RADIATION BIOLOGY

VOLUME I—PART II

RADIATION BIOLOGY

VOLUME I: HIGH ENERGY RADIATION

Edited by

ALEXANDER HOLLAENDER
Director of Biology Division
Oak Ridge National Laboratory

With the cooperation of

AUSTIN M. BRUES　　BERWIND P. KAUFMANN
HERMANN J. MULLER　　LAURISTON S. TAYLOR

Prepared under the Auspices of the Committee
on Radiation Biology, Division of Biology and Agriculture
National Research Council
National Academy of Sciences
Washington, D.C.

PART II
CHAPTERS 9 TO 18

NEW YORK　TORONTO　LONDON
McGRAW-HILL BOOK COMPANY, INC.
1954

RADIATION BIOLOGY

VOLUME I—PART II

Library of Congress Catalog Card Number: 53-6042

THE MAPLE PRESS COMPANY, YORK, PA.

CHAPTER 9

Chromosome Aberrations Induced in Animal Cells by Ionizing Radiations[1]

BERWIND P. KAUFMANN

Department of Genetics, Carnegie Institution of Washington, Cold Spring Harbor, New York

Introduction. Nature of the induced rearrangements: Methods of diagnosis—Types of induced chromosomal aberrations. The process of structural rearrangement: The breakage process. Differences in sensitivity to ionizing radiations: Relative sensitivity of different organisms—Effect of ploidy—Relative sensitivity of chromosomes in different types of cells of the same species—Changes in sensitivity of chromosomes in cells of the same type. Chemical and cytochemical studies. References.

1. INTRODUCTION

The effects on living cells of higher plants and animals of exposure to ionizing radiations are evidenced by various alterations in the constitution and behavior of cellular materials. Among the most readily detectable reactions are those that modify the form and pattern of association of chromosomes and the course of their separation in the cycle of mitosis. Cytologic examination of irradiated cells has disclosed a variety of aberrant types, in which the chromosomes were either adherent or clumped, fragmented or reconstituted, excessive or deficient in number. Many of these abnormalities were observed in the pioneer studies of the biologic effects of radiation carried on during the early years of the century (for example, Bergonié and Tribondeau, 1904, 1906, on rat testes; Krause and Ziegler, 1906, on various mammalian tissues; Perthes, 1904, P. Hertwig, 1911, Payne, 1913, and Holthusen, 1921, on eggs of *Ascaris;* Koernicke, 1905, and Gager, 1908, on somatic and meiotic cells of plants; Mohr, 1919, on testes of grasshoppers; Amato, 1911, and Grasnick, 1918, on cells of amphibia). However, no consistent interpretation of the nature and sequence of origin of the various types of aberrations was developed. This was partly because most of the observations were made

[1] This manuscript was prepared prior to Apr. 1, 1951. Although a few changes have been made since then, this essentially represents the literature available at that time.

on sectioned material, in which induced breaks were not easily diagnosed. Moreover, adequate consideration was not given to the effect on the induced reaction of the length of time elapsing between irradiation and fixation of the cell.

Recognizing the need for a more extensive evaluation of these factors, Alberti and Politzer (1923, 1924) examined entire cells of the corneal epithelium of salamander larvae, fixed at varying periods of time after the animals had been exposed to X-ray treatments of different intensities. The observed types of cellular disturbance were interpreted as revealing a reaction system that involves (1) a period of "primary effect," beginning shortly after irradiation, characterized by a decline in the frequency of mitoses and the appearance, especially after treatment with high doses, of pycnotic nuclei with adherent chromosomes, (2) a subsequent period of mitotic inactivity, and (3) a period of "secondary effects," characterized by abnormal mitoses with fragmented or reconstituted chromosomes, whose frequency is dependent on the duration of the treatment.

It is now recognized that during the period of "primary" or "physiological" effect the materials of the chromosomes are altered, and the mitotic mechanism governing the normal orderly distribution of the chromatids into daughter nuclei is inhibited. In cells that have been exposed to moderate doses of radiation, the chromosomes in late prophase, metaphase, or anaphase stages may continue the course of division, but the mitotic progress of cells in earlier prophases is arrested, and at times their chromosomes evince regressive changes that suggest a return to interphasic conditions (see, for example, Carlson, 1940). Because the onset of new mitoses is inhibited, there occurs shortly after irradiation a period of mitotic inactivity, in which practically all cells appear to be in resting stages. If the treatment has not been too intense, the mitotic rhythm may subsequently be reestablished, whereupon the condensed chromosomes may reveal various types of induced abnormalities. At times the delay effected by radiation may be followed by precocious differentiation of the treated cells (e.g., primary spermatocytes into giant spermatids, Creighton and Evans, 1941).

When the treatment is more drastic, the chromonematic threads of early mitotic stages may reveal nodal thickening along their lengths, and the condensed chromosomes may adhere or clump to form irregular aggregates of chromatin material, presumably as a consequence of changes in viscosity of component proteins and nucleic acids. Such alteration disrupts the normal pattern of chromosome division, at times producing bizarre mitotic figures (see, for example, Helwig, 1933, White, 1937, Carlson, 1938a, Carothers, 1940, Creighton and Evans, 1941, and Bishop, 1942, on grasshopper cells; Bauer and LeCalvez, 1944, on eggs of *Ascaris;* Tansley, Gray, and Spear, 1948, Duryee, 1949, and Rugh, 1950, on amphibian cells; Welander *et al.*, 1948, on cells of embryos and larvae of salmon; Lasnitzki, 1943b, 1948, on avian tissue cultures; Pfuhl and Küntz, 1939, on connective tissue cells of rabbits; Koller, 1947, on normal and malignant cells of man). A few selected illustrations are presented in Fig. 9-1. Alberti and Politzer realized that pycnotic chromosome masses represent one aspect of cellular necrosis. When alteration of the chromosomes is so complete that individual members of the set cannot be recognized, the aberrations are not serviceable for quantitative studies of breakage, but are useful, as will be shown presently, for chemical and cytochemical analysis of the changes effected in the nucleic acids and proteins that represent the major organic constituents of chromosomes.

Of greater use in quantitative studies are those "secondary" or "genetic" effects induced by moderate doses of radiation, in which

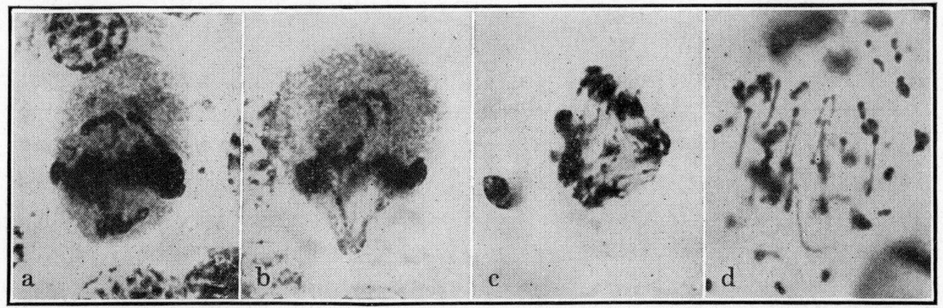

FIG. 9-1. Abnormal mitoses, with adherent chromosomes resulting from exposure of cells to ionizing radiations. (*a*) (*b*) From grasshopper neuroblasts (*Carlson*, 1941b); (*c*) (*d*) from malignant cells of man (*Koller*, 1947).

damage is sufficiently localized to break the chromosomes without impairing permanently the synthetic and reparative processes essential to mitotic and other vital cellular activities. Under these conditions the chromosomes may establish new associations by union of their broken ends. The resulting rearrangements can be detected by examination of the treated cells or their descendants, or by genetic analysis of individuals carrying the aberrations. Production of such viable chromosomal exchanges by X-ray treatment was first reported by Muller (1928a, b) and Muller and Altenburg (1928, 1930), who designed excellent methods for detection and preservation of the induced rearrangements. These furnished a wealth of experimental material, whose analysis during the second quarter of this century has greatly furthered understanding of the mechanisms of heredity and evolution. Determination of the frequency of these gross chromosomal aberrations under various experimental conditions has also furnished basic data for a preliminary analysis of the processes involved in chromosome fragmentation and reconstitution. The significance of such data in supplying information about the mode of action of ionizing radiations and the possible control of deleterious effects has become increasingly apparent in recent years.

Many aspects of such studies have been examined in extensive detail in a series of reviews, texts, and symposia since the publication of Duggar's "Biological Effects of Radiation" in 1936 [e.g., Timoféeff-Ressovsky, 1937; Timoféeff-Ressovsky and Zimmer, 1939; Bauer, 1939c; Delbrück, 1940; Muller, 1940, 1950b; Fano and Demerec, 1944; Catcheside, 1945, 1946, 1948; Lavedan, 1945; Gray, 1946; Spear, 1946; Lea, 1946; Giese, 1947; Buzatti-Traverso and Cavalli, 1948; Fano, Caspari, and Demerec, 1950; Sparrow, 1951; and the numerous contributions to the 1941 Cold Spring Harbor Symposium on Genes and Chromosomes, the 1946 London Conference on Certain Aspects of the Action of Radiations on Living Cells (published in 1947), the 1948 Brookhaven Conference on Biological Applications of Nuclear Physics, the FIAT Review of German Science from 1939 to 1946 (published in 1948), and the 1948 Oak Ridge Symposium on Radiation Genetics (published in 1950)].

The present review will deal with chromosomal aberrations induced in animal cells by ionizing radiations. Separation of animal from plant materials, even for the sake of description, imposes arbitrary limitations that are not always advantageous; accordingly, pertinent botanical literature will be cited when it seems desirable. Designation of chromosome aberrations and gene mutations as sharply delimited classes is also to a large extent arbitrary. Small chromosomal aberrations cannot always be distinguished from the so-called "point mutations." Moreover, radiation studies have clearly shown that the reaction system responsible for the characteristic phenotypic expression of a gene may be profoundly altered by a realignment of parts of chromosomes in the process of structural rearrangement. It is thus apparent that no sharp line can be drawn between gene mutations and chromosome aberrations; but this article will be limited to a consideration of the types of gross chromosomal alterations that can be detected either by direct cytological examination or by breeding tests. Even with attention focused on this restricted segment of a large body of information, it will not be possible to review all the available experimental evidence, and the discussion will be concerned primarily with the types of induced aberrations, the methods used in their diagnosis, and their significance with respect to evaluation of the processes of chromosome breakage and recombination. The effects of radiations in retarding mitosis and in modifying the normal distribution of chromosomes on the spindle are considered in Chap. 11 by Carlson.

2. NATURE OF THE INDUCED REARRANGEMENTS

Various types of cells from many different species of plants and animals have been irradiated in order to obtain information about the process of structural rearrangement, but the majority of available data have been obtained in studies of the effects of treating microspores, or pollen grains, of plants of the genus *Tradescantia*, and spermatozoa, or male gametes, of flies of the genus *Drosophila*. Analysis has been facilitated by the relatively small number of chromosomes in these two types; in the species of *Tradescantia* most commonly used the haploid number is six, and in *D. melanogaster*, the most widely studied species of *Drosophila*, the hap-

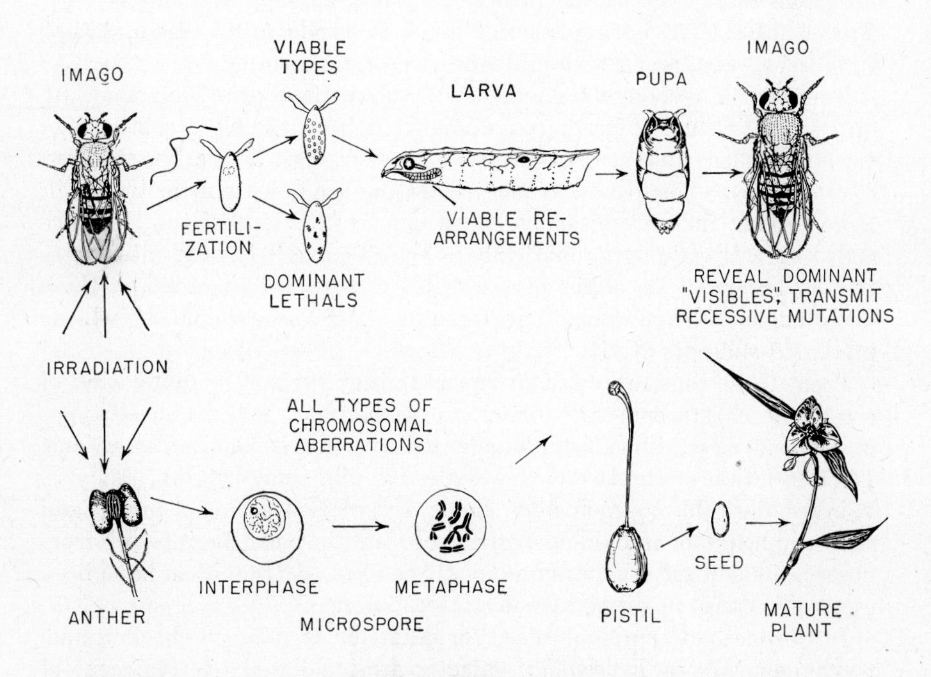

Fig. 9-2. Diagram of development stages in *Drosophila* and *Tradescantia*, indicating sources of materials for cytogenetic studies described in text. (*From Kaufmann*, 1948a.)

loid number is four (either X, 2, 3, 4 or Y, 2, 3, 4—the letters indicating the sex chromosomes, the numerals the autosomes). The techniques employed in studying these organisms illustrate the methods commonly used to detect chromosomal aberrations (Fig. 9-2).

2-1. METHODS OF DIAGNOSIS

In studies on *Tradescantia* the irradiated cells are themselves examined after an interval of time sufficient to permit the treated chromosomes to reach the condensed stages, when determination of the number of fragments or chromosome exchanges is feasible. The earlier studies, on both plant and animal cells, employed this method in basic form; but the development of smear techniques, especially for spreading and staining the microspores of plants (Taylor, 1924; Kaufmann, 1927), presented the opportunity—used advantageously in the work on *Tradescantia*—of irradiating large numbers of cells in a known stage of microsporogenesis and obtaining, by subsequent inspection of the stained metaphases and anaphases, extensive and comprehensive data on the frequency of induction of fragments and various types of chromosomal rearrangements. Diagrams illustrating the kinds of aberrations detected in such studies of *Tradescantia* have been presented by Catcheside (1945, 1946, 1948); Catcheside, Lea, and Thoday (1946a); and Lea (1946).

Comparable although less extensive studies have also been made by direct examination of irradiated animal cells (for example, the studies of Carlson, 1938a, 1941b, on neuroblast chromosomes of the grasshopper, *Chortophaga*). The effects of the treatments are detectable as breaks or lesions along the chromosomes, or as new associations of the breakage ends (represented diagrammatically in Figs. 9-3 and 9-4). An interpretation of the mode of origin of the types of breaks designated in these diagrams as "chromosome," "chromatid," and "isochromatid" will be presented subsequently.

From these illustrations it is apparent that cytologic examination of condensed chromosomes at metaphase or anaphase will reveal all types of induced aberrations, including lethal as well as viable aberrations. Differentiation of the two classes is desirable in some types of analysis. It is also desirable to know more about the precise location of breaks and the complexity of individual rearrangements than can be inferred from observations of mitotic chromosomes. Studies on *Drosophila* have been especially useful in supplying such information.

In the method commonly used for detection of induced chromosomal rearrangements in *Drosophila*, gametes are irradiated by treatment of males, which are then mated with untreated virgin females. Experiments with *D. melanogaster* by Muller and Settles (1927) and Demerec and Kaufmann (1941) have indicated that doses of X rays approaching the limit of tolerance of the adult fly (ca. 5000–10,000 r) do not usually inactivate the spermatozoa, which fertilize the eggs and participate in zygote formation. Some of the fertilized eggs fail to hatch, death of the embryos being attributable in many cases to loss or duplication of sections of chromosomes in early cleavage mitoses (Sonnenblick, 1940). The abortive embryos constitute a class of so-called "dominant lethals," whose frequency can be determined by counting the number of eggs laid and the number from which larvae do not emerge.

Larvae hatching from eggs fertilized by irradiated spermatozoa may or may not carry detectable chromosomal rearrangements. The relative frequencies of the two classes resulting from any given treatment can be determined by either cytological or genetical techniques. The cytologic

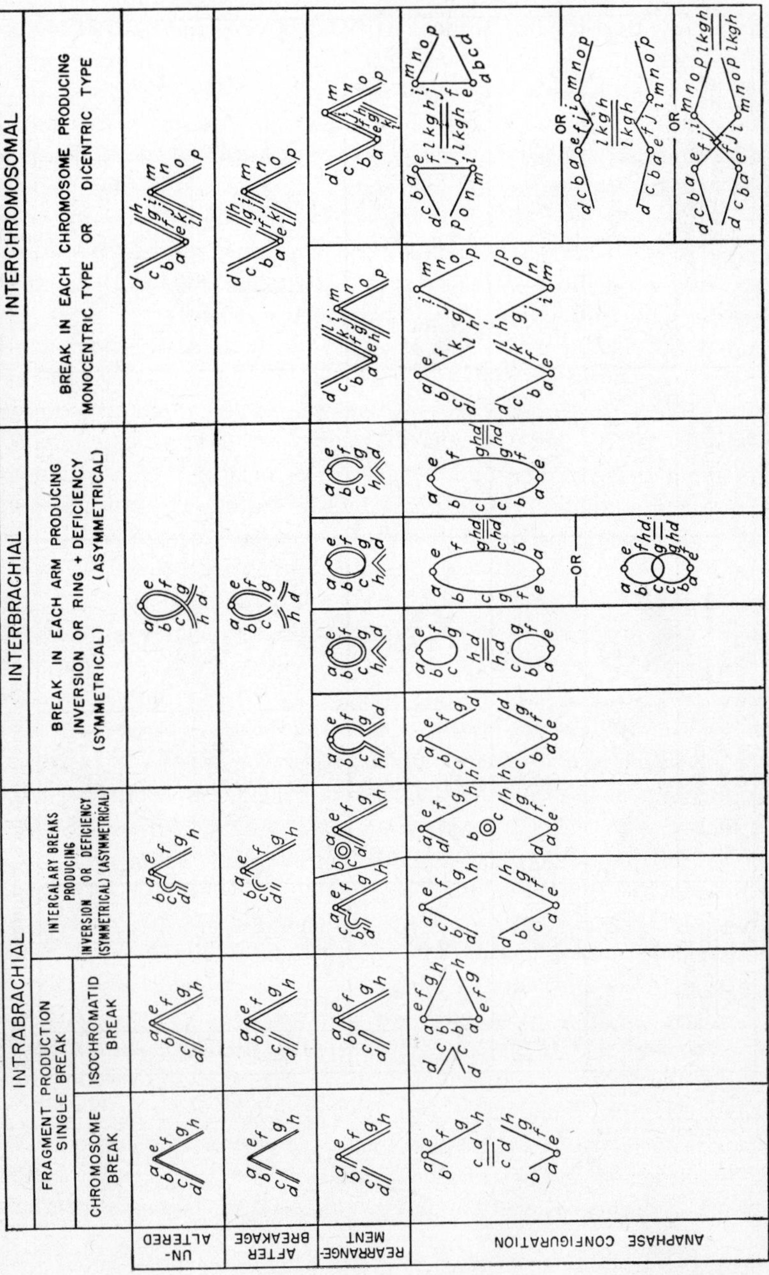

FIG. 9-3. Diagram of types of chromosome aberrations detected after irradiation of animal cells. Continued in Fig. 9-4; further description in text.

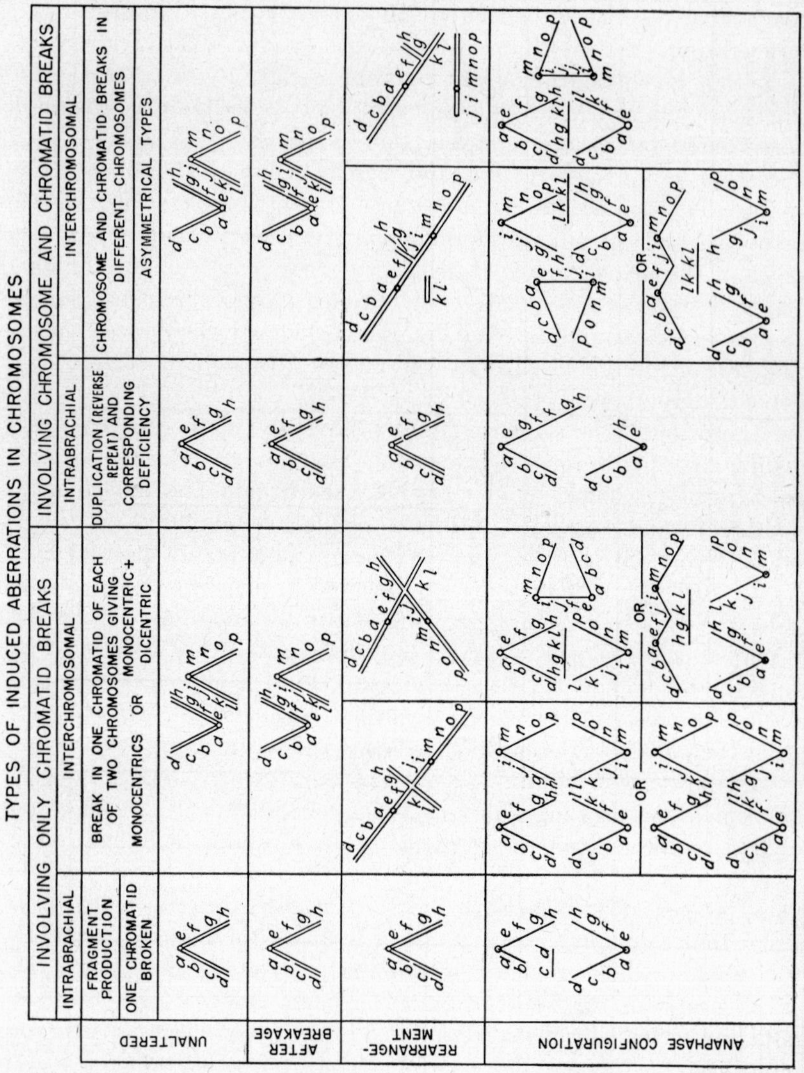

TYPES OF INDUCED ABERRATIONS IN CHROMOSOMES

	INVOLVING ONLY CHROMATID BREAKS		INVOLVING CHROMOSOME AND CHROMATID BREAKS	
	INTRABRACHIAL	INTERCHROMOSOMAL	INTRABRACHIAL	INTERCHROMOSOMAL
	FRAGMENT PRODUCTION ONE CHROMATID BROKEN	BREAK IN ONE CHROMATID OF EACH OF TWO CHROMOSOMES GIVING MONOCENTRICS OR MONOCENTRIC + DICENTRIC	DUPLICATION (REVERSE REPEAT) AND CORRESPONDING DEFICIENCY	CHROMOSOME AND CHROMATID BREAKS IN DIFFERENT CHROMOSOMES ASYMMETRICAL TYPES
UNALTERED				
AFTER BREAKAGE				
REARRANGEMENT				
ANAPHASE CONFIGURATION		OR		OR

Fig. 9-4. Diagram of types of chromosome aberrations detected after irradiation of animal cells. Other types shown in Fig. 9-3; further description in text.

approach involves inspection of the salivary-gland chromosomes of the first generation (F_1) larval progeny of the irradiated fathers. Since analysis of a given rearrangement by this method is restricted to the chromosomes of a single individual, aberrations of special interest cannot be perpetuated for genetic analysis and subsequent experimental use. On the other hand, the large size and precise pattern of banding of the salivary-gland chromosomes (as shown in Figs. 9-5, 9-6) offer unparalleled opportunities for determining the complexity of a rearrangement and the positions of the breaks involved in its production—as was first demonstrated by Painter in 1933. Methods of preparing for cytological examination the aceto-carmine or aceto-orcein smears from which these photographs were made are briefly outlined in the "Drosophila Guide," by Demerec and Kaufmann (1950).

One limitation of the salivary-gland-chromosome method of diagnosis is the difficulty of detecting rearrangements that are restricted to proximal heterochromatic regions; these parts of the chromosome have poorly defined bands, and aggregate to form a so-called "chromocenter" (illustrated in Fig. 9-5a). Exchanges involving breaks in proximal heterochromatic regions can sometimes be detected in neuroblast cells of the larva by the pattern of somatic pairing of the chromosomes. Thus the cross-shaped configuration shown in the small inset of Fig. 9-5a (cf. Fig. 9-7b), results from the side-by-side association of unaltered second and third chromosomes, maternal in origin, with second and third chromosomes of the paternal set that had exchanged parts (reciprocal translocation) as a result of irradiation of the spermatozoon. Identification of intrachromosomal exchanges in neuroblast cells is difficult, but is sometimes possible because of the presence of constrictions, including those associated with the formation of the nucleoli, that are visible in late prophase stages (Fig. 9-7a, c, d, e). From these considerations it is apparent that a comprehensive quantitative study of induced rearrangements should include analysis of both salivary-gland and neuroblast chromosomes from the same larva. The labor involved in cytological examination of the neuroblasts is so considerable, however, that they are rarely utilized for this purpose. Before the advantages of salivary-gland chromosomes were recognized, cytological studies of genetically detected rearrangements were made exclusively on chromosomes of neuroblast cells of larvae or gonial cells of adults (see, for example, Dobzhansky, 1936; Stern, 1931).

Genetic techniques for determination of induced chromosomal exchanges were described by Muller and Altenburg (1930) and Dobzhansky (1929, 1930). Both intra- and interchromosomal rearrangements had previously been known in *Drosophila*. Sturtevant (1926) had shown that a reduction of crossing over in the third chromosome of *D. melanogaster* was due to inversion (rotation through 180° as a consequence of breakage

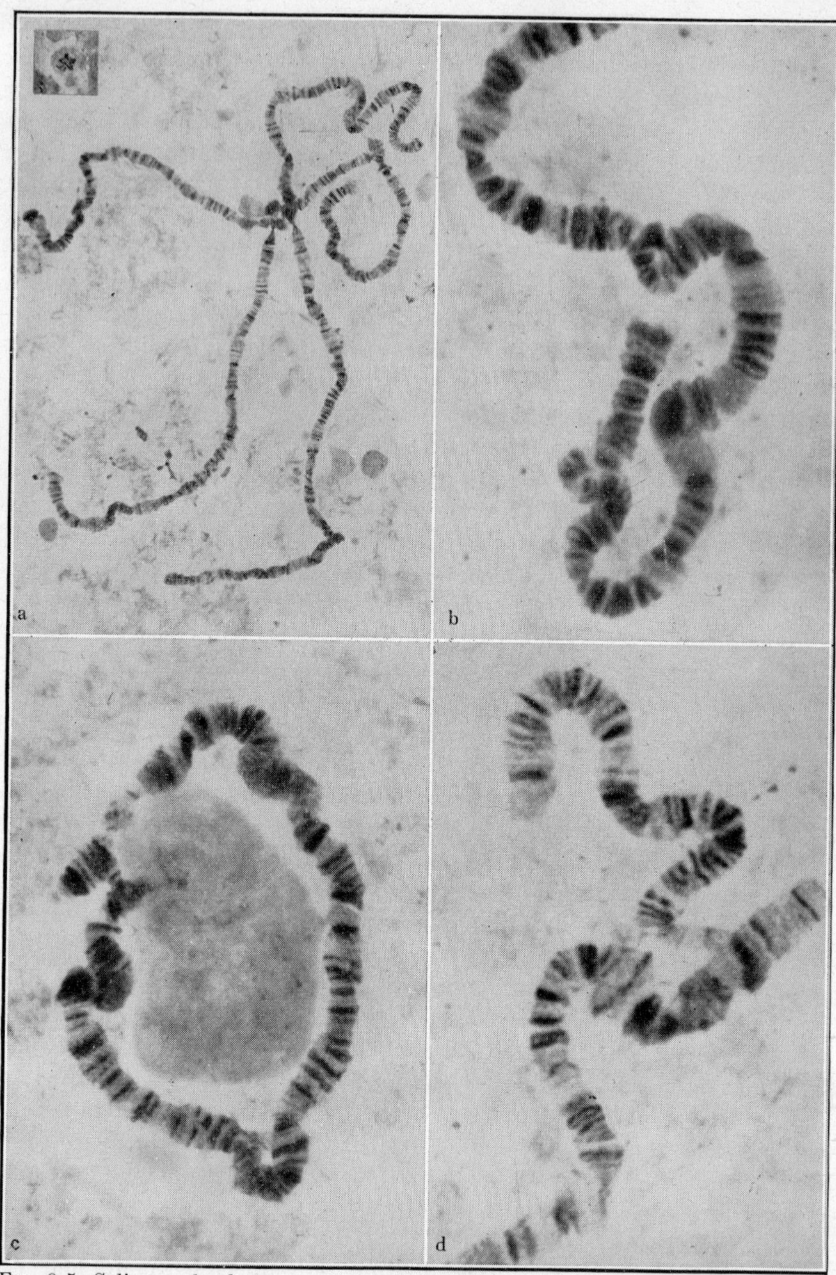

FIG. 9-5. Salivary-gland chromosomes of *Drosophila melanogaster*. Rearrangements detected in larval progeny of irradiated fathers. (*a*) Unaltered complement; chromosomes aggregated at their proximal heterochromatic regions to form the chromocenter. (Insert shows chromosomes of neuroblast cell, not from same individual but photographed to same scale as salivary-gland chromosomes.) (*b*) Transposition of section of right limb of third chromosome. (*c*) Inversion in X chromosome; inversion loop surrounds nucleolus. (*d*) Intercalary duplication (reverse repeat) in left limb of third chromosome. (*Photographs of preparations by the author.*)

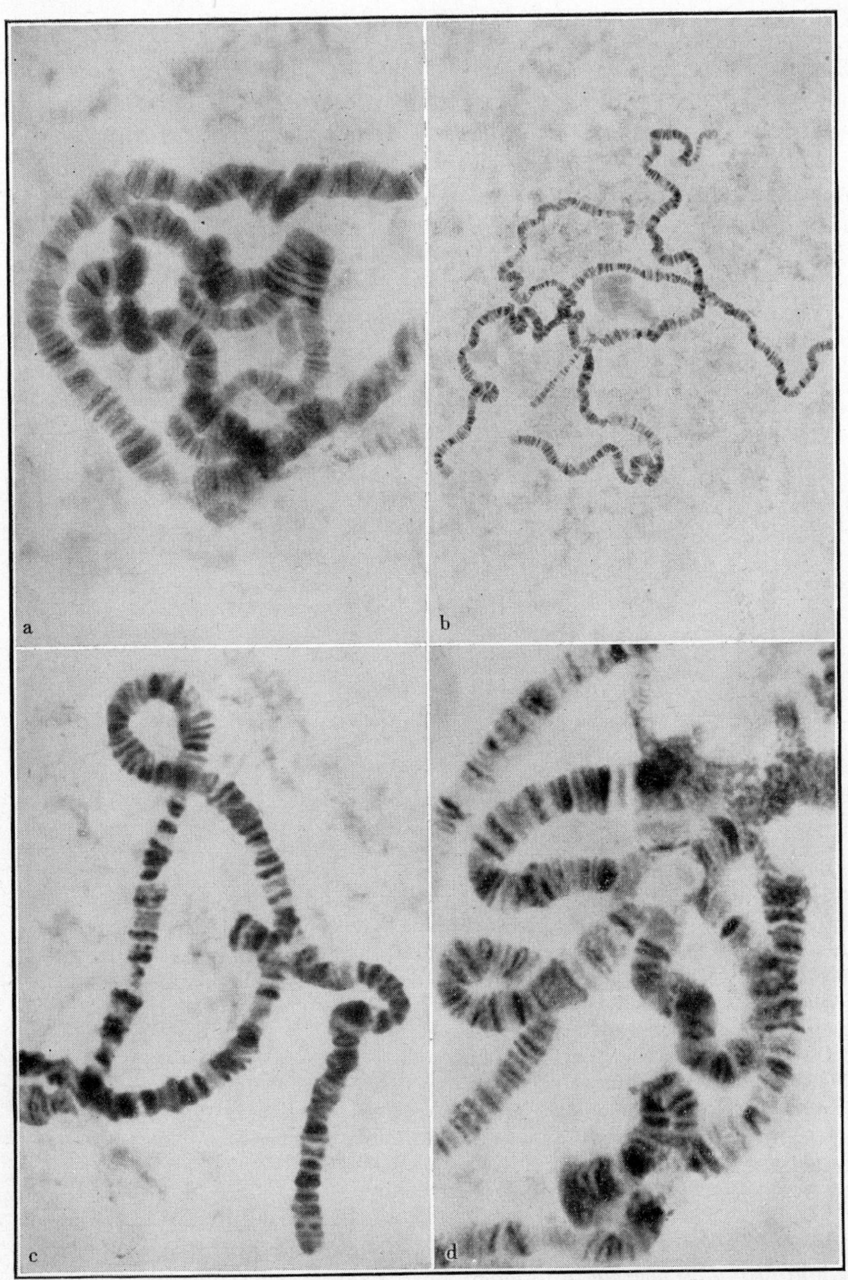

FIG. 9-6. Salivary-gland chromosomes of *Drosophila melanogaster*. Rearrangements detected in larval progeny of irradiated fathers. (*a*) Duplication of terminal section of left limb of second chromosome. (*b*) Reciprocal translocation between the Y chromosome and the right limb of the third chromosome. (*c*) Reciprocal translocation between the left limb of the second chromosome and the right limb of the third chromosome. (*d*) An inversion-translocation complex involving breaks in 2L, 2R, and 3L. (*Photographs of preparations by the author.*)

and reinsertion) of a section of that chromosome. This inversion, and others analyzed by Sturtevant (1931), were found in nature or arose spontaneously in laboratory cultures. Determination of crossover values is laborious, and this has acted as a deterrent to study of induced inversions by means of genetic techniques. Spontaneously arising translocations had also been detected in *Drosophila* by genetic analysis (Bridges, 1923; Bridges and Morgan, 1923; Stern, 1926, 1929). The method of

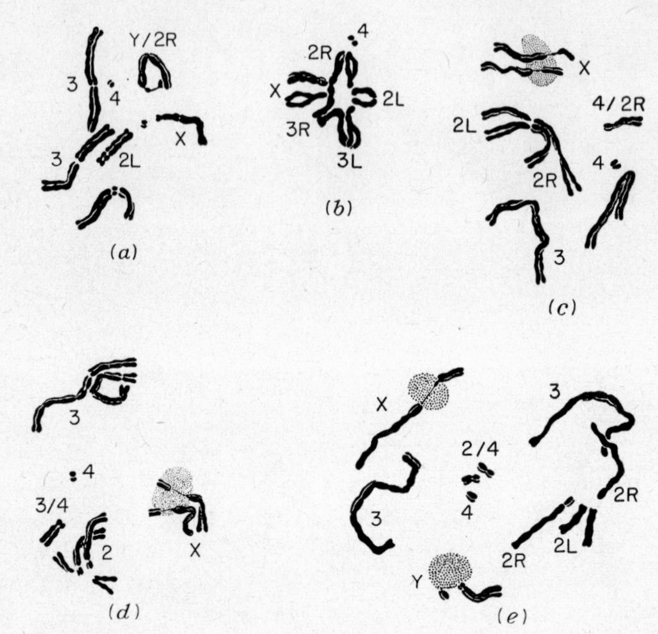

FIG. 9-7. Chromosome exchanges as revealed in late prophase or metaphase stages in neuroblast cells of larvae of *Drosophila melanogaster*. (*a*) Reciprocal translocation between the right limb of the second chromosome and the Y chromosome (2R/Y). (*b*) An exchange between the second and third chromosomes; characteristic cross-shaped configuration results from somatic pairing. (*c*) A reciprocal translocation between the second and fourth chromosomes. (*d*) An exchange between the third and fourth chromosomes. (*e*) An exchange between the second and fourth chromosomes; the fourth chromosome carrying the translocated tip of the second is represented in duplicate, in addition to the normal fourth chromosome. Nucleoli stippled. (*Original drawings by the author.*)

diagnosis of the induced types is based on the finding that translocations produce linkages between genes located in different chromosomes that would normally segregate independently.

In the genetic, as in the cytologic, method for detection of translocations, males are usually irradiated and mated with untreated virgin females. If the males are wild type, they may be crossed with females whose chromosomes carry marking mutant genes. In a typical experiment of this type, outlined in Fig. 9-8, irradiated males having wild-type

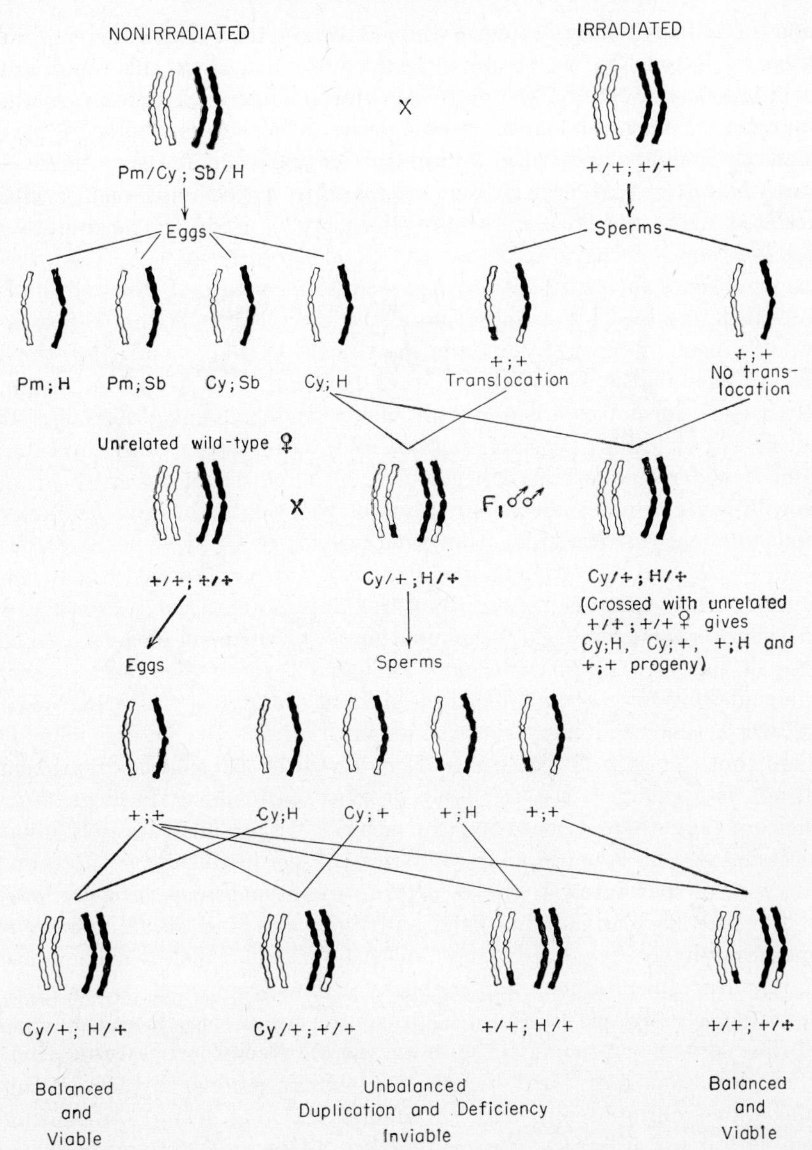

FIG. 9-8. Diagram of the genetic method for detecting reciprocal translocations between the second and third chromosomes in *Drosophila melanogaster*. Second chromosomes shown at left in outline, third chromosomes at right in solid color. The chromosomes with dominant marking genes carry inverted sections which are not indicated in the diagram. Only crosses involving Curly and Hairless (*Cy;H*) are detailed, but similar results are obtainable with Plum and Hairless (*Pm;H*), Plum and Stubble (*Pm;S,b*) and Curly and Stubble (*Cy;Sb*).

second and third chromosomes (represented by the symbols +;+) are mated with females whose second chromosomes carry the dominant markers Curly (*Cy*) and Plum (*Pm*), and the third chromosomes the dominants Hairless (*H*) and Stubble (*Sb*). The heterozygous F_1 flies, which are of four types with respect to the dominant marking genes—namely, *Cy*;*H*, *Cy*;*Sb*, *Pm*;*H*, and *Pm*;*Sb*—are mated individually with unrelated wild-type flies of the opposite sex. Figure 9-8 represents a cross between heterozygous F_1 males and wild-type females. The presence or absence of translocations between the second and third chromosomes is determined by examination of the F_2 cultures. If no translocation has been induced by irradiation, each of the second and third chromosomes of the F_1 males, whether paternal or maternal in origin, will carry a normal complement of genes. Independent assortment at meiosis will yield four types of spermatozoa, with respect to the mutants under consideration, which will produce, by fertilization of eggs bearing the wild-type chromosomes, four kinds of F_2 progeny in approximately equal numbers (for example, from the cross *Cy*;*H* ♂ by +;+ ♀ *Cy*;*H*, *Cy*;+, +;*H*, and +;+ males and females). If, on the other hand, an induced translocation is present, only the maternally derived second and third chromosomes will carry an unaltered complement of genes, since those of paternal origin will have exchanged parts with each other. Independent assortment at meiosis will yield four types of spermatozoa, but two of them will carry some genes in duplicate and be deficient for others (bottom row of Fig. 9-8). Eggs fertilized by such spermatozoa will not as a rule give rise to viable progeny, although a duplication or deficiency zygote may occasionally survive to produce an individual possessing special somatic characteristics. Eggs fertilized by the other two types of spermatozoa (those carrying the second and third chromosomes with the dominant markers, and those carrying the two chromosomes that have exchanged parts), both of which transmit a complete set of genes, will produce viable progeny. The occurrence, in the cross illustrated, of only two classes of F_2 progeny—namely, *Cy*;*H* and +;+—will thus serve as an index to the induction of a reciprocal translocation.

Translocations may be detected in a similar manner by irradiating males whose chromosomes carry dominant marking genes, and mating them with nonirradiated wild-type females. This procedure is described in detail by Dobzhansky (1936).

Another technique for the detection of translocations involving a particular chromosome is based on phenotypic modification accompanying change in position of a specific gene. Thus the cubitus interruptus (*ci*) position effect in *D. melanogaster*, which alters the normal pattern of wing venation, is caused by a translocation involving the fourth chromosome, whereby the dominance of the wild-type allele of cubitus interruptus is weakened (Dubinin and Sidorow, 1934). Using this criterion of assay,

Eberhardt (1939) irradiated flies carrying a normal fourth chromosome and determined the frequency of translocations from the proportion of progeny showing interruptions in the cubital vein.

In a more elaborate experiment designed to disclose exchanges among all four chromosomes of an irradiated spermatozoon, Patterson, Stone, Bedichek, and Suche (1934) mated irradiated wild-type males with females having attached-X chromosomes homozygous for the mutant gene yellow ($\widehat{yy}$), the second chromosome homozygous for brown (*bw*), the third for ebony (*e*), and the fourth for eyeless (*ey*). The heterozygous F_1 males were backcrossed individually to $\widehat{yy}$; *bw*; *e*; *ey* females.

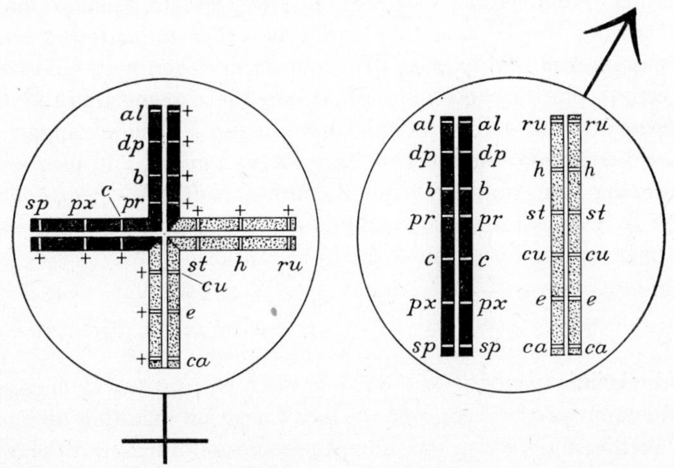

Fig. 9-9. Diagram illustrating the genetic technique for determining points of exchange between chromosomes in *Drosophila melanogaster*. A translocation-carrying female heterozygous for a series of genes (left) is crossed to a male free from the translocation and homozygous for the same genes (right). (*From Dobzhansky, in Duggar's "Biological Effects of Radiation,"* 1936.)

Since these males carried X chromosomes received from their irradiated fathers, many different types of reassociation could be detected by examination of F_2 cultures, e.g., X;2, X;3, X;4, 2;3, 2;4, 3;4, X;2;3, X;2;4, X;3;4, 2;3;4, and X;2;3;4. Some duplication and deficiency types were also viable and could be detected by criteria that will be indicated presently. Translocations involving the Y chromosome were not detected in these experiments because the females that came from eggs fertilized by Y-bearing spermatozoa were not tested.

When translocations have been diagnosed by such genetic methods, they can usually be perpetuated in cultures, and the positions of the breaks involved in the rearrangement can subsequently be determined by either of two procedures. The most informative and least laborious is examination of salivary glands of individuals carrying the translocation in heterozygous condition. The alternative method, which was the first to be used, requires determination of crossover values between the chromosomes involved in a translocation and their homologues. As indicated previously, the apparent linkage between genes located in different chromosomes in translocations is attributable to the inviability of the recombination classes carrying duplications and deficiencies. This apparent linkage can be utilized for determining genetically the loci at which the chromosomes were broken and reunited. The method was outlined by Dobzhansky (1936) in the review from which Fig. 9-9 is reproduced. This represents a translocation between the second (black) and third (stippled) chromosomes, both of which had been broken near the middle. Females heterozygous for this translocation, which carried in their normal homologues the series of genes indicated, were mated with normal males that carried the same series of marking genes. Crossing over took place in the female between the chromosomes involved in the translocation and their normal homologues. The strongest linkage was observed in this case between the genes *cu* and *c*, and between *st* and *pr*, indicating that breakage and recombination had occurred between these loci. The validity of this method of diagnosis has been confirmed in several instances by parallel cytologic studies.

2-2. TYPES OF INDUCED CHROMOSOMAL ABERRATIONS

Any deviation from the standard pattern in number of chromosomes or arrangement of their component units may be regarded as an aberration (Dobzhansky, 1936). Although changes conforming to these specifications regularly occur under natural conditions, the frequency of their occurrence can be increased enormously by ionizing radiations. The types of alterations that have been induced in this manner include duplications and deficiencies affecting individual chromosomes and sets of chromosomes, and inter- and intrachromosomal rearrangements.

2-2a. *Haploids and Polyploids.* Diploid individuals normally have every chromosome represented in duplicate in cells that have not undergone meiosis. In such individuals occasional cells, or groups of cells, may have three, four, or more sets of chromosomes, as a result of failure of chromatids to separate after their multiplication by normal mitotic processes or by endomitosis. Such polyploid cells can sometimes be induced in a diploid organism by irradiation. Makino (1939) detected tetraploid spermatocytes in testes of adults of *Podisma mikado* (Acrididae) developing from irradiated nymphs. The observations, which were restricted to three individuals, were not in themselves conclusive, since polyploid cells occur in nature in the testes of some Orthoptera (Mickey, 1942; Ray Chaudhuri and Bose, 1948). However, Creighton and Evans (1941) reported the formation in *Chorthippus* of giant spermatids by direct transformation of primary spermatocytes whose normal course of development was inhibited by X-ray treatment; and White (1935a, b) and Carlson (1941b) reported the induction by X rays in Orthoptera of tetraploid spermatogonial cells containing diplochromosomes (tetraploid with respect to chromatids but only double with respect to centromeres). It is suggested that they may have originated in prophase cells that reverted in phase at the time of treatment, and whose chromosomes underwent a second doubling as they progressed toward metaphase the second time.

Individuals of a species in which both sexes are normally diploid may occasionally have one, three, four, or more sets of chromosomes. For example, Fankhauser (1945) noted the occurrence of haploid, triploid, tetraploid, and pentaploid individuals among normal embryos raised from eggs of diploid salamanders. Triploid females of *D. melanogaster* arise spontaneously in normal diploid lines (Morgan, Bridges, and Sturtevant, 1925). Deviations in the number of sets of chromosomes may also be induced by ionizing radiations. Thus, in the classic experiments of G. Hertwig (1911, 1927), P. Hertwig (1916, 1924), and Dalcq and Simon (1932), exposure to radiations inactivated the nuclei of amphibian eggs, which upon insemination with untreated spermatozoa produced haploid embryos (androgenesis). In other experiments (cf. Hertwig, 1911, 1913; G. Hertwig, 1927; and Dalcq and Simon, 1932), treatment of spermatozoa with doses of radiation that did not impair their motility or ability to penetrate the egg altered the subsequent behavior of their chromosomes so that haploid embryos developed with only egg chromosomes (gynogenesis). In more recent experiments by Rugh (1939), treatment of spermatozoa of *Rana pipiens* with doses of X rays ranging from 15–10,000 r caused progressive decrease in the frequency of viable embryos; at 10,000 r only 1.6 per cent hatched. With further increase in dosage, however, the number of viable embryos increased, so that at 50,000 r about 90 per cent hatched. These embryos were presumably gynogenetic haploids (see also Rugh and Exner, 1940).

The method of inactivating a gamete nucleus by irradiation has been used by A. R. Whiting (1946) to secure androgenetic males in the wasp *Habrobracon juglandis*. Diploid males, which are nearly always sterile, can be produced experimentally in this species, although the fertile males are normally gynogenetic and haploid. Whiting irradiated females of an inbred wild-type stock, whose egg chromosomes were in the metaphase stage of the first meiotic division, with doses of X rays (up to 42,000 r); they were then mated with untreated males carrying recessive marking genes. Among the surviving progeny were fertile males showing the characters of the recessive mutants (haploid and paternal in origin), in addition to the expected wild-type males (haploid and maternal) and females (diploid and biparental). Cytologic examination (A. R. Whiting, 1948) indicated that the treatment retards and distorts the egg pronucleus to such a degree that the sperm pronucleus cleaves and develops into a normal, fertile, haploid male with paternal traits only.

2-2b. *Monosomic and Polysomic Types.* If, in an otherwise diploid organism, three chromosomes of one type are present, the individual is called "trisomic." If one of the chromosomes is represented only once, the individual is called "monosomic." Irregularities in the mitotic mechanism account for such deviations from the normal diploid condition. Nondisjunction of chromatids in somatic mitosis, or of homologues in meiosis, may result in the passage of both to one pole of the spindle. Bridges (1916) found that eggs of normal, untreated females of *D. melanogaster* may occasionally carry two X chromosomes or none, rather than a single X. If such females are mated with males carrying sex-linked dominant markers, the progeny arising from these exceptional eggs can readily be detected. They will be either recessive females (XXY, derived from XX eggs fertilized by a Y-transmitting spermatozoon) or dominant males (XO, derived from no-X eggs fertilized by an X-transmitting sperm), in contrast with the normal progeny, which are dominant females and recessive males. Although the exceptional eggs originate for the most part as a result of nondisjunction of the X, they apparently can also arise from losses of that chromosome, since XX eggs are less frequent (1:2500) than no-X eggs (1:600).

The frequency of nondisjunction and chromosome elimination can be increased by treatment of females with X rays, as was shown in the studies of Mavor (1922, 1924a) and Anderson (1924, 1925a, b, 1931) on *D. melanogaster*, and Demerec and Farrow (1930a, b) on *D. virilis*. Loss of an X chromosome in a cleavage division of a normal female may give rise to a gynandromorph composed of XX and XO tissues, and such individuals have been obtained in X-ray experiments (Mavor, 1924b; Patterson, 1930; Bonnier, Lüning, and Perje, 1949). Losses of X and Y chromosomes following irradiation of spermatozoa, which result in death of the embryos, will be considered in the discussion of dominant lethals.

Individuals that are monosomic for the fourth chromosome arise spontaneously in *Drosophila,* and may also be induced experimentally. Dobzhansky (1930) observed mosaics among the progeny of treated flies, which were haplo-fourth in part of the body. The mosaic individuals described by Mohr (1932) presumably belonged to this category, as did some of the Minutes described by Muller (1928a, 1930) and others. Flies that are trisomic for the fourth chromosome are viable (cf. Fig. 9-7e), although individuals tetrasomic for this chromosome are not.

Nondisjunction or loss of the second or third chromosomes as a result of irradiation of gametes would also lead to the formation of zygotes that were either monosomic or trisomic for these longer autosomes; but individuals of these types have not been detected by genetic or cytologic methods of analysis, and presumably are eliminated in embryonic stages.

2-2c. *Deficiencies and Duplications.* A segment, rather than an entire chromosome, may be eliminated from the normal complex or added to it as a result of irradiation damage. The loss of a section of a chromosome is designated as a "deficiency," and the repetition of a section as a "duplication." The length of the section removed or added and the genetic properties of the chromatin involved determine the extent of genic unbalance and the capacity of the cells receiving the altered chromosomal complement to survive. Deficiencies and duplications confined to heterochromatic ("inert") regions, such as exist in the proximal third of the X chromosome and throughout the Y chromosome of *D. melanogaster*, have less effect in modifying normal developmental processes than alterations of comparable length within the euchromatic ("genetically active") portions of the chromosomes. (As indicated previously, the loss of the entire Y leads to the production of an XO male, which is viable though sterile; and the addition of a Y, as in an XXY female, does not appreciably reduce viability or fertility.)

Deficiencies confined to euchromatic regions have, in general, more deleterious effects than duplications of comparable length. Studies on *Drosophila* have indicated that deficiencies are usually lethal when homozygous or hemizygous (as, for example, when a deficient X chromosome is present in duplicate in an XX female zygote, or as a single X in an XY male zygote), although some short terminal deficiencies are not (Demerec and Hoover, 1936). Many of the so-called "lethal mutations" of *Drosophila* are attributable to minute deletions (Slizynski, 1938). A deficiency may at times be detected by the absence of specific marking genes. Thus, a deficiency induced in the 1A5–8 region of the X chromosome of *D. melanogaster* by irradiation of wild-type males, which were mated with *y sc* females, was detected by the appearance of female progeny with yellow body color (Sutton, 1943). A deficiency for band 3C7 of the X chromosome acts as a dominant (Notch), producing flies with serrated or notched wings (Demerec, in Demerec and Kaufmann, 1937). Such correlations of phenotypic effects with chromosomal aberrations have been useful in determining the loci of specific genes on the chromosomes, as is illustrated in Fig. 9-10.

Deficiencies may be either terminal or intercalary in position. Terminal deficiencies are frequently detected in irradiated cells as fragments separated from the portion of the chromosome having the centromere or spindle-attachment region (Figs. 9-3 and 9-4). A terminal fragment detached from an ordinary, or monocentric, chromosome lacks the centromere essential for its normal transportation to the spindle pole at anaphase. Consequently, it is usually not included in either of the daughter nuclei (however, see Carlson, 1938b). Fragments detached from chromosomes having compound or diffuse centromeres—such as those of *Ascaris*, the coccids, or the bearberry aphid—provide an exception to the general rule, since they are transported to the spindle poles together with the main body of the chromosomes from which they have been detached (White, 1936; Bauer and LeCalvez, 1944; Hughes-Schrader and Ris, 1941; Ris, 1942). Exclusion of detached fragments from the daughter nuclei upsets genic balance; it has been suggested that the reduction in fertility that follows irradiation of gametes in various species of animals is due in large measure to fragment production. This topic has been reviewed by Lea (1947b).

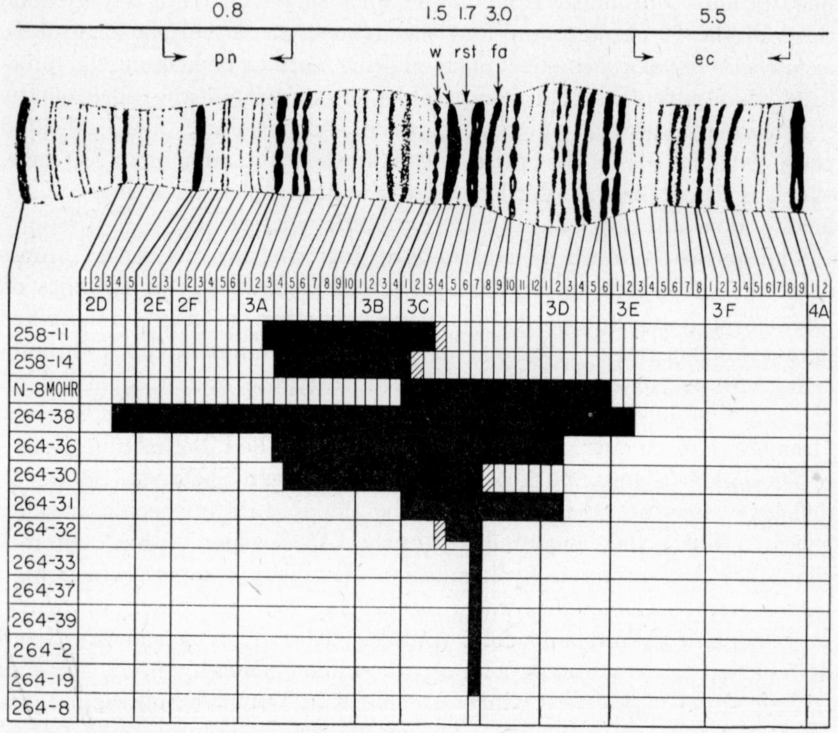

FIG. 9-10. Salivary-gland chromosome map of the prune-echinus region of the X chromosome of *Drosophila melanogaster*, indicating the extent of 14 deficiencies that have been studied. (*From Demerec, in Demerec and Kaufmann*, 1937.)

Terminal deficiencies are probably produced by irradiation of spermatozoa of *Drosophila*, but they presumably have dominant lethal effects (Pontecorvo, 1941, 1942; Pontecorvo and Muller, 1941; Muller, 1941; Fano, 1941; Demerec and Fano, 1944; Lea and Catcheside, 1945; Catcheside and Lea, 1945a). Loss of a fragment from one of the longer autosomes in cleavage mitosis will upset genic balance and cause abortion of the embryo. The mechanism probably involves establishment of a breakage-fusion-bridge cycle in the centric portion of the chromosome (similar to that described by McClintock, 1939, for maize) as a consequence of end-to-end union of sister chromatids at the site of the break, formation of a chromatin bridge between the two separating centromeres at anaphase, and subsequent breakage of the extended strand at an indeterminate position. The irregular cleavage mitoses lead to abnormal embryonic development, and occasionally cellular multiplication may occur without differentiation (Sonnenblick and Henshaw, 1941).

If the breakage-fusion-bridge cycle occurred in either the fourth chromosome or a sex chromosome, it might not be expected to prove lethal in all cases, since haplo-fourth and XO individuals are viable. Muller (1940) and Pontecorvo (1941) found, however, that the number of individuals surviving loss of a sex chromosome was much lower than expected. It thus appears that the actual mechanism of loss may involve mechanical difficulties that upset the course of mitosis and modify subsequent developmental processes, even though the absence of the chromosome from the complex would not in itself cause death of the embryo (cf. Fano and Demerec, 1944; Catcheside and Lea, 1945b; Catcheside, 1948). Viable losses, which occur with a frequency of about 1 per cent at 4000 r according to Pontecorvo (1942), presumably occur when the break is produced close to the centromere, so that a short bridge is formed at anaphase. Formation of daughter nuclei could presumably then proceed without interference from the chromosome in the process of elimination (see also Catcheside, 1948).

For the reasons indicated, most of the detectable deficiencies induced by irradiation of spermatozoa of *Drosophila* are intercalary rather than terminal. Some exceptions have been reported, however (Demerec and Hoover, 1936; Sutton, 1940; Catcheside and Lea, 1945a), and it has also been noted that terminal inversions occur in nature (e.g., by Kaufmann, 1936 and Kikkawa, 1938, on *D. ananassae*). These observations present an objection to Muller's suggestion (1941) that the induced losses are always intercalary rather than terminal, the deleted section approaching the tip but not including the terminal band or bands. Muller's assumption (1940) that the chromosomes of *Drosophila* contain specialized terminal chromomeres or telomeres essential to their survival has also been contested, on the basis of an analysis of breaks induced in ring-X chromosomes (Catcheside and Lea, 1945b).

The extent of an induced intercalary deficiency may be determined roughly by a method designed by Painter and Muller (1929), which measures the suppressing action of genes in the remaining or centric portion of the chromosome. Irradiated males are mated with females having attached-X chromosomes carrying recessive marking genes. When a spermatozoon carrying an X from which a section has been deleted as a result of radiation injury fertilizes an egg with attached-X chromosomes, the individual created has X-chromosome material in excess of that of a normal diploid female. The wild-type genes in the duplicated section will suppress the expression of recessives in the attached X's. Dobzhansky (1936) has summarized data from one of his experiments in which the females were homozygous for *y*, w^a, *ec*, and *f*. The results are shown in Table 9-1.

TABLE 9-1. PROGENY OBTAINED IN A CROSS BETWEEN IRRADIATED WILD-TYPE MALES OF *D. melanogaster* AND ATTACHED-X FEMALES HOMOZYGOUS FOR THE SEX-LINKED RECESSIVES *y*, w^a, *ec*, AND *f*
(Dobzhansky, 1936)

y w^a *ec f* ♀ (normal offspring)	2185	w^a *ec f* ♀ (duplication for *y*)	8
Wild-type ♂ (normal offspring)	1879	*ec f* ♀ (duplication for *y*, w^a)	9
Superfemales	4	*f* ♀ (duplication for *y*, w^a, *ec*)	6
Wild-type ♀ (from detachment of attached X's)	3	Wild-type ♀ (duplication for *y*, w^a, *ec*, *f*)	1
y w^a *ec f* ♂ (from detachment of attached X's)	1	*y* w^a *ec* ♀ (duplication for *f*)	1

A more accurate measure of the extent of an induced duplication or deficiency may be obtained by cytological analysis. The procedure has generally involved examination of the salivary-gland chromosomes of the F_1 larval progeny of irradiated fathers, although a duplication may occasionally be recognizable in neuroblast prophases (Fig. 9-7e). In the salivary-gland-chromosome studies many of the longer duplications have been detected as mosaics, being present in some, but not all, cells of the gland. Since individuals have rarely been detected in which all the cells of the gland carried extensive duplications, it seems probable that aberrations of these types interfere with normal embryonic development, although they are not necessarily lethal in salivary-gland cells.

The nature and extent of several different duplications is represented in diagram form in Fig. 9-11. These aberrations are readily recognized because a portion of the chromosome is present in triplicate, two strands having been contributed by the irradiated father, and one by the untreated mother (as is shown by the photographs reproduced as Figs. 9-5d and 9-6a). Figure 9-11g represents a duplication covering practically the entire length of the right limb of the third chromosome; it was observed in some cells of a mosaic gland. The rearrangement diagramed in Fig. 9-11a was present in some cells of the salivary gland as a duplication of the region 5F to 15F of the X chromosome; other cells of the same gland were deficient for this region. This aberration indicates that a duplication and a deficiency may arise as complementary types as a result of exchange between sister chromatids and their separation into daughter nuclei (Kaufmann, in Demerec, Kaufmann, and Sutton, 1939; diagram in Fig. 9-4, column 3, of this chapter).

The origin of intercalary duplications by sister-chromatid exchange reveals the method whereby replicated sections have been built into the chromosomes of various species of Diptera in the course of phylogeny

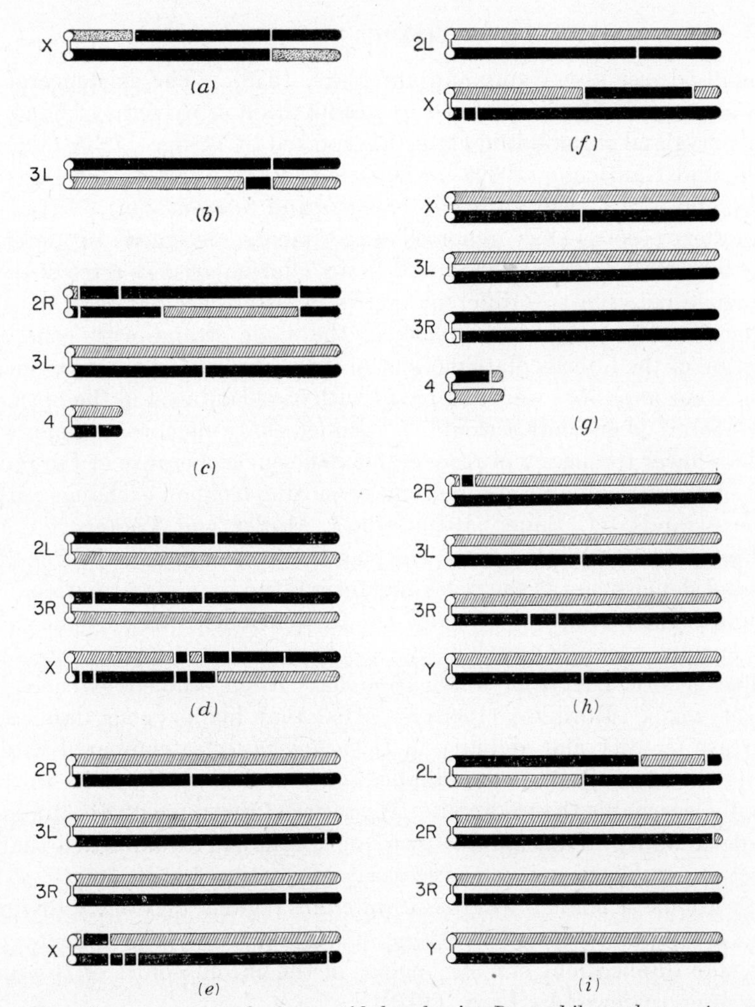

FIG. 9-11. Chromosome and chromatid breaks in *Drosophila melanogaster*. Diagrams showing positions of breaks in nine rearrangements having duplicated sections in one of the chromosomes represented. The chromosomes (2L, 2R, 3L, 3R, X, 4) are diagramed in the two-strand stage; centromeres are shown at left. Approximate positions of breaks are indicated by gaps, the chromosome type occurring at the same level in both strands, the chromatid type represented in only one strand. Portions of the chromosomes that were identified in the salivary-gland nuclei are represented in solid color; portions not recovered, in cross hatching. The rearrangement indicated in (*a*) appeared as a mosaic, some nuclei of the salivary gland showing a duplication of the reversed-repeat type, other nuclei showing a deficiency resulting from recombination of the stippled parts of the chromosome. When chromosomes other than those showing the duplicated sections were involved in a complex rearrangement, the positions of breaks in these chromosomes are also indicated. Thus, in (*i*) duplicated sections of 2L were identified, but the rearrangement also involved breaks in 2R, 3R, and the Y chromosome. The rearrangement diagramed in (*d*) had 14 breaks, although only 12 are shown because the positions of the breaks in one of two reversed repeats could not be identified. The rearrangement represented in (*g*), which is a duplication for the entire length of 3R, was found in some cells of a salivary gland but was lacking in others.

(Fig. 9-5d; see also Kaufmann and Bate, 1938). The existence of such repeats can readily be disclosed by examination of patterns of banding of salivary-gland chromosomes (e.g., as reported by Bridges, 1935, Offerman, 1936, and Kaufmann, 1939a, in *D. melanogaster;* by Metz and Lawrence, 1938, and Metz, 1947, in *Sciara ocellaris* and *S. reynoldsii*).

Muller (1950a) has reported experiments designed to determine whether small deficiencies induced by irradiation arise as a result of such exchange between two different breaks in sister chromatids or as a consequence of two adjacent breaks in the same strand with consequent deletion of the intermediate piece. In these studies the effects induced in ring-X chromosomes were compared with those induced in the normal X. On theoretical grounds it would be assumed that ring chromosomes would yield a lower frequency of recoverable deficiencies because of the production of dicentric double chromosomes resulting from an exchange between sister strands (cf. Bauer, 1939a, 1942; Muller and Pontecorvo, 1942; Pontecorvo, 1941). However, the ring chromosomes gave just as high a yield of deficiencies as the non-rings for a given dose of irradiation. It is assumed, therefore, that very few minute deficiencies arise by the method of "unequal crossing over."

The genetic effects of duplication have been studied extensively in recent years. Burdette (1940) reported that homozygous duplications decrease fertility and viability in *D. melanogaster* as compared with the corresponding heterozygous duplications, and that these in turn are usually less viable than normal. The series of rearrangements studied by Burdette and by Patterson, Brown, and Stone (1940) indicated that the effect of a duplication is not necessarily proportional to its length, so that duplications of similar lengths in different regions may have dissimilar effects on phenotype, fertility, and viability. Specific phenotypical effects of duplications of short regions of the chromosomes of *Drosophila* have been reviewed by Lewis (1950).

2-2d. *Intrachromosomal and Interchromosomal Rearrangements.* For descriptive purposes it will be assumed that in these aberrations, as contrasted with those previously mentioned, there is no gain or loss as compared with the normal condition, but merely a realignment of parts of one or more chromosomes.

The viable types of intrachromosomal rearrangement include *inversions* and *transpositions.* In the former, a section between two breaks is displaced and reinserted in reverse order, as if revolved through 180° (Fig. 9-5c). Thus, in a chromosome in which the normal sequence of genes is represented by the letters *ab cdef ghij*, the arrangement may be altered by inversion to *ab fedc ghij*. Two or more inversions may occur in the same chromosome, and occasionally they are observed in tandem, with one point of breakage common to the two inverted sections (Hoover, 1937).

The term *transposition* is applied to a rearrangement in which a segment is transferred from one position to another within the chromosome. Three breaks are involved. If the unaltered chromosome is represented by the letters *ab cdefg hi j*, transposition may produce such types as *ab hi cdefg j*, or *ab ih cdefg j*, in which the loci of the transposed segment are either in their normal sequence or inverted. Pairing between a chromosome with a transposed section and its normal homologue produces the type of configuration indicated in Fig. 9-5b. The rearrangements shown in Fig. 9-5b and c are intrabrachial, or paracentric; that is, they are restricted to one limb of a chromosome. An interbrachial, or pericentric, inversion, which extends across the centromere and encompasses both limbs of a chromosome, furnishes a pattern of pairing with its normal homologue in salivary-gland cells of *D. melanogaster* similar to that of a reciprocal translocation, because the characteristic inversion loop is distorted by the chromocentral attraction of the heterochromatic regions adjoining the centromere.

A *reciprocal translocation*, involving a mutual exchange between two different chromosomes, is clearly defined in salivary-gland cells by the cross-shaped configuration established by pairing of the rearranged chromosomes and their normal homologues. The translocation illustrated in Fig. 9-6c is between the left limb of the second chromosome and the right limb of the third. If we assign the letters *abcde fghij* to the normal sequence of parts in 2L and the letters *klmnopq rst* to the normal sequence in 3R, we may indicate the new sequences produced by translocation as *abcde rst* and *klmnopq fghij*, the inequality in length being due to the location of one break near the tip of 3R and the other near the middle of 2L. A reciprocal translocation between the right limb of the third chromosome and the Y chromosome is illustrated in Fig. 9-6b. Since the Y chromosome is represented in the salivary-gland cells of male larvae of *D. melanogaster* by only a few bands that form part of the chromocenter, the position of breakage in the Y is not determinable in these cells, but can at times be determined by inspection of neuroblast chromosomes, as is shown in Fig. 9-7a.

An inversion-translocation complex is illustrated in Fig. 9-6d. In the production of this rearrangement, the distal part of the left limb of the second chromosome (2L) was transferred to the base of 2R, the distal part of 3L to the base of 2L, and the distal part of 2R to the base of 3L. Pairing between these rearranged chromosomes and their normal homologues produced the pattern of radiating arms shown in the photograph. Descriptive details of other rearrangements have been published by Kaufmann (1939b).

Several independent two- or three-break rearrangements may be produced in the same irradiated spermatozoon. A large number of breaks within a single spermatozoon may also combine to form one or more complex cyclic rearrangements. In the most complex rearrangement so far reported (induced in a spermatozoon of *D. melanogaster*), at least 32 breaks were involved, and the broken ends had reassociated to form several independent exchanges (Kaufmann, 1943). Because of difficulties of diagnosing breaks in the proximal heterochromatic regions of the chromosomes, it was not possible to determine exactly all the details of recombination, but on the simplest possible explanation there were seven independent exchanges: four with two breaks, one with four breaks, and two with ten breaks each. In one of the latter a cyclic rearrangement occurred among the ends of chromosomes broken at the ten points indicated by the map numbers 87B/51E/81/49F/70C/33E/42C/56B/64C/76A. (Using this system of notation a simple reciprocal translocation would be represented by two breaks, such as 3C/24D.)

Chromosomal aberrations in *Drosophila*, even though they reveal no perceptible loss of chromosomal material when examined in salivary-gland preparations, are for the most part inviable when homozygous (Schultz, 1936, has reviewed the supporting evidence in considerable detail). This suggests that the production of a rearrangement alters the genetic constitution of the chromosomes involved. Analysis of radiation-induced lethal mutations has shown that a considerable fraction of them are associated with chromosomal rearrangements. The frequency varies with the dose (Oliver, 1932; Demerec, 1937; Herskowitz, 1946); it is about 35 per cent at 3000 r. (The association of a high proportion of chemically induced lethals with chromosomal aberrations has also been established by Slizynska and Slizynski, 1947.) Demerec (1937) tested a series of 26 X-ray-induced lethals associated with chromosomal rearrangements, and found that in 24 the locus of the lethal coincided with one of the breakage points. This correlation suggests either that a submicroscopic change (in the nature of a gene mutation or inactivation) has occurred adjacent to a break, as a consequence of the passage of an ionizing particle through the chromosome at that position, or that functional modification has followed displacement of a gene from its normal relations with adjacent regions of the chromosome (position effect). Evidence in favor of the former of these alternatives has been obtained in *Drosophila* by analysis of the dose-frequency relations determined experimentally in studies of lethal mutations and chromosomal aberrations (Lea and Catcheside, 1945; Lea, 1946; Herskowitz, 1946), and by analysis of the modifying effect of near-infrared radiation on the frequency of X-ray-induced lethals and chromosomal rearrangements (Kaufmann and Gay, 1947). When spermatozoa of *D. melanogaster* were exposed to near-infrared radiation before treatment with X rays, they showed an increase in frequency of chromosomal rearrangements, as compared with controls that received only the X-ray treatment; but there was no increase in the frequency of sex-linked recessive lethals, although about one-third of them were associated with gross chromosomal aberrations. An increase would be expected if the lethals were dependent for their expression on the production of rearrangements involving two independent breaks (Fano, in Kaufmann *et al.*, 1947). This evidence, and that afforded by the dose-frequency analyses of Lea, Catcheside, and Herskowitz, indicate that the lethals associated with induced chromosomal rearrangements in *Drosophila* do not represent a special class caused by a position effect. Muller (1950a) has objected to this interpretation, with the suggestion that near-infrared pretreatment may actually increase the frequency of position-effect lethals associated with gross chromosomal exchanges, but that such increase is counterbalanced by a decrease in the frequency of lethals associated with small rearrangements. This explanation involves the assumption, for which there is no experimental evidence, that small rearrangements, unlike the gross ones, are not increased in frequency by pretreatment of spermatozoa with near-infrared radiation.

Another aspect of the phenomenon of chromosomal exchange involves the breakage and recombination of homologous chromosomes, designated by the term "crossing over." In females of *Drosophila*, crossing over occurs regularly in the course of meiosis, presumably during prophase in the oöcyte. In males crossing over occurs spontaneously with very low frequency, but can be induced by X rays, as shown by Friesen (1933, 1934), Patterson and Suche (1934), and others. The frequency of crossing over in the female may also be increased by irradiation (see, for example, Whittinghill, 1938). Naturally occurring and induced crossing over have many similarities; exchange takes place at identical loci while the chromosomes are in the four-strand stage, and the recombinants are usually not lethal when homozygous (references in Shapiro, 1945). Many cases of mosaic formation in X-rayed larvae are assumed to result from crossing over that is induced in somatic tissues (Stern, 1936). In these cells the presence of chiasmalike configurations, which may afford the structural basis conducive to crossing over, has been demonstrated by Kaufmann (1934). Similar configurations have been observed by Cooper (1949) in spermatogonial cells.

The question thus arises whether irradiation promotes crossing over by facilitating a method of exchange comparable to that normally operating in the course of meiosis in the female, or whether the breakage-recombination process resembles that involved in exchange between nonhomologous regions. A related problem concerns the stage of gametogenesis during which induced crossing over occurs. Solution of these problems has generally been assumed to require analysis of the progeny of individual irradiated flies so as to detect the possible occurrence of "clusters" of crossover types. The production of such clusters has been interpreted as indicating that crossing over is induced in gonial stages (e.g., Whittinghill, 1938, 1950; Hinton and Whittinghill, 1950). Some parallel lines of evidence conform with this interpretation. It has been reported that the exceptional flies which result from interchange between X and Y chromosomes in attached-X females of *D. melanogaster* (Kaufmann, 1933) frequently occur in clusters, suggesting that they originate in a gonial cell (Neuhaus, 1936; Cooper, 1946). Whittinghill (1947) has observed that the presence of a Curly inversion in the second chromosome of males of *D. melanogaster* does not influence the induced frequency of crossing over in the third chromosome, although it is known (e.g., Schultz and Redfield, 1932) that the presence of an inversion may affect the frequency of recombination when crossing over occurs in the course of meiosis in the female.

On the other hand, Parker (1948) suggests that induced crossing over in the male may result from breakage in the spermatocyte of both homologous chromosomes by the action of a single ionizing particle—a phenomenon that will be discussed subsequently. This hypothesis assumes that synapsis of homologues occurs within a restricted region of the chromosomes being tested, since it was found that crossing over is limited to a short portion of the chromosome at any time. The production of clusters is attributed to similarity of all cells in a cyst with respect to their crossing-over potentialities. Dose-frequency relations as determined by Parker for the 500- to 2000-r range were in accord with the assumption that a single ionizing particle is concerned; there was an increase in crossing over with increase in dosage, but no increase in the proportion of double crossovers. Shapiro (1945), however, observed a much higher frequency of crossing over at 3000 than at 1500 r (0.69 as compared with 0.23 per cent in one experiment), but only a slight additional increase (to 0.79 per cent) when the dose was increased to 4500 r. He concluded that crossing over may be the result of breakage of chromosomes by ionization, especially in late spermatogonia or in spermatocytes, but that selective elimination of germ cells may account for the declining proportion of detectable recombinants with increasing dosage. A further line of evidence that the frequency of crossing over is a function of the distribution of ionizations is afforded by the observation of Lefevre (1948) that neutrons are relatively more effective per ionization than are γ rays in inducing somatic crossing over in *Drosophila*. It thus seems probable that irradiation-stimulated crossing over involves the production of chromosomal breaks as a consequence of ionization; but the period of gametogenesis during which this occurs is not clearly defined.

3. THE PROCESS OF STRUCTURAL REARRANGEMENT

From the foregoing discussion it is evident that the breakage and recombination phases must both be considered in an analysis of the process of induced structural rearrangement. Whether breakage precedes recombination, or whether both phases are part of a single process and occur simultaneously, could not be decided with certainty from the data obtained in the earlier genetic experiments; but more recent evidence, both genetical and cytological, is in accordance with the first of these alternatives (reviewed in Bauer, 1939c; Muller, 1940). After the breaks—or potential breaks—have been induced, the establishment of new associations of ends is influenced by movement of the chromosomes. In dividing cells such movement takes place as mitosis progresses, with the result that breakage and recombination occur in close succession. In the sperm head of *Drosophila*, the chromosomes are quiescent, so that the types of rearrangement that depend on establishment of associations among breakage ends at different loci are not realized until after the spermatozoon has penetrated the egg in fertilization, when chromosome movement incident to the formation of the male pronucleus presumably provides opportunities for recombination (Muller, 1940; Kaufmann, 1941a; Dempster, 1941a; Makhijani, 1945). The delay between breakage and recombination, which can be controlled by withholding the treated males from copulation, permits experimental determination of the time and method of combination of breakage ends in the production of detectable aberrations.

3-1. THE BREAKAGE PROCESS

3-1a. *Induction of Breaks.* Physical data indicate that ionizations are localized along the paths of ionizing particles throughout the cells of an irradiated tissue. The sequence of events that transpires between ionization and the production of chromosomal lesions remains largely conjectural (see Zirkle, 1949), although an understanding of possible intermediate steps is slowly emerging. It is now generally agreed that ionization produces chemical changes in the irradiated tissue (see, for example, the discussion of Allsopp, 1948; Allsopp and Catcheside, 1948). Available evidence suggests that chemical changes resulting from ionization of materials within the chromosome itself may initiate the series of reactions that lead to its breakage. Whether the chemical reactions originate for the most part in molecules of constituent nucleic acids and proteins, or are mediated through associated aqueous solutions, remains to be determined. For this reason the process of induced chromosome breakage cannot at present be described as exclusively direct or indirect according to the definition formulated by Bacq (1951), which restricts the direct effects to changes initiated by ionizations occurring in or on the surface of organic molecules. Studies conducted in the past few years showing the dependence of the yield of chromosomal aberrations on the physiological conditions of the cell or organism speak strongly in favor of the indirect reaction. Thus Baker and Sgourakis (1950) have shown with *Drosophila* that the frequency of dominant and recessive lethals is

40–70 per cent lower if the flies are irradiated in an atmosphere of nitrogen than when they are irradiated in an atmosphere of oxygen. (Similar and more extensive results have been obtained in studies of plant chromosomes; e.g., by Thoday and Read, 1947, 1949, and by Giles and Riley, 1949.)

One of the criteria of the indirect effect is the protection afforded by dissolved substances, other than those being tested, present in the aqueous medium. Further evidence, therefore, of the indirect nature of the reaction system is afforded by the findings that various substances, such as cysteine, glutathione, thiourea, ethyl alcohol, azides, and cyanides, when used in proper concentrations, afford protection against the effects of ionizing radiations. Pioneering work along these lines with respect to biologically active materials has been done on isolated enzymes (e.g., the studies of Dale, 1940, 1942; Dale, Davies, and Meredith, 1949; and McDonald, reported in Kaufmann *et al.*, 1950), and has recently been extended to whole-body irradiation (reviewed in Bacq, 1951). From the results obtained in irradiating entire animals, which indicated that the median lethal dose is much higher when protective agents are used, it can only be inferred that chromosome breaks are involved, although the dosage in most of these experiments was of the order of magnitude that is known to produce chromosomal rearrangements.

Whatever the precise course of events in the production of any specific break may be, it appears probable that molecules near a high concentration of ionizations may undergo chemical change although not themselves ionized, and that a large number of chemical activations per chromosome is required before any observable breaks occur (Fano, Caspari, and Demerec, 1950).

If an indirect reaction system can produce chromosome breaks, it may conceivably originate in some part of the cell other than the chromosome (a remote effect). Duryee (1939, 1949) has reported that the chromosomes of isolated oöcyte nuclei of amphibia are much less sensitive to radiation damage than chromosomes in the intact cell. Chromosomal injuries are also produced by exposure of isolated nonirradiated nuclei to irradiated cytoplasmic brei. Although these findings may suggest "that nuclear damage results mainly from chemical change in the cytoplasm," as Duryee has proposed, the intense X-ray doses used and the surgical procedures employed in isolating nuclei involve a reaction system different from that which leads to the formation of viable chromosomal rearrangements in the intact cell. It has been shown, however, that the types of viable aberrations induced by ionizing radiations can be produced by treating cells with chemical mutagens, which do not reach the nucleus directly but diffuse into it, either in their original form or as degradation products. For example, chromosome breaks have been induced in *Drosophila* by mustard gas and nitrogen mustard (Auerbach and Robson, 1946; Auerbach, 1949, 1950; Kaufmann, Gay, and Rothberg, 1949), and in chick fibroblasts by urethane (Paterson and Thompson, 1949).

Such results have raised the question whether breaks in chromosomes are ordinarily produced by a series of reactions originating in remote parts of the cell. A. R. Whiting (1949, 1950) examined this question in considerable detail. Her experiments on *Habrobracon* confirm and extend the earlier findings on various species, including *D. melanogaster* (reviewed in Schultz, 1936). Cytoplasmic injury produced in eggs by very intense doses of radiation inhibits the development of all embryos. After lower doses, however, which still may be twenty times greater than that required to induce dominant lethals in all the egg chromosomes, androgenetic males may develop (from nonirradiated chromosomes in X-rayed cytoplasm). No mutations are induced in these males, which are normal in morphology and fertility and produce fully viable progeny. If irradiated cytoplasm exerts any mutagenic action, it must be effected within a shorter period than that tested in these experiments. Auerbach and Robson (1947) also concluded that there was no delayed effect on untreated chromosomes of cytoplasm treated with mustard gas. Other studies indicate that the lethal effects of radiation, such as killing of *Drosophila* eggs, depend primarily on nuclear damage (e.g., Langendorff and Sommermeyer, 1940).

It appears improbable, therefore, that ionizing radiations or chemical mutagens effect genetically significant types of chromosome breaks through the accumulation of toxic substances in the cytoplasm. The fact that chemicals can induce rearrangements similar to those induced by radiations may merely indicate that breaks are produced with comparable potentialities regardless of the agent used in their production; it does not, as some authors have assumed, dispose of the possibility that the sequence of events leading to breakage can originate within the chromosome. Similar end results, as represented by a series of breaks or rearrangements, may conceivably be mediated through a variety of channels. A more specific definition of the radiation-induced reaction system therefore depends on more precise information concerning the effects of ionizations on the genetically active materials of the chromosome and on other cellular materials. This being the case, the question whether an effect is localized or remote is reduced to a choice of probabilities between the effectiveness of a sequence of events originating in the chromosome and that of one initiated elsewhere in the cell (Kaufmann, 1948a).

The target theory, in its more general terms, is formulated in accordance with the first of these alternatives. Primary production of breaks occurs with a frequency that is proportional to dose over a wide range of wave lengths, including X rays and γ rays. The effect is independent of the duration of a given dose or the number of treatments into which it is divided, and is not appreciably modified by temperature within the narrow range that can be utilized while maintaining viability (and, in some cases, fertility) of the test organisms (summary of evidence in Catcheside, 1945). These experimental results add further weight to the argument that chromosome breakage is not primarily attributable to a long chain of chemical reactions operating over considerable distances within the cell. But, as Fano, Caspari, and Demerec (1950) have pointed out, experiments on time distribution could only show interaction between separate events whose activity, even though not permanent, lasts much longer than that of a chemical activation. Phenomena exhibiting such properties are not among the usual physical effects of radiation on matter and must therefore be characteristic of biological materials. These authors have also pointed out that the direct proportionality between dosage and genetic effect would hold for indirect as well as direct action of radiation, provided that the efficiency of the indirect mechanism was not sensitive to changes in temperature and other factors.

The more rigid concept of the target theory, that a single ionization within a sensitive zone suffices to induce a break, was an outgrowth of earlier studies of the conditions governing the induction of gene mutations (summary of experimental data in Timoféeff-Ressovsky, 1937; and critical evaluation in Muller, 1940, 1950a; Fano, 1942; Fano, Caspari, and Demerec, 1950). This view has been tempered in recent years by development of the interpretation that chromosome breakage is referable to a cluster of ionizations produced by the passage of a single ionizing particle. Such clustering takes place at the tail end of the electron track, or at places where the main track branches out into other short tracks; it may occur along the entire length of the track of a recoil proton (Lea and Catcheside, 1942; Fano, 1943a). Relative efficiencies of different wave lengths and types of radiation have been explained on this basis (Giles, 1940; Lea and Catcheside, 1942; Lea, 1946, 1947a; Gray, 1946; Catcheside, 1948). For example, soft X rays of wave length 4 A produce more breaks per roentgen than harder X rays, because the spacing of ionizations is such that the whole track corresponds to the "tail" end of tracks of hard X rays. If the spacing is too close there is a loss of efficiency owing to oversaturation. Thus, wave length 8 A is less effective per roentgen than other wave lengths. Additional evidence in support of the concept that the large concentrations of energy resulting from clusters of ionizations are required to induce chromosome breakage has been obtained from comparative studies of X rays and neutrons (summarized in Fano, Caspari, and Demerec, 1950). Thus the concept that a single ionization serves to induce a chromosome break no longer seems tenable. "When the identification of a hit as a chemical activation is abandoned, the concept itself of a hit acquires a macroscopic significance, while the possibility of establishing a direct atomic physical link between the hit and its biologic consequence becomes more remote." (Fano, Caspari, and Demerec, 1950.)

3-1b. *The Sphere of Action of an Ionizing Particle.* Development of the interpretation that a single ionizing particle, rather than a single ionization, produces a chromosome break has modified the original concept that methods using ionizing radiations are adequate to determine the number of component strands of a chromosome at the time of treatment. On the assumption that a single ionization would suffice to induce a break, it was inferred that irradiation of the divided, or double, chromosome would produce breaks independently in the two chromatids (chromatid breaks), whereas irradiation of the undivided, or single, chromosome would produce breaks that would be transmitted in the subsequent division equally to the daughter chromatids (chromosome breaks). The experimental results indicated in a general way that prior to a certain stage in mitosis the chromosome reacts as a unit to the ionizing radiations (as shown in Fig. 9-3, column 1) and that subsequently each of the two chromatids is affected independently (Fig. 9-4, column 1). As an example, Carlson (1941b) presented the data shown in Table 9-2, which

TABLE 9-2. PERCENTAGE NEUROBLASTS OF THE GRASSHOPPER, *Chortophaga*, REVEALING CHROMOSOME ABERRATIONS AT STATED TIME INTERVALS AFTER TREATMENT WITH 125 R OF X RAYS
(Carlson, 1941b)

Hours after X irradiation	96	72	48	36	24	12
Chromatid translocations	0	0	1	3	12	12
Chromatid + chromosome translocations	0	0	0	0	4	0
Chromosome translocations	13	25	26	15	8	0
Chromosome fragments	17	34	41	43	57	38

indicate the frequency of interchanges involving chromosome and chromatid breaks in neuroblast cells of the grasshopper *Chortophaga viridifasciata.* In cells irradiated 72 to 96 hours before they reached metaphase, at which stage they were examined cytologically, only chromosome breaks were produced; and in those irradiated 12 hours before examination only chromatid breaks appeared; but in the intervening period both types of breaks were produced. In some cases chromosome and chromatid breaks were detected in the same chromosome. The underlying structural basis for such response has been examined in detail by several investigators (reviewed by Kaufmann, 1948b). There is convincing evidence from studies on *Tradescantia,* in which cytological examination sometimes permits determination of the number of strands in the chromosomes at the stage of mitosis during which they are irradiated, that two chromatids may be severed conjointly by a single ionizing particle to produce a so-called "isochromatid break" (Sax, 1941; Swanson, 1943; Catcheside, Lea, and Thoday, 1946b; Catcheside, 1948; Bishop, 1950). In the grasshopper, *Chortophaga*, isochromatid breaks were observed by Creighton (1941) in cells that presumably were irradiated in late prophase stages. She suggested that in these cases breakage was probably attributable to an ion cluster rather than to a single ionization. The present author (unpublished data) has confirmed by direct observation on living neuroblasts of *Chortophaga* the fact that isochromatid breaks can be produced by irradiation at late prophase stages when the chromosomes are visibly separated into chromatids (Fig. 9-3, column 2). Such evidence provides no support for the contention of Darlington and Koller (1947) that isochromatid breaks are "fictitious." Accepting the validity of their occurrence—and there are many other reasons for doing so, as Catcheside (1948) has indicated—it follows, as Lea (1946) has emphasized, that evidence obtained from X-ray studies that a chromosome is unsplit is far from conclusive.

Some of the rearrangements detected in *Drosophila* by salivary-gland-chromosome analysis have involved both chromosome and chromatid breaks in the same chromosome. A typical rearrangement (Fig. 9-11c) included two chromosome breaks, one proximal and the other distal, and in the region between them two chromatid breaks, one in each of the two sister strands. On the assumption that chromatid and chromosome breaks reveal whether a chromosome has or has not divided, the chromosomes of the spermatozoon at the time of irradiation in this case would appear to have been in the process of division. The condensed, inactive condition of the chromosomes of the sperm head, however, makes division at this stage highly improbable. On the assumption that the chromosome was single at the time of treatment, potential breaks were induced at the four loci indicated, and were duplicated subsequently in each sister chromatid. Restitution must then have occurred in each of the two strands at that locus at which a break is detectable only in the sister strand. Under such conditions a higher proportion of duplications might be expected than the analysis of a large group of induced alterations has indicated, for the reason that broken ends in both sister strands would be available for recombination. On the assumption that the chromosome was longitudinally double in the mature spermatozoon, either chromatid or isochromatid breaks might be produced, as revealed in the described rearrangement. An unequivocal decision in favor of one or another of these alternatives is complicated by the fact that the chromosomes have not been identified in the spermatozoon, so that no cytological evidence is available concerning the time of division into chromatids.

Despite this lack of direct evidence, individual rearrangements have been observed that can best be interpreted on the assumption that the chromosomes of the spermatozoon are longitudinally double (Kaufmann,

1941b, 1948b). One of these, reported by Demerec and Sutton (1940) involved a change in the Notch region of the X chromosome of *D. melanogaster*. Cytogenetic analysis showed that a deficiency in one chromatid extended from 3C8 to 3E5, inclusive, whereas in the other the deficiency extended from 3C7 to 3E5. Thus the two breaks to the right occurred at the same point, the two to the left at different points although very close together. It seems probable that the breaks in 3C7 and 3C8 were caused by the passage of a single ionizing particle but that the spread of the effect was greater along one chromatid than along the other.

Such observations on chromosome rearrangements, and a comparable series on gene mutations in *Drosophila*, are difficult to reconcile with the theory that the chromosomes of the spermatozoon are unsplit, as some investigators have assumed (e.g., Muller, 1940, 1941). Treatment of *Drosophila* spermatozoa with chemical agents, such as nitrogen mustard, produces types and proportions of lethals and chromosomal rearrangements that can be explained most readily on the assumption that to a large extent they originate as mosaics (Kaufmann, Gay, and Rothberg, 1949). Perhaps the specific action of this type of agent will provide the precise information that X-ray treatment does not provide concerning the number of experimentally separable strands that comprise the chromosomes of the spermatozoon of *Drosophila*.

In some materials lesions or constrictions are seen at anaphase in chromosomes that have been irradiated at an earlier stage, and these have been interpreted as half-chromatid breaks (e.g., in Carlson, 1938a, on *Chortophaga*). Half-chromatid breaks have also been observed in *Tradescantia* (Swanson, 1943, 1947), especially after treatment of the cells with ultraviolet radiation. Since the sphere of action of an ultraviolet quantum rarely encompasses more than one strand of a longitudinally split chromosome, the half-chromatid breaks suggest that under certain conditions radiations may act selectively on the component units of a multiple-strand chromosome. A striking demonstration of such action has been reported by Slyzinski (1950), confirming an earlier observation of Marshak (1936) that X-ray treatment of *Drosophila* embryos induces structural rearrangements affecting only a few of the chromonemata of the chromosomes that will form the giant structures seen in the salivary-gland cells. In these bodies the rearrangements are discernible as deficiencies, inversions, and translocations, involving in some cases less than one-sixteenth of the diameter of the chromosome (Fig. 9-12).

3-1c. *The Distribution of Breaks.* Cytological examination of salivary-gland chromosomes permits precise determination of the location of radiation-induced breaks participating in viable recombinations. Examination of many hundreds of rearrangements has shown that the breaks occur in the intervals between bands, suggesting that the integrity of the chromomeric regions is maintained. Moreover, breaks rarely occur between the halves of a "doublet" (exceptions are discussed by Metz, 1947), although in some cases the doublets unquestionably represent duplicated regions rather than a single gene locus. These observations suggest that breakage does not represent an indiscriminate severance of the chromosome but an uncoupling of specific linkages.

The breaks that have been located in *Drosophila* are distributed among the chromosomes of the set in proportion to their respective lengths (Bauer, Demerec, and Kaufmann, 1938; Bauer, 1939b; Helfer, 1940; Koller and Ahmed, 1942). Summarized data from the first two of these

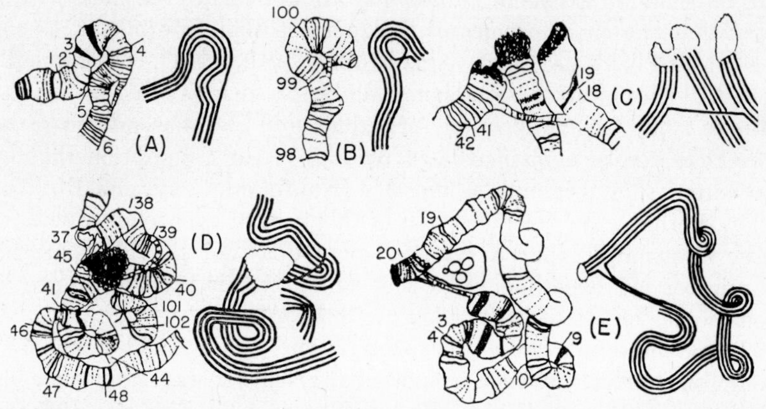

FIG. 9-12. Examples of partial structural changes in salivary-gland chromosomes of *Drosophila melanogaster*. (*A*) Deficiency. (*B*) Inversion. (*C*) Translocation. (*D*) Deficiency. (*E*) Ring formation. (*From Slizynski*, 1950.)

studies, based on the analysis of larval F_1 female progeny of irradiated fathers, are presented in Table 9-3. Expected values were computed on

TABLE 9-3. DISTRIBUTION OF INDUCED BREAKS AMONG THE LIMBS OF THE CHROMOSOMES OF *D. melanogaster*. EXPECTED FREQUENCIES BASED ON METAPHASE CHROMOSOME LENGTH
(Bauer, 1939b)

	X	2L	2R	3L	3R	4	Totals
Observed.......	325	268	298	303	394	18	1606
Expected.......	299.8	279.3	325.7	296.9	386.2	18.0	1605.9
	$\chi^2 = 5.2$ $N = 5$ $P = 0.5 - 0.3$						

the basis of length of the chromosome limbs in mitotic cells. Although there is no direct evidence that the chromosomes of the spermatozoon are structurally comparable to those of a mitotic cell, they give an intense Feulgen-positive coloration similar to that of metaphase and anaphase chromosomes, and also seem to be coiled in a similar manner [as inferred from analysis of patterns of recombination, which suggest that the X chromosome of the spermatozoon is coiled in a series of 13 or 14 gyres (Kaufmann, 1946a)].

In a parallel study of the salivary-gland chromosomes of male larvae, it was found that breakage occurs in the Y chromosome with a frequency that is approximately equal to that in the limbs of the autosomes (Kaufmann and Demerec, 1937). Only 262 breaks were diagnosed in these experiments, as compared with the 1606 indicated in Table 9-3, and there was much greater variability in the distribution of breaks among the chromosomes. Fewer breaks were detected in the Y chromosome than would be expected on the basis of length in mitotic cells, but this was in part due to inability to recognize in salivary-gland chromosomes the types of rearrangements that are restricted to heterochromatin. Since the Y chromosome is essentially heterochromatic, and is represented in the salivary-gland nucleus by only a few discs, practically all inversions and intercalary deficiencies escape detection. If the estimated number of breaks involved in such rearrangements is added to the observed number, the total for the Y chromosome approaches that expected on the basis of mitotic chromosome length. These findings do not support the assumption of Lea (1946) and Catcheside (1948) that greater sensitivity of the X chromosome, as compared with the Y, accounts for the fact that in some studies (e.g., Bauer, 1942; Catcheside and Lea, 1945a) the proportion of female flies hatching from eggs fertilized by irradiated spermatozoa was found to be lower than the proportion of male flies. Demerec and Fano (1944), on the contrary, found only a slight effect of irradiation on sex ratio, and questioned its significance. They suggested that loss, as a result of a breakage-fusion-bridge cycle, may occur in either Y or X chromosomes with approximately equal frequency, and that the numbers of dominant lethals contributed by these two chromosomes are roughly comparable.

The close correspondence between break frequency in the Y chromosome, which is largely heterochromatic, and the autosomes, which are largely euchromatic, suggests that breaks are distributed at random and in proportion to length of the chromosome at the time of irradiation, regardless of its euchromatic or heterochromatic properties. On the other hand, recent studies, by genetic methods, of the frequencies of translocations induced by X rays in *D. virilis* suggest that the Y chromosome participates in exchange only about half as frequently as the various autosomes, although it is of similar length (Baker, 1949). To what extent this result depends on primary break production and to what extent on subsequent behavior of breakage ends remains to be determined. Muller and his associates also had decided, primarily on the basis of genetic analysis of X-chromosome inversions in *D. melanogaster*, that breaks in this chromosome are not distributed at random. They suggested that breaks are produced at only a few points between blocks that are virtually unbreakable (Muller and Gershenson, 1935; Muller, Raffel, Gershenson, and Prokofyeva-Belgovskaya, 1937). On this assumption the close correlation between break frequency and mitotic chromosome length revealed in the cytological studies would be attributable to mere coincidence (Muller, 1945).

In order to evaluate these two alternatives more adequately, an extensive study was made of the distribution of breaks along the X chromosome of *D. melanogaster* (Kaufmann, 1939a, 1946a). The proximal third of this chromosome is heterochromatic in mitotic cells of the stock studied, being represented in salivary-gland chromosomes by only a few discs, whereas the distal two-thirds is primarily euchromatic and constitutes the major portion of the salivary-gland chromosome. The locations of about 1400 breaks were determined with reference to the lettered subdivisions of Bridges' salivary-gland map of this chromosome. About one-fourth of these were in the proximal heterochromatin, but rearrangements confined to this region were not detected. When the estimated number of breaks involved in such rearrangements was added to the observed number, the proportion in the proximal region was increased to about one-third of the total for the entire chromosome. This value corresponds closely to that expected on the basis of length in late prophase stages of mitosis. A similar close correlation between mitotic chromosome length and break frequency in the proximal heterochromatic regions of the second and third chromosomes was presented by Bauer (1939b). The frequency of breaks induced in the second and third chromosomes by treatment of spermatozoa with the chemical mutagen, nitrogen mustard, also showed close correlation with mitotic chromosome length (Kaufmann, Gay, and Rothberg, 1949). Approximately equal numbers of breaks occurred in each of the four arms, and the proportion in the proximal heterochromatic regions was similar to that obtained in X-ray experiments (e.g., 17.6 and 13.6 per cent in the second and third chromosomes, respectively, after nitrogen mustard treatment of males, as compared with 18.3 and 12.5 after X-ray treatment).

In the light of these findings it seems highly probable that break distribution is a function of chromosome length at the time of irradiation. Breakage disrupts the fundamental structural units that give the chromosome its linear continuity; and there is no evidence that the chromatids and their subsidiary strands have different basic patterns of organization in heterochromatin and in euchromatin, although there may be considerable differences in the types and proportions of constituent nucleic acids and proteins. The discrepancy in expression of euchromatin and heterochromatin as the mitotic-type chromosome becomes transformed into the salivary-gland type of structure is a problem of differentiation (see Krivshenko, 1950), and does not necessarily reflect any dissimilarity in structure at the time of irradiation. All these considerations indicate that more convincing evidence is needed if the close correlation between break frequency and mitotic chromosome length is to be regarded as merely coincidental, especially since cytogenetic studies have shown that the presumably indivisible blocks in the proximal region of the X may be broken in a number of different places by X-ray treatment (Kaufmann, 1944). The general conclusion drawn from these various lines of investigation is that breaks induced in the spermatozoa of *Drosophila* are distributed at random among the chromosomes and along their lengths, and represent a random sample of the number originally induced by the ionizing radiations.

In the study of the distribution of breaks along the X chromosome of *D. melanogaster* it was found that certain intercalary subdivisions, such as 11A, 12D, and 12E (Table 9-9; see also Kaufmann, 1944, 1946a), have high coefficients of breakage (determined by comparing the number observed with that expected on the basis of length represented in the salivary-gland chromosome). These regions thereby simulate the behavior of the proximal heterochromatin, and it is suggested, in the light of the foregoing considerations, that they also contain heterochromatin. The probability that other intercalary heterochromatic regions are scattered along the chromosome is indicated by the essentially normal frequency distribution curve obtained by plotting the coefficients of breakage.

Breaks detected in salivary-gland chromosomes of *Sciara* after irradiation of oöcytes are not distributed at random among chromosomes (Bozeman and Metz, 1949). The rearrangements, however, are almost exclusively intrachromosomal (Crouse, 1950), suggesting a recombination pattern different from that of breaks induced in chromosomes of spermatozoa of *Drosophila*. The absence, in the chromosomes of most organisms, of the clear pattern of linear differentiation that characterizes the salivary-gland structure makes precise determination of break position much more difficult. There are, however, several reports of nonrandom break distribution. In the Orthoptera some members of the chromosome set appear to be more susceptible to fragmentation than others (White, 1935b; Bishop, 1942), and some regions of the chromosomes also appear to be especially fragile (Helwig, 1933, 1938), although they are not necessarily characterized by any special morphological features (Bishop, 1942). If it is assumed that breaks are distributed at random among and along these chromosomes, the observed departures from randomness are to be attributed to the subsequent behavior of the breakage ends with respect to restitution or recombination, or to the difficulty of detecting all breaks in later stages of the same mitotic cycle in which they are produced. These aspects of the problem will be discussed later.

3-1d. *Dose-Frequency Relations.* Breaks that are detected cytologically represent only a part of those induced by ionizing radiations.

Some of the breaks primarily produced are eliminated by *restitution*, or restoration of the original sequence of parts, so that the sites of the original lesions are not recognizable in the repaired chromosome (see, for example, Carlson, 1941a; Fabergé, 1940; Sax, 1940). Calculations by Lea and Catcheside (1945), based on a limited number of observations, indicate that about a third of the breaks induced in the X chromosomes of spermatozoa of *Drosophila* by a 3000-r X-ray treatment undergo restitution. It has been suggested that all recessive lethal mutations not associated with cytologically detectable chromosomal aberrations represent restitutional breaks (Lea and Catcheside, 1945; Lea, 1946); but Fano (1947) and Muller (1950a) have noted the difficulty of reconciling this theory with the total data available for the production of recessive and dominant lethals at different dosage levels.

Breaks that do not undergo restitution are detectable, either because they remain "open" or "unhealed," or because the breakage ends join *inter se* or participate in structural rearrangement. Several lines of experimental evidence indicate that the detectable breaks are scattered at random within and among cells, and therefore presumably represent a random sample of those originally induced.

Single breaks, such as those that separate fragments from the centromeric portions of the chromosomes, are produced with frequencies proportional to the dose, at least when the dose is sufficiently low that the mean number of breaks per cell is less than one (Fano, 1941). The dose-frequency relation is expressed by the formula $N/N_0 = kD$, in which N is the number of breaks occurring in N_0 cells, D the dose, and k a proportionality constant. When the frequency N/N_0 approaches 100 per cent, the deviations from linearity that occur can be attributed to the production of more than one break per cell. The linear relation of breaks to dose suggests that breakage is due to a single "hit," use of this term being subject to the various qualifications that have been outlined by Muller, Fano, and others (summarized in Fano, Caspari, and Demerec, 1950).

The experimental results are well illustrated by Carlson's study (1941a) of fragment production in neuroblast cells of the grasshopper, *Chortophaga viridifasciata*, by X-ray treatment. The distribution of the fragments among nuclei was found to conform to a Poisson distribution. The number of breaks was proportional to the amount of the dose within the range tested, which extended from 7.8 to 125 r (Fig. 9-13a). Apparently there is no threshold below which breaks are not produced; it thus appears to be an all-or-none effect.

In *Drosophila* the increase in frequency of dominant lethals induced by X rays, as determined from the proportions of eggs that fail to hatch, is essentially linear at lower dosage levels, indicating that the single-break type of aberration is primarily involved (Demerec and Fano, in Demerec, Kaufmann, Sutton, and Hinton, 1940; Demerec and Fano, 1944; Catcheside and Lea, 1945a). At higher dosage levels the frequency increases more rapidly than the first power of the dose. This deviation from linearity has been attributed to the dominant-lethal effects of deficiencies and asymmetrical exchanges involving two or more breaks, which are produced with higher frequencies at higher doses (Fano and Demerec,

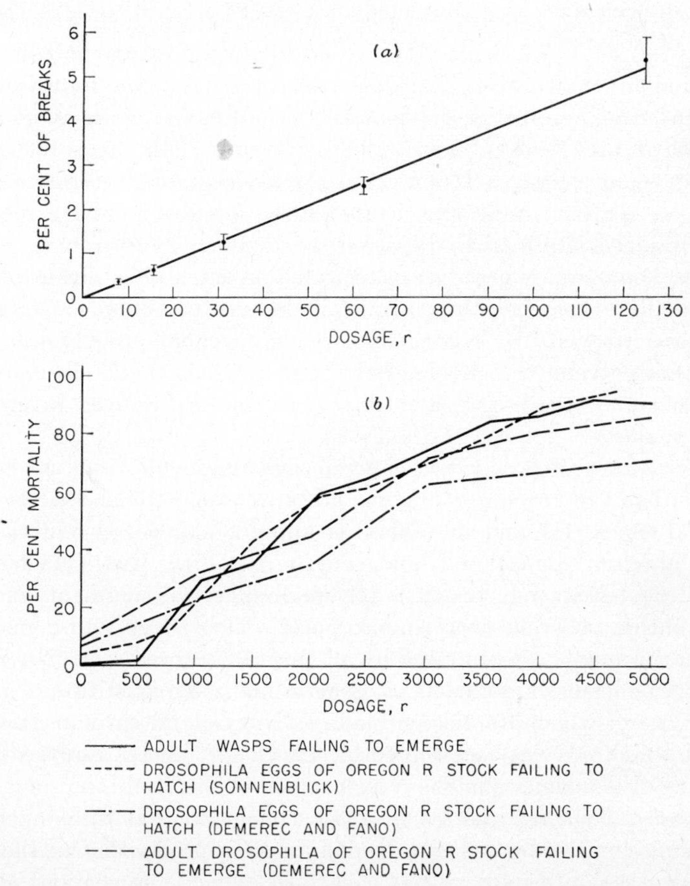

FIG. 9-13. (*a*) Relation between X-ray dose and the production of single breaks in neuroblasts of *Chortophaga*. (*From Carlson*, 1941a.) (*b*) Dose-frequency relations for dominant lethals in *Drosophila* and *Habrobracon*. (*Data of Demerec and Fano*, 1944; *Sonnenblick*, 1940; *Heidenthal*, 1945.)

1941; Demerec and Fano, 1944; Lea and Catcheside, 1945; cf. also the study of Bauer and Lerche, 1943, on the midge, *Phryne fenestralis*). Another line of evidence that the frequency of the single-break type of dominant lethal in *Drosophila* is directly proportional to dose has been obtained by Bauer (1942), in a study of the distortion of the sex ratio resulting from X-ray treatment of spermatozoa carrying a ring-X chromosome. In studies of *Habrobracon* (Heidenthal, 1945; cf. A. R. Whiting,

1945b, P. W. Whiting, 1938a, b), it was found that the proportion of adult wasps failing to emerge among the offspring of irradiated haploid males gave a dose-frequency curve closely paralleling that for dominant lethals in *Drosophila*. The results are illustrated in Fig. 9-13b.

Dose-frequency relations determined in studies of induced crossing over have been discussed previously. Related studies concern the frequency of separation of attached-X chromosomes in irradiated cells. Separation in nonirradiated $\widehat{XX}Y$ females involves crossing over with the Y chromosome, so that the detached X carries either the short or the long arm of the Y (Kaufmann, 1933). Mainx (1940) found that the frequency of exceptional flies resulting from separation of attached-X chromosomes after irradiation of unfertilized females increased approximately linearly with increased dose in the 1000- to 3000-r range. There was a marked increase over values expected on the basis of linear proportionality, however, when the dose was increased to 4000 and 4500 r. It is assumed that at the higher dose a considerable proportion of the exceptional progeny was derived from eggs in which the X chromosomes were broken by processes other than the process involved in crossing over with the Y.

The frequency of production of small deficiencies, detected by genetic methods, has been reported in some cases as proportional to dose (e.g., Muller, 1940, 1941) and in others as approaching a "two-hit" curve (e.g., Panschin, Panschina, and Peyrou, 1946). Rick (1940) also reported dose-frequency relations for small spherical fragments induced by irradiation of *Tradescantia* microspores which suggest that many of the rearrangements are produced by a "two-hit" process. In *Drosophila* the small deficiencies detected by genetic methods constitute a graded series, some of which are discernible in salivary-gland chromosomes and some of which are not (see Slizynski, 1938). From an analysis of the frequency of deficiencies in the Notch region of the X chromosome of *D. melanogaster*, Demerec and Fano (1941) concluded that the longer deficiencies involve two breaks and depend for their production on the passage of two separate ionizing particles. Deficiencies of sections shorter than 15 bands on the salivary-gland chromosome (or ca. 60 mμ on the sperm chromosome) presumably involve single events, and therefore increase in number in proportion to dose. Breakage in these cases may be visualized as a process whereby the effect of the radiation spreads along the chromosome for a short distance and produces two uncouplings rather than one.

Another type of two-break rearrangement that is apparently produced with a frequency proportional to the dose involves breaks, often in separate chromosomes, induced by irradiation with neutrons (e.g., the studies of Giles, 1940, and Thoday, 1942, on *Tradescantia*). The results suggest that both strands involved in the exchange are disrupted simultaneously by the densely ionizing track of a single recoil proton. Comparison with X rays indicated that neutrons produce a higher frequency of chromosomal aberrations for the same dose. Studies on *Drosophila* have not afforded such convincing data as those obtained from the *Tradescantia* experiments. The frequency of viable types of aberrations induced in *D. melanogaster* spermatozoa was determined by salivary-gland-chromosome examination at two levels of neutron dosage (Demerec, Kaufmann, and Sutton, 1942). The frequency at the lower dose did not differ appreciably from that induced by an equivalent dose of X rays; but the higher dose of neutrons was less efficient than X rays, as determined by the frequency of rearrangements and by the total number of breaks. The types of rearrangements induced by neutrons and X rays seemed to differ only with respect to the proportion of intercalary deficiencies, which was greater in the neutron than in the X-ray series (Kaufmann, 1941b). Genetic tests for translocations made by Catsch, Peter, and Welt (1944) also indicated that neutrons are less effective than X rays (Table 9-4), whereas similar tests by Dempster (1941b) suggested that neutrons are slightly more effective. Differences in results may stem in part from the difficulty of equilibrating doses of X rays and neutrons. Marshak (1942) has presented data which suggest that neutrons are more effective than X rays in inducing chromosomal changes in mouse tumors, but diagnosis was based on abnormal anaphase figures, and presumably included single-event as well as two-break processes.

TABLE 9-4. FREQUENCIES OF TRANSLOCATIONS BETWEEN THE SECOND AND THIRD CHROMOSOMES OF *D. melanogaster* INDUCED BY X RAYS AND FAST NEUTRONS (Catsch, Peter, and Welt, 1944)

Dose	Frequency of translocations	
	No. of sperms tested	Per cent translocations
X rays, 1000 r	6,016	1.33 ± 0.15
Neutrons, 1050 r-eq	3,287	1.07 ± 0.18
X rays, 2000 r	5,775	3.79 ± 0.25
Neutrons, 2160 r-eq	3,159	1.87 ± 0.24
X rays, 4000 r	10,223	11.09 ± 0.30
Neutrons, 4480 r-eq	2,665	4.09 ± 0.38

The frequency of two-break rearrangements induced by X rays, in which each break would be caused by a separate ionizing particle, would be expected to increase as the square of the dose in accordance with the formula $N/N_0 = k'D^n$, in which n indicates the number of independent events. The observational data for two-break rearrangements conform in general with this expectation. Inversions, deficiencies, and translocations detected by genetic methods by Timoféeff-Ressovsky (1939) increased in frequency approximately as the square of the dose (Fig. 9-14a). Data furnished by Makki and Muller (Muller, 1940) and by Catsch, Radu, and Kanellis (1943; see also Catsch, Peter, and Welt, 1944; Catsch, 1948) for translocations between the second and third chromosomes induced by X rays in the range from 400–4000 r, can be fitted to a curve that represents the 1.5 power of the dose. This deviation from the anticipated second power is attributed to the scoring of multiple-

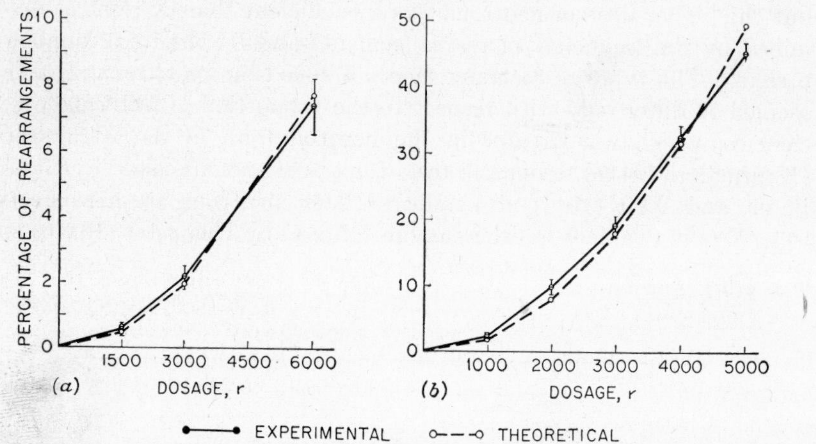

FIG. 9-14. Dose-frequency relations for viable types of chromosomal rearrangements induced by irradiation of spermatozoa of *Drosophila melanogaster*. (*a*) Dose-frequency relations determined by genetic tests for inversions, deficiencies, and translocations. Broken line represents the theoretical exponential ("two-hit") curve. The vertical bars indicate the range of the standard error for each of the experimentally derived values. (*Data from Timoféeff-Ressovsky*, 1939.) (*b*) Dose-frequency relations determined by cytological tests for chromosomal rearrangements. Exponential curve represented by broken line and limits of error by vertical bars as in Fig. 9-14a. (*Data from Bauer*, 1939c.)

break rearrangements as two-break events, and to the disproportionately greater chance for the production of inviable recombinations (dominant lethals) when many breaks are available in the same nucleus.

The frequencies of inversions, deficiencies, translocations, and more complex rearrangements, as determined by salivary-gland-chromosome analysis of the progeny of males irradiated at various dosage levels, in the studies made by Bauer, Demerec, and Kaufmann (1938) and Bauer (1939b), are indicated in Fig. 9-14b. It will be seen that the frequency of cells carrying the viable types of rearrangements increases more rapidly than the first power of the dose, approaching the second power at the lower levels of treatment.

The frequencies of complex rearrangements detected in these studies appear to be much lower than expected at low doses, and to increase less rapidly than would be expected on the general assumptions of the "hit theory." Data summarized by Fano (1941) are presented in Table 9-5. Expected frequencies (shown in parentheses) have been computed on the assumption that the relative frequencies do not depend on the dose. It will be seen that the relative frequencies of the different types of changes—two-break, three-break, four-break, of both the 2+2 and the 4 type—are nearly constant at all doses. As a possible explanation of deviation from expectancy, Fano (1943b) has suggested that potential breaks may be influenced, by mechanical perturbations, to participate in rearrangement whenever two other breaks initiate the process. There is also the possibility that these mechanical disturbances may in themselves cause breakage that is not attributable to the action of the ionizing radiations. Because of such factors it is not possible at present to formulate any simple theoretical interpretation of the relation of frequency of complex chromosomal rearrangements to dose.

In all these considerations it must be kept clearly in mind that an observed rearrangement represents the climax of a series of processes involving breakage and recombination. Efforts to separate these two phases experimentally and thereby elucidate the process of structural rearrangement have included studies of the relation between frequency of aberrations and such factors as wave length, time, and intensity of the ionizing radiations. It was shown by Muller and Ray Chaudhuri (reported in Muller, 1940) that γ rays and 50-kv X rays are equally efficient per roentgen in inducing translocations. Thus 2000 r of 50-kv X rays produced 2.9 $\pm$ 0.3 per cent translocations between the second and third chromosomes of *D. melanogaster*, and 2000 r of γ rays produced 3.8 $\pm$ 0.6 per cent. These values do not differ significantly, nor do those obtained by Catsch, Kanellis, Radu, and Welt (1944) in a study of the frequency of translocations between the second and third chromosomes induced by doses of 1000, 2000, and 4000 r at wave lengths of 0.5, 0.4, and 0.15 A.

It has also been shown that variation of time or intensity of treatment does not alter the frequency of viable types of rearrangements induced by a given dose of radiation (Muller, 1940; Kaufmann, 1941a; Dempster, 1941a; Makhijani, 1945). Muller and Makhijani (reported in Muller, 1940) found by genetic tests that doses of 2000 r given at intensities ranging from 0.05 to 250 r per minute induced similar frequencies of translocations between the second and third chromosomes. In these experiments spermatozoa were treated after they had been transferred to females in insemination; and the translocation frequencies were similar for a given dose of X rays, whether it was administered in a single treatment, with immediate or delayed opportunities for egg laying, or in a series of four treatments. A like absence of effect of discontinuous treatment when males were irradiated was established by cytological examina-

TABLE 9-5. RELATIVE FREQUENCIES OF VARIOUS TYPES OF REARRANGEMENTS INDUCED BY X RAYS IN THE SPERMATOZOA OF *D. melanogaster* (Fano, 1941)

Dose, r	2	2 + 2	3	4	2 + 3	5	6	2 + 2 + 2	2 + 2 + 3	2 + 4 3 + 3	Other	Total
1000	80% 12 (9.1)	.... (1.8)	13.3% 2 (1.8)	6.7% 1 (0.7)	.... (0.5)	.... (0.1)	.... (0.1)	.... (0.1)	.... (0.1)	.... (0.4)	.... (0.4)	100% 15
2000	73.4% 47 (38.7)	12.5% 8 (7.6)	12.5% 8 (7.7)	.... (2.7)	1.6% 1 (2.0)	.... (0.3)	.... (0.4)	.... (0.6)	.... (0.5)	.... (1.6)	.... (1.7)	100% 64
3000	66.0% 74 (67.8)	11.6% 13 (13.2)	12.5% 14 (13.4)	5.4% 6 (5.0)	2.7% 3 (3.5)	.... (0.6)	.... (0.7)	.... (1.1)	.... (1.9)	1.8% 2 (2.8)	.... (2.9)	100% 112
4000	59.6% 86 (87.1)	14.6% 21 (17.1)	11.8% 17 (17.3)	4.2% 6 (6.4)	2.1% 3 (4.5)	.... (0.7)	0.7% 1 (1.0)	.... (1.4)	2.1% 3 (1.2)	2.8% 4 (3.6)	2.1% 3 (3.8)	100% 144
5000	54.5% 149 (166.3)	11.0% 30 (32.2)	11.5% 32 (32.8)	5.1% 14 (12.2)	6.4% 12 (8.5)	1.1% 3 (1.3)	1.1% 3 (1.8)	2.2% 6 (2.7)	0.7% 2 (2.2)	3.2% 9 (6.7)	4.8% 13 (7.2)	100% 273
Total	60.5% 368	11.9% 72	12.0% 73	4.4% 27	3.1% 19	0.5% 3	0.6% 4	1.0% 6	0.8% 5	2.5% 15	2.6% 16	100% 608

tion of salivary-gland chromosomes (Kaufmann, 1941a). This method permits detection not only of rearrangements, but also of their types and proportions, and of the total number of breaks involved. The results are given in Table 9-6.

TABLE 9-6. COMPARISON OF FREQUENCIES OF INDUCED CHROMOSOME BREAKS RESULTING FROM CONTINUOUS AND DISCONTINUOUS X-RAY TREATMENT OF MALES (Kaufmann, 1941a)

(No errors are furnished for the percentage of breaks, since the distribution of the number of breaks is not given by a Poisson series; 1 × 3000 r and 1 × 4000 r refer to continuous treatment.)

Dose, r	Total glands	No. with chromosomal aberrations	Percentage altered	No. of breaks	Percentage of breaks
1 × 3000[a]	595	112	18.82 ± 1.60	293	49.24
1 × 3000[b]	132	28	21.21 ± 3.56		
3 × 1000 at 24-hr intervals	184	43	23.37 ± 3.12	96	52.17
1 × 4000[b]	271	79	29.15 ± 2.76	227	83.76
4 × 1000 at 24-hr intervals	44	15	34.09 ± 7.15	36	81.82
2 × 2000 at 16-day intervals	140	39	27.86 ± 3.79	117	83.57
Total discontinuous treatment	184	54	29.35 ± 3.36	153	83.15

[a] Data from Bauer, 1939b.

[b] Includes data from Bauer, Demerec, and Kaufmann, 1938.

These findings have been interpreted as indicating that breaks produced by irradiation of the mature spermatozoon do not participate in the formation of new rearrangements until after the sperm has entered the egg in fertilization; but, as will be discussed subsequently, this conclusion can apply only to the viable class of aberrations that are available for diagnosis by genetical or cytological techniques.

Experiments to determine the effect of differences in temperature on the production of rearrangements have given conflicting results. The earlier studies of Papalashwili (1935) and Mickey (1939), which indicated that low temperature during irradiation results in a higher frequency of chromosomal rearrangements than high temperature, were not confirmed by the extensive work of Muller (1940) and Makhijani (1949), in which similar frequencies of translocations between the second and third chromosomes of *D. melanogaster* were obtained when temperatures as different as 4.5 and 37.5°C were applied either at the time of irradiation or at the time of fertilization. In another series of experiments (Kaufmann, 1946b, 1948a), it was found that there was no significant difference in frequency of rearrangements or in total number of induced breaks when flies were exposed to temperatures of 8, 18, or 28°C before, during, or after exposure to X rays. More recent studies of sex-linked lethals by King (1947) and of translocations by Kanellis (1946) and Baker (1949) indicate that irradiation at a temperature in the 0-to-4°C range gives a higher frequency of aberrations than irradiation at 20 to 32°C. As an illustration, Fig. 9-15a and b shows the frequencies of exchanges among the second, third, fourth, fifth, and Y chromosomes of *D. virilis* determined at two temperature levels by Baker. The data indicate that not only the frequency of rearrangements, but also the slopes of the dose-

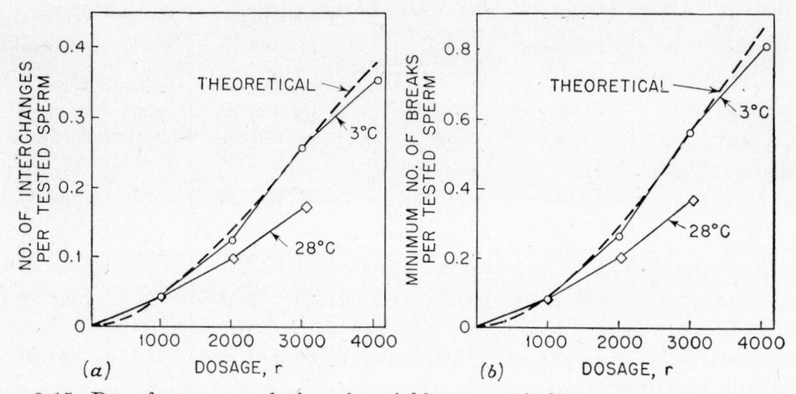

Fig. 9-15. Dose-frequency relations for viable types of chromosome rearrangements induced by irradiation of spermatozoa of *Drosophila virilis*. (*a*) Number of exchanges per tested sperm. (*b*) Minimum number of breaks per tested sperm. The method of determining the shapes of the theoretical curves presented in these figures is described in detail in the original article. (*From Baker*, 1949.)

frequency curves are influenced by the temperature at the time of treatment. Either more breaks are produced when irradiation is carried on at a low temperature (as Baker concluded), or the properties of breakage ends of chromosomes are modified so as to increase the number of viable types of exchange (as Kanellis concluded). Evidence that such modification can occur has accumulated in recent years, and will be considered in the next section.

3-1e. *Qualitative Differences among Breaks*. There is considerable evidence that the capacity of breakage ends to participate in recombination varies greatly in different organisms and types of cells. In some cases, as in the irradiated eggs of *Ascaris*, the ends of chromosomes bordering on induced breaks appear to have no capacity for uniting with one another, for chromosomal rearrangements do not occur (Bauer and LeCalvez, 1944; cf. the similar studies of Hughes-Schrader and Ris, 1941, and Ris, 1942, on Hemiptera). That differences may exist in the behavior of breakage ends in different tissues of the same organism was clearly shown by McClintock (1939). If a broken chromosome is present in the endosperm or gametophyte tissue of maize, union of sister chromatids will occur at the breakage point, but no such sister-strand reunion occurs in the tissues of the embryo.

Another aspect of the problem of qualitative differences among breaks concerns the different fates of the breakage ends produced in cells of a single type, such as the spermatozoa of *Drosophila*. Of the breaks primarily induced in a cell by irradiation, some may be restituted, some may participate in structural rearrangement, and others may remain "open" or "unhealed." When breakage ends are capable of rejoining, the probability of restitution or participation in structural change "appears not to depend on a difference in the breakage process, but mainly on whether other breaks are available with which interchange can occur" (Lea, 1946). Existing data suggest that restitution and recombination occur with approximately equal frequencies (Lea and Catcheside, 1945; Baker, 1949).

If neither restitution nor recombination takes place, it is difficult to determine whether the breakage ends are different in some way from other breakage ends, or whether they are capable of joining but have been prevented from doing so by chance circumstances (Lea, 1947a). Analysis of the proportions of breakage ends that failed to recombine in experiments treating *Tradescantia* chromosomes with different types of radiation favored the former of these alternatives (Catcheside, Lea, and Thoday, 1946a; Lea, 1946). It thus seems probable that some breaks may be qualitatively different from others with respect to their capacities for subsequent recombination.

Data obtained in studies of *Drosophila* suggest that such qualitative differences in breakage ends may exist from the time of their origin (Kaufmann, Hollaender, and Gay, 1946; Kaufmann and Wilson, 1949). These studies involved treatment of spermatozoa with near-infrared radiation before exposure to X rays. The near-infrared portion of the spectrum, centering around wave length 10,000 A, was not in itself effective in inducing chromosome breaks or gene mutations; but when used before X rays it significantly increased the frequency of viable types of rearrangements as compared with the frequency in controls receiving only the X rays. On the other hand, treatment with near-infrared radiation *after* exposure to X rays did not increase the frequency of rearrangements. The frequency of induced dominant or recessive lethals was not modified by near-infrared pretreatment or posttreatment. The experimental data are summarized in Table 9-7. Additional posttreatment data were obtained by Kaufmann and Wilson (1949) from exposure of females inseminated by X-ray-treated spermatozoa to near-infrared radiation. As in the experiments summarized above there was no significant increase in frequency of rearrangements or percentage of breaks as compared with values obtained from controls that received only the X-ray treatment.

Comparable results were obtained when near-infrared radiation was used in combination with nitrogen mustard in treating spermatozoa; pretreatment effected an increase of about 50 per cent in the frequency of rearrangements, but there was no significant increase when near-infrared radiation was used after the spermatozoa had been exposed to the chemical (Kaufmann, Gay, and Rothberg, 1949).

Since pretreatment did not increase the frequency of single-break dominant lethals, no general increase in number of all types of breaks was involved in its effect. The action of near-infrared radiation in "sensitiz-

TABLE 9-7. EFFECTS OF TREATMENT WITH X RAYS AND WITH X RAYS PLUS NEAR-INFRARED RAYS
(Kaufmann, Hollaender, and Gay, 1946)

Treatment of males	Frequency of chromosomal breaks				
	Total sperms	Rearrangements	Per cent rearrangements	No. of breaks	Breaks per 100 sperms
24–72 hr of infrared + 4000 r of X rays	721	312	43.27 ± 1.8	850	117.9
4000 r alone	549	169	30.78 ± 2.0	435	79.2
4000 r of X rays + 24–72 hr of infrared	483	133	27.50 ± 2.0	386	79.9

ing" the chromosomes therefore appears to be restricted to the control of processes involved in the formation of chromosomal aberrations. In other words, the subsequent behavior of some breakage ends is modified by conditions created as a consequence of pretreatment, whereas that of others is not. In explanation of this difference it has been suggested that the single-break, dominant-lethal aberrations originate at the time of irradiation of the spermatozoa, whereas the recombination of other breakage ends is delayed until after fertilization. Supplementary lines of evidence in support of this interpretation have been presented in detail by Kaufmann and Wilson (1949).

In the light of these observations, the breaks induced by irradiation have been classified as "complete," or thoroughgoing, and "potential" (the latter in conformity with the concept developed by Muller, 1940, 1941; Kaufmann, 1941b; Fano, 1941). Various lines of experimental evidence indicate that the potentialities of individual breaks to become restituted or to participate in structural rearrangement can be modified by various kinds of supplementary treatment (e.g., by treatment of spermatozoa with radiation of wave length 2537 A after treatment with

X rays, or by exposure of eggs to near-infrared radiation at the time of their fertilization by X-ray-treated spermatozoa; see Kaufmann and Hollaender, 1946, and Kaufmann, 1946b). Potential breaks that fail to establish new contacts during the period of recombination presumably undergo restitution soon thereafter, although some experimental evidence suggests that recombination may be delayed until after the first cleavage mitosis (Helfer, 1940).

3-1f. *Break Recombination.* The random distribution of breaks among the chromosomes of *Drosophila* having been established by analysis of viable rearrangements, the question remains whether breakage ends unite with equal freedom to produce inviable types of exchanges. Information on this question is available with respect to some of the alternative possibilities of recombination within and among chromosomes.

Intrachromosomal rearrangements involving two breaks usually eventuate as either inversions or deletions (the symmetrical and asymmetrical types diagramed in Fig. 9-3). Evidence from studies on *Drosophila* suggests that deletions are produced about as frequently as inversions of the same length (Fano, 1941). The frequency of X-chromosome inversions used in this comparison was determined by salivary-gland-chromosome analysis; the frequency of X-chromosome deletions, which cannot be ascertained accurately by that method, was determined by genetic analysis of the exceptional females produced in a cross between an irradiated wild-type male and a female carrying attached-X chromosomes with recessive marking genes (Bishop, 1941).

Other analyses of two-break rearrangements indicate that recombination within a chromosome limb is essentially at random. When inversions were grouped in classes, according to length in number of divisions within the euchromatic portions of the chromosomes (ranging from 0–18 divisions), the numbers corresponded closely with those expected on the basis of random recombination (Bauer, Demerec, and Kaufmann, 1938; Bauer, 1939b). A more intensive study of length of X-chromosome two-break rearrangements, in terms of subdivisions (ranging from 0 to 113 subdivisions, since each of the 19 divisions has 6 subdivisions), revealed some departures from the values expected with random recombination (Kaufmann, 1946a). Rearrangements measuring about 13 subdivisions or multiples thereof were somewhat more frequent than those of other lengths. This modal grouping suggests a pattern of coiling within the X chromosome at the time of recombination that slightly increases the opportunities for reunion of parts separated by the distance of the turn of the coil, as compared with regions separated by shorter or longer distances.

No accurate measurements can be made of the length of rearrangements having one break in the proximal heterochromatic region (as in division 20 of the X) and one elsewhere along the chromosome (as in divisions 1 to 19 of the X), because of uncertainty concerning the exact position of the proximal break. These "heterochromatic-euchromatic" rearrangements have been used, however, to determine the distribution of breaks in divisions 1 to 19 of the X chromosome that combine with those in division 20 (Kaufmann, 1946a). Breakage ends in division 20 combined freely with other broken regions throughout the X; no evidence was obtained of preferential recombination with the intercalary heterochromatic regions that lie scattered along the X chromosome. Combined data from this study are shown in Table 9-8.

TABLE 9-8. DISTRIBUTION OF 143 BREAKS IN DIVISIONS 1 TO 19 OF THE X CHROM- 20) COMPARED WITH DISTRIBUTION OF ALL (Kauf-

Division number	Break					
	1	2	3	4	5 6[a]	7
Observed	5	11	14	6	10	8
Expected[b]	8.65	7.45	10.93	9.49	10.57	9.37
Observed	67	51	77	73	78	70
Expected[b]	63.35	54.55	80.07	69.51	77.43	68.63
						$\chi^2 = 15.5$

[a] Grouping required for χ^2 determinations.
[b] Expected values are based on random recombination.

Salivary-gland-chromosome studies on *Drosophila* by Catcheside (1938, 1948) and Bauer (1939b) indicate that the frequency of inversions having both breaks in the same arm of a chromosome (intrabrachial) is not significantly different from that of inversions having the two breaks in different arms (interbrachial). However, in an extensive series of studies in which the frequency of rearrangements of *Drosophila* having two breaks within one chromosome arm was compared with that of rearrangements having one break in one arm and the other break in any of the other arms of the chromosome complex, it was found that the former is much lower and the latter is much higher than chance recombination would permit (Bauer, Demerec, and Kaufmann, 1938, Catcheside, 1938, and Bauer, 1939b, on *D. melanogaster;* Helfer, 1941, and Koller and Ahmed, 1942, on *D. pseudoobscura*). The X-chromosome data presented by Kaufmann (1946a), for example, show that inversions within the X are about two and a half times as frequent as expected on the basis of random recombination (see Table 9-9).

The disparity between intra- and interchromosomal exchanges is even more pronounced when unfertilized eggs are irradiated. It was found, for example, that X-ray treatment of oöcytes of *Drosophila* or *Sciara* produced inversions but practically no translocations (Glass, 1940; Bozeman, 1943; Crouse, 1950).

Two breaks in different chromosomes may also conceivably lead to the formation of an asymmetrical exchange, for example, a dicentric chromosome and an acentric fragment (Figs. 9-3 and 9-4). Since such types would not be perpetuated in *Drosophila* for salivary-gland-chromosome analysis, a comparison cannot be made in that organism between the frequencies of the viable or symmetrical two-break interchromosomal exchanges and their asymmetrical counterparts. From studies on

osome Utilized in Exchanges with the Proximal Heterochromatin (Division
1048 Breaks Recorded in These Divisions
mann, 1946a)

distribution

8	9 10[a]	11	12	13	14 15[a]	16	17 18[a]	19	Total
8	9	12	9	10	9	15	12	5	143
8.17	13.45	11.89	11.17	7.57	8.89	8.89	9.61	6.97	143.07
60	103	87	84	53	65	59	68	53	1048
59.83	98.55	87.11	81.83	55.43	65.11	65.11	70.39	51.03	1047.93

$N = 14$ $P = 0.346$

Tradescantia it appears that the symmetrical and asymmetrical types occur with about equal frequencies (Lea, 1946). In Carlson's study of neuroblast chromosomes of *Chortophaga*, 14 chromatid interchanges were analyzable, of which 5 were symmetrical and 9 asymmetrical.

Analyses of patterns of recombination have also been made for the three- and four-break rearrangements. In computing expected values, the proportion of viable to inviable types must be considered for each possible type of break distribution (Bauer, 1939b; Kaufmann, 1946a). Among the viable three-break exchanges, observed frequencies conformed closely to values expected on the basis of random recombination (Bauer, 1939b, as shown in Table 9-10). There was in this study, however, and also in that of Kaufmann (1946a), a disproportionately large number of rearrangements with all three breaks in the same chromosome limb (in the latter, eight in the X as compared with the expected 2.5). Among the four-break rearrangements, the type having two independent exchanges (2+2) was more frequent than expected, and the single cyclic rearrangement (4) much less frequent. Although the number of rearrangements falling into each of these two classes was small, the breaks utilized in the rearrangements were distributed among the chromosomes with frequencies that corresponded fairly well with random recombination, as is illustrated by the data of Kaufmann (1946a) presented in Table 9-11.

The low incidence of rearrangements of each of the complex types involving five or more breaks precludes their analysis on a similar basis, although Fano (1943b) and Kaufmann (1943) have shown that a concentration of the breaks in one or two limbs often occurs in these multiple-break rearrangements. Fano suggested that in the recombination process adjustments among the chromosomes originally involved may cause mechanical disturbances of sufficient intensity to produce new breaks, which then participate in the development of the complex rearrangement. Another possibility, which does not require the participation of mechanically induced breaks, is that heterochromatic breaks initiate the process of recombination on an intrabrachial level, and the developing rearrangement then incorporates adjacent potential breaks. This alternative is based on the suggestion of Kaufmann (1946a) that potential breaks in

TABLE 9-9. FREQUENCY OF X-CHROMOSOME INVERSIONS (X/X) AND OF TRANSLOCATIONS BETWEEN THE X AND THE AUTOSOMES (X/A)

(Data listed in first four lines involve only breaks in divisions 1–19, data in fifth line involve breaks in division 20. Expected values are calculated on basis of random recombination among five long limbs.)

(Kaufmann, 1946a)

Source material	Numbers of inversions and translocations				χ^2	P
	X/X		X/A			
	Observed	Expected	Observed	Expected		
All 2-break rearrangements[a]	87	34.22	305	357.78	89.2	<0.0001
All 2-break exchanges[b]	131	48.36	423	505.64	154.7	<0.0001
2-break exchanges with at least 1 X break in intercalary heterochromatin[c]	53	23.70	111	140.30	42.3	<0.0001
2-break exchanges with X breaks in intercalary euchromatin[d]	78	26.60	312	363.40	106.6	<0.0001
2-break exchanges with 1 break in division 20	53	24.90	142	170.10	36.4	<0.0001

[a] From nuclei having only one inversion or one translocation.

[b] From more complex rearrangements in addition to 2-break rearrangements.

[c] Regions included are 1F, 3C, 4A, 4E, 7B, 9A, 11A, 12D, 12E, 16F, 19E.

[d] X-chromosome breaks in subdivisions not listed in preceding line.

TABLE 9-10. DISTRIBUTION AMONG THE CHROMOSOMES OF BREAKS UTILIZED IN 3-BREAK REARRANGEMENTS
(Bauer, 1939b)

	Break distribution		
	1:1:1	2:1	3
Observed	14	25	5
		30	
Expected	13.89	27.79	2.32
		30.11	
$\chi^2 = 0.005$	$N = 1$	$P =$ ca. 0.95	

TABLE 9-11. DISTRIBUTION OF BREAKS UTILIZED IN 4-BREAK REARRANGEMENTS
(Kaufmann, 1946a)

		Distribution among the chromosome limbs				
		1:1:1:1	2:1:1	2:2	3:1	4
Single-contact 4-break rearrangements	Observed	3	23	6	12	0
	Expected	5.35	28.07	4.46	5.94	0.19
					6.13	
		$\chi^2 = 8.10$ $N = 3$ $P = 0.044$				
Independent 2 + 2 exchanges	Observed	19	44	9	8	1
	Expected	19.11	42.99	7.96	10.61	0.33
					10.94	
		$\chi^2 = 0.50$ $N = 3$ $P =$ ca. 0.92				

heterochromatin may be able to initiate the production of rearrangements somewhat sooner than breaks in euchromatin.

4. DIFFERENCES IN SENSITIVITY TO IONIZING RADIATIONS

On the basis of the more general considerations of the process of induced structural rearrangement outlined in the preceding pages, some attention can be given to the factors responsible for differences in sensitivity of cells to ionizing radiations.

It has been recognized since the early years of the century that the X-ray sensitivity of a tissue is related to its reproductive capacity (Bergonié and Tribondeau, 1906). It has also been reported that cells with a short mitotic cycle and intermitotic period are more sensitive to radiation and suffer greater damage than those with a longer cycle (Koller, 1947; Knowlton and Widner, 1950). Since high reproductive activity of a tissue indicates that many of its cells are dividing, it seems probable that cells in the course of mitosis are especially sensitive to the deleterious effects of radiations. This is, in fact, clearly demonstrated by experiments which show that a much larger dose of radiation is required to kill a cell immediately than to cause its death at or after its next division. As an example, 2500 r or more is required to kill chick tissue-culture cells while they are in resting stages, but irradiation of these cells with 100 r is sufficient to kill a high proportion of the cells when they subsequently attempt to divide (Lasnitzki, 1943a, b). Irradiation of *Pandorina*, a colonial member of the Volvocales, with doses of X rays ranging from 3000 to 300,000 r did not kill the cells immediately, but death occurred when they subsequently attempted to divide (Halberstaedter and Back, 1942). In another study, hematopoietic cells of tadpoles of the bullfrog exposed to 500 r of X rays showed visible damage only upon entering prophase (Schjeide and Allen, 1950). Some of the latent damage that causes cell destruction during division in these cases is presumably due to chromosomal injury. Many of the physiological disturbances effected in tissues and organisms by ionizing radiations have also been referred to alterations in the structure of chromosomes. In determining the basis for differences in the response of tissues and cells to ionizing radiations it thus becomes essential to ascertain to what extent the observations of such differences are dependent on differences in breakability of chromosomes, to what extent on opportunities for recombination of breakage ends, and to what extent on experimental procedures that permit identification of aberrations more readily in some types of cells than in others.

4-1. RELATIVE SENSITIVITY OF DIFFERENT ORGANISMS

A few selected illustrations will serve to indicate the considerable differences in frequencies of radiation-induced chromosomal aberrations in different species. About 24 r of X rays will induce breaks in 1 per cent of the chromosomes in the neuroblast cells of *Chortophaga* (Carlson, 1941a). About 400 r is required to produce breaks in 1 per cent of the X chromosomes of the spermatozoa of *Drosophila*, as determined by frequencies of dominant lethals (Fano and Demerec, 1941; Pontecorvo, 1942). At the other extreme it was reported by Cleveland and Day (cited in Sax and Swanson, 1941) that doses of X rays in the range between 3000 and 20,000 r did not produce any chromosome aberrations in the protozoon *Holomastigotoides*.

Blumel (1950) reported a difference in the survival of eggs of *D. virilis* and *D. melanogaster* exposed to comparable doses of β radiation from P^{32} combined in H_3PO_4 added to the culture medium. Pairs of mature flies were placed in shell vials, and the cultures were subsequently examined. Few flies hatched in the cultures of *virilis*, many in the *melanogaster* cultures. Parallel genetical and cytological studies of fertile progeny in the *virilis* cultures indicated that radioactive P^{32} produces both mutations and chromosomal aberrations. The *melanogaster* flies were not tested for mutations.

There are some reports that the rate of occurrence of aberrations may differ in different stocks of the same species. For example, the frequency of dominant lethals was found to be higher in the Oregon-R strain of *D. melanogaster* than in the Swedish-b strain when both were exposed simultaneously to X rays (Demerec, Kaufmann, and Hoover, 1938; Dempster, 1941b). In a more recent study, however, Demerec and Fano (1941) questioned the statistical significance of the observed differences because of the considerable range of variability from experiment to experiment in studies of frequencies of dominant lethals.

4-2. EFFECT OF PLOIDY

It has been shown in several experiments that the radiation sensitivity of a cell is related to the number of sets of chromosomes it contains. Haploid microspores of *Tradescantia* are about twice as sensitive as diploid microspores with respect to the production of chromosomal aberrations by a given dose of X rays (Sax and Swanson, 1941). Tetraploid seeds of barley are more resistant than diploid seeds to the effects of irradiation, as determined by growth rates and vigor (Müntzing, 1941). Haploid yeast plants are more sensitive than diploids, as determined by rates of survival (Latarjet and Ephrussi, 1949). In contrast with these results, it was reported by Lamy and Muller (1939) that the mortality rates are not significantly different in triploid and diploid embryos of *Drosophila* exposed to X rays. From this it was concluded that the lethal effects of X rays on embryos must be "physiological" rather than genetic in nature. However, it has been shown that in another insect, the wasp *Habrobracon*, haploid male larvae are more sensitive than diploid female larvae (Whiting and Bostian, 1931); and these observations have recently been extended by Clark and Kelly (1950). Lethal effects were determined by Clark and Kelly by measuring rates of eclosion after treatment of prepupae and pupae. Haploid males were found to be more sensitive than either diploid males or diploid females.

4-3. RELATIVE SENSITIVITY OF CHROMOSOMES IN DIFFERENT TYPES OF CELLS OF THE SAME SPECIES

The frequencies of aberrations induced by X-ray treatment in various types of cells of the plant *Tradescantia* were determined by Sax and Swanson (1941). The order of sensitivity in the cells examined, beginning with the most sensitive, was as follows: microsporocytes, microspores, root-tip cells, and the generative cell. Microspores and root-tip cells of *Allium* were less sensitive than those of *Tradescantia*. Differential sensitivity in these cases was attributed to differences in chromosome development, in speed of nuclear changes, and especially in degree of freedom and capacity for chromosome movement.

Marshak and Bradley (1945) found that the chromosomes of the Walker 256 rat carcinoma were more sensitive to X rays and neutrons than those of a rat lymphosarcoma throughout the greater portion of the resting stage. They concluded that there are physiological differences in

TABLE 9-12. FREQUENCY OF TRANSLOCATIONS AMONG SPERMATOZOA UTILIZED IN INSEMINATION AT DIFFERENT PERIODS OF TIME AFTER IRRADIATION (Catsch and Radu, 1943)

Days after treatment	Total sperm tested	No. with aberrations	Percentage of aberrations
1	2559	306	11.96 ± 0.64
2–7	1483	92	6.21 ± 0.63
8–13	1133	78	6.89 ± 0.75
14–19	1532	21	1.37 ± 0.30
20–25	1028	1	0.10 ± 0.10

TABLE 9-13. FREQUENCY OF DOMINANT LETHALS AMONG SPERMATOZOA UTILIZED IN INSEMINATION AT DIFFERENT PERIODS OF TIME AFTER IRRADIATION (Timoféeff-Ressovksy, 1931)

Days after treatment	No. of eggs laid	No. of larvae emerging	Percentage of egg mortality
10–15	1829	437	76.1
15–30	2172	1463	32.6
Control	4763	3738	14.5

the chromosomes of two different tissues (lymphoid and epithelial) of the same species.

In such experiments the aberrations were scored during a later stage of the same mitotic cycle in which the cells were exposed to the ionizing radiations. In other cases, where the method of assay determined the frequency of aberrations surviving a series of cell generations, as in *Drosophila* studies, the possibility must be considered that the survival value may differ in different types of cells. When males of *Drosophila* are irradiated, the frequency of induced rearrangements is fairly uniform among spermatozoa transferred in the earlier copulations, but significantly lower among those transferred in later matings. Typical data for chromosomal rearrangements are shown in Tables 9-12 and 9-13; similar data for sex-linked lethals have been summarized and discussed by Schultz (1936).

The marked reduction in frequency after 12 to 15 days has been attributed to the fact that in actively copulating males the spermatozoa that were mature at the time of irradiation are used up, and are replaced by cells that then existed as spermatocytes or spermatogonia. According to this explanation, these cells are subject to germinal selection; that is, they are eliminated from the germ line if they carry aberrations that prove cell-lethal, and as a result the spermatozoa maturing after irradiation are for the most part free of chromosomal rearrangements. Although this theory may seem adequate to account for the decline in frequency of aberrations, it does not take into consideration the fact that the viable types of exchanges such as translocations and inversions, which are perpetuated through cleavage and embryonic mitoses if induced in mature spermatozoa, are eliminated if induced in spermatogonia or spermatocytes. Histological examination of irradiated testes of *Drosophila* showed some necrotic apical cells to be present, but no necrosis of spermatogonia, spermatocytes, or spermatids was seen (Pontecorvo, 1944). On the basis of this observation the conclusion was reached that no germinal selection takes place. Lea (1947b) suggested, however, that germinal selection operates among spermatogonia. He attributed the decline in dominant lethals in later matings to the elimination of affected germ cells in spermatogonial stages. This explanation implied that mature and immature germ cells are equally sensitive with regard to the induction of the dominant-lethal type of aberration, and Lea stated that there is little basis for assuming that chromosomes in spermatogonia are less sensitive to lethal changes than those in the sperm. As regards the induction of viable types of chromosome change, on the other hand, this author concluded that "spermatogonia are much less sensitive than mature sperm" (Lea, 1947b).

Because of this series of conflicting interpretations, the problem of germinal selection and relative sensitivity of different stages in the male germ line of *Drosophila* requires further consideration. Clarification may possibly be obtained through the study of chemical-induced rearrangements, since it was shown by Kaufmann, Gay, and Rothberg (1949) that the frequency of translocations induced by nitrogen mustard treatment of *Drosophila* males is higher among spermatozoa transferred 13–18 days after treatment than among those utilized in earlier matings.

Differences in radiation sensitivity of cells of the testis of the grasshopper, *Decticus*, were reported by Cocchi and Uggeri (1944). Treatment of males with moderate doses of X rays caused chromosomal damage that could be detected after a few days, whereas high doses were required to effect more rapid necrosis. A dose of 25 r affected cells in telophases of the last spermatogonial division, the damage being detected by pycnosis of these cells or of the primary spermatocytes into which they were transformed. A dose of 100 r affected all secondary spermatogonia.

Much larger doses were required to damage all spermatocytes and spermatids; and primitive spermatogonia, mature spermatozoa, and the epithelial cells of the testis were found to be even more resistant.

Differential sensitivity of cells of rodents in various stages of spermatogenesis has been determined by fertility tests and by histological examination of the irradiated testes (see, for example, Snell, 1935, 1941; Snell and Ames, 1939; P. Hertwig, 1938, 1941; Henson, 1942; von Wattenwyl and Joël, 1941, 1944). Histological examination of testes of irradiated mice by P. Hertwig (1938) showed that the sensitivity of the germ cells to radiation decreased with their increasing maturity. The youngest cells disappeared first, and the mature spermatozoa last (Table 9-14). Similar

TABLE 9-14. DISAPPEARANCE AND REAPPEARANCE OF VARIOUS TYPES OF SPERMATOGENOUS CELLS IN THE IRRADIATED TESTIS OF THE MOUSE
(P. Hertwig, 1938)

Stage of development	Days after irradiation													
	2	4	6	7	9	11	13	16	18	21	26	32	39	46
Spermatogonia	..	..	..	..	..	..	X	X	X	X	X	X	X	X
	..	..	..	..	0	..	..	*	..	*	*	*	*	*
Young spermatocytes	X	X	X	..	..	..	..	..	..	..	X	X	X	X
	..	*	*	..	..	..	0	0	..	0	*	*	*	*
Large spermatocytes	X	X	X	X	X	..	..	..	..	..	..	X	X	X
	..	*	*	..	*	..	*	..	..	0	*	*	*	*
Meiotic divisions	X	X	X	X	X	X	..	..	..	..	..	..	X	X
	..	*	*	..	*	..	*	..	..	0	*	*	*	*
Prospermatids	X	X	X	X	X	X	..	..	..	..	..	..	X	X
	..	*	*	..	*	..	*	0	..	..	..	*	*	*
Spermatids	X	X	X	X	X	X	X	X	X	..	..	..	..	X
	..	*	*	..	*	..	*	*	..	..	..	0	*	*
Spermatozoa	X	X	X	X	X	X	X	X	X	X	0	..	..	X
	..	*	*	..	*	..	*	*	..	*	*	0	..	*

The symbol X indicates the presence of cells after a treatment of 800 r; the symbol * indicates the presence of cells after a treatment of 200 r; the symbol 0 indicates the occasional appearance of the cells in question. Testes in the 200-r series were fixed only 4, 6, 9, 13, and 21 to 46 days after irradiation.

results were obtained in studies in which mice were irradiated by injection of P^{32} in isotonic saline (Warren, MacMillan, and Dixon, 1950). Females inseminated by irradiated spermatozoa often produce abnormally small litters (see, for example, Snell, 1935; Brenneke, 1937), which suggests that the ionizing radiations induce dominant-lethal chromosomal aberrations. Among the viable progeny fertility may be reduced. Snell (1935, 1941) attributed such semisterility to the presence of chromosomal aberrations, induced in the paternal gamete (see also P. Hertwig, 1941; Koller and Auerbach, 1941).

P. Hertwig (1941) found that doses of radiation sufficient to inhibit spermatogenesis led to temporary sterility when the supply of mature spermatozoa had been exhausted. When fertility was restored, the newly formed spermatozoa produced litters of approximately normal size. This result suggests either that few chromosomal breaks are induced in the primordial spermatogonia, or that germinal selection in the course of spermatogenesis eliminates most of the cells with chromosomal aberrations.

Evidence of differences of sensitivity in germ cells of female mice at different stages of development was presented by Murray (1931). After exposure to 150 r of X rays, all primary follicles disappeared within two days, and no follicles were seen after 43 days. Details of these various experiments and the extensive literature pertaining thereto have been summarized by Glücksmann (1947).

Another aspect of the general problem concerns the relative sensitivity of male and female gametes. Metz and Boche (1939) found that the chromosomes of the spermatozoon and the oöcyte of *Sciara* responded differently to X rays. Numerous rearrangements were found among the progeny of irradiated males, but none among the offspring of treated females. Subsequent studies have shown that this difference is not a matter of sex, but depends on the condition of the chromosomes at the time of treatment (Crouse, 1950). In *Drosophila*, dominant-lethal effects may be induced by irradiation of the eggs. When oöcytes are irradiated before fertilization, a higher proportion of the zygotes fail to hatch than when spermatozoa are irradiated with an equivalent dose (Sonnenblick, 1940); but as Glass (1940) has shown, irradiation of eggs produces many fewer chromosomal aberrations—inversions but no translocations—than irradiation of sperm. In the gnat, *Phryne fenestralis*, irradiation of oöcytes apparently produces only the dicentric single-break type of aberration, whereas irradiation of spermatozoa also produces multiple-break recombinations (Bauer and Lerche, 1943).

Such comparisons have at times been interpreted as indicating that some of the dominant-lethal effects produced by irradiation of eggs may not be attributable to induced chromosomal alterations (Muller, 1938). Lea (1946) suggested, however, that dominant lethals induced in unfertilized eggs, as well as in sperm, can be explained by structural alterations of chromosomes, if it is assumed that the probabilities differ in sperm and egg that a breakage end will join with another breakage end in preference to undergoing sister-union. Similar calculations suggest that chromosome aberrations are largely responsible also for lethals induced in fertilized eggs (see Lea and Catcheside, 1945; Lea, 1946; Haldane and Lea, 1947). It is suggested that if primary breaks occur at random, and if joinable breaks unite at random, differences in the frequencies of viable types of exchange induced by a given dose of radiation in mature sperms and eggs depend on the proportion of the primary breaks that are incapable of restitution or participation in exchange and accordingly eventuate as dominant lethals. If this proportion is high, the treated cells will readily be inactivated by radiations and will yield few structural rearrangements (as happens when mature eggs are irradiated). If the proportion is low, the cells will be less sensitive to the dominant-lethal effects of radiation and will yield more structural rearrangements (as happens when mature spermatozoa are irradiated).

4-4. CHANGES IN SENSITIVITY OF CHROMOSOMES IN CELLS OF THE SAME TYPE

4-4a. *Effect of Aging.* The effect of age of mature spermatozoa on the frequency of induction of dominant lethals has been studied in *D. melanogaster.* Mature spermatozoa present in the testes at the time of emergence will be retained if the flies are withheld from copulation. By storing males, and controlling the time of irradiation, it was found that in early developing males the sensitivity of the chromosomes to irradiation, as determined by dominant-lethal counts of eggs, increased with increase in age (Strømnaes, 1949; cf. Dempster, 1941b). It has been suggested that this dependence on age of sperm and rate of development of the males may explain the discrepancies between the dose-frequency relations for dominant lethals reported by different workers (Strømnaes, 1949).

4-4b. *Effect of Stage of Mitosis.* In 1906 Krause and Ziegler found evidence that cells were most sensitive to irradiation at the time of organization of the equatorial plate. During the second quarter of the century extensive data assembled by a number of investigators suggested that chromosomes were most sensitive to breakage during interphase or early prophase stages. In some cases, studies of the same type of cell in the same species led to different conclusions about relative sensitivities at different mitotic phases. Obviously, the experimental methods were not uniform, and no standard method had been developed for assessing the full extent of radiation damage to the chromosomes. In more recent years, critical studies of induced chromosomal aberrations have led to conclusions agreeing with those of Krause and Ziegler. The extensive literature bearing on the question has recently been surveyed by Whiting (1945a), Bozeman and Metz (1949), and Sparrow (1951). Our attention here will be restricted to a few illustrations of differences in sensitivity at different phases of the mitotic cycle, as indicated by the production of chromosomal aberrations.

Information concerning relative sensitivities of chromosomes at different stages of gametogenesis has been obtained in studies of *Habrobracon.* In this wasp, cells in various stages of oögenesis are arranged seriatim along the length of each of the four ovarioles. Criteria have been developed for determining whether the chromosomes of eggs at the time of irradiation are in first meiotic metaphase, or in prophase. Eggs are permitted to develop parthenogenetically so that the effect of the treatment can be detected directly by its influence on hatchability (Whiting, 1940, 1945a). The results obtained in such experiments indicate that eggs whose chromosomes are in metaphase of the first meiotic division are much more sensitive than those in prophase stages of this division. Embryonic abortion in these cases is presumably due in large measure to single-break dominant-lethal chromosomal aberrations (Whiting, 1945b). Germinal selection cannot explain the observed differences, since the eggs continue meiosis and initiate the cleavage mitoses at rates not noticeably different from the controls, after doses greatly exceeding those necessary to inhibit embryonic development.

Apparently the situation in *Drosophila* is similar, although the stage of development of the egg at the time of treatment cannot be determined with as great precision as in *Habrobracon*. Patterson, Brewster, and Winchester (1932) found a higher proportion of dominant lethals among eggs laid within 24 hours after irradiation than among those laid on the third day, which presumably were in an earlier stage of oögenesis at the time of treatment. Sonnenblick (1940) also noted that the most mature oöcytes are especially sensitive to irradiation.

In *Sciara* the sensitivity of the oöcyte increases as it passes from late prophase to metaphase and anaphase, as determined by the percentage of rearrangements detected and by egg hatchability (Reynolds, 1941; Metz and Bozeman, 1942). In these fungus flies all oöcytes develop synchronously, so that the meiotic stage at the time of irradiation can readily be distinguished. More detailed information regarding sensitivity in *S. ocellaris* is furnished in a later paper (Bozeman and Metz, 1949). Sensitivity is almost zero before the breakdown of the nuclear membrane at the beginning of the first meiotic division. It then rises rapidly to a peak in anaphase, and drops off in late anaphase, when mitotic activity is arrested pending fertilization. The types of induced rearrangements include inversions, duplications, deletions, and transpositions, but almost no translocations. Summarized data based on salivary-gland-chromosome analyses are presented in Fig. 9-16.

The most exhaustive studies of differences in sensitivity during the nuclear cycle have been made by Sparrow (1944, 1948, 1951) on *Trillium*. Meiotic divisions are generally well synchronized in the anthers of the buds of this plant. The stage during which irradiation was carried out could thus be determined with a high degree of accuracy, and the effects of the treatment could be studied during the course of meiosis or in either of the two postmeiotic mitoses. Determination of fragment number in successive mitoses gave a more adequate estimate of the frequency of induced aberrations than had been possible with methods previously used. Since other investigators did not use this double scoring technique, their data do not represent total sensitivity, but only a portion of the induced effect. Breaks that are not perceptible in the condensed chromosome immediately after treatment may appear after an intervening interphase (as Reynolds, 1941, also showed in *Sciara*). Results of Sparrow's studies showed that sensitivity increases during prophases of the first meiotic division, reaching a peak in the interval between diplotene and first

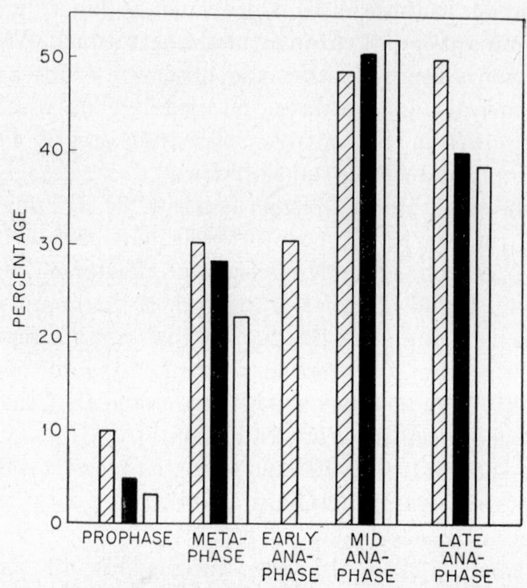

FIG. 9-16. X-ray sensitivity during various stages of first meiotic division, as determined by salivary-gland-chromosome analysis of F_1 progeny of irradiated *Sciara* females. Left column (diagonally striped) represents calculations based on wild stock; open column at right, based on yellow stock; solid black column, based on totals of both stocks. (*From Bozeman and Metz*, 1949.)

metaphase, and then falls off through the stages of the second meiotic division, to reach a low in the postmeiotic interphase (Fig. 9-17). More recent studies by Sparrow and Maldawer (1950) indicate that part of the observed difference in sensitivity is due to a difference in the frequency of recombination of breakage ends, which is significantly higher in cells irradiated in early interphase than among those irradiated in first meiotic metaphase. However, these authors state that this difference in recombination is not sufficient to account for the aforementioned differences in frequency of fragments. The recent results thus indicate that chromosomes in the condensed form have a high proportion of "potential" breaks, which subsequently produce chromosomal aberrations. These results stand in vivid contrast to many of the earlier plant studies, from which it was inferred that chromosomes are most sensitive to breakage in resting or early prophase stages.

The factors responsible for changes in sensitivity during the cycle of mitosis cannot at this time be clearly defined. Movements of chromosomes incident to the coiling of the chromonemata and formation of the equatorial plate may be of importance in modifying the reaction system. As mitosis progresses, nuclear membrane and nucleoli normally disappear and are later re-formed. Profound changes are thus effected in the structure of the chromosome and its cellular environment. Chemical changes that have been detected within chromosomes and nucleoli in the course of these events involve the types, proportions, and patterns of association of nucleic acids and proteins. Very little is known about the

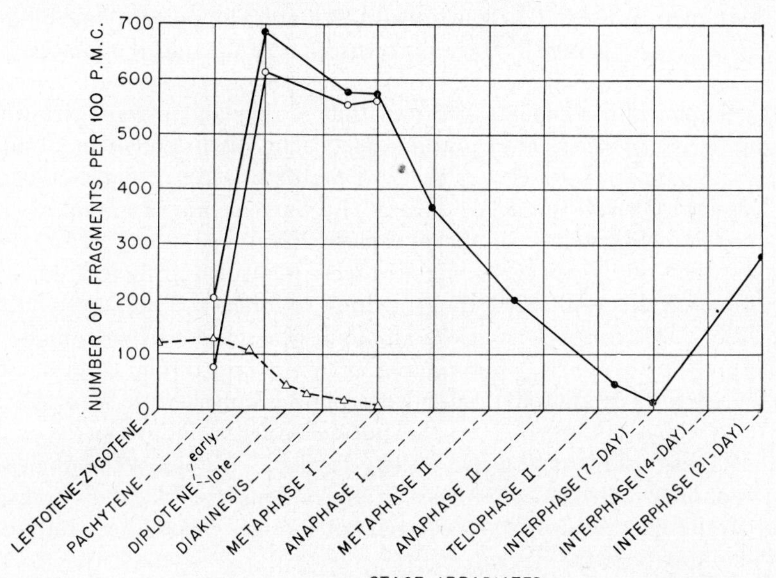

FIG. 9-17. Graph showing the numbers of fragments induced by 50 r of X rays at various stages of the nuclear cycle during microsporogenesis in *Trillium erectum*. (*From Sparrow*, 1951.)

cyclic alterations in associated cellular materials. Structural and functional modifications of cellular components may be effected by a multitude of physical and chemical agents (listed in Sparrow, 1951). To the extent that such modifications affect the reaction system initiated by ionizing radiations, the agents used will alter the radiosensitivity of cells.

5. CHEMICAL AND CYTOCHEMICAL STUDIES[2]

Numerous attempts have been made in recent years to correlate the cytologically detectable effects of ionizing radiations with changes in

[2] This section has been prepared in collaboration with Miss Helen Gay, to whom the author expresses his sincere thanks.

the chemical composition of cellular materials. The experimental procedures have involved cytochemical study of irradiated cells and chemical analysis of materials extracted therefrom. Supplementary studies have been made on nucleic acids and proteins that were irradiated after extraction from the cells. Attention has been focused, in all these studies, on nucleic acids and proteins because they are considered to be the major structural components essential to the synthetic and reparative processes of the cell. It has been established that ionizing radiations effect changes in the physical and chemical properties of these materials, and in their quantities and proportions. The more important question of the alterations effected in their patterns of organization remains largely unexplored.

Cytochemical methods have shown that X rays and γ rays, within the dosage range of 40–4000 r, produce metabolic disturbances in proliferating and undifferentiated cells that are characterized by inhibition of the synthesis of desoxyribonucleic acid in the nucleus, and accumulation of ribonucleic acid, mainly in the cytoplasm (Mitchell, 1940, 1942, 1943, 1944). The two types of nucleic acid were identified in these studies by digestion of the cells with the enzymes ribonuclease and desoxyribonuclease. Determinations of the amounts of nucleic acid were made by a method of ultraviolet photomicrography. Comparable areas of nonirradiated and irradiated tissues were photographed with wave length 2537 A, which is absorbed by the purine and pyrimidine bases of the nucleic acids. The sections were then digested with one of the nucleases and rephotographed. Differences in the amount of blackening of the photographic plate afforded an estimate of changes effected by irradiation in the amounts of the nucleic acids.

Inhibition of the synthesis of desoxyribonucleic acid by ionizing radiations has been confirmed in other experiments. Cytochemical studies have used spectrophotometric methods to determine the amount of nucleic acid in irradiated and control sections of the same tissue. Absorption of ultraviolet rays (wave length 2537 A) by purines and pyrimidines was determined on unstained preparations (Ely and Ross, 1948a, b), and absorption of visible light (around wave length 5460 A) was determined on preparations stained by the Feulgen reagent (Stowell, 1945; Petrakis, Ashler, and Ferkel, 1949). Radioactive phosphorus has also been used to determine the amount of newly formed desoxyribonucleic acid in X-ray-treated and nonirradiated tissue (e.g., studies by von Euler and von Hevesy, 1942, 1944; Hevesy, 1945—see Table 9-15; and Holmes, 1947). Hevesy (1945) reported that doses of X rays at or above the therapeutic level inhibited the formation of desoxyribonucleic acid about equally in growing and differentiated tissue. Approximately 75 per cent of the inhibiting action disappeared within 2 hours after irradiation.

Inhibition of synthesis of desoxyribonucleic acid after irradiation has been attributed to failure of conversion of ribose into desoxyribonucleic acid (Mitchell, 1940, 1942, 1943, 1944), since ribonucleic acid accumulates in the irradiated cell. The greatest accumulation seems to be in the cytoplasm, but an increase has also been detected in the nucleus by Mitchell (1944), and by Koller (1947), who noted that nucleoli, which are known to contain ribonucleic acid, are formed precociously in tumor cells after their irradiation.

In contrast with the foregoing observations, there have been some reports that the amount of ribonucleic acid in the cell decreases after its irradiation (e.g., Holmes, 1947; Ely and Ross, 1948a, b). The problem was examined by Petrakis *et al.* (1949), who made a quantitative

TABLE 9-15. RATIO OF NEWLY FORMED DESOXYRIBONUCLEIC ACID MOLECULES BEFORE AND AFTER IRRADIATION OF JENSEN'S SARCOMA OF THE RAT (von Hevesy, 1945)

Dosage, r	Time interval between irradiation and injection	Time elapsed between injection and sacrificing rat, hours	Ratio of newly formed nucleic acid in the controls and in the irradiated sarcoma
750–1500	Few minutes	0.5	3.2
335–1500	Few minutes	1	2.4
450–1500	Few minutes	2	2.2
1500	Few minutes	4–6	2.8
1230–1500	3–7 days	2	1.7

histochemical study of rat-liver epithelium over a 6-day period after irradiation of the animals with either 600 or 1500 r. The results of these investigators showed that the detectable amounts of ribonucleic acid varied with the dose and the interval of time elapsing between irradiation and fixation of the tissue. After the 600-r dose there was an increase during the first 24 hours in the concentration of ribonucleic acid in cytoplasmic granules and nucleoli, as determined by their stainability with the basic dye methylene blue; but subsequent examination indicated that a marked decrease occurred between the second and sixth days. After the 1500-r dose, there was a decrease in cytoplasmic basophilia during the first 3 hours, followed by an increase during the next 3 hours to about 40 per cent in excess of the control value, and again a marked decrease detectable at 24 hours after irradiation. Similar results, indicating that the concentration of ribonucleic acid depends on the dose and on the time interval between treatment and fixation of the cell, have been obtained by the author and his associates in cytochemical studies of sections of irradiated plant and animal tissues stained with various basic and acidic dyes (unpublished data). In these studies the ribonucleic acid was identified by using purified, crystalline ribonuclease. It is suggested that the differences in the reports of various workers concerning the accumulation or loss of ribonucleic acid after irradiation may be due in part to differences in dosage and time between treatment and examination, and in part to differences in the response of the tissues being studied.

Hevesy (1945) has noted that cells are highly radiosensitive if the synthesis of nucleic acids and associated materials is proceeding rapidly, but are more resistant if synthetic activity is low. Differences in sensitivity between actively dividing and differentiated tissues are explained on the assumption that cells in actively growing tissues do not have time to recover from the deleterious effects of radiation before initiating division, whereas there is ample time for recovery in differentiated cells. The high content of desoxyribonucleic acid in tumor cells may be a factor in their radiosensitivity (Sparrow, 1944).

Another problem that has been attacked by chemical and cytochemical methods concerns the nature of the changes induced by ionizing radiations that lead to the adhesion and deformation of chromosomes (the "primary" or "physiological" effect). Adhesion of chromosomes suggests that changes have occurred in the viscosity of their constituent materials. It has frequently been assumed that such changes in viscosity are due to depolymerization of desoxyribonucleic acid (see, for example, Darlington, 1942). There is little question that X rays can depolymerize salts of desoxyribonucleic acid in vitro, as has been shown, for example, by Sparrow and Rosenfeld (1946); Taylor, Greenstein, and Hollaender (1948); G. C. Butler (1949); Scholes, Stein, and Weiss (1949); Limperos and Mosher (1950); and Smith and Butler (1951). The data of Sparrow and Rosenfeld for sodium thymonucleate are given in the last column of Table 9-16.

TABLE 9-16. RELATION OF X-RAY DOSAGE TO RELATIVE VISCOSITIES OF SOLUTIONS OF THYMONUCLEOHISTONE AND SODIUM THYMONUCLEATE
(Sparrow and Rosenfeld, 1946)

Dosage, r	Relative viscosity	
	Nucleohistone	Sodium thymonucleate
0	3.47	3.97
7,500	3.27	3.50
15,000	3.10	3.13
30,000	2.72	2.26
45,000	2.54	1.99
60,000	2.21	1.61
90,000	1.79	1.25
120,000	1.74	1.15

High doses of radiation were used in all such experiments; in the studies just cited the minimum dose required to abolish structural viscosity completely in a 0.2 per cent solution was 22,400 r. It may well be questioned, therefore, whether the comparatively low doses required to effect adhesion and pycnosis of chromosomes in living cells—in some cases as little as 25 r—operate in a similar manner. It may also be asked whether depolymerization, which leads to a decrease in viscosity of solutions of nucleic acid in vitro, would bring about an increase in stickiness of the materials of the chromosomes.

In an effort to answer these questions, cytochemical studies have been made of the effect of the exposure to ionizing radiations on methyl green stainability of chromosomes. Purified methyl green, when used under suitable experimental conditions, stains polymerized but not depolymerized desoxyribonucleic acid (Kurnick, 1947, 1950; Pollister and Leuchtenberger, 1949). Methyl green stainability of meiotic cells of *Trillium erectum* was not impaired, as determined by spectrophotometric methods, when the living buds were exposed to doses as high as 20,000 r, although such doses reduce the viscosity of solutions of desoxyribonucleic acid (Moses, DuBow, and Sparrow, 1951). It is apparent that depolymerization of desoxyribonucleic acid (which can be produced by treatment of fixed cells with hot water or with the enzyme desoxyribonuclease) is not induced in the living cells of this plant by exposure to X rays. Similar results were obtained by the author in studies of plant and animal cells in which X-ray treatment had produced deformed and adherent metaphase and anaphase chromosomes. No reduction of methyl green stainability of these chromosomes was effected by doses as high as 16,000 r. These results agree with those of Himes (1950), who found that the "stickiness" of chromosomes caused by the "sticky" gene in maize and by chemical treatment of root tips of onion is not due to depolymerization of the desoxyribonucleic acid.

In the light of these experimentally derived data it appears that the attempts to interpret the effects of X rays on chromosomes in terms of depolymerization of desoxyribonucleic acid are premature and inconclusive. Attachment and detachment of desoxyribonucleic acid are not simple coupling and uncoupling phenomena, since it has been shown that the chromosome is a complex aggregate of both desoxyribose and ribose nucleic acids, intimately associated with each other and with histones and more acidic proteins (Kaufmann, McDonald, and Gay, 1951). Some studies have also indicated that there is very little increase in the amount of desoxyribonucleic acid between mid-interphase and metaphase (e.g., Swift, 1950; Lison and Pasteels, 1950; Pasteels and Lison, 1950), although other experiments (e.g., those of Ogur *et al.*, 1951, on *Lilium*) suggest that the amount of desoxyribonucleic acid increases during mitosis as well as during interphase. It has also been reported that changes occur during mitotic prophases in the amount and type of chromosomal ribonucleic acid (Kaufmann, McDonald, and Gay, 1948).

Since in the living cell nucleic acids exist in association with proteins, the possible effects of ionizing radiations on proteins and nucleoproteins must also be assessed. Changes occur in the viscosity of solutions of gelatin, egg albumin, and serum albumin exposed to X rays or radium (see, for example, the review of Arnow, 1936). The action of X rays in lowering the viscosity of a solution of nucleohistone is shown in Table 9-16. When nucleoproteins prepared from chicken erythrocytes and carp spermatozoa in the form of stiff gels were irradiated, the gels gradually liquefied (Errera, 1946). If the cells were first subjected to intense irradiation (50,000 r), and the nucleoproteins were then extracted, the latter formed liquid solutions rather than gels. Von Euler and Hahn (1946) irradiated nuclei isolated from calf thymus with 65,000 r but did not detect any change in the nucleoproteins. Cytological examination of cells of the testis of the salamander, *Triturus*, that had been irradiated with heavy doses of X rays (from 5,000 to 50,000 r) revealed chromosomal material that had spread out along the spindle fibers (Rugh, 1950). It was suggested that denaturation of protein might have been responsible for the lowered viscosity leading to this dislocation.

In the light of these various lines of experimental evidence it is apparent that a satisfactory understanding of the action of ionizing radiations on the materials of the chromosome must await the accumulation of information about the types and patterns of association of nucleic acids, proteins, and related materials during the various phases of the mitotic cycle.

REFERENCES

Information regarding availability of government reports indicated by an asterisk may be obtained from the Office of Technical Services, Department of Commerce, Washington, D.C.

Alberti, W., and G. Politzer (1923) Über den Einfluss der Röntgenstrahlen auf die Zellteilung. Arch. mikroskop. Anat. Entwicklungsmech., 100: 82–109.

——— and ——— (1924) Über den Einfluss der Röntgenstrahlen auf die Zellteilung. Arch. Entwicklungsmech. Organ., 103: 284–307.

Allsopp, C. B. (1948) Theories of the biological action of ionizing radiations. Brit. J. Radiology, 21: 72–74.

——— and D. G. Catcheside (1948) Chemical breakage of chromosomes. Nature, 161: 1011–1012.

Amato, A. (1911) Über die Wirkung der Röntgenstrahlen auf in Karyokinese begriffene Zellen. Z. Röntgenk., 13: 1–14.

Anderson, E. G. (1924) X-rays and the frequency of nondisjunction in *Drosophila*. Michigan Acad. Sci., 4: 523–525.

——— (1925a) Crossing over in a case of attached X-chromosomes in *Drosophila melanogaster*. Genetics, 10: 403–417.

——— (1925b) The proportion of exceptions in the offspring of exceptional females from X-ray treatment in *Drosophila*. Michigan Acad. Sci., 5: 355–356.

——— (1931) The constitution of primary exceptions obtained after X-ray treatment of *Drosophila*. Genetics, 16: 386–396.

Arnow, L. E. (1936) Effects produced by the irradiation of proteins and amino acids. Physiol. Revs., 16: 671–685.

Auerbach, C. (1949) Chemical mutagenesis. Biol. Revs., 24: 355–391.

——— (1950) Differences between effects of chemical and physical mutagens. Pubbl. staz. zool. Napoli (Suppl.), 22: 1–23.

——— and J. M. Robson (1946) Chemical production of mutations. Nature, 157: 302.

——— and ——— (1947) The production of mutations by chemical substances. Proc. Roy. Soc. Edinburgh, B62: 271–283.

Bacq, Z. M. (1951) L'action indirecte du rayonnement X et ultraviolet. Experientia, 7: 11–19.

Baker, W. K. (1949) The production of chromosome interchanges in *Drosophila virilis*. Genetics, 34: 167–193.

——— and E. Sgourakis (1950) The effect of oxygen concentration on the rate of X-ray-induced mutations in Drosophila. Proc. Natl. Acad. Sci. U.S., 36: 176–184.

Bauer, H. (1939a) Röntgeninduktion von Chromosomenmutationen bei *Drosophila*. Proc. Seventh Intern. Congr. Genetics, 38.

——— (1939b) Röntgenauslösung von Chromosomenmutationen bei *Drosophila melanogaster*. I. Chromosoma, 1: 343–390.

——— (1939c) Die Chromosomenmutationen. Z. indukt. Abstamm.- u. Vererbungsl., 76: 309–322.

——— (1942) Röntgenauslösung von Chromosomenmutationen bei *Drosophila melanogaster*. II. Die Häufigkeit des primären Bruchereignisses nach Untersuchungen am Ring-X-Chromosom. Chromosoma, 2: 407–458.

———, M. Demerec, and B. P. Kaufmann (1938) X-ray-induced chromosomal alterations in *Drosophila melanogaster*. Genetics, 23: 610–630.

——— and J. LeCalvez (1944) Das Verhalten der Chromosomen von *Ascaris megalocephalus* nach Röntgenbestrahlung. Chromosoma, 2: 593–617.

——— and W. Lerche (1943) Die Auslösung von Zygotischlethalen Mutationen bei *Phryne fenestralis* durch Röntgenbestrahlung der Spermien. Chromosoma, 2: 482–492.

Bergonié, J., and L. Tribondeau (1904) Action des rayons X sur le testicule du rat blanc. Compt. rend. soc. biol., 57: 400–402; 592–595.

——— and ——— (1906) Interpretation de quelques résultats de la radiothérapie et essai de fixation d'une technique rationelle. Compt. rend., 143: 983–985.

Bishop, C. J. (1950) Differential X-ray sensitivity of *Tradescantia* chromosomes during the mitotic cycle. Genetics, 35: 175–187.

Bishop, D. W. (1942) Spermatocyte chromosome aberrations in grasshoppers subjected to X-radiation during embryonic stages. J. Morphol., 71: 391–429.

Bishop, M. (1941) The recovery of simple and multiple breaks of the X-chromosome of *Drosophila melanogaster*. University of Texas M.A. thesis.

Blumel, J. (1950) The action of radioactive phosphorus in *Drosophila*. Science, 111: 205–206.

Bonnier, G., K. G. Lüning, and A. M. Perje (1949) Formation of gynandromorphs and other kinds of mosaics. Hereditas, 35: 301–335.

Bozeman, M. L. (1943) Effects of irradiation on oöcytes of *Sciara*. Genetics, 28: 71.

——— and C. W. Metz (1949) Further studies on sensitivity of chromosomes to irradiation at different meiotic stages in oöcytes of *Sciara*. Genetics, 34: 285–314.

Brenneke, H. (1937) Strahlenschädingung von Mäuse- und Rattensperma, Beobachtet an der Frühentwicklung der Eier. Strahlentherapie, 60: 214–238.

Bridges, C. B. (1916) Nondisjunction as proof of the chromosome theory of heredity. Genetics, 1: 1–52; 107–163.

——— (1923) The translocation of a section of chromosome II upon chromosome III in *Drosophila*. Anat. Record, 24: 426.

——— (1935) Salivary chromosome maps. J. Heredity, 26: 60–64.

——— and T. H. Morgan (1923) The third chromosome group of mutant characters of *Drosophila melanogaster*. Carnegie Inst. Wash. Pub. 327: 1–251.

Brookhaven National Laboratory Conference (1948) on biological applications of nuclear physics, USAEC Report BNL-C4.*

Burdette, W. J. (1940) The effect of artificially produced tetraploid regions of the chromosomes of *Drosophila melanogaster*. Univ. Texas Pub. 4032: 157–163.

Butler, G. C. (1949) The effect of X- and γ-rays in aqueous solutions of sodium thymonucleate. Can. J. Research, B27: 972–987.

Buzzati-Traverso, A., and L. L. Cavalli (1948). Teorio del urto ed unita biologische elementari. Milan.

Carlson, J. G. (1938a) Some effects of X-radiation on the neuroblast chromosomes of the grasshopper, *Chortophaga viridifasciata*. Genetics, 23: 596–609.

——— (1938b) Mitotic behavior of induced chromosomal fragments lacking spindle attachments in the neuroblasts of the grasshopper. Proc. Natl. Acad. Sci. U.S., 24: 500–507.

——— (1940) Immediate effects of 250 r of X-rays on the different stages of mitosis in neuroblasts of the grasshopper, *Chortophaga viridifasciata*. J. Morphol., 66: 11–23.

——— (1941a) An analysis of X-ray-induced single breaks in neuroblast chromosomes of the grasshopper (*Chortophaga viridifasciata*). Proc. Natl. Acad. Sci. U.S., 27: 42–47.

——— (1941b) Effects of X-radiation on grasshopper chromosomes. Cold Spring Harbor Symposia Quant. Biol., 9: 104–112.

Carothers, E. E. (1940) A cytological study of X-rayed grasshopper embryos. J. Morphol., 66: 529–559.

Catcheside, D. G. (1938) Frequency of induced structural changes in the chromosomes of *Drosophila*. J. Genetics, 36: 307–320.

——— (1945) Effects of ionizing radiations on chromosomes. Biol. Revs., 20: 14–28.

——— (1946) Genetic effects of radiations. Brit. Med. Bull., 4: 18–23.

——— (1948) Genetic effects of irradiations. Advances in Genetics, 2: 271–358.

——— and D. E. Lea (1945a) The rate of induction of dominant lethals in *Drosophila melanogaster* sperm by X-rays. J. Genetics, 47: 1–9.

——— and ——— (1945b) Dominant lethals and chromosome breaks in ring X-chromosomes of *Drosophila melanogaster*. J. Genetics, 47: 25–40.

———, ———, and J. M. Thoday (1946a) Types of chromosome structural change induced by the irradiation of *Tradescantia* microspores. J. Genetics, 47: 113–136.

———, ———, and ——— (1946b) The production of chromosome structural changes in *Tradescantia* microspores in relation to dosage, intensity and temperature. J. Genetics, 47: 137–149.

Catsch, A. (1948) Versuche an Drosophila über die Dosisabhängigkeit strahleninduzierter Chromosomenmutationen. Z. indukt. Abstamm.- u. Vererbungsl., 82: 155–163.

———, A. Kanellis, G. Radu, and P. Welt (1944) Über die Auslösung von Chromosomenmutationen bei *Drosophila melanogaster* mit Röntgenstrahlen verschiedener Wellenlänge. Naturwissenschaften, 32: 228.

———, O. Peter, and P. Welt (1944) Vergleich der chromosomenmutations-auslösenden Wirkung von Röntgenstrahlen und schnellen Neutronen bei *Drosophila melanogaster*. Naturwissenschaften, 32: 230–231.

——— and G. Radu (1943) Über die Abhängigkeit der röntgeninduzierten Translokationrate von Reifezustand der bestrahlen Gameten bei *Drosophila melanogaster*. Naturwissenschaften, 31: 368–369.

———, ———, and A. Kanellis (1943) Die Dosisproportionalität der durch Röntgenbestrahlung ausgelöstem Translokationen zwischen II und III Chromosom bei *Drosophila melanogaster*. Naturwissenschaften, 31: 368.

Clark, A. M., and E. M. Kelly (1950) Differential radiosensitivity of haploid and diploid prepupae and pupae of *Habrobracon*. Cancer Research, 10: 348–352.

Cocchi, U., and B. Uggeri (1944) Die Wirkung der Röntgenstrahlen auf den Heuschreckenhoden. Strahlentherapie, 75: 96–109.

Cold Spring Harbor Symposia on Quantitative Biology (1941) Genes and chromosomes. Structure and organization. Vol. 9, pp. 1–315.

Cooper, K. W. (1946) Detachment frequency of attached-X chromosomes in autosomal structural heterozygotes of *Drosophila melanogaster*. Proc. Natl. Acad. Sci. U.S., 32: 273–275.

——— (1949) The cytogenetics of meiosis in *Drosophila*. Mitotic and meiotic autosomal chiasmata without crossing over in the male. J. Morphol., 84: 81–122.

Creighton, M. (1941) The effects of X-rays on mitotic and meiotic chromosomes and cell division in *Chorthippus longicornis* (Orthoptera). J. Exptl. Zool., 37: 347–369.

——— and B. H. Evans (1941) Some effects of X-rays on the germ cells of *Chorthippus longicornis* (Orthoptera). J. Morphol., 69: 187–205.

Crouse, H. V. (1950) The differential response of male and female germ cells of *Sciara coprophila* (Diptera) to irradiation. Am. Naturalist, 84: 195–202.

Dalcq, A., and S. Simon (1932) Contributions à l'analyse des fonctions nucléaires dans l'ontogénèse de la grenouille. II. Le rôle dynamique des chromosomes mis en évidence par lesion mécanique ou irradiation des gamètes. Protoplasma, 14: 497–555.

Dale, W. M. (1940) Effect of X-rays on enzymes. Biochem. J., 34: 1367–1373.

——— (1942) Effects of X-rays on the conjugated protein *d*-amino acid oxidase. Biochem. J., 36: 80–85.

———, J. V. Davies, and W. J. Meredith (1949) Further observations on the protection effect in radiation chemistry. Brit. J. Cancer, 3: 31–41.

Darlington, C. D. (1942) Chromosome chemistry and gene action. Nature, 149: 66–69.

——— and P. C. Koller (1947) The chemical breakage of chromosomes. Heredity, 1: 187–221.

Delbrück, M. (1940) Radiation and the hereditary mechanism. Am. Naturalist, 74: 350–362.

Demerec, M. (1937) Relationship between various chromosomal changes in *Drosophila melanogaster*. Cytologia, Fujii Jubilee vol., pp. 1125–1132.

——— and U. Fano (1941) Mechanism of the origin of X-ray-induced notch deficiencies in *Drosophila melanogaster*. Proc. Natl. Acad. Sci. U.S., 27: 24–31.

——— and ——— (1944) Frequency of dominant lethals induced by radiation in sperms of *Drosophila melanogaster*. Genetics, 29: 348–360.

——— and J. G. Farrow (1930a) Non-disjunction of the X-chromosomes in *Drosophila virilis*. Proc. Natl. Acad. Sci. U.S., 16: 707–710.

——— and ——— (1930b) Relation between the X-ray dosage and the frequency of primary nondisjunction of X-chromosomes in *Drosophila virilis*. Proc. Natl. Acad. Sci. U.S., 16: 711–714.

——— and M. E. Hoover (1936) Three related X-chromosome deficiencies in *Drosophila*. J. Heredity, 27: 207–212.

——— and B. P. Kaufmann (1937) The Gene. Carnegie Inst. Wash. Year Book, No. 36, pp. 44–51.

——— and ——— (1941) Time required for *Drosophila* males to exhaust the supply of mature sperm. Am. Naturalist, 75: 366–379.

——— and ——— (1950) Drosophila guide. Carnegie Inst. Wash., Washington, D.C.

——— and E. Sutton (1940) Unequal breaks in two sister chromatids induced by X rays in *Drosophila melanogaster*. Proc. Natl. Acad. Sci. U.S., 26: 532–536.

———, B. P. Kaufmann, and M. E. Hoover (1938) The gene. Carnegie Inst. Wash. Year Book, No. 37, pp. 40–47.

———, ———, and E. Sutton (1939) The gene. Carnegie Inst. Wash. Year Book No. 38, pp. 185–191.

———, ———, and ——— (1942) Genetic effects produced by neutrons in *Drosophila melanogaster*. Genetics, 27: 140.

———, ———, ———, and O. T. Hinton (1940) The gene. Carnegie Inst. Wash. Year Book, No. 39, pp. 211–217.

Dempster, E. R. (1941a) Absence of a time factor in the production of translocations in *Drosophila* sperm by X irradiation. Am. Naturalist, 75: 184–187.

——— (1941b) Dominant vs. recessive mutation. Proc. Natl. Acad. Sci. U.S., 27: 249–250.

Dobzhansky, T. (1929) Genetical and cytological proof of translocations involving the third and fourth chromosomes of *Drosophila melanogaster*. Biol. Zentr., 49: 408–419.

——— (1930) Translocations involving the third and fourth chromosomes of *Drosophila melanogaster*. Genetics, 15: 347–399.

——— (1936) Induced chromosomal aberrations in animals, *in* Biological effects of radiation, ed. B. M. Duggar. McGraw-Hill Book Company, Inc., New York, Vol. II, pp. 1167–1208.

Dubinin, N. P., and B. N. Sidorow (1934) Relation between the effect of a gene and its position in the system. Am. Naturalist, 68: 377–381.

Duggar, B. M. (ed.) (1936) Biological effects of radiation. McGraw-Hill Book Company, Inc., New York, 2 vols.

Duryee, W. R. (1939) Comparative effects of X radiation on isolated and non-isolated nuclei. Anat. Record (Suppl.), 75: 144.

——— (1949) The nature of radiation injury to amphibian cell nuclei. J. Natl. Cancer Inst., 10: 735–796.

Eberhardt, K. (1939) Über den Mechanismus strahleninduzierter Chromosomenmutationen bei *Drosophila melanogaster*. Chromosoma, 1: 317–335.

Ely, J. O., and M. H. Ross (1948a) Nucleic acid content in intestines of rats after X radiation. Cancer Research, 8: 285–294.

——— and ——— (1948b) Nucleic acid content in intestines of rats after neutron radiation. Cancer Research, 8: 607–612.

Errera, M. (1946) Action des radiations sur les nucléoprotéines du noyau cellulaire. Bull. soc. chim. biol., 28: 472–477.

von Euler, H., and L. Hahn (1946) Influence of roentgen rays on isolated cell nuclei. Acta Radiol., 27: 268–280.

——— and G. v. Hevesy (1942) Wirkung der Röntgenstrahlen auf den Umsatz der Nukleinsäure im Jensen-Sarkom. Kgl. Danske Videnskab. Selskab Biol. Medd., 17: 1–38.

——— and ——— (1944). Wirkung der Röntgenstrahlen auf den Umsatz der Nukleinsäure im Jensen-Sarkom. II. Arkiv Kemi, Mineral. Geol., 17A(30): 1–60.

Fabergé, A. C. (1940) Chromosome fragmentation by X-rays. J. Genetics, 39: 229–248.

Fankhauser, G. (1945) The effects of changes in chromosome number on amphibian development. Quart. Rev. Biol., 20: 20–78.

Fano, U. (1941) On the analysis and interpretation of chromosomal changes in *Drosophila*. Cold Spring Harbor Symposia Quant. Biol., 9: 113–121.

——— (1942) On the interpretation of radiation experiments in genetics. Quart. Rev. Biol., 17: 244–252.

——— (1943a) Production of ion clusters by X rays. Nature, 151: 698.

——— (1943b) Mechanism of induction of gross chromosomal rearrangements in *Drosophila* sperms. Proc. Natl. Acad. Sci. U.S., 29: 12–18.

——— (1947) Note on the theory of radiation-induced lethals in Drosophila. Science, 106: 87–88.

———, E. Caspari, and M. Demerec (1950) Genetics, *in* Medical physics, ed. O. Glasser. Year Book Publishers, Chicago, Vol. 2, pp. 365–385.

——— and M. Demerec (1941) Measurements of the frequency of dominant lethals induced in sperm of *Drosophila melanogaster* by X-rays. Genetics 26: 151.

——— and ——— (1944) Genetics: physical aspects, *in* Medical physics, ed. O. Glasser. Year Book Publishers, Chicago, pp. 495–512.

FIAT (1948) Review of German science, 1939–1946. Biophysics, Part 1. Biol. Strahleneinwirkungen, pp. 51–122.

Friesen, H. (1933) Artificially induced crossing-over in males of *Drosophila melanogaster*. Science, 78: 513–514.

——— (1934) Künstliche Auslösung von Crossing-over bei Drosophila-Männchen. Biol. Zentr., 54: 65–75.

Gager, C. S. (1908) Effects of the rays of radium on plants. Mem. N.Y. Botan. Garden, 4: 1–278.

Giese, A. C. (1947) Radiations and cell division. Quart. Rev. Biol., 22: 253–282.

Giles, N. H. (1940) The effect of fast neutrons on the chromosomes of *Tradescantia*. Proc. Natl. Acad. Sci. U.S., 26: 567–575.

——— and H. P. Riley (1949) The effect of oxygen on the frequency of X-ray-induced chromosomal rearrangements in *Tradescantia* microspores. Proc. Natl. Acad. Sci. U.S., 35: 640–646.

Glass, H. B. (1940) Differential susceptibility of the sexes of *Drosophila* to the effect of X-rays in producing chromosome aberrations. Genetics, 25: 117.

Glücksmann, A. (1947) The effects of radiation on reproductive organs. Brit. J. Radiology, Suppl. 1, pp. 101–108.

Grasnick, W. (1918) Die Wirkung der Radiumstrahlen auf tierisches Gewebe. Experimentell-histologische Untersuchung an Geweben von Amphibien larven. Arch. mikroskop. Anat., 90: 1–38.

Gray, L. H. (1946) Comparative studies of the biological effects of X-rays, neutrons, and other ionizing radiations. Brit. Med. Bull., 4: 11–18.

Halberstaedter, L., and L. Back (1942) The effect of X rays on single colonies of *Pandorina*. Brit. J. Radiology, 15: 124–128.

Haldane, J. B. S., and D. E. Lea (1947) A mathematical theory of chromosomal rearrangements. J. Genetics, 48: 1–10.

Heidenthal, G. (1945) The occurrence of X-ray-induced dominant lethal mutations in *Habrobracon*. Genetics, 30: 197–205.

Helfer, R. G. (1940) Two X-ray-induced mosaics in *Drosophila pseudoobscura*. Proc. Natl. Acad. Sci. U.S., 26: 3–7.

——— (1941) A comparison of X-ray induced and naturally occurring chromosomal variations in *Drosophila pseudoobscura*. Genetics, 26: 1–22.

Helwig, E. R. (1933) The effect of X-rays upon the chromosomes of *Circotettix verruculatus* (Orthoptera). J. Morphol., 55: 265–311.

——— (1938) The frequency of reciprocal translocations in irradiated germ cells of *Circotettix verruculatus* (Orthoptera). Arch. biol., 49: 144–158.

Henson, M. (1942) The effect of roentgen irradiation of sperm upon the embryonic development of the albino rat (*Mus norvegicus albinus*). J. Exptl. Zool., 91: 405–433.

Herskowitz, I. H. (1946) The relationship of X-ray-induced recesssive lethals to chromosomal breakage. Am. Naturalist, 80: 588–592.

Hertwig, G. (1911) Radiumbestrahlung unbefruchteter Froscheier und ihre Entwicklung nach Befruchtung mit normalem Samen. Arch. mikroskop. Anat. Entwicklungsmech., 77(II): 165–209.

——— (1927) Beiträge zum Determinations- und Regenerations-problem mittels der Transplantation haploidkerniger Zellen. Arch. Entwicklungsmech. Organ., 111: 292–316.

Hertwig, O. (1911) Die Radiumkrankheit tierischer Keimzellen. Arch. mikroskop. Anat. Entwicklungsmech., 77(II): 1–164.

——— (1913) Versuche an Tritoneiern über die Einwirkung bestrahlter Samenfäden auf die tierische Entwicklung. Arch. mikroskop. Anat. Entwicklungsmech., 82(II): 1–63.

Hertwig, P. (1911) Durch Radiumbestrahlung hervorgerufene Veränderungen in den Kernteilungsfiguren der Eier von *Ascaris megalocephala*. Arch. mikroskop. Anat. Entwicklungsmech., 77(II): 301–312.

——— (1916) Durch Radiumbestrahlung verursachte Entwicklung von halbkernigen Triton- und Fischembryonen. Arch. mikroskop. Anat. Entwicklungsmech., 87(II): 63–122.

——— (1924) Bastardierungsversuche mit entkernten Amphibieneiern. Arch. mikroskop. Anat. Entwicklungsmech., 100: 41–60.

——— (1938) Die Regeneration des Samenepithels der Maus nach Röntgenbestrahlung unter besonderer Berücksichtigung der Spermatogonien. Arch. exptl. Zellforsch. Gewebezücht., 22: 68–73.

——— (1941) Erbänderungen bei Mäuse nach Röntgenbestrahlung. Proc. Seventh Intern. Genetics Congr., pp. 145–146.

von Hevesy, G. (1945) Effect of roentgen rays on cellular divisions. Revs. Modern Physics, 17: 102–111.

Himes, M. H. (1950) Studies on the chemical nature of "sticky" chromosomes. Genetics, 35: 670.

Hinton, C. W., and M. Whittinghill (1950) The distribution of X-ray induced crossovers from Curly inversion heterozygotes of *Drosophila melanogaster* females. Proc. Natl. Acad. Sci. U.S., 36: 552–558.

Holmes, B. E. (1947) The inhibition of ribo- and thymonucleic synthesis in tumor tissue by irradiation with X rays. Brit. J. Radiology, 20: 450–453.

Holthusen, H. (1921) Beiträge zur Biologie der Strahlenwirkung. Untersuchungen an Askarideneiern. Arch. ges. Physiol. (Pflügers), 187: 1–24.

Hoover, M. E. (1937) A tandem inversion in *Drosophila melanogaster*. Genetics, 22: 634–640.

Hughes-Schrader, S., and H. Ris (1941) The diffuse spindle attachment of coccids, verified by the mitotic behavior of induced chromosome fragments. J. Exptl. Zool., 87: 429–456.

Kanellis, A. (1946) Abhängigkeit der Rate strahleninduzierter Chromosomenmutationen bei *Drosophila melanogaster* von der Temperatur während der Bestrahlung. Naturwissenschaften, 33: 27.

Kaufmann, B. P. (1927) The value of the smear method for plant cytology. Stain Technology, 2: 88–90.

——— (1933) Interchange between X- and Y-chromosomes in attached-X females of *Drosophila melanogaster*. Proc. Natl. Acad. Sci. U.S., 19: 830–838.

——— (1934) Somatic mitosis of *Drosophila melanogaster*. J. Morphol., 56: 125–155.

——— (1936) A terminal inversion in *Drosophila ananassae*. Proc. Natl. Acad. Sci. U.S., 22: 591–594.

——— (1939a) Distribution of induced breaks along the X-chromosome of *Drosophila melanogaster*. Proc. Natl. Acad. Sci. U.S., 25: 571–577.

——— (1939b) Induced chromosome rearrangements in *Drosophila melanogaster*. J. Heredity, 30: 179–190.

——— (1941a) The time interval between X radiation of sperm of *Drosophila* and chromosome recombination. Proc. Natl. Acad. Sci. U.S., 27: 18–24.

——— (1941b) Induced chromosomal breaks in *Drosophila*. Cold Spring Harbor Symposia Quant. Biol., 9: 82–92.

——— (1943) A complex induced rearrangement of *Drosophila* chromosomes and its bearing on the problem of chromosome recombination. Proc. Natl. Acad. Sci. U.S., 29: 8–12.

——— (1944) Cytology. Carnegie Inst. Wash. Year Book, No. 43, pp. 115–120.

——— (1946a) Organization of the chromosome. I. Break distribution and chromosome recombination in *Drosophila melanogaster*. J. Exptl. Zool., 102: 293–320.

——— (1946b) Modification of the frequency of chromosomal rearrangements induced by X rays in *Drosophila*. III. Effect of supplementary treatment at the time of chromosome recombination. Genetics, 31: 449–453.

——— (1948a) Radiation-induced chromosome aberrations. Brookhaven Conf. Rept., USAEC Report BNL-C-4,* pp. 27–35.

——— (1948b) Chromosome structure in relation to the chromosome cycle. II. Botan. Rev., 14: 57–126.

——— and R. C. Bate (1938) An X-ray-induced intercalary duplication in *Drosophila* involving union of sister chromatids. Proc. Natl. Acad. Sci. U.S., 24: 368–371.

——— and M. Demerec (1937) Frequency of induced breaks in chromosomes of *Drosophila melanogaster*. Proc. Natl. Acad. Sci. U.S., 23: 484–488.

——— and H. Gay (1947) The influence of X-rays and near-infrared rays on recessive lethals in *Drosophila melanogaster*. Proc. Natl. Acad. Sci. U.S., 33: 366–372.

———, ———, and H. Rothberg, Jr. (1949) The influence of near infrared radiation on the production by nitrogen mustard of chromosome rearrangements in *Drosophila*. J. Exptl. Zool., 111: 415–436.

——— and A. Hollaender (1946) Modification of the frequency of chromosomal rearrangements induced by X-rays in *Drosophila*. II. Use of ultraviolet radiation. Genetics, 31: 368–376.

———, ———, and H. Gay (1946) Modification of the frequency of chromosomal rearrangements induced by X-rays in *Drosophila*. I. Use of near infrared radiation. Genetics, 31: 349–367.

———, M. R. McDonald, and H. Gay (1948) Enzymatic degradation of ribonucleoproteins of chromosomes, nucleoli, and cytoplasm. Nature, 162: 814.

———, ———, and ——— (1951) The distribution and interrelation of nucleic acids in fixed cells as shown by enzymatic hydrolysis. J. Cellular Comp. Physiol., 38 (Suppl. 1): 71–99.

———, ———, ———, K. Wilson, and R. Wyman (1947) Organization of the chromosome. Carnegie Inst. Wash. Year Book, No. 46, pp. 136–146.

———, ———, ———, N. O. Belser, J. M. Pennoyer, M. R. Lennihan, and J. T. Judge (1950). Organization of the chromosome. Carnegie Inst. Wash. Year Book, No. 49, pp. 168–177.

——— and K. Wilson (1949) Modification of the frequency of chromosomal rearrangements induced by X rays in *Drosophila*. IV. Posttreatment with near-infrared radiation. Genetics, 34: 425–436.

Kikkawa, H. (1938) Studies on the genetics and cytology of *Drosophila ananassae*. Genetica, 20: 458–516.

King, E. D. (1947) The effect of low temperature upon the frequency of X-ray-induced mutations. Genetics, 32: 161–164.

Knowlton, N. P., Jr., and W. R. Widner (1950) The use of X rays to determine the mitotic and intermitotic time of various mouse tissues. Cancer Research, 10: 59–63.

Koernicke, M. (1905) Über die Wirkung der Röntgen- und Radiumstrahlen auf pflanzliche Gewebe und Zeller. Ber. deut. botan. Ges., 23: 404–415.

Koller, P. C. (1947) The effect of radiation on the normal and malignant cell in man. Brit. J. Radiology, Suppl. 1, pp. 84–96.

——— and I. A. R. S. Ahmed (1942) X-ray-induced structural changes in the chromosomes of *Drosophila pseudoobscura.* J. Genetics, 44: 53–72.

——— and C. A. Auerbach (1941) Chromosome breakage and sterility in the mouse. Nature, 148: 501–502.

Krause, P., and K. Ziegler (1906) Experimentelle Untersuchungen über die Einwirkung der Röntgenstrahlen auf tierisches Gewebe. Forschr. Gebiete Röntgenstrahlen, 10: 126–182.

Krivshenko, J. D. (1950) The structure of the heterochromatic part of the Y-chromosome in *Drosophila buscki.* Proc. Natl. Acad. Sci. U.S., 36: 703–707.

Kurnick, N. B. (1947) Discussion, appended to paper by L. Michaelis. Cold Spring Harbor Symposia Quant. Biol., 12: 141–142.

——— (1950) The quantitative estimation of desoxyribonucleic acid based on methyl green staining. Exptl. Cell Research, 1: 151–158.

Lamy, R., and H. J. Muller (1939) Evidence of the nongenetic nature of the lethal effects of radiation on *Drosophila* embryos. Proc. Seventh Intern. Congr. Genetics, pp. 180–181.

Langendorff, H., and K. Sommermeyer (1940) Strahlenwirkung auf Drosophilaeier. I. Die Schädigung der 6 Stunden alten Eier durch Röntgenstrahlen in Abhängigkeit von der Wellenlänge. Strahlentherapie, 68: 656–668.

Lasnitzki, I. (1943a) The effect of X rays on cells cultivated *in vitro.* II. Recovery factor. Brit. J. Radiology, 16: 61–67.

——— (1943b) The response of cells *in vitro* to variations in X-ray dosage. Brit. J. Radiology, 16: 137–141.

——— (1948) The effect of beta rays on cells cultivated *in vitro.* Brit. J. Radiology, 21: 265–269.

Latarjet, R., and B. Ephrussi (1949) Courbes de survie de levures haploides et diploides soumises aux rayons X. Compt. rend., 229: 306–308.

Lavedan, J. (1945) L'action des radiations sur le cellule normale. Gauthier-Villars & Cie, Paris.

Lea, D. E. (1946) Actions of radiations on living cells. Cambridge University Press, London (The Macmillan Company, New York, 1947).

——— (1947a) The induction of chromosome structural changes by radiation: detailed quantitiative interpretation. Brit. J. Radiology, Suppl. 1, pp. 75–83.

——— (1947b) Effects of radiation on germ cells: Dominant lethals and hereditary partial sterility. Brit. J. Radiology, Suppl. 1, pp. 120–137.

——— and D. G. Catcheside (1942) The mechanism of the induction by radiation of chromosome aberrations in *Tradescantia.* J. Genetics, 44: 216–245.

——— and ——— (1945) The relation between recessive lethals, dominant lethals, and chromosome aberrations in *Drosophila.* J. Genetics, 47: 10–24.

Lefevre, Geo., Jr. (1948) The relative effectiveness of fast neutrons and gamma rays in producing somatic crossing over in *Drosophila.* Genetics 33: 113.

Lewis, E. B. (1950) The phenomenon of position effect. Advances in Genetics, 3: 73–115.

Limperos, G., and W. A. Mosher (1950) Roentgen irradiation of desoxyribonucleic acid. I. Mechanism of the action of irradiation on aqueous solution. Am. J. Roentgenol. Radium Therapy, 63: 681–693.

Lison, L., and J. Pasteels (1950) Mesures photométriques de la teneur en acide désoxyribosenucléique des noyaux au cours de la mitose. Acad. roy. Belg., Classe sci., Mem., 36: 348–354.

London Conference (1947) Certain aspects of the action of radiation on living cells. Brit. J. Radiology, Suppl. 1.

McClintock, B. (1939) The behavior in successive nuclear divisions of a chromosome broken at meiosis. Proc. Natl. Acad. Sci. U.S., 25: 405–416.

Mainx, F. (1940) Die Wirkung von Röntgenstrahlen auf die Trennung der attached-X Chromosomen bei *Drosophila melanogaster*. Z. Abstamm.- u. Vererbungsl., 78: 238–245.

Makhijani, J. K. (1945) Mutation frequency as conditioned by the manner of application of radiation. Indian J. Genetics Plant Breeding, 5: 15–31.

——— (1949) The ineffectiveness of temperature in influencing the production of mutations by X-rays. J. Univ. Bombay, 13: 1–13.

Makino, S. (1939) On the tetraploid spermatocytes produced by irradiation in *Podisma mikado* (Acrididae). Japanese J. Genetics, 15: 80–82.

Marshak, A. (1936) The structure of the chromosomes in the salivary gland of *Drosophila melanogaster*. Am. Naturalist, 70: 181–184.

——— (1942) Effects of X-ray and neutrons on mouse lymphoma chromosomes in different stages of the nuclear cycle. Radiology, 39: 621.

——— and M. Bradley (1945) Relative sensitivity of chromosomes to neutrons and X-rays. III. Comparison of carcinoma and lymphosarcoma in the rat. Proc. Natl. Acad. Sci. U.S., 31: 84–90.

Mavor, J. W. (1922) The production of non-disjunction by X-rays. Science, 55: 295–297.

——— (1924a) The production of non-disjunction by X-rays. J. Exptl. Zool., 39: 381–432.

——— (1924b) Gynandromorphs from X-rayed mothers. Am. Naturalist, 58: 525–529.

Metz, C. W. (1947) Duplication of chromosome parts as a factor in evolution. Am. Naturalist, 81: 81–103.

——— and R. D. Boche (1939) Observations on the mechanism of induced chromosome rearrangements in *Sciara*. Proc. Natl. Acad. Sci. U.S., 25: 280–284.

——— and M. L. Bozeman (1942) Chromosome studies on *Sciara*. Carnegie Inst. Wash. Year Book, No. 41, pp. 237–242.

——— and E. G. Lawrence (1938) Preliminary observations on *Sciara* hybrids. J. Heredity, 29: 179–186.

Mickey, G. H. (1943) The influence of low temperature on the frequency of translocations produced by X-rays in *Drosophila melanogaster*. Genetica, 21: 386–407.

——— (1942) Polyploid gametes in the Louisiana lubber grasshopper. Proc. Louisiana Acad. Sci., 6: 82.

Mitchell, J. S. (1940) Increase in ultra-violet absorption of cytoplasm after therapeutic X and gamma irradiation. Nature, 146: 272–273.

——— (1942) Disturbance of nucleic acid metabolism produced by therapeutic doses of X and gamma radiations. I. Methods of investigation. II. Accumulation of pentose nucleotides in cytoplasm after irradiation. III. Inhibition of synthesis of thymo-nucleic acid by radiation. Brit. J. Exptl. Path., 23: 285–313.

——— (1943) Metabolic effects of therapeutic doses of X and gamma radiations. Brit. J. Radiology, 16: 339–343.

——— (1944) Disturbance of nucleic acid metabolism produced by therapeutic doses of X and gamma radiations. Brit. Empire Cancer Campaign, 21st Ann. Rept., pp. 62–63.

Mohr, O. L. (1919) Mikroskopische Untersuchungen zu Experimenten über den Einfluss der Radiumstrahlen und der Kältewirkung auf die Chromatinreifung und das Heterochromosom bei *Decticus veruccivorus* (♂). Arch. mikroskop. Anat. Entwicklungsmech., 92: 300–368.

——— (1932) Genetical and cytological proof of somatic elimination of the fourth chromosome in *Drosophila melanogaster*. Genetics, 17: 60–80.

Morgan, T. H., C. B. Bridges, and A. H. Sturtevant (1925) The genetics of *Drosophila*. Bibliographia Genetica, 2: 1–262.

Moses, M. J., R. DuBow, and A. H. Sparrow (1951) The effects of X-rays on desoxypentose nucleic acid *in situ*. Quantitative cytochemical studies on *Trillium*. J. Natl. Cancer Inst., 12: 232–235.

Muller, H. J. (1928a) The problem of genic modification. Z. indukt. Abstamm.- u. Vererbungsl., Suppl. 1, pp. 234–260.

——— (1928b) The production of mutations by X rays. Proc. Natl. Acad. Sci. U.S., 14: 714–726.

——— (1930) Types of visible variations induced by X-rays in *Drosophila*. J. Genetics, 22: 299–334.

——— (1938) Biological effects of radiation with special reference to mutation. Actualités sci. et ind., No. 725, pp. 477–494.

——— (1940) An analysis of the process of structural change in chromosomes of *Drosophila*. J. Genetics, 40: 1–66.

——— (1941) Induced mutations in *Drosophila*. Cold Spring Harbor Symposia Quant. Biol., 9: 151–167.

——— (1945) The non-equivalence of the blocks and the salivary "heterochromatin." Genetics, 30: 15.

——— (1950a) Some present problems in the genetic effects of radiation. J. Cellular Comp. Physiol., 35 (Suppl. 1): 9–70.

——— (1950b) Radiation damage to the genetic material. Am. Scientist, 38: 33–59; 126; 399–425.

——— and E. Altenburg (1928) Chromosome translocations produced by X-rays in *Drosophila*. Anat. Record, 41: 100.

——— and ——— (1930) The frequency of translocations produced by X-rays in *Drosophila*. Genetics, 15: 283–311.

——— and S. M. Gershenson (1935) Inert regions of chromosomes as the temporary products of individual genes. Proc. Natl. Acad. Sci. U.S., 21: 69–75.

——— and G. Pontecorvo (1942) The surprisingly high frequency of spontaneous and induced breakage and its expression through dominant lethals. Genetics, 27: 157–158.

———, D. Raffel, S. M. Gershenson, and A. A. Prokofyeva-Belgovskaya (1937) A further analysis of loci in the so-called "inert region" of the X-chromosome of *Drosophila*. Genetics, 22: 87–93.

——— and F. Settles (1927) The non-functioning of the genes in spermatozoa. Z. indukt. Abstamm.- u. Vererbungsl., 43: 285–312.

Müntzing, A. (1941) Differential response to X-ray treatment of diploid and tetraploid barley. Kgl. Fysiograf. Sällskap. (Lund) Förh., 11: 1–10.

Murray, J. M. (1931) A study of histological structure of mouse ovaries following exposure to roentgen therapy. Am. J. Roentgenol. Radium Therapy, 25: 1–45.

Neuhaus, M. J. (1936) Crossing-over between the X- and Y-chromosomes in the female of *Drosophila melanogaster*. Z. indukt. Abstamm.- u. Vererbungsl., 71: 265–275.

Oak Ridge Symposium (1948) Radiation genetics, Biology Division, Oak Ridge National Laboratory. J. Cellular Comp. Physiol., 35 (Suppl. 1) (1950).
Offermann, C. A. (1936) Branched chromosomes as symmetrical duplications. J. Genetics, 32: 103–115.
Ogur, M., R. Erickson, G. U. Rosen, K. B. Sax, and C. Holden (1951) Nucleic acids in relation to cell division in *Lilium longiflorum*. Exptl. Cell Research, 2: 73–89.
Oliver, C. P. (1932) An analysis of the effect of varying the duration of X-ray treatment upon the frequency of mutations. Z. indukt. Abstamm.- u. Vererbungsl., 61: 447–488.
Painter, T. S. (1933) A new method for the study of chromosome rearrangements and the plotting of chromosome maps. Science, 78: 585–586.
——— and H. J. Muller (1929) The parallel cytology and genetics of induced translocations and deletions in *Drosophila*. J. Heredity, 20: 287–298.
Panschin, I. B., A. N. Panschina, and P. P. Peyrou (1946) Die Dosisabhängigkeit der röntgeninduzierten Chromosomenmutationen mit kleinen Bruchabständen bei *Drosophila melanogaster*. Naturwissenschaften, 33: 27–28.
Papalashwili, G. (1935) The effect of a combined action of X-rays and low temperature on the frequency of translocations in *Drosophila melanogaster*. Biol. Zhur., 4: 587–591.
Parker, D. R. (1948) Observations on crossing over induced by X-rays in the males of *Drosophila*. Genetics, 33: 304–310.
Pasteels, J., and L. Lison (1950) Recherches histophotométriques sur la teneur en acide désoxyribosenucléique au cours de mitoses somatiques. Arch. biol., 61: 445–474.
Paterson, E., and M. V. Thompson (1949) Effect of urethane combined with X-rays on chick fibroblasts. Nature, 163: 563.
Patterson, J. T. (1930) The production of mosaics in *Drosophila* by X-rays. Anat. Record, 47: 394–395.
———, W. Brewster, and A. M. Winchester (1932) Effects produced by aging and X-raying eggs. J. Heredity, 23: 325–333.
———, M. S. Brown, and W. Stone (1940) Experimentally produced aneuploidy involving the autosomes of *Drosophila melanogaster*. Univ. Texas Pub. 4032, pp. 167–189.
———, W. Stone, S. Bedichek, and M. Suche (1934) The production of translocations in *Drosophila*. Am. Naturalist, 68: 359–369.
——— and M. L. Suche (1934) Crossing over induced by X-rays in *Drosophila* males. Genetics, 19: 223–236.
Payne, F. (1913) A study of the effect of radium upon the eggs of *Ascaris megalocephala univalens*. Arch. Entwicklungsmech. Organ., 36: 287–293.
Perthes, G. (1904) Versuche über den Einfluss der Röntgenstrahlen und der Radiumstrahlen auf die Zellteilung. Deut. med. Wochschr., 30(17): 632–634; 668–670.
Petrakis, N. L., F. M. Ashler, and R. L. Ferkel (1949) Histochemical studies of the effect of total body X-irradiation in the alkaline phosphatase, ribo- and desoxyribonucleic acid content of rat liver cells. Naval Radiol. Def. Lab. Report AD-126 (B).*
Pfuhl, W., and H. Küntz (1939) Die pathologischen Mitosen in Bindegewebszellen nach einmaliger Röntgenbestrahlung. Z. Anat. Entwicklungsgeschichte, 110; 98–121.
Pollister, A. W., and C. Leuchtenberger (1949) The nature of the specificity of methyl green for chromatin. Proc. Natl. Acad. Sci., 35: 111–116.
Pontecorvo, G. (1941) The induction of chromosome losses in *Drosophila* sperm and their linear dependence on dosages of irradiation. J. Genetics, 41: 195–215.

——— (1942) The problem of dominant lethals. J. Genetics, 43: 295–300.
——— (1944) Drosophila Inform. Serv., 18.
——— and H. J. Muller (1941) The lethality of dicentric chromosomes in *Drosophila*. Genetics, 26: 165.
Ray Chaudhuri, S. P., and I. Bose (1948) Meiosis in diploid and tetraploid spermatocytes of *Attractomorpha* sp. (Acrididae). Proc. Zool. Soc. Bengal, 1: 1–12.
Reynolds, J. P. (1941) X-ray-induced chromosome rearrangements in the females of *Sciara*. Proc. Natl. Acad. Sci. U.S., 27: 204–208.
Rick, C. M. (1940) On the nature of X-ray-induced deletions in *Tradescantia* chromosomes. Genetics, 25: 466–482.
Ris, H. (1942) A cytological and experimental analysis of the meiotic behavior of the univalent X-chromosome in the bearberry aphid *Tamalia* (=Phyllaphis) *coweni* (Ckll.). J. Exptl. Zool., 90: 267–330.
Rugh, R. (1939) Developmental effects resulting from exposure to X-rays. I. Effect on the embryo of irradiation of frog sperm. Proc. Am. Phil. Soc., 81: 447–471.
——— (1950) The immediate and delayed morphological effects of X-radiations on meiotic chromosomes. J. Cellular Comp. Physiol., 36: 185–203.
——— and F. Exner (1940) Developmental effects resulting from exposure to X-rays. II. Development of leopard frog egg activated by bull frog sperm. Proc. Am. Phil. Soc., 83: 607–617.
Sax, K. (1940) An analysis of X-ray-induced chromosomal aberrations in *Tradescantia*. Genetics, 25: 41–68.
——— (1941) Types and frequencies of chromosomal aberrations induced by X-rays. Cold Spring Harbor Symposia Quant. Biol., 9: 93–103.
——— and C. P. Swanson (1941) Differential sensitivity of cells to X-rays. Am. J. Botany, 28: 52–59.
Schjeide, O. A., and B. M. Allen (1950) The relation of mitosis to the manifestation of X-ray damage in hematopoietic cells of tadpoles. USAEC Report UCLA-94.*
Scholes, G., G. Stein, and J. Weiss (1949) Action of X-rays on nucleic acids. Nature, 164: 709–710.
Schultz, J. (1936) Radiation and the study of mutations in animals, *in* Biological effects of radiation, ed. B. M. Duggar. McGraw-Hill Book Company, Inc., New York, Vol. II, pp. 1209–1261.
——— and H. Redfield (1932) The constitution of germinal material in relation to heredity. Carnegie Inst. Wash. Year Book, No. 31, pp. 303–307.
Shapiro, N. P. (1945) On the nature of crossing-over induced by X-rays in males of *Drosophila melanogaster*. Compt. rend. acad. sci. U.R.S.S., 49: 292–295.
Slizynska, H., and B. M. Slizynski (1947) Genetical and cytological studies of lethals induced by chemical treatment in *Drosophila melanogaster*. Proc. Roy. Soc. Edinburgh, B62: 234–242.
Slizynski, B. M. (1938) Salivary chromosome studies of lethals in *Drosophila melanogaster*. Genetics, 23: 283–290.
——— (1950) Partial breakage of salivary gland chromosomes. Genetics, 35: 279–287.
Smith, D. B., and G. C. Butler (1951) On the mechanism of the action of ionizing radiations on sodium thymonucleate. J. Am. Chem. Soc., 73: 258–261.
Snell, G. D. (1935) The induction by X-rays of hereditary changes in mice. Genetics, 20: 545–567.
——— (1941) Induction by roentgen rays of hereditary changes in mice. Radiology, 36: 189–196.
——— and F. B. Ames (1939) Hereditary changes in the descendants of female mice exposed to roentgen rays. Am. J. Roentgenol., 41: 248–255.

Sonnenblick, B. P. (1940) Cytology and development of the embryos of X-rayed adult *Drosophila melanogaster*. Proc. Natl. Acad. Sci. U.S., 26: 373–381.

——— and P. S. Henshaw (1941) Influence on development of certain dominant lethals induced by X-rays in *Drosophila* germ cells. Proc. Soc. Exptl. Biol. Med., 48: 74–79.

Sparrow, A. H. (1944) X-ray sensitivity changes in meiotic chromosomes and the nucleic acid cycle. Proc. Natl. Acad. Sci. U.S., 30: 147–155.

——— (1948) Relative X-ray sensitivity of metaphase and interphase chromosomes. Nature, 162: 651.

——— (1951) Radiation sensitivity of cells during mitotic and meiotic cycles with emphasis on possible cytochemical changes. Ann. N. Y. Acad. Sci., 51: 1508–1540.

——— and M. Maldawer (1950) Differential rejoining as a factor in apparent sensitivity of chromosomes to X-ray breakage. Proc. Natl. Acad. Sci. U.S., 36: 636–643.

——— and F. M. Rosenfeld (1946) X-ray induced depolymerization of thymonucleohistone and of sodium thymonucleate. Science, 104: 245–246.

Spear, F. G. (1946) The biological effects of penetrating radiations. A review. Brit. Med. Bull., 4: 2–10.

Stern, C. (1926) Eine neue Chromosomenaberration von *Drosophila melanogaster* und ihre Bedeutung für die Theorie der linearen Anordnung der Gene. Biol. Zentr., 46: 505–508.

——— (1929) Untersuchungen über Aberrationen des Y-Chromosoms von *Drosophila melanogaster*. Z. indukt. Abstamm.- u. Vererbungsl., 51: 253–353.

——— (1931) Zytologisch-genetische Untersuchungen als Beweise für die Morgansche Theorie des Factorenaustauschs. Biol. Zentr., 51: 547–587.

——— (1936) Somatic crossing over and segregation in *Drosophila melanogaster*. Genetics, 21: 625–730.

Stowell, R. E. (1945) The effects of roentgen radiation on the thymonucleic acid content of transplantable mammary carcinomas. Cancer Research, 5: 169–178.

Strømnaes, Øistein (1949) The production of dominant lethals with X-rays in aged *Drosophila melanogaster* sperm. Genetics, 34: 462–474.

Sturtevant, A. H. (1926) A cross-over reducer in *Drosophila melanogaster* due to inversion of a section of the third chromosome. Biol. Zentr., 46: 697–702.

——— (1931) Known and probable inverted sections of the autosomes of *Drosophila melanogaster*. Carnegie Inst. Wash. Pub. 421, pp. 1–27.

Sutton, E. (1940) Terminal deficiencies in the X chromosome of *Drosophila melanogaster*. Genetics, 25: 628–635.

——— (1943) A cytogenetic study of the yellow-scute region of the X-chromosome in *Drosophila melanogaster*. Genetics, 28: 210–217.

Swanson, C. P. (1943) Differential sensitivity of prophase pollen tube chromosomes to X-rays and ultraviolet radiation. J. Gen. Physiol., 26: 485–494.

——— (1947) X-ray and ultraviolet studies on pollen tube chromosomes. II. The quadripartite structure of the prophase chromosomes of *Tradescantia*. Proc. Natl. Acad. Sci. U.S., 38: 229–232.

Swift, H. H. (1950) The desoxyribose nucleic acid content of animal nuclei. Physiol. Zool., 23: 169–198.

Tansley, K., L. H. Gray, and F. G. Spear (1948) A preliminary note on some biological effects of alpha radiation on the frog tadpole. Brit. J. Radiology, 21: 567–570.

Taylor, B., J. P. Greenstein, and A. Hollaender (1948) Effects of X-radiation on sodium thymus nucleate. Arch. Biochem., 16: 19–31.

Taylor, W. R. (1924) The smear method for plant cytology. Botan. Gaz., 78: 236–238.

Thoday, J. M. (1942) The effects of ionizing radiations on the chromosomes of *Tradescantia bracteata.* A comparison between neutrons and X-rays. J. Genetics, 43: 189–210.

——— and J. Read (1947) Effect of oxygen on the frequency of chromosome aberrations produced by X-rays. Nature, 160: 608.

——— and ——— (1949) Effect of oxygen on the frequency of chromosome aberrations produced by alpha rays. Nature, 163: 133–134.

Timoféeff-Ressovsky, N. W. (1931) Einige Versuche an *Drosophila melanogaster* über der Art der Wirkung des Röntgenstrahlen auf den Mutationsprozess. Arch. Entwicklungsmech. Organ., 124: 654–665.

——— (1937) Mutationsforschung in der Vererbungslehre. Wiss. Forsch. Ber. Naturw. Reihe, 42.

——— (1939) Zur Frage der Beziehungen zwischen strahlenausgelösten Punkt- und Chromosomenmutation bei *Drosophila.* Chromosoma, 1: 310–316.

——— and K. G. Zimmer (1939) Strahlengenetik. Strahlentherapie, 66: 684–711.

Warren, S. H., J. C. MacMillan, and F. I. Dixon (1950) Effects of internal irradiation of mice with P^{32}. II. Gonads, kidneys, adrenal glands, digestive tract, spinal cord, lungs, and liver. Radiology, 55: 557–570.

Wattenwyl, H. v., and C. A. Joël (1941) Die Wirkung der Röntgenstrahlen auf den Rattenhoden. III. Mitteilung: Verlauf der Degeneration bzw. Regeneration des Samenepithels nach Bestrahlung mit 60 bis 2400 r bis zu 50 Tagen nach der Bestrahlung. Strahlentherapie, 70: 588–631.

——— and ——— (1944) Die Wirkung der Röntgenstrahlen auf den Rattenhoden. II. Mitteilung: Verlauf der Degeneration bzw. Regeneration des Samenepithels im unreifen Hoden nach Bestrahlung mit 60 bis 1500 r bis zu 173 Tagen nach der Bestrahlung. Strahlentherapie, 75: 295–322.

Welander, A. D., L. R. Donaldson, R. F. Foster, K. Bonham, and A. H. Seymour (1948) The effect of roentgen rays on the embryos and larvae of the Chinook salmon. Growth, 12: 203–242.

White, M. J. D. (1935a) Eine neue Form von Tetraploidie nach Röntgenbestrahlung. Naturwissenschaften, 24: 390–391.

——— (1935b) The effects of X-rays on mitosis in the spermatogonial divisions of *Locusta migratoria* L. Proc. Roy. Soc. London, B119: 61–84.

——— (1936) Chromosome cycle of *Ascaris megalocephala.* Nature, 137: 783.

——— (1937) The effect of X rays on the first meiotic division in three species of *Orthoptera.* Proc. Roy. Soc. London, B124: 183–196.

Whiting, A. R. (1940) Sensitivity to X-rays of different meiotic stages in unlaid eggs of *Habrobracon.* J. Exptl. Zool., 83: 249–269.

——— (1945a) Effects of X-rays on hatchability and on chromosomes of *Habrobracon* eggs treated in first meiotic prophase and metaphase. Am. Naturalist, 79: 193–227.

——— (1945b) Dominant lethality and correlated chromosome effects in *Habrobracon* eggs X-rayed in diplotene and late metaphase. Biol. Bull., 89: 61–71.

——— (1946) Motherless males from irradiated eggs. Science, 103: 219–220.

——— (1948) Incidence and origin of androgenetic males in X-rayed *Habrobracon* eggs. Biol. Bull., 95: 354–360.

——— (1949) Androgenesis, a differentiator of cytoplasmic injury induced by X-rays in *Habrobracon* eggs. Biol. Bull., 97: 210–220.

——— (1950) Absence of mutagenic action of X-rayed cytoplasm in *Habrobracon.* Proc. Natl. Acad. Sci. U.S., 36: 368–372.

——— and C. H. Bostian (1931) The effects of X-radiation of larvae in *Habrobracon.* Genetics, 16: 659–680.

Whiting, P. W. (1938a) Decrease in biparental males by X-raying sperm in *Habrobracon.* Proc. Penn. Acad. Sci., 12: 74–76.

——— (1938b) The induction of dominant and recessive lethals by radiation in *Habrobracon.* Genetics, 23: 562–572.

Whittinghill, M. (1938) The induction of oögonial crossing over in *Drosophila melanogaster.* Genetics, 23: 300–306.

——— (1947) Spermatogonial crossing over between the third chromosomes in the presence of the Curly inversions of *Drosophila melanogaster.* Genetics, 32: 608–614.

——— (1950) Consequences of crossing over in oögonial cells. Genetics, 35: 38–43.

Zirkle, R. E. (1949) Relationship between chemical and biological effects of ionizing radiations. Radiology, 52: 846–855.

Manuscript received by the editor May 1, 1951

CHAPTER 10

Radiation-induced Chromosome Aberrations in *Tradescantia*[1]

NORMAN H. GILES, JR.

*Osborn Botanical Laboratory, Yale University, and
Biology Division, Oak Ridge National Laboratory*

Introduction. Methods; aberration types and their relationships: General experimental techniques—Types of aberrations—Ratio of symmetrical and asymmetrical exchanges—Distribution of breaks in chromosomes—Distribution of aberration types among nuclei—Spontaneous chromosome aberrations—Time of chromosome division. Variations in radiosensitivity during the nuclear cycle. Quantitative radiation results: The relation of aberration yield to dose—The relation of aberration yield to intensity—The space factor in reunion—Proportion of breaks that undergo restitution—Relative efficiencies of various radiations—Aberration production by absorbed radiosotopes—Aberration production by slow neutrons. Recapitulation. Effects of modifying factors: Centrifugation; Sonic vibration—Colchicine—Ultraviolet—Infrared—Temperature—Oxygen. Conclusions. References.

INTRODUCTION

Studies on the effects of ionizing radiation on the chromosomes of species of the spiderwort genus *Tradescantia* have all appeared since the publication of the volumes edited by Duggar (1936), "Biological Effects of Radiation," and, as a consequence, the present review does not constitute in any way a revision and extension of earlier observations presented in these volumes. There have appeared, however, within the past few years a number of more or less complete treatments of the early radiation studies on *Tradescantia*. In particular, the discussions by Lea (1946) and by Catcheside (1945, 1948) have been quite extensive. Under the circumstances, it does not seem desirable to review in as great detail as would otherwise be necessary the material already covered in these publications. In order to make the present discussion reasonably complete, however, an attempt will be made to present the essential details of earlier observations, together with references to selected original papers and review articles on these subjects. In addition, a particular effort will be made to provide a more detailed discussion of recent research in this field, with emphasis on those results which appear to necessitate a

[1] Work at Oak Ridge performed under Contract No. W-7405-eng-26 for the Atomic Energy Commission.

modification of earlier concepts or which have contributed to a better understanding of the basic mechanisms by which ionizing radiations produce chromosome aberrations.

A complete evaluation of the significance of current research in this field, especially as it relates to earlier results, is not an easy task. As a consequence, many of the conclusions drawn at the present time may require considerable revision in the near future. This is particularly true with respect to the recent discovery of the significance of oxygen in increasing the frequency of aberrations. It seems clear that an understanding of this effect is fundamental to any interpretation of the physicochemical mechanism of aberration production by ionizing radiations. At the present time, however, it is obvious that many questions concerning the nature of the oxygen effect remain to be answered.

The first utilization of *Tradescantia* for quantitative X-ray experiments is that of Sax (1938). Previous workers (Riley, 1936; Husted, 1936) had, however, demonstrated the suitability of this material, especially the developing microspores, for the cytological analysis of radiation effects. The initial quantitative X-ray observations of Sax were soon extended by him and by his students at Harvard and elsewhere utilizing X rays as well as other types of radiation. Sax presented the early X-ray results in terms of a comprehensive theory of the effects of radiation on the chromosomes of *Tradescantia* in 1940. The *Tradescantia* investigations were initiated shortly thereafter in England by Catcheside, Lea, and others. These investigators, on the basis of the earlier studies together with their own observations, developed a detailed, quantitative theory of chromosome aberration production in *Tradescantia* by ionizing radiations. Certain aspects of this theory are presented in a review by Catcheside (1945), and a comprehensive account is given in the volume by Lea (1946). A later review, including additional literature appearing since 1945, has been written by Catcheside (1948).

METHODS; ABERRATION TYPES AND THEIR RELATIONSHIPS

GENERAL EXPERIMENTAL TECHNIQUES

Most of the observations on radiation effects in *Tradescantia* have been carried out on diploid species in which the haploid chromosome number is 6. Several different species have been studied including *T. gigantea*, *T. bracteata*, *T. canaliculata*, and especially *T. paludosa*. Although certain differences in quantitative results have been noted when supposedly equivalent irradiation treatments have been applied in different laboratories, such differences appear not to result from marked differences in species sensitivity (Sax and Swanson, 1941), but rather from differences in exposure conditions and dosage measurements. It is possible, however, that a certain degree of genetically controlled difference in sensitivity among species or within a given species may exist.

The stage in the life cycle of *Tradescantia* which has proved most favorable for observations of radiation effects on chromosomes is the first postmeiotic mitosis in the developing microspores. Following meiosis, the haploid microspores (having six chromosomes) go through a regular mitotic cycle, and the chromosomes can be observed at metaphase or anaphase, utilizing simple acetocarmine or other smear techniques. The various mitotic stages are usually fairly well synchronized in the six anthers of one bud, and a smear preparation of an appropriately selected single bud will usually contain from 100–400 cells in a stage of mitosis suitable for chromosome observations. Since the different buds on a single inflorescence contain microspores in successive stages of development, it is possible with one radiation exposure to treat cells in different stages of mitosis. Observations of nuclei at metaphase or anaphase can then be made at intervals after irradiation and the types and frequencies of various chromosome aberrations determined. Since the duration of the various stages in microspores has been determined (Sax and Edmonds, 1933), it is possible to make certain correlations of aberration types and frequencies with particular stages in the mitotic cycle, especially with the resting stage and prophase.

When inflorescences are exposed to penetrating radiation and the cells in metaphase and anaphase examined immediately afterward, the chromosomes can be seen to exhibit a type of stickiness during which certain chromosome parts, especially ends, tend to adhere. This adherence may lead occasionally to bridging and fragmentation at anaphase. Such a condition has been attributed to an effect of the radiation on the nucleic acid forming the matrical material of the chromosome (Darlington, 1942). This type of transient aberrant behavior is soon replaced, as seen in cells examined a few hours after exposure, by the typical permanent aberration types resulting from chromosome breakage and the reunion of broken ends with which the subsequent discussion will be concerned.

TYPES OF ABERRATIONS

Observations at increasing intervals of time following irradiation have shown the existence of two major categories of aberration types differing in whether they are derived from chromosomes which are effectively single or double at the time of irradiation.

Chromatid Aberrations. The first category consists of types produced in chromosomes which are effectively double at the time of irradiation. Chromatid aberrations appear first, within a few hours after irradiation, reach a peak 12–20 hours later, and are the only types present up to about 26 hours (under spring and summer growing conditions; see Sax, 1941). Following a relatively brief transition period, in which both chromatid and chromosome types may occur in the same cell—or rarely, even in the same chromosome (Sax and Mather, 1939)—chromosome types replace the chromatid types and are present exclusively from about 31 hours on. The frequency of chromosome aberrations rises rapidly to a maximum shortly after this type appears, and this frequency is maintained for several days after irradiation. The typical periods for observation of

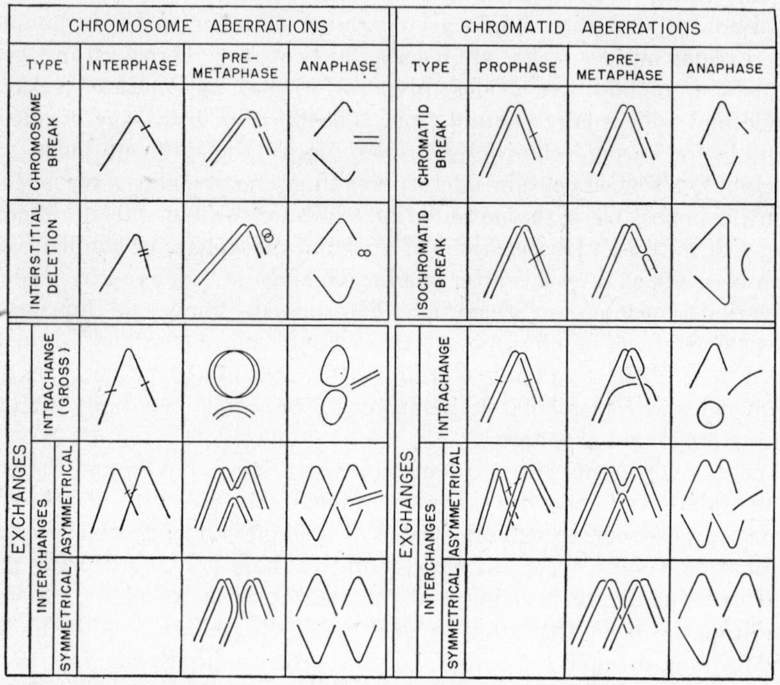

CHROMOSOME ABERRATIONS				CHROMATID ABERRATIONS			
TYPE	INTERPHASE	PRE-METAPHASE	ANAPHASE	TYPE	PROPHASE	PRE-METAPHASE	ANAPHASE
CHROMOSOME BREAK				CHROMATID BREAK			
INTERSTITIAL DELETION				ISOCHROMATID BREAK			
EXCHANGES — INTRACHANGE (GROSS)				EXCHANGES — INTRACHANGE			
EXCHANGES — INTERCHANGES — ASYMMETRICAL				EXCHANGES — INTERCHANGES — ASYMMETRICAL			
EXCHANGES — INTERCHANGES — SYMMETRICAL				EXCHANGES — INTERCHANGES — SYMMETRICAL			

FIG. 10-1. Diagrammatic representation of the origin and types of aberrations, both chromosome and chromatid, induced in *Tradescantia* microspores by ionizing radiations. Only the types of major importance which can be recognized at metaphase and anaphase in cytological analyses are shown. Original break positions at interphase or prophase are indicated by short diagonal lines. (*Modified from Sax,* 1940. *Reproduced by permission of the author and the editor of Genetics.*)

chromatid and chromosome aberration frequencies are 20–24 hours and 4–5 days following irradiation, respectively. The time and duration of the transition period appears to depend rather markedly on environmental factors.

The various kinds of chromatid and chromosome aberration types produced in *Tradescantia* microspores have been diagramed and discussed in considerable detail by Sax (1940), Lea (1946), and especially by Catcheside, Lea, and Thoday (1946a) and Catcheside (1948). The present discussion will consider in detail only certain selected types which occur most frequently and which have been of major importance in the quantitative data on radiation effects. The mode of origin of these types is shown diagrammatically in Fig. 10-1, and photomicrographs of the various types are presented in Plate I.

There are three major chromatid aberration types: (1) *chromatid breaks*, in which one of the two chromatids in a metaphase chromosome has a transverse fracture, giving rise to a free acentric fragment at anaphase (Plate I-E, F); (2) *isochromatid breaks* (chromatid dicentrics), in which the two sister chromatids of a single chromosome are broken at the same locus, the broken ends typically undergoing lateral union to produce a dicentric and a U-shaped fragment (Plate I-B). At the succeeding anaphase a bridge and a free acentric fragment result (Plate I-C). The interpretation of the manner in which ionizing radiations produce isochromatid breaks has been a controversial one. For example, Darlington and La Cour (1945) have maintained that this aberration type arises as a result of chromosome breakage before effective division, apparent sister union resulting from a reproductive error in the chromosome thread and not from true reunion. Catcheside (1948) has summarized the evidence against this view and in favor of the alternative one, that isochromatid breaks, in general, arise as a result of the simultaneous breakage at the same level of the two chromatids of a single chromosome. (3) *Chromatid exchanges* are derived from two chromatid breaks, either in two separate chromosomes, yielding interchanges, or in the same chromosome, yielding intrachanges. The commonest category is the interchange in which the union of broken ends gives rise to symmetrical (reciprocal translocation, Plate I-D) or to asymmetrical (dicentric and acentric fragment, Plate I-E) types. Additional exchange types, which are in general much less frequent, involve recombination between two isochromatid breaks or between one isochromatid and one chromatid break, and have been described and diagramed by Catcheside, Lea, and Thoday (1946a).

Chromosome Aberrations. This second major category of aberration types is made up of those arising in chromosomes which are effectively single at the time of exposure. There are also three major chromosome aberration types: (1) *chromosome breaks* (terminal deletions), in which the unsplit chromosome suffers a transverse fracture giving rise at metaphase to two shortened chromatids and two acentric fragments (Plate I-G); (2) *interstitial deletions* (minute, isodiametric fragments), involving two breaks close together in one arm of an unsplit chromosome, the broken ends uniting to produce a small acentric ring which appears following division as a pair of dotlike fragments at metaphase (Plate I-G, N). This aberration is actually a type of intra-arm exchange (intrachange) but is listed separately because of the frequency with which it occurs. (3) *Chromosome exchanges*, which arise from two chromosome breaks either in two different chromosomes, yielding interchanges, or in different arms of the same chromosome, yielding large intrachanges. In general, only the

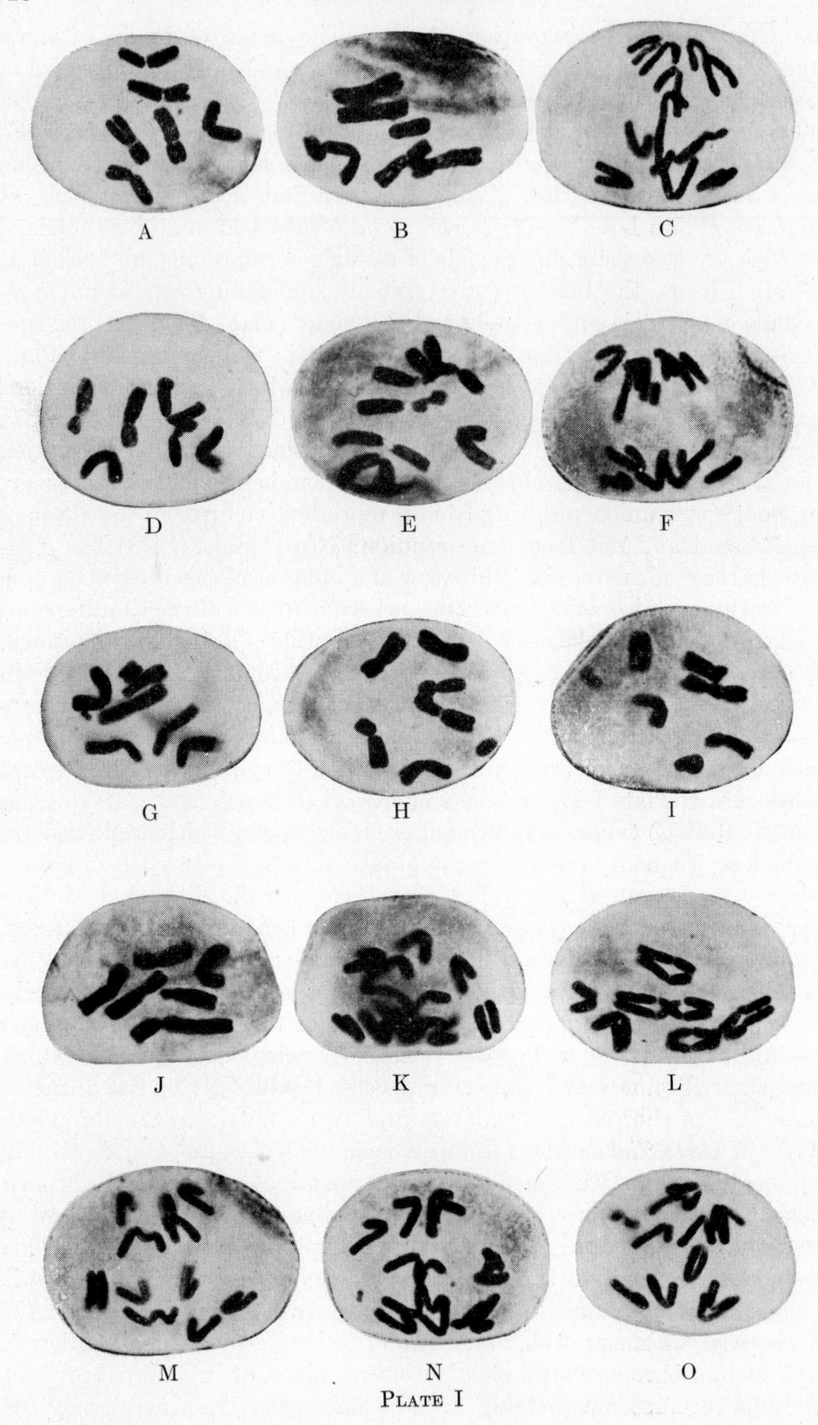

PLATE I

Description of Plate I

Photomicrographs of *Tradescantia* microspore chromosomes showing the major types of aberrations induced by ionizing radiations (*from Sax*, 1940). Figures A–F are chromatid aberration types; Figs. G–O are chromosome aberration types. (*Reproduced by permission of the author and the editor of Genetics.*)

FIG. A. Untreated. Six normal chromosomes at metaphase.

FIG. B. An isochromatid break at metaphase. Acentric fragment (U-shaped) at left.

FIG. C. Similar isochromatid aberration at anaphase. Partially straightened fragment to right.

FIG. D. Symmetrical chromatid interchange at metaphase.

FIG. E. Asymmetrical chromatid interchange (at top) and a chromatid break (center).

FIG. F. Chromatid break at anaphase, shortened arm and acentric fragment visible at upper center. Also probable chromatid-isochromatid intrachange giving duplication-deficiency chromatids (to left).

FIG. G. A chromosome break (upper center) and a chromosome interstitial deletion (to right).

FIG. H. An asymmetrical chromosome interchange (dicentric); paired acentric fragments at lower right.

FIG. I. An asymmetrical chromosome interchange (dicentric) at upper right, and an asymmetrical chromosome intrachange (centric ring) at lower center. Two pairs of acentric fragments at top, center and left.

FIG. J. A symmetrical chromosome interchange.

FIG. K–N. Types of separation at anaphase of asymmetrical chromosome interchanges (dicentrics). An interstitial deletion is also present in Fig. N.

FIG. O. Anaphase separation of an asymmetrical chromosome intrachange as a continuous ring. Somatic nondisjunction has also occurred.

asymmetrical types in these two categories—dicentrics (Plate I-H, I, K, L, M, N) and centric rings (Plate I-I, O), respectively—can be regularly scored, although symmetrical interchanges can be detected occasionally when they are very unequal (Plate I-J).

RATIO OF SYMMETRICAL AND ASYMMETRICAL EXCHANGES

Symmetrical and asymmetrical chromatid interchanges appear to be about equally frequent according to Catcheside, Lea, and Thoday (1946a), although the data of Sax (1940) suggest that asymmetrical interchanges are more frequent. These latter results are probably biased somewhat, since cells at anaphase as well as at metaphase were scored, and symmetrical exchanges cannot be detected at anaphase. The observations of Catcheside *et al.* (1946a) also indicate that symmetrical and asymmetrical chromatid intrachanges are equally frequent and these authors state that such results argue against the existence of any polarization in chromosomes which would prevent the random joining of breakage ends.

DISTRIBUTION OF BREAKS IN CHROMOSOMES

It is not possible to determine directly in *Tradescantia* the distribution of initial breakage, since the processes of restitution and reunion, to be considered later, intervene. There is, in fact, evidence that more aberrations tend to arise from breaks produced in the proximal rather than in the distal regions of a chromosome (Sax, 1940). Although such evidence may indicate a nonrandom distribution of initial breaks, it appears more likely that it indicates a nonrandom reunion of broken ends, resulting from the operation of secondary factors influencing reunion and restitution. The more proximal distribution of aberrations has been attributed by Sax (1940) to stresses imposed in the region of the centromere by the various coiling mechanisms.

DISTRIBUTION OF ABERRATION TYPES AMONG NUCLEI

The distribution of various chromatid and chromosome aberration types among nuclei following X irradiation and neutron irradiation has been studied by Catcheside, Lea, and Thoday (1946a) and Rick (1940). The distributions observed are in accordance with the Poisson formula, and this evidence, especially that for chromatid breaks, is taken as compatible with the view that single breaks in a given chromosome are produced by the action of single ionizing particles and are unaffected by the presence or absence of other breaks in the cell.

SPONTANEOUS CHROMOSOME ABERRATIONS

Of interest in connection with radiation experiments are observations on the types and frequencies of spontaneous aberration types in microspores. Such data are in fact necessary as controls for comparison with experimental material. Studies of spontaneous chromosome aberrations have demonstrated that the same aberration types occur in unirradiated material, but that the frequencies are usually very low (Giles, 1940a; Sax and Luippold, 1952). Even this low rate is much too high to be accounted for in terms of natural radiation. Further, there is evidence that the spontaneous rate may be considerably higher in material of hybrid origin (Giles, 1940a, 1941; Darlington and Upcott, 1941).

TIME OF CHROMOSOME DIVISION

Observations on the kinds and sequence of aberration types have been used to draw certain conclusions about the time and degree of chromosome duplication during mitosis (Riley, 1936; Mather, 1937; Sax, 1940, 1941; Catcheside, 1948). The transition from chromosome to chromatid aberrations, which corresponds in general to the late resting stage, has been taken to indicate the time in the nuclear cycle at which duplication occurs (Mather, 1937). One of the difficulties with this interpretation, however, is the observation that chromosome breaks may occur in the same cell with chromatid breaks. Some investigators (Darlington and La Cour, 1945) have, in fact, maintained that chromosomes are broken by radiation only when they are undivided and that reunion then takes place after division, giving rise to either chromosome or chromatid break types. Catcheside (1948) has summarized the evidence favoring the view that chromatid aberrations actually arise as a result of breaks in divided chromosomes, and has concluded that, while a small proportion of chromatid breaks may be derived from chromosome breaks, most are not. It thus seems likely that the average time of chromosome splitting should be about halfway between the peaks of chromatid and chromosome breakage, and thus does correspond in general to the transition from chromosome to chromatid types.

It can still be argued, however, that actual duplication has occurred earlier, but that the chromosome or chromatid is the unit of reunion. There is, in fact, some evidence from radiation studies (Swanson, 1947) for a quadripartite condition of the chromosomes at prophase in pollen tube nuclei. This condition appears to be the exception rather than the rule, however, since even in pollen tubes, chromatid rather than half-chromatid break types predominate in nuclei where the chromosomes can be seen microscopically to be divided at the time of treatment (Swanson, 1943).

VARIATIONS IN RADIOSENSITIVITY DURING THE NUCLEAR CYCLE

The original studies of Sax (1938, 1940) demonstrated that more aberrations were produced for the same X-ray dose in prophase as compared with resting stage chromosomes of *Tradescantia* microspores. It was later shown (Sax and Swanson, 1941), that the sensitivity apparently was greatest shortly before mid-prophase, somewhat less in early prophase, and only about one-third the prophase maximum during the microspore resting stage. Comparative studies with diploid microspores from tetraploid *Tradescantia* species indicated a similar sensitivity cycle, but also demonstrated that the diploid spores were only one-half to one-third as sensitive as the haploid, in terms of aberrations per chromosome. Further evidence from the tetraploids indicated that meiosis was much more sensitive than mitosis. Chromosomes in root tip mitoses in the diploid were found to be less sensitive than those in the haploid microspores. Bishop (1950) has studied the radiosensitivity of chromosomes in the postmicrospore mitosis (in the generative nucleus of the pollen grain) which is initiated after the microspore division and completed in the pollen tube, at which time cytological analyses at metaphase can be made. He finds evidence for two sensitivity peaks, one at 3 days and one at 5 days before the dehiscence of the anthers. These peaks are considered to correspond, respectively, to the time of chromosome doubling during prophase of the pollen tube mitosis (cf. Koller, 1946), and to metaphase-anaphase of the microspore mitosis. The range of sensitivity, from the low point at the postmitotic resting stage, is estimated to be approximately 2.4 times as great for the prophase maximum and ten times as great for the metaphase-anaphase maximum.

The extensive studies of Sparrow (1951) on the radiosensitivity of *Trillium* chromosomes are in general agreement with the *Tradescantia* data. The more detailed data on *Trillium*, particularly at meiosis, indicate that late prophase and metaphase of the first meiotic division are over fifty times as sensitive as the least sensitive stage, early interphase in the microspore. Complete data are not yet available for the entire microspore cycle.

The factors responsible for such marked changes in sensitivity during the nuclear cycle are not yet completely elucidated (Sparrow, 1951). It is clear that any change in sensitivity (i.e., any change in the frequency of aberrations produced by the same dose) may be attributed either (1) to an actual difference in the number of initial breaks, or (2) to a change in the proportion of breaks which undergo reunion and/or restitution, or (3) to both these factors. There is evidence in *Trillium* (Sparrow and Maldawer, 1950), from a comparison of the ratios of fragments to dicentrics and rings induced at metaphase of meiosis and at microspore interphase, that a greater amount of reunion occurs at interphase, the stage of lowest sensitivity. However, the increase in reunion is not of sufficient magnitude to account for the observed decrease in fragmentation. It thus appears that both factors mentioned may be involved in changes in sensitivity.

Many possible reasons for variations in the incidence of primary breakage or of restitution and reunion during the nuclear cycle have been suggested (Sparrow, 1951). Differences in primary breakage may reflect variations in the chemical composition of the chromosomes during mitosis and meiosis, for example, in their desoxyribonucleic acid (DNA) content, as suggested by Darlington and La Cour (1945). [However, quantitative measurements by Ris (1947) and by Sparrow, Moses, and Steele (1950) indicate that there is no significant change in the amounts of either desoxyribonucleic acid or pentose nucleic acid during meiosis and mitosis.] It is also possible that changes in the cellular environment (e.g., changes in oxygen tension during mitosis and meiosis) may be responsible for modifying the relative efficiency of ionizing radiations in breaking chromosomes. Among the factors that have been suggested as possibly influencing reunion and restitution are the type of coiling present in the chromosomes and the degree of chromosome duplication (plus the relative proximity of the duplicated sister strands) at the time of irradiation (Sax and Swanson, 1941; Bishop, 1950).

QUANTITATIVE RADIATION RESULTS

THE RELATION OF ABERRATION YIELD TO DOSE

The initial development of a quantitative theory of chromosome aberration production in *Tradescantia* microspores by radiation resulted primarily from studies of the relation between the yield of various aberrations with dosage and intensity of X rays and neutrons. The early experiments of Sax (1938; 1940) with X rays demonstrated two types of relationship: (1) a linear relation with dose for certain aberration types, e.g., for isochromatid breaks, and (2) a nonlinear (geometric-exponential) relation (the exponent of the dose being greater than one) for other aberrations, such as chromatid and chromosome exchanges. In the first experiments of Sax, in which the radiation dose was administered at a constant intensity, the exponent of the dosage curve for exchanges was approximately 1.5. In later experiments, when the time of irradiation was kept constant and the intensity varied, the exponent of the dosage curve for exchanges was approximately 2 (Fig. 10-2).

These results were interpreted as indicating that with X rays certain aberration types (one-hit) are produced by single events, whereas, other aberrations (two-hit types) are produced by two separate events (which must be related in time and space, as will be discussed later). The nature of the event producing the break, whether related to a single ionization or to the passage of a single ionizing particle, could not be determined from the initial X-ray experiments alone.

Subsequently, experiments with fast neutrons (Giles, 1940b) showed that with this radiation the frequencies of all aberration types studied, including chromatid and chromosome exchanges, were linearly related to dose (Fig. 10-3). Further, when equal doses of X rays and neutrons were compared, neutrons were found to be much more efficient than X rays in producing aberrations. These results were interpreted as indicating that with fast neutrons all aberrations are produced by single events, and that the passage of an ionizing particle, rather than the occurrence of a single ionization, constitutes the event, or hit.

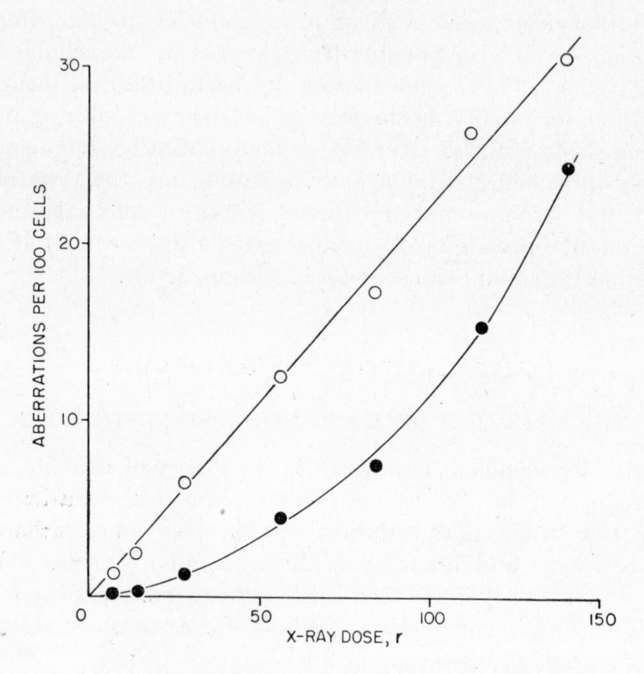

FIG. 10-2. Relation between X-ray dosage and frequency of isochromatid breaks (one-hit) and chromatid exchanges (two-hit). Time of exposure constant. (*Data of Sax,* 1940. *Dosage values multiplied by correction factor, cf. Catcheside, Lea, and Thoday,* 1946.)

These observations on X-ray and fast-neutron effects on *Tradescantia* chromosomes have been subsequently confirmed and extended in numerous independent experiments. The following general conclusions relating the frequency of various aberration types to dose can be made. Simple (one-hit) break types, i.e., chromosome and chromatid breaks and isochromatid breaks, increase in approximately linear proportion to dose for all types of radiations tested—X and γ rays (Sax, 1938; 1940; 1941; Thoday, 1942; Newcombe, 1942; Rick, 1940; Catcheside *et al.*, 1946b), neutrons (Giles, 1940b; 1943; Thoday, 1942), and α particles (Kotval and

Gray, 1947). Break types involving exchanges, i.e., chromatid interchanges and chromosome dicentrics and rings, increase more rapidly than the first power of the dose when X rays or γ rays are used. The actual exponent obtained in a given experiment depends on the intensity of the radiation. With high intensities (e.g., ca. 150 r/minute) aberration frequency is approximately proportional to the square of the dose (Sax, 1941; Thoday, 1942; Sax and Brumfield, 1943). At intermediate and low intensities (e.g., ca. 20 r/minute and 3 r/minute), the exponent

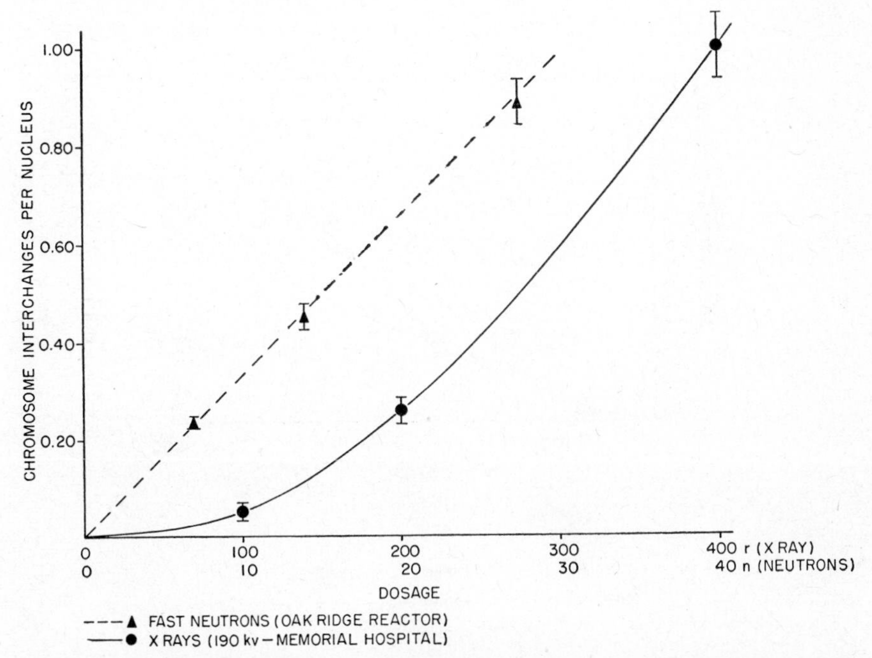

FIG. 10-3. Relation between frequencies of chromosome interchange (dicentric and centric rings) and dosages of fast neutrons and X rays. 1 n unit = ca. 2.5 r. (*Data of Giles, unpublished.*)

becomes progressively less than 2 (Fig. 10-4) (Sax, 1941). A dosage-squared relationship is also obtained if the time of irradiation is kept constant and the intensity varied (Sax, 1940, 1941), provided the total irradiation time is relatively short (Sax, 1950b). It is concluded from these results that, fundamentally, exchange aberration frequencies increase as the square of the dose with X rays, the two breaks involved being produced by separate X-ray hits. Modifications of the dosage-squared relationship are attributed indirectly to an effect of intensity, such that at low intensities relatively greater restitution, as compared with reunion, occurs and hence proportionally more exchanges arise as a result of single hits.

Although the majority of the X-ray-induced interchanges appear to result from two separate hits, a certain fraction has been shown to originate as a result of single hits. This proportion has been investigated for chromatid exchanges, by Catcheside, Lea, and Thoday (1946b) in experiments in which two similar dosage curves were obtained at constant, but widely different, exposure times. The results indicate that one-hit exchanges are of relatively minor consequence at high intensities, but make a substantial contribution to the total aberration yield at low

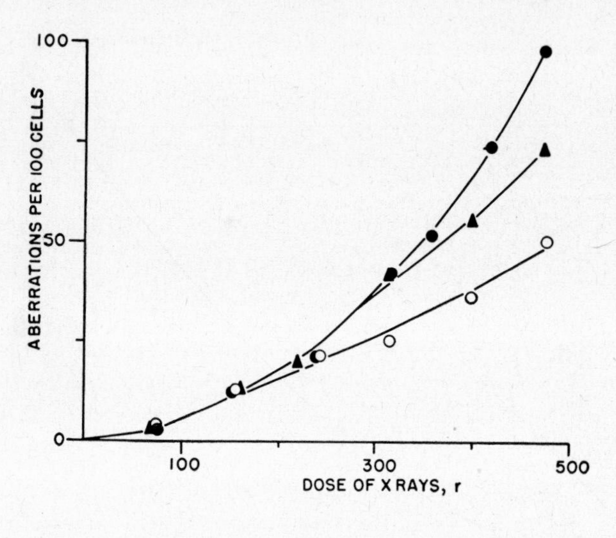

Fig. 10-4. Effect of dosages of X rays at different intensities upon the yield of chromosome exchanges. (*Data from Sax,* 1941.)

intensities. Similar conclusions have been arrived at by Sax for chromosome exchanges (1950b).

Rick (1940) has shown that the yield of interstitial deletions increases as the 1.5 power of the dose when irradiations are performed at constant time and at relatively high intensities, and has concluded that these types represent a mixture of one- and two-hit aberrations.

With fast neutrons (Giles, 1940; 1943; Giles and Conger, 1950; Thoday, 1942) and α particles (Kotval and Gray, 1947), all types of exchange aberrations increase linearly with dose. As indicated previously, these results are compatible with the view that such two-break aberrations are produced by the passage of a single ionizing particle. The special case of slow-neutron effects will be considered later.

THE RELATION OF ABERRATION YIELD TO INTENSITY

Some of the results just discussed under dosage relationships indicated the existence of an intensity effect on the yield of certain aberration types in *Tradescantia*. This effect has been investigated in detail in X-ray experiments by Sax (1939, 1940, 1950a, b, 1952), Fabergé (1940), Marinelli, Nebel, Giles, and Charles (1942), Catcheside, Lea, and Thoday (1946b), and Lane (1951).

The most direct way in which an intensity effect can be demonstrated is in experiments in which the same X-ray dose is administered at several

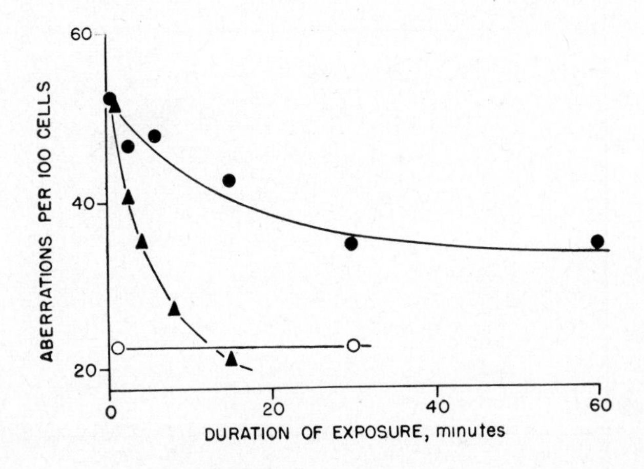

FIG. 10-5. Effect of intensity of radiation dose on yield of chromosome interchanges induced by X rays and neutrons.

different intensities. When this is done, it is found that there is a marked decrease in the frequencies of exchange-type aberrations, both chromosome and chromatid; whereas, the yields of chromatid and isochromatid breaks are not affected (Figs. 10-5, 10-6). The general conclusion drawn from such experiments is that the two independently produced breaks necessary for the production of an exchange aberration must occur within a certain time in order for reunion, and thus aberration formation, to result. This is the case, since restitution is constantly taking place; and if the second break is not produced before restitution of the first break occurs, no exchange can result. Consequently, when a given X-ray dose is administered at a high intensity, most breaks are simultaneously present in a given nucleus and numerous reunions can occur;

when the same dose is extended over a long period of time, restitution intervenes to reduce the number of breaks which can participate in reunion. On this view, absence of an intensity effect with chromatid and isochromatid breaks is expected, since these are one-hit aberration types.

The data from neutron experiments (Giles, 1943) indicate that, contrary to the X-ray results, there is no intensity effect with either exchanges

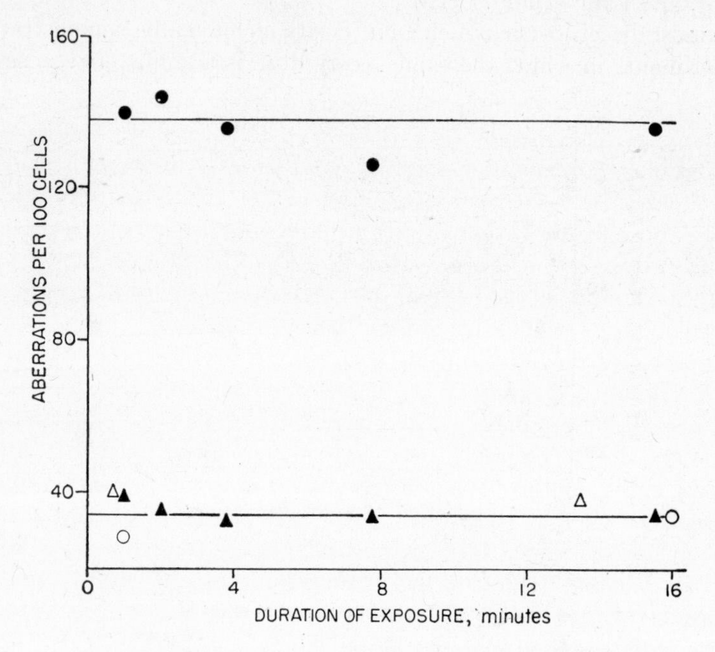

FIG. 10-6. Effect of intensity of radiation dose on yield of chromatid and isochromatid breaks induced by X rays and neutrons.

or simple break types (Figs. 10-5, 10-6). The absence of an intensity effect with exchanges affords strong support for the previously outlined mechanism of aberration production, since these aberrations have been shown by dosage data to be one-hit types, both breaks being produced by a single proton path; consequently, an intensity effect is not anticipated.

Lea and Catcheside (1942), Lea (1946), and Catcheside, Lea, and Thoday (1946b) have used the experimental data on the intensity effect for exchanges to calculate the average restitution time (τ), i.e., the average time elapsing between breakage and restitution. Using the original data of Sax (1939, 1940), the value of τ is approximately 4 minutes for both chromosome and chromatid breaks. In later experiments (Catcheside *et al.*, 1946b), when irradiation was prolonged beyond about 30 minutes, however, the experimental results were not in very good agreement with the theoretical predictions, since there was an unexpected persistence of interchanges even in experiments in which the irradiation extended over several hours. These investigators studied this situation in an attempt to determine whether the discrepancy could be accounted for on the basis that some exchanges are one-hit rather than two-hit aberrations. Although a certain proportion of exchanges were found to be one-hit types, this value was not sufficient to account for the observed discrepancy. Consequently, it was concluded that, in addition to a short-term component ($\tau 1$), there is also a long-term component ($\tau 2$) involved in restitution and that the value of $\tau 2$ is of the order of hours, not minutes. It is suggested that biologically this situation may result from the circumstance that, if two broken ends of a given break do not restitute within a few minutes, they may then become separated beyond the spatial limits of restitution, and a considerable period may elapse before they are accidentally brought together again.

In addition to experiments with varying intensity, other experiments with fractionated doses have been performed to investigate the mechanism of aberration production. In general, the results of these experiments (Sax, 1939, 1940; Fabergé, 1940) are in agreement with those of the intensity experiments. When a given dose is divided into two or more fractions, the yield of exchange aberrations decreases, but that of one-hit types is not affected. By utilizing increasing time intervals between doses, Sax (1939, 1940) concluded that some breaks may remain open and capable of reunion for as long as 1 hour, but that most breaks undergo restitution or reunion in a considerably shorter period.

The results of experiments by Lane (1951) on dose fractionation are similar to those of Sax in showing a pronounced reduction in exchange aberrations when intervals up to 4 hours between doses are employed. However, when longer intervals of 6 or 8 hours were used, a recovery effect was noted, the aberration yield returning, with an 8-hour interval between fractions, to almost the level obtained with an equivalent dose delivered without fractionation. This result, plus the observation that the aberration yield from a given dose delivered in two equal fractions often appeared to be *less* than twice the yield obtained when half that dose was used, led to the conclusion that the so-called intensity effect was actually to be interpreted in terms of a temporary inhibition of chromosome breakage by radiation, such that an initial dose rendered the chromosomes more resistant to breakage by a subsequent dose. That this inhibition was temporary was shown by the subsequent recovery effect with time intervals between doses longer than 4 hours. These over-all results and interpretations are clearly incompatible with much of the theory of aberration production as outlined previously. The experiments of Lane have, however, been repeated by Sax (1952)—the only difference being that a higher radiation intensity was used—and on the basis of a much more extensive analysis in terms of numbers of cells scored, no evidence of an inhibition or recovery effect is found, even with an interval between doses as long as 12 hours (Table 10-1). Thus

TABLE 10-1. EFFECT OF X-RAY DOSE FRACTIONATION ON YIELD OF CHROMOSOME INTERCHANGES, 180 R/MINUTE
(Data from Sax and Luippold, 1952)

Dose, r	Time interval between doses, hr	No. of cells	No. of interchanges	Interchanges per cell
360	0	2802	2055	0.732
180 + 180	4	2970	1534	0.516
180 + 180	8	1665	847	0.509
180 + 180	12	1000	487	0.487
180	0	2817	726	0.258 (× 2 = 0.516)

the rejection by Lane, on the basis of his experiments, of the theory of relatively rapid reunion and restitution, appears not to be warranted.

THE SPACE FACTOR IN REUNION

Sax (1940) pointed out that the observed ratio of certain types of chromosome inter- and intrachanges (i.e., dicentric-centric rings = 3.3:1) was not as expected (10:1) on the basis of random reunion of broken ends, intrachanges being favored. These data are interpreted as indicating that space limitations influence the reunion process, and that most breaks must be relatively close together in order for reunion to occur. The further conclusion is drawn that the limitations to reunion imposed by this factor of proximity must mean that most of the breaks induced by radiations do not lead to the production of aberrations. Rather, the two broken ends simply reunite in the original position (the process of *restitution*) and no structural alteration is visible at succeeding metaphases or anaphases.

Lea (1946, 1947) has developed several quantitative methods for estimating the average distance over which reunion occurs. One of these depends on the use of biological and physical data on exchanges induced by fast neutrons and X rays. It is possible to calculate the number of ionizing particles, either protons or photoelectrons, which will pass through a given *Tradescantia* microspore nucleus irradiated with equivalent physical doses of neutrons of X rays. Since neutron-induced exchanges are primarily one hit, the data on protons can be used to set an upper limit to the distance from a given break at which a second break normally taking part in an exchange must occur. Since X-ray-induced exchanges are primarily two hit, the data on photoelectrons can be used to set a lower limit to the distance from a given break at which the second break must occur. Calculations based on physically equivalent neutron and X-ray doses, e.g., at 50 r, indicate that 23 protons and 303 photoelectrons pass through a nucleus of diameter 12 μ and set these limits as <1.3 and >0.9 μ, respectively. Thus the average distance over which reunion occurs is concluded to be approximately 1 μ. Independent estimates derived from the ratio of interstitial deletions to asymmetrical exchanges and from the most frequent size of interstitial deletions are in agreement with this calculation.

PROPORTION OF BREAKS THAT UNDERGO RESTITUTION

Evidence has been presented in the preceding section that reunion is not at random, and that breaks separated by distances greater than approximately 1 μ usually do not undergo reunion. From this evidence, plus the results of the intensity experiments, it can be concluded that the majority of breaks undergo restitution. Further general evidence for restitution comes from data on the frequencies of different kinds of breaks observed in individual cells. For example, as pointed out by Catcheside (1948), it seems clear that chromatid exchanges and chromatid breaks arise from a similar initial event, a chromatid break, reunion occurring in one case and not in the other. If, in fact, chromatid exchanges do arise in this manner from reunion of two chromatid breaks, and if all chromatid breaks not participating in such reunions were preserved, it is apparent that the occurrence of chromatid exchanges should affect the distribution of surviving chromatid breaks. However, in cells with exchanges, there is no evidence of an excess of odd as compared with even numbers of surviving chromatid breaks. Lea (1946) and Catcheside, Lea, and Thoday (1946b) have developed several quantitative methods for calculating from the number of observed aberrations of various types the number of breaks primarily produced, and hence the proportion of breaks which restitute. These include (1) a comparison of the frequencies of incomplete reunion and restitution in various chromatid aberration types; (2) a consideration of the departure at high doses from the dose-squared relation for X-ray-induced exchanges; (3) comparisons of expected and observed break frequencies with fast neutrons; (4) comparisons, based on the observed ratio of chromatid exchanges to chromatid-isochromatid exchanges, and of chromatid to isochromatid breaks, of the relative proportions of primary chromatid and isochromatid breaks which persist; and (5) a consideration of the relative frequencies of chromatid and isochromatid breaks. All these calculations agree in indicating that only a minority of the breaks primarily produced in *Tradescantia* microspores are scored and that the majority restitute and escape recognition. The estimates of the fraction (f) of unjoinable breaks are 0.09, 0.09, and 0.5 for X rays, neutrons, and α particles, respectively.

The over-all evidence thus indicates that a substantial fraction of originally induced breaks undergo restitution. Only failure of restitution permits new reunion and the two processes of restitution and reunion are thus competing ones in which both space and time factors are important.

RELATIVE EFFICIENCIES OF VARIOUS RADIATIONS

Comparisons of the relative efficiencies of various ionizing radiations and of X rays of various wave lengths in producing breaks and aberrations have been of considerable importance in the development of the theory of aberration production in *Tradescantia*. As indicated previously, the greater efficiency of fast neutrons as compared with 160-kv X rays provided part of the initial evidence that single ionizations were insufficient to produce chromosome breaks. The conclusion that several ionizations (or related chemical events, as will be discussed later) are necessary for chromosome breakage arises from the following consideration: Ionizations are much more densely spaced along a proton track (derived from neutron radiation) than along an electron track (derived from X radiation). Hence, when a proton traverses a chromosome, many ionizations will be produced within its volume; if only one ionization were required for breakage, neutrons should be less rather than more efficient than X rays, since additional ionizations produced within the chromosome would be wasted, contributing to the physical dose but not to the biological effect.

Utilizing the neutron–X-ray comparisons, Lea and Catcheside (1942) attempted to determine the approximate number of ionizations required to produce a break. Their conclusion was that seventeen ionizations, on the average, are required for breakage to occur. Further, with the usual X-irradiation procedures, in which relatively hard X rays are employed, it appears that breakage arises primarily from the concentrated ionization produced at the end (tail) of the electron path. The conclusion that the tail of the electron path is responsible for break production with X rays was tested experimentally by comparing the efficiencies of X rays of different wave lengths, particularly in the soft X-ray range. For this purpose, the effects on pollen tube chromosomes were examined and the experimental results were found to agree well with the theoretical predictions (Catcheside and Lea, 1943).

The calculations of Lea and Catcheside (1942) indicated that the probability of break production when a proton (from a fast neutron) traverses a chromosome is somewhat less than one. On this basis α particles, because of their much greater ionization density, should be actually less efficient than fast neutrons. The studies of Kotval and Gray (1947), however, indicate that α particles are actually more efficient than neutrons. It is possible to conclude from these results that α particles need not always traverse a chromosome in order to produce a break, but that breaks may also arise when the particle passes in the immediate vicinity of the chromosome. Such a view implies an indirect action of the radiation in producing chromosome breaks, a topic which will be considered in detail later.

ABERRATION PRODUCTION BY ABSORBED RADIOISOTOPES

The abundant production by atomic reactors of radioactive isotopes of various elements has stimulated interest in the use of these substances, not only as tracer, but also as radiation, sources. Experiments have been performed with two different isotopes, P^{32} and C^{14}, both producing β rays, to determine the effects of these substances in producing chromosome aberrations in *Tradescantia* microspores (Giles, 1947; Giles and Bolomey, 1948). When cut stems of inflorescences were placed in solutions of various activities, containing one or the other of the two isotopes, aberrations similar to those produced by X rays were observed in the microscopes. The types, frequencies, and temporal sequence of aberrations were recorded over a period of several days following the initial treatments. Quantitative measurements of β activity from disintegrations of P^{32} molecules in individual half-anthers showed good correlations with the relative frequencies of aberrations detected cytologically in sister half-anthers (Giles and Bolomey, 1948). It has not been possible, however, in the *Tradescantia* anthers to make sufficiently accurate calculations of dosages from internally distributed isotopes to determine whether aberrations arise as a result of recoil and/or transmutation events in addition to ionization events.

ABERRATION PRODUCTION BY SLOW NEUTRONS

The cytogenetic effects of slow neutrons are being discussed separately from those of other radiations because of certain unique features associated with the interaction of this type of radiation with biological materials. Fast neutrons arising from uranium fission can be moderated by elastic collision with graphite or heavy water in a nuclear reactor until their velocities are reduced to thermal energies (average 2200 meters/second = 0.025 ev). Such neutrons do not behave like fast neutrons, whose principal reaction of significance in biological materials is the ejection of recoil protons from hydrogen atoms. Rather, thermal neutrons, because of their very low velocities and energies, are normally captured by various atoms in biological materials. Such a capture reaction produces an unstable compound nucleus with an excess of energy. This unstable nucleus may then (1) emit a γ ray immediately to form a stable isotope, e.g.,

$$H^1 + n \rightarrow [H^2] \rightarrow H^2 + \gamma$$

(2) emit a heavy particle immediately to form a stable isotope, e.g.,

$$B^{10} + n \rightarrow [B^{11}] \rightarrow Li^{7} + \alpha$$

or (3) emit a capture radiation immediately, forming a radioactive daughter which then emits β or γ rays at a rate characteristic of the isotope formed, e.g.,

$$N^{14} + n \rightarrow [N^{15}] \rightarrow C^{14} + p \xrightarrow{\text{half life ca. 6000 years}} N^{14} + \beta^{-}$$

The radiations of biological importance are the immediate "capture" radiations and the delayed or "decay" radiations, since these produce ionization. Thermal neutrons do not themselves appear to produce any effect, since they are uncharged particles of low energies.

The reactions outlined indicate that there are two principal classes of radiations arising from slow neutrons which should be of biological significance, γ radiation and heavy-particle radiations. As has been shown, exchanges in *Tradescantia* microspores are linearly related to doses of protons and α particles, but show a geometrical relation to doses of γ rays. Thus it should be possible, by determining the kind of dosage curve obtained for slow neutron-induced exchanges, to decide the relative biological importance in chromosome aberration production of these two classes of radiations arising from slow neutron exposures. Such experiments have been performed, utilizing a special exposure facility in the thermal column of the Oak Ridge reactor (Conger and Giles, 1950). The results obtained indicate that the relationship with doses of slow neutrons is linear for all types of aberrations, giving biological evidence that capture reactions resulting in the emission of particulate radiations are of major consequence in producing aberrations. Physical calculations indicate that the boron and nitrogen reactions are responsible for approximately 32 and 52 per cent of the total rep of ionization absorbed in *Tradescantia* tissue, while the hydrogen reaction accounts for 16 per cent, practically all the remainder.

Simultaneous X-ray exposures were made in order to compare the relative biological efficiencies of thermal neutrons and X rays for the production of chromatid and isochromatid breaks. After appropriate corrections were made for γ-ray contamination in the neutron exposure chamber, the observed thermal neutron–X-ray ratio for chromatid aberration production was found to be approximately 11:1. If only the nitrogen protons and boron α particles from thermal neutron capture are considered, their efficiency compared with X rays seems to be about 15:1. The expected ratio, calculated on the basis of previous radiation results from external sources, was ca. 5.2:1. Thus it appears that particulate radiations originating internally from capture reactions are considerably more efficient (about three times) in break production than are similar radiations from external sources. Since some evidence indicates a nonrandom distribution of boron and possibly of nitrogen in cells, with higher relative concentrations in the nucleus and possibly in the chromosomes, it is suggested that this may account in part for the observed efficiency differences. In addition, recoil and transmutation effects may also be of importance. It thus seems probable that the greater effectiveness of particulate radiations originating internally from capture reactions results from both the site and mode of origin of these radiations.

RECAPITULATION

Before considering the effect of modifying factors, it seems appropriate to summarize briefly the general theory of aberration production by ionizing radiation as discussed in the previous sections.

On this theory, as originally proposed by Sax and Lea and Catcheside, a break in either a single (resting stage) or divided (prophase) chromosome is due to the direct action on the chromosome of the ionization produced by the passage through the chromosome of a single particle, such as an electron, a proton, or an α particle. Such a break may then remain as such giving rise to a terminal deletion, rejoin in the original position (the process of restitution) and thus be undetected, or join with another adjacent break in the same or in a different chromosome (the process of reunion) to produce various types of aberrations.

Comparative experiments with different radiations under various conditions indicate that several ionizations (average ca. 17) are required to produce a chromosome break; that the majority of breaks produced undergo restitution; that restitution is, for most breaks, a relatively rapid process (the average restitution time being ca. 4 minutes, although some breaks may remain "open" for considerably longer periods); and that reunion is not at random, since for an exchange to occur the two breaks involved must be produced with an initial separation of not more than ca. 1 μ.

The quantitative relationship between a dose of radiation and the yield of aberrations depends on both the type of aberration and the kind of radiation. With X and γ rays, certain types of breaks (simple, one-hit) are linearly related to dose and are apparently produced by the relatively concentrated ionization at the tail of a single electron track. Other types, principally those involving breaks in separate chromosomes (exchanges, two-hit types) increase as some power of the dose greater than one. These aberrations apparently arise from the production of the two separate breaks by the tails of two separate electron tracks. An intensity effect with X rays exists for exchange breaks, as indicated by the fact that the yield for exchanges, but not for simple breaks, is lower when the same dose is delivered at a low as compared with a high intensity. If the dose is given in a short time, all the initial breaks are present in the nucleus simultaneously, reunion is favored, and the exchange yield is proportional to the square of the dose. If the dose is extended over a considerable period (at a low intensity), restitution is favored over reunion and the exchange yield is reduced.

With fast neutron and α-particle experiments, in which many fewer ionizing particles traverse the nucleus than do electrons in comparable X-ray exposures, all aberrations exhibit a linear relationship with dose. Thus exchange aberrations apparently arise as the result of the simultaneous production by the same ionizing particle of the two breaks taking part in the exchange. Confirmation of this fact comes from the evidence that there is no effect of neutron intensity on aberration yield.

The interpretation of chromosome aberration production as just outlined has been quite generally successful in accounting for most of the quantitative results of radiation experiments with *Tradescantia.* Recently, however, experimental data of two sorts have been obtained which indicate that this theory in its simplest form is not entirely adequate. The first evidence was that obtained by Kotval and Gray (1947) in their studies with α particles. On the basis of comparative ionization distribution and particle numbers, the theory predicts that a given amount of ionization produced by α particles should be considerably less efficient in producing chromosome breaks than an equal ionization dose produced by fast neutrons; whereas, the experimental results indicate that, for equal ionization doses, α particles are somewhat more efficient. It was concluded that a proportion of the breaks produced by α particles arise from ionization produced in the immediate vicinity of, but not within, a chromosome, thus suggesting the involvement of an *indirect* as well as a direct mechanism. The second, and even more striking, evidence was that obtained by Thoday and Read (1947), who noted a pronounced effect of oxygen on the frequency of X-ray-induced aberrations in the root-tip mitosis of the broad bean, *Vicia faba.* Their experiments indicated that the absence of oxygen during irradiation resulted in a marked decrease in aberration frequency and consequently supplied additional evidence for the probable presence of indirect mechanisms responsible for chromosome breakage. Extensive studies of the oxygen effect on aberration production in *Tradescantia* microspores have also been performed and the results of these experiments will be discussed in one of the next sections on modifying factors. In that discussion an attempt will be made to evaluate the significance of all these more recent findings in relation to the mechanism of aberration production as previously described.

EFFECTS OF MODIFYING FACTORS

The effects of various modifying factors applied before, during, or after exposures to radiations have been extensively studied in attempts to elucidate further the mechanisms of chromosome breakage and reunion. In certain instances, for example centrifugation effects, such studies have served primarily to support previous hypotheses as to the process involved. In other cases (e.g., infrared effects) the investigations have revealed pronounced effects which may require modification of original views, but for which no clear explanations are as yet available. Finally, certain studies (the oxygen effect) have yielded results of paramount significance for any interpretation of the biophysical and biochemical mechanism of aberration production and appear to necessitate a definite revision of certain aspects of older hypotheses. In view of the past and probable future importance of studies of modifying factors, it appears desirable to devote a rather considerable amount of space to a consideration of these effects. Since it is felt that the oxygen effect is of special significance, a major portion of the discussion will be devoted to the available evidence relating to this effect. It should be borne in mind, however, that many of the conclusions arrived at in this latter discussion must be, of necessity, tentative ones, since such investigations have only recently been initiated and much work remains to be done to clarify various aspects of the problem.

CENTRIFUGATION; SONIC VIBRATION

Experiments of Sax (1943) have shown that centrifugation (2080 rpm) during X irradiation approximately doubles the yield of chromosome and chromatid interchanges as well as of isochromatid aberrations. When centrifugation followed irradiation (the interval between cessation of irradiation and initiation of centrifugation being 5 minutes) there was no increase in aberration frequency. In control experiments, centrifugation alone produced no effect. In analogous experiments in which sonic energy (9100 cycles/second) was applied during X irradiation (Conger, 1948), an increased frequency of both chromosome interchanges and deletions resulted, although the magnitude of the effect was less than that found with centrifugation. In control experiments, no effect of this treatment alone was detected, although chromosome breakage following supersonic treatment (400,000 cycles/second) alone has been reported in other plant material (Wallace, Bushnell, and Newcomer, 1948). These experiments are interpreted as indicating that factors such as mechanical stresses or vibrations can cause movement of broken ends produced by irradiation, and thus promote new reunions yielding aberrations, as opposed to restitution.

COLCHICINE

Brumfield (1943) has studied the effect of pretreatment with colchicine on the frequency of X-ray-induced aberrations in *Allium* root tips. The experimental roots were placed in a 0.05 per cent solution of colchicine for

45 minutes immediately before exposure to 300 r of X rays. Subsequent to irradiation, both experimental and control roots were kept in a colchicine solution and a cytological analysis was made 48 hours later. There was a marked reduction, by about two-thirds, in the frequency of X-ray-induced chromatid aberrations in the root tips pretreated with colchicine; whereas, chromosome aberrations were about equally frequent in the experimental and control roots. These results are interpreted as arising from an effect of colchicine in reducing the amount of chromosome movement in prophase, where chromatid effects are induced, thus favoring restitution as opposed to recombination. Since chromosome movement at the resting stage is presumably at a minimum, the absence of an effect of colchicine on chromosome breaks is as expected.

ULTRAVIOLET

The investigations of Swanson (1940, 1942) utilizing pollen tube chromosomes (in *Tradescantia*) have shown that ultraviolet differs from X rays in that this radiation produces only chromatid breaks and no isochromatid breaks or chromatid exchanges. Subsequent to these studies of the comparative effects of ultraviolet and X radiation individually, experiments were performed (Swanson, 1944) in which ultraviolet was used in combination with X rays. Pretreatment with ultraviolet (2537 A) 1 hour before X irradiation produces an inhibition of all types of visible X-ray breaks. Chromatid breaks and translocations are relatively more affected than are isochromatid breaks. The degree of inhibition depends on the dosage of ultraviolet, but the nature of this proportionality was not established. The suggestion is made that the inhibition resulting from ultraviolet pretreatment arises from an effect on the chromosome matrix. This effect may result from a greater resistance of the matrix to subsequent X-ray breakage, or from the failure of broken ends having an ultraviolet-treated matrix to undergo new reunion, thus presumably favoring restitution.

Posttreatment with ultraviolet has no inhibitory effect on isochromatid breaks. However, translocations are inhibited, the effect decreasing as the time after radiation at which the ultraviolet is applied increases (up to 1 hour). Chromatid breaks are inhibited even when ultraviolet is applied as late as 1 hour after X irradiation. These posttreatment inhibitory effects on chromatid translocations and deletions are interpreted as indicating an effect of ultraviolet in facilitating restitution as opposed to reunion.

Similar experiments in *Drosophila* (Kaufmann and Hollaender, 1946) involving posttreatment with ultraviolet of X-rayed spermatozoa also resulted in a decrease in the frequency of gross chromosomal rearrangements. Dominant lethals, however, were not affected. These results are interpreted in the same way as those obtained in *Tradescantia*—as indicating an effect of ultraviolet in favoring restitution as opposed to recombination.

INFRARED

The original investigations of Kaufmann, Hollaender, and Gay (1946) demonstrated a marked effect of pretreatment with infrared in increasing the frequency of X-ray-induced chromosomal rearrangements in *Drosophila.* This effect was subsequently confirmed in experiments with *Tradescantia* microspores by Swanson and Hollaender (1946) and Swanson (1949). Pretreatment of whole inflorescences was carried out with infrared (between 6000 and 11,500 A with maximum energy transmission at 10,000 A) for varying periods of time (up to 96 hours) before exposure to X rays, and cytological analyses were made at 22 hours following X-ray exposure. All such pretreatments resulted in an increase in all types of chromatid rearrangements with the increase in interchanges being most marked. Posttreatments with infrared also resulted in an increase in the frequency of chromatid breaks and exchanges. (In the initial pretreatment experiments no effect on isochromatid breaks was found, but in later experiments these also showed an increase.) As with pretreatment, the effect on interchanges was most marked, and increased yields were obtained even when posttreatments were delayed as much as 18 hours after X irradiation. In order to explain the fact that both pre- and posttreatments are effective, the hypothesis is proposed that both infrared and X rays alone are capable of weakening the chromosome structure (in addition to the normally produced X-ray breaks) and that such changes only become realized as complete breaks upon the addition of the other type of radiation.

Yost (1951) has investigated the effect of infrared pre- and posttreatments on the frequency of chromosome breaks induced at the resting stage. Again, both these treatments resulted in an increase in the frequency of the aberrations scored—dicentrics and centric rings. Pretreatments were followed immediately by X irradiation and cytological examinations made 96 hours later. The frequency of aberrations in buds pretreated with infrared was, on the average, approximately doubled. For tests of posttreatment effects, buds were X-rayed and samples then given a single exposure to infrared at several successive intervals following the X irradiation, up to 96 hours, at which time cytological analyses were made. As indicated, increases were noted in each test and these were of approximately equal magnitude at all intervals (and of the same order of increase as for the pretreatments). Further, the unexpected result was obtained that all the aberration types observed were chromosome types, even in instances where the infrared exposures were made just before the cytological examination at 96 hours, when the chromosomes were obviously in the prophase stage where they respond to X-irradiation breakage as double structures. It is concluded that the type of aberration (whether chromosome or chromatid) is determined by the time of X irradiation and is independent of the time at which the infrared is applied. It is not yet clear why the additional reunion taking place during infrared treatment does not correspond to the singleness or doubleness of the chromosome as shown by X irradiation.

The *Drosophila* results obtained when infrared is used as a supplementary treatment with X irradiation differ in certain ways from those obtained in *Tradescantia*. In an extensive series of experiments, Kaufmann and his co-workers (Kaufmann, Hollaender, and Gay, 1946; Kaufmann and Hollaender, 1946; Kaufmann, 1946; Kaufmann and Gay, 1947; Kaufmann and Wilson, 1949) found that pretreatment results in an increased frequency of translocations, but not of dominant lethals (analogous to isochromatid breaks in *Tradescantia*) or of recessive lethals. Further, posttreatment of mature sperm has no effect. If, however, posttreatment is carried out at the time of fertilization (when chromosome recombination is usually assumed to occur), the frequency of translocations is increased. The action of infrared in *Drosophila* thus appears to be restricted to an effect on processes involved in the formation of chromosomal interchanges. The failure to detect an increase in the single-break type of dominant lethal indicates that the higher frequency of translocations is not simply a result of an over-all increase in chromosome breakage. These observations, together with the evidence that infrared alone has no detectable effect, have led to the hypothesis that this radiation acts in *Drosophila* to facilitate recombination (as opposed to restitution) among breaks produced by X radiation. It also appears that breaks may fall into two qualitatively different classes, since the subsequent behavior of the broken ends of some is modified by pretreatment while that of others remains unchanged. On this basis the proposal is made that dominant lethals in *Drosophila* may arise at the time of irradiation as a result of sister chromatid reunion; whereas, breaks resulting in translocations do not undergo recombination until the time of fertilization.

It is at present difficult to provide a comprehensive and unified interpretation of the supplementary effects of infrared applicable to both *Drosophila* and *Tradescantia*. The evidence that in *Tradescantia* all types of breaks are increased in frequency by pretreatment appears to constitute a real difference from *Drosophila*. However, the major effect of pretreatment in *Tradescantia* seems to be on translocation frequency. Again the major increase of posttreatment effects in *Tradescantia*, on the basis of available data, appears to be on translocation frequency.

Evidence against the idea of a weakened chromosome structure giving rise to true breaks upon subsequent irradiation as postulated by Swanson and Hollaender (1946) is available from the experiments of Sax (1942).

In these experiments the X-irradiation of microspores during the resting stage did not increase the subsequent sensitivity of the chromosomes in these same cells when they were X-rayed in prophase. In view of these results it appears improbable that infrared treatments following X irradiation would be more likely to produce additional true breaks.

It is possible that these difficulties may be resolved and a better understanding of the mechanisms of the infrared effect be achieved as a result of future research based on experiments briefly reported by Swanson and Yost (1951). These authors find that a heat shock applied after infrared exposure, and before X irradiation, will remove the infrared effect in *Tradescantia* microspores. They suggest that infrared may act to produce a metastable state in the chromosome which renders it more sensitive to X-ray breakage, and that this state is replaced by the normal state following heat shock. They also state that a similar effect is obtained when the order of treatment is X rays, heat, infrared and suggest that X rays, too, may produce, in addition to the usual breaks, incipient breaks or metastable states that are acted upon by infrared.

TEMPERATURE

As might perhaps be expected, temperature was the first modifying factor whose effect was studied in *Tradescantia* microspores. Sax and Enzmann (1939) demonstrated that the yield of chromatid aberrations of all types was greater at low than at high temperatures for a given X-ray dose. They interpreted these results as indicating an effect of temperature on the recovery process, such that restitution is favored at high and reunion at low temperatures, since it was supposed that at low temperature a break would remain open longer allowing the broken ends a greater chance, following chromosome movement, of undergoing reunion as opposed to restitution. Although there was evidence in the early experiments of an effect of postirradiation temperature changes, later experiments failed to demonstrate this effect, and Sax (1947) concluded that the temperature of the cells at the time of irradiation was the factor of major importance. The general observations of Sax and Enzmann were confirmed in independent investigations by Fabergé (1940) on X-ray-induced "fragments" and by Catcheside, Lea, and Thoday (1946b) on chromatid aberrations, although the latter investigators failed to find much temperature effect on chromatid deletions. Darlington and La Cour (1945) have maintained that most or all of the temperature effect in modifying aberration frequency is an indirect one resulting from an influence of this factor on the timing of the nuclear cycle, and thus on chromosome sensitivity to radiation. This objection has been met by Sax (1947) and especially by Catcheside (1948), who showed that the relatively brief exposures to high or low temperatures at the time of irradiation had little or no effect on the relative temporal positions of the peak frequencies of various chromatid aberrations although the magnitudes of the peaks was greater at low than at high temperatures. These results indicate that there had been no major modification by temperature of the timing of the nuclear cycle.

The discovery of the oxygen effect (to be discussed later) served to reopen the problem of the temperature effect, especially the interpretation of this effect as operating solely on the recovery mechanism. Since X-ray-induced aberration frequencies are positively correlated with oxygen concentration and oxygen is more soluble in water at low than at high temperatures, it seemed possible that all the apparent temperature

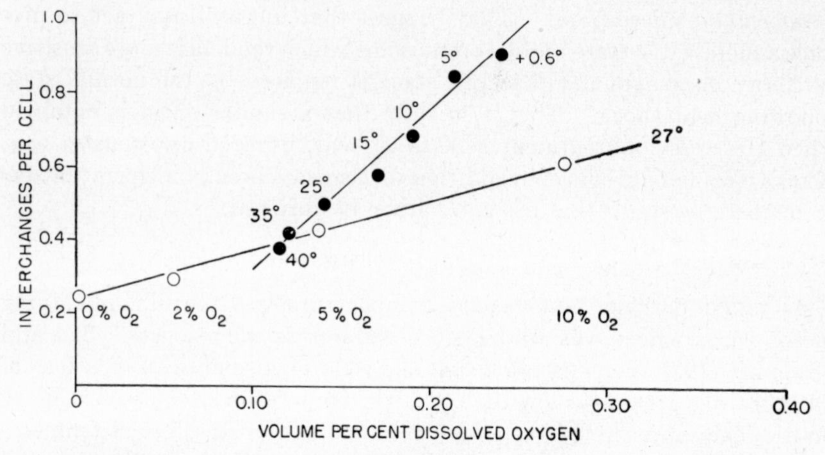

FIG. 10-7. Comparative effects of temperature and dissolved oxygen on chromosome interchange yield induced by 400 r of X rays. (*Giles, Beatty, and Riley, unpublished.*)

effects might be due to an indirect effect on oxygen availability. However, experiments of Giles, Beatty, and Riley (1951; and unpublished) indicate that the relation between chromosomal aberration yield and temperature can be attributed only in part to an effect of temperature on oxygen solubility. In addition, there appears to be a rather large effect of low temperature alone in increasing aberration frequency, such that chromosome interchanges and interstitial deletions are much more frequent than expected on the basis of an oxygen solubility effect alone at low as compared to high temperatures as long as oxygen is present during irradiation (Fig. 10-7). Whether this additional effect of temperature—beyond that portion probably associated with oxygen solubility and thus very likely with the initial breakage frequency—is to be attributed to an influence on the recovery mechanism, in accordance with the earlier interpretations, is not clear. It is also possible that the additional effect may result from an influence of temperature on the formation or effectiveness of substances responsible for actual breakage (to be discussed in detail later). If, for example, the "half life" of such mutagenic substances is increased at low temperature, this might permit these substances to increase their relative spheres of effectiveness, within the nucleus, in aberration production at low temperatures.

Additional evidence regarding the temperature effect is provided by experiments (Giles, Beatty, and Riley, 1951; and unpublished) performed in the absence of oxygen (in helium). The relation between

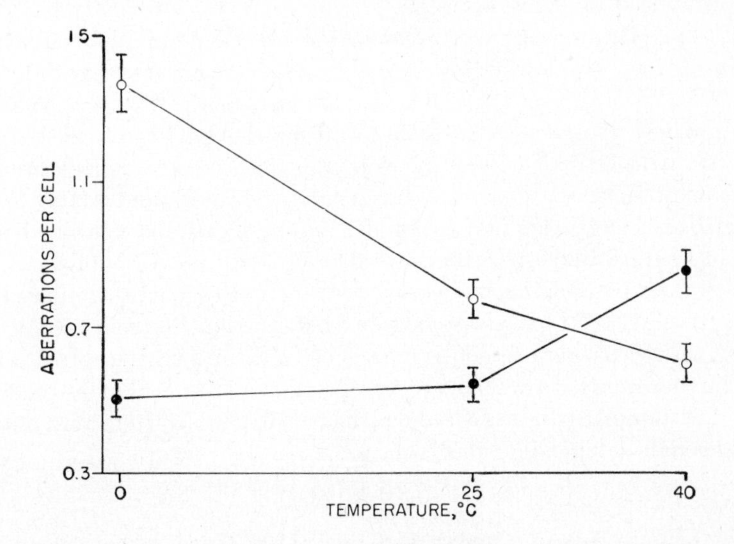

FIG. 10-8. Effect of temperature on yield of chromosome interchanges when X irradiation is performed in 5 per cent oxygen (400 r at 50 r/minute), helium (900 r at 300 r/minute). (*Data of Giles, Beatty, and Riley, unpublished.*)

temperature and chromosome aberration frequency under these circumstances is just the reverse of that found when oxygen is present, more interchanges and deletions being present in helium at high than at low temperatures. The same relationship holds for all types of chromatid aberrations as well. Data for isochromatid aberrations are shown in Fig. 10-8. How this result is to be interpreted is not yet clear. If the action of X rays in the absence of oxygen is considered to be largely direct, as some evidence indicates (Giles and Beatty, 1950), then the temperature effect would presumably be on the recovery process, such that restitution is favored at low and reunion at high temperatures. However, if the production of aberrations in the absence of oxygen is assumed to result largely from the production of OH radicals, which is certainly a possible interpretation (to be discussed later), then the temperature effect may result from an influence on either the production or, more likely, the effectiveness of the OH radicals. The discovery of this reversal of the temperature effect in the absence of oxygen makes it unlikely that the effect of temperature is to be attributed solely to a modification of the behavior of broken chromosome ends during the recovery process. Hollaender *et al.* (1951) have reported preliminary experiments indicating a similar reversal of the temperature effect with X-ray-induced killing of bacteria.

Fabergé (1948, 1950) has investigated the effect of X irradiation of pollen at very low temperatures and finds that the breakage frequency at −192°C is only about one-fifth that at +25°. Furthermore, the sensitivity curve for intermediate temperatures resembles, in general character, that for hydrogen peroxide production plotted against temperature when water containing oxygen is X-rayed (Bonet-Maury and Lefort, 1948). Experiments have been performed also to investigate the combined effects of temperature and of nitrogen (Fabergé, 1950 and unpublished). At +25°C the aberration frequency is reduced in nitrogen, as compared with air. At −192°C there is a reduction in aberration frequency in air compared with +25° as previously observed; and in nitrogen, sensitivity is still further reduced by about one half. Fabergé feels that nitrogen and very low temperature both reduce the sensitivity by the same amount, but through independent mechanisms.

OXYGEN

The experiments of Thoday and Read (1947), using root tips of *Vicia faba*, demonstrated that oxygen has a marked effect on chromosome sensitivity to X radiation as measured by induced aberrations visible at anaphase. The absence of oxygen during X irradiation reduced the aberration frequency to about one-third that observed when the irradiation was performed in the presence of air. Subsequent studies by the same investigators (1949) showed that the oxygen effect was markedly less when α-particle radiation was used.

A series of investigations (Giles and Riley, 1949, 1950; Giles and Beatty, 1950; Giles, Beatty, and Riley, 1951; Riley, Giles, and Beatty, 1952; Giles, Beatty, and Riley, 1952; and Giles, 1952, and unpublished) has been carried out utilizing *Tradescantia* inflorescences in order to confirm and extend these observations. In most of the experiments special exposure chambers have been used to make possible the rapid removal or introduction of various gases either before, during, or after irradiation and to control the temperature of the inflorescences during exposures. Most of the cytological observations have been confined to chromosome aberrations—interchanges and interstitial deletions. However, some data are also available for chromatid effects. The major experimental conclusions which have emerged from these studies may be summarized as follows.

1. There is a pronounced effect of oxygen in increasing the frequency of X-ray-induced aberrations of all types. Results of experiments with chromosome interchanges are shown in Fig. 10-9. The possibility that other gases are responsible for the effect has been excluded.

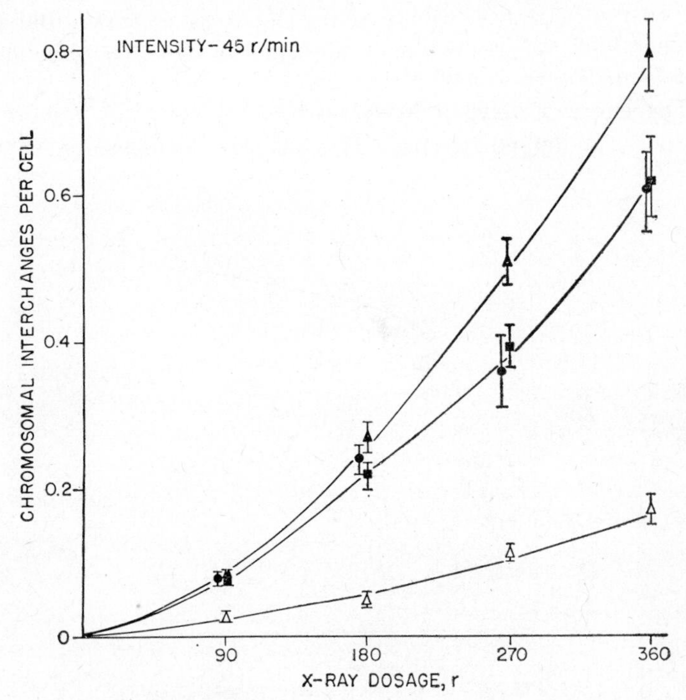

FIG. 10-9. X-ray dosage curves for chromosome interchanges induced in atmospheres of oxygen, air, or nitrogen. (*Giles and Riley*, 1949. *Figure reproduced by permission of the authors and the editor of the Proceedings of the National Academy of Sciences.*)

2. Oxygen must be present during the actual X irradiation to be effective. Pre- and posttreatment exposures of cells to pure oxygen or to anaerobic conditions for periods of time up to 1 hour have no effect. The results with pure oxygen in microspores contrasts with the effects observed by Conger and Fairchild (1951), who found that oxygen alone can produce aberrations in pollen grain chromosomes.

3. Even in the complete absence of oxygen, in so far as this gas can be completely removed from microspore cells, there is still an appreciable aberration frequency.

4. The percentage of increase in aberration frequency above this base line depends on the percentage of oxygen present during irradiation. This relationship is approximately linear between 0 and 10 per cent oxygen, after which the increase in aberration frequency becomes more gradual, until an approximate plateau is reached at 21 per cent. Data for chromosome interchanges at a constant dose are given in Fig. 10-10. Similar results have been reported by Baker (Hollaender, Baker, and Anderson, 1952) for reciprocal translocations detected genetically in *Drosophila virilis*.

5. The effect of oxygen in increasing the yield of X-ray-induced aberrations is an immediate one. This has been demonstrated by experi-

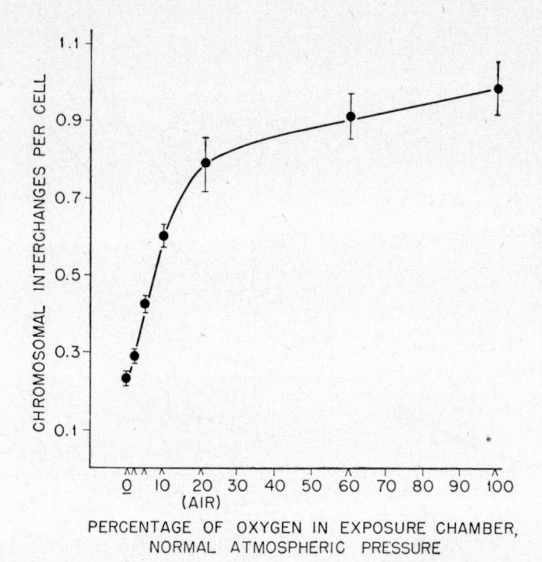

Fig. 10-10. Relation between percentage of oxygen and yield of X-ray-induced chromosome interchanges (400 r at 50 r/min). (*Giles and Beatty*, 1950. *Figure reproduced by permission of the authors and the editor of Science.*)

ments in which a rapid introduction of oxygen into cells during irradiation is effected. It has also been shown that the removal of oxygen during irradiation results in a decreased aberration yield. Data for chromosome interchanges are presented in Table 10-2.

6. The effect of pressure during irradiation depends on the amount of oxygen present in the gas mixture used. These studies provide further evidence that the increase in aberration frequency is related to the actual amount of oxygen dissolved in the cells.

7. Irradiation in pure hydrogen at normal pressure and under three atmospheres of pressure effects little or no significant decrease in aberration yield.

8. In agreement with previous studies on the temperature effect, an increased aberration yield at low temperatures is observed when irradiations are performed in the presence of oxygen in the range between approximately 1° and 35°C (see Fig. 10-7), but this result cannot be attributed entirely to an effect of temperature on oxygen solubility.

TABLE 10-2. EXPERIMENTS DEMONSTRATING THAT THE EFFECT OF OXYGEN ON THE YIELD OF X-RAY-INDUCED CHROMOSOME INTERCHANGES IN *Tradescantia* IS CONFINED TO THE PERIOD OF X-RAY EXPOSURE. (ALL DOSES: 300 R AT 300 R/MINUTE)
(Data from Giles and Riley, 1949)

Series No.	Condition of buds			No. of cells	Inter-changes per cell	Interstitial deletions per cell
	Pre-treatment	Exposure	Posttreatment			
1	Vacuum	Vacuum	Vacuum—10 min	880	0.12 ± 0.01	0.11 ± 0.01
2	Vacuum	Vacuum	Oxygen introduced (within 3 sec) to 1500 mm Hg—10 min	700	0.09 ± 0.01	0.10 ± 0.01
3	Oxygen	Oxygen at 1500 mm Hg	Oxygen at 1500 mm Hg —10 min	150	0.70 ± 0.07	0.83 ± 0.07
4	Oxygen	Oxygen at 1500 mm Hg	Evacuation (within 25 sec); vacuum—10 min	200	0.72 ± 0.06	0.85 ± 0.07
5	Vacuum	1st 30 sec: vacuum 2d 30 sec: oxygen introduced (within 3 sec) to 1500 mm Hg	Evacuation (within 25 sec); vacuum—10 min	350	0.39 ± 0.03	0.50 ± 0.04
6	Oxygen	1st 30 sec: oxygen at 1500 mm Hg 2d 30 sec: evacuation (within 25 sec) to 1–2 mm Hg	Oxygen introduced (within 3 sec) to 1500 mm Hg—10 min	518	0.61 ± 0.03	0.59 ± 0.03

9. In the absence of oxygen, a reversal of the temperature effect is noted, aberration frequencies being higher at high than at low temperatures (see Fig. 10-8).

10. When fast neutron radiation is used, an oxygen effect is also found, but the magnitude of the effect is considerably less for all types of aberrations than it is with X radiation.

11. Experiments on the intensity effect with X rays in oxygen and in nitrogen, using dosages of equivalent biological effect, have shown similar decreases in the yields of chromatid exchanges in the two gases at low intensities.

As a working hypothesis, to explain the oxygen effect, the view will be taken that this effect results from an increased frequency of initial chromosome breakage as a consequence of the action of certain active substances produced in the aqueous cellular medium when oxygen is present during irradiation. Before discussing the evidence for this view and for the possible identity of the intermediate substances involved, it is necessary to consider the evidence against other possible explanations for the oxygen effect. The three other principal explanations for this effect on chromosome aberration production, especially in *Tradescantia*, appear to be the following: (1) an effect of oxygen, as compared with oxygen lack, on some metabolic system or systems in the cell resulting in increased radiosensitivity; (2) an effect of oxygen itself on the recovery process such that the reunion of broken ends, which results in aberrations, is favored over restitution, which restores the original conditions; and (3) an effect of oxygen, when present during irradiation, not on the breakage process, but on the subsequent recovery process. Such a situation could arise either from the production in the presence and absence of oxygen of qualitatively different types of breaks with respect to their subsequent behavior in restitution or reunion, or from the effect on the recovery process of some product arising when oxygen is present during irradiation.

There would appear to be a distinct possibility that oxygen lack might influence radiosensitivity by modifying certain aspects of cellular metabolism, thus causing a decrease in chromosome aberration frequency. For example, there is good evidence that radiosensitivity varies with different stages in the mitotic cycle (cf. Sparrow, 1951), and an effect of oxygen (as compared with nitrogen) in modifying the timing of this cycle might result in an effect on aberration frequency (cf. Gaulden, Carlson, and Tipton, 1949). Further, it seems possible that modifications in the rate of cellular respiration might influence radiosensitivity. Other effects on cellular metabolism (e.g., on nucleic acid synthesis) of a lowering or increase in oxygen tension might also be anticipated. The major evidence against the view that the oxygen effect operates by way of disturbed cellular metabolism comes from the comparative studies of this effect with different kinds of radiations, as emphasized by Thoday (1950). Although there is a marked oxygen effect with X rays on chromosome aberration frequency in *Vicia* root tips, there is little or no effect with α particles. Similar observations have been made in *Tradescantia* (Conger, unpublished) and, in addition, the oxygen effect with fast neutrons has been found to be intermediate (Giles, Beatty, and Riley, 1952) between that for X rays and α particles. If the effect of oxygen were a metabolic one, there is no reason to suppose that the resulting modification in radiosensitivity would vary with different kinds of radiations.

Further evidence against the possibility that a disturbance of the mitotic cycle can explain the oxygen effect comes from the experiments (Giles and Riley, 1950; Giles, 1952) in which it was shown that this effect is an immediate one, since the introduction of the gas *during* irradiation results in a marked increase in aberration frequency. That oxygen could have influenced the timing of the mitotic cycle in these experiments is clearly impossible. Furthermore, the experiments were performed on chromosomes in the resting stage, a part of the mitotic cycle where there is relatively little variation in radiosensitivity (Sax, 1938; Koller, 1946). It also appears highly improbable that the introduction of oxygen during irradiation could have modified nucleic acid synthesis rapidly enough to have affected chromosome radiosensitivity if, in fact, the course of such synthesis does influence radiosensitivity (Darlington and La Cour, 1945).

The possibility must also be considered, especially in *Tradescantia*, that the effect of oxygen is on the recovery mechanism—the reunion, or restitution of broken chromosome ends—rather than on the initial breakage mechanism. Experiments have been performed (Giles and Riley, 1950) which appear to eliminate the possibility that oxygen itself may be influencing the recovery process. In these experiments, buds were X-irradiated in a vacuum, and oxygen was introduced immediately following the exposure. There was no increase in aberration frequency over control experiments in which buds were irradiated in vacuum and maintained in this condition for ca. 15 minutes following the exposure.

These experiments do not completely rule out the possibility that the oxygen effect may still operate by way of the recovery process, since as noted in possibility (3) above, it is conceivable that some substance produced in the cells when oxygen is present during X irradiation might influence the reunion of broken chromosome ends or that broken ends produced in the presence and absence of oxygen might be qualitatively different with respect to their subsequent behavior during the recovery process. Evidence against this interpretation is provided by intensity experiments in oxygen and in nitrogen (Riley, Giles, and Beatty, 1952), in which the restitution times for breaks giving rise to chromatid exchanges in the presence and absence of oxygen are found to be essentially identical. If the oxygen effect were operating by way of the recovery process, a difference in the average restitution time might well be anticipated. Further general support of the view that a major effect on the recovery process is not involved comes from the comparative oxygen effect with different types of radiations. It is found that the effect of oxygen on aberration frequencies is inversely correlated with the specific ionization of the radiation used (X rays, fast neutrons, and alpha particles). There appears to be no reason to assume that breaks produced by these radiations, especially by X rays and fast neutrons, should differ qualitatively with respect to a possible oxygen effect on the recovery process. It is possible, however, to provide a reasonable hypothesis to explain these observations on the basis of differential initial breakage, as will be discussed later. It should be noted that, despite the evidence just presented, the possibility cannot yet be excluded that the oxygen effect, even though operating primarily on the breakage mechanism, may also exert some influence on the recovery process.

The preceding evidence is taken to indicate that the effect of oxygen in modifying X-ray-induced chromosome aberration frequencies does not arise as a result of general metabolic disturbances within cells produced by the presence or by the absence of this gas. Further, the evidence favors the view that the effect of oxygen is not on the recovery mechanism, involving the restitution or reunion of broken chromosome ends. It thus appears that the increased aberration frequencies observed in the presence of oxygen probably result from an increased frequency of radiation-induced chromosome or chromatid breaks when this gas is present during irradiation. Consequently, the problem remains to determine what mechanism or mechanisms can explain this increased frequency of chromosome breakage by radiation, especially by X radiation, in the presence of oxygen. Further, consideration must be given to the way in which the results of the oxygen-effect studies can best be fitted into an over-all interpretation of the mechanism of chromosome aberration production by ionizing radiations.

During the past few years, increasing evidence has accumulated which indicates that many radiation effects in aqueous systems are largely indirect, mediated by active substances resulting from the radiodecomposition of water. Weiss (1944) concluded that these initial substances are OH radicals and H atoms and has discussed their mode of origin in irradiated water. Weiss (1944, 1947) and others (e.g., Allsopp, 1944; Lea, 1946; Allen, 1948; Bonet-Maury and Lefort, 1948; Sparrow and Rubin, 1952; Gray, 1952) have discussed the subsequent interactions of these primary products with one another and with dissolved substances, especially with oxygen, when water is irradiated with various radiations.

When pure water is irradiated the following reactions are believed to occur:

$$H_2O \ldots H_2O \xrightarrow[\text{(ionization)}]{\text{radiation}} H_2O^+ \ldots H_2O^- \qquad (1)$$

$$H_2O^+ \longrightarrow H^+ + OH \qquad (2)$$

$$H_2O^- \longrightarrow H + OH^- \qquad (3)$$

The result of the electron transfer in reaction (1) and the subsequent decompositions in reactions (2) and (3) are to produce H atoms and OH radicals. The relative magnitude of the various reactions which follow depends upon the type of radiation and the resulting geometric distribution of these primary products. The following reactions are all thought to occur (Allen, 1948):

$$H + OH \rightarrow H_2O \qquad (4)$$

$$OH + OH \rightarrow H_2O_2 \rightarrow H_2O + O \qquad (5)$$

$$H + H \rightarrow H_2 \qquad (6)$$

$$OH + H_2 \rightarrow H_2O + H \qquad (7)$$

$$H + H_2O_2 \rightarrow H_2O + OH \qquad (8)$$

If oxygen is present in the water, as is normally the case in most biological systems, the following reactions can also occur:

$$H + O_2 \rightarrow HO_2 \quad (9)$$
$$HO_2 + H \rightarrow H_2O_2 \quad (10)$$

The experimental evidence, particularly that of Bonet-Maury and Lefort (1948) and Allen (1948), indicates that in the absence of oxygen there is very little decomposition of water by X rays, since little or no H_2, O_2, or H_2O_2 can be detected. However, pure water is readily decomposed by α particles. The amount of H_2O_2 formed [presumably by reaction (5)] is directly proportional to the dose. There are few experimental data for other radiations, but Allen's results (1948) indicate that neutrons also produce appreciable amounts of H_2O_2 in oxygen-free water. When dissolved oxygen is present, H_2O_2 is produced by X rays, presumably by way of reactions (9) and (10). The influence of such factors as dose rate, pH, temperature, and amount of dissolved oxygen have been investigated by Bonet-Maury and Lefort (1948). With α particles, the yield of H_2O_2 when oxygen is present is approximately the same as in the absence of this gas. This absence of an oxygen effect is apparently related (Allen, 1948) to the closely spaced distribution of the H atoms and OH radicals, such that reactions (4), (5), and (6) are favored, and consequently H atoms are unavailable to participate in reaction (9). With X rays, the more widely spaced distribution of the H atoms and OH radicals does not favor reaction (6) and consequently reaction (9) does occur. When dissolved hydrogen is present in water in place of oxygen, a back reaction to form water, and thereby remove the OH radicals, takes place [reaction (7)].

As a result of their observations that there is a marked effect of oxygen on chromosome aberration production by X rays, and little or no such effect with α particles, Thoday and Read (1949) suggested that the active substance responsible for aberration production might be H_2O_2. Further striking parallelisms between H_2O_2 production in water under various conditions of irradiation, such as temperature and pH, and chromosome aberration production under similar conditions, are discussed by Giles (1952). Much of the radiochemical and biological evidence may be interpreted as furnishing indirect support to the view that H_2O_2 is important in aberration production. There is also direct evidence that H_2O_2 is mutagenic in such organisms as bacteria (Wyss *et al.*, 1948) and molds (*Neurospora*) (Wagner *et al.*, 1950; Jensen *et al.*, 1951). The difficulty of introducing this substance into cells such as microspores has precluded a direct test of aberration production by H_2O_2 in *Tradescantia*.

Although the H_2O_2 hypothesis has considerable evidence to support it, the radiochemical data, especially for X irradiation, suggest that other active substances are probably involved in aberration production in the presence of oxygen. It seems particularly likely that the HO_2 radical [resulting from reaction (9)] would itself be highly active biologically and should produce effects similar to H_2O_2. Furthermore, recent evidence from experiments on the oxygen effect with fast neutrons has made it clear that there is an inverse relationship between the specific ionization (ionization density) for a given radiation and the magnitude of the oxygen effect (Giles, Beatty, and Riley, 1952). The best data, for isochromatid breaks, indicate that the nitrogen-oxygen dose ratios (the ratio of the dose of a given radiation in nitrogen to that in oxygen producing an equal aberration yield) for α particles, fast neutrons, and X rays are, in order, 1.0, 1.4, and 2.6. These data serve to reemphasize the importance of ionization (and subsequent radical) distribution as a factor in radiobiological effects.

This inverse relationship between specific ionization and the oxygen effect apparently can be interpreted best as arising from differences in the distribution, and consequently in the interactions, of the primary radiation products in water (H atoms and OH radicals) and dissolved oxygen. Thus with α particles, the OH radicals and H atoms are closely spaced and reactions (4), (5), and (6) are favored. Even with oxygen present there is little opportunity for reaction (9) to occur, since H atoms are rapidly removed by reaction (6). Thus no HO_2 radicals are produced and no oxygen effect is noted. With X rays, however, the primary radiation products are more widely spaced and dissolved oxygen can react with H atoms to produce HO_2 [reaction (9)]. With radiations having intermediate specific ionization, such as recoil protons produced by fast neutrons, some oxygen effect might be anticipated, since reaction (6) would be less favored in comparison with reaction (9) than is the case with α particles.

It seems quite possible that reactions produced by OH and HO_2 radicals (and possibly by H atoms) rather than by H_2O_2 molecules, are principally effective in producing chromosome aberrations and that a certain average concentration of such radicals may be required for a chromosome break to result. It should be noted, however, that the probability also exists that H_2O_2 molecules are involved in α-particle effects, even if they prove to be relatively unimportant in X-ray effects, since the close proximity of OH radicals along the paths of these particles should favor their rapid reaction to form H_2O_2. At the present time it does not appear possible to decide whether OH radicals (and possibly also H atoms) or H_2O_2 molecules are primarily responsible for the α-particle effects. Further, there is the additional possibility that active products of secondary reactions, such as organic peroxides which are known to be mutagenic (Dickey *et al.*, 1949), are involved. This seems rather unlikely, however, in view of the apparent localization of the effects to the immediate vicinity of particle paths, a point which will be discussed later.

It will be recalled that in the absence of oxygen, i.e., in X irradiations performed in other gases such as nitrogen or helium or in a vacuum, there is still an appreciable frequency of aberrations. The question may be raised as to whether this residual frequency is due largely to indirect radical effects even in the absence of oxygen, as has been assumed in the immediately preceding discussion, or whether this effect arises from the direct absorption of the radiation energy by the nucleoprotein structure of the chromosome. The whole problem of distinguishing between direct and indirect effects, particularly in a situation such as this one, becomes exceedingly difficult. The distinction may in fact become largely meaningless in instances where such complex structures as chromosomes are involved, in which, for example, water molecules giving rise to active radicals upon irradiation may occur within the volume of the chromosome and probably even to some extent bound to it.

Despite these difficulties, it appears worth while to consider the available evidence bearing on the question of the mechanism of the radiation effect in the absence of oxygen. On a priori grounds, it seems reasonable to expect that an indirect effect by way of OH radicals, and possibly H atoms, would occur in an aqueous system such as a cell in the absence of oxygen. The difficulty of demonstrating such an effect experimentally is considerable, however. In the first place it is difficult to prove that all the oxygen has been removed from cells by the evacuation procedure employed. If it is assumed that the oxygen is in fact removed, then the existence of an indirect effect in the absence of oxygen can best be demonstrated by the efficacy of some protective substance in decreasing this effect by reacting with the intermediate active radicals or atoms before they can produce their biological result, in this instance, a chromosome break. A major difficulty in testing for such an effect arises from the problem of ensuring that the protective substance is actually penetrating the cell. For *Tradescantia* inflorescences, penetration by gases has been shown to be effective, hence an attempt was made to test for a protective effect using H_2, which is known on radiochemical evidence (Allen, 1948) to promote the back reaction to form H_2O in X-irradiated water by combining with the OH radical [reaction (7)]. However, no clearly significant decrease in aberration frequencies was found following irradiation in hydrogen at normal pressure or at three atmospheres above normal, compared with irradiation in a vacuum or in nitrogen at three atmospheres above normal pressure (Giles and Beatty, 1950).

Evidence that a hydrogen effect can be detected, at least in a chemical system possibly similar to the one in this biological experiment, is indicated by the experiments of Scholes and Weiss (1950) who found a decreased effect of X rays in disrupting nucleic acid (as measured by the ammonia yield) when hydrogen was present during irradiation, as compared with irradiation in a vacuum or in oxygen. The negative results of the *Tradescantia* experiment may be taken to indicate that OH radicals are in fact not effective in producing chromosome breaks, and that the X-ray effect in the absence of oxygen is primarily a direct one. However, there is no unequivocal evidence that hydrogen is actually present in the cell in sufficient amounts or in the appropriate locations to ensure that the back reaction will occur, although the evidence indicating a rapid penetration and effectiveness of oxygen would suggest that a similar situation exists for hydrogen. Furthermore, it is also possible that H atoms rather than OH radicals are responsible for the biological effect. That this may be true for certain chemical reactions is again suggested by the experiments of Scholes and Weiss (1950), in which evidence is presented that the liberation of phosphate from X-irradiated nucleic acid may result from reactions involving H atoms rather than OH radicals. The conclusion is thus not yet warranted that all or most of the X-ray effect on chromosomes in the absence of oxygen is a direct one. In other biological studies, such as those involving the killing of bacteria by X rays (Hollaender, 1952), there is evidence that chemical protection in the absence of oxygen can occur.

Further general evidence for the probable importance of the indirect effect comes from observations on the relatively greater radioresistance of dry as compared with soaked seeds (cf. Gustaffson, 1947), even though these experiments have been performed in air and not in the absence of oxygen. Regardless of the relative magnitude of the direct and indirect effects in the absence of oxygen, it appears to be quite clear that the indirect effect is of major importance when oxygen is present.

Even if the identity of the intermediate substances responsible for radiation-induced chromosome breakage were unequivocally established, the problem of determining the chemical structures involved and the chemical reactions leading to breakage would remain to be elucidated. It is not known, for example, whether the protein or the nucleic acid or both components of chromosomes are ruptured in the initial breakage reactions. Certain studies on the effects of irradiation on nucleic acid and proteins in vitro and in vivo are pertinent to this problem, however. The experiments of Sparrow and Rosenfeld (1946) demonstrated that X rays can induce depolymerization of thymonucleohistone and of sodium thymonucleate. The studies of Scholes and Weiss (1950) already referred to indicate that this effect on nucleic acid may result largely from indirect radical action. This conclusion is supported by the observation (G. C. Butler, 1949) that the presence of glucose or methanol in the solution during irradiation partially protects the nucleic acid. J. A. V. Butler and Smith (1950) conclude that the degradation of DNA can be produced by the action of OH radicals. Taylor *et al.* (1948) demonstrated that there is a continuing depolymerization of nucleic acid after the cessation of radiation. The recent work of J. A. V. Butler and Conway (1950) indicates that this latter effect occurs only if oxygen is present in the nucleic acid solutions at the time of irradiation. The immediate depolymerization effect of X radiation is independent of oxygen concentration. It is noteworthy that the radiosensitivity of nucleic acid to X rays increases by a factor of $\sim$3 in the presence of oxygen over that found under anaerobic conditions. This numerical increase is substantially the same as that found for chromosomal aberrations induced in *Vicia* root tips and *Tradescantia* microspores. Additional experiments are described (ibid.) from which the conclusion is reached that H_2O_2 is not the effective agent when irradiation is performed in the presence of dissolved oxygen.

In addition to the experiments on irradiation of nucleic acid in vitro, others have been reported (Limperos and Mosher, 1950) on the effects of irradiation in vivo. These workers conclude that substantial depolymerization occurs in living cells during irradiation, since they were able to isolate almost completely depolymerized DNA from the thymus of recently X-rayed rats.

Although these experiments on the effects of X radiation on nucleic acid are important in suggesting possible mechanisms of chromosome breakage, they do not establish that depolymerization is necessarily involved in this process. It is still not at all clear, for example, that changes in the nucleic acid of chromosomes, as opposed to those in the protein component, are the significant ones in chromosome breakage. These experiments do indicate, however, that the structure of one important component of chromosomes can be markedly modified by indirect radiation effects mediated by radicals or related active substances.

CONCLUSIONS

In concluding this discussion of radiation-induced chromosome aberrations in *Tradescantia,* it appears desirable to consider to what extent recent evidence, particularly that derived from the oxygen effect, necessitates a modification of earlier conceptions of the mechanism of chromosome aberration production by ionizing radiations. Prior to the discovery of the oxygen effect, the view was usually taken that the effect of radiations on chromosomes was a direct one resulting from the ionization of the bonding electrons of the molecules composing the chromosomes by the passage of the ionizing particles (Catcheside and Lea, 1943; Lea, 1946). However, the demonstration of the marked effect of oxygen in modifying the frequency of X-ray-induced aberrations, plus the evidence that this effect is probably on the breakage and not on the recovery process, appear to invalidate this opinion that direct molecular ionization is the only mechanism involved. Rather, it now seems most probable that the major fraction of the radiation effect on chromosomes is an indirect one, resulting from the action of active radicals, or of related substances derived from them, produced in the aqueous medium of the cell. Despite this indicated modification of earlier views on the basis of the recent results, it must be recalled that the major emphasis in the theory of radiation-induced chromosome changes in *Tradescantia* has been that a particular chromosome break results from several ionizations produced by one particular particle (whether an electron, a proton, or an α particle) and not from a single ionization or from a cumulative effect of several particles. Thus an essential feature of this theory, for which the major evidence has been derived from comparative experiments with X rays and fast neutrons, has been the localization of the biological effect along particle tracks, and the influence on this effect of differences in the patterns of ionization distribution along such tracks with various radiations (Lea, 1946). Since the original experiments were all performed in the presence of oxygen (in air), the evidence that chromosome breakage stems from events produced by single particle tracks remains valid, whether such events result from direct ionization of the molecules of the chromosome or from indirect effects produced by radicals arising in the water along the particle track. The types of dosage curves for interchanges induced by X rays and fast neutrons in the absence of oxygen are similar to those found when oxygen is present, again indicating a localized breakage mechanism involving the passage of single particles, regardless of whether the breakage in the absence of oxygen arises from direct or indirect effects. Thus the major modification required of earlier opinions is simply concerned with the nature of the chemical events involved in chromosome breakage. Consequently, it is only necessary to replace the concept of characteristic columnar patterns of ionization along various particle tracks, with one of columns of active radicals having similar patterns (or columns of their immediate products arising from radical interactions or from reactions with other solute molecules, such as oxygen). As emphasized by Thoday (1950) and Allsopp and Catcheside (1948), the principal point at issue is one of the relative localization of effects to the immediate vicinity of particle tracks. Even though indirect effects involving radical formation are involved, the evidence indicates that the effective diffusion of such substances is very limited. As a consequence, although a particle involved in producing a chromosome break by way of indirect radical effects may not actually traverse the chromosome thread, it seems clear that it must at least pass in the immediate vicinity of the site of breakage.

REFERENCES

Allen, A. O. (1948) Radiation chemistry of aqueous solutions. J. Phys. & Colloid Chem., 52: 479–490.

Allsopp, C. B. (1944) Radiochemistry. A review of recent progress. Trans. Faraday Soc., 40: 79.

——— and D. G. Catcheside (1948) Chemical breakage of chromosomes. Nature, 161: 1011–1012.

Bishop, C. J. (1950) Differential X ray sensitivity of *Tradescantia* chromosomes during the mitotic cycle. Genetics, 35: 175–187.

Bonet-Maury, P., and M. Lefort (1948) Formation of hydrogen peroxide in water irradiated with X- and alpha-rays. Nature, 162: 381–382.

Brumfield, R. T. (1943) Effect of colchicine pretreatment on the frequency of chromosomal aberrations induced by X-irradiation. Proc. Natl. Acad. Sci. U.S., 29: 190–193.

Butler, G. C. (1949) The effect of X and γ rays on aqueous solutions of sodium thymonucleate. Can. J. Research, 27B: 972–987.

Butler, J. A. V., and B. E. Conway (1950) The action of ionizing radiations and of radiomimetic substances on deoxyribonucleic acid. Part II. The effect of oxygen on the degradation of nucleic acid by X-rays. J. Chem. Soc., pp. 3418–3421.

——— and K. A. Smith (1950) Degradation of deoxyribonucleic acid by free radicals. Nature, 165: 847–848.

Catcheside, D. G. (1945) Effects of ionizing radiations on chromosomes. Biol. Revs., 20: 14–28.

——— (1948) Genetic effects of radiations, *in* Advances in genetics. Academic Press, Inc., New York, Vol. 2, pp. 271–358.

——— and D. E. Lea (1943) The effect of ionization distribution on chromosome breakage by X-rays. J. Genetics, 45: 186–196.

———, ———, and J. M. Thoday (1946a) Types of chromosome structural change induced by the irradiation of *Tradescantia* microspores. J. Genetics, 47: 113–136.

———, ———, and ——— (1946b) The production of chromosome structural changes in *Tradescantia* microspores in relation to dosage, intensity, and temperature. J. Genetics, 47: 137–149.

Conger, A. D. (1948) The cytogenetic effect of sonic energy applied simultaneously with X-rays. Proc. Natl. Acad. Sci. U.S., 34: 470–474.

——— and L. M. Fairchild (1951) The induction of chromosomal aberrations by oxygen. Genetics, 36: 547–548.

——— and N. H. Giles, Jr. (1950) The cytogenetic effect of slow neutrons. Genetics, 35: 397–419.

Darlington, C. D. (1942) Chromosome chemistry and gene action. Nature, 149: 66.

——— and L. F. La Cour (1945) Chromosome breakage and the nucleic acid cycle. J. Genetics, 46: 180–267.

——— and M. B. Upcott (1941) Spontaneous chromosome change. J. Genetics, 41: 297–338.

Dickey, F. H., G. H. Cleland, and C. Lotz (1949) The role of organic peroxides in the induction of mutations. Proc. Natl. Acad. Sci. U.S., 35: 581–586.

Duggar, B. M. (1936) Biological effects of radiations. McGraw-Hill Book Company, Inc., New York, 2 vols.

Fabergé, A. C. (1940) An experiment on chromosome fragmentation in *Tradescantia* by X rays. J. Genetics, 39: 229–248.

——— (1948) Chromosome aberrations in *Tradescantia* produced by X-ray treatment at liquid air temperature. Genetics, 33: 609.

——— (1950) Chromosome breakage by X-rays at low temperature and the radiodecomposition of water. Genetics, 35: 104.

Gaulden, M. E., J. G. Carlson, and S. R. Tipton (1949) Effects of carbon dioxide and nitrogen gas on mitosis as observed in living neuroblasts of grasshopper embryo. Anat. Record, 105: 16.

Giles, N. H., Jr. (1940a) Spontaneous chromosome aberrations in *Tradescantia*. Genetics, 25: 69–87.

——— (1940b) The effect of fast neutrons on the chromosomes of *Tradescantia*. Proc. Natl. Acad. Sci. U.S., 26: 567–575.

——— (1941) Spontaneous chromosome aberrations in triploid *Tradescantia* hybrids. Genetics, 26: 632–649.

——— (1943) Comparative studies of the cytogenetical effects of neutrons and X-rays. Genetics, 28: 398–418.

——— (1947) Chromosome structural changes in *Tradescantia* microspores produced by absorbed radiophosphorus. Proc. Natl. Acad. Sci. U.S., 33: 283–287.

——— (1952) Recent evidence on the mechanism of chromosome aberration production by ionizing radiations. Symposium on radiobiology (Oberlin, 1950), ed. J. J. Nickson. John Wiley & Sons, Inc., New York, pp. 267–284.

——— and A. V. Beatty (1950) The effect of X-irradiation in oxygen and in hydrogen at normal and positive pressures on chromosome aberration frequency in *Tradescantia* microspores. Science, 112: 643–645.

———, ———, and H. P. Riley (1951) The relationship between the effects of temperature and of oxygen on the frequency of X-ray induced chromosome aberrations in *Tradescantia* microspores. Genetics, 36: 552.

———, ———, and ——— (1952) The effect of oxygen on the production by fast neutrons of chromosomal aberrations in *Tradescantia* microspores. Genetics, 37: 641–649.

——— and R. A. Bolomey (1948) Cytogenetical effects of internal radiations from radioisotopes. Cold Spring Harbor Symposia Quant. Biol., 13: 104–112.

——— and A. D. Conger (1950) Chromosomal interchanges induced in *Tradescantia* microspores by fast neutrons from uranium fission. J. Cellular Comp. Physiol., 35 (Suppl.1): 83–88.

——— and H. P. Riley (1949) The effect of oxygen on the frequency of X-ray induced chromosomal rearrangements in *Tradescantia* microspores. Proc. Natl. Acad. Sci. U.S., 35: 640–646.

——— and ——— (1950) Studies on the mechanism of the oxygen effect on the radiosensitivity of *Tradescantia* chromosomes. Proc. Natl. Acad. Sci. U.S., 36: 337–344.

Gray, L. H. (1952) Biological actions of ionizing radiations, *in* Progress in biophysics. Academic Press, Inc., New York, Vol. 2.

Gustafsson, A., (1947) Mutations in agricultural plants. Hereditas, 33: 1–100.

Hollaender, A. (1951) Physical and chemical factors modifying the sensitivity of cells to high energy and ultraviolet radiation, *in* Symposium on radiobiology (Oberlin, 1950), ed., J. J. Nickson. John Wiley & Sons, Inc., New York, pp. 285–295.

———, W. K. Baker, and E. H. Anderson (1951) Effect of oxygen tension and certain chemicals on the X-ray sensitivity of mutation production and survival. Cold Spring Harbor Symposia Quant. Biol., 16: 315–326.

———, G. E. Stapleton, and F. L. Martin (1951) X-ray sensitivity of *E. coli.* as modified by oxygen tension. Nature, 167: 103–107.

Husted, L. (1936) An analysis of chromosome structure and behavior with the aid of X-ray induced rearrangements. Genetics, 21: 537–553.

Jensen, K. A., Inger Kirk, G. Kolmark, and M. Westergaard (1951) Chemically induced mutations in *Neurospora*. Cold Spring Harbor Symposia Quant. Biol., 16: 245–261.

Kaufman, B. P. (1946) Modification of the frequency of chromosomal rearrangements induced by X-rays in *Drosophila*. III. Effect of supplementary treatment at the time of chromosome recombination. Genetics, 31: 449–453.

——— and H. Gay (1947) The influence of X rays and near infrared rays on recessive lethals in *Drosophila melanogaster*. Proc. Natl. Acad. Sci. U.S., 33: 366–372.

——— and A. Hollaender (1946) Modification of the frequency of chromosomal rearrangements induced by X-rays in *Drosophila*. II. Use of ultraviolet radiation. Genetics, 31: 368–376.

———, ———, and H. Gay (1946) Modification of the frequency of chromosomal rearrangements induced by X-rays in *Drosophila*. I. Use of near infrared radiation. Genetics, 31: 349–367.

——— and K. Wilson (1949) Modification of the frequency of chromosome rearrangements induced by X-rays in *Drosophila*. IV. Posttreatment with near infrared radiations. Genetics, 34: 425–436.

Koller, P. C. (1946) The response of *Tradescantia* pollen grains to radiation at different dosage-rates. Brit. J. Radiology, 19: 393–404.

Kotval, J. P., and L. H. Gray (1947) Structural changes produced in microspores of *Tradescantia* by α radiation. J. Genetics, 48: 135–154.

Lane, G. R. (1951) X-ray fractionation and chromosome breakage. Heredity, 5: 1–35.

Lea, D. E. (1946) Actions of radiations on living cells. The University Press, Cambridge (also The Macmillan Company, New York, 1947).

——— (1947) The induction of chromosome structural changes by radiation: detailed quantitative interpretation. Brit. J. Radiology, Suppl. 1, pp. 75–83.

——— and D. G. Catcheside (1942) The mechanism of the induction by radiation of chromosome aberrations in *Tradescantia*. J. Genetics, 44: 216–245.

Limperos, G., and W. A. Mosher (1950) Roentgen irradiation of desoxyribosenucleic acid. II. Physicochemical properties of desoxyribosenucleic acid from irradiated rats. Am. J. Roentgenol. Radium Therapy, 63: 691–700.

Marinelli, L. D., B. R. Nebel, N. H. Giles, and D. R. Charles (1942) Chromosomal effects of low X-ray doses on five-day *Tradescantia* microspores. Am. J. Botany, 29: 866–874.

Mather, K. (1937) The experimental determination of the time of chromosome doubling. Proc. Royal Soc. (London), B124: 97–106.

Newcombe, H. B. (1942) The action of X-rays on the cell. II. The external variable. J. Genetics, 43: 237–248.

Rick, C. M. (1940) On the nature of X-ray induced deletions in *Tradescantia* chromosomes. Genetics, 25: 467–482.

Riley, H. P. (1936) The effect of X rays on the chromosomes of *Tradescantia gigantea*. Cytologia, 7: 131–142.

———, N. H. Giles, Jr., and A. V. Beatty (1952) The effect of oxygen on the induction of chromatid aberrations in *Tradescantia* microspores by X irradiation. Am. J. Botany 39: 592–597.

Ris, Hans (1947) The composition of chromosomes during mitosis and meiosis. Cold Spring Harbor Symposia Quant. Biol., 12: 158–160.

Sax, Karl, (1938) Induction by X-rays of chromosome aberration in *Tradescantia* microspores. Genetics, 23: 494–516.

——— (1939) The time factor in X-ray production of chromosome aberrations. Proc. Natl. Acad. Sci. U.S., 25: 225–233.

——— (1940) An analysis of X-ray induced chromosomal aberrations in *Tradescantia*. Genetics, 25: 41–68.

——— (1941) Types and frequencies of chromosomal aberrations induced by X-rays. Cold Spring Harbor Symposia Quant. Biol., 9: 93–101.

——— (1942) The mechanisms of X-ray effects on cells. J. Gen. Physiol., 25: 533–537.

——— (1943) The effect of centrifuging upon the production of X-ray induced chromosomal aberrations. Proc. Natl. Acad. Sci. U.S., 29: 18–21.

——— (1947) Temperature effects on X-ray induced chromosome aberrations. Genetics, 32: 75–78.

——— (1950a) The cytological effects of low-intensity radiation. Science, 112: 332–333.

——— (1950b) The effect of X-rays on chromosome structure. J. Cellular Comp. Physiol., 35 (Suppl. 1): 71–81.

——— and R. T. Brumfield (1943) The relation between X-ray dosage and the frequency of chromosomal aberrations. Am. J. Botany, 30: 564–570.

——— and H. W. Edmonds (1933) Development of the male gametophyte in *Tradescantia*. Botan. Gaz., 95: 156–163.

——— and E. V. Enzmann (1939) The effect of temperature on the frequency of X-ray induced chromosome aberrations. Proc. Natl. Acad. Sci. U.S., 25: 397–405.

——— and H. Luippold (1952) The effect of fractional X-ray dosage on the frequency of chromosome aberrations. Heredity, 6: 127–131.

——— and K. Mather (1939) An X-ray analysis of progressive chromosome splitting. J. Genetics, 37: 483–490.

——— and C. P. Swanson (1941) Differential sensitivity of cells to X-rays. Am. J. Botany, 28: 52–59.

Scholes, G., and J. Weiss (1950) Chemical action of ionizing radiations on nucleic acids in aqueous systems. Nature, 166: 640–642.

Sparrow, A. H. (1951) Radiation sensitivity of cells during mitotic and meiotic cycles with emphasis on possible cytochemical changes. Ann. N.Y. Acad. Sci., 51: 1508–1540.

——— and M. Maldawer (1950) Differential rejoining as a factor in apparent sensitivity of chromosomes to X-ray breakage. Proc. Natl. Acad. Sci. U.S., 36: 636–643.

———, J. J. Moses, and R. Steele (1950) Sensitivity of chromosomes to breakage by X rays and its relationship to the nucleic acid cycle in dividing cells. Cancer Research, 10: 241–242.

——— and F. M. Rosenfield (1946) X-ray-induced depolymerization of thymus nucleohistone and of sodium thymonucleate. Science, 104: 245–246.

——— and B. A. Rubin (1952) Effects of radiations on biological systems, *in* Survey of biological progress, ed. G. S. Avery, Jr. Academic Press, Inc., New York, Vol. 2.

Swanson, C. P. (1940) A comparison of chromosomal aberrations induced by X-ray and ultraviolet radiations. Proc. Natl. Acad. Sci. U.S., 26: 366–373.

——— (1942) The effects of ultraviolet and X-ray treatment on the pollen tube chromosomes of *Tradescantia*. Genetics, 27: 491–503.

——— (1943) Differential sensitivity of prophase pollen tube chromosomes to X-rays and ultraviolet radiation. J. Gen. Physiol., 26: 485–494.

——— (1944) X-ray and ultraviolet studies on pollen tube chromosomes. I. The effect of ultraviolet (2537 Å) on X-ray induced chromosomal aberrations. Genetics, 29: 61–68.

——— (1947) X-ray and ultraviolet studies on pollen tube chromosomes. II. The quadripartite structure of the prophase chromosomes of *Tradescantia*. Proc. Natl. Acad. Sci. U.S., 33: 229–232.

——— (1949) Further studies on the effect of infrared radiation on X-ray-induced chromatid aberrations in *Tradescantia*. Proc. Natl. Acad. Sci. U.S., 35: 237–244.

——— and A. Hollaender (1946) The frequency of X-ray induced chromatid breaks in *Tradescantia* as modified by near infrared radiation. Proc. Natl. Acad. Sci. U.S., 32: 295–302.

——— and H. T. Yost, Jr. (1951) The action of infrared radiation on the chromosomes of *Tradescantia*. Genetics, 36: 579.

Taylor, Babette, J. P. Greenstein, and A. Hollaender (1948) Effects of X-radiation on sodium thymus nucleate. Arch. Biochem., 16: 19–31.

Thoday, J. M. (1942) The effects of ionizing radiations on the chromosomes of *Tradescantia bracteata*. A comparison between neutrons and X-rays. J. Genetics, 43: 189–210.

——— (1950) Oxygen and chromosome mutation in plants. Brit. Sci. News, 3: 66–69.

——— and J. Read (1947) Effect of oxygen on the frequency of chromosome aberrations produced by X-rays. Nature, 160: 608–610.

——— and ——— (1949) Effect of oxygen on the frequency of chromosome aberrations produced by alpha-rays. Nature, 163: 133–134.

Wagner, R. P., C. H. Haddox, R. Fuerst, and W. S. Stone (1950) The effect of irradiated medium, cyanide, and peroxide on the mutation rate in *Neurospora*. Genetics, 35: 237–248.

Wallace, R. H., R. S. Bushnell, and E. H. Newcomer (1948) The induction of cytogenetic variations by ultrasonic waves. Science, 107: 577–578.

Weiss, J. (1944) Radiochemistry in aqueous solutions. Nature, 153: 748–750.

——— (1947) Some aspects of the action of radiations on aqueous solutions. Brit. J. Radiology, Suppl. 1, pp. 56–59.

Wyss, O., J. B. Clark, F. Haas, and W. S. Stone (1948) The role of peroxide in the biological effects of irradiated broth. J. Bact., 56: 51–57.

Yost, H. T., Jr. (1951) The frequency of X-ray induced chromosome aberrations in *Tradescantia* as modified by near infrared radiation. Genetics, 36: 176–184.

Manuscript received by the editor Jan. 5, 1952

CHAPTER 11

Immediate Effects on Division, Morphology, and Viability of the Cell

J. Gordon Carlson

Department of Zoology and Entomology, The University of Tennessee,[1] and Biology Division, Oak Ridge National Laboratory[2]

Introduction. Action of high-energy as compared with ultraviolet radiations. Measurement of effect. High-energy radiations: Mitotic effects—Morphological effects—Cell viability effects. Ultraviolet radiations: Mitotic effects—Cell morphology effects—Viability effects. References.

INTRODUCTION

Among the earliest known effects of ionizing and ultraviolet radiations on the living organism were their capacities to produce changes in cell morphology that were frequently followed by death of the cell and to reduce the mitotic activity in tissues. The last two decades have seen a great increase in interest in this field and in the publication of papers dealing with the results of research into these effects. As a natural consequence, the subject of cytological effects has been subdivided in these volumes into several topics, each delimited by somewhat arbitrary and often overlapping boundary lines, more often than not determined by the special interests and the particular points of view of the authors. The subject matter of this chapter will be confined to a review of those radiation-induced cytological effects that are ordinarily evident within a single mitotic cycle of treatment. Omitted are such important subjects as chromosome aberrations, protective agents, photorecovery, developmental effects, physiological effects, and effects on microorganisms, which are dealt with in other chapters.

For discussions of certain aspects of the effects considered in this chapter the reader is referred to reviews by Packard (1931), Duggar (1936), Warren (1942), Lea (1946), Spear (1946), Giese (1947), Rajewsky and Schön (1948), and Carlson (1950).

[1] Contribution No. 67 from the Department of Zoology and Entomology.

[2] Work performed under Contract No. W-7405-eng-26 for the Atomic Energy Commission.

ACTION OF HIGH-ENERGY AS COMPARED WITH ULTRAVIOLET RADIATIONS

The cytological effects of treatment with high-energy radiations are probably the results of chemical and physical changes induced in certain molecules by the release of energy inside the living cell. This assumedly results directly or indirectly from ionizations induced by the radiation. Through the selection of the kind of radiation one can control the manner in which the energy is distributed within the cell. Gamma rays, β rays, and short wave-length (hard) X rays, for example, which have a low specific ionization in air, release their energy in relatively scattered rather than clustered loci. The ionizing particles produced by long wave-length (soft) X rays, however, give off energy in dense clusters, while α rays and protons release their energy in very densely ionizing columns. The quantity of energy absorbed by different structures in the cell depends on the nature of the ionizing particle and not on the chemical composition of the cell part affected. For this reason, different kinds of high-energy radiation give biologically detectable effects that are quantitatively, but not qualitatively, different.

On the other hand, the different wave lengths of ultraviolet radiation of interest to the biologist, i.e., those in the range of 2250–3650 A, induce cytological changes that may be both quantitatively and qualitatively different. Ultraviolet quanta are selectively absorbed by the different molecules of the cell, a given molecule absorbing a certain quantum only if it has a corresponding energy level. The energy of a given ultraviolet wave length will, therefore, be absorbed with a resulting change in certain types of molecules. Wave lengths around 2600 A, for example, will be highly absorbed by the nucleic acids of the cell, while those around 2800 A will be more highly absorbed by certain proteins. The absorbing molecules are altered in the process, and these changes may be reflected in morphological and functional alterations of the cell constituents.

The kind of radiation determines the types of biological materials and the methods of study that can be used. The greatest latitude is possible with deeply penetrating radiations, such as γ rays, neutrons, and hard X rays. Beta rays, α rays, and soft X rays, however, impose definite limitations, for their paths in tissue are very short. If the cells to be studied for effect are single cells or if they are situated at the surface of a tissue, the amount of energy reaching them can be determined with reasonable accuracy. If deeper lying cells are to be studied, however, more penetrating radiation must be used. An alternative is the method used by Gray and Read (1942), wherein root tips were immersed in radon solution, which readily penetrates the material and emits α particles within the cells.

MEASUREMENT OF EFFECT

In determining the relation of a dose of radiation to the biological changes induced, it is essential that allowance be made for two factors that characterize this kind of experiment: (1) latency in the appearance of the effect and (2) the extent to which recovery may have occurred between treatment and observation. Each warrants a more detailed analysis.

Biological effects do not become observable immediately on the cessation of treatment, even though the ionizations and excitations produced by radiations occur within a fraction of a second after the impingement of the photons. Different biological effects may become detectable in minutes, hours, days, or even years after treatment. In part, this is due to the time required for the series of physical and chemical changes that must intervene between the photon absorption and the morphological change. For example, in alteration of the form of the nucleolus by ultraviolet the maximum observable change occurs at about 35 minutes after treatment (Carlson and McMaster, 1951). In part the latency is due to the series of biological changes that must run their course before the appropriate stage for detecting the change is reached. Changes in rate of mitosis can be determined only at the end of an interval of time during which the rate is measured. Chromosomal aberrations are first detectable hours or days after treatment and then only at certain mitotic stages and in certain kinds of tissues, while gene mutations may have to pass through two or three generations of individuals, and so may not be detected for months or years after they have been produced. Though the present chapter deals only with what we term immediate effects, these may not be observable until several hours after treatment.

A striking characteristic of living substance is the capacity to repair deleterious changes produced within it by external agents. The effects dealt with in this chapter, with the exception of cell lethality and possibly the chromosome "stickiness" evident soon after treatment, are subject to repair within the cell.

The intermediaries by which ionizations within the cell lead to changes in the rate of mitosis are not known. Probably the initial effect may be viewed as either the destruction of something within the cell—perhaps an enzyme or substrate that is necessary for mitotic progression—or the production of a substance that exerts a toxic effect on mitosis. Recovery, then, would result either from the replacement of the destroyed enzyme or substrate or from the removal of the toxic substance. From the time that treatment begins and the first effects are induced, therefore, the recovery processes will begin and the cell will act to restore the original conditions. At any given time between the start of irradiation and the completion of recovery, the amount of radiation effect within the cell will be the *initial effect* less the amount of recovery. This is referred to as the *residual effect.* The dose of radiation that would be required at any instant to produce an effect quantitatively identical with the residual effect is known as the *cumulative dose.* Ideally the residual effect should be expressed in terms of a deficiency of an essential substance or in the amount of toxic material that is acting to produce the biological effect, but this is not possible at present because of our lack of information on the radiation-induced chemical and physical changes responsible for the effect observed.

It is these two factors, latency and recovery, that often make it difficult to determine accurately the immediate effect of a given dose of radiation. The measurement of mitotic delay, for example, depends on the timing of irradiated cells or the making of cell counts at certain intervals of time following treatment. Since recovery may be assumed to be in progress during this period and since the maximum observed biological effect appears some time after the primary changes are induced, the accuracy of our determination of initial and residual effect has definite limitations, and these must not be overlooked in choosing a material and a method and in interpreting results.

HIGH-ENERGY RADIATIONS

MITOTIC EFFECTS

Methods. The type of material selected by the researcher for study determines to a large extent the type of mitotic problem that can profitably be studied. The most direct approach to the problem of how radiations affect mitosis is offered by observations on individual living cells. Hanging-drop preparations of neuroblasts of the grasshopper, *Chortophaga viridifasciata,* in artificial culture medium are very useful for such studies. These cells are large, the internal structures are clearly visible in the living cell, and all the mitotic stages are readily identifiable. It is possible, therefore, to treat a cell at a known mitotic stage and then record its behavior and time its progress subsequent to irradiation. A present shortcoming of this method is our inability to maintain these cells at a normal rate of division for more than 6–8 hours after the preparation is made up; as a result, experiments designed to test recovery from large doses, which may delay mitosis for several hours, are not feasible.

The marine invertebrate egg, such as that of *Arbacia,* also makes possible treatment at a known stage of division and accurate timing of subsequent mitotic progress, but the means of obtaining the data is quite different. All of a lot of eggs from a single female will progress mitotically at about the same rate after fertilization. Since stages in the mitotic cycle of the zygote can be identified accurately only in fixed material, the procedure is to determine the mitotic stage at any desired time by fixing a sample of the eggs for future examination. Cleavage delay is customarily expressed as the difference in time required by the treated and the control eggs to progress from the stage of treatment to cleavage of 50 per cent of the zygotes. If sperm or unfertilized eggs are treated, cleavage time is measured from insemination. In addition to giving precise data on the relation of dose to cleavage delay, this material is useful in obtaining quantitative data on the degree and rate of recovery from mitotic retardation.

Mitotically active parts of living plants or animals in vivo or in vitro may be irradiated and fixed at the end of a certain time interval. The effect on mitosis can then be determined by comparing the proportions of cells in different mitotic stages with those of controls. Since the frequency of different stages after treatment depends on both the dose and the time after treatment at which the material is fixed, an accurate picture of mitotic events following treatment is secured only by the analysis of a series of preparations fixed at short time intervals after irradiation. Unlike the marine invertebrate egg, this kind of tissue will ordinarily consist of cells in interphase and various stages of mitosis at the time of irradiation. The results are therefore expressed as changes in the proportion of cells in different stages at different times after irradiation. Part of the error inherent in the use of different preparations for different counts can be eliminated by the use of culture preparations in which successive counts can be made of the same group of cells.

It cannot be emphasized too strongly, however, that valid conclusions regarding the effect of a given treatment on mitosis cannot be drawn from counts alone of cells in different stages of the mitotic cycle at intervals following treatment. For example, an increase in the number of cells in middle prophase following a certain treatment must be the result of cells entering middle prophase at a faster rate than they leave it. This may be brought about in different ways, none of which could be confirmed or negated by counts alone. It could result from: (1) an increase in the mitotic rate of cells in early prophase, so that a number greater than normal enters middle prophase in a given time; (2) a decrease in the mitotic rate of cells in middle prophase, so that a number smaller than normal leaves middle for late prophase in a given time interval; (3) a reversal of mitotic progress in late prophase, so that late prophase cells regress to become middle prophase cells; or (4) any combination of these. It may be seen, therefore, that a simple conclusion that treatment has accelerated division, or that it has retarded it, cannot be reached merely by comparing mitotic counts made at intervals after treatment. All too often one comes across the wholly unjustifiable conclusion that, because the proportion of dividing cells in the tissue under consideration is greater under one set of experimental conditions than another, the mitotic activity has been increased or mitosis has been stimulated.

Nature of Effect. Direct observations of mitosis in hanging-drop preparations of living *Chortophaga* neuroblasts following X irradiation have demonstrated that there exists in these cells what we may term a critical period between late and very late prophase (Fig. 11-1) (Carlson,

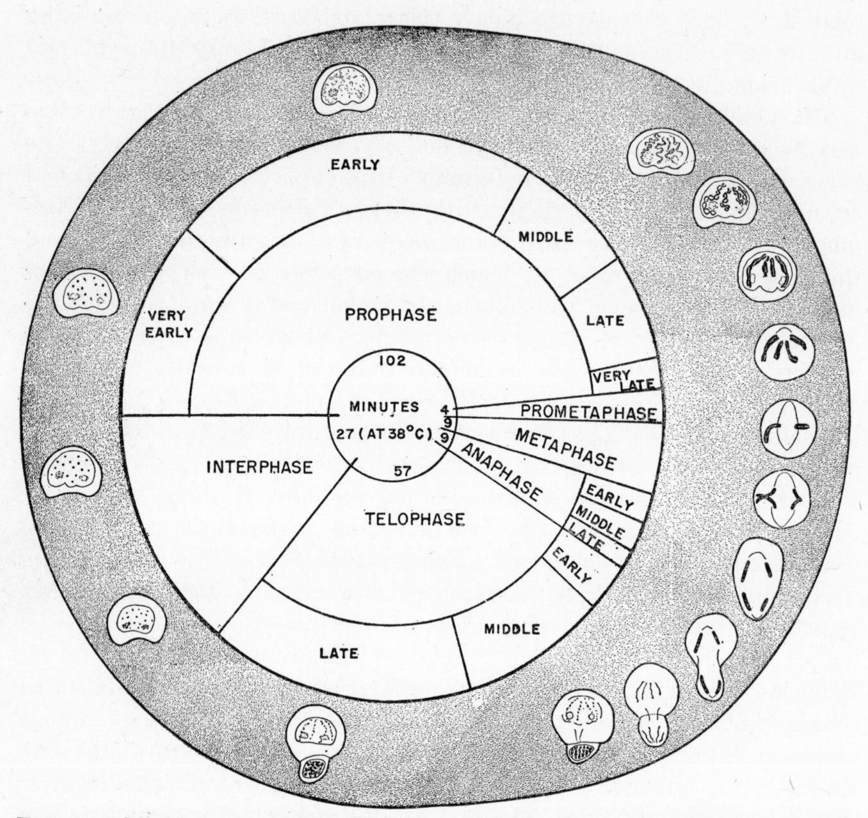

Fig. 11-1. Mitotic cycle of *Chortophaga* neuroblast in vitro at 38°C (*from Carlson and Hollaender*, 1948).

1941, 1950). Irradiation of a cell before it has reached this period usually causes it to stop or even to revert mitotically; irradiation after it has passed this period affects its progress through mitosis little if at all. The cell passes through this critical period about 5 minutes before the nuclear membrane disappears. At this time the chromosomes have almost reached the end of prophase contraction, the shape of the cell is changing from concavo-convex to spherical, the nucleoli are disappearing, and the cytoplasmic viscosity is falling rapidly (Carlson, 1946). Neuroblasts that have passed this stage at the time of treatment complete mitosis with little or no delay, if the dose is less than 250 r. Larger doses produce a delay that increases with the dose. This seems to result partly from delay in the breakdown of the nuclear membrane and partly from chromosome "stickiness," which prolongs the anaphase separation of daughter chromosomes. The more recently the irradiated cell has passed the critical period, the greater is the delay in completing mitosis. If the cell is in prophase at the time of treatment, but has not reached the critical period, the effect on mitosis is determined both by the dose of radiation and by the nearness of the cell to the critical period. After a very small dose, such as 8 or 16 r, most cells in middle or late prophase,[3] which have not reached the critical period, are stopped mitotically for a length of time that increases with increase of dose and decreases with rise of temperature. The cell treated in interphase or early prophase is gradually slowed as it approaches the critical period. Larger doses, 250 r, for example, produce mitotic stoppage of those prophase cells that are nearing the critical period. This is followed by reversion or simulated reversion to a stage in which the chromatin resembles that of interphase (Carlson, 1940, 1941, 1950). Prophases are entirely absent from the tissue until recovery has occurred; then these cells, together with those retarded in interphase, again progress mitotically.

The most extensive series of studies yet made to determine the effect of irradiation on the mitotic rate of cells treated at a known stage of mitosis have been carried out by Henshaw and his co-workers on the marine invertebrate egg. If *Arbacia* eggs or sperm are X-rayed and used immediately afterward in insemination, the first cleavage division is delayed, and the larger the dose of radiation to which they have been exposed, the greater is the delay (Fig. 11-2) (Henshaw, 1932, 1940a). Irradiation of either sperm or egg is about equally effective in retarding cleavage (Henshaw and Francis, 1936; Henshaw, 1940b; Henshaw and Cohen, 1940). When sperm alone are treated, it is found that the amount of delay varies linearly with the logarithm of the dose (Henshaw, 1940a). If the eggs and sperm are both treated, the zygote shows a greater delay in the first cleavage division than if one or the other is treated (Henshaw and Francis, 1936), but the effects are not additive in the sense that the delay in the zygote formed from irradiated egg and irradiated sperm is equal to the sum of the delays produced in zygotes formed from irradiated

[3] Recent unpublished studies in our laboratory by Nancy D. Wolfson indicate that appreciable numbers of neuroblasts treated at late prophase with 32 r of X rays pass the critical period and complete mitosis with little or no delay. Since mitotic activity falls to zero after this dose, however, cells in middle prophase at treatment must suffer complete temporary blockage at some stage between middle prophase and the breakdown of the nuclear membrane. After so small a dose perhaps a certain amount of time is necessary for the physical and chemical changes induced to be translated into mitotic blockage.

egg and untreated sperm and from untreated egg and irradiated sperm. An additive effect in this sense would hardly be expected, unless recovery from the irradiation effects took place successively in the maternal and paternal parts of the zygote. It seems more likely that it would occur concurrently in both. If such is the case, cleavage of the fertilized egg would always have to await the recovery of the gamete with the greater radiation-induced effect. The combining at random, therefore, of irradiated eggs and sperm, which show individual variation with respect to their radiation-induced damage, would in itself result in a greater average delay than if eggs or sperm alone had been treated.[4] Lea (1938b, 1946), concluded that one would expect the cumulative doses, but not the effects

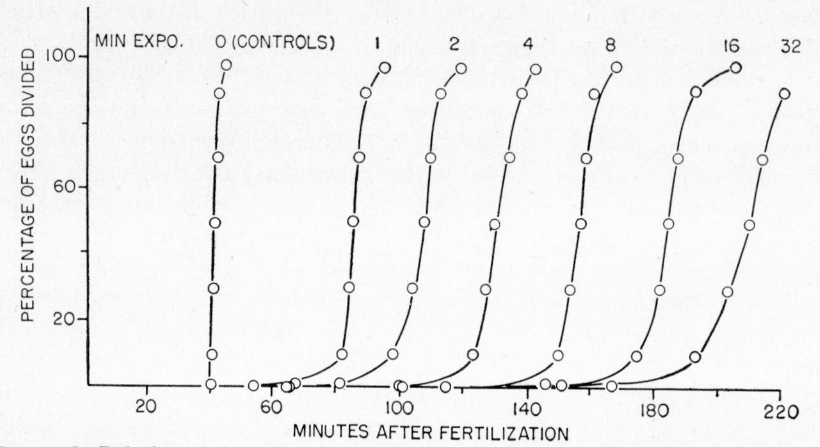

FIG. 11-2. Relation of time after insemination to per cent of *Arbacia* eggs cleaved for several doses of X rays administered at 7800 r/min to sperm before fertilization (*after Henshaw*, 1940a).

as measured by delay in cell division, to be additive. He found that the curve calculated on this basis fitted the experimental observations satisfactorily.

In order to determine whether cleavage delay is due to a retardation of one stage or is spread over the whole period from insemination to cleavage, Henshaw (1938, 1940b) fixed samples of fertilized eggs, in which sperm or

[4] I am indebted to Mr. Jack Moshman for some calculations bearing on this point. Using the variation in cleavage time after treatment of the sperm (Henshaw, 1940a, Table I, 4-minute exposure), which shows a normal distribution, and assuming that the range and delay would be similar in the egg, we find that a random combination of the gametes would increase the time for 50 per cent cleavage by about 3½ minutes. This is approximately half the increase in delay produced by treatment of both gametes over sperm alone, as indicated in another paper (Henshaw and Francis, 1936, Fig. 1) for a comparable dose. It should be pointed out that this test, as set up, gives a maximum increase in delay for irradiation of both gametes over either alone. If one gamete is more sensitive than the other, the effect for irradiation of both will be closer to that resulting from irradiation of the more sensitive one.

egg had been X-rayed, at short time intervals after insemination to compare their progress with that of untreated controls. He found no retardation from entrance of the sperm head through fusion of the pronuclei; considerable retardation from crescent formation (early prophase) through late prophase, and slight retardation at metaphase, anaphase, and telophase (Fig. 11-3).

The relative radiosensitivities of the different stages of the sea urchin egg from insemination to first cleavage were tested by Yamashita, Mori, and Miwa (1939) and Henshaw and Cohen (1940). Their results are in

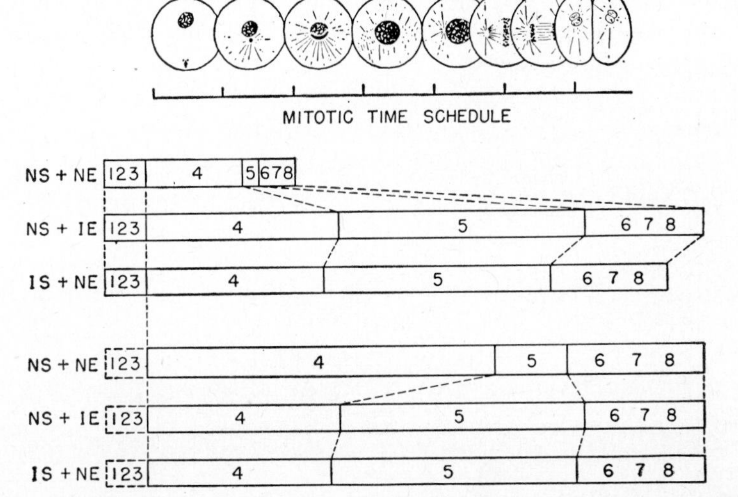

FIG. 11-3. Diagram to show the effects of X radiation on the duration of the different stages of the first cleavage division of *Arbacia*. At top is a semidiagrammatic representation of the mitotic time schedule of *Arbacia* (*patterned after Fry*, 1936). 1, Entrance of sperm head into egg; 2, elaboration of sperm aster; 3, fusion of pronuclei; 4, crescent formation and disappearance; 5, prophase; 6, metaphase; 7, anaphase; 8, telophase. N, normal; I, Irradiated; S, sperm; E, egg (*after Henshaw*, 1940b).

close agreement. The former investigators, using *Pseudocentrotus*, found that maximum delay of the first cleavage division results when irradiation (X, γ, or β rays) takes place during the period extending from fusion of the pronuclei into early prophase. Treatment during approach of the sperm to the egg nucleus was somewhat less effective, while treatment during late prophase, metaphase, anaphase, and telophase caused little delay. Henshaw and Cohen (1940) X-rayed similar samples of *Arbacia* zygotes at 5-minute intervals during the first 45 minutes after insemination. Using the *Arbacia* mitotic time schedule of Fry (1936) (see Fig. 11-3) to determine the stage at which each sample of zygotes was irradiated, these investigators concluded that sensitivity as measured by cleavage delay was greatest in zygotes treated during fusion of pronuclei.

Stages arranged in successively decreasing order of sensitivity were: entrance of sperm head into egg cytoplasm and its approach to the egg nucleus, early prophase, and late prophase. No delay resulted from treatment at metaphase.

Yamashita, Mori, and Miwa (1939) also determined the effect of irradiating different stages of one- and two-celled *Pseudocentrotus* eggs on the length of the second cleavage division. They found that it was delayed only slightly by treatment of the one-celled stage at metaphase or earlier, markedly by treatment at anaphase and telophase, and maximally by treatment at the beginning of the two-celled stage.

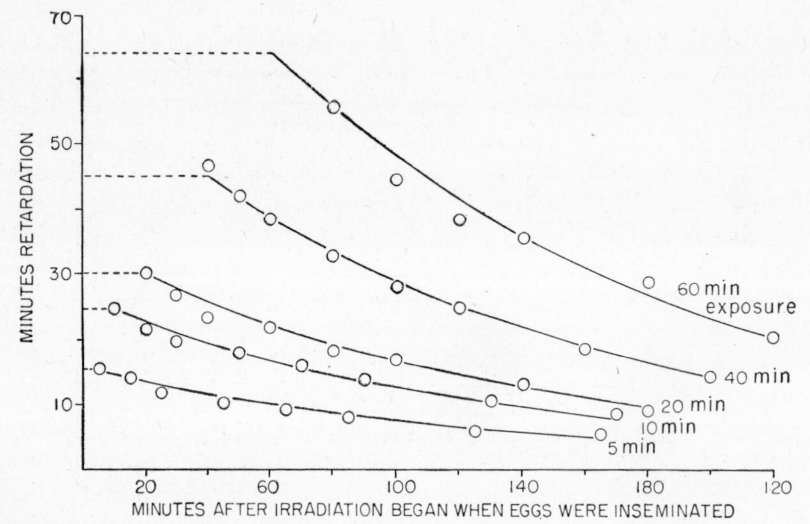

FIG. 11-4. Relation of time intervening between beginning of X irradiation and insemination of *Arbacia* eggs to the cleavage delay, showing recovery from effect; dosage rate, 520 r/min (*after Henshaw*, 1932).

The rate of recovery in the *Arbacia* egg has been shown by Henshaw (1932) to be exponential. Eggs exposed to different doses of X rays at the same dosage rate were inseminated at different times after the end of treatment. For a series of exposures ranging from 5–60 minutes at 520 r/minute he found that the longer the delay between irradiation and insemination, the less the first cleavage was delayed (Fig. 11-4). When minutes delay on a logarithmic scale was plotted against minutes intervening between irradiation and insemination, a straight line was obtained.

The doses and dosage rates used in these experiments on the sea urchin are large, ranging from 2600 to 249,600 r delivered at rates of 120 to 7800 r/minute. These doses are of a much greater order of magnitude than those used with most other kinds of material. Cleavage delays recorded are from a few minutes to somewhat less than 3 hours.

Both *Chortophaga* neuroblast and sea urchin egg experiments indicate that prophase is the mitotic stage most prolonged when the cell is irradiated at an earlier stage. Exact comparisons, however, are not possible at present, for Henshaw has not tested the immediate effect of irradiation on the duration of the stage treated, and we as yet have little data on the times required for neuroblasts X-rayed in different stages of mitosis to complete mitosis.

In dealing with a tissue in which the cells are in different mitotic stages and in which the stage of any given cell is not known at the time of irradiation, the experimental procedures are quite different and the interpretation of the results considerably more involved than when the individual cells or groups of cells are in known stages during irradiation. A brief survey of the postirradiation changes in the proportion of cells in different mitotic stages will be followed by a comparison of the results and conclusions of different investigators who have studied different kinds of tissues. Exposure of a tissue to ionizing radiations is followed by a decrease in the number of prometaphases, metaphases, anaphases, and telophases present, the amount of the decrease being positively correlated with the dose of radiation to which the material is exposed. If the dose is sufficient to reduce the numbers of cells in these stages to zero, the length of time during which they will remain at zero is directly related to the dose. In such experiments the order of disappearance of the stages is prometaphases first, then metaphases, then anaphases, and finally telophases (Carlson, 1942). During recovery from the irradiation effect these stages reappear in the same order. As the number of cells in these stages increases, it will temporarily exceed the normal if the dose is so small as to produce mitotic delay only during part of the mitotic cycle. If the dose is large enough to affect cells at all periods of the mitotic cycle, however, the number of cells in these stages as a rule never exceeds the original. With this general picture in mind of the events that follow irradiation of a mitotically active tissue, we can undertake a more detailed analysis of the radiation-induced changes.

While there is general agreement that cells in prometaphase, metaphase, anaphase, and telophase at the time of irradiation subsequently complete mitosis with little or no delay and that cells in interphase at treatment may be prevented from entering mitosis by sufficiently large doses of radiation, difference of opinion exists about the immediate reaction of prophase cells to irradiation. Because the number of cells in prophase is reduced as a result of irradiation, it has generally been assumed that cells in this stage, like those in prometaphase-through-telophase, are not very radiosensitive and so complete mitosis after irradiation with little or no delay. This conclusion has been reached from studies of mammalian tumors (Mottram, Scott, and Russ, 1926; Warren, 1937), chick fibroblasts in vitro (Strangeways and Hopwood, 1926; Canti and Spear, 1929; Spear, 1931, 1932; Love, 1931; Lasnitski,

1940), rat retina cells (Tansley, Spear, and Glücksmann, 1937), crocus root tips (Stone, 1933), and *Tradescantia* pollen grains (Koller, 1943). In the *Chortophaga* neuroblast, on the other hand, middle and late prophase cells show the greatest radiosensitivity, with early prophases and interphases exhibiting successively less sensitivity (Carlson, 1941, 1950). Deufel (1951) has also described a slowing down of prophases in the *Vicia* root tip soon after treatment. Three possible explanations of these apparently contradictory results may be considered.

First, the method used to determine the stage of greatest sensitivity may not be adequate. Decrease in number or disappearance of prophase cells from an irradiated tissue does not necessarily mean that blockage is at late interphase and that the prophases have continued through mitosis unchecked. As pointed out in an earlier section (p. 769), X irradiation may lead to a disappearance of prophases by causing them to revert to a condition resembling interphase, the real point of blockage being in late prophase.

Second, the mitotic stage of greatest sensitivity may differ in different kinds of cells, so that in certain cells blockage occurs at late interphase or early prophase while in others it takes place at late prophase. If this were true it would mean that the mitotic radiosensitivity of the cell depends on factors other than those we commonly use in distinguishing interphases and early, middle, and late prophases, namely, chromosome morphology.

Third, the appearance of the prophase chromosomes of different kinds of cells may be so different, because of differences in size and visibility, that early prophase in one tissue may resemble late prophase in another (Carlson, 1942), especially when examined in the living condition. According to the description of Strangeways (1922) of the chick fibroblast in vitro the beginning of prophase is preceded by spheration of the cell and followed immediately by the disappearance of the nucleoli, the duration of prophase averaging about seven minutes at 39°C. In the *Chortophaga* neuroblast culture, on the other hand, both the rounding-up of the cell and the disappearance of the nucleoli occur within a few minutes of the end of a prophase that extends over an average period of 102 minutes at 38°C (Carlson and Hollaender, 1948; Carlson, 1950). It would seem, therefore, that the long early and middle prophases of the grasshopper neuroblast, which are characterized by slender, highly convoluted intranuclear chromosomal threads, are passed over very briefly or even omitted, perhaps because of the invisibility of the fine threads in the smaller fibroblast, and what is termed late prophase in the neuroblast may correspond to what is thought of as the whole prophase in the fibroblast. In their study of the effects of γ rays on the rat retina, Tansley *et al.*, (1937) classed as prophase "all the early changes in the nucleus up to the appearance of discrete chromosomes," and as metaphase, the stage from the "appearance of chromosomes to the beginning of the journey to the poles." The fact that their "prophases" are about half as abundant as their "metaphases," as determined by counts in untreated preparations, suggests that their "prophase" represents a portion of the mitotic cycle comparable in extent to that in the chick fibroblast. Regardless of the terminology adopted by the particular worker, until contradictory evidence from observations of the mitotic history of living, irradiated cells other than grasshopper neuroblasts is forthcoming, the conclusion seems justifiable that the mitotic radiosensitivity is greatest shortly before breakdown of the nuclear membrane when the chromosomes are clear and well formed, and that whether or not an irradiated cell will continue through mitosis or be stopped mitotically depends on whether or not it has passed this stage.

Comparison of the results obtained from studies by different investigators of the effects of ionizing radiations on the mitotic activity of different tissues is difficult, especially in certain of the earlier studies, because investigators (1) failed to control the temperature following treatment, (2) used the term "mitosis" to include different and often undesignated division stages, (3) made mitotic counts at very infrequent and irregular intervals, or (4) did not make accurate measurements of the doses given. Nevertheless, some general conclusions can be reached from an analysis of the various studies.

The rate of decrease of mitotic activity immediately after irradiation is greater in animal than in plant tissue. This is probably correlated with the length of the mitotic cycle, which apparently is usually shorter in animals (Lewis and Lewis, 1917; Strangeways, 1922; Wright, 1925; Carlson, 1941; Carlson and Hollaender, 1948) than in plants (Gray and Scholes, 1951). The times after treatment for the number of dividing cells to reach a minimum are shown in Table 11-1. The mitotic activity of the animal cells reaches a minimum ½–6 hours and that of plants 9–21 hours after treatment. An exception is the value of 3 hours found by Marshak (1937) for root tips of several plant genera and by Gray *et al.*, (1940) for root tips of *Vicia* after small doses. The former paper contains so little information on this particular point that it is not possible to evaluate the evidence. In the latter paper it is actually stated that "mitosis is not far from its minimum 3 hours after irradiation."[5] The small dose used may also have some bearing on this low value (see Table 11-2).

When the exposure time is short, the duration of the postirradiation period of mitotic decrease is positively correlated with the dose; the larger the dose, the more extended is the time interval between treatment and the period of minimum mitotic activity (Table 11-2, Fig. 11-5). The

[5] Gray in a personal communication to me states that "the true value could easily have been as late as 6 hours, since the minimum tends to be rather flat."

TABLE 11-1

Organism	Tissue	Radiation	Temp. between treat. and exam.[a], °C	Interval between treat. and minimal mitotic activity, hours[b]	Reference
Grasshopper	Embryonic cells exclusive of neuroblasts	X	28	3	Creighton, 1941
	Neuroblasts	X	26	1½	Carlson, 1940, 1942
		γ	38	1	Carlson *et al.*, 1949
Salamander	Cornea	X	—	6	Alberti and Politzer, 1924
Tadpole	Brain and eye	γ	RT	2	Spear and Glücksmann, 1938
Chick embryo	Neural epithelium, mesenchyme	X	39	½	Regaud *et al.*, 1925
	Neural tube	X	39	½	Butler, 1932
	Fibroblasts in vitro	X	39	1⅓	Strangeways and Oakley, 1923; Strangeways and Hopwood, 1926; Lasnitski, 1940
		γ	39	⅔–2	Canti and Spear, 1929; Spear, 1931; Wilson *et al.*, 1935; Simon-Reuss and Spear, 1947
		γ, X	39	1	Kemp and Juul, 1930; Juul and Kemp, 1933
		β	39	1⅓	Lasnitski, 1948
Rat	Retina	γ	BT	1–3	Tansley *et al.*, 1937
		Fast neutrons	BT	1–3	Spear and Tansley, 1944
	Carcinoma	γ	BT	1½–3⅔	Warren, 1937
		X	BT	2	Luther, 1943
Mouse	Epidermis, adrenal gland, lymph node, jejunum	X	BT	1–2	Knowlton *et al.*, 1948; Knowlton and Hempelmann, 1949
	Sarcoma	X	BT	3	Marshak, 1937
Vicia	Root tip	γ	—	9	Mottram, 1936
		γ	25	3	Gray *et al.*, 1940
		X	—	18	Jüngling and Langendorff, 1930
			RT	19–21	Pekarek, 1927
			18	12	Deufel, 1951
Scilla	Root tip	X	—	>7½	Marquardt, 1938
Vicia, *Pisum*, *Allium*, *Lycopersicum*	Root tip	X	—	3	Marshak, 1937

[a] —, no information on temperature. RT, room temperature. BT, body temperature.
[b] In most of these studies the minimal mitotic activity was zero or close to zero.

overlaps between certain of these doses shown in Table 11-2 are obviously not real but due to the fact that counts were not made frequently enough to bring out minor differences. After doses up to those barely sufficient to cause a fall to zero in mitotic activity, the duration of the period of decreasing mitotic activity of a given tissue is determined by the rate at which the cells recover and begin to progress mitotically after treatment. Since, after small doses, recovery begins sooner than after large doses, the

TABLE 11-2

Organism	Tissue	Radiation	Dose, r	Temp. after treat.[a], °C	Time between treat. and minimal mitotic activity, min	Reference
Chick embryo	Fibroblasts in vitro	γ	50	39	40	Spear, 1931
			83		80	
			300		80	
			1000		120	
Mouse	Epidermis	X	5	BT	60	Knowlton *et al.*, 1948; Knowlton and Hempelmann, 1949
			15		60	
			25		90	
			35		90	
			325		120	
Chortophaga	Neuroblast	γ	8	38	66	Carlson, unpublished
			64		66	
			128		88	
			256		88	
Vicia	Root tip	γ	Small	25	180[b]	Gray *et al.*, 1940
			Large	—	540	Mottram, 1936

[a] BT, body temperature; —, no information on temperature given.
[b] See p. 775 and footnote 5.

rise in mitotic activity that marks the end of the period of mitotic fall occurs somewhat earlier after small than large doses.

Prolongation of the period of mitotic decrease after doses larger than those sufficient barely to reduce the mitotic count to zero is apparently due to two factors: a radiation-induced retardation in the mitotic rate of those cells that complete mitosis immediately after treatment and an increase in the time required by cells to pass through anaphase, if the dose is large enough to cause stickiness of the chromosomes. Jüngling and Langendorff (1930) found that in the *Vicia* root tip cessation of mitosis occurred 18 hours after 420 r but 33 hours after 550 r. Increased doses of X rays cause increased delay in the breakdown of the nuclear membrane and increased stickiness of the chromosomes of the *Chortophaga* neuroblast, both of which tend somewhat to delay the completion of mitosis (Carlson, 1941). The amount of delay is directly related to the nearness of the neuroblast at the time of treatment to the stage of mitotic stoppage; the more recently the treated cell has passed this stage, the greater is the delay.

The interval of time elapsing between treatment and the virtual disappearance of mid-mitotic stages[6] is considerably greater than the average interval of time required by the untreated cell to complete mitosis from

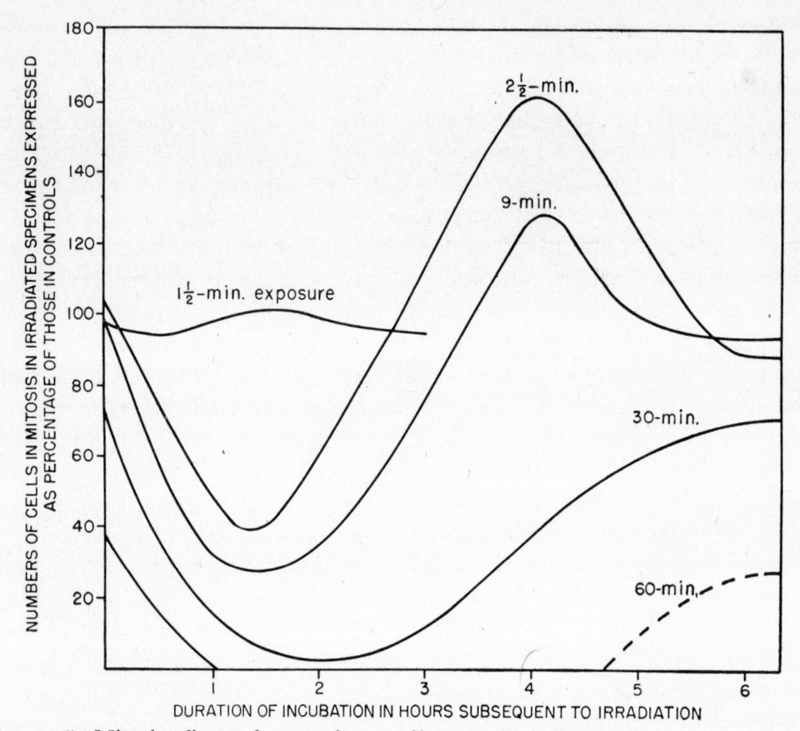

FIG. 11-5. Mitotic effects of γ rays from radium on chick fibroblasts in vitro. Curves from top to bottom represent effects of 50, 83, 300, 1000, and 2000 r, respectively, given at 33 r/min (*after Cade*, 1948, *after Canti and Spear*, 1929).

the stage just following that at which radiation blockage occurs. The untreated chick fibroblast requires about 35 minutes on the average to pass from the beginning of prophase to the formation of the daughter nuclei (Strangeways, 1922) or about 20 minutes to complete metaphase, anaphase, and telophase (Simon-Reuss and Spear, 1947), but it is not until 2 hours after irradiation that mid-mitotic stages have virtually disappeared (Canti and Spear, 1929). The root-tip cells of *Vicia* require

[6] Mid-mitosis is used in this chapter to include prometaphase, metaphase, and anaphase stages, i.e., the period between breakdown of the nuclear membrane and the loss of the smooth form of the chromosomes after they have reached the poles.

about 2½ hours to progress from early prophase through telophase (Gray and Scholes, 1951), while mitosis does not fall to zero until 9–12 hours after treatment (Mottram, 1936; Deufel, 1951). Simon-Reuss and Spear (1947) found that as small a dose of γ rays as 88 r retarded temporarily or permanently mitotic progression in over one-half the cells treated in metaphase, anaphase, and telophase. Neuroblast cells of the grasshopper require on the average about 26 minutes to progress through very late prophase, prometaphase, metaphase, and anaphase (Carlson and Hollaender, 1948), but after irradiation the zero level is not reached until about 50 minutes after treatment. Recent studies carried out in our laboratory on neuroblasts of *Chortophaga* seem to indicate that doses of 250 r and greater delay the completion of mitosis by retarding the dissolution of the nuclear membrane, by producing chromosome stickiness and delayed separation of the chromatids at anaphase, or by retarding the formation of the cleavage furrow (Carlson and Harrington, unpublished). Smaller doses do not affect appreciably the rate at which cells past the critical period complete mitosis (Carlson and Harrington, unpublished; Wolfson, unpublished). After small doses, e.g., 32 r, up to half of the late prophase cells may pass the block and thus contribute to this discrepancy, but this does not appear to take place at 128 r. Our present conclusion, reached from studies of the grasshopper neuroblast in vitro, is that among both treated and control cells considerable variation exists in the duration of very late prophase, so that, although most cells require no more than 26 minutes to progress from the beginning of very late prophase to the end of anaphase, enough cells require a longer time to account for the presence of mid-mitoses 44 minutes after treatment. These data cast doubt on the validity of using the time required for mitosis to disappear after treatment as a measure of the average time required for the cells to pass through the stages in question, unless a correction is made for this variation.

Knowlton and Widner (1950) have recently proposed a method of using X-ray-induced stoppage of mitosis to calculate the duration of the intermitotic period. In any given tissue the ratio of the number of mitotic to intermitotic cells should equal the ratio of the duration of mitotic to intermitotic stages. In the equation,

$$\frac{\text{No. of mitotic cells}}{\text{No. of intermitotic cells}} = \frac{\text{duration of mitosis}}{\text{duration of intermitotic period}}$$

the number of mitotic and intermitotic cells is obtained by direct counts and the duration of mitosis is determined from rate of fall of the number of mitotic cells following treatment. The accuracy of this method depends on the validity of certain assumptions that can be determined only with difficulty in many kinds of biological materials; therefore, certain information about the material and the X-ray effect must precede its application. First, the stage of blockage must not be among the stages classed as mitotic. If any of the prophase cells that are being included in the counts of mitotic cells are blocked by the X rays or caused to revert mitotically (Carlson, 1940, 1941), the rate of fall in numbers of mitotic cells after treatment will not be a true measure of the normal mitotic rate of these cells. Second, the stage of blockage must precede by only a short interval of time the stages included among those designated as mitotic stages. If the stage of blockage precedes by a long interval the stage at which counts are being made, cells will enter mitosis as fast as they leave it until the supply is depleted. By this time a certain proportion of the blocked cells will have begun to recover and enter mitosis, thus making it difficult to determine accurately the rate of fall of mitosis. Third, the dose must be large enough to prevent all but an inappreciable number of cells from leaking through the stage of blockage or recovering early enough to swell the mitotic count in the postirradiation period. Fourth, the dose must be small enough that delay is not induced in the progress of cells through the mitotic stages in which cells are being counted. A dose of 256 r, for example, as determined by timing experiments on living *Chortophaga* neuroblasts in vitro will delay appreciably the progress of cells through mid-mitosis (Carlson and Harrington, unpublished). These cells were treated in very late prophase, that is, just past the blockage stage. Such a delay decreases the rate of fall of mitoses following irradiation. Fifth, the tissue must be homogeneous with respect to the mitotic activity of its cells. If, for example, only one-tenth of the cells in a certain tissue divide regularly, then the intermitotic period of these cells must be one-tenth as long as that calculated by this method, in order to account for the number of mitotic cells present. If we were to apply the method of Knowlton and Widner (1950) to the *Chortophaga* neuroblast, for which we have much information on the conditions just discussed, we would proceed as follows. Extensive series of counts of mid-mitotic cells at 22-min intervals after treatment of neuroblasts in vitro with 64 r of X rays give average counts of approximately 10, 7, 2, and 0 at 0, 22, 44, and 66 min after treatment, respectively. The slope of this curve is steepest from 22 to 44 min. A straight line with the same slope drawn through 10 on the Y axis intersects the X axis at approximately 44. Substituting this value for the duration of mid-mitosis, 10 for the average number of mid-mitotic cells, and 190, which has been obtained by averaging direct counts, for the number of intermitotic[7] cells, we have

$$\frac{10}{190} = \frac{44}{\text{duration of intermitotic period}}$$

[7] For the sake of simplifying this analysis, "intermitotic" as used in this paragraph refers to the period from the end of one to the beginning of the next mid-mitotic period. This includes telophase, interphase, and prophase.

The answer arrived at is 836 min, or about 14 hr for the duration of the intermitotic period; yet we know from direct observations that under good conditions most neuroblasts in hanging-drop preparations will go through a complete mitotic cycle in 5–6 hr. Where is the error in this calculation? In the first place, we know from direct timing experiments that the average neuroblast passes through prometaphase, metaphase, and anaphase, in 22 min while the 44 used above is approximately the time taken by the slowest cells. If we use 22 instead of 44 in the above equation, we arrive at an intermitotic time of about 7 hr, which is still considerably higher than we observe. Probably this is not far from a correct average figure when we take into account the fact that occasional neuroblasts spend an excessively long time in interphase or early pro-

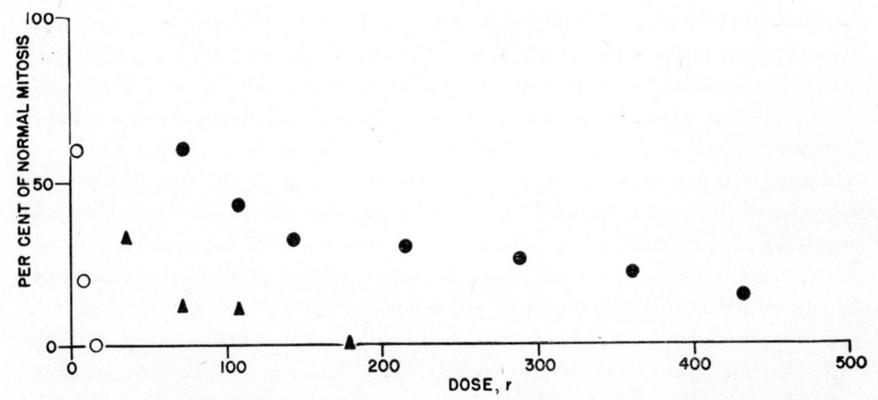

FIG. 11-6. Relation of dose of radiation to maximum depression of mitotic activity. Solid circle, chick fibroblast (*Spear and Grimmet*, 1933); triangle, cell of developing rat retina (*Tansley, Spear, and Glücksmann*, 1937); open circle, *Chortophaga* neuroblast.

phase, and so are often disregarded in the calculations as "abnormal" cells.

The efficiencies of different doses of radiation in decreasing mitotic activity—as measured at the time after treatment when the effect is greatest—are quite different for different kinds of cells. The mitotic activity of *Chortophaga* neuroblasts is reduced to a much greater degree than that of either rat retinal cells or chick fibroblasts by a given dose of radiation (Fig. 11-6). A comparison of these efficiencies with those obtained when testing the capacity of radiation to retard the mitotic progress of the same cells treated in mid-mitosis points to the fallacy of concluding that the relative radiosensitivities of different kinds of cells as measured by one effect are necessarily correlated with their radiosensitivities as determined by another effect. A dose of 88 r, for example, which reduces the mid-mitotic count of the neuroblast to zero and that of the fibroblast to 20 per cent of normal, has no detectable effect on the mitotic progress of neuroblasts treated in metaphase, anaphase, or telophase, but retards considerably over half the fibroblasts treated in these stages.

After doses of radiation, up to and including those barely sufficient to reduce the mid-mitotic count to zero, recovery from the radiation effect is accompanied by a rise of the mid-mitotic count at a rate roughly similar to the rate of fall in the count immediately after treatment, with no prolonged low count intervening (Fig. 11-5) (Canti and Spear, 1929; Kemp and Juul, 1930; Spear, 1931, 1932, 1935; Wilson *et al.*, 1935; Mottram, 1936; Tansley *et al.*, 1937; Lasnitski, 1940; Carlson, 1942; Simon-Reuss and Spear, 1947; Knowlton, Hempelmann, and Hoffman, 1948; Knowlton and Hempelmann, 1949; Deufel, 1951). This rise in the mid-mitotic count does not stop at the normal level but continues above it before returning to the normal level. Following very small doses, the rise above the normal after recovery compensates approximately for the fall below normal that precedes it (Fig. 11-5) (Canti and Spear, 1929; Spear, 1931, 1932, 1935; Wilson *et al.*, 1935; Tansley *et al.*, 1937; Knowlton and Hempelmann, 1949; Carlson, Snyder, and Hollaender, 1949). From what we know of the behavior of individual cells after treatment, this is exactly what we would expect. In the grasshopper neuroblast, for example, blockage from irradiation affects not only the cells at the most sensitive stages (namely, middle and late prophase) but also cells entering these after treatment in earlier stages, so that an excessively large number of cells accumulates during the period of decreased mitotic activity. A similar increase has been found by Mallet and Perrot (1951) in the *Allium* root tip. With recovery and the resumption of mitotic progression, these cells will complete mitosis and their numbers should compensate exactly for the previous deficit. With larger doses, however, the number of mitoses never exceeds the normal and with still larger doses the return to normal may be greatly prolonged (Alberti and Politzer, 1924; Pekarek, 1927; Canti and Spear, 1929; Kemp and Juul, 1930; Spear, 1931, 1935; Tansley *et al.*, 1937; Lasnitski, 1946, 1948; Simon-Reuss and Spear, 1947; Knowlton *et al.*, 1948; Knowlton and Hempelmann, 1949; Carlson *et al.*, 1949). Failure of the mid-mitotic count to surpass the normal is apparently due to the extension of the radiation effect to earlier and earlier stages of the mitotic cycle as the dose is progressively increased, until cells in all stages of the cycle are retarded.

If the dose is large enough to lower the mid-mitotic count to zero, the larger the dose, the more prolonged is the period of zero activity. Few studies have been made of the relation of the length of this period to dosage, probably because, for most purposes, the investigator has found it more profitable to work with doses that do not completely inhibit mitosis. A dose of 2000 r of γ rays reduced the mitotic count of chick fibroblasts in vitro to zero until about 5 hours after treatment (Fig. 11-5). Jüngling and Langendorff (1930) reported that in the *Vicia* root tip mitosis remained at zero for about 16, 18, and 24 hours after doses of 175, 420, and 550 r, respectively. In the *Chortophaga* neuroblast the time from irradiation to the reappearance of the first metaphases after mitotic cessation approximates the curves shown in Fig. 11-7 for 26 and 38°C. None of the tissues of *Ambystoma* larvae exposed to 15,000 r of X rays exhibited any mitoses one week later (Rugh, 1949).

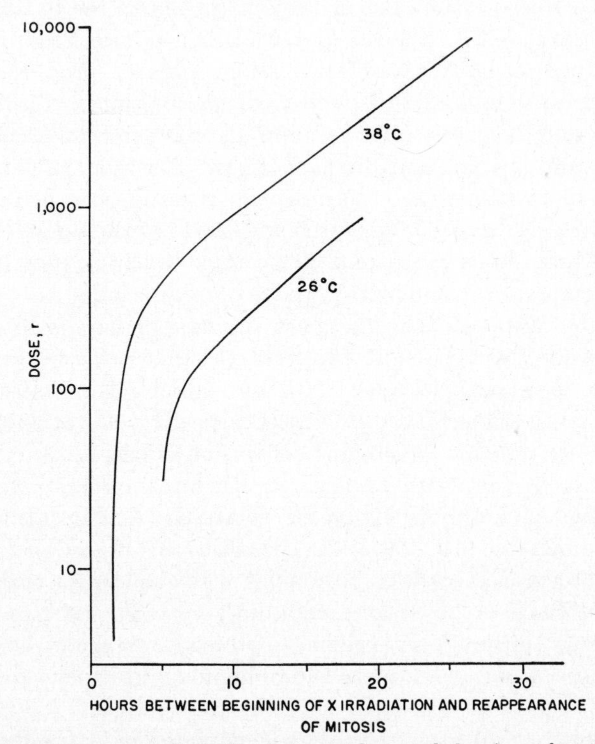

Fig. 11-7. Graph showing the relation between dose and the time after the beginning of X-ray treatment when mitoses reappear. Postirradiation temperature, 26° and 38°C; material, *Chortophaga* neuroblast.

In contrast to the foregoing investigations, which point only to depression of mitotic activity as a result of treatment with ionizing radiations, a few studies have indicated that certain exposures may actually speed up the mitotic rate. Richards (1915) reached the conclusion that exposure of the fertilized egg of the snail, *Planorbis,* to X rays during the spindle formation period of the maturation or early cleavage divisions stimulated the cell to complete its division much more rapidly than if untreated; one experiment, for example, showed a change from 75 to 3 minutes for the time of the first cleavage division. The next succeeding division was usually faster than normal, but following divisions showed a progressive retardation. If the exposure was made, therefore, during the first cleavage division, development of the treated eggs would usually be behind that of the untreated eggs at the 24-celled stage. No stimulation and probably some depression of the division rate was produced by treatment of the resting stage. Packard (1916) reported a γ-ray-induced acceleration of the first cleavage division of *Arbacia* that amounted to a 5–15 per cent increase in the speed of division. Richards and Good (1919) found that a small dose of X rays applied to the fertilized egg of *Cumingia* stimulated division at first, and then retarded it. Irradiation of sperm or eggs or both before fertilization, however, produced either no effect or a retardation of subsequent cleavage divisions. More recently, Darlington and La Cour (1945) found increases in the frequencies of metaphases and anaphases of *Vicia* root tips 4 hours at 24°C after treatment with 45 r of X rays. Since the numbers of cells in these stages exhibited decreases at other doses (90 and 135 r) at the same temperature and at all three doses at 16 and 30°C, they conclude that there is an optimum temperature and dose at which mitosis may be temporarily stimulated by X rays. The numbers of metaphases and anaphases in the controls for their different experiments differ widely, however, and they give no tests of significance for these numbers. La Cour (1951) also reports an X-ray-induced acceleration of mitosis by 90 r at 20°C but does not include the data on which this conclusion is based. In view of the fact that, except for these studies, no other researchers seem to have found evidence of a stimulating effect of radiation, confirmation by other workers, duplicating as exactly as possible the procedures originally used, would seem worth while. An attempt to confirm the earlier studies was made by Seide (1925), who used a different biological material, however. He treated the *Ascaris* egg in the pronuclear stage with small doses of X and γ radiation, but was unable to demonstrate a constant increase in the mitotic rate as determined by the time required for the treated cells, as compared with the controls, to complete the first and the second divisions.

Evidence relating to the means by which ionizing radiations interfere with mitosis has pointed strongly to a primary effect on the nucleus. The first cleavage division of the *Arbacia* zygote is delayed to about the same extent, whether the sperm or the egg is irradiated (Henshaw and Francis, 1936; Henshaw, 1940b; Henshaw and Cohen, 1940). Since the sperm consists almost entirely of nuclear material, it is natural to conclude that the X-ray effect must involve changes induced in the nucleus rather than in the cytoplasm. Further, if nucleated and nonnucleated egg fragments obtained by centrifugation are irradiated and then fertilized with untreated sperm, it is found that a delay is produced in the nucleated fragments comparable to that produced in the whole egg, while no delay is produced in the nonnucleated fragments (Henshaw, 1938).

Miwa, Yamashita, and Mori (1939b), on the other hand, obtained evidence that mitotic delay may be induced by treatment of the cytosome. Unfertilized eggs of the sea urchin, *Pseudocentrotus*, were irradiated with α rays through aluminum filters varying from 0 to 45 μ in thickness. Sensitivity of the eggs as measured by delay in the first cleavage division decreased markedly as the increased thickness of the filters used prevented the α rays from penetrating to the nucleus, but even with α-ray ranges that fell short of the nucleus, some eggs showed marked delay.

It has also been demonstrated that the amount of cleavage delay resulting from X-raying *Arbacia* sperm is not influenced by the concentration of the sperm or the composition of the medium in which they are irradiated (Evans *et al.*, 1942). When *Arbacia* sperm were mixed with heavily irradiated water containing X-ray-induced hydrogen peroxide, and then used to fertilize untreated eggs, delay of the first cleavage division resulted (Evans, 1947). The amount of delay was positively correlated with the dose. Heilbrunn and Young (1935), however, found that, while the concentration of unfertilized *Arbacia* eggs X-rayed in sea water had no effect on the delay of the first cleavage division, irradiation in the presence of ovarian tissue produced a considerably greater delay than irradiation of the eggs in sea water alone or in concentrated suspension. They suggest that ovarian cells exposed to X rays produce a substance or substances that act on the eggs to enhance the direct effect obtained in their absence.

Increased absorption of 2537 A ultraviolet radiation in the cytoplasm of irradiated neoplastic cells is interpreted by Mitchell (1942a, b, 1943), to result from radiation-induced inhibition of desoxyribonucleic acid (DNA) formation and the consequent accumulation of pentose nucleotides in the cytoplasm. He suggests that this might cause inhibition of mitosis.

That the cytosome, however, may be responsible for *recovery* from radiation effects is suggested by the findings of Henshaw (1940a) using X rays, and Miwa *et al.* (1939a) and Mori, Miwa, and Yamashita (1939) using β rays, who state that there is no recovery in sea urchin sperm between treatment and insemination. Since the same investigators have found that sea urchin eggs undergo recovery between treatment and insemination, it seems likely that the cytosome of the egg is responsible for recovery.

Kind of Radiation. Of special importance in the interpretation of the mechanism of the action by which radiations are able to alter the rate of so complex and yet so precise a living process as cell division are studies of the relative capacities of different kinds of radiations to interfere with mitosis. From the point of view of the biologist, different radiations are of interest because of their different ion distributions or densities. These range from the widely separated ions produced by high energy β and γ

radiation (about 8.5 ions/μ in tissue), the denser ionizations of medium X rays (about 100 ions/μ), the still more densely ionizing recoil protons from fast neutron irradiation (up to 1100 ions/μ), to α particles with densities of 3700–4500 ions/μ (Gray, 1946, 1947). Knowledge of the relative efficiencies of the different radiations in interfering with mitosis might give us a clue to the means by which radiation energy is transformed into observable effects on cell morphology and behavior. Since such determinations depend directly on the accuracy with which the dose absorbed by the cells is measured, conclusions reached from comparative studies of this type are valid only insofar as the energy measurements are accurate. As might be expected, only quantitative, not qualitative, differences in the effects produced by different radiations have been demonstrated.

Fast neutrons have been found to be more effective than γ rays in reducing the mitotic activity of a number of different kinds of cells. Zirkle, Aebersold, and Dempster (1937), who compared the efficiencies of neutrons and X rays by irradiating fern spores, germinating them, and determining the proportion that had undergone their first cell division at the end of 10 days (normally this division occurs on the sixth day of germination), found that neutrons were 2.5 times as effective as X rays in reducing division by 50 per cent. Small doses of neutrons were found by Gray *et al.* (1940) to be 2.1 times as effective as γ rays in reducing the number of mitoses in broad bean root tips 3 hours after the mid-point of the treatment period. Similar experiments carried out with chick fibroblasts in culture also showed neutrons to be more effective than γ rays, as determined by the reduction in mitotic activity 80 minutes after irradiation. When the percentage of normal mitoses was plotted against dose, the neutron curves were exponential and the γ-ray curves sigmoid, the two intersecting at some dose higher than any used in the study. They postulated that the neutron effect may result from the passage of a single recoil proton within a certain limited volume of radius 2 or 3 μ in the cell, and that the γ radiation effect would require some two hundred secondary β particles.

The evidence with regard to the effectiveness of α particles in inhibiting mitosis, however, is conflicting. Gray and Read (1950) found α rays to be less effective than either neutrons or γ rays in lowering the mitotic count 3 hours after the mid-point of treatment in the broad bean root tip (Fig. 11-8). The relative efficiencies of γ rays, neutrons, and α rays were about 1:2.1:0.6. They point out that these relative efficiencies of neutrons and α rays are in good agreement with the ion density ratios of recoil protons to α rays, if reasonable assumptions be made for the δ-ray ionization. On the other hand, in the frog tadpole treated with α radiation by immersion of the animal in water containing radon and subsequently sectioned and stained at intervals for study, α particles proved to be twice as effective as γ rays (Spear and Glücksmann, 1938; Tansley *et al.*, 1948). A dose of 134 energy units of α radiation reduced the numbers of eye and brain cells in mitosis to approximately the same level as 268 r of γ rays (tissue exposed to 1 energy unit has received the same increment of energy/g as water exposed to 1 r of γ rays).

Miwa *et al.* (1939b) observed in *Pseudocentrotus* that after β irradiation the cleavage delay of all the treated eggs was about the same (with a spread of 30 minutes), while after α irradiation the spread was much greater, some eggs being delayed hardly at all and others 3 or more

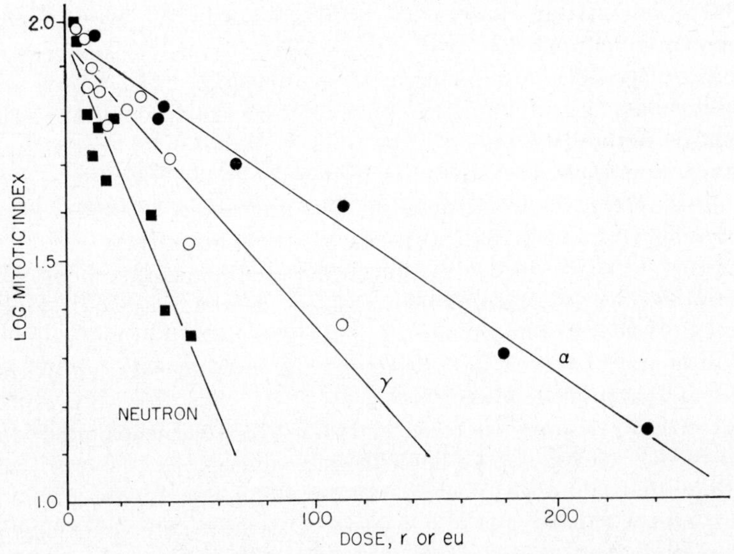

FIG. 11-8. Relative efficiencies of α rays (solid circle), γ rays (open circle), and fast neutrons (square) in reducing the mitotic index in *Vicia* root tip meristems 3 hours after irradiation (*after Gray and Reed*, 1950).

hours. Because their study did not include careful measurements of the doses used, it is difficult to relate these results to those of other α-ray studies.

Lasnitski and Lea (1940) compared the efficiencies of γ rays with medium X rays, and hard X rays with soft X rays in reducing the prophase, metaphase, and anaphase-telophase counts in chick fibroblasts in vitro. For several doses within the range of 20–200 r, the hard and soft X rays were found to be equally effective, but the γ rays were found to be less effective than medium X rays by a factor of about 2:1. These conclusions are based on the assumption that the low point is reached at 80 minutes after each kind of radiation, when all counts were made; if it is not, the different values may be measures of the rapidity at which the mitotic count falls or at which recovery takes place.

Lasnitski (1948) determined the relative efficiencies of β and X rays in lowering the mitotic count in the chick fibroblast culture. She found that, although the over-all depression of mitotic activity during the 24-hour period following treatment and the maximum reduction of mitosis was comparable for the two radiations, mitotic activity fell off more abruptly and during recovery rose more rapidly in the β- than in the X-irradiated material (Fig. 11-15). This illustrates very clearly the danger of interpreting the extent of radiation-induced mitotic depression on the basis of mitotic counts made at the end of a single time interval after treatment.

Dosage Rate. In the great majority of studies in the field of radiation biology treatment administered is expressed in terms of dose, with little emphasis placed on the time-intensity relationship. The dose, however, represents only the total quantity of radiant energy dissipated in a tissue. It tells us nothing of the intensity of the radiation or of the time of exposure, and these may be quite important in determining the effect produced. Excellent discussions of these factors in biological research are presented by Lea (1938a, 1946) and Gray *et al.* (1944).

The time-intensity factor is important, and at the same time peculiarly difficult to deal with experimentally for several reasons. First, if recovery of the cell from radiation effects occurs at all, it begins immediately after the first effects are produced and continues during treatment (Canti and Donaldson, 1926; Henshaw *et al.*, 1933); therefore the biological effect as determined at the end of a long treatment period, during which recovery from the earlier effects produced has occurred, will be less than that obtained after a corresponding dose delivered at high intensity in a shorter period. Second, a certain detectable biological effect may depend on interaction between the products of two or more primary effects that are subject to recovery during the treatment period—perhaps at the molecular level or perhaps at the microscopic level, e.g., broken chromosomes which by interaction (fusion) give rise to translocations. If these are subject to recovery during the treatment period, small doses will produce little or no effect, whether delivered in a short period at high intensity or in a long period at low intensity, because the primary changes will be so few and far between on the average that little or no interaction will take place. At successively larger doses, however, interaction will have a successively better opportunity of occurring and the observed effect will increase theoretically as the square of the dose—actually it is usually less than this because of the recovery that takes place during treatment. Third, since the living cell is dynamic and not static and since visible biological effects cannot be detected immediately after treatment but only at some later phase of a cell's physiological and morphological state, and then may be manifest maximally for only a brief period, results will often depend on the time after treatment at which the determination is made. As the treatment becomes lower in intensity and more prolonged in time, the choice of the appropriate time at which the effect is to be determined becomes more and more difficult. Fourth, the cell and its parts undergo a whole series of cyclic changes in their physical and chemical nature during mitosis; treatment extending over a long period of time will increase the chances of a certain highly sensitive stage in the mitotic cycle receiving radiation, while a brief treatment will decrease this possibility. The proportion of a given quantity of radiation that a cell receives in a particularly sensitive or insensitive stage, therefore, should not be overlooked in the interpretation of dosage-rate effects. Though recovery processes in the cell usually begin as soon as the first effect of the radiation is produced, damage to the cell during the treatment period—unless the dosage rate is very low—will occur at a faster rate than repair, and the maximum residual effect will be present at the end of the radiation period. From this time on recovery will take place gradually until the capacity of the cell to progress mitotically has been restored to its original state. If, on the other hand, the dosage rate is extremely low, e.g., about 0.8 r/hour in treatment of the grasshopper neuroblast with γ rays, an equilibrium between radiation damage and tissue repair will be established soon after the start of treatment, the residual effect remaining relatively constant over a long portion of the treatment period (Carlson and Harrington, 1953). Not only is it essential that these factors be taken into account in the interpretation of radiation results, but they may also be utilized in designing experiments to test certain hypotheses relating to the effects of radiations on living material.

The interpretation of the results of studies of the effects of different dosage rates on mitosis in selected cells that were in known stages of mitosis at the time of treatment and that can be observed at desired intervals after treatment, e.g., marine invertebrate eggs and hanging-drop preparations of grasshopper neuroblasts, offers no particular difficulties, if treatment is not so prolonged that deterioration sets in during the course of the experiments. The *Arbacia* sperm and egg offer, in fact, a unique opportunity for time-intensity studies. As described previously, Henshaw (1932) found that recovery of eggs occurred between treatment and cleavage. Further, Henshaw *et al.* (1933) found that recovery took place between the beginning and end of irradiation. If *Arbacia* eggs were exposed to a given dose of X rays administered at different rates, the cleavage delay produced by the lower dosage rate was 20–40 per cent less than a dosage rate eight times as high and therefore given in one-eighth the time. On the other hand, the sperm gives no evidence of recovery before insemination (Miwa *et al.*, 1939a; Henshaw, 1940a). These results would lead us to expect that the *Arbacia* egg would exhibit a dosage-rate effect, while the sperm would not; and such, indeed, is the case. Using dosage rates of 120–960 r/minute, Henshaw and Francis (1936) found that X irradiation of the sperm was more effective than X irradiation of the egg in producing mitotic delay in the zygote. On the other hand, a dose given at 7800 r/minute produces greater mitotic delay when administered to the egg than to the sperm (Henshaw, 1940b; Henshaw and Cohen, 1940). Apparently the initial effect of irradiation is greater in eggs than in sperms, but, owing to recovery during the treatment period, the residual effect at the end of treatment will be less in the egg than in the sperm, if the treatment period is prolonged.

Accurate comparisons of the effects of different dosage rates on tissues, however, in which the results are based on counts of cells in different mitotic stages at certain intervals of time following treatment, introduce special difficulties. We may consider separately the problems presented by relatively short and relatively long exposures.

If the times of irradiation are short, i.e., occupying only a small part of the period during which the number of mitoses is falling and therefore a small portion of the duration of one mitotic cycle, the minimum levels of mitotic activity reached following treatment can be compared to determine the effectiveness. In such experiments, where a single count of certain mitotic stages following irradiation is used as a measure of effectiveness, the results will be different depending on whether the mitotic count is made a certain number of minutes after the *beginning*, the *midpoint*, or the *end* of the treatment period. Probably timing from the *midpoint* of the treatment period is the most reliable procedure, when comparisons of the effects of different exposure times are to be made, unless the time of the low-intensity treatment is greatly prolonged. The results of the γ-ray studies on dosage-rate effect by Canti and Spear (1927) and Spear and Grimmett (1933) on chick fibroblast in vitro are based on counts of the numbers of cells in mitosis in treated cultures fixed 80 minutes after the end of the irradiation period and expressed as the percentage of the number of mitoses in the controls. Both studies indicated that at dosage rates of approximately 20 r/minute and higher, the dose required to produce a given reduction in mitosis—to 50 per cent of that in the controls in the former study and to 40 per cent in the latter—was independent of the dosage rate. At rates below 20 r/minute, however, Canti and Spear found that the dose increased successively with successively lower dosage rates, while Spear and Grimmett's more detailed study in the 4–20 r/minute region shows a fall in dosage from 17.2 to 8.7 r/minute and a rise from 8.7 to 4.3 r/minute. This apparent demonstration of an optimum dosage rate below or above which the mitotic depression is less might be due to the fact that all their results were based on counts made on cultures fixed 80 minutes after the *end* of the treatment period, while the suppression of mitosis by irradiation is initiated at the *beginning* of irradiation. At the time the counts were made, therefore, all the primary effects produced by the high dosage-rate irradiation would have had less time for recovery than all except the last effects produced by the low dosage-rate treatment. An optimum effectiveness would then be expected for the dosage rate for which a minimum of recovery had occurred at 80 minutes after the end of treatment.

A more laborious but at the same time more informative procedure is to make counts at intervals following irradiation. Comparison can then be made of the rates of fall and rise, as well as the minimums of mitotic activity at certain times after the beginning, mid-point, or end of the irradiation period.

Using a dose of 100 r delivered at rates of 9.3, 29.8, and 103 r/minute, Lasnitski (1946) determined that depression of mitotic activity was approximately the same 80 minutes after treatment for all three dosage rates. Recovery occurred more rapidly after 103 r/minute than after 29.8 r/minute and more rapidly after 29.8 r/minute than after 9.3 r/minute. After 2500 r, however, no mitotic cells were present within 24 hours if the dose was delivered at 101 r/minute, 0.4 per cent of the cells were in mitosis at 24 hours if the rate was 29.8 r/minute, and about 1 per cent if the rate was 9.3 r/minute. (The per cent of mitotic cells in the control cultures at any one time during the same period ranged from 2.6 to 8.0.) Counts of the mid-mitotic cells in hanging-drop preparations of grasshopper neuroblasts give comparable results. Curves based on twenty successive counts of ten to fourteen embryos made at 22-minute intervals beginning 20 minutes after the mid-point of the radiation period were not significantly different for doses of 8 and 64 r at high (32 r/min) and low (2 r/min) dosage-rate γ radiation (Carlson *et al.*, 1949). After doses of 128 and 256 r the rate of fall in mitotic activity and the length of the cessation period are comparable for both the 2 and 32 r/minute dosage rates, but the return of the mitotic count to normal is much slower after the 32 than after 2 r/minute treatment (Fig. 11-9).

Another method of comparing the efficiencies of different dosage rates in reducing the mitotic activity of a tissue is to compare the *totals* of the mitotic counts obtained at uniform intervals over a certain period following treatment. The time interval at which counts are made may be fixed arbitrarily, but, if the interval taken represents the average time required for the cells to pass through the mitotic stage or stages to be counted, the total of the average counts will approximate closely the number of cells passing through the stages counted and therefore through mitosis during the period under consideration. This method presupposes, however, that the stages counted are not prolonged to such an extent by either of the treatments that the same cell is counted twice; otherwise a high count and, therefore, a false indication of increased mitotic activity will result when mitotic retardation actually occurs. This procedure can be used with confidence, then, only when it is possible to check the mitotic time schedule by direct observations of living cells. Carlson *et al.* (1949), using this method, showed that the γ-ray-induced reduction in prometaphase-through-anaphase stages during a 7-hour period following treatment was not appreciably different after dosage rates of 2 and 32 r/minute at doses of 8, 32, and 64 r, but that the 32 r/minute rate caused a much greater reduction than the 2 r/minute rate at 128 and 256 r.

The problem becomes quite different if the dosage is spread over a long period, e.g., hours or days. In such experiments the recovery factor

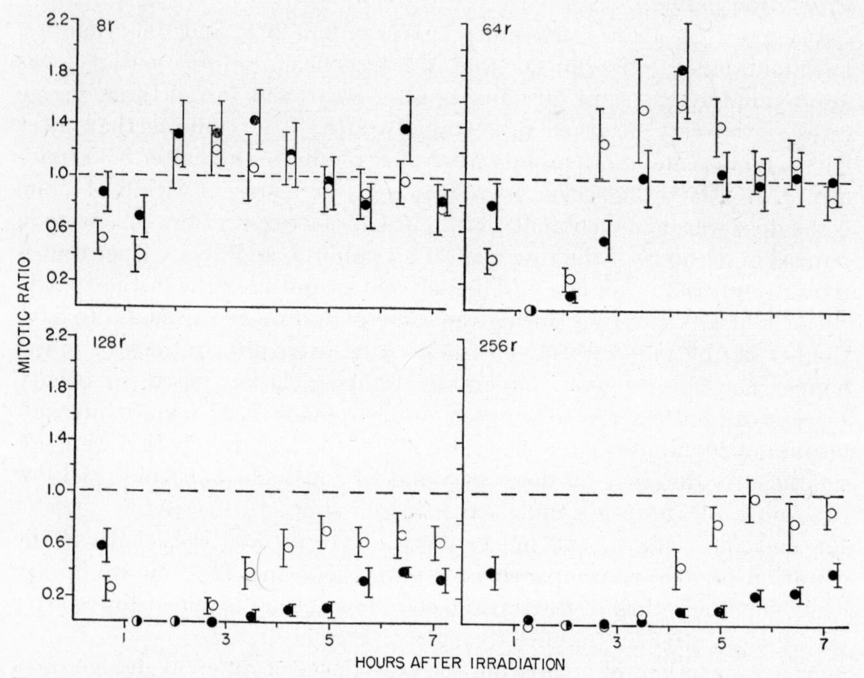

FIG. 11-9. Effects of different doses of γ rays delivered at different dosage rates on mitosis in the *Chortophaga* neuroblast: open circle, 2 r/min; solid circle, 32 r/min (*after Carlson, Snyder, and Hollaender*, 1949).

dominates the picture. A brief high-intensity treatment will be completed before the mitotic activity will have had time to fall off appreciably, while at the end of a prolonged low-intensity treatment, radiation effect and recovery processes will have reached equilibrium and the mitotic activity will be at a minimum; therefore the shape of the mitotic activity curves, based on a series of counts immediately following treatment, will be so different as not to be readily comparable. If the mitotic activities after a certain dose delivered over a short and over a long period are compared at corresponding times measured from the *beginning* or *mid-point* of the radiation period, all the primary effects produced by the high-intensity treatment will have had approximately the same long period for recovery, while only the first of the primary effects produced by low-intensity treatment will have had a correspondingly long period for recovery. The cells given a brief, high-intensity treatment may have recovered completely, while those subjected to the prolonged, low-intensity treatment, even though they received the same dose, will exhibit a decrease in the number of cells in mitosis. Probably the most accurate method of comparing the mitotic depression after short and very long exposures to the same dose is to obtain a series of mitotic counts at short time intervals for a few hours immediately following each treatment. The mitotic picture during the long exposure can be obtained by running other material at the same dosage rate and making a single count immediately after any desired length of exposure to determine the

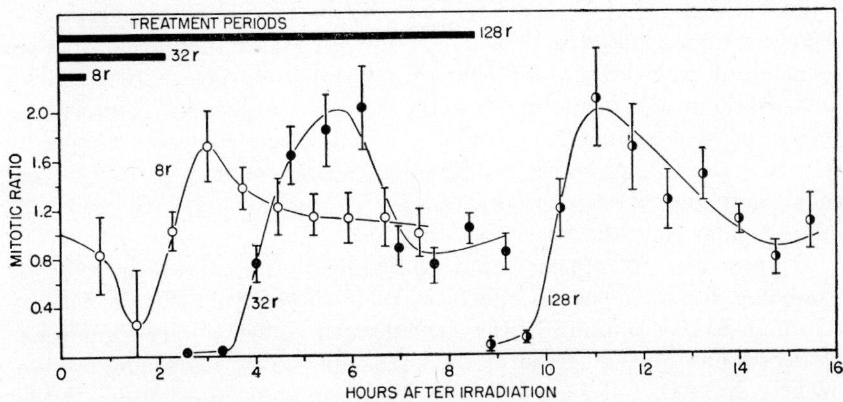

FIG. 11-10. Relation of mitotic rate to time after γ irradiation for different doses given at 0.25 r/min; *Chortophaga* neuroblasts at 38°C: open circle, 8 r; solid circle, 32 r; divided circle, 128 r (*from Carlson*, 1950).

mitotic activity at that time. A curve illustrating the mitotic picture from the beginning to several hours after the termination of a prolonged, low-intensity treatment can thus be obtained. It can be seen, for example, that the 128-r curve in Fig. 11-10, if projected to the left, would parallel closely the zero ordinate to a point to the left of the first 32-r count and then upward through the first 8-r count.

Fractionated Treatment. A given dose of radiation may be delivered not only in different periods of time and at different dosage rates but also in two or more portions with intervening nonirradiation intervals. Fractionated or spaced irradiation resembles low-intensity treatment in that it reduces the possibility of interaction between primary effects by giving time for recovery from one group of effects before the next group is produced. Because mitosis is a cyclical process, however, with some phases of the cycle more highly radiosensitive than others, the interpretation of the effects of fractionated treatment must take into account not only the reduced opportunity for interaction of effects, but also the mitotic stages of the cells at the time of treatment and at observation and the relation of these to the radiosensitivity of the stages involved.

Spear (1932) compared the effects of 2½- and 5-minute continuous exposures of fibroblast cultures to a given radium source with two 2½-minute exposures, separated in the one case by 80 minutes and in the other by 160 minutes. In the former, the second dose of γ rays was delivered at the depth of depression of mitotic activity, which was lowered still further. The mitotic activity was thus lowered to a greater extent and for a longer time after the two 2½-minute exposures than after the continuous 5-minute exposure. In the latter experiment the second fraction was given at the time the mitotic activity had returned to normal, and the curve representing the resulting change in mitotic count closely resembled the first one. These experiments suggest that there is an optimum dose that is more effective per r than other doses in reducing mitotic activity and that the 2½-minute exposure represents a dose nearer to the optimum than the 5-minute exposure. This is substantiated by a comparison of the 2½- and 5-minute continuous exposure curves. The former shows a minimum mitotic count only about 7 per cent lower and a return of mitotic activity to normal only about 20 minutes later than the latter.

Temperature. It appears that the temperature at which cells are irradiated has little or no effect on their subsequent mitotic activity (Gorman S. Hill, unpublished). Grasshopper embryos were given 8 r of X rays while at temperatures of 2, 18, and 38°C, maintained subsequently at 38°C, and fixed at 44, 88, 132, 176, and 220 minutes. There were no significant differences in the number of neuroblasts in prometaphase, metaphase, and anaphase at any of these time intervals for the three temperatures tested.

The times after treatment at which the mitotic activity will reach a minimum and then will begin to rise during recovery are functions of the temperature at which the cells are maintained after irradiation. Maintenance of the cells at a low temperature after irradiation prolongs the period of mitotic decrease and delays the return of mitotic activity. In the *Allium* root tip, the time of minimum mitotic activity after 150 r is about 10 hours at 24° and about 24 hours at 16°C (Darlington and La Cour, 1945). In the grasshopper neuroblast, the low point of mitotic activity is reached at about 66 minutes after 32 r of γ rays at 38°C (Carlson *et al.*, 1949) and at about 100 minutes after 31 r of X rays at 26°C (Carlson, 1942); the time intervals between treatment and resumption of mitotic activity are about 165 and 195 minutes at 38 and 26°C, respectively.

Low temperature following X irradiation also delays both the fall in the mitotic count immediately after treatment and its rise during recovery. Walter G. Adams (unpublished) has studied the effect of low

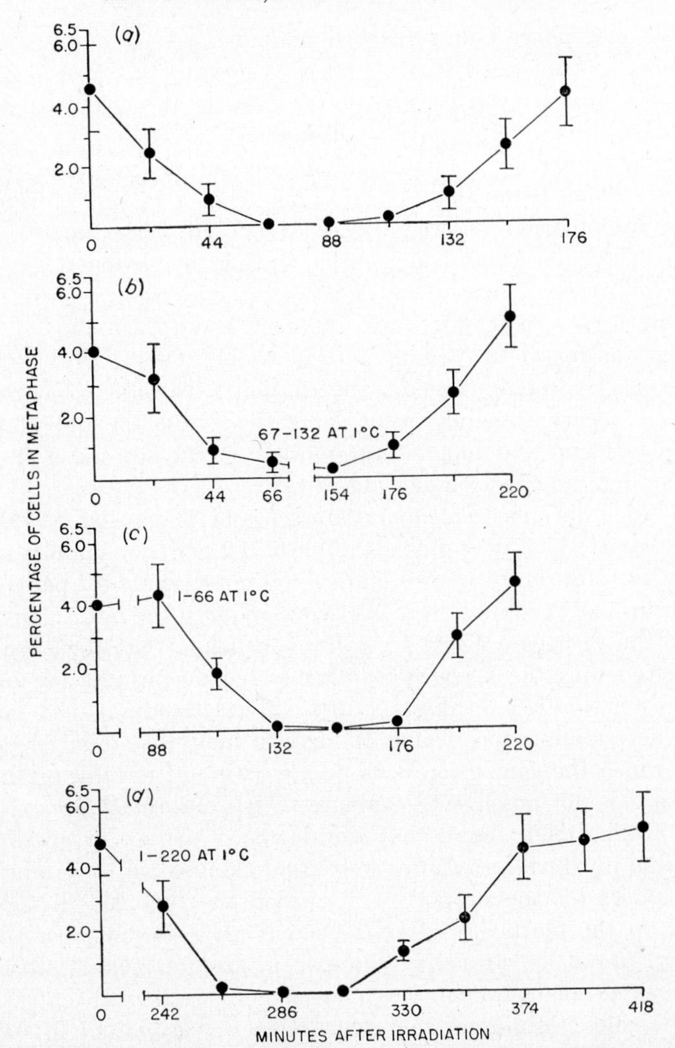

FIG. 11-11. Per cent of *Chortophaga* neuroblasts in metaphase at different times after 32 r of X rays. These cells were kept at 38°C except for different intervals after irradiation. The periods during which the cells were at 1°C are not included in the graph. A, Control, B, 1°C from 57 to 132 minutes after X irradiation; C, 1°C from 1 to 66 minutes after X irradiation; D, 1°C from 1 to 220 minutes after X irradiation (*after Adams*, unpublished).

temperature after treatment on X-ray-induced changes in mitotic activity in the grasshopper neuroblast. He found that exposure to 3°C for 220 minutes immediately after irradiation (32 r), followed by incubation at 38°C, delayed the fall to zero in the metaphase count and the subsequent return of metaphases, as compared with cells kept at 38°C from treatment on, by only slightly less than the time of the cold treatment (Fig. 11-11). If the embryos were changed from 38 to 3°C at the beginning of the period when the metaphase count reached zero, i.e., at 66 minutes after X irradiation, and returned to 38°C after 66 minutes, the reappearance of metaphases was delayed by almost the time of the cold treatment, as compared with cells kept at 38°C throughout. Exposure to 3°C, therefore, brings almost to a standstill both mitotic progress and recovery. Henshaw (1940c) found that *Arbacia* eggs, when kept at 0°C from treatment to insemination, showed less recovery and, consequently, greater cleavage delay than those kept at 24°C during this period.

Chemical Agents. Immersion of unfertilized *Arbacia* eggs in 0.35 *M* potassium citrate to remove most of the calcium from the cell during X-raying was found by Wilbur and Recknagel (1943) to decrease the cleavage delay normally caused by irradiation. The effect, however, was slight and occurred mainly after large doses (30,400 and 53,200 r). Increased calcium and magnesium content of the sea water during X irradiation had no effect on cleavage delay.

Using chick fibroblast cultures, Paterson and Thompson (1949) found that urethane, which in a concentration of 0.2 per cent inhibits mitosis, when added to the culture medium in a concentration of 0.1 per cent just before or up to 40 minutes after X-raying, reduced the mitosis-inhibiting effect of the X rays. They draw the conclusion that the capacity of urethane to reduce the X-ray effect when added after irradiation indicates that X-ray action is incomplete at the end of irradiation. The method used in determining the degree of metotic inhibition induced and the data on which the conclusion is based are omitted from this preliminary report, so it is not possible to evaluate their interpretation.

pH. Zirkle (1936) found that the degree of acidity or alkalinity of the medium in which fern spores were X-rayed affected their sensitivity, as determined by the proportion in which the first cell division had occurred by the tenth day after treatment—it normally occurs on the sixth day. In 0.006 *M* carbon dioxide in culture medium the radiosensitivity was greatest, being less in stronger or weaker concentrations of carbon dioxide. Minimum radiosensitivity was exhibited in 0.003 *M* ammonia; it was greater in either stronger or weaker concentrations of ammonia.

Oxygen Concentration. A series of studies has recently been made by Gaulden, Nix, and Moshman (1953) on the mitotic effects of exposing the grasshopper egg during X irradiation to different concentrations of oxygen. In concentrations of 0, 2, 5, 10, 21, and 100 per cent oxygen, 64 r of X rays reduced the number of prometaphase, metaphase, and anaphase cells to zero about 1 hour after treatment. The greater the per cent of oxygen, however, the longer these stages remained at zero and the longer the time interval between irradiation and the peak of mitotic activity following recovery. Treatment with 8 r of X rays, however, which does not reduce the mitotic activity to zero, resulted in no significant difference in the extent to which mitosis was depressed, whether irradiation was carried out in vacuum or in 100 per cent oxygen. It seems, therefore, that the concentration of oxygen at the time of treatment has no effect on the degree to which mitotic activity is reduced but does determine the rate of mitotic recovery. The results were the same whether 100 per cent carbon dioxide, 100 per cent nitrogen, or a vacuum was used; therefore it was clear that the oxygen concentration of the gas mixtures determined the effectiveness of the X rays in these experiments.

Type of Preparation and Kind of Tissues. The effects on mitosis of γ irradiation of pre- and postcirculatory chick embryos have been com-

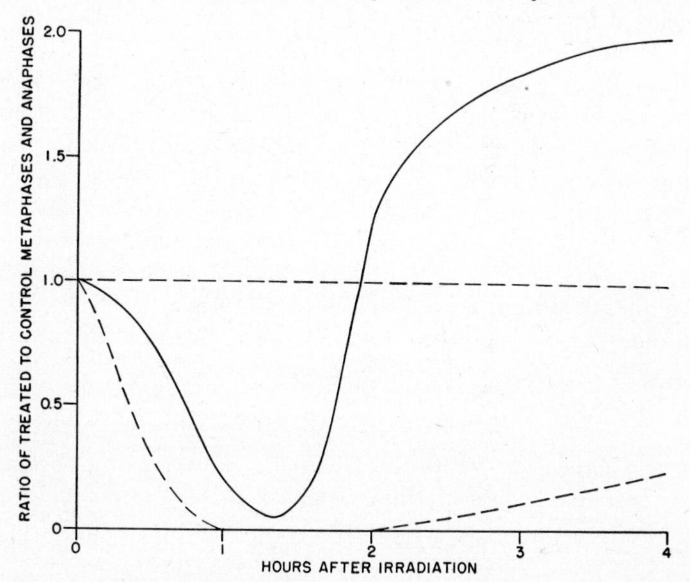

FIG. 11-12. Comparison of effects of approximately 130 roof γ rays from radium on mitosis in chick embryo tissues differing in age. Precirculatory chick designated by broken line; postcirculatory chick by solid line (*reconstructed from Spear*, 1935; *Wilson et al.*, 1935).

pared with the effects produced by comparable doses in the chick fibroblast culture preparation (Wilson *et al.*, 1935; Spear, 1935). The mitotic count of the embryo with blood circulation established fell to a minimum in about the same length of time as the culture preparation, but recovery was earlier and more abrupt (Fig. 11-12). In the precirculatory embryo, mitosis reached a minimum sooner and recovery was greatly delayed. A comparison of the effects of γ radiation on malignant cells of the mouse in vitro and in vivo showed no difference in the time required for the mitotic activity to reach a minimum (Lasnitski, 1945). Mitotic activity recovered, however, more rapidly in vivo than in vitro.

The postirradiation picture of mitotic activity in a number of different tissues in the mouse has been determined by Knowlton and Hempelmann

(1949). No striking differences in the relation of dose to rate of decrease of mitotic activity after X radiation are evident. Only the adrenal gland shows a typical compensatory effect a few hours after treatment; epidermis, jejunum, and lymph nodes give little or no indication of a rise of mitotic activity above normal. A greatly delayed overshooting does occur 3 and 7 days after treatment in the epidermis and lymph nodes, respectively, but, as the authors point out, this may be due to secondary physiological factors.

Chromosome Number. Marshak and Bradley (1944) found that the inhibition of mitotic activity in root tips of three species of *Triticum* and two species of *Bromus* with diploid chromosome numbers of 14, 28, 42, 56, and 84, as determined by mitotic counts made 3 hours after X irradiation, was neither directly nor inversely proportional to chromosome length but did vary inversely as the chromosome number. Evidence from other studies on plant root tips suggests that mitotic activity has not reached a minimum value at 3 hours. If that is true in these species these results might be a measure of the rate of fall of mitotic activity rather than of minimum activity, and rate of fall is mainly determined by the normal mitotic rate (see p. 775). The inverse relation to chromosome number could be due, therefore, as well to a lower mitotic rate in cells with more chromosomes as to increased resistance to radiation-induced mitotic delay in cells with the larger chromosome number.

MORPHOLOGICAL EFFECTS

Nuclear Components. Effects of ionizing radiations on chromosomes fall into two main classes: those referred to as "primary," "physiological," or "stickiness" effects, and those termed "secondary" or "aberration" effects. Primary effects may be described as changes of a general, or not highly localized, character in the physical, and possibly also the chemical, nature of the chromosome, which are evidenced during the ensuing metaphase and anaphase in a tendency of sister chromatids or of different chromosomes to adhere. Sister chromatid fusion results in bridge formation at anaphase. Secondary effects, or chromosome aberations, are highly localized alterations of the chromatid or chromosome that are evident as breaks, exchanges, or inversions in metaphase and anaphase cells subsequent to irradiation. For obvious reasons the terms "primary," "physiological," "stickiness," and "secondary," as applied to effects on the chromosome are objectionable. The terms "nonlocalized" and "localized" are used here as substitutes for "primary" and "secondary," respectively.

Localized effects are of interest in this chapter only insofar as the time of their appearance is related to that of nonlocalized effects and the period of mitotic inhibition. It seems apparent from evidence now available that nonlocalized effects are limited to cells that complete mitosis immediately after irradiation during the period of diminishing mitotic activity, while localized effects occur most frequently in those cells that enter metaphase and anaphase after the period of irradiation-induced minimum mitotic activity. That localized effects are not restricted to the postinhibition period is evidenced by the recording of acentric fragments 7½ hours after treatment in *Scilla* root tips (Marquardt, 1938), shortly after irradiation in *Tradescantia* microspores (Sax and Swanson, 1941), at 4 hours in *Trillium, Allium,* and *Vicia* root tips (Darlington and La Cour, 1945), in anaphases of the first meiotic division in *Habrobracon* eggs treated in late prophase or metaphase (Whiting, 1945), at 1 hour in root tips of *Vicia* (Deufel, 1951), and 22 minutes after treatment in neuroblasts of the grasshopper (Gaulden, unpublished). The explanation offered by Sax and Swanson that such fragments may be due to breaks resulting from stresses imposed by stickiness of sister chromatids at anaphase may also apply to the *Habrobracon* egg treated at prophase I, for anaphases of the latter showed fusions between separating chromosomes. It is unlikely that this would explain their presence at anaphase I in the *Habrobracon* egg treated in metaphase I or at anaphase in the grasshopper neuroblast treated in very late prophase, for in these no fusions between separating chromosomes were evident. It will certainly not account for their presence in *metaphases* of *Scilla, Vicia, Allium,* and *Trillium* root tips. The frequency of fragments in irradiated cells before the period of minimum mitotic activity is very low in most cells compared to the number found in cells after the resumption of mitotic activity. The high percentage of cells with fragments found by Deufel (1951) in root tips of *Vicia* as early as 1 hour after 150 r may not be inconsistent with other results because he includes in his tabulation "fragments" connected by constrictions with the remainder of the chromosome as well as those completely separated from it, and no breakdown of the two types is given. It may be that the ion densities of X rays of the wave lengths usually used is not high enough to produce many breaks of the heavily condensed late prophase-through-anaphase chromosomes; perhaps neutrons or α particles would produce a greater frequency of breaks during this period. It is of interest to note that, though localized and nonlocalized effects in the form of breaks and fusions, respectively, may occur during the period of decreasing mitotic activity, fusions apparently do not occur at the breakage loci to give translocations, as Marquardt (1938) has pointed out.

Nonlocalized effects in the form of clumping of metaphase chromosomes or the sticking together of sister chromatids to give anaphase bridges have been described by numerous investigators (Alberti and Politzer, 1923, 1924; Strangeways and Oakley, 1923; Kemp and Juul, 1930; Lewitsky and Araratian, 1931; Crow, 1933; White, 1937; Marquardt, 1938, 1950; Sax and Swanson, 1941; Carlson, 1941; Koller, 1943;

Darlington and La Cour, 1945; Rugh, 1950; Deufel, 1951). For the most part these effects have been seen in fixed and stained material soon after treatment, and the mitotic stage at which they were induced is not known with certainty. Direct observations of the postirradiation history of selected living grasshopper neuroblasts in stages of mitosis identified before treatment has provided us with some exact information regarding the stages at which these nonlocalized effects are produced and the relation of this to dosage (Carlson and Harrington, unpublished). With a series of doses ranging from 64 to 4096 r it is found that successively increasing doses give rise to successively increasing degrees of response as follows: (1) delayed anaphase separation of a few of the sister chromatids

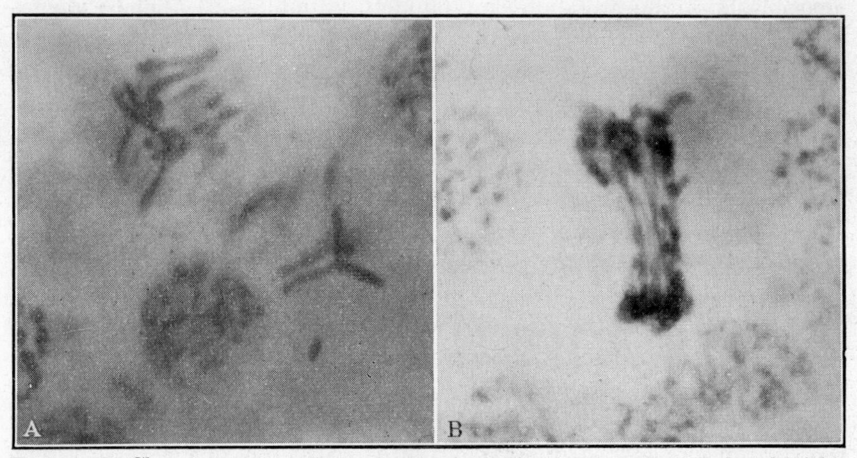

FIG. 11-13. Chromosomes of *Chortophaga* neuroblast, showing X-ray-induced stickiness at anaphase. 512 r; 30 minutes after treatment: A, early anaphase; B, late anaphase.

in cells that were in very late prophase at the time of treatment and, therefore, the last cells to pass through mitosis before the interval of minimal mitotic activity, (2) a similar effect but with many sister chromatids involved (Fig. 11-13), (3) stickiness involving different chromosomes, induced at very late prophase and evident in prometaphase, and anaphase, (4) fusion of different chromosomes by treatment at the same stage in which it is observed, viz., prometaphase, metaphase, or anaphase, and (5) fusion of all the chromosomes into a single, irregular mass at prometaphase, metaphase, or anaphase as a result of treatment at the same stage. Subsequently, this chromosomal mass elongates in the direction of the poles and appears to be divided by a pressing inward of the cleavage furrow (Carlson, 1941).

It has been postulated that the stickiness induced in chromosomes by irradiation is due to depolymerization of the thymonucleic acid of the chromosomes (Darlington, 1942) and to an excess of nucleic acid charge

(Darlington and La Cour, 1945). The in vitro nucleic acid studies of Sparrow and Rosenfeld (1946) and Taylor, Greenstein, and Hollaender (1947, 1948) showed a viscosity fall that indicated at least a partial depolymerization of the nucleic acid, and the viscosity continued to fall for several hours after the cessation of X irradiation. This parallels the results obtained by Harrington and Koza (1951), who found that the methyl green staining reaction of X-rayed grasshopper chromosomes reached a minimum as late as 10 hours after X-raying. It is probable that many of the abnormal anaphases studied by Marshak (1938) in *Vicia* and *Allium* root tips 3 hours after X irradiation were the result of nonlocalized rather than localized effects. Though depolymerization of nucleic acids is interfered with at high pH, it seems doubtful whether the capacity he found for increasing concentrations of ammonium hydroxide to decrease the percentage of X-ray-induced abnormal anaphases could be due to a raising of the intracellular pH to the level necessary for such an effect.

Changes may also be induced by X rays in the intranuclear chromosomes. The studies of Duryee (1939, 1947, 1949, 1950) were made on the later stages of amphibian oöcytes, when the "lampbrush" chromosomes of the large germinal vesicle consist of chromonemata with chromomeres spaced at intervals along them and numerous lateral loops attached at both ends to the central chromonemata. Doses of 5000–10,000 r and more produced breakage in the lateral loops. Chromonemata were occasionally broken by 10,000 r; multiple fragmentation was produced by 30,000 r and more of X rays (Fig. 11-14). Such changes, which were visible 15 minutes after treatment, appear to be prophase manifestations of chromosome breakage that are not discernible in most cells until the succeeding metaphase and anaphase, when they would be classed as chromosome aberrations.

The chromosomes of the *Chortophaga* neuroblast, after 250 r of X rays, undergo changes suggestive of reversion to an earlier stage of mitosis (Carlson, 1940). The diameter of the chromosome thread resembles, successively, that of the middle prophase and then of early prophase cells. Instead of being uniform in diameter from end to end, however, it has a beaded appearance, consisting of granules separated by narrower regions. It finally acquires the coarsely granular character of the interphase nucleus. This is a reversible, and not a degenerative, change, however, for at the time of recovery these cells pass through mitosis in an apparently normal fashion.

Marquardt (1938) described excessive relational coiling of chromatids in *Bellevalia* microspores 2–3 hours and abnormally short metaphase chromosomes 3–4 hours after X-raying. Defective internal and relational coiling of the chromatids, according to Darlington and La Cour (1945), results from X-ray-induced depolymerization of the chromosome

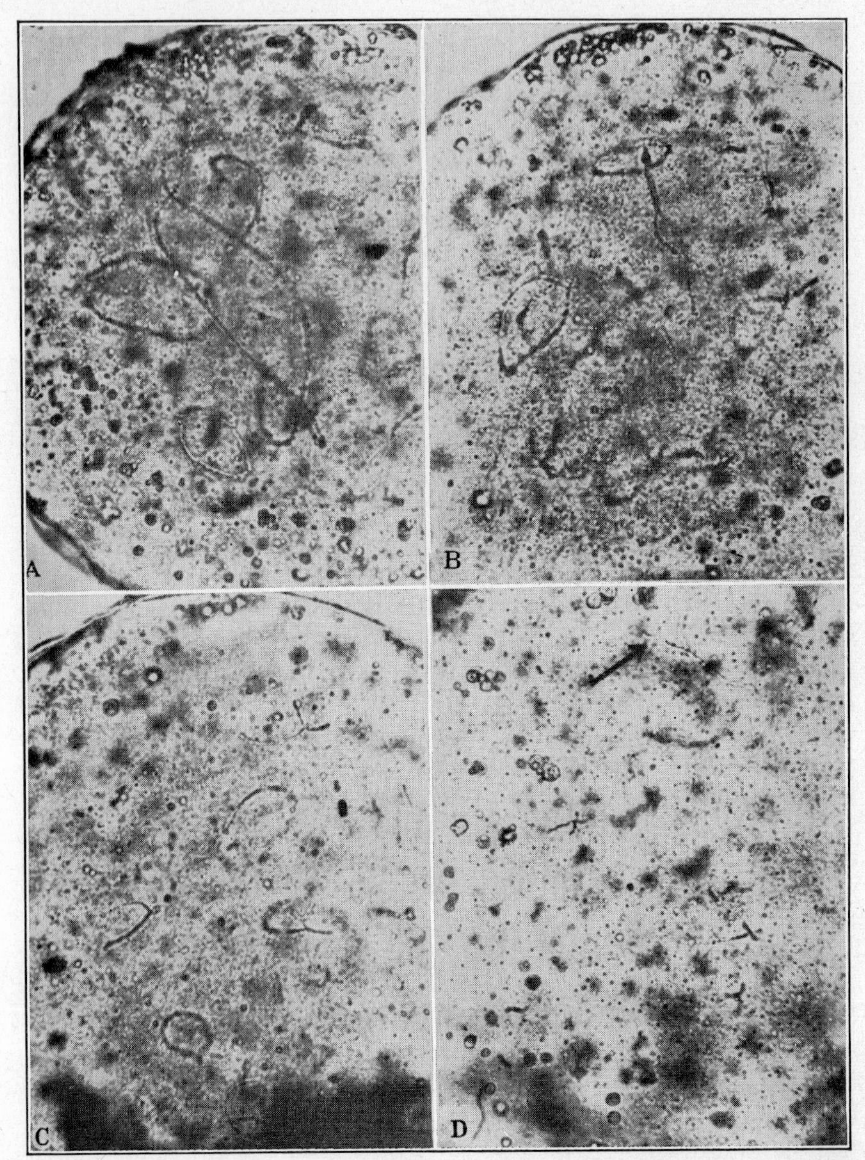

Fig. 11-14. X-ray-induced fragmentation of intranuclear chromosomes of ovarian eggs. *Rana catesbiana.* A, control; B, 2000 r, some fragmentation of chromosomes; C and D, 50,000 r, much chromosome fragmentation (*Duryee*, 1949).

nucleic acid. Elongation of the chromonemata of *Trillium* chromosomes between diakinesis and the first meiotic anaphase is reduced to considerably less than half of normal by X-raying cells in the first meiotic prophase (Sparrow, 1946). It is suggested by Sparrow that this may result from X-ray-induced DNA deficiency.

Irradiation of isolated amphibian eggs with as little as 1000 r of X rays is sufficient to affect the appearance of the nucleoli (Duryee, 1949). They are changed from small, rounded bodies somewhat irregular in shape and with small internal vacuoles to much larger bodies more nearly spherical in form and with large internal vacuoles. Cattley (1909) noted an increase in the number of nucleoli per cell in plant root tips soon after X irradiation. Grasshopper neuroblasts subjected to a dose of 10,000 r of X rays at telophase exhibit shortly afterward several spherical instead of the usual two nucleoli (Carlson and McMaster, 1951). Treatment of neuroblasts at other stages of the mitotic cycle or at interphase fails to alter the nucleoli.

With regard to the means by which high-energy radiations act on the nucleus, Duryee (1939, 1947, 1949) has made a strong case for an indirect effect through the cytosome. Fragmentation of chromosomes and their lateral loops and vacuolation and enlargement of nucleoli were used as criteria of radiation damage. X irradiation of nuclei *in situ* or microinjection of the cytosome of nonirradiated eggs with cytoplasm withdrawn from irradiated ones produced these changes. Immersion of isolated, untreated nuclei in irradiated cytoplasmic brei led to loss of chromosomal loops and heavy nucleolar damage. On the other hand, nuclei irradiated with comparable doses after removal from the egg cytosome exhibited no detectable injury. Duryee has concluded, on the basis of these results, that the primary physical or radiochemical changes are produced in the cytosome, that substances toxic to the nucleus accumulate in the cytosome, and that the subsequent movement of these toxins into the nucleus effect the morphological changes seen after irradiation.

Achromatic Figure and Cleavage. It has generally been found that only very large doses of radiation, i.e., many thousands of r, affect the achromatic figure of the dividing cell. Henshaw (1940d, 1941) demonstrated that 62,400 r administered to either gamete of *Arbacia* produced multipolar cleavage in almost 100 per cent of the zygotes. Polyspermy was ruled out as a cause of this, for cytological examination showed that the percentage of polyspermy was no greater in treated than control specimens. He concluded, because multipolar cleavage was present after treatment of the sperm, which contains almost no cytoplasmic material, as well as the egg, which contributes no aster in fertilization, that the supernumerary asters must result from an effect on nuclear rather than cytoplasmic material. Unless one is willing to assume that the effectiveness of the treatment depends on the quantity of cytoplasm irradiated or that the sperm is devoid of cytoplasm exclusive of centrioles, the possibility of an indirect effect through the cytoplasm is not eliminated completely. As much as 8000 r applied to the dividing grasshopper neuroblast has no demonstrable effect on the structure or functioning of the spindle.

In the amphibian egg, X-ray doses of 50,000 r and more have been shown by Duryee (1949) to produce enough solvation of the karyoplasm, or presumptive spindle substance, to disorient certain of the chromosome pairs within the nucleus. In the light of present information the γ-irradiated *Chaetopterus* "chromosomes" that failed to move to the poles at anaphase (Packard, 1918) were apparently acentric fragments instead of chromosomes with radiation-induced destruction of the capacity to develop spindle fibers, as postulated by Packard. Large doses applied to dividing animal cells lead to an immediate fusion of all the metaphase or anaphase chromosomes to form a single mass from which chromatin material seems to flow toward opposite poles, but there appears to be no change in spindle appearance or behavior (Alberti and Politzer, 1923, 1924; Carlson, 1941; Rugh, 1950).

On the other hand, Marquardt (1938) and Koller (1943), whose observations were made on *Scilla* root tips and *Tradescantia* microspores, respectively, have concluded that small doses of X rays (360 r in *Tradescantia*) can lead to abnormal orientation or complete suppression of spindle formation soon after treatment. Koller used delay of the chromosomes in attaining metaphase after breakdown of the nuclear membrane and clumping of chromosomes without any orientation as evidence of the absence of the metaphase spindle in the *Tradescantia* microspore. In *Scilla*, absence of the spindle led to a certain disorientation of the metaphase and anaphase chromosomes, but the latter exhibited repulsion of sister chromatids toward the opposite sides of the cell and a certain degree of stickiness.

CELL VIABILITY EFFECTS

Nature of Effect. The presence of pyknotic and degenerating cells in tissues after irradiation, the destruction of malignant growths, and the failure of animals to hatch or seeds to germinate may all be the result of irradiation-induced cell-lethal effects. We are concerned in this chapter only with those cell-lethal effects that are evident very soon after irradiation.

Degenerative changes in irradiated cells of the tadpole brain and eye are described as follows by Spear and Glücksmann (1938). At first there is separation of chromatic from nonchromatic nuclear material, the former gradually accumulating in the peripheral region of the nucleus, while the latter forms a large central vacuole. Following this, the nucleus breaks up into a number of parts, some of which contain deeply staining chromatin scattered through the cytosome. Eventually the cell undergoes fragmentation and dissolution. The chromatic elements of the nucleus, which change from Feulgen positive to eosin positive, gradually become smaller as they dissolve. A similar description is given by Lasnitski (1943b, 1946) for the degeneration occurring in resting cells following large doses of radiation (2500 r or more). She recognizes also "mitotic degeneration" resulting from the unsuccessful attempt of irradiated cells to undergo mitosis. In this type "the chromatic material (chromatopycnosis) is assembled in bands (hyperchromatosis) which later tend to accumulate at the nuclear membrane and finally (chromatolysis), undergo shrinkage and lysis. The cytoplasm of these cells undergoes fatty or colloquative degeneration at an early stage, shrinks, and disappears."

The formation of large intranuclear vacuoles surrounded by irregular layers of desoxypentose nucleic acid within a few hours of the injection of P^{32} is described for the intestinal cells of rats by Warren, Holt, and Sommers (1951). Such changes lead to eventual degeneration.

On the basis of direct observations of living chick fibroblasts in culture, Strangeways and Oakley (1923) described the "breaking down" of cells after X irradiation and concluded that this resulted from damage to cells about to divide. Some cells were not affected until telophase, when one or both of the daughter cells broke down. Their observations have been confirmed and extended by more recent investigations based mainly on material fixed and stained at intervals following treatment. Degenerate cells in irradiated tissues seem to belong to one of three classes:

(1) After doses of ionizing radiation sufficiently small for mitotic recovery to take place within a few hours after treatment, the maximum number of degenerating cells coincides more or less closely in time with the high point of mitotic activity that marks recovery from the mitosis-depressing effect of radiation (Strangeways and Fell, 1927; Tansley *et al.*, 1937; Spear and Glücksmann, 1938; Glücksmann and Spear, 1939; Lasnitski, 1940, 1943a; Tansley *et al.*, 1948). The close correspondence between rise in mitotic activity and the degenerate cell count suggests that the effect of the irradiation has been to render cells about to enter division incapable of completing it, so that they degenerate during or after division. If the radiation dose and other conditions are such that a large proportion of the dividing cells complete mitosis instead of or before degenerating, the degenerate cell high will follow the mitotic high; if they are such that few of the cells that undertake division complete it, undergoing degeneration instead, the degenerate cell high may precede the mitotic high (Glücksmann and Spear, 1939; Lasnitski, 1943a). Glücksmann and Spear (1939), who altered the mitotic activity of the cells of the tadpole eye by fasting and by exposure of the animals to low temperatures, were able to correlate the amount of cell degeneration following γ irradiation with the amount of mitotic activity of the tissues. Since the degenerate cell counts in many of their experiments greatly exceeded the mitotic counts, they reached the conclusion that it was not the cells in division at the time of treatment, but those approaching division, that subsequently constituted the bulk of the degenerating cells.

Feeding one week after irradiation, which occurred on the seventh day of fasting, led to the appearance of degenerate cells, presumably because feeding stimulated the cells to undertake division.

(2) After the exposure of chick fibroblasts in vitro to such large doses of X radiation that mitosis did not reappear within at least 24 hours of treatment, Lasnitski (1943b) found that there nevertheless occurred an appreciable rise in the number of degenerate cells. This reached a maximum 3 hours after the end of treatment. Doses of 2500, 5000, and 10,000 r were followed by 53, 58, and 75 per cent, respectively, of degenerate cells. She has postulated that the lethal radiosensitivity of these cells may be positively correlated with their proximity to mitosis, so that at successively higher doses, cells successively farther removed from mitosis may be killed, even though they make no attempt at cell division.

(3) Whether the radiation dose is large or small as judged by its effect on mitotic activity, degenerate cells are generally present at least in small numbers, very soon after treatment, when the mitotic activity is at a minimum or completely absent (Strangeways and Fell, 1927; Tansley *et al.*, 1937; Spear and Glücksmann, 1938; Glücksmann and Spear, 1939; Lasnitski, 1943a, b, 1945). Their interpretation that this is an effect on cells that were in division during treatment is confirmed by the work of Simon-Reuss and Spear (1947), who observed the breaking up of living fibroblasts that were in metaphase, anaphase, or telophase at the time of treatment. Such degenerating cells represent only a small proportion of the total number of cells present, regardless of the dosage, because in the tissues studied (tadpole brain and eye, avian fibroblasts, rat retinal cells, mouse malignant cells), the number of dividing cells is small in relation to the number of resting cells. It is interesting to note that in contrast to the results obtained with chick fibroblast preparations, in which cells may break up before completing mitosis after as small a dose as 88 r (Simon-Reuss and Spear, 1947), neuroblasts of *Chortophaga* complete mitosis almost without exception after doses at least as large as 4000 r, yet the latter cells are much more radiosensitive than the former when the criterion is decreased mitotic activity (Fig. 11-6).

By comparing the lethal effects of X radiation on malignant cells of the mouse in vitro and in vivo Lasnitski (1947) concluded that the immediate effect of the treatment was mainly a direct one, for the amounts of cell degeneration in the two were similar. A much higher percentage of cell degeneration in vivo than in vitro occurred on the second day after treatment, however, which suggested an indirect effect through damaged blood circulation.

The nuclear changes leading to pyknosis and cell disintegration in the amphibian egg are described by Duryee (1949) as follows:

(1) Prophase chromosomes normally transparent and invisible become shorter, thicker, darker, and beaded. (2) In young ovocytes the nascent chromomere

lateral loops swell and disintegrate. (3) Nucleoli along the inner surface of the nuclear membrane evert their contents into the cytoplasm, and their residual shells swell and disintegrate. (4) The central nuclear ground substance . . . changes from a gel to a sol, thereby allowing the chromosomes to tangle, mat, and clump. (5) Later radiation damage with advanced pyknosis consists of formation of a clumped central nuclear body.

Nuclear damage is induced in ovarian eggs of *Triturus* within 2 days at 22–24°C by doses of 2000 and more r of X rays applied to the whole body of the female (Duryee, 1949). Experiments in which the ovaries were shielded during irradiation showed that this was the result of direct effects on the eggs and was not secondarily induced through the body of the female. If the animals were kept at 4°C from the end of treatment on, the pyknotic changes were temporarily arrested, but not for more than about two weeks. After warming to 22°C, pyknosis appeared. Maintenance of animals at 27°C, however, after irradiation increased the rate of nuclear disintegration.

Lea (1946) has discussed at some length radiation-induced lethal effects and their causes in higher organisms. From evidence based largely on radiation of the *Drosophila* sperm, the *Tradescantia* microspore, and the bean root tip cell, he has concluded that chromosome losses resulting from asymmetrical interchanges and simple breaks are responsible for at least some of the cell deaths that occur at or following division. It should be pointed out, however, that the evidence from these organisms, in which the analysis of chromosome changes is possible, cannot justifiably be applied to the elucidation of evidence from cells that have been used in the study of immediate lethal effects, which are manifest in the treated cells before, during, or immediately following the first postirradiation division of the cell. The test of a lethal effect induced in the *Drosophila* sperm is failure of the egg fertilized by that sperm to hatch. Chromosome losses might be expected to lead to faulty differentiation and death of the embryo, but this appears to me to be a quite different cause of death from the immediate effect that would result in the death of the zygote or one or both of its daughter cells. The same is true of the bean root-tip cell where the test of lethal effect is the death of the root many cell generations and many days (about 14) after treatment. The one example cited by Lea of an immediate lethal effect is the failure of the irradiated *Tradescantia* microspore to differentiate or failure of the pollen tube to develop. The microspore, however, is a haploid cell and any chromosome loss might be expected to produce an immediate lethal effect. The chick fibroblast, the cells of the brain and eye of the tadpole, malignant cells of the mouse, and rat retinal cells are not haploid. Unless both members of a chromosome pair suffered the loss of corresponding regions, and this would be a rare event except after large doses, there is no reason to think that the loss would cause the death of the cell. It seems to me, therefore, that we should look to some effect other than chromosome loss for the cause of immediate lethal effects on cells.

Hevesy (1945) believes that the basic effect of X rays on cells is the inhibition of DNA formation. A comparison of the amounts of P^{32} incorporated in the nucleic acid molecules of irradiated and unirradiated tissues of the rat showed a significantly higher amount in the latter than in the former. The percentage of DNA formed was not appreciably different in dividing and nondividing cells. In order to account for the greater lethal effect in dividing than in nondividing cells—in both the percentage of DNA formed is about the same—he concludes that inhibition of DNA formation in a fully developed, rarely dividing group of cells is not critical, because on the average most of these cells will have time to eliminate this disturbance before it is their time to divide. The more frequently the cells of a tissue are dividing, the greater will be the number of degenerate cells formed, because the cell will attempt to divide before recovery has had a chance to take place.

The diverse radiosensitivities of different kinds of cells to immediate lethal effects as compared with mitotic effects are very striking. Tansley *et al.* (1937), for example, found that 72 r of γ rays, which reduced the mitotic count in cells of the developing rat retina to a minimum of about 10 per cent of normal, produced a lethal effect on 11 per cent of the total cells as determined 6 hours after treatment. In the *Chortophaga* neuroblast, however, the mitotic count is reduced to the same extent by as little as a ninth of that dose, or 8 r of X rays, while 1250 times that dose, or 10,000 r, causes virtually no neuroblast deaths within at least 8 hours after treatment (Gaulden, unpublished). This is unrelated to the kinds of radiation used; for no comparable difference has been detected so far in the efficiencies of γ rays and medium X rays in reducing mitotic activity or killing cells. Apparently, some basic biological difference in the cells themselves is responsible. This also demonstrates the fallacy in comparing radiosensitivities of different biological materials, when these sensitivities are based on different criteria.

Under the heading of immediate lethal effects we might also include chromosome destruction or inactivation produced in *Habrobracon* eggs by large doses of X rays (Whiting, 1948). If eggs treated with doses of 14,420–36,050 r in the first meiotic prophase or metaphase are laid by females mated with untreated males, a small percentage of haploid males will develop, which contain only the chromosome set of the male parent. The maternal chromosomes are so adversely affected, presumably by chromatin bridges which interfere with their anaphase movement and with the subsequent movement and internal changes of the female pronucleus, that they take no part in cleavage and are eventually eliminated.

Kind of Radiation. Lasnitski (1948) discovered no striking differences in the proportion of degenerate avian fibroblasts in vitro exposed to either 1000 r of X or β rays (Fig. 11-15). Degenerate cells made their appearance slightly earlier, however, after β-raying than after X-raying.

A comparison of the efficiencies of fast neutrons and γ rays in producing cell degeneration of the developing rat retina led Spear and Tansley (1944) to conclude that the former were 6.5 times as effective as the latter per n unit. The degenerate cell count rises more rapidly after neutron treatment than after γ irradiation. Also after neutron treatment the

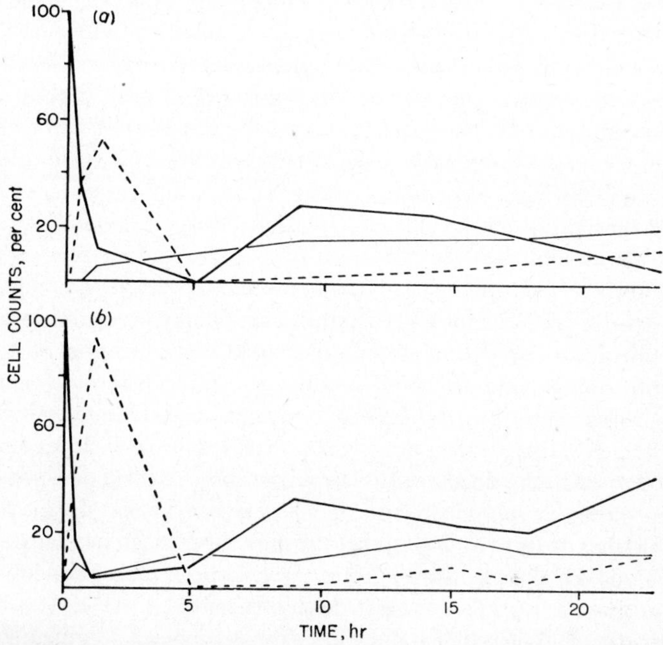

FIG. 11-15. Effects of 1000 r of X rays (*a*) and β rays (*b*) on mitosis (heavy, solid line), abnormal mitoses (broken line), and degeneration of cells (light, solid line) of avian fibroblasts in vitro (*after Lasnitski*, 1948).

time of appearance of the degenerate cells does not vary with the dose as it does after γ irradiation, when the larger the dose, the greater is the delay in their appearance. This is interpreted to indicate that, while after each irradiation the degenerate cells are made up of those killed outright during mitosis and those that die later when they attempt, but fail, to complete mitosis, in the case of neutrons a larger proportion of the degenerating cells represent direct kills. The much greater effectiveness of fast neutrons than γ rays in killing mice by whole-body irradiation is attributed by Mitchell (1947), at least in part, to degeneration of radiosensitive cells, such as bone marrow. He also suggests that neutrons can probably kill cells in interphase as well as early prophase, while γ rays have their main lethal effects on the latter alone.

Tansley *et al.* (1948) compared the cell degeneration induced in the germinative zones of the eye and brain of the frog tadpole by α rays with that induced by γ rays. Small doses of each were found to produce comparable amounts of degeneration, but larger doses of α rays produced a degree of cell degeneration out of all proportion to that following similar doses of γ rays. They suggest that the greater effectiveness of α rays may be caused either by an effect on cells farther removed from mitosis than those killed by γ rays or by an abnormally great accumulation of injured cells that break up on attempting mitosis.

Dosage Rate. In order to test the efficiencies of different dosage rates in causing cell degeneration in the brain and eye of the tadpole, Glücksmann, Tansley, and Wilson (1945) administered a dose of 336 r of γ rays at rates of 5.05, 8.37, 12.6, 15.0, and 20.1 r/minute. They found that the dosage rate is positively correlated with the maximal degeneration count and with the length of the interval of time between irradiation and the maximal count, but that the total amount of degeneration is greatest at 15.0 r/minute. Lasnitzki (1946) determined the relative efficiencies of dosage rates of 9.7, 29, and 101 r/minute in producing cell degeneration in chick fibroblasts in vitro. After a dose of 100 r the number of degenerations expressed as percentage of resting cells was negatively correlated with the dosage rate, but the differences were very slight. After 2500 r, however, there was a positive correlation of dosage rate with degeneration. At the lower dose the degenerations were mainly mitotic ones, but at the higher dose they were mainly resting cell degenerations. Her interpretation of these apparently contradictory dosage-rate efficiencies at small and large doses is based on the relation of degeneration to the lowering of mitotic activity after the different dosage rates.

Temperature. The experiments of Strangeways and Fell (1927) indicate that the amount of cell degeneration that would normally result after X raying, if chick embryos are incubated at 38°C, is greatly reduced if they are kept at 0 or 5°C for 5 to 24 hours after irradiation. This is indicated not only by the lowered frequency of degenerating cells seen in fixed and stained preparations after cold treatment, but also in the greater proportion of successful in vitro cultivations obtained from cells that had been cold treated as contrasted with those incubated only at 38°C after treatment.

ULTRAVIOLET RADIATIONS

Unlike X-ray studies, ultraviolet radiation investigations have of necessity been limited to single, isolated cell types or to cells that are situated or can be grown in cultures on the surface of tissue masses and in which, therefore, penetration of the radiation is not a serious problem.

MITOTIC EFFECTS

Nature of Effect. Reduction of mitotic activity immediately following treatment with mixed wave lengths of ultraviolet radiation has been described for chick fibroblasts in vitro (Kemp and Juul, 1932; Juul and Kemp, 1933; Mollendorff and Laqueur, 1938), marine invertebrate eggs (Nebel, Harvey, and Hollaender, 1937; Chase, 1938; Blum *et al.*, 1949; Blum *et al.*, 1950; Blum and Price, 1950), salamander corneal eipthelium (Politzer and Alberti, 1924) and rat corneal epithelium (Buschke, Friedenwald, and Moses, 1945). After monochromatic radiation, division of the marine invertebrate egg is retarded by various wave lengths of 2260–3130 A inclusive (Hertel, 1905; Nebel *et al.*, 1937; Giese, 1938a, b, 1939a, b, c, 1946; Marshak, 1949; Wells and Giese, 1950). Mitotic activity is reduced in the rat corneal epithelium by wave lengths 2480 through 3160 A (Friedenwald *et al.*, 1948). In the grasshopper neuroblasts, only 2250 and 2537 A have been studied in detail and found to retard division (Carlson and Hollaender, 1944, 1945, 1948) but preliminary experiments indicate that longer wave lengths, up to and including 3130 A, are probably also effective.

Comparative studies of the effectiveness of different wave lengths point to the 2480–2804 A region inclusive as producing the greatest retardation of mitosis (Mayer and Schreiber, 1934; Giese, 1938b, 1939a, b; Friedenwald *et al.*, 1948). Giese (1946) found that treatment of certain echinoderm sperm gave an action spectrum for delay through the third cleavage that resembles the absorption spectrum of nucleoprotein (high at 2600 A), while treatment of the unfertilized egg gave an action spectrum resembling protein (high at 2800 A). He suggested that cleavage may be slowed by different types of induced changes in the sperm and egg. Friedenwald *et al.* (1948), however, found that the action spectrum for mitotic activity in the rat corneal epithelium was high at 2480 and 2804 and lower at 2650 A.

Of the tissues so far examined only periblem cells of the root tip of *Vicia* have given evidence of an increase in the percentage of cells in mitosis immediately after treatment with ultraviolet radiation. Takamine (1935) found that after exposure of one side of root tips to the radiations from a quartz mercury vapor lamp, 2–3 hours after an exposure of ½–3 hours, the percentage of cells in mitosis (prophase, metaphase, anaphase, and telophase) on the exposed side of the root tip was about 1 per cent higher than on the opposite side. Subsequently, the percentage on the treated side fell until at 15 hours it was about 1 per cent less than the control side; and the percentage was still below normal at 48 hours. The effects of monochromatic radiation of 2537 and 3650 A were also studied. The latter gave a slight increase in the number of dividing cells during the first 3 hours after treatment, while the former reduced the number of mitoses to slightly below normal during 24 hours after treatment. Since the numbers of cells on which these percentages are based are not given, it is not apparent how significant they are. It is noteworthy, however, that exposures of 0.5, 1.0, 1.5, and 3.0 hours all showed a consistently similar effect on mitosis. It is a question also whether the ultraviolet—especially the shorter wave lengths—would penetrate the root tip to the periblem, let alone to its deeper layers. A differential penetration by the wave lengths used is indicated by the different effects of 2537 and 3650 A. Seide (1925) treated *Ascaris* eggs in various stages of the first cleavage division with small doses of ultraviolet radiation of 2804 A and of mixed wave lengths from the mercury quartz lamp, but was unable to demonstrate a positive shortening of the time required by the eggs to reach the two- and four-celled stages. In 1945 Buschke, Friedenwald, and Moses described what appeared to be increased mitotic activity following weak doses of nonmonochromatic ultraviolet radiation of the rat cornea, but it was demonstrated in a later study (Friedenwald *et al.*, 1948) that the effective agent was a gas—probably ozone—generated by the ultraviolet lamp used in the treatments.

Of the tissues examined for mitotic activity after exposure to ultraviolet, only the corneal epithelium of the rat exhibits a compensatory effect at recovery, i.e., a temporary increase in the number of mitoses in excess of normal immediately after recovery (Friedenwald *et al.*, 1948). This peak is reached approximately 12 hours after treatment.

It appears from present evidence that interphase and early prophase are the stages most sensitive to ultraviolet radiation. Investigating the radiosensitivity of different parts of the interval between the first and second cleavages of the *Arbacia* egg, Blum and Price (1950) found that a dose of radiation applied in the early part of this interval caused the greatest mitotic delay, the radiosensitivity then diminished to a minimum at 12 minutes; and from this time to the completion of the second cleavage division, irradiation did not induce delay. In studying the effects on the grasshopper neuroblast of 2250 and 2537 A radiation, Carlson and Hollaender (1944, 1948) found that, if the radiosensitivity was measured by the time required for a cell treated in one stage to reach the next stage, early prophase was the most sensitive; for cells treated in either interphase or early prophase remained in early prophase an excessively long time. If, on the other hand, the increase in the time required by the cell to progress from the stage in which it was treated to anaphase was the criterion of sensitivity used, at both wave lengths interphase was found to be more sensitive than early prophase (Carlson and Hollaender, 1948). A detailed analysis of the radiosensitivities of different stages of mitosis to 2250 A, as indicated by their delay in reaching anaphase, showed middle and late prophase to be only slightly less affected than early prophase, and metaphase to be much less sensitive. Cells in middle prophase were caused to undergo temporary regression by a dose of 34,650 ergs/cm^2 and late prophase by one-fourth as large a dose. Recovery and progression through anaphase followed. Delay induced in prometaphase and metaphase cells is probably the result of damage to the spindle-forming substance and spindle, respectively (see p. 814).

Intensity. In time-intensity studies the problems encountered in the choice of materials and methods and in the interpretation of results are essentially the same for ultraviolet as for high-energy radiations (see p.

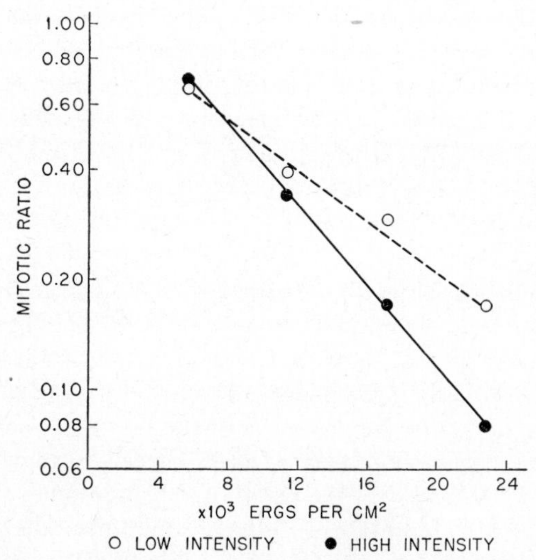

FIG. 11-16. Effects of different intensities of 2537 A ultraviolet radiation on the mitotic ratio of treated to control cells (*Chortophaga* neuroblasts) (*after Carlson and Hollaender*, 1945).

788). In addition, the relatively slight penetration of many ultraviolet wave lengths into organic materials limits drastically the kinds of cells amenable to mitotic studies. Carlson and Hollaender (1945) compared the effectiveness of selected doses of 2537 A radiation delivered in 3.5–13 seconds and in 3.75–4 hours. It was found that the number of cells passing through mitosis in a 2-hour period beginning approximately 4 hours after the mid-point of the irradiation period was decreased to approximately the same extent by doses of 5760 or 11,520 ergs/cm^2, but that at doses of 17,280 or 23,040 ergs/cm^2 the brief, high-intensity exposure was considerably more effective in reducing the mitotic activity than the prolonged, low-intensity one (Fig. 11-16).

Chemical Agents. Marshak (1949) found that none of the following chemical agents were effective in altering 2537 A ultraviolet-induced cleavage delay in *Arbacia:* streptomycin, adenosine, folic acid, 2,4-diamino-5-*p*-chlorphenoxypyrimidine, or riboflavin.

CELL MORPHOLOGY EFFECTS

Chromosomes. After generative nuclei of *Tradescantia* pollen tubes growing on artificial sugar-agar-gelatin medium had been treated in prophase with a sublethal dose (3000 ergs/mm^2) of 2537 A radiation, the metaphase chromosomes were much shorter and thicker than normal (Swanson, 1942). This was apparently due to partial despiralization of the chromonemata, for the number of coils in these chromosomes was reduced from the normal twenty to about seven to ten per chromosome and the gyres were increased in width. The chromosome matrix, which was rarely seen under normal conditions, appeared as a transparent hyaline mass surrounding and holding together the two chromatids. Frequently the matrixes of two or more chromosomes were fused, a change suggestive of the nonlocalized or "stickiness" effect found immediately after large doses of ionizing radiations. None of these changes were seen after treatment with a mixture of 2967 and 3022 A radiation.

If neuroblasts of the grasshopper are exposed to large doses of 2537 or 2650 A radiation and examined subsequently in the living, unstained state, the chromosomes of cells in prometaphase, metaphase, and anaphase appear blurred and indistinct. Fusions between chromosomes may lead to defective anaphase separation and the hourglass-shaped telophase chromatin masses seen soon after large doses of ionizing radiations (Carlson, 1941). A change in the prophase chromosomes from threads of uniform diameter to a moniliform shape accompanies ultraviolet-induced mitotic reversion at this stage.

Achromatic Figure and Cleavage. One of the striking effects of certain wave lengths of ultraviolet is their inhibitory action on spindle development (Nebel *et al.*, 1937; Carlson and Hollaender, 1948) and their destructive action on the fully formed spindle (Carlson and Hollaender, 1948). Ultraviolet of 2250 A acts on the spindle and its precursor, the karyolymph, in the grasshopper neuroblast very much as colchicine does (Gaulden and Carlson, 1951). If the spindle is not well formed, the karyolymph of the nucleus accumulates in one or more hyaline globules and the spindle remains small, the centromeres of the chromosomes being held in a compact group by the small spindle. Later, certain of these centromeres may move poleward along the spindle, but anaphase is not initiated until all have returned to the equatorial plate. Wave length 2804 A is equally effective in altering the spindle; wave lengths 2399, 2537, 2650, 2967, and 3022 A are less effective (Carlson and McMaster, unpublished). The action spectrum resembles, therefore, a protein absorption curve. Destruction of the spindle probably accounts for the binucleate cells observed by Takamine (1923) in *Allium* root tips 1 hour after treatment with 2500 A radiation.

Normally, in the grasshopper neuroblast, the cleavage furrow forms near one end of the elongated anaphase cell and the resulting daughter cells are unequal in size; the daughter neuroblast is large, while the

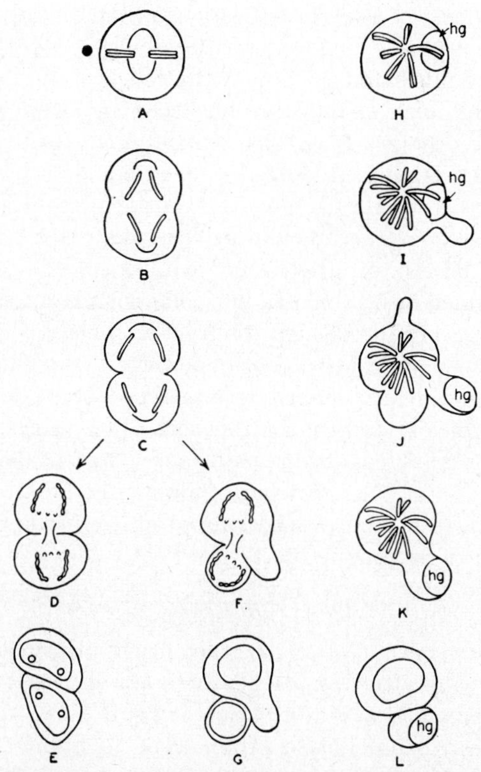

FIG. 11-17. Diagram showing ultraviolet-induced abnormalities in mitosis of the *Chortophaga* neuroblast. A-G, treatment at late metaphase or early anaphase; spindle abnormally short (A), cleavage furrow appears at cell equator (B, C) to give an equal division (D, E) or a secondarily produced unequal division (F, G). H-L, treatment at prometaphase or early metaphase with a dose sufficiently large to prevent centromere division and chromosome separation. Spindle greatly reduced, its substance mainly in the form of a hyaline globule (hg); note pseudopodia and distal separation of chromatids (I-K) (*from Carlson and Hollaender*, 1948).

daughter ganglion cell is small. The reduction in spindle size induced by 2250 A radiation is apparently correlated with a tendency of the cleavage furrow to form at the cell equator (Fig. 11-17) (Carlson and Hollaender, 1948). In many cells, as the cleavage furrow deepens, the bulk of the cytoplasm flows toward one of the poles, so that two more or less normal daughter cells of unequal size are formed. In some cells, however, no shift occurs and two cells approximately equal in size result. That this is caused by the reduced spindle size is evidenced by a similar phenomenon in colchicine-treated neuroblasts, in which the spindle is also reduced in size (Gaulden and Carlson, 1951). If the dose of radiation is large enough to damage the spindle to such an extent that the chromosome halves do not separate, even at the time when pseudopodia-like outpushings of the cell indicate the onset of telophase, the chromosomes may all be incorporated in a single nucleus. One of the pseudopodia is eventually cut off by a furrow from the nucleated portion of the cell.

Nucleolus. The form of the neuroblast can be altered drastically by all ultraviolet wave lengths from 2250 to 3130 A (Carlson and McMaster, 1951). This effect is studied most readily in hanging-drop preparations of the living cell. Normally the nucleolus of the neuroblast appears as an irregular mass of low refractility during interphase and most of the prophase. Within 25–35 minutes after irradiation the nucleolar mass becomes transformed into about ten nucleolar fragments, which gradually separate to form a cluster of highly refractile spherules. If the dose is large, these subsequently fuse to form fewer and larger spheres, until, ultimately, a single, clearly defined, spherical body results. If the dose is less than that sufficient to produce this series of changes, recovery by a return to the original condition may take place at any stage. The 2399–2804 A region of the spectrum is most effective in producing this change, which suggests that absorption by both protein and nucleic acid may be involved in its production.

VIABILITY EFFECTS

Few studies have been made on the capacity of ultraviolet radiations to kill animal cells soon after treatment; these are all based on mixed wave lengths and contain no exact information on the doses used. Politzer and Alberti (1924) described necrosis of the cells of the upper two layers of the cornea of salamander larvae 1 hour after ultraviolet irradiation. Möllendorff and Laqueur (1938) found that, after moderate doses, fibroblasts in culture recover and progress through mitosis normally, but after large doses they break down on attempting division at the end of the radiation-induced, mitosis-free period. They suggest that ultraviolet irradiation produces a toxic substance, which acts at the time of division to prevent the successful completion of mitosis. Buschke *et al.* (1945) recorded aggregation of nuclear chromatin in clumps, followed by fragmentation of nuclei within 6 hours of treatment, and finally complete destruction of the cells of the two uppermost layers of the rat cornea. Both low temperature and anaerobiosis, produced either by immersion of the enucleated eye in buffer solution without stirring or by maintaining it in a vacuum, caused a lag in the appearance of nuclear fragmentation. From this they concluded that cell disintegration resulting from ultraviolet irradiation depends on secondary intracellular processes that follow the treatment and that, at least in part, can be identified as oxidative ones.

REFERENCES

Alberti, M., and G. Politzer (1923) Über den Einfluss den Röntgenstrahlen auf die Zellteilung. Arch. Mikroskop. Anat. Entwicklungsmech., 100: 83–109.

——— and ——— (1924) Über den Einfluss der Röntgenstrahlen auf die Zellteilung. II. Mitteilung. Arch. Entwicklungsmech. Organ., 103: 284–307.

Blum, H. F., G. M. Loos, J. P. Price, and J. C. Robinson (1949) Enhancement of "visible" light recovery from ultra-violet irradiation in animal cells. Nature, 164: 1011.

———, ———, and J. C. Robinson (1950) The accelerating action of illumination in recovery of *Arbacia* eggs from exposure to ultraviolet radiation. J. Gen. Physiol., 34: 167–181.

——— and J. P. Price (1950) Delay of cleavage of the *Arbacia* egg by ultraviolet radiation. J. Gen. Physiol., 33: 285–304.

Buschke, W., J. S. Friedenwald, and S. G. Moses (1945) Effects of ultraviolet irradiation on corneal epithelium: Mitosis, nuclear fragmentation, post-traumatic cell movements, loss of tissue cohesion. J. Cellular Comp. Physiol., 26: 147–164.

Butler, E. G. (1932) On some cellular reactions to X-radiation. J. Exptl. Biol., 9: 107–116.

Cade, S. (1948) Malignant disease and its treatment by radium. The Williams & Wilkins Company, Baltimore.

Canti, R. G., and M. Donaldson (1926) The effect of radium on mitosis *in vitro*. Proc. Roy. Soc. (London), B100: 413–419.

——— and F. G. Spear (1927) The effect of gamma irradiation on cell division in tissue culture *in vitro*. Proc. Roy. Soc. (London), B102: 92–101.

——— and ——— (1929) The effect of gamma radiation on cell division in tissue culture *in vitro*. Part II. Proc. Roy. Soc. (London), B105: 93–98.

Carlson, J. G. (1940) Immediate effects of 250 r of X-rays on the different stages of mitosis in neuroblasts of the grasshopper, *Chortophaga viridifasciata*. J. Morphol., 66: 11–23.

——— (1941) Effects of X-radiation on grasshopper chromosomes. Cold Spring Harbor Symposia Quant. Biol., 9: 104–111.

——— (1942) Immediate effects of 31 r of X-rays on the different stages of mitosis in neuroblasts of *Chortophaga*. J. Morphol., 71: 449–460.

——— (1946) Protoplasmic viscosity changes in different regions of the grasshopper neuroblast during mitosis. Biol. Bull., 90: 109–121.

——— (1950) Effects of radiation on mitosis. J. Cellular Comp. Physiol., 35 (Suppl. 1): 89–102.

———, N. Harrington, and M. E. Gaulden (1953) Mitotic effects of prolonged irradiation with low-intensity gamma rays on the *Chortophaga* neuroblast. Biol. Bull., 104: 313–322.

——— and A. Hollaender (1944) Immediate effects of low doses of ultraviolet radiation of wavelength 2537 A on mitosis in the grasshopper neuroblast. J. Cellular Comp. Physiol., 23: 157–169.

——— and ——— (1945) Intensity effects of ultraviolet radiation of wavelength 2537 A on mitosis in the grasshopper neuroblast. J. Cellular Comp. Physiol., 26: 165–173.

——— and ——— (1948) Mitotic effects of ultraviolet radiation of the 2250 A region with special reference to the spindle and cleavage. J. Cellular Comp. Physiol., 31: 149–137.

——— and R. McMaster (1951) Nucleolar changes induced in the grasshopper neuroblast by different wavelengths of ultraviolet radiation and their capacity for photorecovery. Exptl. Cell. Research, 2: 434–444.

———, M. L. Snyder, and A. Hollaender (1949) Relation of gamma-ray dosage rate to mitotic effect in the grasshopper neuroblast. J. Cellular Comp. Physiol., 33: 365–372.

Cattley, R. (1909) Cytological changes produced by the action of X-rays on growing root tips of plants. J. Path. Bact., 13: 380–381.

Chase, H. Y. (1938) The effect of ultraviolet light upon cleavage in certain marine eggs. I. Some studies on cleavage rate. Biol. Bull., 75: 134–144.

Creighton, M. (1941) The effect of X-rays on mitotic and meiotic chromosomes and cell division in *Chorthippus longicornis* (Orthoptera). J. Exptl. Zoöl., 87: 347–369.

Crow, H. E. (1933) The effects of a minimal lethal dose of X-rays upon chick embryos. Kansas U. Sci. Bull., 21: 479–523.

Darlington, C. D. (1942) Chromosome chemistry and gene action. Nature, 149: 66–69.

——— and L. F. La Cour (1945) Chromosome breakage and the nucleic acid cycle. J. Genetics, 46: 180–267.

Deufel, J. (1951) Untersuchungen ueber die Einfluss von Chemikalien und Roentgenstrahlen auf die Mitose von *Vicia faba*. Chromosoma, 4: 239–272.

Duggar, B. M. (1936) Biological effects of radiation. McGraw-Hill Book Company, Inc., New York.

Duryee, W. R. (1939) Does the action of X-rays on the nucleus depend upon the cytoplasm? Biol. Bull., 77: 326.

——— (1947) The effect of X-rays on chromosomes and nucleoli in ovarian eggs of the salamander, *Triturus pyrrhogaster*. Biol. Bull., 93: 206–207.

——— (1949) The nature of radiation injury to amphibian cell nuclei. J. Natl. Cancer Inst., 10: 735–795.

——— (1950) Chromosomal physiology in relation to nuclear structure. Ann. N.Y. Acad. Sci., 50: 920–953.

Evans, T. C. (1947) Effects of hydrogen peroxide produced in the medium by radiation on spermatozoa of *Arbacia punctulata*. Biol. Bull., 92: 99–107.

———, J. C. Slaughter, E. P. Little, and G. Failla (1942) Influence of the medium on radiation injury of sperm. Radiology, 39: 663–680.

Friedenwald, J. S., W. Buschke, J. Crowell, and A. Hollaender (1948) Effects of ultraviolet irradiation on the corneal epithelium. II. Exposure to monochromatic radiation. J. Cellular Comp. Physiol., 32: 161–173.

Fry, H. J. (1936) Studies of the mitotic figure. V. The time schedule of mitotic changes in developing *Arbacia* eggs. Biol. Bull., 70: 89–99.

Gaulden, M. E., and J. G. Carlson (1951) Cytological effects of colchicine on the grasshopper neuroblast in vitro with special reference to the origin of the spindle. Exptl. Cell. Research, 2: 416–433.

———, M. Nix, and J. Moshman (1953) Effects of oxygen concentration on X-ray-induced mitotic inhibition in living *Chortophaga* neuroblasts. J. Cellular Comp. Physiol., 41: 451–470.

Giese, A. C. (1938a) The effects of ultraviolet radiation of 2537 A upon cleavage of sea urchin eggs. Biol. Bull., 74: 330–341.

——— (1938b) The effects of ultra-violet radiations of various wave-lengths upon cleavage of sea urchin eggs. Biol. Bull., 75: 238–247.

——— (1939a) Retardation of early cleavage of *Urechis* by ultraviolet light. Physiol. Zool., 12: 319–327.

———(1939b) Ultraviolet radiation and cell division. Nuclear sensitivity: effect of irradiation of sea urchin sperm. J. Cellular Comp. Physiol., 14: 371–382.

——— (1939c) Nuclear and cytoplasmic effects of ultraviolet light. Science, 89: 266–267.

——— (1946) Comparative sensitivity of sperm and eggs to ultraviolet radiations. Biol. Bull., 91: 81–87.

——— (1947) Radiations and cell division. Quart. Rev. Biol., 22: 253–282.

Glücksmann, A., and F. G. Spear (1939) The effect of gamma radiation on cells in vivo. Part II. 1. Single exposure of the fasting tadpole at room temperature. 2. Single exposures of the normal animal at low temperature. Brit. J. Radiology, 12: 486–498.

———, K. Tansley, and C. W. Wilson (1945) The effect of variations in the dosage-rate of gamma radiation on cell degeneration in the frog tadpole. Brit. J. Radiology, 18: 158–164.

Gray, L. H. (1946) Comparative studies of the biological effects of X rays, neutrons and other ionizing radiations. Brit. Med. Bull., 4: 11–18.

——— (1947) The distribution of the ions resulting from the irradiation of living cells. Brit. J. Radiology, Suppl. 1, pp. 7–15.

———, F. Ellis, G. C. Fairchild, and E. Paterson (1944) Dosage-rate in radiotherapy. Symposium. Brit. J. Radiology, 17: 327–342.

———, J. C. Mottram, J. Read, and F. G. Spear (1940) Some experiments upon the biological effects of fast neutrons. Brit. J. Radiology, 13: 371–388.

——— and J. Read (1942) The effect of ionizing radiations on the broad bean root. IV. The lethal effect of alpha radiations. Brit. J. Radiology, 15: 320–336.

——— and ——— (1950) The effect of ionizing radiations on the broad bean root. VII. The inhibition of mitosis by alpha radiation. Brit. J. Radiology, 23: 300–303.

——— and M. E. Scholes (1951) The effect of ionizing radiations on the broad bean root. VIII. Growth rate studies and histological analyses. Brit. J. Radiology, 24: 82–92, 176–180, 228–236, 285–291, 348–352.

Harrington, N. J., and R. W. Koza (1951) Effect of X-radiation on the desoxyribonucleic acid and on the size of grasshopper embryonic nuclei. Biol. Bull., 101: 138–150.

Heilbrunn, L. V., and R. A. Young (1935) Indirect effects of radiation on sea urchin eggs. Biol. Bull., 69: 274–278.

Henshaw, P. S. (1932) Studies of the effect of roentgen rays on the time of the first cleavage in some marine invertebrate eggs. I. Recovery from roentgen-ray effects in *Arbacia* eggs. Am. J. Roentgenol. Radium Therapy, 27: 890–898.

——— (1938) The action of X-rays on nucleated and non-nucleated egg fragments. Am. J. Cancer, 33: 258–264.

——— (1940a) Further studies on the action of roentgen rays on the gametes of *Arbacia punctulata.* I. Delay in cell division caused by exposure of sperm to roentgen rays. Am. J. Roentgenol. Radium Therapy, 43: 899–906.

——— (1940b) Further studies of the action of roentgen rays on the gametes of *Arbacia punctulata.* II. Modification of the mitotic time schedule in the eggs by exposure of the gametes to roentgen rays. Am. J. Roentgenol. Radium Therapy, 43: 907–912.

——— (1940c) Further studies on the action of roentgen rays on the gametes of *Arbacia punctulata.* V. The influence of low temperature on recovery from roentgen-ray effects in the eggs. Am. J. Roentgenol. Radium Therapy, 43: 921–922.

——— (1940d) Further studies on the action of roentgen rays on the gametes of *Arbacia punctulata.* VI. Production of multipolar cleavage in the eggs by exposure of the gametes to roentgen rays. Am. J. Roentgenol. Radium Therapy, 43: 923–933.

——— (1941) The induction of multipolar cell division with X-rays and its possible significance. Radiology, 36: 717–724.

——— and I. Cohen (1940) Further studies on the action of roentgen rays on the gametes of *Arbacia punctulata.* IV. Changes in radiosensitivity during the first cleavage cycle. Am. J. Roentgenol. Radium Therapy, 43: 917–920.

——— and D. S. Francis (1936) The effect of X-rays on cleavage in *Arbacia* eggs: evidence of nuclear control of division rate. Biol. Bull., 70: 28–35.

———, C. T. Henshaw, and D. S. Francis (1933) The effect of roentgen rays on the time of the first cleavage in marine invertebrate eggs. II. Differential recovery and its influence when different experimental methods are used. Radiology, 21: 533–544.

Hertel, E. (1905) Ueber die Einwirkung von Lichtstrahlen auf den Zellteilungsprozess. Z. allgem. Physiol., 5: 535–565.

Hevesy, G. (1945) On the effect of roentgen rays on cellular division. Rev. Mod. Phys., 17: 102–111.

Jüngling, O., and H. Langendorff (1930) Über die Wirkung verschieden hoher Röntgendosen auf den Kernteilungsablauf bei *Vicia faba* equina. Strahlentherapie, 38: 1–10.

Juul, J., and T. Kemp (1933) Über die Einfluss von Radium-und Röntgenstrahlen, ultraviolettem Licht und Hitze auf die Zellteilung bei warmblütigen Tieren. Studien on Gewebekulturen. Strahlentherapie, 48: 457–499.

Kemp, T., and J. Juul (1930) Influence of various agents (X-rays, radium, heat, ether) upon mitosis in tissue cultures. Acta Path. Microbiol. Scand., 7: 279–308.

——— and ——— (1932) Influence of ultraviolet rays upon mitosis in tissue cultures. Acta Path. Microbiol. Scand., 9: 222–235.

Knowlton, N. P., Jr., and L. H. Hempelmann (1949) The effect of X-rays on the mitotic activity of the adrenal gland, jejunum, lymph node and epidermis of the mouse. J. Cellular Comp. Physiol., 33: 73–91.

———, ———, and J. G. Hoffman (1948) The effects of X-rays on the mitotic activity of mouse epidermis. Science, 107: 625–626.

——— and W. R. Widner (1950) The use of X-rays to determine the mitotic and intermitotic time of various mouse tissues. Cancer Research, 10: 59–63.

Koller, P. C. (1943) The effects of radiation in pollen grain development, differentiation, and germination. Proc. Roy. Soc. Edinburgh, B61: 398–429.

La Cour, L. F. (1951) Combined effects of X-rays and temperature on mitosis. Nature, 167: 318–319.

Lasnitski, I. (1940) The effect of X-rays on cells cultivated *in vitro.* Brit. J. Radiology, 13: 279–284.

——— (1943a) The effect of X-rays on cells cultivated *in vitro.* Part II. Recovery factor. Brit. J. Radiology, 16: 61–67.

——— (1943b) The response of cells in vitro to variations in X-ray dosage. Brit. J. Radiology, 16: 137–141.

——— (1945) A quantitative analysis of the effect of gamma radiation on malignant cells *in vitro* and *in vivo.* Brit. J. Radiology, 18: 214–220.

——— (1946) The effect of dose rate variations on mitosis and degeneration in tissue cultures of avian fibroblasts. Brit. J. Radiology, 19: 250–256.

——— (1947) A quantitative analysis of the direct and indirect action of X-radiation on malignant cells. Brit. J. Radiology, 20: 240–247.

——— (1948) The effect of β rays on cells cultivated in vitro. Brit. J. Radiology, 21: 265–269.

——— and D. E. Lea (1940) The variation with wavelength of the biological effect of radiation. Brit. J. Radiology, 13: 149–162.

Lea, D. E. (1938a) A theory of the action of radiations on biological materials capable of recovery. Part I. The time-intensity factor. Brit. J. Radiology, 11: 489–497.

——— (1938b) A theory of the action of radiations on biological materials capable of recovery. Part II. Delay in cell division. Brit. J. Radiology, 11: 554–566.

——— (1946) Action of radiations on living cells. Cambridge University Press, Cambridge (also The Macmillan Company, New York, 1947).

Lewis, W. H., and M. R. Lewis (1917) The duration of the various phases of mitosis in the mesenchyme cells of tissue cultures. Anat. Record, 13: 359–367.

Lewitsky, G. A., and G. A. Araratian (1931) Transformations of chromosomes under the influence of X-rays. Bull. Appl. Botany, 27: 265–303.

Love, W. H. (1931) Some effects of X-radiation on dividing cells in tissue cultures. Parts I, II, III, IV. Arch. exptl. Zellforsch., 11: 435–447, 448–454, 455–462, 463–471.

Luther, W. (1943) Untersuchungen über die Wirkung von einzeitigen Röntgenbestrahlungen auf die Impfkarzionom der weissen Ratte. Strahlentherapie, 72: 679–696.

Mallet, L., and M. Perrot (1951) Effets mitotiques des radiations ionizatés sur le meristem d'Allium capa. J. radiol. électrol., 32: 497–498.

Marquardt, H. (1938) Die Röntgenpathologie der Mitose I und II. Z. Botan., 32: 401–482.

——— (1950) Neuere Auffassungen über einige Probleme aus der Pathologie der Kernteilung. Naturwissenschaften, 18: 416–424, 19: 433–438.

Marshak, A. (1937) The effect of X-rays on chromosomes in mitosis. Proc. Natl. Acad. Sci. U.S., 23: 362–369.

——— (1938) Alteration of chromosome sensitivity to X-rays with NH_4OH. Proc. Soc. Exptl. Biol. Med., 38: 705–713.

——— (1949) Recovery from ultra-violet induced delay in cleavage of *Arbacia* eggs by irradiation with visible light. Biol. Bull., 97: 315–322.

——— and M. Bradley (1944) X-ray inhibition of mitosis in relation to chromosome number. Proc. Natl. Acad. Sci. U.S., 30: 231–237.

Mayer, E., and H. Schreiber (1934) Die Wellenlängenabhängigkeit der Ultraviolettwirkung auf Gewebekulturen, Protoplasma, 21: 34–61.

Mitchell, J. S. (1942a) Disturbance of nucleic acid metabolism produced by therapeutic doses of X- and gamma-radiations. II. Accumulation of pentosenucleotides in cytoplasm after irradiation. Brit. J. Exptl. Path., 23: 296–308.

——— (1942b) Disturbance of nucleic acid metabolism produced by therapeutic doses of X- and γ-radiations. III. Inhibition of synthesis of thymonucleic acid by radiation. Brit. J. Exptl. Path., 23: 309–313.

——— (1943) Metabolic effects of therapeutic doses of X and gamma radiations. Brit. J. Radiology, 16: 339–343.

——— (1947) Experiments on the mechanism of the biological action of fast neutrons using the summation method for lethal effects in mice (with a section on dosimetry of fast neutrons). Brit. J. Radiology, 20: 368–380.

Miwa, M., H. Yamashita, and K. Mori (1939a) The action of ionizing rays on sea-urchin. I. The effects of roentgen, gamma and beta rays upon the unfertilized eggs and sperms. Gann, 33: 1–12.

———, ———, and ——— (1939b) The action of ionizing rays on sea urchin. IV. The effects of alpha rays upon fertilized eggs. Gann, 33: 323–330.

Möllendorff, W. V., and G. Laqueur (1938) Zur Kenntnis der Mitose. III. Über die Wirkung von ultravioletten Strahlen auf den Wachstumsrhythmus und auf die Zellteilung in Fibrozytenkulturen. Z. Zellforsch. u. mikroskop. Anat., 28: 310–340.

Mori, K., M. Miwa, and H. Yamashita (1939) The action of ionizing rays on sea urchin. III. Further observations on recovery phenomenon in the effects of beta rays upon fertilized eggs and sperm with some studies on the time factor problems. Gann, 33: 316–321.

Mottram, J. C. (1936) On the spacing of radiation according to variation in radiosensitivity. Brit. J. Radiology, 9: 824–832.

———, G. M. Scott, and S. Russ (1926) Effects of β-rays upon division and growth of cancer cells. Proc. Roy. Soc. (London), B100: 326–335.

Nebel, B. R., E. B. Harvey, and A. Hollaender (1937) The cytology of *Arbacia punctulata* activated by monochromatic ultraviolet radiation. Biol. Bull., 73: 365–366.

Packard, C. (1916) The effect of radium radiations on the rate of cell division. J. Exptl. Zool., 21: 199–212.

——— (1918) The effect of radium radiations on the development of *Chaetopterus*. Biol. Bull., 35: 50–70.

——— (1931) The biological effects of short radiations. Quart. Rev. Biol., 6: 253–280.

Paterson, Edith, and M. Thompson (1949) Effect of urethane combined with X-rays on chick fibroblasts. Nature, 163: 563.

Pekarek, J. (1927) Ueber den Einfluss der Roentgenstrahlen auf die Kern- and Zellteilung von *Vicia faba.* Planta, 4: 299–357.

Politzer, G., and W. Alberti (1924) Ueber die Einwirkung des ultravioletten Lichtes auf tierisches Gewebe. Z. Zellen-Gewebelehre, 1: 413–444.

Rajewsky, B., and M. Schön (1948) Naturforschung und Medizin in Deutschland. Dieterich'sche Verlagsbuchhandlung, Wiesbaden, 21.

Regaud, C., A. Lacassagne, and J. Jovin (1925) Lésions microscopiques déterminées par les rayons X dans l'embryon de poulet. Compt. rend. soc. biol., 93: 1587–1589.

Richards, A. (1915) The effect of X-rays on the rate of cell division in the early cleavage of *Planorbis*. Biol. Bull., 27: 67–96.

——— and D. J. Good (1919) Notes on the effect of X-radiation on the development of *Cumingia* eggs. Biol. Bull., 37: 209–221.

Rugh, R. (1949) Histological effects on the embryo following X-irradiation. J. Morphol., 85: 483–502.

——— (1950) The immediate and delayed morphological effect of X-radiations on meiotic chromosomes. J. Cellular Comp. Physiol., 36: 185–194.

Sax, K., and C. P. Swanson (1941) Differential sensitivity of cells to X-rays. Am. J. Botany, 28: 52–59.

Seide, J. (1925) Zur Kenntnis der biologischen Strahlenwirkung. Untersuchungen am Ascaris-Ei mit ultravioletten, Röntgen und Radiumstrahlen. Z. Wissensch. Zoöl., 124: 252–304.

Simon-Reuss, J., and F. G. Spear (1947) The effect of gamma radiation on mitosis in vitro. Brit. J. Radiology, 20: 63–70.

Sparrow, A. H. (1946) Reduced chromonema elongation and abnormal spiralization following X-ray treatment of meiotic chromosomes. Genetics, 30: 23.

——— and F. M. Rosenfeld (1946) X-ray-induced depolymerization of thymonucleohistone and of sodium thymonucleate. Science, 104: 245–246.

Spear, F. G. (1931) Immediate and delayed effects of radium (gamma rays) on tissue cultures in vitro. Brit. J. Radiology, 4: 146–165.

——— (1932) The effect of spaced radiation on tissue cultures in vitro. Proc. Roy. Soc. (London), B110: 224–234.

——— (1935) Tissue cultures. II, III. Its application to radiological research. Brit. J. Radiology, 8: 68–86, 280–297.

——— (1946) The biological effects of penetrating radiations. Brit. Med. Bull., 4: 2–11.

——— and A. Glücksmann (1938) The effect of gamma radiation on cells in vivo: single exposures of the normal tadpole at room temperature. Brit. J. Radiology, 11: 533–553.

——— and L. G. Grimmett (1933) The biological response to gamma rays of radium as a function of the intensity of radiation. Brit. J. Radiology, 6: 387–402.

——— and K. Tansley (1944) The action of neutrons on the developing rat retina. Brit. J. Radiology, 17: 374–379.

Stone, L. H. A. (1933) The effect of X-radiation on the meiotic and mitotic divisions of certain plants. Ann. Botany, 47: 815–826.

Strangeways, T. S. P. (1922) Observations on the changes seen in living cells during growth and division. Proc. Roy. Soc. (London), B94: 137–141.

——— and H. B. Fell (1927) A study of direct and indirect action of X-rays upon the tissues of the embryonic fowl. Proc. Roy. Soc. (London), B102: 9–29.

——— and F. L. Hopwood (1926) The effects of X-rays upon mitotic cell division in tissue cultures in vitro. Proc. Roy. Soc. (London), B100: 283–293.

——— and H. E. H. Oakley (1923) The immediate changes observed in tissue cells after exposure to soft X-rays while growing in vitro. Proc. Roy. Soc. (London), B95: 373–381.

Swanson, C. P. (1942) The effects of ultraviolet and X-ray treatment on the pollen tube chromosomes of *Tradescantia*. Genetics, 27: 491–503.

Takamine, N. (1923) On the effect of ultraviolet rays upon nuclear division of plants. Bot. Mag. Tokyo, 37: 109–113.

——— (1935) On the influence of ultraviolet rays upon the frequency of nuclear division in plants. Cytologia, 6: 444–456.

Tansley, K., L. H. Gray, and F. G. Spear (1948) A preliminary note on some biological effects of alpha radiation on the frog tadpole. Brit. J. Radiology, 21: 567–570.

———, F. G. Spear, and A. Glücksmann (1937) The effect of gamma rays on cell division in the developing rat retina. Brit. J. Ophthalmol., 21: 273–298.

Taylor, Babette, J. P. Greenstein, and A. Hollaender (1947) Effects of X-radiation on thymus nucleic acid. Science, 105: 263–264.

———, ———, and ——— (1948) Effects of X-radiation on sodium thymus nucleate. Arch. Biochem., 16: 19–31.

Warren, S. (1937) The effect of gamma radiation on mitosis. Am. J. Roentgenol. Radium Therapy, 38: 899–902.

——— (1942) Effects of radiation on normal tissues. I. Introduction. II. Effects on the cell. Arch. Pathol., 34: 443–450.

———, M. W. Holt, and S. C. Sommers (1951) Some early nuclear effects of ionizing radiation. Proc. Soc. Exptl. Biol. Med., 77: 288–291.

Wells, P. H., and A. C. Giese (1950) Photoreactivation of ultraviolet light injury in gametes of the sea urchin *Strongylocentrotus purpuratus*. Biol. Bull., 99: 163–172.

White, M. J. D. (1937) The effect of X-rays on the first meiotic division in three species of Orthoptera. Proc. Roy. Soc. (London), B124: 183–196.

Whiting, Anna R. (1945) Effects of X-rays on hatchability and on chromosomes of *Habrobracon* eggs treated in first meiotic prophase and metaphase. Am. Naturalist, 79: 193–227.

——— (1948) Incidence and origin of androgenetic males in X-rayed *Habrobracon* eggs. Biol. Bull., 95: 354–360.

Wilbur, K. M., and R. O. Recknagel (1943) The radiosensitivity of eggs of *Arbacia punctulata* in various salt solutions. Biol. Bull., 85: 193–200.

Wilson, C. W., A. F. Hughes, A. Glücksmann, and F. G. Spear (1935) Bestrahlungsversuche an Hühnerembryonen in vitro und in vivo mit Radiumgammastrahlen. Strahlentherapie, 52: 519–524.

Wright, G. P. (1925) The relative duration of the various phases of mitosis in chick fibroblasts cultivated in vitro. J. Roy. Microscop. Soc., 45: 414–417.

Yamashita, H., K. Mori, and M. Miwa (1939) The action of ionizing rays on sea urchin. II. The effects of roentgen, gamma, and beta rays upon the fertilized eggs. Gann, 33:117–121.

Zirkle, R. E. (1936) Modification of radiosensitivity by means of readily penetrating acids and bases. Am. J. Roentgenol. Radium Therapy, 35: 230–237.

———, P. C. Aebersold, and E. R. Dempster (1937) The relative effectiveness of fast neutrons and X-rays upon different organisms. Am. J. Cancer, 29: 556–562.

Manuscript received by the editor Nov. 23, 1951

CHAPTER 12

Genetic Effects of Radiation in Mammals[1]

W. L. Russell

Biology Division, Oak Ridge National Laboratory

Introduction: Effect of radiation on reproduction. Dominant lethals, semilethals, and subvitals: Offspring of presterile-period matings of irradiated males—Offspring of irradiated females—Offspring of poststerile-period matings of irradiated males—Sex ratio. Dominant sterility. Dominant partial sterility. Dominant visibles. Recessive lethals, semilethals, and viables. Human hazards. References.

INTRODUCTION

Most of the information on the genetic effects of radiation in mammals has come from work on the mouse. The small amount of data obtained from rats, rabbits, and guinea pigs is, in general, confirmatory of the results on mice. The only form of ionizing radiation that has been used extensively is X radiation. There is a little information from limited investigations with neutrons and γ rays.

Short general review articles have been presented by Snell (1941b) and Russell (1952). The paper by Lea (1947) includes a review of the work on dominant lethals and hereditary partial sterility. Methods for the detection of mutations in mammals have been discussed by Hertwig (1932), Snell (1935, 1945), Catcheside (1947), Falconer (1949), and Russell (1951, 1952).

Mutations are commonly divided into two categories, chromosomal and point mutations, according to whether or not a structural change in the chromosomes can be detected. Whether radiation-induced point mutations include gene mutations, or represent only certain types of chromosomal change, is still debated. Regardless of its exact nature, the distinction between chromosomal and point mutations has proved to be descriptively useful in *Drosophila*. In this organism, where observation of the fine details of chromosome structure is possible, and where the chromosomes are so thoroughly marked genetically, even minute structural changes in chromosomes can be detected, and the level below which they would no longer be apparent is sharply definable. In mammals, the

[1] Work at Oak Ridge and preparation of manuscript under Contract No. W-7405-eng-26 for the Atomic Energy Commission.

available cytological and genetic tests for structural chromosomal changes are far less critical. The category "point mutations," or mutations in which structural change has not been detected, is not, therefore, a particularly useful one in mammals at the present time. In this chapter, mutations are classified according to their dominance relations and phenotypic effects. Wherever there is proof, or evidence, that a chromosomal change is involved, this is, of course, discussed.

Effect of Radiation on Reproduction. In investigating the genetic results of radiation in mammals the experimental procedures are in some respects limited, and in others aided, by the effects of the radiation on the reproduction of the exposed animals. It is desirable, therefore, to give an outline of these effects before considering the results of genetic studies. Furthermore, the two subjects are not unrelated: some of the effects on reproduction are themselves the result of damage to the genetic material of the germ cells.

The procedure used in most genetic studies has been the exposure of males to a single, high intensity dose of X rays. Considering, first, the effects on reproduction of this treatment, it is now well established by the results of many investigators that within the range of approximately 400–1000 r, the limits depending on the species and on other factors, a period of fertility immediately following irradiation is succeeded by an interval of sterility after which fertility returns. A sample of data on the lengths of the initial fertile period and the temporary sterile period is given in Table 12-1. The length of the initial fertile period is probably underestimated in some of the experiments because of its dependence on number of copulations (Snell, 1933b; Brenneke, 1937; Hertwig, 1938a), or because of insufficient testing of males. The data are erratic and there is no clear-cut dependence on dose. The length of the sterile period, however, is apparently affected by dose. This conclusion is confirmed by the findings of Strandskov (1932) who showed that the length of time during which no motile sperm were present in electrically induced ejaculations of guinea pigs was related to the dose received by the males. Litter size in the first fertile period is reduced and is related to dose. After the sterile period the litter size is probably slightly below normal, but so close to it that a difference is hard to establish. Details on litter size are presented later.

For doses below about 400 r there is no clear-cut period of complete sterility. As the dose increases above 1000 r the litter size in the period immediately following irradiation reduces toward zero, most matings producing no young at all. At very high doses it appears that some permanent sterility is induced (Table 12-2), but whether this results from direct damage to the testis or from the systemic effects, which are noticeable even with the partial-body irradiation, is not known. In either case, there appear to be differences in response attributable to the strains of

TABLE 12-1. MAXIMUM LENGTH OF INITIAL FERTILE PERIOD AND MINIMUM LENGTH OF TEMPORARY STERILE PERIOD OF MALES EXPOSED TO VARIOUS DOSES OF RADIATION

(The results shown for each group are the extreme values, not the means)

Reference	Species	Radiation	Whole- or part-body	Dose, r	Presterile-period matings		Poststerile-period matings	
					No. ♂♂	Days after irrad. of last fertile mating	No. ♂♂	Interval between last presterile- and first poststerile-period mating
Snell (1933b)	Mouse	X rays	P	600	...	.....	1	20 weeks
			P	800	?	16–18	1	10 weeks
Brenneke (1937)	Mouse	X rays	P	800	13	16		
			P	1400	2	11		
			P	1800	2	13		
			P	2200	2	11		
	Rat	X rays	P	800	5	19		
			P	1400	3	15		
			P	1800	4	15		
Hertwig (1938a)	Mouse	X rays	P	400	...	.....	10	1 month
			P	500	...	.....	5	2½–3 months
			P	600	...	.....	10	2½–3 months
			P	800	?	20–25	36	2½–3 months
			P	1000	...	.....	36	2½–3 months
			P	1200	...	.....	6	2½–3 months
			P	1500	...	.....	21	3–5 months
Russell *et al.*[a]	Mouse	X rays	W	500	4	21	4	8 weeks
			W	600	378	27	78	4½ weeks
			W	800	2	12–14	6	10 weeks
			P	1000	4	13	21	11 weeks
Snell and Aebersold (1937)	Mouse	Neutrons	P	110–160 "r"[b]	9	20	5	10 weeks

[a] Unpublished data of W. L. Russell, Josephine S. Gower, Gloria J. Jasny, and J. C. Kile.

[b] Cyclotron neutrons measured on r scale of Victoreen condenser-type dosimeter.

mice used, or to other variables in experimental conditions, for it can be seen from Table 12-2 that the data of Hertwig show appreciable incidences

TABLE 12-2. INCIDENCE OF PERMANENT STERILITY IN MALE MICE EXPOSED TO VARIOUS DOSES OF X RADIATION

Reference	Dose, r	Whole- or part-body irrad.	No. ♂♂ tested	Permanently sterile	
				Number	Per cent
Hertwig (1938a).....	400	P	10	0	0.0
	500	P	5	0	0.0
	600	P	10	1	10.0
	800	P	36	5	13.9
	1000	P	36	11	30.6
	1200	P	6	2	33.3
	1500	P	21	17	81.0
	3000–4000	P	5	5	100.0
Russell *et al.*[a]........	500	W	4	0	0.0
	[600	W	1717	2 + 2?[b]	0.12–0.23
	[Control	..	1134	3 + 1?[b]	0.26–0.35
	800	W	6	0	0.0
	[1000	P	414	3?[c]	0.00–0.72
	[Control	..	392	2 + 2?[c]	0.51–1.02

[a] Unpublished data of W. L. Russell, Josephine S. Gower, Gloria J. Jasny, and J. C. Kile.

[b] Died less than twelve weeks after mating and tested against only one female each.

[c] Tested against only one female each.

of permanent sterility with doses of 1000 r and below, while those of Russell *et al.* show no difference from the controls even with 1000 r.

Up to the dose level above which breeding experiments become impracticable, no effects on the viability or motility of mature sperm have been observed. In electrically induced ejaculations from guinea pigs, Strandskov (1932) found motile sperm up to four weeks following exposure to 2592 r of X rays. Snell (1933b) performed a bilateral vasa efferentia ligation on six mice and irradiated three of them with 800 r of X rays. There was no difference between the irradiated and nonirradiated animals in length of survival of motile sperm in the epididymides.

The testis was one of the first organs studied histologically for the effects of X rays and has since been the object of numerous investigations. The references cited, particularly Schinz and Slotopolski (1925) and Glücksmann (1947), may be used as an introduction to the voluminous literature which can be only briefly summarized here. Hertwig (1938b) and Schaefer (1939) have studied the subject with particular regard to its bearing on genetic problems. There is now almost unanimous agreement that spermatocytes, spermatids, and sperm, along with Sertoli cells and interstitial tissue, are resistant to radiation, and that spermatogonia are quite sensitive.[2] Reduction in numbers is found first in the spermatogonia. The later germ cell stages disappear in the order in which they are formed in spermatogenesis and at approximately the same rate as that of the spermatogonial disappearance (Hertwig, 1938b; Eschenbrenner and Miller, 1950; Fogg and Cowing, 1951a, b). As there is evidence that the spermatocytes and spermatids present at the time of irradiation complete their development (Schaefer, 1939; Eschenbrenner and Miller, 1950), the disappearance of these classes is attributable to failure of replacement by the depleted spermatogonia. Since Fogg and Cowing (1951a, b, 1952) nowhere mention this commonly accepted view, and even wrongly imply that Eschenbrenner and Miller adopted another explanation, it must be concluded that their own suggestion, that the progressive disappearance of later stages reflects a delay in response to irradiation correlated with cell specialization, was made in unawareness of the consequence of loss of spermatogonia. The number of spermatogonia rapidly reaches a minimum. The reduction in number was measured, in mice, by Hertwig (1938b) for a dose of 800 r, by Eschenbrenner and Miller (1950) for 400 r and, less quantitatively, by Fogg and Cowing (1951a, b) for other doses (Table 12-3). The number of sperma-

TABLE 12-3. REDUCTION IN NUMBER OF SPERMATOGONIA IN MICE EXPOSED TO VARIOUS DOSES OF X RAYS

Reference	Dose, r	Days after irradiation when minimum number of spermatogonia observed	Number of cross sections of tubules examined	Per cent of cross sections showing any spermatogonia[b]	Per cent of normal number of spermatogonia
Fogg and Cowing (1951a)	300	7	1000	10	
Eschenbrenner and Miller (1950)	400	7[a]	....	..	1.5[c]
Hertwig (1938b)	800	4–6	59	14	0.76[d]
Fogg and Cowing (1951b)	1440	10	200	1	

[a] No observation made at earlier time.

[b] Fogg and Cowing state that normal testis shows spermatogonia in 80 per cent of cross sections of tubules.

[c] Based on reduction of resting spermatogonia to 3.3 per cent and of mitotic spermatogonia to 0 per cent. Eschenbrenner, Miller, and Lorenz (1948) give the ratio of these two types in testes of unirradiated mice of similar age as 8.9 : 11.1.

[d] Hertwig found a total of 9 spermatogonia in the 59 cross sections examined and states that a cross section of a tubule of a normal testis contains 20 spermatogonia.

togonia then increases, and eventually the later germ cell stages reappear in the order in which they disappeared (Hertwig, 1938b; Eschenbrenner and Miller, 1950; Fogg and Cowing, 1951a, b). The time taken, from the

[2] Unpublished data, obtained by E. F. Oakberg at this laboratory since this manuscript was submitted, show that primary spermatocytes, as well as spermatogonia, show appreciable sensitivity to radiation.

first reappearance of mitotic spermatogonia to the production of sperm, is approximately four weeks in the mouse. The interesting results of Howard and Pelc (1950), who used autoradiographs, following P^{32} injection, to measure the times taken by various stages of spermatogenesis in the mouse, show that the interval from spermatogonial metaphase to immature sperm is more than 10 days.

The surviving cells have been referred to as spermatogonia. This is the view taken by most authors, including Hertwig (1938b) who identifies the cells as spermatogonia with "dusty," pale, oval nuclei. Other interpretations are mentioned by Hertwig. Among the spermatogonia there is great variety in size and appearance of nuclei. The frequencies of these types at various intervals after irradiation, together with interpretations of what stages in spermatogonial divisions the types represent, are also presented by Hertwig.

From the histological observations it appears that matings made in the initial period of fertility following irradiation utilize sperm that were mature at the time of irradiation, and that copulations occurring in the latter part of the period may use some sperm that matured from cells that were spermatids or spermatocytes when irradiated. The period of temporary sterility corresponds to the interval in which replacement of later germ cell stages has not yet been completed owing to the depletion of spermatogonia. Matings made after the sterile period use sperm that were in the spermatogonial stage at the time of irradiation. The sterile period is thus a useful marker for separating genetic changes induced in spermatogonia from those induced in later germ cell stages. The reduction in litter size in the initial fertile period is not accounted for by the histological findings described above, but is explained by the results described in the next section.

The breeding results and histological changes in the gonads following exposure to neutrons or γ rays, and following the use of X rays on females, will be described only briefly since these treatments have had only limited use in genetic studies.

Snell and Aebersold (1937) have shown that the effects on reproduction, following a single exposure of male mice to cyclotron neutrons, are similar to those produced by X rays. However, measured on the roentgen scale of a Victoreen condenser-type dosimeter, neutrons are from five to six times as potent as X rays in reducing the litter size in pre-sterile-period matings.

The effects on the gonads and on fertility of long exposure to low intensity γ radiation have been described by Lorenz *et al.* (1947) and Eschenbrenner *et al.* (1948). Vigorous hybrid male mice exposed to a total dose of 1100 r at 8.8 r per day from a radium source and then removed from the radiation field gave litters of reduced size in early matings and normal litters later. Those exposed to 1760 r at the same rate were sterile at first, but recovered fertility after two months. Exposure to 1100 r at 4.4 r per day did not affect fertility. Hybrid females exposed to total doses of from 770 to 880 r, regardless of rate, and then mated, were either sterile or became so after the production of one, or rarely two, litters of reduced size. When inbred strains were used instead of hybrids, the same effects in males and females were produced at lower doses. Histological observations on the testis showed reduction in spermatogenic elements to stable levels which were dependent on dose rate. The relative proportions of the cell types were, however, normal except in males exposed to 8.8 r per day. In these animals, after ten months, the sperm were relatively few in number and multinucleated spermatids were common. Eschenbrenner *et al.* suggest that these effects resulted from the degeneration of Sertoli cells which was observed only in this material.

Acute X-ray exposure of female mice with a dose of 150 r, or perhaps lower, results in permanent sterility. One, and occasionally two, litters can be obtained, even at much higher doses, before the sterility sets in. The figures, 800 to 1500 r, given by Glücksmann (1947) as the permanent sterilizing dose for the female mouse and rat are too high by a factor of about 10, and are perhaps either a misprint or refer to the dose at which even the temporary fertility following irradiation is suppressed. The litter size in this temporary fertile period is reduced, and Snell and Ames (1939) report that it falls off more rapidly with increasing dose than does the litter size from irradiated males.

DOMINANT LETHALS, SEMILETHALS, AND SUBVITALS

For purposes of discussion here, lethals are defined as mutations that cause death usually before birth, semilethals as those which cause death usually between birth and reproductive age, and subvitals as mutations that sometimes cause death.

Offspring of Presterile-period Matings of Irradiated Males. Radiation-induced dominant lethal effects in mammals were reported as early as 1908 by Regaud and Dubreuil who observed a high proportion of abnormal embryos in rabbits sired by males that had been exposed to X rays. It was not until many years later, however, that it became probable, and was finally demonstrated, that induced chromosomal aberrations are a cause of this class of abnormalities. Strandskov (1932) found a markedly reduced litter size in the immediate progeny of X-rayed male guinea pigs. Since electrically induced ejaculations showed numerous motile sperm during the times the litters were produced, Strandskov assumed that the normal number of eggs was fertilized, but that some were later resorbed. He cited the results of Regaud and Dubreuil, and similar findings in amphibia, in support of the view that some embryos died.

He concluded: "The most plausible interpretation seems to be the induction of dominant lethal mutations." Snell (1932, 1933b), working on mice, also found a reduction in litter size in early matings of X-irradiated males and no effect on motility of sperm. In the same material he found that many embryos died usually at, or shortly after, implantation. He also demonstrated the presence of both male and female pronuclei in all of fourteen eggs fixed and sectioned 16 hours after impregnation. Snell concluded that the reduction in litter size, caused by the death of embryos, is most plausibly explained by the induction of chromosome abnormalities. Final proof of the correctness of the interpretations of Strandskov and Snell was provided by Hertwig (1935), Hertwig and Brenneke (1937) and Brenneke (1937). In the first place, it was demonstrated that fertilizing capacity of mouse and rat sperm is unaltered even by high doses. Table 12-4 shows the results obtained for doses up to

TABLE 12-4. LACK OF EFFECT OF RADIATION ON THE PERCENTAGE OF UNFERTILIZED EGGS IN PRESTERILE-PERIOD MATINGS OF X-IRRADIATED MALE MICE AND RATS
(Data from Brenneke, 1937)

Species	Dose, r	No. of eggs examined	Unfertilized		$Prob._{Diff.}$
			Number	Per cent[a]	
Mouse	800	447	24	5.37	
	1400	134	8	5.97	
	1800	171	14	8.19	
	2200	95	3	3.16	
	Total irrad.	847	49	5.79	0.14
	Control	158	14	8.86	
Rat	800	288	14	4.86	
	1400	186	10	5.38	
	1800	54	7	12.96	
	Total irrad.	528	31	5.87	0.64
	Control	106	5	4.72	

[a] Percentages given in Brenneke's table have been changed to agree with the numbers given by her.

2200 r in the mouse and 1800 r in the rat. Hertwig and Brenneke (1937) state that even with 4000 r, the highest dose used, there was still no effect on fertilizing ability of mouse sperm. Second, the authors showed that as soon as the eggs cleave, differences between experimentals and controls become apparent. Supernumerary nuclei were found sometimes in the blastomeres of the two-cell stage and more often in the cells of later stages. In metaphase of cleavage mitoses, portions of chromatin lying away from the equatorial plate could be found, and, in anaphase, lagging chromosomes were observed. Amoroso and Parkes (1947), using arti-

TABLE 12-5. LITTER SIZE IN PRESTERILE-PERIOD MATINGS OF IRRADIATED MALES

Reference	Species	Radiation	Dose, r	Early matings[a]		Late matings[a]		Total		
				No. of litters	Mean litter size	No. of litters	Mean litter size	No. of litters	Mean litter size	Per cent of control litter size
Strandskov (1932)	Guinea pig	Control	...	...	....	...	....	140	2.69	
	Guinea pig	X rays	173–2592	...	....	...	....	23	1.70	63
Snell (1933b)	Mouse	Control	...	...	....	...	....	24	7.71	
	Mouse	X rays	200	...	....	...	....	2	5.50	71
	Mouse	X rays	400	...	....	...	....	5	4.20	54
	Mouse	X rays	600	...	....	...	....	12	3.25	42
	Mouse	X rays	800	27	2.85	12	2.17	39	2.64	34
	Mouse	X rays	1200	...	....	...	....	3	1.33	17
Rokizky[b]	Rabbit	Control	...	...	....	...	....	?	7.71	
	Rabbit	X rays	500	...	....	...	....	?	4.38	57
Hertwig (1938a)	Mouse	Control	...	...	....	...	....	472	5.54	
	Mouse	X rays	200	4	6.00	3	4.00	7	5.14	93
	Mouse	X rays	400	17	4.29	7	4.29	24	4.29	77
	Mouse	X rays	500	11	4.45	2	4.00	13	4.38	79
	Mouse	X rays	600	17	2.71	3	2.67	20	2.70	49
	Mouse	X rays	800	69	2.45	38	1.76	107	2.21	40
	Mouse	X rays	1000	34	2.12	7	1.43	41	2.00	36
	Mouse	X rays	1200–1400	6	1.67	1	1.00	7	1.57	28
Snell and Aebersold (1937)	Mouse	Control	...	...	....	...	....	9	8.44	
	Mouse	Neutrons	110–160 "r"[c]	6	5.00	8	1.75	14	3.14	37
Henson (1942)	Rat	Control	...	...	....	...	....	33	7.67	
	Rat	X rays	100	...	....	...	....	7	6.71	88
	Rat	X rays	500	...	....	...	....	2	6.00	78
	Rat	X rays	1000	...	....	...	....	10	4.30	56
Russell *et al.*[d]	Mouse	Control	...	...	....	...	....	670	5.70	
	Mouse	X rays	600	163	3.40	182	3.97	345	3.70	65

[a] Early and late matings in Snell's X-ray data are respectively 1–6 and 7–15 days after irradiation, in Hertwig's data are 1–8 days and 8–14 days, in Snell's neutron data are 1 week and 2–3 weeks, and in the data of Russell *et al.* are 1–7 and 8–14 days.

[b] As quoted by Brenneke (1937).

[c] Cyclotron neutrons measured on r scale of Victoreen condenser-type dosimeter.

[d] Unpublished data of W. L. Russell, Josephine S. Gower, and Mary H. Major.

ficial insemination of rabbit spermatozoa irradiated in vitro, have confirmed both the lack of effect of high doses on fertilizing capacity of sperm and the occurrence of blastomeres with supernumerary nuclei.

Turning to some of the details of the experimental findings, data for effect on litter size in presterile-period matings of irradiated males are given in Table 12-5. The litter sizes are based on the numbers of litters actually born. This underestimates the effect of radiation, particularly at higher doses, because some pregnancies, the proportion increasing with dose, fail to produce any young at term. Even without this correction, the data in Table 12-5 clearly show that litter size is dependent on dose. An effect of dose on litter size is also indicated in the few litters allowed to go to term in the work of Amoroso and Parkes (1947) on artificial insemination of rabbit spermatozoa irradiated in vitro. In the data of both Snell and Hertwig, the reduction in litter size is greater for the later matings within the presterile period. The proportion of pregnancies that fail to reach term is, according to Hertwig (1938a), also greater in the later matings. Although the results of Russell *et al.* do not show a greater drop in litter size in the later matings, it should be pointed out that they were obtained from an experiment in which each male was mated to only one female in each of the two weeks and, therefore, possibly expended his store of sperm at a slower rate than that occurring in the experiments of Snell and Hertwig. The data of Brenneke (1937) show that the proportion of eggs having abnormal cleavages may increase both with number of matings and time. These data also provide the most direct evidence that the increased effect in later matings is attributable to a higher incidence of dominant lethals.

Information on the time of death of the embryos carrying dominant lethals is given in Table 12-6. Additional information is provided by the studies of Brenneke (1937) on the proportion of abnormal cleavages found at various times after fertilization. Brenneke's results for 800 r showed abnormality in 23.2 per cent of 186 two-cell stages, 44.4 per cent of 90 three- to six-cell stages and 41.9 per cent of 105 seven- to twelve-cell stages. Because of the possibility of further cleavage of some of the abnormal embryos found at any one stage, the total percentage of abnormality cannot be accurately estimated from these data. However, it is clearly higher than the percentage of preimplantation death estimated from the 800 r data of Snell and of Russell *et al.* If the difference proves to be real, it would indicate that some of the embryos showing abnormal cleavages actually survive to implantation. Most of the dominant lethal types that survive to implantation were found by Snell to die shortly thereafter. This appeared to be true in the material of Russell *et al.*, but, with the females opened at a later stage in pregnancy, the time of death could not be accurately determined. Henson found degeneration occurring shortly after implantation in six of eleven rat embryos examined on the eighth or ninth day of pregnancy of females mated to males exposed to 1000 r. There is some evidence, from a comparison of implantation data for 1200 r with the two sets of data for 800 r (Table 12-6), that the effect of raising the dose is to increase the ratio of preimplantation to postimplantation death; for, although no controls are given for the 1200 r data, the low mean number of implantations indicates a high incidence of preimplantation death. This effect of an increase in dose, as Lea (1947) pointed out, could be attributed to more of the sperm carrying more than one lethal chromosome change and to this resulting in a relatively greater death in early stages. The data of Amoroso and Parkes (1947) on irradiation of rabbit spermatozoa in

TABLE 12-6. TIME OF DEATH OF EMBRYOS CARRYING X-RAY-INDUCED DOMINANT LETHALS

Reference	Species	Dose to ♂♂, r	No. pregnant ♀♀	Day after fertilization when ♀♀ dissected	Mean no. implants per pregnancy			Estimated per cent of induced death occurring before implantation
					Living embryos	Dead embryos and resorption sites	Total	
Snell (1933b)	Mouse	Control	9	5–11	7.22	0.33	7.56[a]	
	Mouse	800	8	5–11	2.63	3.88	6.50[a]	23
Brenneke (1937)	Mouse	1200	19	9–13	0.74	3.05	3.79	
Henson (1942)	Rat	Control	5	8–14	....	....	9.00	
	Rat	1000	8	8–14	....	....	7.13	
Russell *et al.* (1951)	Mouse	Control	47	16–18	8.19	0.98	9.17	
	Mouse	800	50	16–18	3.92	3.64	7.56	38

[a] Excludes an insignificant proportion of unclassified embryos.

vitro show that, when very high doses are given to the sperm, death of embryos takes place still earlier in preimplantation development.

The exact nature of the chromosomal aberrations that cause dominant lethality in mammals is not known. Snell (1933b) pointed out that his data, Table 12-5, fit the interpretation that litter size falls off logarithmically with dose. This would be expected if the dominant lethals were the result of single-hit effects. However, the data are not extensive enough to warrant definite conclusions on the relation of lethality to dose. It is difficult to obtain accurate information on this relation because with increasing dose there is an increasing proportion of fertile matings that produce no young at term and possibly an increasing proportion of stillbirths, some of which may be missed. The cytological observations of Brenneke (1937) and Amoroso and Parkes (1947), as far as they go, strengthen the view that dominant lethals in the mouse and rat are analogous to those of *Drosophila*. The much higher rate of induction in mammals than in *Drosophila* would be expected from the larger number of chromosomes. Lea (1947) has speculated on the frequency of chromosome breakage that would account for the observed results. The higher frequency of dominant lethals in offspring of later matings within the presterile period was attributed by Hertwig (1938a) to fertilizations by germ cells that had been irradiated in prespermatozoal stages which were assumed to be more sensitive. Although the observed frequency of major chromosomal disturbances is adequate to account for most of the radiation-induced reduction in litter size, it is, however, possible that dominant lethal, or subvital, point mutations also occur and contribute a small portion of the cause of death of embryos.

The percentage of stillborn offspring from presterile-period matings of irradiated males is higher than in the controls in the data of both Snell (1933b) and Hertwig (1938a). However, both authors believe that much of this effect is not due to genetic damage in the stillborns, but to difficulties of parturition when litter size is small and the young consequently bigger at birth. Snell provides evidence for this by showing that the percentage of stillbirths is higher for the smaller litter sizes within one dose group. In guinea pigs, Strandskov (1932) found no significant difference between presterile-period matings and controls in percentage of stillbirths. In the guinea pig, the normal litter size is much lower (2.79 in Strandskov's material) than in the mouse, so there is presumably less likelihood of parturition difficulties resulting from a reduction in litter size. Among the stillborns found by Hertwig and Snell there were, however, a few pathological cases that could hardly be accounted for by difficulties in parturition. These indicate that, as would be expected, at least a portion of the stillbirths are the result of chromosomal aberrations or dominant point mutations in the affected individuals. It is clear, however, that, because of the difficulty of distinguishing between internal and external causes of death, stillbirths are particularly unsuitable material for the estimation of mutation rates.

Hertwig (1938a) found a significantly higher percentage of death between birth and 75 days of age in the offspring of presterile-period matings than in the controls. The percentage of death was greater for later than for earlier matings within the presterile period. Autopsies did not reveal the causes of death, but retarded growth was a frequent characteristic of the animals that died. Strandskov (1932) found a slight, but insignificant, increase in death in the 0- to 30-day age interval in progeny of presterile-period matings of irradiated male guinea pigs. The mean 30-day weight of the survivors was lower than that of the controls, especially after correction for litter size. This is all the more striking in view of the fact that the mean 0-day weight of these same animals, i.e., of those raised to 30 days, was actually, though not significantly, higher than the controls in both the uncorrected and corrected figures. In 102 offspring of matings made within three weeks after exposure of male rats to doses of from 100 to 1000 r, Henson (1942) was able to raise only 46 per cent to weaning as against 79 per cent of 96 controls. An effect of radiation on postnatal viability is also indicated in the few litters allowed to come to term in the work of Amoroso and Parkes (1947) on irradiation of rabbit spermatozoa in vitro. Thus the data so far obtained indicate an appreciable manifestation of dominant, deleterious, postnatal effects in offspring of presterile-period matings of irradiated males. The relative importance of chromosomal aberrations and of semilethal and subvital point mutations as causes of the postnatal mortality is not known.

Offspring of Irradiated Females. Information on the radiation induction of dominant lethals in females does not go beyond the observation of a reduction in litter size. Snell and Ames (1939) state that, as the dose is increased, litter size in the mouse falls off more rapidly for females than for males, and they attribute the greater effect to a radiation damage of the mother which interferes with development of the young. Another factor that should be kept in mind is that, as the second maturation division of oogenesis in the mouse is not completed until after fertilization, the germ cells in the female are irradiated in oocyte stage. The results obtained may, on this account alone, prove to be different from those observed for irradiated sperm.

Offspring of Poststerile-period Matings of Irradiated Males. In contrast to the marked effect of irradiation of the male on litter size in presterile-period matings, there is little reduction in litter size in matings made in the poststerile period (Table 12-7). The germ cells utilized in poststerile-period matings received the radiation in spermatogonial stages. There is no reason to doubt that dominant lethals are induced in spermatogonia, but, as suggested by Strandskov (1932), it is quite likely that many of them would fail to pass through the cell divisions between spermatogonia and sperm. Chromosome aberrations of the types which, when induced in sperm, cause breakdown in early cleavages would seem to be especially subject to elimination by germinal selection if they are induced in spermatogonia. That such elimination is occurring is suggested by the observed reduction in number of spermatogonia following irradiation. Schinz and Slotopolski (1925), Hertwig (1938b) and Fogg and Cowing (1952) have reported finding degenerating cells at short intervals after irradiation. The fact that Eschenbrenner and Miller (1950) found little evidence of degenerating spermatogonia at later times (one week or more) after irradiation of mice with 400 r hardly justifies the authors' conclusion that the effect on the spermatogonia "is not one of cell death but is one of inhibition of division." There may well be some inhibition of mitosis, but it is difficult to see how this could result in a reduction in number of spermatogonia to 1.5 per cent of normal. The results of Eschenbrenner and Miller perhaps indicate not the absence of killing, but rather the rapid disappearance of degenerating cells. This would also explain the fact that the number of degenerating cells found by those investigators who have reported seeing them is not high enough, at any one time, to account for the magnitude of the reduction in number of spermatogonia.

TABLE 12-7. LITTER SIZE IN POSTSTERILE-PERIOD MATINGS OF IRRADIATED MALES

Reference	Species	Radiation	Dose, r	No. of litters	Mean litter size	Per cent of control litter size
Strandskov (1932)	Guinea pig	Control	....	140	2.69	
	Guinea pig	X rays	173–2592	62	2.16	80
Snell (1933b)	Mouse	Control	....	24	7.71	
	Mouse	X rays	600–800	4	8.00	104
Hertwig (1938a)	Mouse	Control	....	472	5.54	
	Mouse	X rays	200	13	5.24	95
	Mouse	X rays	400	78	5.42	98
	Mouse	X rays	500	30	5.67	102
	Mouse	X rays	600	36	4.86	88
	Mouse	X rays	800	136	5.06	91
	Mouse	X rays	1000	110	5.36	97
	Mouse	X rays	1200–1400	30	5.70	103
	Mouse	X rays	1500–1600	14	4.64	84
	Mouse	X rays	Total irrad.	447	5.26[a]	95
Snell and Aebersold (1937)	Mouse	Control	....	9	8.44	
	Mouse	Neutrons	120–140 "r"[b]	4	5.75	68
Russell *et al.*[c]	Mouse	Control	....	9,710	5.75	
	Mouse	X rays	600	12,986	5.58	97

[a] Not given by Hertwig. Calculated as weighted mean of mean litter sizes for each dose.

[b] Cyclotron neutrons measured on r scale of Victoreen condenser-type dosimeter.

[c] Unpublished data collected by W. L. Russell, Josephine S. Gower, Gloria J. Jasny, Elizabeth M. Kelly, Mary H. Major, and Patricia A. Sarvella. Litter size recorded three weeks after birth.

The view that spermatogonia are killed is supported by extensive data showing that cells of other rapidly dividing animal tissues are destroyed by moderate doses of radiation and that the degeneration occurs at cell division. It, therefore, seems plausible to attribute at least the major part of the radiation-induced reduction in number of spermatogonia, and the consequent sterile period, to dominant cell lethals. If this interpretation is correct, then dominant lethals are apparently induced with greater frequency in spermatogonia than in sperm, for the loss of spermatogonia for given doses (Table 12-3) is much greater than would be expected from the reduction in litter size produced by the same doses given to sperm. Several factors could be involved. In the first place, the spermatogonia are diploid and the sperm haploid. Furthermore, the frequency of chromosome breakage, and the proportion of breaks that result in lethal aberrations may be influenced by the state of the chromosomes, the phases of the mitotic cycle in the spermatogonia, and the oxygen tension or other metabolic characteristics. The total effect of these possible factors cannot be accurately estimated. All that can be said is that there is still plenty of latitude for the assumption that more dominant lethals are induced in spermatogonia than in sperm.

If the reduction in litter size shown in Table 12-7 is real, and certainly some effect of mutation would be expected, it could be attributed to dominant lethal chromosomal or point mutations that are not eliminated by germinal selection, to dominant subvital mutations, or, perhaps, to a combination of these. The effect is apparently too slight, however, for easy analysis of the time and nature of death of the missing individuals.

The percentages of stillbirths and of postnatal deaths before 75 days of age in progeny of poststerile-period matings are slightly, but not significantly, higher than in the controls in Hertwig's (1938a) data on mice. Strandskov's (1932) data on the guinea pig show no difference between experimentals and controls in postnatal death before 30 days of age, but the experimentals had a higher percentage of stillbirths and lower 0-day and 30-day corrected weights. The differences are on the borderline of significance and conditions that could have affected the 30-day weights were not exactly matched in experimentals and controls. Some effect, through the induction of dominant mutations, would be expected, but, as with litter size, it is apparently too small for easy detection.

Sex Ratio. Death of embryos from dominant lethals could, through differential mortality of males and females, result in a disturbed sex ratio at birth. Certain types of chromosomal aberration, such as loss of part or perhaps all of the X chromosome, could conceivably upset the sex ratio without affecting survival. The available data do not present a consistent picture. Parkes (1925), who exposed male mice to an X-ray dose below that which produces temporary sterility, reported a barely significant increase in proportion of males born from matings made from 0 to 4 days after irradiation (59.4 per cent of 133 animals as against 51.6 per cent of 735 controls) and a significant drop in proportion of males born from 5- to 18-day matings (33.6 per cent of 143 animals). In the offspring of still later matings (19–57 days), the sex ratio was normal (54.4 per cent of 217 animals). Hertwig (1938a), however, found, for male mice exposed to 400–1400 r, no effect on sex ratio at birth in the progeny of presterile-period matings as a whole and no difference between the 1- to 8-day and 8- to 14-day mating groups. Unpublished data on the sex ratio at birth from our experiments, tabulated according to the division into time intervals made by Parkes, show, for male mice exposed to 600 r, 54.1 per cent males in 218 offspring of 0- to 4-day matings and 54.6 per cent males in 370 offspring of 5- to 14-day matings. Thus Parkes' results are not confirmed by later work at higher doses. Furthermore, the low proportion of males in the 5- to 18-day mating group in Parkes' data is hard to explain. An increased death rate of male embryos can scarcely be the cause, because the litter size is only slightly depressed. The question, therefore, arises as to whether the disturbance in sex ratio may have been the result of causes other than irradiation. It is also possible that the fluctuations were random ones. The probability of this is not necessarily as remote as the tests of significance indicate, because the time sequences were apparently chosen on the basis of the differences shown by them and not on a priori biological grounds.

The sex ratio at birth in the offspring of poststerile-period matings of mice shows, in the data of Hertwig (1938a), a larger proportion of males than in the controls in all except the lowest of seven dose groups ranging from 400 to 1600 r. The difference from the controls is significant for doses of 1200 r and above. The total number of animals in the irradiated group was 2240, in the controls 2595. On the other hand, the sex ratio, recorded at three weeks of age, in unpublished data from our extensive experiment with exposure of male mice to 600 r shows a slight decrease in proportion of males in progeny of poststerile-period matings (50.35 per cent males in 72,472 offspring as against 51.00 per cent in 55,828 controls).

DOMINANT STERILITY

The sterility described in this section is, like the lethality already discussed, called "dominant" solely because it appears in the F_1 of an irradiated parent. Its dominance precludes transmission to later generations and consequently makes analysis of its nature difficult. For dominant lethals, there is, as has already been mentioned, cytological evidence that chromosomal aberration is at least the major cause. The cytology of the chromosomes of dominant steriles has not yet been described. The available information on dominant sterility is limited to the incidence and to the morphology and histology of the defect.

Data from various experiments with mice on the incidence of dominant sterility in the offspring of irradiated male or female parents is given in Table 12-8. Although far more attention has been paid by all investigators to the partial sterility described in the next section, it is apparent that the rate of induction of sterility in the offspring of presterile-period matings of irradiated males is far from negligible. In the male offspring it may be taken as about 10 per cent for a 700-r X-ray exposure of the

TABLE 12-8. INCIDENCE OF STERILITY IN THE OFFSPRING OF IRRADIATED MICE

Reference	Radiation	Dose, r	Parent irrad.	Presterile-period matings				Poststerile-period matings			
				♂ offspring		♀ offspring		♂ offspring		♀ offspring	
				Total no.	No. sterile	Total no.	No. sterile	Total no.	No. sterile	Total no.	No. sterile
Snell (1935)	Control	...	..	47	1?	59	2?				
	X rays	200–1200 (mostly 600–800)	♂	65	6	56	1				
Hertwig (1938a, 1940)	Control	...	..	158	1	130	1	158	1	130	1
	X rays	400	♂	30	0	37	0	7	0	8	0
	X rays	500	♂	13	0	15	0	1	0	4	0
	X rays	600	♂	14	1	22	4				
	X rays	800	♂	45	7	38	5	21	0	31	1
	X rays	1000	♂	14	3	21	1	37	0	38	1
	X rays	1200	♂	...	...	...	...	25	0	20	0
	X rays	1500–1600	♂	7	2	7	0	5	0	3	0
Snell (1939)	Control	...	..	3	0	19	0				
	Neutrons	110–140 "r"[a]	♂	23	3	10	0				
Russell (1950)	X rays	500	♂	11	2	5	0				
	X rays	750	♂	10	1	7	0				
	X rays	1000	♂	1	0	3	0				
Snell and Ames (1939)	Control	...	..	?[b]	0	?[b]	0				
	X rays	240–280	♀	?[c]	2	?[c]	1				
Total of all investigations except last	Control		..	208	1 + 1?	208	1 + 2?	158	1	130	1
	Irradiated		♂	233	25	221	11	96	0	104	2

[a] Cyclotron neutrons measured on r scale of Victoreen condenser-type dosimeter.
[b] Total of 71 offspring of both sexes. Sex distribution not given.
[c] Total of 151 offspring of both sexes. Sex distribution not given.

sire. This is nearly one-half the rate of induction of partial sterility at the same dose level.

The data for presterile-period matings in Table 12-8 show a higher incidence of sterility in males than in females. The material is too heterogeneous for an accurate test of significance, but it is noteworthy that the sex difference is in the same direction in all investigations.

The only data tabulated to show the proportion of steriles produced by early and late matings within the presterile period of irradiated males are those of Hertwig (1938a). Of the 10 male steriles listed in that publication, 8 occurred in 88 offspring of matings made from 1 to 8 days after irradiation and 2 in 24 offspring of matings made from 8 to 14 days after exposure.

As shown in Table 12-8, Hertwig's results indicate that radiation-induced dominant sterility does not appear in the progeny of poststerile-period matings.

Only scattered information is available on the nature of the sterility. Hertwig (1935) reports that in one sterile male, spermatogonia and spermatocytes were present in the testes, but all later stages of spermatogenesis were lacking and no sperm could be found in the epididymis or vas deferens. The histological information on the three sterile males obtained by Snell (1939) in his neutron experiment is as follows: One male proved to have spermatogonia and spermatocytes, but no spermatids; one had a few spermatids, some in a rather advanced stage, but no spermatozoa; and the remaining male showed a very few motile sperm in the left epididymis, a few immotile sperm in the left vas, and no sperm in the right reproductive tract. Of the two sterile males found by Snell and Ames (1939) in the offspring of X-irradiated females, one had spermatogonia and spermatocytes, but no spermatids or spermatozoa, and the other lacked testes, although epididymides and vasa deferentia were present. The sterile female obtained in this experiment was small and died at seven months of age. The ovaries, which were invaded by a lymphoblastoma, showed primordial follicles, but no mature ones.

The mutational changes involved in the production of dominant sterility in mice are not known. Snell (1935) suggested that fragmentation or deletion of the Y chromosome in irradiated Y-bearing sperm could, as in *Drosophila*, account for sterile males. This hypothesis could probably be tested by cytological examination. Sterility might also result from damage to the X chromosome in eggs or X-bearing sperm, and this, too, might be checked cytologically. Some of the animals classified as sterile may have had chromosomal aberrations, such as multiple translocations, that gave a high proportion of aneuploidy in the gametes. However, the animals examined histologically were clearly sterile from causes other than aneuploidy of mature gametes. More information is needed on the anatomical and histological nature of the sterility in both males and females, and on the incidence in the two sexes. Is absence of testes a common cause and does this occur in offspring of irradiated males? Whatever the exact nature of the mutational changes, it seems likely, from the high incidence, that most of the sterility will turn out to be the result of chromosomal aberrations rather than gene mutations. The failure to complete the later stages of spermatogenesis, which appears to be the commonest cause of sterility in males, suggests chromosome damage of a type that interferes with the maturation divisions. This, in turn, provides a plausible explanation for the lack of sterility in the progeny of poststerile-period matings of irradiated males. A mutation that had such an effect would, if induced in spermatogonia, fail to pass through to mature sperm.

DOMINANT PARTIAL STERILITY

The radiation induction of hereditary partial sterility in mammals was reported first by Snell (1933a, 1934, 1935) and shortly afterward by Hertwig (1935). In Snell's work, male mice were exposed to doses of from 200 to 1200 r of X rays and mated to nonirradiated females. The fertility of each of several offspring sired in the presterile period was tested by repeated matings to nonirradiated animals. The distribution of the mean sizes of the litters produced proved to be bimodal, whereas that of the controls was unimodal. The upper mode in the experimental group corresponded approximately to the mode in the controls, and the lower mode was at about one-half the litter size of the upper mode. Snell referred to the animals that consistently produced small litters, that is, the animals grouped around the lower mode, as "semi-sterile." The term "partially sterile," adopted by some authors, is used in preference here because it avoids any implication as to the extent of reduction in fertility. Snell showed that the reduction in litter size could be accounted for by the death of embryos. He found that partial sterility was transmitted, like a dominant, to one-half of the surviving progeny of outcrosses of partially sterile animals. He pointed out that the results fitted the interpretation that the partially sterile animals were heterozygous for a reciprocal translocation. After laborious linkage tests, Snell (1941a, 1946) finally achieved genetic proof of this in one partially sterile line. In this line, the normally unlinked genes *a* and *b* were found to be linked. Cytological confirmation of translocation was provided by Koller and Auerbach (1941) and Koller (1944) who demonstrated the association of four chromosomes at synapsis in each of three partially sterile lines examined. Hertwig (1935, 1938a) confirmed Snell's early findings and, in addition, showed that there was little or no induced partial sterility in the offspring of poststerile-period matings of irradiated males.

The above historical account summarizes the major findings. Detailed aspects, and some additional results, follow. It should be kept in mind that most of the partially sterile animals obtained in the experiments to be discussed were not actually proved cases of translocation and that some of them were not even tested for transmission of partial sterility to descendants. Furthermore, if any translocations in heterozygous condition show considerably more than 50 per cent fertility, these would usually not have been detected. It is also possible that some of the partially sterile animals carried more than one translocation. In spite of these qualifications, however, it seems safe to assume that the frequency of induction of translocations is represented, in at least a rough way, by tabulation of partial sterility.

The frequency of occurrence of partial sterility in the offspring of presterile-period matings of male mice exposed to various doses of X rays is shown in Table 12-9. Since Snell found no clear-cut cases of translocation in his controls, and Charles (1950) only two in 2755 animals, it is likely that in Hertwig's controls, which were not tested for transmission of partial sterility to their descendants, most, or all, of the observed partial sterility was not due to translocations, but was simply an expression of the variation, apparently large in Hertwig's material, of other factors affecting fertility. Although these factors presumably did not contribute greatly to the results in Hertwig's irradiated material, some of which, in contrast to the controls, was tested for transmission, it is possible that they accounted for some of the recorded partial sterility and perhaps for more in females than in males. Making allowance for this, the data in Table 12-9, for all investigations combined, indicate that induced partial sterility occurs with approximately equal frequencies in the male and female offspring of presterile-period matings of irradiated mice. The data are still not sufficient for an accurate analysis of the relation between frequency and dose. They do, however, show that the rate is much higher than that for translocations in *Drosophila*. The yield from a dose of about 700 r in the mouse is comparable to that from 4000 r in *Drosophila melanogaster*. A difference of about this magnitude would be expected from the larger number of chromosomes in the mouse, but whether or not other factors are involved is not known.

Since, as will be discussed later, the yield of partially sterile offspring from irradiated oocytes may be lower than that from irradiated sperm, it might be expected that the yield from irradiated spermatocytes would also be low. If this assumption is correct and if, as Hertwig has maintained, later matings within the presterile period of irradiated males utilize some sperm that was irradiated in spermatocyte stage, then these later matings should give a lower percentage of partial sterility than the earlier matings. The difference between spermatocytes and sperm would thus be in the opposite direction to that obtained for dominant lethals.

TABLE 12-9. INCIDENCE OF PARTIAL STERILITY IN THE OFFSPRING OF MICE EXPOSED TO SINGLE DOSES OF HIGH-INTENSITY RADIATION

Reference	Radiation	Dose, r	Parent irrad.	Presterile-period matings					Poststerile-period matings				
				♂ offspring		♀ offspring		Total offspring	♂ offspring		♀ offspring		Total offspring
				Total no.	No. part. sterile	Total no.	No. part. sterile	Per cent part. sterile	Total no.	No. part. sterile	Total no.	No. part. sterile	Per cent part. sterile
Snell (1935)........	Control	....	..	47	0	59	0?	0.0?					
	X rays	200–1200 (mostly 600–800)	♂	65	21	56	17	31.4					
Hertwig (1938a, 1940)...........	Control	....	..	158	6	130	12	6.3	158	6	130	12	6.3
	X rays	400	♂	30	4	37	7	16.4	7	0	8	1	6.7
	X rays	500	♂	13	2	15	5	25.0	1	0	4	0	0.0
	X rays	600	♂	14	3	22	7	27.8					
	X rays	800	♂	45	5	38	12	20.5	21	1	31	3	7.7
	X rays	1000	♂	14	4	21	8	34.3	37	0	38	2	2.7
	X rays	1200	♂	...	..	...	..	....	25	0	20	0	0.0
	X rays	1500–1600	♂	7	2	7	1	21.4	5	0	3	0	0.0
Snell (1939)........	Control	....	..	3	0	19	0	0.0					
	Neutrons	110–140 "r"[a]	♂	23	3	10	1	12.1					
Russell (1950)......	X rays	500	♂	11	3	5	1	25.0					
	X rays	750	♂	10	1	7	4	29.4					
	X rays	1000	♂	1	0	3	1	25.0					
Snell and Ames (1939)...........	Control	....	..	?[b]	0	?[b]	0	0.0					
	X rays	240–280	♀	?[c]	2	?[c]	1	2.0					

[a] Cyclotron neutrons measured on r scale of Victoreen condenser-type dosimeter.
[b] Total of 71 offspring of both sexes. Sex distribution not given.
[c] Total of 151 offspring of both sexes. Sex distribution not given.

The only data that can be analyzed with regard to this factor are those of Hertwig (1938a) and she tabulates only the results for partially sterile male progeny. In these she found 12 partially steriles in 88 offspring from matings made 1–8 days after irradiation and 2 partially steriles in 24 offspring from the 8- to 14-day matings. As far as these data go, they are in agreement with the above assumption, but they are obviously not extensive enough to be considered a satisfactory test.

The information obtained by Snell (1939) on the incidence of partial sterility in the offspring of presterile-period matings of male mice irradiated with fast neutrons is also given in Table 12-9. As would be expected from their effect on chromosome breakage in other organisms, neutrons appear to be more effective than X rays in producing partial sterility, but it is clear that data obtained with modern methods of irradiation and dosimetry are needed to establish the ratio of effectiveness.

The incidence of partial sterility in offspring of X-irradiated female mice was determined by Snell and Ames (1939), as shown in Table 12-9. Comparison of the result with incidence in offspring of irradiated males is difficult because there are no data from males exposed at this dose level, and the data from higher doses are, as has already been pointed out, not adequate for establishing the frequency-dose curve. However, the incidence of partial sterility in the offspring of females appears to be lower than what would be expected from males irradiated with the same dose. Since, in *Drosophila*, the incidence of translocations in irradiated female germ cells is much below that in irradiated sperm (Glass, 1940), some consideration should be given to the possibility that the frequency in progeny of irradiated female mice may be even lower than the results of Snell and Ames indicate. The fact that two of the three partially sterile animals found in the 151 offspring came from the same female suggests the possibility that this female was herself carrying dominant partial sterility. As she had only one other offspring that was tested, no definite conclusion can be reached. This uncertainty, coupled with the limited total of only three partially sterile animals obtained, still leaves some latitude for assuming that in mice, as in *Drosophila*, translocation induction in females may be much less frequent than in males.

As Hertwig (1935, 1938a) first clearly showed, Table 12-9, there is no evidence for the occurrence of radiation-induced partial sterility in the offspring of poststerile-period matings of X-irradiated male mice. This indicates either that translocations are not induced in spermatogonia or that they occur and are eliminated by germinal selection. However, elimination seems unlikely in view of the fact that translocations are easily transmitted through descendant generations. The hypothesis of lack of occurrence, therefore, seems to be the more plausible one to adopt. Since there is evidence, from the great reduction in number of spermatogonia following irradiation, that chromosome breakage resulting in dominant lethals does occur, the absence of translocations is probably not attributable to lack of breaks. Thus, it appears that it is the process of segmental interchange which fails to occur.

Using γ rays from a radium source, Lorenz *et al.* (1947) found, by fertility tests, no evidence of translocations in the offspring of male mice exposed to 8.8 r given in 8 hours per day to a total dose of 1100 r, or in the offspring of female mice exposed to 8.8 r given 24 hours per day to a total dose of 770 r. The details of this experiment were presented in an earlier report by Deringer *et al.* (1946). In all, forty-two offspring of irradiated males and thirty-one offspring of irradiated females were tested. The offspring of the irradiated males came partly from matings made immediately after removal of the males from the radium field and partly from later matings, but the proportions and time intervals are not given. The absence of partial sterility in the offspring of the irradiated males in this experiment is just what would have been expected from the earlier work of Snell and Hertwig. For, firstly, even if all the offspring had been obtained from matings made immediately after removal from the field, the total dose received in spermatozoal stages, and perhaps in all post-spermatogonial stages, would hardly have been high enough, even if it had been given as an acute dose, to produce any translocations in the number of animals tested. Secondly, although the average dose received in spermatogonial stages may have been close to the total dose of 1100 r given, Hertwig had already found no translocations in a slightly larger sample of offspring of poststerile-period matings of males exposed to acute doses of from 1200 to 1600 r (Table 12-9). Since the dose of radiation to which the sperm were exposed in the experiment of Lorenz *et al.* was not sufficient, even if it had been given as acute radiation, to have produced any translocations in the sample tested, the data do not answer the question of whether chronic irradiation of sperm is less effective in translocation production than acute irradiation, or equally effective, as would be expected if the chromosome breaks in mouse sperm are like those in *Drosophila* sperm and remain open until after fertilization. Taking Snell's data on the incidence of partial sterility in the offspring of females exposed to acute irradiation at face value and comparing them with the results of Lorenz *et al.* for irradiated females, it appears that, if translocations are induced in oocytes, chronic irradiation is less effective.

The only information on the incidence of partial sterility in the descendants of mammals exposed to repeated small doses of high intensity radiation is that provided by Charles (1950). He exposed male mice to 0.1, 0.5, 1.0, or 10.0 r of X rays daily, for 6 days a week, mated them to unexposed females throughout the weeks of irradiation and tested the fertility of the offspring. The average accumulated exposures at time of mating for the different dose levels were 13, 69, 134, and 238 r, respectively, and 60 r for all dose levels combined, but there was a wide range of accumulated exposure within each group. Seven partially sterile animals were found in 3072 tested offspring. This rate does not differ significantly from that of two in 2755 found in the controls. It is not possible in Charles' data to separate accurately the dose received by spermatozoal stages from that received by prespermatozoal stages, a distinction which, as has already been shown, is all important. It is probable that any real excess over the controls was due solely to that portion of the total irradiation which was received by the sperm but, even if this is assumed, the data are not suitable, or extensive enough, for answering the question as to whether or not fractionated doses to the sperm are less effective than a single dose.

It may be concluded from Charles' data and from the work of Snell, who found no translocations in 196 control mice in all his experiments combined, that the rate of occurrence of spontaneous translocations is quite low in mice. Charles has not yet presented any detailed information on the two spontaneous cases reported by him. The only spontaneous mammalian translocation thoroughly analyzed is one in the rat investigated by Waletzky and Owen (1942), Tyler and Chapman (1948), and Bouricius (1948). The pattern of fertility reduction, abnormal embryos, and cytological aberrations described falls well within the range of variability found for X-ray-induced translocations in the mouse.

Turning to a consideration of the characteristics of the translocations, the degree of effect on the fertility of the animals that are heterozygous for a translocation is of first importance. Hertwig (1940) found that the fertility, expressed as percentage of control litter size at birth, of translocation heterozygotes in eleven of her X-ray-induced partially sterile lines of mice ranged from 42 to 59 per cent. The mean of these lines was 45 per cent. Uterine dissections in the same eleven lines and a few others showed similar reductions in fertility as measured by number of living embryos. Hertwig concluded that the differences between lines could be attributed to chance. The mean fertility of heterozygotes in three translocation lines of mice studied by Koller (1944) was 30–39 per cent in one line, 46 per cent in another, and 44–46 per cent in the third. Cytological analysis showed correlation between reduction in fertility and frequency of nondisjunctional coorientation of chromosomes in the ring-of-four in first meiotic division. In the six translocation stocks investigated in detail by Snell (1946), the fertility of heterozygotes ranged from 38 to 62 per cent for females and from 41 to 69 per cent for males. Differences between lines were significantly greater than could be expected by chance. In five of the six lines, the percentage fertility of males was higher than that of females and the difference was significant in two of these lines. The assumption that the percentage fertility corresponds to the percentage of orthoploid gametes is supported by the observed proportion of normal embryos in one of the lines, and is tenable as part of the explanation of the results obtained from the matings of partially sterile to partially sterile made within two of the lines. Snell and Picken (1935) report a presumed translocation in which the fertility of heterozygotes was almost normal. This case was discovered through the occurrence of a few abnormal offspring. It should be kept in mind that, as has already been mentioned, translocations showing considerably more than 50 per cent fertility in the heterozygote would usually not be detected by fertility tests. Present determinations of the average fertility of translocation heterozygotes may, therefore, be biased.

The time of death and nature of the abnormal embryos produced by the aneuploid gametes in translocation stocks obtained from irradiated mice have been studied by Snell, Bodemann, and Hollander (1934), Snell and Picken (1935), Hertwig (1938a, 1940), and Otis (1949). These investigations show that the commonest time of death is at implantation or shortly after. There is evidence of some death before this time and also of some survival even to birth. The proportions falling into these classes vary considerably among the translocation lines. Snell and his associates found that failure of the neural groove to close at its anterior end was a common type of defect in the small proportion of abnormal embryos that survive to later stages.

The expected proportion of partially sterile animals in the viable offspring of a mating of a translocation heterozygote with a normal is one-half. It would, however, be lower than this if the heterozygotes were less viable than the normals. On the other hand the proportion of normals would be depressed if any aneuploid zygotes were viable. Hertwig (1940), using the mean-litter-size test for partial sterility, found that the percentage of partially steriles in the offspring of such crosses fell below 50 per cent in ten out of eleven translocation lines. The mean for the eleven lines was 45 per cent. In contrast, Snell (1946), who made use of genetic markers to establish the proportion of partial sterility, found no significant departure from a 1:1 ratio. In all of five sets of his data, involving three marker genes for one translocation and two marker genes for another, there was actually a slight, though not significant, excess of the classes marked by the gene that entered the cross with partial sterility.

Translocations have been obtained in homozygous condition in two, or possibly three, of six lines tested by Hertwig (1940) and in both of two lines tested by Snell (1946). The failure to obtain the homozygotes in Hertwig's other lines could be attributed to limitations of the test rather than to lethality of the homozygotes. The bearers of the homozygous translocations proved to be phenotypically normal with the exception of one of Snell's which showed "a suggestion of a reduced viability." Thus, as far as they go, the data for the mouse indicate that position effect may be less important than it is in *Drosophila*.

The translocations produced by irradiation in mice are proving increasingly useful as tools for genetic and cytological research. Snell (1946) has attempted a genetic analysis of the frequencies of occurrence of the nondisjunction classes of gametes found in two translocation lines and has also obtained some information on the positions of the centromeres on the two chromosomes involved in one of these lines. Slizynski (1952) has begun the task of determining, in the mouse, which genetically determined linkage group corresponds to which cytologically identifiable chromosome.

DOMINANT VISIBLES

No dominant mutations with externally visible effects were observed by Snell (1935) in 178 offspring of male mice given a mean dose of 681 r of X rays (numbers obtained from Snell, 1933b). However, autopsies in the third generation revealed what proved to be a dominant mutation affecting spleen shape. Penetrance was incomplete. Affected individuals had markedly reduced vigor and somewhat subnormal fertility. The autopsied F_3 mice were descended from ninety-one offspring of treated males, but, as the descendant lines were not always large enough to give near certainty of recovering even dominant mutations, the mutation rate must be taken as one mutation in something less than ninety-one sperm for a dose of approximately 700 r.

Charles (1950) found seven dominant visible mutations, including those detected only by autopsy, in 3072 offspring of male mice exposed to a mean dose of 60 r. The difference from the controls, in which there were no mutations in 2755 animals, is significant. Two of the mutant phenotypes were characterized by abnormal connections of minor tributaries of the vena cava, one had extra nodules of adrenal cortical tissue, one showed incomplete suture of the parietal bones, one exhibited "confused" behavior occasionally associated with cataract and deafness and two had altered hair color, one of these also having reduced eye size and lowered fertility.

Five dominant visible mutations in approximately 30,000 offspring of poststerile-period matings of male mice exposed to 600 r of X rays are recorded by Russell (1951) in a preliminary account of an investigation designed primarily for the detection of recessive mutations at seven specific loci. The loci were chosen so that recessives could be detected by rapid examination of the coat color and ears. Dominant mutations, anywhere in the genome, that had effects on these characters were, therefore, automatically detected. In order not to interfere appreciably with the rapidity of observation necessitated by the large number of animals required for the determination of mutation rates at the specific loci, the only additional character routinely observed for dominants was the tail. For this reason, the mutation rate must be far below the over-all rate to dominant visibles and is, therefore, of only limited value as an absolute rate. It is, however, interesting to compare the results obtained for dominants with the data on mutations at the specific loci. Two of the dominants affected the tail, one affected the ears and possibly the coat color, one produced white spotting and one mottling. Thus, only three of the dominants affected the characters associated with the specific loci. In the population in which these now established dominants were found, thirty-two mutations were observed at the specific loci. It can be concluded that, at least for the coat color and ears, the mutation rate to dominant visibles at all loci is lower than the mutation rate to recessive visibles at a total of only seven selected loci.

It was mentioned by Russell (1951) that about one-half of the twenty-eight induced mutations at the *S* locus showed, in addition to the recessive spotting effect, a dominant reduction in body size. With the accumulation of more data on body weights in descendant generations it now appears that most, or perhaps all, of the *S*-locus mutations will show this effect to some extent. There is also increasing evidence for an associated reduction in viability which would place these mutations under the classification of dominant subvitals. In any case, it is apparent that the mutation rate to dominants detected by a change at the *S* locus is much higher than would have been anticipated from the over-all rate to dominants affecting coat color, ears, and tail. It is possible that dominant mutations affecting size are far more frequent than those causing coat color changes or gross morphological abnormalities. It is also possible that the *S*-locus mutations fall in a special class.

RECESSIVE LETHALS, SEMILETHALS, AND VIABLES

The only data on the possible occurrence of radiation-induced sex-linked recessives in mammals is that presented by Charles (1950) who briefly reports two sex-linked lethals in 3072 offspring of male mice exposed to a mean dose of 60 r of X rays and one in 2755 control animals. The rest of this section is concerned with information obtained on autosomal recessives.

Hertwig (1939, 1941) reports two recessive visibles, both causing retarded growth, and four recessive lethals in the descendants of thirty-six male offspring of presterile-period matings of male mice exposed to from 600 to 1200 r of X rays. Three visibles, one causing anemia, one oligodactyly (both described in detail in Hertwig, 1942a, b), and one causing dwarfism, were found in the descendants of eighty-two male offspring of poststerile-period matings of irradiated males. The dose range, 800–1600 r, is given only for the first fifty-eight (sixty ?) male offspring tested. Two other possible lethals are reported as incompletely tested, but it is not stated whether these came from presterile- or poststerile-period matings. Two lethals were found in the descendants of seventy-two control males. In later publications Hertwig (1942a, b, 1944, 1949, 1951) describes two recessive visibles, shaker-syndactyly and "Kreisler," that were recovered from presterile-period matings. These are first described as having come from males exposed to 1000 r and would, therefore, appear to be additional to the visibles from presterile-period matings reported in 1939 which were recorded as coming from males treated with 800 r. There seems to be some confusion over doses, however, because shaker-syndactyly is later described as having come from a male exposed to 1500 r, and the dose given to the male that produced anemia in descendants of a poststerile-period mating is reported as 1500 r in one place and 1000 r in another. Combining offspring of presterile- and poststerile-period matings, taking the total number of visibles as from five to seven, assuming that the total number of offspring tested was the 118 reported in the 1941 publication, and using the weighted mean dose of that portion of the data for which the doses are recorded, the induced mutation rate to recessive visibles is from 4.1 to 5.7×10^{-5} per r. All of the four mutations that have been described in detail fall on the borderline between semilethals and subvitals, and only one has shown any fertility. Taking the number of lethals as from four to six in 118 tested offspring, assuming the mean dose used above, and subtracting the control rate, the induced mutation rate to lethals is from 0.59 to 2.2×10^{-5} per r. Since visibles with not easily recognizable effects were probably not detected, and since lethals are difficult to detect with the methods available in mammals, the above rates are probably much below the over-all mutation rates to visibles and lethals.

In the investigation by Russell (1951), which has already been mentioned in the section on dominant visible mutations, wild-type male mice were exposed to a single whole-body dose of 600 r of X rays and, after their period of temporary sterility, mated to a stock homozygous for seven autosomal recessive visible genes. Control, unexposed, males were also mated to the test stock. The offspring were observed for mutations at the seven specific loci. Presumed mutants were saved and breeding tests made to determine the allelism and the effect of the mutations in homozygous condition. Thus, the method used detects mutations to recessives, including those with lethal effect when homozygous, at a limited number of specific loci. The mutations obtained at each locus are listed in Table 12-10. Table 12-10 includes the results from a pilot experiment conducted mainly to determine the relation of dose to survival and productivity of the exposed animals. Various doses were used in the pilot experiment and detailed tabulation with regard to this and other variables was postponed until completion of that experiment.

Taking the total number of mutations in the irradiated group in the main experiment as fifty-three and subtracting the control from the experimental rate, the mean induced mutation rate, in spermatogonia, for the seven loci is $(25.0 \pm 3.7) \times 10^{-8}$ per roentgen, per locus. The observed variation in induced rates at the different loci is significantly greater than chance variation.

The characteristics of the mutations are of interest from several points of view. It has already been mentioned that most, or all, of the *S*-locus mutations have, in addition to the recessive spotting effect, a dominant effect causing reduction in body size and possibly lowered viability. No marked dominant effects have been observed for the other mutations, but

TABLE 12-10. X-RAY-INDUCED MUTATIONS AT SPECIFIC LOCI IN THE MOUSE (Russell, 1951)

Dose	No. of animals examined	Number of mutations at locus							
		A	*B*	*C*	*D*	*P*	*S*	*Se*	Total
Pilot experiment[a]		. .	. .	1	1	2	(3–4[b])[c]	1	8–9
600 r	48,007	. .	11	3–4[b]	6	8	25	. .	53–54
Control	37,868	. .	. .	. . . .	1	. .	1	. .	2

[a] See text for explanation.
[b] Two of the four mutations may be a cluster from a single mutation.
[c] In the pilot experiment, mutations at the *S* locus were scored on a smaller sample of animals than that on which mutations at the other loci were determined.

TABLE 12-11. VIABILITY OF HOMOZYGOTES OF X-RAY-INDUCED MUTATIONS AT SPECIFIC LOCI IN THE MOUSE

Viability of homozygote	Tested number of mutations at locus						
	B	*C*	*D*	*P*	*S*	*Se*	Total
Viable.	2	2	. .	3	. . . .	1	8
Semilethal.	. .	. .	5	2	. . . .	. .	7
Lethal.	1	2	. .	1	2+[a]	. .	6+

[a] Other mutations at this locus that have been partially tested indicate a considerable addition to the lethal category.

the possibility of a slight reduction in viability has not yet been excluded. Three of the induced mutations, one at the *B* locus, one at the *C* locus and one at the *P* locus, were to intermediate alleles. The effect of the mutations in homozygous condition is still being tested. The available information, which includes some not published before, is given in Table 12-11. The mutations listed do not constitute a random sample because their inclusion depended on the speed with which the test could be completed and this, in turn, was affected by the nature of the mutation and the locus involved. When all the mutations have been tested, the proportion of viables in the total may turn out to be lower than that in

Table 12-11. The results already indicate that the relative frequencies of viable, semilethal, and lethal types differ according to the locus. Most striking is the uniformity of *D*-locus mutations. Not only are all of the five tested mutations at this locus semilethal; they also exhibit the same phenotypic effect: a coat color which is like that produced by the *d* allele, but, combined with this, a curious behavior defect characterized by convulsive fits exhibiting clonus of the limbs and opisthotonos of the body. Furthermore, this phenotype is indistinguishable from that of the spontaneous *D*-locus mutation obtained in this investigation and of the spontaneous mutation found by Searle (1951).

The question arises as to how many of the induced mutations scored by the specific loci test are deficiencies. The following evidence bears on this question, although it does not provide a definite answer. The frequency of the homozygous lethal effect suggests that at least some of the mutations may be deficiencies. The occurrence of three mutations that appear to be intermediate alleles is presumptive, though not conclusive, evidence of gene mutation in these cases. The most favorable loci for the detection of deficiencies by phenotypic effect are the *D* and *Se* loci which are closely linked (average crossover percentage 0.16). Of the total of eight mutations obtained at these loci in the experimental group, none shows the phenotypic effect that would be expected from a deficiency involving the linked locus.

HUMAN HAZARDS

The genetic hazards of radiation in man have been discussed by Haldane (1947), Muller (1950a, b, c; also see Chap. 7, this volume), Wright (1950), and others. No attempt will be made here to review the concepts of population genetics used or the resulting estimates of the hazard, which have been calculated mainly on the basis of mutation rates in *Drosophila*. The present section is limited to a brief discussion of the application of the experimental results that have been presented in this chapter.

Considering, first, the dominant defects, such as lethality, sterility, and partial sterility, that appear in the offspring following irradiation of the later stages in spermatogenesis, it is well established that the rate of induction of these is much higher in mice than in *Drosophila*. This would be expected if most of them are due to major chromosomal aberrations, for the haploid number of chromosomes in the mouse is twenty, while in *Drosophila melanogaster* it is four. It is reasonable to suppose that, with twenty-four chromosomes in man, the rate in man might be somewhat higher than that in the mouse. Some of the effects, for example, death of early embryos caused by dominant lethals or by aneuploid gametes from translocation heterozygotes, might bring little or no distress, and might pass unnoticed as individual occurrences, but the rate of induction of those dominant defects, such as complete sterility and lowered viability in postnatal or late prenatal life, which are important at the individual level, is far from negligible. Fortunately, there is ample evidence to show that the high incidence in the offspring is found only after irradiation of later germ-cell stages. It is clear that if the gonads of a man are exposed to a considerable dose of radiation at one time, or within the few weeks required for a spermatogenic cycle, the chance of transmission of the mutational changes responsible for these defects can be greatly reduced by abstention from fertile matings for a period of a few weeks following exposure.

Turning to a consideration of point mutations and small deficiencies or other minor chromosomal changes, it must be remembered that the ratio of induced mutation rates in spermatogonia and spermatozoa for these types of mutation has not been measured in mammals. However, from results on *Drosophila*, it seems likely that the practice recommended above for avoiding the transmission of major chromosomal changes would result in much less of a reduction in the probability of transmitting point mutations and minor chromosomal changes. If this is true, then, for these mutations, it is more important to know the induced mutation rate in spermatogonia than that in spermatozoa, because most of the total dose received in the ontogeny of a spermatozoon in man will usually have been accumulated in the spermatogonial stage.

The induced mutation rate in spermatogonia for mutations with clear-cut dominant effects has not been adequately determined in mammals. The results of Charles (1950) indicate that the rate to dominant visibles may be appreciable, but, in his data, the effects of irradiation on early and late germ-cell stages cannot be separated. In the investigation by Russell (1951), irradiation of spermatogonia gave a low over-all mutation rate to dominants affecting coat color, tail, and ears, but a high rate at one locus to dominants causing reduction in body size and possibly lowered viability.

The reduction in litter size in litters from poststerile-period matings of irradiated males (Table 12-7) may prove to be useful in estimating the total effect from the induction in spermatogonia of dominants that cause mortality in early development. This effect is apparently not large enough for easy measurement by a small sample, because of the presence of variation in the many biological factors that influence litter size, but the extensive data now being collected may prove informative when fully analyzed.

The specific-loci mutations induced in spermatogonia in the mouse (Russell, 1951) have not yet been thoroughly investigated for deleterious effects. However, the majority of those tested have proved to be lethal or semilethal in homozygous condition (Table 12-11). Work on *Drosophila* has shown that most recessive lethals have a deleterious effect on viability even in heterozygous condition (see Chap. 7, this volume). It, therefore, appears likely that mutations induced in spermatogonia in mammals may have appreciable dominant deleterious effects which, in man, will prove to be more of a hazard than the recessive effects.

The mean induced mutation rate for irradiated spermatogonia in the experiment of Russell on specific loci in the mouse is $(25.0 \pm 3.7) \times 10^{-8}$ per roentgen, per locus. This is considerably higher than the rates found in similar experiments on *Drosophila* and indicates that estimates of human hazards based on *Drosophila* mutation rates may have to be revised.

In the same investigation, the observed rate of mutation was not appreciably dependent on the length of interval between irradiation and fertilization. It, therefore, appears that, as far as mutations induced in spermatogonia are concerned, postponement of procreation would be ineffective in reducing the probability of transmission.

The discoveries (reviewed by Hollaender, Baker, and Anderson, 1951) that hypoxia and other treatments protect against the induction by radiation of chromosomal damage, and perhaps other genetic changes, has increased the hope that protective agents will be found that will reduce the genetic hazard of radiation in man. The first test of the effect of hypoxia on radiation induction of genetic damage in mammals has, however, proved discouraging. No protection against the X-ray induction of dominant lethals in sperm in mice was found (Russell *et al.*, 1951). It is possible, of course, that hypoxia will prove to afford protection against genetic damage in earlier germ-cell stages, or even against some types of genetic damage in sperm.

REFERENCES

(Information regarding availability of government reports indicated by an asterisk may be obtained from the Office of Technical Services, Department of Commerce, Washington, D.C.)

Amoroso, E. C., and A. S. Parkes (1947) Effects on embryonic development of X-irradiation of rabbit spermatozoa *in vitro*. Proc. Roy. Soc. (London), B134: 57–78.

Bouricius, J. K. (1948) Embryological and cytological studies in rats heterozygous for a probable reciprocal translocation. Genetics, 33: 577–587.

Brenneke, H. (1937) Strahlenschädigung von Mäuse- und Rattensperma, beobachtet an der Frühentwicklung der Eier. Strahlentherapie, 60: 214–238.

Catcheside, D. G. (1947) Genetic effects of radiations. Brit. J. Radiology, Suppl. 1, pp. 109–116.

Charles, D. R. (1950) Radiation-induced mutations in mammals. Radiology, 55: 579–581.

Deringer, M. K., W. E. Heston, and E. Lorenz (1946) Biological effects of long-continued whole body irradiation with gamma rays on mice, guinea pigs, and rabbits. Part IV. Biological action of gamma radiation on the breeding behavior of mice. USAEC Report MDDC-1247,* pp. 1–30. Also National Nuclear Energy Series, Div. IV, Vol. 22B (in press).

Eschenbrenner, A. B., E. Miller, and E. Lorenz (1948) Quantitative histologic analysis of the effect of chronic whole-body irradiation with gamma rays on the spermatogenic elements and the interstitial tissue of the testes of mice. J. Natl. Cancer Inst., 9: 133–147.

——— and ——— (1950) Effect of roentgen rays on the testis. Arch. Path., 50: 736–749.

Falconer, D. S. (1949) The estimation of mutation rates from incompletely tested gametes, and the detection of mutations in mammals. J. Genetics, 49: 226–234.

Fogg, L. C., and R. F. Cowing (1951a) The changes in cell morphology and histochemistry of the testis following irradiation and their relation to other induced testicular changes. I. Quantitative random sampling of germinal cells at intervals following direct irradiation. Cancer Research, 11: 23–28.

——— and ——— (1951b) The changes in cell morphology and histochemistry of the testis following irradiation and their relation to other induced testicular changes. II. Comparison of effects of doses of 1440 r and 5050 r with 300 r. Cancer Research, 11: 81–86.

——— and ——— (1952) Post-irradiation studies on mammalian testes. Effect at hourly intervals for first 24 hours. Proc. Soc. Exptl. Biol. Med., 79: 88–92.

Glass, H. B. (1940) Differential susceptibility of the sexes of *Drosophila* to the effect of X-rays in producing chromosome aberrations. Genetics, 25: 117.

Glücksmann, A. (1947) The effects of radiation on reproductive organs. Brit. J. Radiology, Suppl. 1, pp. 101–109.

Haldane, J. B. S. (1947) The dysgenic effect of induced recessive mutations. Ann. Eugenics, 14: 35–43.

Henson, M. (1942) The effect of roentgen irradiation of sperm upon the embryonic development of the albino rat (*Mus norvegicus albinus*). J. Exptl. Zoöl., 91: 405–434.

Hertwig, P. (1932) Wie muss man züchten, um bei Säugetieren die natürliche oder experimentelle Mutationsrate festzustellen? Arch. Rassen- u. Gesellschaftsbiol., 27: 1–12.

——— (1935) Sterilitätserscheinungen bei röntgenbestrahlten Mäusen. Z. indukt. Abstammungs- u. Vererbungslehre, 70: 517–523.

——— (1938a) Unterschiede in der Entwicklungsfähigkeit von F_1 Mäusen nach Röntgen-bestrahlung von Spermatogonien, fertigen und unfertigen Spermatozoen. Biol. Zentr., 58: 273–301.

——— (1938b) Die Regeneration des Samenepithels der Maus nach Röntgenbestrahlung, unter besonderer Berücksichtigung der Spermatogonien. Arch. exptl. Zellforsch., 22: 68–73.

——— (1939) Zwei subletale rezessive Mutationen in der Nachkommenschaft von röntgenbestrahlten Mäusen. Erbarzt, 4: 41–43.

——— (1940) Vererbare Semisterilität bei Mäusen nach Röntgenbestrahlung, verursacht durch reziproke Chromosomentranslokationen. Z. indukt. Abstammungs- u. Vererbungslehre, 79: 1–27.

——— (1941) Erbänderungen bei Mäusen nach Röntgenbestrahlung. Proc. Intern. Genetic Congr. 7th Congr. Edinburgh, 1939, J. Genetics Suppl., pp. 145–146.

——— (1942a) Neue Mutationen und Koppelungsgruppen bei der Hausmaus. Z. indukt. Abstammungs- u. Vererbungslehre, 80: 220–246.

——— (1942b) Sechs neue Mutationen bei der Hausmaus in ihrer Bedeutung für allgemeine Vererbungsfragen. Z. menschl. Vererbungs- u. Konstitutionslehre, 26: 1–21.

——— (1944) Die Genese der Hirn- und Gehörorganmissbildungen bei röntgenmutierten Kreisler-Mäusen. Z. menschl. Vererbungs- u. Konstitutionslehre, 28: 327–354.

——— (1949) Untersuchungen über die Taubheit bei einem Stamm von röntgenmutierten Mäusen, den "syndactylen Schüttlern." Proc. 8th Intern. Congr. Genetics, Stockholm, 1948, Hereditas Suppl., pp. 592–593.

——— (1951) Entwicklungsgeschichtliche Untersuchungen über Bewegungsstörungen bei Mäusen. Verhandl. anat. Ges., 49: 97–107.

——— and H. Brenneke (1937) Die Ursachen der herabgesetzten Wurfgrösse bei Mäusen nach Röntgenbestrahlung des Spermas. Z. indukt. Abstammungs- u. Vererbungslehre, 72: 483–487.

Hollaender, A., W. K. Baker, and E. H. Anderson (1951) Effect of oxygen tension and certain chemicals on the X-ray sensitivity of mutation production and survival. Cold Spring Harbor Symposia Quant. Biol., 16: 315–326.

Howard, A., and S. R. Pelc (1950) P^{32} autoradiographs of mouse testis. Preliminary observations of the timing of spermatogenic stages. Brit. J. Radiology, 23: 634–641.

Koller, P. C. (1944) Segmental interchange in mice. Genetics, 29: 247–263.

——— and Charlotte A. Auerbach (1941) Chromosome breakage and sterility in the mouse. Nature, 148: 501–502.

Lea, D. E. (1947) Effects of radiation on germ cells: dominant lethals and hereditary partial sterility. Brit. J. Radiology, Suppl. 1., pp. 120–141.

Lorenz, E., W. E. Heston, A. B. Eschenbrenner, and Margaret K. Deringer (1947) Biological studies in the tolerance range. Radiology, 49: 274–285.

Muller, H. J. (1950a) Radiation damage to the genetic material. Am. Scientist, 38: 33–59, 126, 399–425.

——— (1950b) Some present problems in the genetic effects of radiation. J. Cellular Comp. Physiol., 35 (Suppl. 1): 9–70.

——— (1950c) Our load of mutations. Am. J. Human Genetics, 2: 111–176.

Otis, E. M. (1949) Intra-uterine death time in semi-sterile mice. Anat. Record, 105: 533.

Parkes, A. S. (1925) The effects on fertility and the sex-ratio of sub-sterility exposures to X-rays. Proc. Roy. Soc. (London), B98: 415–436.

Regaud, C., and G. Dubreuil (1908) Perturbations dans le développement des oeufs fécondés par des spermatozoides Roentgénisés chez le lapin. Compt. rend. soc. biol., 64: 1014–1016.

Russell, W. L. (1950) The incidence of sterility and partial sterility in the descendants of X-irradiated mice. Genetics, 35: 689.

——— (1951) X-ray-induced mutations in mice. Cold Spring Harbor Symposia Quant. Biol., 16: 327–336.

——— (1952) Mammalian radiation genetics, *in* Symposium on radiobiology (Oberlin, 1950), ed. J. J. Nickson. John Wiley & Sons, Inc., New York, pp. 427–440.

———, J. C. Kile, and L. B. Russell (1951) Failure of hypoxia to protect against the radiation induction of dominant lethals in mice. Genetics, 36: 574.

Schaefer, H. (1939) Die Fertilität von Mäusemännchen nach Bestrahlung mit 200 r. Z. mikroskop. anat. Forsch., 46: 121–152.

Schinz, H. R., and B. Slotopolsky (1925) Der Röntgenhoden. Ergeb. med. Strahlenforsch., 1: 443–526.

Searle, A. G. (1951) A lethal allele of dilute in the mouse. Heredity, 5: 302.

Slizynski, B. M. (1952) Pachytene analysis of Snell's T(5:8)*a* translocation in the mouse. J. Genetics, 50: 507–510.

Snell, G. D. (1932) The effect of X-rays on the fertility of the male house mouse. Proc. 6th Intern. Congr. Genetics, Brooklyn Botanic Garden, Brooklyn, N.Y., 2: 188.

——— (1933a) Genetic changes in mice induced by X-rays. Am. Naturalist, 67: 24.
——— (1933b) X-ray sterility in the male house mouse. J. Exptl. Zoöl., 65: 421–441.
——— (1934) The production of translocations and mutations in mice by means of X-rays. Am. Naturalist, 68: 178.
——— (1935) The induction by X-rays of hereditary changes in mice. Genetics, 20: 545–567.
——— (1939) The induction by irradiation with neutrons of hereditary changes in mice. Proc. Natl. Acad. Sci. U.S., 25: 11–14.
——— (1941a) Linkage studies with induced translocations in mice. Genetics, 26: 169.
——— (1941b) Induction by roentgen rays of hereditary changes in mice. Radiology, 36: 189–194.
——— (1945) The detection of mutations. Relative efficiency of various systems of brother-sister inbreeding in mice. J. Heredity, 36: 275–278.
——— (1946) An analysis of translocations in the mouse. Genetics, 31: 157–180.
——— and P. C. Aebersold (1937) The production of sterility in male mice by irradiation with neutrons. Proc. Natl. Acad. Sci. U.S., 23: 374–378.
——— and F. B. Ames (1939) Hereditary changes in the descendants of female mice exposed to roentgen rays. Am. J. Roentgenol. Radium Therapy, 41: 248–255.
———, E. Bodemann, and W. Hollander (1934) A translocation in the mouse and its effect on development. J. Exptl. Zoöl., 67: 93–104.
——— and Dorothea Picken (1935) Abnormal development in the mouse caused by chromosome unbalance. J. Genetics, 31: 213–235.
Strandskov, H. H. (1932) Effect of x-rays in an inbred strain of guinea-pigs. J. Exptl. Zoöl., 63: 175–202.
Tyler, W. J., and A. B. Chapman (1948) Genetically reduced prolificacy in rats. Genetics, 33: 565–576.
Waletzky, E., and R. Owen (1942) A case of inherited partial sterility and embryonic mortality in the rat. Genetics, 27: 173.
Wright, S. (1950) Discussion on population genetics and radiation. J. Cellular Comp. Physiol., 35 (Suppl. 1): 187–205.

Manuscript received by the editor June 6, 1952

CHAPTER 13

The Effects of Radiation on Mammalian Prenatal Development[1]

LIANE BRAUCH RUSSELL

Biology Division, Oak Ridge National Laboratory

Introduction. Experimental findings: The preimplantation period—The period of major organogenesis; Mortality, Body size, Sex ratio, Morphology—The period of the fetus; Mortality, Morphology, Time of parturition, Isotope studies. Mechanisms of radiation effect on the embryo: Influence of the maternal organism—Nature of the primary damage and intermediate effects—Dosage relations; variability—Comparison with other agents affecting development. Clinical literature on the effects of radiation on embryo and fetus; human implications of experimental work. Summary. References.

I. INTRODUCTION

Studies on the effects of radiation on mammalian prenatal development are of special interest not only because of their human and medical implications but by virtue of their contributions to the fields of mammalian experimental embryology and of developmental mechanics in general.

Certain inherent peculiarities in the biological material set it apart from the more conveniently studied invertebrates and lower vertebrates. Since the mammalian embryo develops within the body of its mother and cannot, in general, be irradiated without irradiating some maternal tissues, the question of how much of the damage to the conceptus is direct and how much is caused indirectly through damage to the mother must always be in the background of an investigation and was, in fact, almost the sole subject of much of the early work. The dependent nature of mammalian development is, however, of some advantage for embryological studies since it probably permits abnormal development to proceed to more advanced stages than it would in the unprotected embryos of other forms. Since the embryo is usually not observed at the time of irradiation, its developmental stage can be designated only by its chronological age, which—because of variations in rate between litters (especially of different genetic backgrounds) and even within litters—provides only an

[1] Work at Oak Ridge and preparation of manuscript were performed under Contract No. W-7405-eng-26 for the Atomic Energy Commission.

approximate measure. Unfortunately, the importance of controlling even the postconceptional interval has eluded some investigators altogether.

For a few reasons, then, the mammal is not the most suitable material for investigating the effects of radiation on development. Conversely, however, radiation is an excellent tool for approaching mammalian embryology from an experimental point of view. As opposed to other deleterious agents (e.g., injected poisons), radiation does not have to "pass the placental barrier" and it reaches the embryo in calculable quantities. Timing of treatment is not complicated by the unknowns existing for other agents (e.g., how soon effective concentrations are built up in the circulation or how rapidly the poison is destroyed or eliminated by the organism). Finally, since the action of radiation has a general distribution throughout the organism, selective response of structures may be expected to indicate patterns of sensitivity intrinsic to the embryo.

Work on the effects of radiation on mammalian prenatal development will thus be reviewed from the points of view of (1) the contributions to mammalian experimental embryology and developmental mechanics, and (2) the human implications of the existing experimental material supported by pertinent clinical findings.

The early investigations in the field were, unfortunately, not well controlled, not only with respect to radiation factors, as might be expected, but especially as regards timing of developmental stages. They, therefore, do not contribute substantially to point (1) except for scattered incidental information. For this reason, they will not be discussed in detail but are, for the sake of completeness, included in the summarizing tabular material (Tables 13-1, 2, 7).

II. EXPERIMENTAL FINDINGS

Although it would be most profitable to discuss separately the results of irradiating each of the conveniently landmarked stages from conception to birth, only a very small number of past investigations is suitable for this type of analysis, and rougher groupings must, therefore, be made. Convenient points of division can be derived from a survey of the entire gestation period of the mouse (Russell, 1950) in which irradiated stages, differing by 24-hour intervals, ranged from day ½ postfertilization to near term. The three broad phases which emerged from this study were as follows: (1) irradiation during the preimplantation period gave a high incidence of prenatal death but almost no abnormalities in survivors to term; (2) irradiation with the same dose during the period of major organogenesis yielded a high incidence of abnormalities at birth but much less prenatal mortality; and (3) irradiation during the fetal period (growth, minor organogenesis) did not cause prenatal death, and no *gross* abnormalities *at birth*. It should be pointed out that the division points do not represent sharp demarkations but merely separate average response for entire periods. Appropriate groupings of the work of other authors support, in general, these broad divisions of prenatal development with respect to response to radiation. Each division will, therefore, be taken up in turn.

An attempt at complete coverage of the literature has been made. The experimental material consists almost entirely of mice, rats, guinea pigs, and rabbits. In the publications here reviewed, the number of investigators, or groups of investigators, concerned with each of these is 11, 9, 8, and 15, respectively. Incomplete data are available on two cats (Toussey, 1905; Schinz, 1923) and one dog (Regaud *et al.*, 1912). Only the mouse and rat have been used in recent experiments, all work with other species having been published before 1935. In order to determine broad developmental divisions, similar to those described in the preceding paragraph, for the species to be discussed, landmarks in development (e.g., blastocyst, first mesoderm, neural plate, first somite, etc.) were entered against coordinates representing days of gestation of mouse and of the animal to be compared with it. It is thus possible to arrive at the following approximate divisions for preimplantation period, period of major organogenesis, and period of the fetus, respectively: mouse—0–5, 6–13, 14 to term (usually days 19 or 20); rat—0–7, 8–15, 16 to term (usually days 21 or 22); rabbit—0–5, 6–15, 16 to term (usually days 31 or 32); guinea pig—0–8, 9–25, 26 to term (approximately 9 weeks; but it must be remembered that birth here does not occur at a comparable stage, a newborn mouse corresponding, approximately, to a 34-day guinea pig fetus).

Whenever possible, work to be reviewed has been placed in a category defined by the animal with which it deals and the time in gestation at which irradiation was applied (see Tables 13-1, 2, 7). A few publications cover two or several categories and are, therefore, listed more than once. In many cases the stage is only vaguely stated (e.g., "second half of pregnancy"), in others, although not stated at all, it can be approximately calculated from incidental information (e.g., by counting back from term). In still other cases, where a treatment interval is reported (either because the irradiation was chronic or because the author is not specific about the date of his acute exposure), there may be overlap into an adjacent broad developmental phase. For these and other reasons, Tables 13-1, 2, 7 may be considered only as organized listings of literature and must not be evaluated as a summary of results. It was felt that this was the most profitable way of presenting the extremely heterogeneous group of investigations, many of which are not definitive by themselves but may add to the picture as a whole. Not included in the tables are experiments in which no clue can be obtained of the stage irradiated (Murphy and de Renyi, Levine, Finkel, von Klot, Försterling, Linser and Helber).

In almost all of the experiments, irradiation was administered from an external source. The whole pregnant female was usually exposed, although several investigators attempted to direct the beam to the abdominal region. Shielding of extra-abdominal regions was part of the technique in experiments by Warkany and Schraffenberger (1947), Job *et al.* (1935), Kaven (1938a, b), Murphy and de Renyi (1930), and Regaud *et al.* (1912). Wilson (1949), and Wilson and Karr (1950, 1951) went so far as to expose only selected embryos. Finally, Raynaud and Frilley (1943a, b, 1947a, b, c, 1949a, b) used a beam of 0.5–3.0 mm diameter to irradiate only selected parts of certain embryos. Radioactive isotopes, Sr^{89} and P^{32}, were injected into the pregnant female by Finkel (1947) and by Burstone (1951), respectively. Bagg (1922) and Gudernatsch and Bagg (1920) injected a solution of sodium chloride which had been exposed to 500 mc of radium emanation to obtain an "active deposit."

A. THE PREIMPLANTATION PERIOD

The rather scanty work on the preimplantation period is summarized in Table 13-1. It may be noted, first of all, that none of the publications report abnormalities while all report prenatal death. This result is particularly meaningful in the case of investigators whose work has also extended into other periods. Thus Job *et al.* (1935), who obtained abnormalities from the irradiation of later stages, report only resorption as a result of 0.8 skin erythema dose (hereafter to be abbreviated to SED)[2] delivered during the preimplantation period. The survivors were normal. The similar contrast found by Russell (1950) in a survey of the gestation period has already been mentioned. Kosaka (1928c) states that ⅓ SED delivered during the preimplantation period to guinea pigs has either no effect at all or kills the embryo. The normality of survivors from very early irradiation (mice or rats?) extends even to normality of postnatal development (Kosaka, 1928e). Parkes obtained litters from all of ten females irradiated in the second and third weeks of gestation, but only two out of thirteen irradiated during the first week carried to term.

[2] The SED is defined (Ellinger, 1941) as the quantity of radiation administered at 23 cm focal skin distance, 180 kv, 0.5 mm Zn + 3 mm Al filter, and a field of 6 × 8 cm. This is equivalent to 600 r in air. However, the radiation factors in most of the experiments using SED dosimetry differ from the standard conditions enumerated and, since the r equivalent to 1 SED varies considerably depending on hardness of radiation and other factors, the practice throughout this review has been to cite the dose exactly as stated by the author. This applies also where other systems of measurement have been used, such as the Holzknecht unit, or the pastille tint method. It has been left to the reader to make attempts at approximate conversion to r units in individual cases where it might be of interest and where the original publication may be consulted for details on radiation factors.

TABLE 13-1. SUMMARY OF THE LITERATURE DEALING WITH IRRADIATION OF MAMMALIAN EMBRYOS DURING PREIMPLANTATION STAGES

Animal	Author	Dose[a]	Region exposed[b]	Stage irradiated[c]	Stage observed[d]	Number		Results[e]			
								Prenatal death		Arrested develop-ment	Normality of survivors
						♀♀ treat.	Young observ.	Presumed preimplant.	Postim-plant.		
Mouse	Burckhard	30 min/exposure	Total	0 + 1 + 2 + · · · + 8	0–8 PC	?	?	+		+	
	Parkes	40 min = ¼ B tint	Total	4, 5, or 6	6–10 PC, T	13	12	+	+		+
	Russell, 1950	100 r, 200 r	Total	½, 1½, . . . , or 4½	12–17 PC, T	35	70	+	+		+
	Russell and Russell, 1950a	200 r	Total	½, 1½, . . . , or 4½	10½, or 13½ PC	154	831	+	+		+
Rat	Bagg	Radium	Injection	7	? PC	10	?		+		
	Job *et al.*	0.8 skin unit	Total	One of 1st–6th	T ?	?	?		+		+
		12–90 r	Total	One of 1st–7th	? PC, T	16	140				+
	de Nobele and Lams, 1925	½–2 SED	Total	5, or 7	9, 14, or 21 PC	18	97	+	+	+	+
Guinea pig	Trillmich	Wk. brown or tint B	Total	0–7? or earlier?	PI to T (externally)	5	4	+	+		
	Kosaka, 1928c	⅙, ⅓, ⅔ SED	?	One of 1–7	1 PI to T	14	?	+	+		+
Rabbit	Driessen	30 H, 10 H	Left side	4	14 PC	2	>3	+		+	
	Saretzky	?	Ovaries	1st few days	?	9	?		+		
	Momigliano, 1934	½–2 SED	Total ?	"Beginning" of pregn.	?	3	?		+		

[a] X rays, unless otherwise indicated. See also text footnote 2.

[b] Refers to mother.

[c] Designates days postconception. See text footnote 3.

[d] PC = postconception, PI = postirradiation, T = term. Numbers designate days.

[e] Positive reports are indicated by +. Absence of a + symbol in the table may indicate either a negative result or lack of observation: many of the original publications do not allow a decision between these two alternatives.

In view of recent results to be discussed in more detail, it is of interest to extract from the literature what information is available as to the stage in gestation when death occurs. In five investigations (Burckhard, Parkes, Russell, de Nobele and Lams, Driessen), in which the uterus was examined within two weeks after irradiation, there is mention of finding no signs of pregnancy in several of the females. This means either that death occurred before implantation or that fertilization failed to occur. Radiation was not administered early enough in any of the experiments to have interfered with fertilization, although Burckhard (who began his treatments earlier than most investigators) suggests that killing of sperm in the female is responsible for nonpregnancy. Since a certain proportion of matings is apparently always nonfertile, the early experiments, which lack adequate controls for the determination of this proportion, provide only suggestive evidence of preimplantation death due to early irradiation. Somewhat more direct evidence comes from Kosaka (1928c) who opened, within 72 hours after irradiation, three of fourteen guinea pig females irradiated during the first week after conception and found disturbances in implantation of embryos that had died earlier. Burckhard (1905) reports retarded cleavage, which may be an indication of disturbances leading to later death, some of it conceivably before implantation. Finally, there are reports (Trillmich, 1910; Parkes, 1927) of finding no sign of pregnancy *externally*, although here there also exists the possibility of early postimplantation death.

Ample evidence for death *after* implantation is presented by all investigators except Burckhard, whose observations do not extend far enough into that period. The usual finding consists of resorbing bodies or decidual rests in the uterus, but two authors (Trillmich, 1910; Parkes, 1927) also mention abortion in later stages of pregnancy. A few reports of arrested development (de Nobele and Lams, 1925; Driessen, 1924), are probably to be classed with more obvious cases of resorption, since there are indications that the embryos may have died shortly before observation.

Following up the indications of the survey experiment (Russell, 1950) in which irradiation during preimplantation stages had reduced the number of litters at term (see Table 13-3), as well as the litter size in surviving litters (see Table 13-4), Russell and Russell (1950a) irradiated a separate extensive series of females ½, 1½, 2½, 3½, or 4½ days after mating. A control was handled simultaneously with each irradiated female. In an attempt to determine at what stages preimplantation death occurred and whether any abnormalities were expressed in animals thus weeded out before term, all uteri were examined either 10½ or 13½ days after mating, i.e., 6–13 days after irradiation. It was found that radiation-induced death was considerable and that, in over-all effect, the earliest stages were most sensitive, the average number of living embryos per treated female being only about 20 per cent of the controls in groups irradiated on days $\frac{1}{2}$, $1\frac{1}{2}$, or $2\frac{1}{2}$, but 31 and 57 per cent following treatment on days $3\frac{1}{2}$ and $4\frac{1}{2}$, respectively (Fig. 13-1*a*). Mortality between days $10\frac{1}{2}$ and $13\frac{1}{2}$ and between days $13\frac{1}{2}$ and term was no higher than in controls and radiation-induced death, therefore, occurred entirely before day $10\frac{1}{2}$, in fact, so long before that stage that abnormalities, if

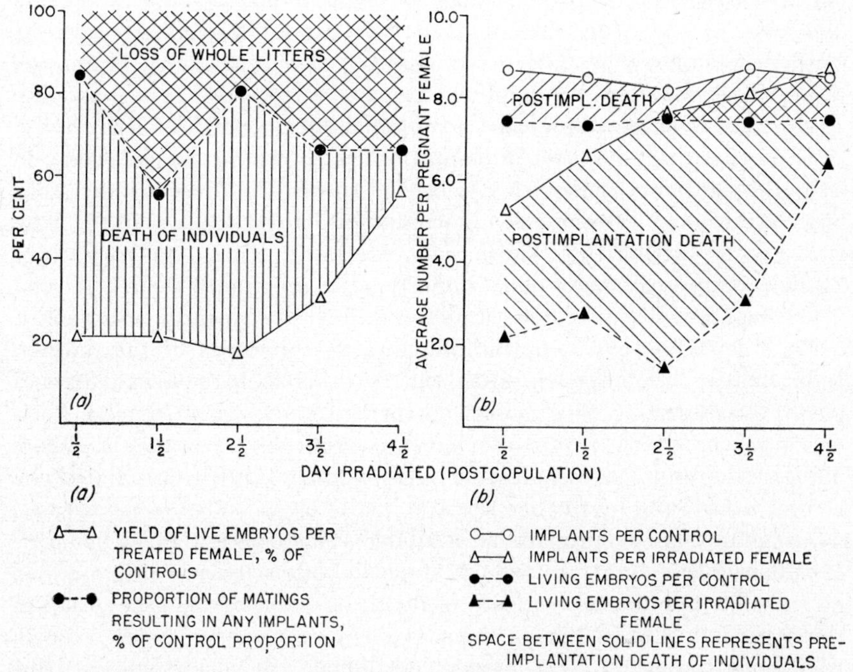

FIG. 13-1. Effects of irradiation with 200 r during the preimplantation stages of the mouse embryo. All observations are made on days $10\frac{1}{2}$ or $13\frac{1}{2}$ postcopulation, and points are based on a total of 521 implants in the controls, 310 in the irradiated groups. Fig. (*b*) based on pregnant females only. (*Russell and Russell*, 1950a.)

any were produced, could no longer be recognized at the time of observation. More specifically, three groups of deaths can be recognized: (1) Preimplantation death of entire litters, i.e., very early termination of pregnancy, is indicated by the excess of nonpregnant females at the time of dissection (see Fig. 13-1*a*). The percentage of copulations resulting in implants observable on days $10\frac{1}{2}$ and $13\frac{1}{2}$ is 79 in controls and 44–67 in different irradiated groups (average, 56 per cent). As a whole, the reduction is highly significant but fluctuations among the different irradiated groups are probably random. Therefore, on the average, about 29 per cent of the embryos irradiated in preimplantation stages are lost in whole-litter death prior to implantation. (2) The balance of the mortality is due to death of individuals within surviving pregnancies (see Fig. 13-1*a*). This accounts for about two-thirds of the total death in groups irradiated on days ½, 1½, and 2½, but by day 4½, when over-all mortality has greatly decreased, death of individuals has become only a minor portion of the total loss. Further analysis of death of individuals (see Fig. 13-1*b*, based on pregnant females only) indicates that it may occur in one of two periods: (*a*) Animals may die before implantation, as shown by deficiency in total implants in irradiated pregnant females. This type of death occurs mostly in embryos irradiated on days ½ and 1½, eliminating respectively 3.3 and 1.9 implants per surviving pregnancy. By day 4½, irradiation no longer causes preimplantation death of individuals. (*b*) Embryos may die after implantation, as shown by the deficiency in living implants. Further work is needed to test the present indications of survival being lowest following irradiation on day 2½.

It can be argued that, since preimplantation death involving whole litters is of approximately equal importance in all groups, the majority of it may not be caused by direct radiation injury to the early embryo but, instead, by some effect on the implantation processes of the mother. Individual preimplantation death, on the other hand, is high only as a result of irradiating precleavage or very early cleavage stages. Post-implantation death is greatly increased following irradiation before implantation but its exact relation to developmental stage irradiated can be elucidated only by further work.

Assuming that the probability of killing a blastomere with a given dose of radiation is equal in the one-cell stage and later cleavage stages, it can be calculated from the incidence of death of embryos that the group of those surviving radiation on days 1½–4½ probably includes some in which one to several blastomeres were killed. Since virtually all survivors from irradiation of cleavage stages are normal, the results, as they stand, indicate a considerable degree of totipotency in the blastomeres of the young mammalian embryo.

B. THE PERIOD OF MAJOR ORGANOGENESIS

The bulk of the work on the effects of radiation on the mammalian embryo deals with the period of major organogenesis and most of the more careful and extensive studies fall into this group. Table 13-2, which presents a condensed summary of the literature, immediately reveals the almost universal discovery of abnormalities following irradiation during that period. The interest in mortality is, in general, only secondary. Only in the rabbit is there a dearth of reported abnormalities, but this may be due to the fact that all the rabbit work was done early in the century and much of it was not critical with respect to experimental procedure.

TABLE 13-2. SUMMARY OF THE LITERATURE DEALING WITH IRRADIATION OF MAMMALIAN EMBRYOS DURING THE PERIOD OF MAJOR ORGANOGENESIS

Animal	Author	Dose[a]	Region exposed[b]	Stage irradiated[c]	Stage observed[d]	Number		Results[f]						
								Mortality			Morphol. changes			Poor devel.
						Mothers[e]	Young obs.	Pre-natal	Neo-natal	Post-natal	Pre-natal	Neo-natal	Post-natal	
Mouse	Kaven, 1938a	200 r	Abdomen	7, 8, . . . , or 14	T, PN	113	650?		+			+	+	
	Kaven, 1938b	200 r	Abdomen	7, or 8	13–19 PC, T	181	1091	+	+		+	+		
	Kosaka, 1927, 1928e	⅛–2½ SED	Total or parts	One of 4–14	½–? PI, PN	?	~500?	+	+		+	+?		+
	Parkes	10 min	Total	9½	T, PN	1	9							
	Raynaud and Frilley	5000–200,000 r	Head of embryo	12 days 6 hr (+13 days 6 hr)	18½ PC	"Many"	?				+			
	Russell and co-workers	25–400 r	Total	5½, 6½, . . . , or 13½	T	241	1660	+	+	+		+	+	
Rat	Hanson	? X rays	Total	"Later" in pregn.	T, PN	?	?					+		+
	Bagg	? Ra	Injection	10–14	? PC	24	?	+			+	+		
	Job *et al.*	12–200 r	Total	One of 8th–15th	9–18 PC, T	>58	>278	+	+			+		
		40–65 r	Posterior ½	9th, 10th, or 11th	T	22	192							
	Kosaka, 1928b	⅙–1½ SED	?	One of 5–15	¼–10 PI, T ?	59	?	+			+			
	de Nobele and Lams	½, 2 SED	Total	8, or 10	12, 14, 23 PC	4	15	+				?		
	Warkany and Schraffenberger	190–1120 r	Lumbosacral	9, 10, . . . , or 15	T	108	568	+				+		
	Wilson and Karr	50–400 r	Individual embryos	9, or 10	11–15 PC, T, PN	>38	>167	+			+	+		
Guinea pig	Dyroff	420 r	Total	18	T, PN	1	?			+				
	Kosaka, 1928c	⅙–1½ SED	?	2d–4th week, one ? exposure	¼ PI to T	54	?	+			+			
	de Nobele and Lams	½, 1 SED	Total	13, or 14	20–55 PC, T	19	22	+			+		?	
	Trillmich	60 min	Total	10?–27? for 6 consec. days	PI externally	5	3	+						
Rabbit	Cohn	3 hours	Head	10–20	PN	?	?							+
	Driessen	10–78 H	Left side	4–13	10–26 PC	6	36	+						
	Fellner and Neumann	5–8 H	Upper ⅔ of abdomen	Two of 5–12	? PC, T	13	?	+						
	v. Hippel and Pagenstecher	21 H	Total, or abdomen shielded	Three of 8–12	T	30	?	+				+		
	Pagenstecher	2–3.4 SED	Abdomen	Three of 9–15	28 PC	7	>4	+			+			
	Kosaka, 1928a, d	⅙–2 SED	?	10, or 15	¼ PI to T ?	77	?	+			+	+		
	Momigliano	½–2 SED	Total ?	"Middle" of pregn.	? PC	3	?	+						
	Nürnberger	15 or 30 min	Abdomen	8	T, PN	2	4		+	+				
	Saretzky	?	Ovaries	1st half of pregn.	PI	10	?	+						
	Schinz	0.85–2 SED	Total	8, 9, 10, 14, or 15	PI to T	5	23?	+						
	Sébileau	Tint. no. 6	Total ?	4 to 9 of 7–30	T, PN	3	?		+	+				

[a] X rays, unless otherwise indicated. See also text footnote 2.
[b] Refers to mother, unless otherwise indicated.
[c] Designates day postconception, unless otherwise indicated. See text footnote 3.
[d] PC = postconception; PI = postirradiation; T = term; PN = postnatal. Numbers designate days.
[e] In the majority of cases, this number refers to females with observable young.
[f] Positive reports are indicated by +. Absence of a + symbol in the table may indicate either a negative result or lack of observation: many of the original publications do not allow a decision between these two alternatives.

1. MORTALITY

a. Prenatal. Mortality is reported by almost all investigators, at least for the higher dose series. For doses comparable to those which were used during the preimplantation period by investigators whose work spans both periods, prenatal death, however, is of decreased importance (Job *et al.*, 1935; Russell, 1950; Bagg, 1922; Parkes, 1927). Russell (1950) showed that complete interruption of pregnancy, which often follows irradiation during the preimplantation stages, occurs only rarely as a result of later irradiation. This is obvious from the almost 100 per

TABLE 13-3. PERCENTAGE OF COPULATIONS RESULTING IN PREGNANCY IN CONTROLS AND FOLLOWING IRRADIATION WITH DIFFERENT DOSES AT DIFFERENT STAGES IN THE PRENATAL DEVELOPMENT OF THE MOUSE

Dose, r	Observation	Yield of litters following treatment on postcopulation day					
		½–4½		5½–8½		9½–13½	
		Pregnancy not diagnosable				Pregnancy diagnosable	
		No. ♀♀ treated	Per cent w. litter	No. ♀♀ treated	Per cent w. litter	No. ♀♀ treated	Per cent w. litter
0	Term[a]	18	72.2	18	72.2		
100	Term[a]	15	46.7	1	100		
200	Term[a]	20	45.0	29	69.0	17	94.1
300	Term[a]	..	....	9	0.0	19	94.7
400	Term[a]	..	....	..	....	4	100.0
0	10½, 13½ PC[b]	77	79.2				
200	10½, 13½ PC[b]	77	55.8				

[a] Russell, 1950.
[b] Russell and Russell, 1950a. PC = postcopulation.

cent yield (see Table 13-3) from females treated with 200, 300, or 400 r in stages when pregnancy can already be diagnosed externally (days 9½ and 10½ usually; days 11½ through 13½ invariably) and no less apparent from comparison with controls of those females irradiated with 200 r at a time when it is unknown whether copulation was fertile (days 5½–8½). The question of whether there is prenatal death of individuals within litters, as judged by decrease of average litter size at term, is more difficult to answer since, with the necessarily limited numbers available after subdivision into stage and dose groups, standard errors are large. To diminish this difficulty, data accumulated at this laboratory from several morphological investigations, in which litter size was only an incidental result, have been pooled in Table 13-4 to give a total popula-

Table 13-4. Average Size of Litters Coming to Term Following Irradiation with Different Doses at Different Stages in the Prenatal Development of the Mouse
(Russell and coworkers)

Day irradiated (postconception)	0 r		25 r		50 r		75 r		100 r		200 r		300 r		400 r	
	No. of litt.	Litt. size	No. of litt.	Litt. size	No. of litt.	Litt. size	No. of litt.	Litt. size	No. of litt.	Litt. size	No. of litt.	Litt. size	No. of litt.	Litt. size	No. of litt.	Litt. size
½			..	...	..	...	..	...	3	6.0	1	3.0				
1½			..	...	..	...	..	...	2	4.0	1	2.0				
2½			..	...	..	...	..	...	2	5.0	1	1.0	1	2.0		
3½			..	...	..	...	..	...	..	...	4	4.0				
4½			..	...	..	...	..	...	..	...	4	6.3	1	7.0		
Total ½–4½			..	...	..	...	..	...	7	5.1	11	4.3	2	4.5		
5½			..	...	..	...	..	...	1	8.0	4	6.5				
6½			..	...	..	...	..	...	..	...	7	5.4	1	1.0		
7½			5	6.0	10	7.0	..	...	19	6.4	11	4.5	1	1.0		
8½			13	6.5	13	5.3	7	7.0	26	6.8	14	4.9	1	1.0		
Total 5½–8½			18	6.4	23	6.0	7	7.0	46	6.7	36	5.1	3	1.0		
9½			..	...	..	...	..	...	16	6.4	12	7.0	3	2.7		
10½			..	...	..	...	..	...	11	6.8	9	4.9	4	7.0		
11½			..	...	..	...	..	...	13	7.7	15	6.8	12	5.8		
12½			..	...	..	...	..	...	6	8.7	5	9.0	7	7.7	3	4.0
13½			..	...	..	...	..	...	..	...	..	...	10	7.1	3	6.3
14½			..	...	..	...	..	...	..	...	..	...	9	6.3		
15½			..	...	..	...	..	...	..	...	..	...	6	7.0		
Total 9½–15½			..	...	..	...	..	...	46	7.2	41	6.7	51	6.5	6	5.2
	122	6.7														

tion of 419 litters (2667 young). (It must be borne in mind that the table includes several genetic strains—distributed *unevenly* among groups—with probable differences in radiation response; see a future section. It is, therefore, suitable only for showing broad trends.) For irradiation of postimplantation stages, doses of 100 r and below have apparently no effect on prenatal viability. A dose of 200 r, which, it may be remembered, caused 80 per cent prenatal death when applied days ½, 1½, or 2½ after fertilization, permits an over-all average litter size of 5.94 ± 0.27 when administered between days 5½ and 12½ inclusive, i.e., causes a decrease of only 11 per cent from the control mean of 6.69 ± 0.18 (t = 2.43). This over-all slight depression is due primarily to the significantly reduced litter sizes of groups irradiated near the beginning of the period, namely, on days 6½, 7½, and 8½ (reduction for these three is 27 per cent; t = 4.46). The 300-r data substantiate the 200-r series in again showing sensitivity to prenatal killing of individuals only in the early part of the period of organogenesis.

The findings of other investigators who have worked on the mouse are in general agreement with the above results. Kaven (1938b) obtained litter sizes of 4.3 and 4.7 following irradiation with 178 r to the uterus on days 7 and 8, respectively. The control litter size was 6.8 (see Table 13-6). Litter sizes for irradiation of later stages cannot be accurately calculated from his data (1938a), but where estimates are possible these are usually considerably higher than the results from the 7- and 8-day stages. Kosaka (1927) found that doses greater than ½ SED would give 100 per cent prenatal death if given between the fourth and tenth days while more than 1 SED was required to accomplish the same result when administered after the tenth day.

Wilson and Karr (1951) concentrated their study on irradiation at day 10 after fertilization in the rat and examined for dead embryos 1–5 days following irradiation. Their results for the last observation day are shown in Table 13-5. These figures and the summation for all observation days indicate that while 50 r does not increase the percentage of prenatal death at all and 100 r not significantly so (t = 1.4 for the sum of all observation days), the significant (t = 5.3) killing action of 200 r should result in at least 88 per cent reduction in average litter size at birth (more if, as is likely, there is further death between day 15 and term). For approximately comparable stages in the mouse (days 7½ and 8½) and the same dose, the reduction in average litter size at birth is only 29 per cent. It is of interest in Wilson's data that while mortality due to 200 r is spread over a 4-day interval beginning 2 days after irradiation, all death with 400 r occurs within 24 hours of exposure. In contrast, Kosaka (1928b), in his work on rats, found that even doses which kill 100 per cent of the embryos—i.e., ⅓ SED and above on any of days 5–10—do not cause death until 48 to 240 hours after irradiation. In an abstract, Wilson and Karr (1950) mention that 200 r applied on day 9 will kill all embryos, which would indicate that stage to be even more critical for prenatal viability than day 10.

While it is tempting to compare the results of Wilson and those of Russell with a view to demonstrating a probable difference between rat and mouse in susceptibility to prenatal killing, three further investigations, all on the rat, serve to show that even in the same species vastly different results may be obtained, depending, perhaps, on genetic differences, details of method, or difficulties in early dosimetry. Job *et al.* (1935) report 100 per cent resorption following exposure to only 95–200 r (see Table 13-5). It must, however, be pointed out that females were opened before irradiation to ascertain their pregnancy and, since no con-

TABLE 13-5. VIABILITY AFTER PRENATAL IRRADIATION IN THE RAT: COMPARISON OF THE RESULTS OF DIFFERENT AUTHORS

Senior author	Day irrad.	Dose, r													
		0	50	100	200	300	400	500	600	700	800	900	1000	1100	1200
		Percentage of embryos or fetuses alive[a]													
Job, 1935	9th–15th			0											
Wilson, 1950	9				0										
Wilson, 1951	10	89(37)[b]	100(2)	89(9)	12(8)		0(10)								
		Percentage of ♀♀ with litter at term—average litter size[c]													
Job, 1935	8th–11th	?%—8.2 (41)	?%—7.4(237)												
Warkany, 1947	9[d]						50%—4.9(44)								
Warkany, 1947	10						79%—3.0(45)								
Warkany, 1947	11						92%—4.9(54)								
Job, 1935	12th–16th	?%—11.0 (22)	?%—8.4(101)												
Warkany, 1947	12									72%—5.2(249)					
Warkany, 1947	13									100%—6.3(50)					
Warkany, 1947	14										92%—7.4(81)				
Warkany, 1947	15											75%—7.5(45)			

[a] Observations recorded in this portion of the table were made as follows: in the work of Job *et al.*, on day 18; in the experiments of Wilson and Karr, on day 15 for 0–200 r, day 12 for 400 r.

[b] Figures in parentheses indicate the number of young on which percentage alive or average litter size is based.

[c] Based only on litters brought to term.

[d] See text footnote 3.

trol figures are cited, the operation itself may have contributed to the prenatal death. It is otherwise hard to imagine how Warkany and Schraffenberger (1947) could have obtained as large a yield as they did with the very much higher doses of 190–1120 r. Summing all treatment stages (days 9–15),[3] 75 per cent of their 144 irradiated females had litters at term and the average litter size was 5.26. Since results for different doses are, in general, not reported separately, it is difficult to compare stages. Table 13-5, however, makes it clear that, as in the mouse, there is more prenatal death from irradiation of the earlier stages. In general keeping with this trend is the report by Kosaka (1928b) that only ⅓ SED suffices to kill all embryos irradiated during the "first stage" (days 5–10), while during the second stage (days 11–15) 1 SED is required to produce 100 per cent mortality. Similar results are obtained in guinea pigs (Kosaka, 1928c). In over-all sensitivity, Kosaka's rat embryos appear intermediate between those of Job and those of Warkany.

In summary, it may be stated that extensive data on the mouse reveal that, for comparable doses, irradiation during the period of major organogenesis causes considerably less prenatal death than does treatment during the preimplantation period. Furthermore, within the period of organogenesis, susceptibility to prenatal killing probably decreases fairly rapidly with embryonic age. This is shown by the mouse results as well as by individual investigations on the rat, although the latter differ greatly amongst themselves with regard to *absolute* sensitivity of the embryo.

b. Neonatal. Only two investigators have reported in a quantitative manner on death at birth following irradiation during the period of organogenesis. In both cases, this is more frequent than prenatal death observed by them in the same sample. Kaven (1938a) reports stillbirth of over three-fourths of those newborns which had been irradiated on day 10, 11, or 12 postfertilization with 178 r. Irradiation on the immediately preceding or following day results in a smaller proportion of death at birth.

A pooling of several experimental series (involving different genetic strains) by Russell and co-workers is represented in Fig. 13-2. This shows that, while 100 r and below has no effect on survival at birth, 200 r (a dose comparable to Kaven's) applied on any one of days 7½ through 11½ inclusive causes neonatal mortality, with a sharp peak for days 9½ and 10½ (75 and 67 per cent respectively). Raising the dose to 300 r increases neonatal mortality in general, the curve paralleling the 200 r curve and the peak reaching 100 per cent (days 9½ and 10½). These

[3] Throughout this review an attempt will be made to name the stage according to the actual time elapsed since fertilization—a procedure which is followed in the publications of Wilson, and of Russell *et al.* Following this system, Warkany and Schraffenberger's "10th day" will be referred to as day 9 (if irradiation took place in the afternoon, it was day 9⅓), etc.

data indicate that the slope of the dose-mortality curve for any given stage is steep around 50 per cent lethality (see also Fig. 13-9*b*). The work of both Kaven and Russell makes it clear that mortality is markedly dependent on the stage irradiated, even when stages are separated by only

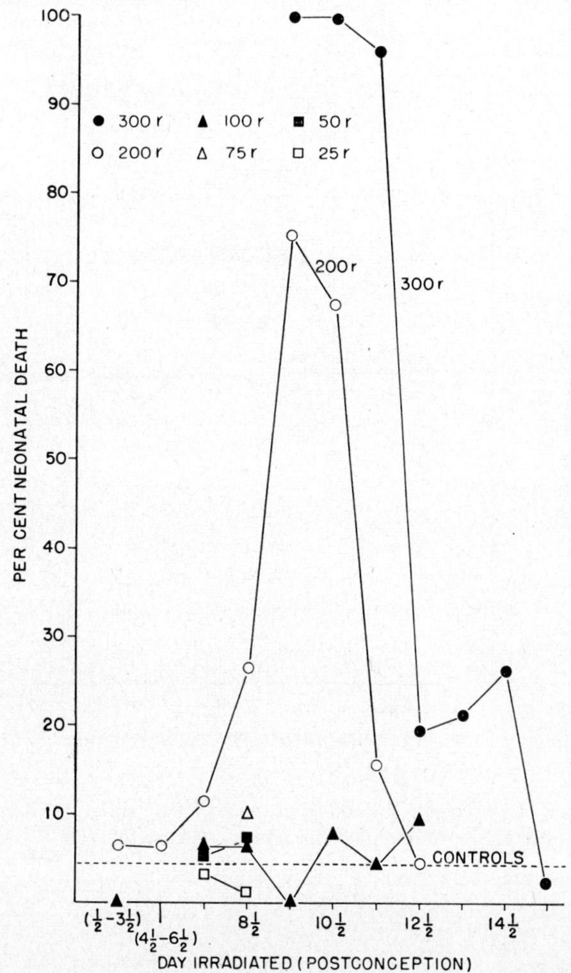

FIG. 13-2. Incidence of neonatal death following irradiation with different doses at different stages in the prenatal development of the mouse. (*Data of Russell and co-workers.*)

24-hour intervals. For the data presented in Fig. 13-2, the LD_{50} at birth varies as follows according to the stage irradiated:

For irradiation on days ½–8½ postconception, $LD_{50} > 200$ r.
For irradiation on days 9½ and 10½ postconception, $LD_{50} < 200$ r.
For irradiation on day 11½ postconception, $200r < LD_{50} < 300r$.
For irradiation on days 12½–15½ postconception, $LD_{50} > 300$ r.

2. BODY SIZE

Although only a few investigators report observations on weight or length of their material, the information available is sufficient to demonstrate an effect on body size of irradiation during the period of major organogenesis. Kosaka (1928b, c, d) mentions generalized hypoplasia from prenatally lethal doses in several rodents. Wilson and Karr (1951) present data on prenatally observable growth retardation in rat embryos. Raynaud and Frilley (1949a) and Russell (1950), both working on mice,

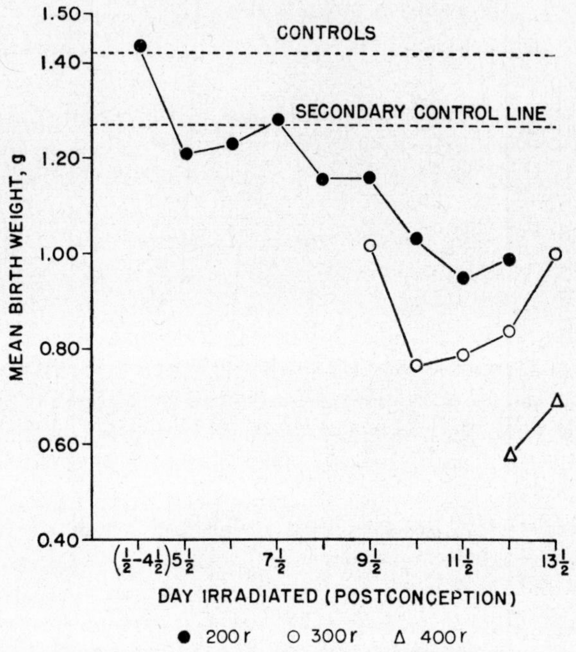

FIG. 13-3. Mean birth weights following irradiation with different doses at different stages in the prenatal development of the mouse. (*Russell*, 1950.)

have measured size at term. Finally, there are two rather vague reports of reduced body size in later life, in the rat (Hanson, 1923), and the rabbit (Cohn, 1907).

Wilson and Karr (1951) found no effect on body weight 2–11 days after irradiation with 50 r on day 10. With 100 r, however, there was a marked growth retardation one day after irradiation, treated embryos weighing 37 per cent less than controls. This high initial retardation may have been due mostly to moribund embryos since the percentage weight reduction in survivors decreased to between 6 and 15 per cent in the succeeding period up to term. With 200 r, weight reduction decreased to 20 per cent in survivors after an initial high of 39 per cent. Finally, embryos irradiated with 400 r, all of which were already dead at the time of first observation, appeared to have undergone at least some growth between irradiation and death. Of the animals which had received 100 r, seven were raised and it was found that they made up their initial weight deficiency (an average of 15 per cent at term) by the age of 70 days.

Russell (1950) presents mean birth weights for groups of animals irradiated in stages differing by 24-hour intervals and ranging from day ½ to day 13½ after fertilization (see Fig. 13-3). Several variables which are known to affect birth weight are controlled: (1) newborns are genetically uniform (F_1 hybrids between two inbred strains); (2) the maternal environment is genetically uniform; (3) parity is controlled, all animals coming from second litters. Other variables, especially litter size, could not be eliminated. A secondary control line was drawn in Fig. 13-3 to provide a liberal allowance for the amount of milk sucked by the time of weighing. It was found that mean birth weights for the 8½- through 13½-day stages of treatment fell considerably below that control line. The 200-r and 300-r curves were, in general, parallel with a mean difference of 0.2 g. Minima for both curves lay between the 10½- and 11½-day stages. The short portion of the 400-r curve available paralleled the 300-r curve in the rising portion between days 12½ and 13½.

Holding the time of irradiation constant, Russell, Russell, and Major (1951) obtained a more complete dose-weight series for day 11½, which is close to the stage of maximum susceptibility to growth retardation. Points for different doses and for the control fall on an approximately straight line, weight reduction per 100 r averaging 0.22 g over the three available intervals (Fig. 13-9*a*).

The experiments of Raynaud and Frilley fall into a special category since they involve very local irradiation with a narrow beam (0.5–3 mm diameter) of very high dosage (100,000 r per exposure) in an attempt at selective destruction of the pituitary. Five male mouse fetuses at term which had been irradiated twice, at 12 days 6 hours and 13 days 6 hours respectively, weighed, on the average, only about 60 per cent as much as their control litter mates (1949a). The loss of weight due to direct destruction of radiation-traversed head tissues does not account for the total weight loss, which is considerable. This is also evident from the fact that the irradiated animals showed a 10 per cent reduction in xiphoid-anal length as well as the expected reduction in crown-anal length. The results may be explained by secondary effects of pituitary destruction, by such uncontrolled factors as scattered radiation to other parts of the body, or, as the authors suggest, by indirect action of radiation-produced toxins.

3. SEX RATIO

The only claim in the literature of an upset sex ratio following prenatal irradiation is by Job *et al.* (1935), who state that treatment between the ninth and eleventh days with 35–50 r yielded 160.6 males per 100 females (i.e., 61.6 per cent males) without modifying the litter size. Control ratios are not reported and even significance of the difference from a 1:1 ratio cannot be calculated since the actual numbers for this group are not given. (In other groups, similar with respect to stages irradiated, the sex ratio appears normal; e.g., treatment between the eighth and eleventh days with 27–90 r gave 141 males and 132 females.) It may, however, be pointed out that a 1:1 sex ratio is not necessarily expected at birth even if it exists at conception. Russell (1950) reports 61.0 per cent newborn males in one group of controls (difference from 50 per cent males = 2.5 × S.E.) in comparison with which the excesses of males in both broad experimental categories (preimplantation and postimplantation) are nonsignificant.

Although it is, of course, quite conceivable that the sex ratio at birth might be affected by prenatal irradiation—either through differential mortality of one sex or through actual sex reversal (e.g., loss of one X chromosome)—valid reports of such effects must to date be considered lacking.

Job *et al.* further claim that males are more susceptible to the induction of abnormalities than are females. In the group irradiated between the eighth and eleventh days, which yielded all the morphological abnormalities reported, 37.4 per cent of 123 males and 24.8 per cent of 109 females treated with 36–90 r were deformed. The difference is at the 5 per cent level of significance ($t = 2.07$). The authors state, however, that only one of the abnormal animals had been irradiated on the eighth day, the other seventy-two between the ninth and eleventh, and the percentage of males obtained following irradiation on these days (as given without actual figures) is 61.6. The sex incidence of 62.7 per cent males among the abnormals then seems as expected on the basis of random distribution. The authors' claim must thus be considered unproved. Again, however, it is quite conceivable that differential sensitivity of the sexes to the induction of abnormalities will be found.

4. MORPHOLOGY

Even within the relatively limited literature on the subject a vast number of abnormalities has been reported as resulting from the irradiation of mammalian embryos during the period of major organogenesis. It is, therefore, unfortunate that some authors failed to realize the importance of timing accurately the stage at which the embryos were subjected to treatment, while others neglected to provide such pertinent information as total numbers (for the calculation of percentage incidence) or exact dosage. However, not many of the later publications fail in this respect, and the earlier ones, which do, were nevertheless useful in demonstrating that there existed a fertile field for future work. The earliest report of abnormalities was by von Hippel and Pagenstecher (1907) who obtained cataracts, microphthalmia, and lid coloboma in newborn rabbits following irradiation with a high dose (21 H = Holzknecht units) on days 7, 9, and 11, or 8, 10, and 12 after fertilization. Bagg (1922) mentions one case of "dislocation" of the spinal column in a rat fetus which had been treated between the tenth and fourteenth days of intra-uterine life with radium emanation. Several other fetuses in this group suffered from extravasations in subcutaneous vessels and along meningeal sinuses (Gudernatsch and Bagg, 1920). But since the same type of lesion could be produced by injecting the mother 22 days *before* conception and since it is unlikely that the activity of the circulating radiation source would be maintained long enough to affect the embryos directly, an indirect nonspecific effect through lasting injury of the mother must be postulated in this case. Hanson (1923) found that rat females in "later stages of pregnancy when given the proper dosage" of X rays produced litters in which one or more of the young had serious eye defects, changes in the shape of the skull, and paralysis of the limbs. When raised, they showed considerable growth retardation and nearly all proved sterile. De Nobele and Lams (1927), reporting on what appears to be the same material as that in which they studied radiation-induced prenatal mortality (1925)—although it is possible that some additional animals are included in the later publication—state that a few of the treated rat embryos which were permitted to come to term were afflicted with microphthalmia, while some of the irradiated guinea pig embryos later developed hydrocephalus and dilatation of the lateral ventricles. Murphy and de Renyi (1930) report foot abnormalities in all of five litters irradiated prenatally with 400 or 800 r. Since, unfortunately, the method consisted of giving a mixed population of virgin and pregnant females a series of exposures and then considering only those whose litters were cast within twenty-two days of the last exposure, it is not known at what stages embryos were irradiated, or even whether they were irradiated once or twice.

On turning to the more extensive and more carefully controlled work, it appears that the field has been explored in two general ways: (*a*) comparison of the results of irradiating a number of different stages in order to determine whether the changes produced are characteristic of the treatment day (Kosaka, 1927, 1928a, b, c, d, e; Job, Leibold, and Fitzmaurice, 1935; Kaven, 1938a; Warkany and Schraffenberger, 1947; Russell, 1949, 1950; Russell and Russell, 1950b); and (*b*) concentration on one or two stages (Raynaud and Frilley, 1943b, 1947a, b, c, 1949a, b; Wilson and Karr, 1950, 1951; Russell *et al.*, 1951), or a certain group of abnormalities (Pagenstecher, 1916; Kaven, 1938b; Hicks, 1950) with the ultimate aim of tracing the genesis of the malformations. All experiments (groups *a* and *b*) will first be briefly outlined in turn. Following this examination of each experiment, particularly with regard to the evidence for critical periods, tabular comparisons between experiments will be made in an attempt to derive some general conclusions about certain of the abnormalities. Many others will have to be ignored, due to limitations in scope of this review.

a. Experiments That Compare Results of Irradiating Different Stages. The first investigator to attempt a survey of the gestation period with regard to radiosensitivity was Kosaka who worked on mice (1927, 1928e), rats (1928b), rabbits (1928a),[4] and guinea pigs (1928c), irradiating during known intervals (though not definite days) postconception with various doses, ranging from ⅛ to 2 SED, and observing effects manifest 6, 12, 24, 48, 72, et seq., hours after irradiation. A large part of the work on all animals was devoted to histological description of tissue damage which was apparently not considered as malformation since special mention is made (1928d) of the fact that malformations (microcephalus, deformity of the extremities) occurred only in the rabbit. For any given stage of irradiation, tissues were ranked in order of decreasing sensitivity, and this rank order was found to change with the stage in a manner parallel to the change in relative growth rates of the particular organs. Early in the period of organogenesis, brain and spinal cord are most sensitive, retina and mesoderm in second place. Shortly thereafter, spinal cord loses much of its sensitivity, while retina joins brain in first place. During the period of the fetus, thymus suddenly becomes extremely sensitive, and liver and spleen move up on the list. A variety of other tissues in the lower ranks of sensitivity must be omitted from mention here. Finally, certain organs showed no marked effects from irradiation at any stage. One interesting finding was that, while the processes of regeneration in most tissues were similar in kind to the growth which had occurred just before irradiation, cerebrum and retina responded to severe damage by forming numerous ependymal canals believed analogous to the neural tube of early stages.

Job *et al.* (1935) posed the question of whether certain periods in development could be demonstrated to be critical either for the rat embryo as a whole or for certain of its organ systems or individual organs. After eliminating higher doses because of excessive mortality, they obtained litters from sixty-six females which had received a single dose of X rays of 90 r or less between the first and sixteenth days of gestation. In all cases where irradiation had been before the eighth day or after the eleventh day, the young were normal. Following irradiation between eighth and eleventh days, 17 of the young (7 per cent) were hydrocephalic, 14 (6 per cent) suffered from jaw abnormalities, and 52

[4] Unlike Kosaka's other publications, the paper on rabbits lacks an English or German summary. This reviewer did not obtain a translation of the Japanese text. Scattered information about the rabbit results was obtained from the other papers of the series, particularly the summary paper (Kosaka, 1928d).

(22 per cent) had eye defects (about ⅔ bilateral) combined in 8 of the animals with one of the other two abnormalities. Breaking down this generally sensitive period, it appeared that hydrocephalus resulted from irradiation on the ninth day and jaw abnormalities on the eleventh day, while most of the eye defects were produced by treatment on the tenth day. Job *et al.* can thus be considered to have brought the first demonstration of well-defined critical periods for abnormalities in different characters. Incidence for individual treatment days cannot be calculated since separate totals are not given, but the qualitative results are included in Figs. 13-4 to 13-7 for purposes of comparison with the findings of other investigators.

In an experiment essentially similar to the above, Kaven (1938a) obtained litters from over 162 mouse females irradiated on any one of days 7 to 19[5] with a constant dose of 178 r (at the level of the embryo or fetus). Two improvements over Job's method were (1) the use of genetically homogeneous material, and (2) observations on a large control group (Kaven, 1938b). Abnormals are reported for each group separately and give clear indications of the existence of critical periods even though percentage incidence can usually be only estimated (since Kaven, like Job, does not report the number of young observed within each group). The qualitative results are included in Figs. 13-4 to 13-7. The most frequently affected structure, the tail (abnormal in over 130 newborns), is sensitive only between days 9 and 14, with peak sensitivity probably on day 11. Brain hernias were obtained exclusively from irradiation on day 8. Although both the incidence and total number in this group were small in the original series, a separate experiment (Kaven, 1938b—see p. 890), in which irradiation was given only on days 7 or 8, established that the original cases had not been spurious. Four other abnormalities are reported, in the survey series, from treatment during the period of organogenesis: head malformation and head hemorrhage, each appearing in one of eighteen litters irradiated on day 10; hydrocephalus (apparent a few days after birth), occurring in about 10 per cent of the animals irradiated on day 12 and in lower proportions from the treatment of days 13 and 10; and skin defects arising later in life as a result of irradiation on days 13 and 14 postconception. (Other abnormalities produced by Kaven—e.g., torsion of limbs, digital abnormalities—were apparently not noticed by him but are apparent from the photo-

[5] Kaven followed two systems of timing pregnancy: (1) by actual observation of copulation, in which case his "first day" equals day ⅔ to 1⅓, depending on hour of mating and hour of irradiation; (2) by looking for vaginal plugs, which, in the majority of cases, represent fertilizations between 1:00 and 4:00 A.M., so that, under this system, his "first day" approximately equals day 1¼ to 1⅔, depending on hour of irradiation. It is thus obvious that within a given one of his stage groups, pregnancies may differ in age by a whole day. In general, the designation of his "first day" as *day one* is probably representative of the majority of his cases and will be followed in this review.

graphs.) The numbers of afflicted animals are small but assume importance in comparison with the results of other workers.

Warkany and Schraffenberger (1947) studied litters from 108 rat females irradiated on any one of days 9 to 15 of gestation (referred to by the authors as "10th to 16th" days)[6] and reported well over a dozen different abnormalities. Unfortunately they do not separate the results for different doses but give only the dose range (often very wide, e.g., 190–900 r) for each stage group. Since, at any one stage, an increase in dose generally increases percentage incidence of a given abnormality (Russell, 1950), it is obviously impossible to determine the most sensitive stages in Warkany and Schraffenberger's experiment by comparing incidence: for a peak may be due merely to a higher dose having been used. Moreover, since, by raising the dose, a primordium or process can usually be affected on days adjacent to that of maximum sensitivity (Russell, 1950), it is not surprising that with the large doses used (up to 1120 r) the authors did not usually get very clearly defined critical periods. Even so, a few emerge when incidences are calculated from their report and when allowance is made for the dosage difficulties discussed above (see Figs. 13-4 to 13-7). Thus, the peak for rib angulation is definitely on day 14, the long bones of the front legs are sensitive almost exclusively on day 12, and those of the hind legs mostly on day 12 except for the tibia which has a peak sensitivity on day 10. These points and others become interesting in comparison with other experiments (see pp. 891–893).

Like Kaven, Russell (1949, 1950) used genetically uniform mice, in her case an F_1 hybrid between two inbred strains to add vigor to uniformity. The scope of the experiment was extended with respect to (1) the number of stages surveyed, (2) doses used (200 r for all stage groups, 300 and 400 r at certain ones), and (3) types of abnormalities observed. The skeleton was chosen for detailed study mainly because its various parts are formed by processes whose periods of maximum activity, taken

[6] See footnote 3.

FIGS. 13-4 to 13-7. Results of several groups of investigators represented to show critical periods for the induction of various abnormalities.

Wherever sufficient data are given in the original publication, representation here is by (*a*) percentage incidence of abnormality (see scale in figures) and (*b*) magnitude of dose required to produce abnormality. Thus, the wider and more heavily shaded a band, the greater the sensitivity. Absence of a band at a particular stage indicates that the abnormality did not occur in the irradiated group (see, e.g., 200 r results of Russell), except where the serrated end of a band indicates that the dose series was not continued to the stage in question (see, e.g., 300 and 400 r results of Russell, all results of Wilson and Karr). For cases where exact incidence for a given stage and dose cannot be calculated from the original data, representation is only roughly quantitative. In general, + = 1–49%, >200 r; ++ = 1–49%, 1–200 r; +++ = 50–100%, >200 r; ++++ = 50–100%, 1–200 r. (J = *Job, Leibold, and Fitzmaurice*, 1935; K = *Kaven*, 1938a,b; R = *Russell*, 1950, 1949; Wi = *Wilson and Karr*, 1951, 1950; Wa = *Warkany and Schraffenberger*, 1947.)

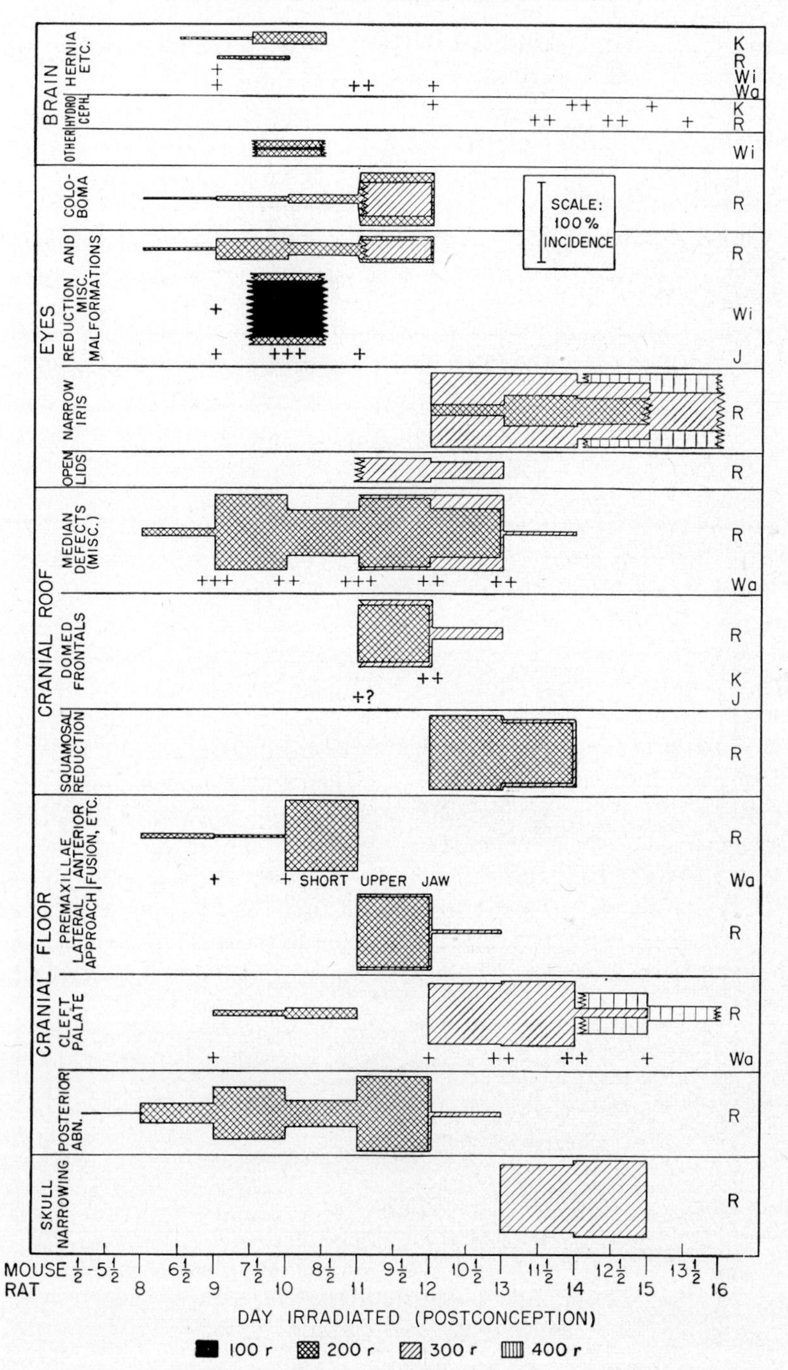

FIG. 13-4. Central nervous system, eyes, skull.

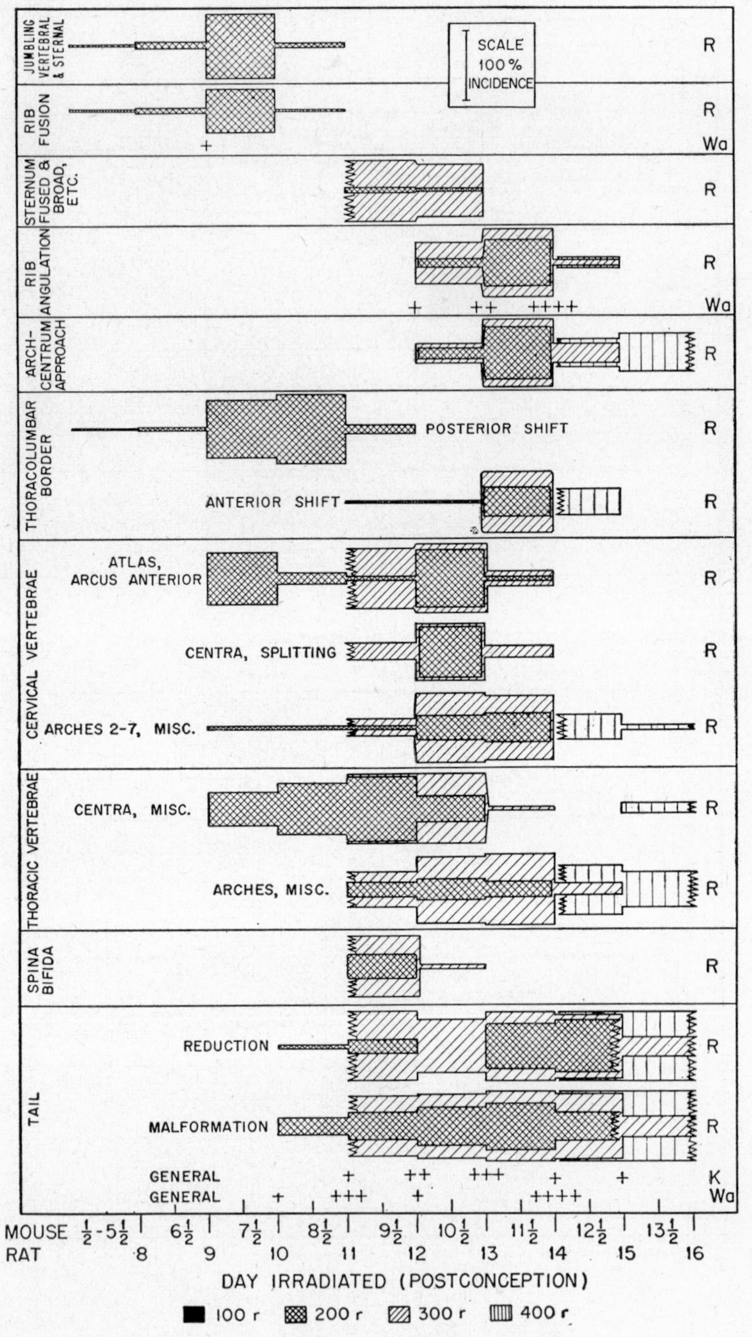

FIG. 13-5. Vertebral column and thorax.

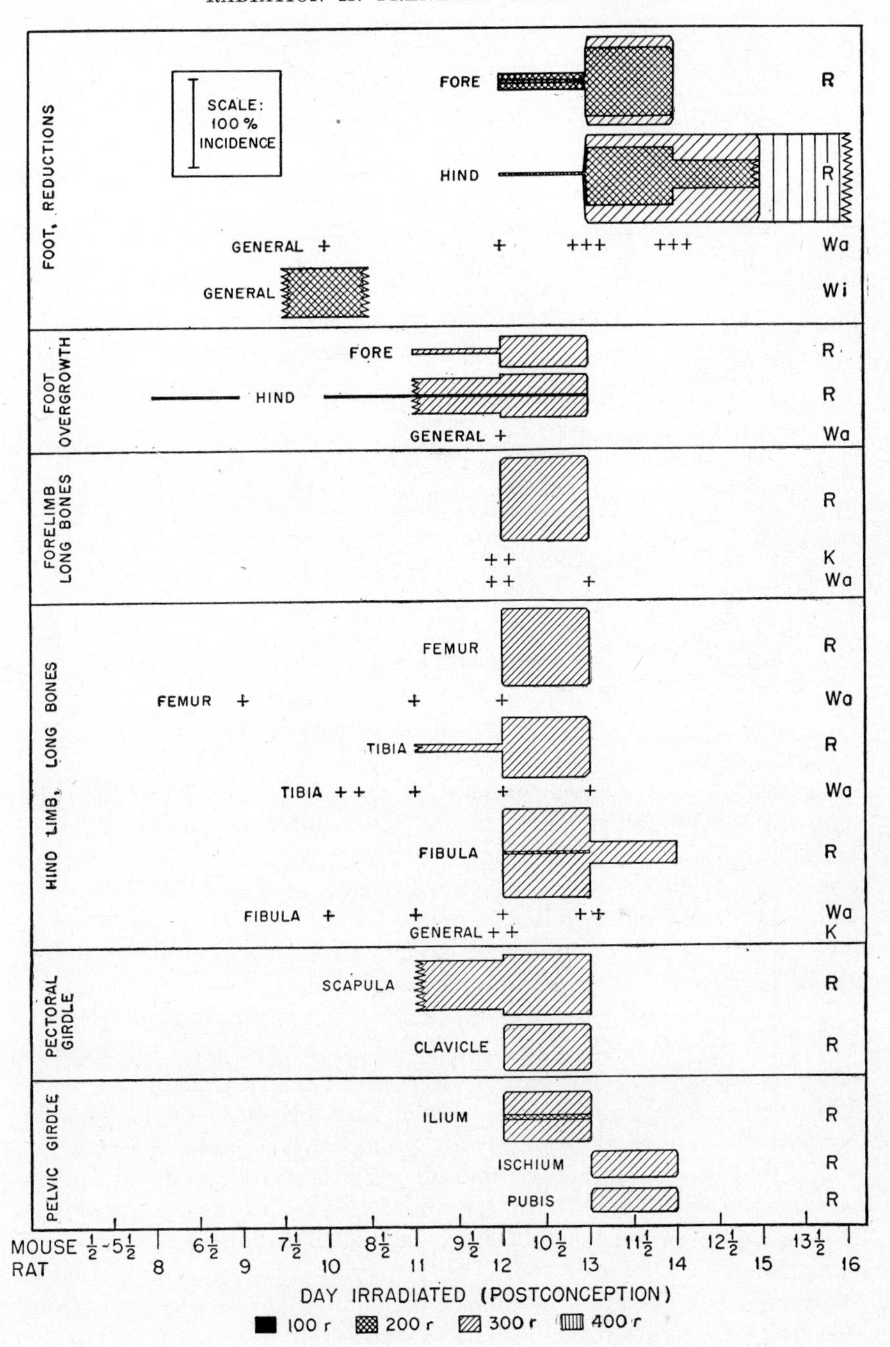

FIG. 13-6. Appendicular skeleton.

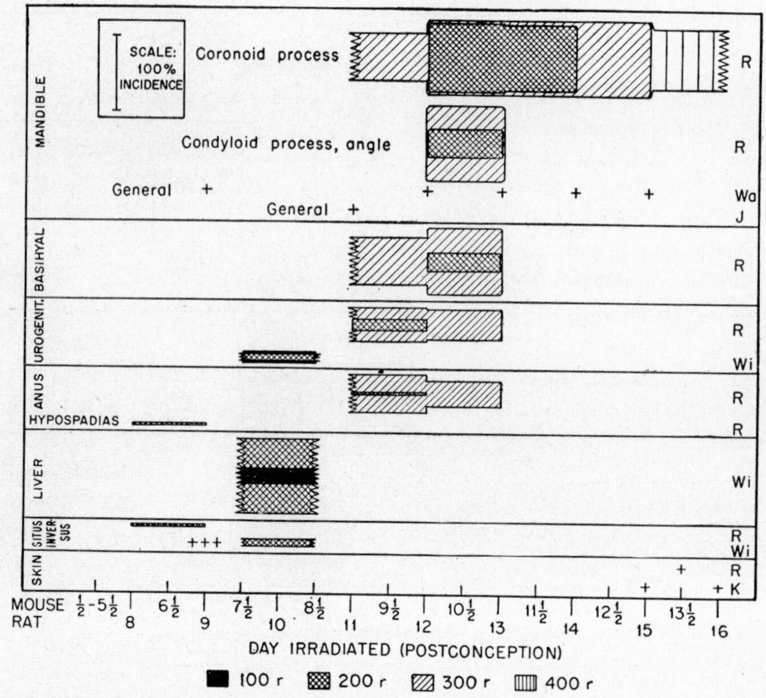

FIG. 13-7. Visceral skeleton, viscera, and miscellaneous.

altogether, spread over a considerable portion of embryonic life. In addition to skeletal abnormalities, changes noted on careful external examination and on gross dissection were recorded. A large control group (372 newborns) was studied in the same manner as 420 newborns which had been irradiated during prenatal life. Since it is impossible to give a complete report of changes observed (the checklist of characters examined included about a hundred items), only the most striking ones and those most useful for comparison with the results of other investigators are represented in Figs. 13-4 to 13-7. These samples will serve to illustrate the general type of result obtained.

Almost all abnormalities represented in Figs. 13-4 to 13-7 were found in newborns or fetuses at term but are projected back upon the stage at which they were apparently induced. Width of the bands represents percentage incidence at term. Without going into details about the abnormalities, several general features of Russell's results may be pointed out. First, it is striking that with the general survey dose of 200 r, abnormalities in a high proportion of the animals are obtained only from embryos exposed after day 5½ (no external and visceral and only 2 per cent slight skeletal abnormalities from irradiation of earlier periods). At the other end, day 13½ is probably the limit beyond which abnormalities of the types looked for at term can no longer be obtained with 200 r.

This broad division of the gestation period has already been mentioned and the special features of the first phase (preimplantation) have been discussed. Second, it is apparent that critical periods[7] for the induction of almost all abnormalities are short. The 200-r series shows many of them to be restricted to one particular stage (e.g., spina bifida, reduction of the ilium, abnormalities of the basihyal, etc.), and even when they span several stages, one often stands out as the main sensitive one on the basis of incidence (e.g., anterior premaxillary fusion, vertebral jumbling, rib fusion, coloboma). Third, the effective period of disturbance is lengthened by raising the dose, indicating that a certain degree of sensitivity exists at stages other than the most critical one. High doses are thus not suitable for the mapping of critical periods except for abnormalities which have high thresholds of induction (e.g., deformities in limbs and girdles). The addition of higher dose series is useful, however, not only for conclusions which can be drawn from dosage comparisons (discussed later in Sect. IIIC) but also for the confirmation of location and shape (e.g., unimodal, or bimodal as in tail reduction, etc.) of any given critical period.

b. Experiments That Concentrate on a Few Stages or on a Group of Abnormalities. In contrast to the experiments discussed so far, Wilson and Karr (1951) confined their X-ray treatment of rat embryos to day 10. Survivors which had received 50, 100, or 200 r (18, 40, and 31 embryos, respectively) were sacrificed 1–5 days later and examined for morphological changes. A small number of embryos in the 100-r group were allowed to come to term and were observed postnatally. All the prenatal findings of aberrant growth in various organs, as well as damage to the liver (classed by the authors with localized retardations rather than with malformations), are represented in Figs. 13-4 to 13-7. It may be noted that 50 r was ineffective except in the production of two cases of slight microphthalmia. For most changes, incidence with 200 r is higher than with 100 r. The eye was the most consistently affected of all organs, giving 75 per cent abnormalities even with 100 r. Defects of the extremities and liver damage cannot be diagnosed until the thirteenth or fourteenth days, when these organs have reached a stage of differentiation adequate for observation. Percentage incidences are, therefore, based on considerably lower totals (14, 27, and 16 animals, respectively, in the three dose groups) but, as they stand, they approximate eye defects in frequency in the 200-r, though not in the 100-r group. Urogenital malformations include (in order of decreasing frequency) incipient horseshoe

[7] The critical period for a given change from normal development may be defined as the developmental moment or interval during which radiation must be applied to produce that change at some specified stage of observation, if the dose of radiation is the lowest one that gives a detectable incidence of that change. The term "critical period" does not necessarily imply that the immediate primordium of the character malformed as a result of irradiation at a certain stage was damaged at that stage.

kidneys, defects in the mesonephros, inhibition or duplication of a metanephric bud, and epispadias. In the central nervous system, the brain was the only part affected by irradiation on day 10; in all but one of the cases, malformations involved the forebrain, mainly the telencephalon. A tendency to reversed asymmetry in dominance of aortic arches, combined in two of three cases with reversed tail curling, gave indications of a certain degree of *situs inversus*. Abnormalities of the extremities were usually more pronounced in, or limited to, the forelimbs. In mild cases only the distal elements were affected, while distortions and deficiencies extended more proximally in more severely afflicted individuals.

Set apart from the malformations are cases of localized retardation, i.e., tardiness in normal processes rather than aberrant growth. Criteria for gauging retardation are considered not completely satisfactory, especially where malformations are superimposed. Brain and urogenital organs are most frequently retarded, but heart, aortic arches, and lungs may also be affected. Also classed with retardation rather than malformation is liver damage, which frequently involves a reduction (occasionally down to complete absence) of hemopoietic elements. While the impairment is only slight and transitory in the 100-r groups, the authors feel that in the 200-r groups it represents a significant functional loss and may be associated with the high rate of prenatal death. As judged by eight 100-r animals allowed to go to term, there may be recovery from localized retardations except in the eye, where microphthalmia may become anophthalmia or malformation, and in the heart (one case).

A few results of irradiation on day 9 are mentioned by Wilson and Karr in an abstract (1950) and used (1951) for occasional comparisons with the day-10 results. While reversal of symmetry was only indicated following irradiation on day 10, treatment on the preceding day may give *situs inversus totalis*. Furthermore, there seems to be a very sharp division for the type of central nervous system anomalies obtainable from the two treatment stages, day-10 irradiation never yielding the class of defects that results from faulty closure of the neural tube, while irradiation on day 9 often produced meningocele, encephalocele, cranioschisis, etc. More prevalent after day-9 exposure were aberrant cell islands of neural origin, growing independently in the mesenchyme surrounding the brain. These are described in more detail by Wilson, Brent, and Jordan (1951) and may be comparable to the regenerative growths found by Kosaka (1928b, c, see p. 880).

In one experimental series, Russell *et al.* (1951) concentrated on the irradiation of day 11½. However, since this experiment also involved irradiation under hypoxia, it will be reviewed in a different section (see Sect. IIIB).

The experiments of Raynaud and Frilley fall into a class by themselves since, because of the method employed, the results cannot be used to indicate differential sensitivity throughout the body. The mother's uterus was exposed by laparotomy and a localized beam (0.5–3 mm diameter—see 1943a for technique) directed from below at the head region of the embryos, particularly at the base of the diencephalon. The traversed region also included the central shaft of the cranium, the buccal cavity, and the primordium of the tongue. The dose range was 5000–200,000 r. The investigators confined exposures to mouse embryos of a certain age, namely, 12 days 6 hours, adding occasionally a second irradiation 24 hours later. All observations were made just before term. In three publications (1943b, 1947a, c), the authors report on effects in structures directly traversed by the pencil of X rays; in another three (1947b, 1949a, b), they describe observations on the reproductive system which was not irradiated but could conceivably have been secondarily affected as a result of pituitary damage.

As expected for the high doses used, there was considerable damage in the radiation path. Externally, the animals treated with 5000–40,000 r were microcephalic, often had open eyelids, and occasionally lacked ears, tongue, salivary glands, or upper or lower jaws. After irradiation with 190,000 r, the head at term was only a small atrophic mass. Condensation of mesenchyme to precartilage was suspended and membranous ossification suppressed even with 5000–40,000 r. The same dose range produced extensive cerebral lesions, and complete destruction of the optic nerve and of both layers of the retina. Following treatment with 60,000 r, the brain at term showed the vesicle configuration characteristic of the stage of irradiation; while 190,000 r left only a necrotic mass with the vesicles no longer recognizable. Complete destruction of the anterior lobe of the pituitary could be achieved only with 200,000 r divided evenly between 12 days 6 hours and 13 days 6 hours. It should be noted that, in spite of the massive damage due to the high doses used, it is possible to find in the data evidence of differential susceptibility of different structures. Thus, only a quarter (or less ?) of the dose required to inactivate the anterior lobe will completely eliminate the pars nervosa; the choroid plexus resists 60,000 r, a dose which causes almost complete destruction of the rest of the brain; the lens of the eye resists doses which completely destroy retina and optic nerve.

Several indirect changes were noted in regions presumably not traversed by radiation. Effects on body size have already been discussed (see p. 877). In addition, there was marked atrophy of the adrenal cortex and a reduction in liver glycogen. In spite of pituitary destruction, the histogenesis of the genital tract, including accessory structures, and the cytological differentiation of the germ cells proceeded normally, which led the authors to suggest that either the hypophysis exerts no gonadotropic influence in development or that its function can be taken over by maternal or placental hormones. There was, however, up to

70 per cent reduction in the number of germ cells in both sexes and somewhat reduced masculinization in the external genitalia of males, which would point to the lack of some normally available trophic influence or to a general toxic effect (e.g., in the blood) caused by the localized radiation.

The experiment of Kaven (1938b) forms a transition between those concentrated on a particular stage and those concentrated on a certain group of abnormalities. His concern was with the latter—namely, meningocele and possibly related changes—but his earlier experiment (1938a) had yielded information on the effective treatment stage. The pertinent features of Kaven's experiment may be read from Table 13-6,

TABLE 13-6. INCIDENCE OF BRAIN ABNORMALITIES AND OF MORTALITY IN FETAL STAGES AND AT BIRTH FOLLOWING IRRADIATION OF 7- OR 8-DAY-OLD MOUSE EMBRYOS (Kaven, 1938b)

	Irradiated day 7			Irradiated day 8			Control
Day observed:	14	17	Birth	13–16	17–19	Birth	Birth
Number of litters	31	24	39	40		47	306
Number of fetuses	237	182	166	118	169	219	2066
Per cent dead	65.8	72.0	11.4	39.0	30.8	13.7	1.7
Per cent extrakranielle Dysencephalie[a]	4.9	0	0	16.7	3.4	0	0
Per cent meningocele[a]	0	17.3	2.4	2.8	19.7	16.1	0
Average litter size:							
Total	7.6	7.6	.....	7.2			
Expected at term[b]	2.6	2.1	.....	4.4			
Found at term	.....	.....	4.3	.....	.....	4.7	6.8

[a] Percentages for prenatal observations are based on living fetuses only, in order to make them more comparable with results at birth, when the majority of prenatally dead animals will not be counted.

[b] That is, living and without "extrakranielle Dysencephalie."

which was compiled from information scattered through his paper. The results show that brain hernias (more correctly, meningoceles) at birth are significantly more frequent following irradiation on day 8 than on day 7 (they were never obtained from later stages—Kaven, 1938a), and that this abnormality becomes macroscopically apparent only late in prenatal development (all cases but one after the sixteenth day). A finding entirely unexpected from the birth data was the presence, in dissected uteri, of fetuses with "icepack" brains, i.e., pseudencephalics. This abnormality, referred to by Kaven as "extrakranielle Dysencephalie," is about five times as frequent in 13- to 16- as in 17- to 19-day fetuses and is apparently missing in litters not observed until shortly after birth.

Reduction in litter size at birth in the group irradiated on day 8 is completely accounted for when these abnormals are added to the number of placental rests (but agreement for day 7 is not very good). Kaven suggests that the various effects may be explained by embryos being in slightly different stages of neural tube closure at the time of irradiation on day 8. The developmentally (not necessarily chronologically) youngest are most sensitive and die early (placental rests at time of observation). This is supported by the finding that irradiation on the preceding day (day 7) gives a greatly increased prenatal mortality. Slightly more advanced embryos respond with development of pseudencephaly and die shortly before term. Still more advanced embryos are at least externally normal for a considerable period, then about 3 days before birth develop meningocele and show reduced postnatal viability. Finally, the most advanced embryos are not affected at all.

Pagenstecher (1916) concentrated his studies on rosette formation in the retina, after von Hippel and Pagenstecher had demonstrated very early (1907) that various eye abnormalities could be obtained from the irradiation of rabbit embryos. In four fetuses, observed 3–4 days before term, which had been irradiated between days 9 and 15 postfertilization, he found three with rosettes (five out of eight eyes). He believed that rosettes were the simplest type of retinal damage and that each represented the apex of an altered fetal fold of the retina.

Hicks (1950) irradiated rat and mouse females "in the second and third week" of pregnancy (without closer timing of the stage of treatment) and reports the resulting nervous system changes. Mention is made of the fact that extraneural damage is not obtained with doses below 400 r. Since this is in contradiction to all other work (already reviewed) on mouse and rat for irradiation during the second week, it seems probable that virtually all of Hicks' data came from exposure during the third week. They will therefore be discussed in the section dealing with irradiation during the period of the fetus.

c. Comparison of Experiments. In an attempt to derive more general conclusions about certain of the abnormalities which have been obtained through irradiation of embryos, Figs. 13-4, 5, 6, 7 have been constructed from data contained in eight publications of five groups of investigators reviewed in preceding sections. The figures include all abnormalities reported by Job *et al.* (1935), Kaven (1938a, b), Warkany and Schraffenberger (1947), Wilson and Karr (1951, 1950); and a sample of the abnormalities reported by Russell (1950, 1949). The data of Kosaka, of Pagenstecher, of Hicks, of Murphy and de Renyi, and of early authors contain either insufficient information or none at all on stage of irradiation. They, therefore, had to be omitted from the comparison since they can contribute little or nothing to conclusions about critical periods. Also omitted are the experiments of Raynaud and Frilley which involved localized radiation and could thus not be expected to indicate differential sensitivities throughout the body.

It should be pointed out that several approximations have had to be made to construct Figs. 13-4 to 13-7. They represent work on two different animals—rat and mouse—which had to be matched according to equivalent developmental stage. In most of the original publications, data are not represented in a manner to indicate critical periods. Many are incomplete: Job does not report totals for calculation of percentage incident, Kaven only occasionally; Kaven's observations were apparently not thorough since he missed limb defects clearly indicated in one of his illustrations; Warkany and Schraffenberger list only wide dose ranges (e.g., 190–900 r) instead of separating results according to dose. It must also be remembered that the thorough work of Wilson and Karr was confined mainly to day 10.

Despite the various limitations, agreement in most cases is good and some of it is striking. Only some of the comparisons can be discussed here. In the work of three authors, the critical periods for all long-bone defects in the forelimbs seem to be strictly confined, both in mouse and rat, to the stage when the anterior limb buds first become apparent as rudder-shaped outgrowths. The total period for the hind limb is somewhat longer and the work of two authors indicates that the tibia is the first bone to be sensitive, the fibula the last. Warkany and Russell agree well, both on polydactyly and on foot reduction (oligodactyly, syndactyly, etc.), but for the latter there is an additional early critical period in the rat (Wilson, Warkany) which has not appeared in the mouse data. The general period sensitive to the induction of eye abnormalities is similar in three experiments.

There is agreement between authors on apparent bimodalities in critical periods of three characters (ribs, tail, palate). In the case of the ribs, two different abnormalities—fusion and angulation—are obviously represented without overlap in times of sensitivity. For the tail, such distinction cannot be made from the end result, but very probably two different developmental processes are affected (Russell, 1950). All cases of cleft palate resulting from early treatment were found by Russell (1949) to be associated with anterior premaxillary fusion, while those following irradiation during the second period were independent of this, thus probably indicating two entirely different precursor processes for the abnormality. Warkany does not report any such distinction but, since short upper jaw occurs in his material irradiated during the early period, a similar situation may exist.

Russell found only one instance of situs inversus in the mouse, but this corresponds well in critical stage with the more frequent cases of Wilson. On the other hand, the urogenital malformations described by these two investigators are probably of different types and it is thus not surprising that the critical periods differ.

C. THE PERIOD OF THE FETUS

Very few of the more recent investigators have concentrated their attention on irradiation during the period of the fetus. Thus, the bulk of Table 13-7 represents either early (often inadequate) work, or newer experimental series in which the main emphasis lay on the period of organogenesis but which, for one reason or another, were extended to include the first few days of the period of the fetus. It will, therefore, suffice to mention only the few highlights on which evidence seems adequate.

1. MORTALITY

Mortality resulting from irradiation of fetal stages has been found to occur mostly in the period between birth and two weeks of age (see also Table 13-7). The mode is probably shortly after birth, but the frequency there is considerably less than for equivalent doses used during the period of major organogenesis (Kaven, 1938a, see p. 874; Russell, see Fig. 13-2). Prenatal death has been noted only by a few authors (Kosaka, 1928c; de Nobele and Lams, 1925; Schinz, 1923) for doses in the neighborhood of 1 SED and above, i.e., even higher than those which will cause early postnatal death. In early experiments where absolute doses were not known (Burckhard, Trillmich, Saretzky), exposures equal to those which would give a high degree of prenatal mortality when given earlier in pregnancy were without effect when given during the period of the fetus.

A kind of acute fatal radiation sickness may occur during the first week or two following birth. Bagg (1922) reports that γ-ray treatment of rats 2 or 3 days before term produces in approximately half the animals of each litter symptoms of anemia, diffuse edema, and meningeal, spinal cord and subcutaneous extravasations, leading to death at about a week of age. Autopsy revealed fatty degeneration of the liver and desquamation of the lining of the intestinal mucosa. Job *et al.* (1935) report postnatal anemia, diarrhea, hemorrhagic exudates in eye and nose, underweight, and abnormal nervousness following X-ray treatment of rat fetuses with more than 1 "skin unit," but no effect from lower doses. (It is not clear whether 1 skin unit = 1 SED.) Lacassagne and Coutard (1923) found that fifty-three of fifty-four rabbits, which had been irradiated 2–3 days before birth, died of "purpura roentgenien." Death occurred always on the tenth day after birth following a relatively invariable syndrome (hemorrhagic spots in skin and viscera; extravasations from peritoneum, pleura, pericardium; edema; torpor; dyspnea;—note resemblance

TABLE 13-7. SUMMARY OF THE LITERATURE DEALING WITH IRRADIATION OF THE MAMMALIAN FETUS

Animal	Author	Dose[a]	Region exposed[b]	Stage irradiated[c]	Stage observed[d]	Number		Results[f]						
						Mothers	Young observ.	Mortality			Specific damage		Poor devel.	No effect
								Pre-natal	Neo-natal	Post-natal	Imme-diate[e]	De-layed		
Mouse	Burckhard	?	Total	2d half	T, PN	?	?							+
	Burstone	5–17 μc/g P^{32}	Injection	One of 14–18	6–28 PN	18	?				+			
	Hicks	35–600 r	Total	Third week	2 hr PI–PN	<46	?				+	+		
	Kaven, 1938a	200 r	Abdomen	15, 16, . . . , or 19	T, PN	>49	>303					+		
	Kosaka, 1927, 1928e	⅛–2½ SED	Total or parts	One of 15–20	½–? PI, PN	?	~250?	+		?	+	+	+	
	Nürnberger	5 min	Abdomen	18?	T, PN	2	9		+					
	Parkes	10–40 min	Total	1 to 3 of 10½–18½	T, PN	9	>48			+		+		
	Russell, Grobman	300 r, 500 r	Total	14½ or 15½	T, PN	16	110		+	+		+		
Rat	Bagg	Ra, or 1300–2900 mc/hrγ	Inject. or through abd.	One of 15–21	T, PN	>31	?			+	+	+		
	Hicks	35–600 r	Total	Third week	2 hr PI–PN	<46	?				+	+		
	Job *et al.*	0.2–1.6 skin unit	Total	16th, 17th, or 18th	T	?	?		+	+				
		12–90 r	Total	16th, 17th, or 18th	T	<14	<123							+
	Kosaka, 1928b	⅓–2 SED	?	One of 16–20	¼ PI–PN	22	?		+		+			
	Hanson	?	Total?	18?	T, PN	?	?				+	+	+	
Guinea pig	Dyroff	350 r	Total	55	T, PN	1	?		+					
	Kosaka, 1928c	⅓–2 SED	?	One exp., 5th–9th week	¼ PI–T	84	?	+			+			
	Lengfellner, 1906	20–60 min	Total?	61, 64?	T	3	9		+					
	de Nobele and Lams	½–1 SED	Total	30, 31, or 32	37 PC–PN	8	15	+				+		
	Nürnberger	X ray or Ra + mesothor.	Total ?	One of 28–53?	T, PN	3	6			+		+		
	Trillmich	60 min	Total	31?–36?, daily	PI externally	1	2			+				
Rabbit	Cohn	3 hours	Head	10–20	PN	?	?						+	
	Fellner and Neumann	5–8 H	Upper ⅔ of abdomen	25 + 28	T	1	6		+					
	Kosaka, 1928a[g]	⅓–2 SED	?	20, 25, or 30	¼ PI–T	54	?							
	Lacassagne *et al.*	5.5–13 H	Abdomen	19, 28, 29, or 30	29 PC–10 PN	>9	>62			+	+			
	Momigliano, 1934	½–2 SED	Total ?	"End" of pregn.	T	3	?		+					
	Nürnberger	30 min	Abdomen	18	T, PN	1	5		+					
	Saretzky	?	Ovaries	2d half	PI	9	?							+
	Schinz	¼–2 SED	Total	15, 16, 18, 20, 22, or 28	PI to T	6	46?	+	+					
	Sébileau	Tint no. 3	Total ?	21?	T, PN	2	>4		+	+				

[a] X rays, unless otherwise indicated. See also text footnote 2.
[b] Refers to mother.
[c] Designates day postconception unless otherwise indicated.
[d] PC = postconception, PI = postirradiation, T = term, PN = postnatal. Numbers designate days unless otherwise indicated.
[e] Before day 10 postnatal.
[f] Positive reports are indicated by +. Absence of a + symbol in the table may indicate either a negative result or lack of observation: many of the original publications do not allow a decision between these two alternatives.
[g] Details of results available only in Japanese.

to Bagg's syndrome), which was first noticeable externally on the fourth day (Lacassagne, Lavedan, and Léobardy, 1922). Coagulation time was progressively decreased, starting with the seventh day, and platelets were absent. Lacassagne and Lavedan (1922) report blood counts on pre-

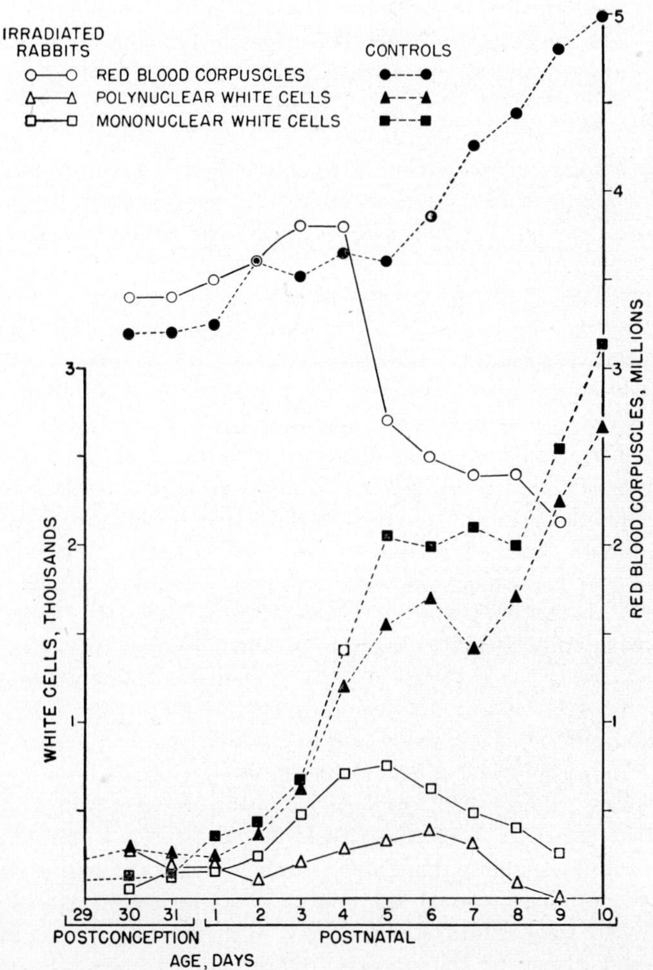

FIG. 13-8. Average counts of red blood corpuscles polynuclear white cells, and mononuclear white cells in rabbits irradiated in utero 2–3 days before term. Counts were begun following irradiation on day 29 postconception and were continued daily until death. (*Graphs constructed from data presented by Lacassagne and Lavedan.*)

sumably the same group of animals. Figure 13-8 was constructed from their data. The red count of irradiated animals is normal until the fourth day after birth when it takes a sharp drop and continues to fall. The effect on total white count is more immediate, consisting of almost complete inhibition of the very sharp rise which normally takes place at birth: while control counts increase from 350 to 5800 by the tenth day, irradiated animals stay at the fetal level except for a temporary rise to 1100 on the fifth day. The deficiency of polynuclear cells is somewhat greater than that of mononuclear cells, the former averaging only about 29 per cent of the total white count for the period from birth to ten days instead of the normal 43 per cent.

2. MORPHOLOGY

Irradiation during the period of the fetus does not lead to the striking changes or malformations in newborns which are produced by irradiation with comparable or even lower doses during the period of major organogenesis (Job, 1935; Kaven, 1938a; Russell, 1950). It is, however, erroneous to assume that exposure during the latter part of pregnancy is without morphological effects. It must be remembered that there is less chance for any damage to express itself as a gross change by the time of birth, for not only is the irradiation-to-observation interval shorter, but the rate of development averages considerably less over that period than over the interval from earlier exposure to birth. On these grounds, it may be expected that gross changes will become expressed later in life and these have indeed been reported by a number of authors (Bagg, 1922; Kosaka, 1928e; Kaven, 1938a; Russell, 1950; Hicks, 1950; Grobman, personal communication). Several studies on fertility point in the same direction (Parkes, 1927; Kosaka, 1928e; Hanson, 1923). The immediate damage which may lead to later gross changes was demonstrated by Kosaka (1928b, c) and Hicks (1950). General growth retardation has also been reported (Kosaka, 1928e; Job *et al.*, 1935). Some of the studies enumerated will be briefly described in the rest of this section.

Delayed morphological effects of irradiation during the fetal period were first noticed by Bagg (1922) in survivors from the group in which acute radiation death had been described (see p. 893). Externally, these animals exhibited opaque pupil and atrophied lens. At autopsy at about a year of age, Bagg also noted smallness of the cerebral hemispheres, especially the neopallium (occasionally even complete absence of the cortex), and arrest of the gonads, ovaries and testes alike. Kosaka (1928e) also found very marked hypoplasia of the cerebrum and the gonads, and occasionally a smaller degree of arrest in lung, liver, heart, and kidney in surviving mice (or rats ?) irradiated after the fourteenth day postconception with ⅔ SED. Both Kaven (1938a) and Russell (1950) report later development of skin defects and of cataracts resulting from irradiation during the period of the fetus but it is not known whether that period is critical for the production of these changes since mice exposed earlier were not kept alive in large enough numbers after birth. Working on the same F_1 hybrid used by Russell, Grobman autopsied twenty-nine mice 37–49 days old which had been irradiated with 300 r on day 14½ or 15½ postconception. He found reduction in size of gonads and secondary sex glands, absence of the corpus callosum, and absence of the gallbladder. Defects in the reproductive system could also be produced by earlier irradiation (day 11½, 12½, or 13½).

Sterility has frequently been observed to result from irradiation during fetal stages. Parkes (1927) raised twenty-five mice treated between days 10 and 18 postconception (mostly days 14 to 17). Only four of sixteen females and neither of two males tested proved fertile. Kosaka (1928e) found that, while irradiation between the seventh and thirteenth days did not affect the fertility of survivors, irradiation after the fourteenth day completely sterilized all but two males (totals not given). Even these two (irradiated on the seventeenth day) were only temporarily fertile. Sterility in all males was due to failure of sperm formation. Some females too were completely sterilized but the majority was poorly fertile and showed reduction in the number of mature ova formed. Hanson (1923) mentions that "nearly all" rats (no numbers given) irradiated in fetal stages proved sterile. Nürnberger (1920) found sterility in the only one of his guinea pigs (a male) which survived the early postnatal period.

Two investigators have made observations on immediate effects of irradiation during the period of the fetus. Kosaka (1928b, c) reports findings on rat and guinea pig fetuses from fourteen and eighty-five litters, respectively, sectioned 6, 12, 24, 48, 72 hours . . . (etc., to term) after irradiation with ⅓–2 SED during the fetal period. In the rat, he finds most tissue damage in the brain, retina, and thymus; liver and spleen take second place, and skin third. In the guinea pig, results are similar for irradiation in early fetal stages. Later in gestation, when the guinea pig fetus is really comparable to a postnatal rat or mouse, brain and retina lose some of their sensitivity but thymus remains in first place. Hicks (1950) irradiated rat and mouse females in late pregnancy (unfortunately without timing the stage of treatment) and observed the resulting nervous system changes ½ to 96 hours after irradiation, as well as at one day to several months after birth. He found 100 per cent brain damage and usually also damage in the retina, cord, and ganglia following doses of 200, 400, or 600 r. With 150 r, the degree and incidence of damage was less; and no necrosis at all was found below 100 r. Acute stages of necrosis were observable as early as 2 hours following irradiation. The periventricular neuroblasts and other regions of rapid growth in the brain, the neuroblastic layer of the retina, and the dorsal gray columns of the cord were affected. Changes seen 2 to several days after irradiation were classed as early malformations. These consist of the formation of ependymal canals and rosettes in brain, cord, and retina, and are therefore interesting in comparison with the results of Kosaka, of Wilson, and of Pagenstecher. Finally, the author lists almost a dozen "late maldevelopments," namely, nervous system changes found in the postnatal period. Among these are: virtual absence of corpus callosum (also found by Grobman—see p. 897), jumbling and reduction of the hippocampus, malformations of the ventricles. It is interesting that extraneural damage could be obtained only with the highest doses and that even then it was rare except in the thymus (cf. Kosaka).

All morphological changes—immediate and delayed—reported for irradiation during the period of the fetus have been summarized in Table 13-8.

TABLE 13-8. MORPHOLOGICAL CHANGES FOLLOWING IRRADIATION DURING THE PERIOD OF THE FETUS

Observation	Author	Affected organ						
		Gonads	Brain	Retina	Lens	Thymus	Skin	Miscellaneous
Immediate	Kosaka	......	++	++	....	+++	+	Liver, spleen
	Hicks	......	+++	++	....	+	..	Cord, ganglia
Delayed	Bagg	++	Cerebrum	?	Cataract, atrophy			
	Kosaka	+++	Cerebrum	......	....	......	..	Occas. liver, lung, heart, kidneys
	Kaven	......	....	......	Cataract	......	+	
	Russell	......	....	......	Cataract	......	+	
	Grobman	++	Corpus callos.	......	....	......	..	Gall bladder
	Parkes	Sterility						
	Hanson	Sterility						
	Nürnberger	Sterility						
	Hicks	......	Corpus callos., hippocampus, etc.	Rosettes	....	......	..	Cord

3. TIME OF PARTURITION

There are a number of scattered reports in the literature to the effect that irradiation during pregnancy causes a delay in parturition. Since most of these statements are concerned with irradiation during the period of the fetus, they will be examined in this section. In rabbits, a delay of 17 hours to 2 days was found by Sébileau (1906a, b—three cases out of seven), of 3–4 days by Nürnberger (1920—three cases out of three), and of 1–2 days by Lacassagne and Coutard (1923—three cases out of nine). In guinea pigs, one instance of slight delay is mentioned by von Klot (1911); de Nobele and Lams (1925) record one case of 3 and one of 8 days delay; and Kosaka (1928c) states that dead fetuses may occasionally be expelled after the expected time. The same is true in rats irradiated in the third week of pregnancy (Kosaka, 1928b) where the young may be stillborn 1–3 days late.

In a class by itself is the claim by Levine (1927) that the irradiation of pregnant mice lengthened the mating-to-birth interval by from 3 to 41 days in twenty-two of twenty-six cases. Examination of his method reveals that the author did not realize that (1) conception may occur a considerable interval after a male and female mouse are caged together, and (2) the first litter conceived may be completely lost as a result of early irradiation, so that the litter observed at birth stems from a later conception. Even where errors are not as crass as this, it should be borne in mind that any claim of delay must be supported by adequate control data, since there is considerable variation in length of gestation period depending on genetic constitution, and even individual variation *within* an inbred strain. Moreover, suckling a previous litter may markedly lengthen the gestation period of the litter being carried. This fact was not known to earlier authors.

Russell (1950) found that 88 per cent of her control mice and 80 per cent of the irradiated females of the same inbred strain delivered by approximately 19½ days after conception. The rest of the control group was born within the following 16 hours and there were no indications (from the developmental state of the fetuses) that the balance of the irradiated animals, which was delivered by caesarean section at 19½ days, would have been born later than that. There is thus no evidence of delayed parturition following irradiation during the preimplantation stages and the period of major organogenesis, but critical data are needed to answer this question for irradiation during the period of the fetus.

4. ISOTOPE STUDIES

It remains to mention two recent studies in which radioactive isotopes were injected into pregnant females and the effects on the resulting young studied. It should be kept in mind that isotope treatment differs from external irradiation in two ways: (1) the period of effective irradiation may extend for a considerable time following injection; (2) the radiation source may be concentrated in certain tissues or organs because of chemical affinities of the isotope or other reasons. Response, therefore, does not necessarily represent relative degrees of radiosensitivity throughout the body.

Burstone (1951) studied the effect of localized electron bombardment produced by the metabolism of P^{32} in fetal tooth primordia of inbred mice. Mothers were injected 2–6 days before expected parturition with 5–17 μc/g and the teeth of the young studied 6–28 days after birth. The following are some of the findings: (1) fetal teeth are more radiosensitive than the teeth of newborns (or P^{32} concentrates in them to a greater degree); also, injections 4–5 days before term were more effective than injections 1–2 days before term; (2) the development of the third molar is completely inhibited, while that of the first and second molars, which had already commenced before injection, is greatly modified; (3) newly differentiated cells are more radiosensitive as shown by greater damage in the second than the first molar and by effects within different cell layers of each tooth; (4) doses of 10–17 $\mu c/g$ produce general postnatal growth retardation which is greater for earlier than for later injections.

Finkel (1947) injected Sr^{89} and plutonium into pregnant females (stages not stated). While very little plutonium reached the fetus, Sr^{89} concentration in the fetus actually exceeded that of the mother if injection was shortly before term. Both treatments increased the percentage of stillbirths, and Sr^{89} produced retardation of growth, fragility, bending and shortening of the long bones, anemia, and osteogenic sarcoma.

III. MECHANISMS OF RADIATION EFFECT ON THE MAMMALIAN EMBRYO AND FETUS[8]

A. INFLUENCE OF THE MATERNAL ORGANISM

One question that has been raised several times in the literature is whether radiation affects the conceptus directly or produces an altered condition in the maternal organism which indirectly damages the embryo or fetus. Archangelsky (1923) suggested that this altered condition might consist of changes in uterine tissues, alterations of hormonal output of the ovaries, or the production of "roentgen leukotoxins" first postulated by Linser and Helber (1905). Obviously, any debilitated condition of the mother could affect viability of the embryo, and several reports from the early investigations in this field—when preoccupation with this particular point was greatest—seem indeed to indicate an indirect influence on viability of the embryo. In most of this early work, however, the doses were extremely high, often high enough to kill the mother before expected term, and factors of shielding may have been incompletely understood. Fellner and Neumann (1907) and Saretzky (1908), who shielded the uterus and irradiated the ovaries of rabbits in the first half of pregnancy, both reported death of embryos (resorption and abortion, respectively). Von Hippel and Pagenstecher (1907) obtained almost as poor a yield of living young at term when the abdomen was shielded as when total-body irradiation was given to rabbits 7–12 days pregnant. They also injected blood from an irradiated animal into one nonirradiated doe presumed to be 9 days pregnant and report that no young were born and that maternal toxins were therefore responsible for prenatal death. Cohn (1907) shielded all but the head of rabbits 10–20 days pregnant and

[8] Since this chapter went to press, the mechanisms of radiation effect on the mammalian embryo have been more extensively and systematically discussed in another publication (L. B. Russell and W. L. Russell, 1954).

observed poor postnatal development of the young. (This may very well have been due to a disturbance of maternal lactation brought about through radiation injury of the pituitary.) Driessen (1924), who irradiated only the left half of the abdomen, found that the more severely affected embryos were as often in the shielded horn as in the exposed one. The work of Wilson and Karr (1950, 1951), in which only individual implantation sites were exposed, should make it clear that a high incidence of prenatal death can be caused, even with relatively low doses, by direct action on the embryo, though indirect effects of certain degenerative changes produced in the placenta (Kosaka, 1927) can even here not be definitely excluded. The possibility of interaction between embryos of the same pregnancy has not been considered in any experiment to date. It is, however, quite conceivable that radiation-induced death of several individuals within a uterus may adversely affect the remainder of the litter, the viability of which was not directly influenced by radiation.

As far as the production of abnormalities is concerned, there seems little doubt that the maternal body need not act as an intermediary in causing damage to the embryo, for similar changes have been produced in oviparous forms. Moreover, in mammals, the methods of several investigators, reporting a variety of malformations, have included shielding of either the anterior half of the mother (Murphy and de Renyi); or of all nonabdominal regions (Kaven; Warkany and Schraffenberger); or of everything except a selected implantation site (Wilson and collaborators); or part of an embryo (Raynaud and Frilley). In investigations where part or all of the mother was exposed, it is, of course, not inconceivable that a few of the embryonic abnormalities had an indirect causation, but two pieces of circumstantial evidence, added to the evidence derived from analogy with oviparous forms, make it likely that the *majority* of abnormalities are due to the action of radiation on the embryo itself: (1) since "radiation sickness" of the mother is not sharply limited to a day, any major influence of maternal pathological conditions on the development of the embryo would presumably result in a much more blurred relation between time of disturbance and effect than is actually encountered in the well-defined critical periods (Russell, 1950); (2) it is unlikely that effects via the mother would become apparent within 2 hours (Hicks, 1950, for changes in neuroblasts).

The only serious evidence against the above arguments is presented by Job *et al.* (1935) who obtained only normal offspring (192) from 22 rat females irradiated with shielding of the anterior half, while 23 other females, irradiated in the same stages of pregnancy and receiving approximately the same dose of *whole-body* irradiation, produced 73 abnormal young among 175. This result is puzzling in the light of later evidence by Warkany and Schraffenberger, and by Wilson and collaborators, who dealt with the same organism in comparable stages of pregnancy.

B. NATURE OF THE PRIMARY DAMAGE AND INTERMEDIATE EFFECTS

Assuming that at least a large part of the damage must be due to the action of radiation on the embryo itself, there arises the more difficult task of elucidating the nature of the primary damage and the pathways that lead to the observed malformations. Although there is little direct evidence on these points available for mammalian embryos, the hypotheses are limited by two end results which have been discussed in preceding sections and must now be considered well established: (1) irradiation at a given stage causes observable changes only in certain specific characters, and (2) a primordium affected at any given stage responds in consistent ways. These points will be considered in turn.

(1) The first end result must be due either to differential primary damage, or, if the primary damage was randomly distributed throughout the body, a differential intermediate effect. A few available facts indicate a possible basis for selectiveness at either step. There is evidence to show that some of the processes specifically affected at any given stage are those engaged in a rapid rate of change at the time. A few examples are: vertebral jumbling—beginnings of primitive streak activity (Russell, 1949); brain hernia and pseudencephaly—early brain differentiation (Kaven, 1938b); microphthalmia—early optic evagination (Wilson and Karr, 1951); coloboma—invagination of optic vesicles (Russell, 1950); digital reductions—limb bud rudder formation (Russell, 1950); second phase for tail reduction—tail bud formation (Russell, 1950). There are also a few examples which show that sensitivity is not always predictable from the visibly fastest rate of change in a primordium: e.g., the critical periods for polydactyly and the first phase of tail reduction occur before limb buds and tail bud, respectively, have made their appearance (Russell, 1950); a high incidence of liver damage is produced by irradiating at a stage when the hepatic primordium is not yet indicated morphologically (Wilson and Karr, 1951). In these cases some process related developmentally (e.g., an organizer), and not necessarily by cellular ancestry, may be sensitive at the time of irradiation.

It is conceivable that the primary intracellular damage—e.g., chromosome breakage, injury of the spindle-forming mechanism—occurs with uneven distribution, possibly dependent on relative proportions of cells in mitosis in various regions. In addition to differential distribution of the primary intracellular (and the subsequent cellular) damage, various intermediate selective mechanisms on a higher level can be postulated. Thus, for example, the different degrees of differentiation reached by various precursors at the time of irradiation may be correlated with different capacities for regeneration. Or, even a slight upset in cellular balance in a region providing trophic influences for a certain primordium may inhibit proper differentiation of the latter but not at all affect other processes.

(2) Having discussed distribution of damage within the body, it is necessary to examine the quality of the change in affected cells in order to arrive at an explanation for the consistency of end results. In the reviewer's opinion, this consistency for any given primordium and stage of irradiation is almost certainly due to an invariable response of cells (e.g., death) which have undergone a *random* type of primary change within them (e.g., any of a number of chromosome aberrations). The alternative hypothesis, namely, that consistency results from primary damage selective within the cell, is hardly tenable. Although it is possible to postulate mechanisms that would give a certain degree of intracellular specificity, e.g., greater susceptibility of terminal regions of chromosomes, or a maximum breakage frequency in the longest chromosome, this type of directed damage cannot be expected to change with stage and type of precursor nor can it be sufficient to account for consistency in a vast number of phenotypic changes. This argument automatically eliminates Wilson and Karr's (1950) suggestion of "subtle genic alterations" leading to failure "to follow the prescribed course in differentiation"—quite apart from the fact that several reasons make gene mutations unlikely as an effective primary change.

Among the possible classes of primary damage are chromosome breakage, damage to the mitotic mechanism, and gene mutations. The last named is, on the basis of frequency alone, unlikely to cause many abnormalities. Thus, with currently available mammalian germinal mutation rates (W. L. Russell, 1951), and assuming the same somatic rate and $2 \times 20,000$ loci, 200 r would give an average of two mutations per cell. The average degree of dominance of these radiation-induced mutations is presumably quite low and only very few cells would thus be affected in diploid tissues. (Of course, embryonic material *can* be used for the study of somatic mutations, but special genetic techniques are necessary for this purpose—Russell and Major, 1952.)

A number of mechanisms may be postulated to account for the consistent nature of the final change, in spite of the random quality within the cell of the primary damage. These include (1) dominant lethal action of chromosomal aberrations which lead to aneuploidy after mitosis and thus to cellular death; (2) retardation in mitotic rhythm brought about by any damage to the mitotic mechanism or by certain types of chromosome aberrations; and (3) change in developmental potency, *provided* there is only one possible abnormal path for the cell, regardless of the type of aberration it contains; this condition is probably met only in a small number of instances, if ever. That selective cellular death occurs following prenatal irradiation and often after only short intervals has been shown by Hicks (1950) and by Kosaka (1927, 1928b, c, d), who describe its various histological manifestations in detail. Temporary mitotic inhibition is harder to demonstrate but the work on other organisms, reviewed in Chap. 10, makes it likely that it can occur in mammals also. In this connection, it should be pointed out that arrests in whole tissues or organs, which have been reported by Wilson and Karr (1951), and which may later turn into abnormality, need not be due to mitotic inhibition but may be caused by death of a certain proportion of cells at a stage preceding observation. Abnormalities involving an apparent *increase* rather than defect, e.g., polydactyly, or the formation of an extra thoracic rib, are quite reconcilable with the idea that the initial change is death or retardation of cells rather than acceleration: thus the selective elimination of a region may divide a primordium, and result in "twinning." Radiation effects on viability (except during cleavage stages, which form a special problem because of the apparently great regulatory powers of blastomeres) may be thought of as resulting from damage to various key tissues or organs (e.g., liver, as suggested by Wilson and Karr, 1951). It is then obvious that incidence as well as time of mortality would vary with the stage irradiated, i.e., with the different critical periods existing at the time of treatment.

The work of Russell, Russell, and Major (1951) has shown that hypoxia protects markedly against radiation-induced abnormalities. By obtaining results at a particular stage for a variety of dosages both in 5 per cent oxygen (+ 95 per cent helium) and in air, it could be demonstrated that the magnitude of protection is approximately similar for all of six characters so far tabulated (see Fig. 13-9). Since hypoxia has been shown to protect against chromosome aberrations (Giles, Baker, and others) and mitotic inhibition (Gaulden and Nix, and others), it may be suggested that the protection against developmental abnormalities is on the level of the intracellular damage, but the results do not provide evidence in favor of any one kind of intracellular damage. The fact that various characters are protected to an approximately equal degree makes it likely that different sensitive primordia are affected in a similar manner by radiation to yield abnormalities. It is also noteworthy from the point of view of the discussion which follows that, both in incidence and degree of change, reduction in oxygen is equivalent to treatment with a lower dose.

C. DOSAGE RELATIONS; VARIABILITY

The commonest results obtained on increasing the dose are: (1) increase in incidence, (2) increase in degree, and (3) extension of the period during which radiation will yield the given abnormality (Russell, 1950, 1949). Exceptions to these points will be discussed. If the probability of affecting a potentially sensitive cell in a given precursor of n cells is p, then the proportions of animals with 0, 1, 2, 3, . . . , n cells of

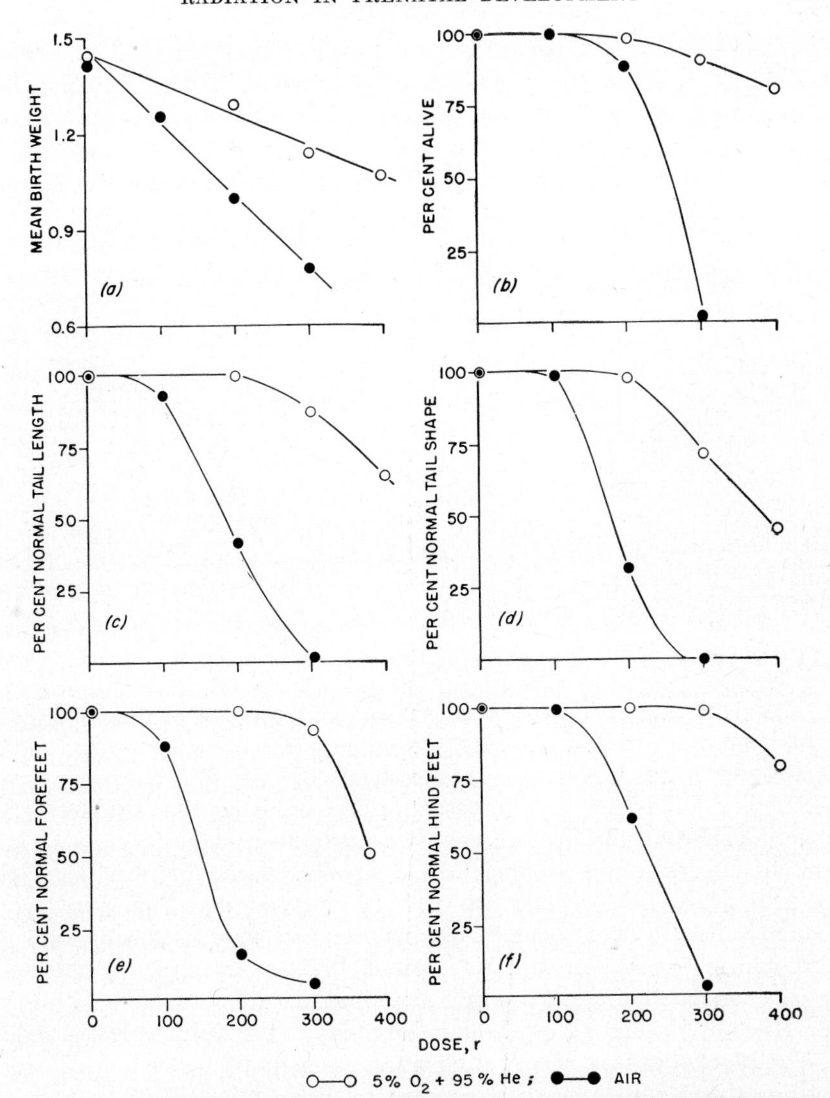

FIG. 13-9. Quantitative comparison between the effects of prenatal irradiation of the mouse in an atmosphere of 5% O_2 + 95% He (○——○) and in air (●——●). All treatments (0, 100, 200, 300, and 400 r) were administered on day 11½ postconception and all observations made at birth. (*Russell, Russell, and Major*, 1951.) a = mean birth weight; b = mortality; c = tail length; d = tail shape; e = forefeet; f = hind feet.

the precursor affected are given by the successive terms of the binomial expansion $[(1 - p) + p]^n$. It may be assumed that precursors with a proportion of from 0 to $\frac{x}{n}$ cells altered can still develop normally, while those with a proportion of from $\frac{x + 1}{n}$ to all cells altered will give rise to a changed character, the degree of abnormality being determined by the number of stricken cells. The larger p becomes on raising the dose, (1) the relatively smaller will be the proportions of animals in the classes with 0, 1, 2, . . . , x cells affected, i.e., the greater the incidence of abnormality, and (2) the larger will be the mean, pn, i.e., the higher the average degree of abnormality. The result, mentioned in the preceding section, that irradiation under hypoxia is equivalent in end result to lower dose treatment in air, indicates that for any given dose, p is lower under hypoxia, since n and x are presumably constant. The fact that irradiation at a stage subsequent to that of maximum sensitivity may still yield abnormality with a higher dose can be explained either by decrease, with age of precursor, in p for a given dose because of some biological reason, e.g., slowing in rate of mitosis, or merely by increase in n (provided $\frac{x}{n} > pn$), or by a combination of these factors.

The above statistical considerations on incidence and degree show that there could be variability in results even in perfectly uniform material, a fact which has not generally been recognized. As it is, however, such variability would be superimposed on three biological variables: (1) genetic variability, which can, however, easily be controlled by the use of inbred material; (2) environmentally determined variability existing even in genetically homogenous material of a given developmental age; (3) differences in developmental age between and within litters of a given chronological age (Allen and MacDowell, 1940); these probably account in part for the finding that certain abnormalities are obtainable with low incidence by irradiating on the days adjacent to the main critical period.

The effect of genetic constitution on radiosensitivity to the induction of certain abnormalities has been studied by Russell and Russell (1950b), choosing characters (homeotic shifts in vertebral borders and related changes in the thorax) in which there is normal variability between as well as within inbred strains. Genetic constitution determines the location of the strain on a scale of developmental *potencies*, while environmental factors, mostly intangible, cause individuals to be distributed about this mean. Because of thresholds of expression, the finally observed characters fall into alternate categories. Data indicate that differences between three strains in the final visible result of a given dose of radiation—and thus in the *apparent* ease of radiation shift—are not attributable to differences in the underlying effect. For example, 200 r on day 8½ postconception increases the presacral number to 27 in 100 per cent of BalbC strain animals, in only 3 per cent of (C57 × NB)F_1's, and in 0 per cent of 129 strain mice. However, control results show the BalbC and 129 distributions to be situated across the $^{25}/_{26}$ thresholds, respectively, while the (C57 × NB)F_1 distribution crosses neither threshold. The positions are such that equal radiation-induced shifts in the mean, on the scale of underlying processes, would account for the results. In the course of this experiment it also became apparent that for the changes studied, i.e., quantitative characters in which even slight shifts are observable, a dose as low as 25 r may be shown to have an effect on prenatal development.

Although the commonest result of an increase in dose is increased incidence and degree of abnormality, there are a few exceptions which point to the possible existence of interesting developmental pathways. In the case of microphthalmia, for instance, the results of both Russell (1950) and Wilson and Karr (1951) indicate a lowering of incidence as the dose is raised. This can be explained by some other abnormality "competing" with microphthalmia at the higher dose but produced only to a slight extent or not at all at the lower.—Certain primordia are apparently capable of only one type of response since degree does not change with dose level even though incidence does. Examples are polydactyly, and hydro-ureter (Russell, 1950).

D. COMPARISON WITH OTHER AGENTS AFFECTING DEVELOPMENT

Radiation-induced developmental abnormalities may be compared with those produced by other agents (Haskins, 1948; Gillman *et al.*, 1948; Hamburgh, 1952; Waddington and Carter, 1952; Fraser and Fainstat, 1951a; Kalter and Fraser, 1952; see also review by Fraser and Fainstat, 1951b). Haskins' (1948) results for nitrogen mustard treatment between days 13 and 16 of rat gestation are similar to (but less extensive than) those obtained by Warkany and Schraffenberger following irradiation at the same stages. On the other hand, Waddington and Carter (1952) point out that trypan blue (used also by Gillman *et al.* and by Hamburgh) produces a smaller variety of abnormalities than found by Russell for irradiation at the comparable stage, and the same seems true of the action of cortisone (Fraser and Fainstat) and of 17-hydroxycorticosterone (Kalter and Fraser). This may well be due to chemical affinity of these deleterious agents for certain primordia. It is also of interest that the high proportion of tail abnormalities found by Waddington and Carter and by Hamburgh for trypan blue injection on day 7 points to the persistence of the deleterious action until somewhat later stages, at which X-ray results have shown the tail to become considerably more sensitive. On the other hand, cleft palate can be produced by the injections of cortisone at stages *following* closure of the nasomaxillary fissure. Fraser and

Fainstat suggest a degenerative change instead of developmental interference, which seems to occur as a result of other agents.

Comparison of radiation-induced developmental abnormalities with the changes produced by mutant genes has been made by Russell (1949, 1950). Although a particular mutant gene is probably present in every cell of the body, primary gene action is in most cases circumscribed by conditions arising in the course of differentiation. It may be limited to one process, depending on the identity of which the ultimate phenotypic effect may be either circumscribed or widespread. Or the primary gene action may be widespread, in which case the ultimate expression is even more likely to be a whole syndrome of changes. In any case, it is unlikely that gene action, evoked, as it is, by certain conditions in differentiation, should exactly parallel the pattern of radiation effect which is probably determined by some generalized state (e.g., high rate of mitosis) of a variety of precusors. It is, therefore, not surprising that there are no cases of perfect correspondence between all the changes brought about by a given gene and the various abnormalities produced by radiation at a given stage. On the other hand, similarity of certain details may point to the weak links in some of the various developmental chains coexisting at a given moment and should indicate that at least some of the secondary gene effect occurs at the time indicated by the radiation effect. Another possible difference between mutant action and radiation is that, *within* the affected tissue, the gene may act in every cell, radiation probably only in a certain proportion. This latter property of radiation damage may also differentiate it from the action of physiological poisons, e.g., certain chemicals, and explain its failure to date to produce many of the classical abnormalities—cyclopia, twinning, otocephaly.

IV. CLINICAL LITERATURE ON THE EFFECTS OF RADIATION ON EMBRYO AND FETUS; HUMAN IMPLICATIONS OF EXPERIMENTAL WORK

The case literature on the subject of prenatal radiation effect is large and diffuse but various summaries facilitate a survey of the field, even though they suffer from a certain amount of overlap. In order of appearance, these are by von Klot (1911), Driessen (1924), Murphy (1929), Goldstein and Murphy (1929) (the same material is also found in Murphy, 1947), Gauss (quoting a thesis by Kraemer, 1930), Flaskamp (1930), Schall (1933—thorough tabular representation), Miller *et al.* (1936), and Jones and Neill (1944). Cases not included in the above summaries are by Lindenfeld (1913) and Murphy *et al.* (1942). Russell and Russell (1952) have discussed the implications for medical practice of findings in experimental animals.

Although reports of normal children following prenatal irradiation are given, among others, by Robinson (1927—twenty-three cases collected from the literature), Lacomme (1931—two cases), Jones and Neill (1944—seven definite and twenty-eight questionable cases), and Hobbs (1950—one case), and have been stressed by various authors as showing that damage need not invariably or even frequently follow prenatal irradiation, there can, of course, be no question, both from experimental and clinical findings, that the human embryo is subject to severe radiation injury. The types of human abnormalities enumerated in the case literature include microcephaly, blindness, microphthalmia, coloboma, cataract, chorioretinitis, ankyloblepharon, strabismus, nystagmus, mental deficiency, hydrocephaly, coordination defects, mongolism, spina bifida, skull malformations, ossification defects of the head, cleft palate, ear abnormalities, deformed arms, club feet, hypophalangea, genital deformities, and general mental and physical subnormality. Microcephaly is present alone or in combination with other changes in 16 of 28 abnormal cases listed by Goldstein and Murphy (1929), and in 27 of 38 tabulated by Schall (1933). It is probable that this classification includes a variety of head abnormalities. Next on the list in Schall's tabulation are various eye defects (14 of 38 cases). Central nervous system abnormalities other than microcephaly are frequent as a group. Thus, the tissues believed to be radioresistant in adult humans are especially sensitive in the embryo.

By equating human and mouse gestation periods developmentally (rather than chronologically, since, e.g., the first one-fourth of mouse prenatal life is equivalent to only the first one-thirtieth of human), as has been done by Otis (1952), it should be possible to predict when the critical period for the production of abnormalities determined in the mouse (see preceding sections) should occur in man. This type of prediction is substantiated by one of the few human cases where stage of irradiation is accurately known (Feldweg, 1927): irradiation during the fourth or fifth week caused arm abnormalities of the newborn similar to those which can be produced in the mouse by treatment at the corresponding stage, day 10½. The period of major organogenesis in man, corresponding to days 6½ to 13½ in the mouse, comprises weeks 2–6. It may be predicted from the animal results that irradiation during those stages will lead to a high percentage of conspicuous abnormalities, while later irradiation will yield a lower incidence, at least insofar as immediately recognizable changes are concerned. Confirmation comes from the tabulation of Kraemer (1930) who found that all of 11 cases of irradiation within the first two months resulted in damage, while only 7 out of 11 (64 per cent) irradiated between the third and fifth months and 3 out of 13 (23 per cent) irradiated between the sixth and tenth months were abnormal at or near term. In Schall's (1933) tabulation, which, in contrast to Kraemer's, lists only positive cases, 57 per cent (20 of 35) were irradiated between conception and the third month, 31 per cent between the third and fifth months, and 11 per cent after the fifth month. In Goldstein and Murphy's compilation (1929), 79 per cent of the abnormals come from pregnancies irradiated before the fifth month.

Russell and Russell (1952) have suggested that, since during at least the early part of the period of major organogenesis, many women are not yet aware that they are pregnant, pelvic irradiation of women of child-bearing age should whenever possible be restricted to the *two weeks following a menstruation* as there is little chance of an unsuspected pregnancy during that time. This type of timing should be feasible for diagnostic irradiation (see following paragraph for discussion of dose), if not always for therapeutic. The dangers of irradiation after the period of major organogenesis, which, predicting from the animal results, consist of the production of possibly delayed and less obvious but, from a human point, at least as undesirable effects (e.g., changes in mental abilities, sterility), occur at a time when there need no longer be any doubt of pregnancy. They are, therefore, already avoided in good current practice.

It was mentioned earlier (see p. 907) that in experimental work a dose as low as 25 r, the lowest used, may be shown to have an effect on prenatal development (Russell and Russell, 1950b), and there is no evidence that lower doses would not also cause damage detectable in man where even subtle defects are likely to be recognized. This is of significance in medical diagnostic practice since Sonnenblick *et al.* (1951) found that about one-fifth of sixty-three fluoroscope machines tested emitted more than 30 r per minute, and Bell's results (1943) indicate that the length of exposure for a standard gastrointestinal series is 4½ to 12 minutes, during which time about 50 r may be received at a depth of 10 cm for a panel dose of 30 r/minute. On the other hand, doses received by the uterus in radiographs are comparatively negligible (Mobius, 1951).

The question of feasibility of radiation-induced therapeutic abortion arose very soon after the beginning of radiological practice. As early as 1911, von Klot discusses its pros and cons at considerable length. Driessen (1924) cites seven references which claim success and seven others which state X rays to be unsuitable for the induction of abortion in man. Murphy (1929) showed that the abortion rate following postconceptional irradiation was probably no higher than in the population at large. In his review, Schall (1933) states that radiation abortion has finally been discontinued in medical practice because of inconstancy of results; but, three years later, Mayer, Harris, and Wimpfheimer (1936) recommend the method and claim a very high percentage of success. The statement has occasionally been made (Robinson, 1927, and others) that doses high enough to cause maldevelopment usually also terminate pregnancy and thus do not present an appreciable hazard. Whether the unreliability in success of X-ray abortion is due to variability in the physical factors of irradiation or to biological variability in the subjects cannot here be determined, but it is clear, both from the animal results discussed in earlier sections and the human cases summarized above, that damaged embryos or fetuses *do* come to term in a large number of instances. Survival of these monsters is, moreover, fairly frequent. Murphy (1929) found no stillbirths among seventy-four cases of postconceptional irradiation which went to (or near) term; yet 34 per cent of the children were grossly deformed. Postnatal viability may be estimated from the lists of Goldstein and Murphy (1929) and of Schall (1933): only 7 of 26 (27 per cent) and 11 of 38 (29 per cent), respectively, of the malformed children died between birth and two and a half years of age; the rest, alive at the last report, ranged from several weeks to twelve years with about two-thirds of the group (in Schall's list) two or over.

The possibility of damaging the human conceptus indirectly through radiation injury of the mother has been stressed by Flaskamp (1929, 1930) and by Faerber (1933), who report abnormal children following irradiation during pregnancy to nonabdominal sites or with the uterus shielded. Schall (1933) evaluates the four cases cited by Flaskamp and three additional ones and comes to the conclusion that, in at least five of the seven, the uterus probably received scattered radiation. Results with experimental animals (discussed earlier) make it likely that at least the majority of the abnormalities are due to the action of radiation on the embryo itself and would thus be avoided by appropriate shielding if nonabdominal regions of a pregnant woman had to be irradiated.

SUMMARY

1. Radiation has proved to be an excellent tool in mammalian experimental embryology and radiation-embryological studies on mammals have yielded results which have important clinical implications.

2. Most of the experimental work in the field has been concerned with rodents and with radiation from an external source. Various degrees of shielding and localization of the beam have been used, ranging from none at all to the exposure of only selected parts of individual embryos. Almost all of the early experiments, and even a few of the more recent ones, suffer greatly from lack of timing of the developmental stage at which radiation was applied.

3. Recent experiments have shown that the stages at which radiation is applied to the embryo can be conveniently grouped by broad end result into (*a*) the preimplantation period, (*b*) the period of major organogenesis, and (*c*) the period of the fetus. Experiments concerning these three periods are reviewed in turn.

4. Irradiation during the preimplantation period causes a high rate

of prenatal mortality. In the mouse, the incidence for a dose of 200 r is 43–79 per cent, depending on the stage irradiated. Death may involve the whole litter, terminating pregnancy prior to implantation, or it may occur in individuals in surviving pregnancies both before or shortly after implantation. The relative proportions of the different types of death depend on the stage irradiated. Virtually all survivors are normal.

5. For comparable doses, irradiation during the early part of the period of major organogenesis causes considerably less prenatal death than does treatment during the preimplantation period and, from then on, susceptibility to prenatal killing probably decreases rapidly with embryonic age. On the other hand, neonatal death assumes considerable importance and, in the mouse, is at a peak following irradiation on days 9½ and 10½. The LD_{50} at birth for prenatal irradiation varies markedly with the stage irradiated, even when stages are separated by only 24-hour intervals.

6. A vast number of varied abnormalities have been reported as resulting from the irradiation of mammalian embryos during the period of major organogenesis. A few critical experiments have shown that sensitive periods for the induction of almost all abnormalities are short: with 200 r, many of them are restricted to one particular day, or, if they span several days, one often stands out as the main sensitive one on the basis of incidence. There are several cases of good agreement of different authors on the critical periods for certain characters.

7. Irradiation during the period of the fetus does not cause the striking changes in newborns produced by comparable doses during the period of major organogenesis. Immediate histological damage can, however, be demonstrated and this leads to gross changes which become expressed later in life. The most frequently reported defects are in the brain, retina, gonads, lens, skin, and thymus.

8. Proportional growth retardation leading to decreased body size can be produced by irradiation at almost any stage after implantation. In the mouse, the maximum reduction in birthweight for any given dose follows irradiation between days 10½ and 11½. Birthweight depression for treatment on day 11½ is directly proportional to dose, averaging 0.22 g per 100 r.

9. Claims of upset sex ratio following prenatal irradiation and of differential susceptibility of the sexes to the induction of abnormalities cannot be considered proved, although it is conceivable that such effects will be found. The same is true of claims that prenatal irradiation prolongs the gestation period.

10. Although high doses to the mother may indirectly affect the viability of the conceptus, there seems little doubt that most of the major embryonic abnormalities are due to the action of radiation directly on the embryo.

11. The finding that irradiation at a given stage causes changes only in certain characters may be explained by either or both of the following: (1) differentially distributed cellular damage; (2) selective mechanisms on a higher level. The basis for (1) may be differential mitotic activity. The fact that a precursor affected at any given stage responds in consistent ways may be explained by the invariable response of cells which have undergone a *random* primary change within them. The most plausible mechanism is cell lethal action of somatic chromosomal aberrations which lead to aneuploidy after mitosis.

12. Hypoxia protects markedly against radiation-induced abnormalities to an approximately equal extent in several characters. Protection is probably on the level of the intracellular damage.

13. Although there are several exceptions, the commonest results obtained on increasing the dose are increase in incidence, increase in degree, and extension of the period during which radiation will yield the given abnormality. These results are as expected on the assumption that a threshold proportion of cells must be affected in a primordium in order to produce any abnormality and that, above this threshold, the number of cells affected determines degree of abnormality. Simple statistical considerations show that there could be variability in result even in perfectly uniform material. This is superimposed on genetic variability, environmental variability, and subtle differences in developmental age among embryos of a given chronological age at the time of exposure.

14. There are certain similarities but also marked differences between the action of radiation on the one hand and of other deleterious agents or of genes on the other.

15. The clinical literature includes many cases in which abnormal children have been born following irradiation of the pregnant mother. In applying experimental results to man, it becomes apparent that critical periods for the majority of gross abnormalities occur at a time which corresponds to weeks 2–6 in human gestation. During at least part of this time, pregnancy may still be unsuspected. It has, therefore, been recommended that, whenever possible, irradiation involving the uterus in women of childbearing age should be restricted to the two weeks following the menses, to preclude the possibility of fertilization having taken place. Experimentally, doses as low as 25 r have been shown to be effective in producing developmental changes if applied at the critical time. This is within the dose range used in diagnostic fluoroscopy.

REFERENCES

(Information regarding availability of government reports indicated by an asterisk may be obtained from the Office of Technical Services, Department of Commerce, Washington, D.C.)

Allen, E., and E. C. MacDowell (1940) Variation in mouse embryos of 8 days gestation. Anat. Record, 77: 165–173.

Archangelsky, B. A. (1923) Zur Frage von der Wirkung der Röntgenstrahlen auf das Frühstadium der Gravidität. Arch. Gynäkol., 118: 1–17.

Bagg, H. J. (1922) Disturbances in mammalian development produced by radium emanation. Am. J. Anat., 30: 133–161.

Bell, A. L. (1943) X-ray therapy in fluoroscopy. Radiology, 40: 139–144.

Burckhard, Georg (1905) Über den Einfluss der Röntgenstrahlen auf den tierischen Organismus, insbesondere auf die Gravidität. Volkmanns Samml. klin. Vorträge, 404 (Gyn. 150): 469–480.

Burstone, M. S. (1951) The effect of radioactive phosphorus upon the development of the embryonic tooth bud and supporting structures. Am. J. Path., 27: 21–31.

Cohn, M. (1907) Discussion of a paper by Försterling. Verhandl. deut. Röntgenges., 3: 128–129.

Driessen, L. F. (1924) Keimschädigung durch Röntgenstrahlen. Strahlentherapie, 16: 656–689.

Dyroff, Rudolf (1927) Experimentelle Beiträge zur Frage der Nachkommenschädigung durch Röntgenstrahlen. Strahlentherapie, 24: 288–312.

Ellinger, F. (1941) The biologic fundamentals of radiation therapy. Elsevier Publishing Co., Inc., New York, pp. 13–16.

Faerber, Ernst (1933) Beitrag zur Frage der Röntgenschädigung des Fötus. Jahrb. Kinderheilk., 89: 33–37.

Feldweg, P. (1927) Ein ungewöhnlicher Fall von Fruchtschädigung durch Röntgenstrahlen. Strahlentherapie, 26: 799–801.

Fellner, O. O., and F. Neumann (1907) Der Einfluss der Röntgenstrahlen auf die Eierstöcke trächtiger Kaninchen und auf die Trächtigkeit. Z. Heilkunde, 28: 162–202.

Finkel, Miriam P. (1947) The transmission of radio-strontium and plutonium from mother to offspring in laboratory animals. Physiol. Zoöl., 20: 405–421.

Flaskamp, W. (1929) Gefahren und Schäden bei gynäkologischer Tiefentherapie, *in* Lehrbuch der Strahlentherapie, ed. H. Meyer. Urban & Schwarzenberg, Berlin and Vienna, Vol. 4, pp. 1133–1199.

——— (1930) Die Fruchtschädigung durch Röntgenstrahlen, *in* Über Röntgenschäden und Schäden durch radioaktive Substanzen, ed. H. Meyer. Sonderbände zur Strahlentherapie. Urban & Schwarzenberg, Berlin, Vol. 12, pp. 247–261.

Försterling, K. (1907) Wachstumsstörung infolge von Röntgenisierung. Verhandl. deut. Röntgenges., 3: 126–128.

Fraser, F. C., and T. D. Fainstat (1951a) Production of congenital defects in the offspring of pregnant mice treated with cortisone. Pediatrics, 8: 527–533.

——— and ——— (1951b) Causes of congenital defects. Am. J. Diseases Children, 82: 593–603.

Gauss, C. J. (1930) Die Klinik der temporären Röntgenamenorrhoe. Strahlentherapie, 37: 511–566.

Gillman, J., Christine Gilbert, T. Gillman, and Isobel Spence (1948) A preliminary report on hydrocephalus, spina bifida and other congenital anomalies in the rat produced by trypan blue: The significance of these results in the interpretation of congenital malformations following maternal rubella. S. African J. Med. Sci., 13: 47–90.

Goldstein, L., and D. P. Murphy (1929) Etiology of the ill-health in children born after maternal pelvic irradiation. II. Defective children born after post-conception pelvic irradiation. Am. J. Roentgenol. Radium Therapy, 22: 322–331.

Gudernatsch, J. F., and H. J. Bagg (1920) Disturbances in the development of mammalian embryos caused by radium emanation. Proc. Soc. Exptl. Biol. Med., 17: 183–187.

Hamburgh, Max (1952) Malformations in mouse embryos induced by trypan blue. Nature, 169: 27.

Hanson, F. B. (1923) The effects of X-rays on the albino rat. Anat. Record, 24: 415.

Haskins, D. (1948) Some effects of nitrogen mustard on the development of external body form in the fetal rat. Anat. Record, 102: 493–509.

Hicks, S. P. (1950) Acute necrosis and malformation of developing mammalian brain caused by X-ray. Proc. Soc. Exptl. Biol. Med., 75: 485–489.

Hippel, v., and H. E. Pagenstecher (1907) Über den Einfluss des Cholins und der Röntgenstrahlen auf den Ablauf der Gravidität. Münch. med. Wochschr., 54: 452–456.

Hobbs, A. A., Jr. (1950) Fetal tolerance to roentgen rays. Radiology, 54: 242–246.

Job, T. T., G. J. Leibold, Jr., and H. A. Fitzmaurice (1935) Biological effects of roentgen rays. The determination of critical periods in mammalian development with x-rays. Am. J. Anat., 56: 97–117.

Jones, H. W., Jr., and W. Neill, Jr. (1944) The treatment of carcinoma of the cervix during pregnancy. Am. J. Obstet. Gynecol., 48: 447–463.

Kalter, H., and F. C. Fraser (1952) Production of congenital defects in the offspring of pregnant mice treated with Compound F. Nature, 169: 665.

Kaven, A. (1938a) Röntgenmodifikationen bei Mäusen. Z. menschl. Vererbungs- u. Konstitutionslehre, 22: 238–246.

——— (1938b) Das Auftreten von Gehirnmissbildungen nach Röntgenbestrahlung von Mäuseembryonen. Z. menschl. Vererbungs- u. Konstitutionslehre, 22: 247–257.

Klot, Bernhard v. (1911) Die Unterbrechung der Schwangerschaft durch Röntgenstrahlen. Inaug.-Diss. München., pp. 1–52.

Kosaka, Shigenobu (1927) Effects of roentgen rays upon the fetus. I. Investigation of the influence and effect of roentgen rays upon the mouse fetus (English). Japan. J. Obstet. Gynecol., 10: 34–39 (Zentr. ges. Radiol., 5: 231, 1928).

——— (1928a) Effects of roentgen rays upon the fetus. II. Investigations on the fetus of the domestic rabbit (Japanese). Nippon Roentgen Gakkai, 5: 519–576.

——— (1928b) Der Einfluss der Röntgenstrahlen auf die Feten. III. Mitt.: Untersuchungen an weissen Ratten (Japanese, with German summary). Okayama-Igakkai-Zasshi, 40: 1893–1919 (Zentr. ges. Radiol., 6: 538, 1929).

——— (1928c) Der Einfluss der Röntgenstrahlen auf die Feten. IV. Mitt.: Untersuchungen an Meerschweinchen (Japanese, with German summary). Okayama-Igakkai-Zasshi, 40: 2214–2234 (Zentr. ges. Radiol., 6: 777, 1929).

——— (1928d) Der Einfluss der Röntgenstrahlen auf die Feten. V. Mitt.: Zusammenfassende Betrachtung der Resultate der Untersuchungen an allen bisher berichteten Versuchstieren (Japanese, with German summary). Okayama-Igakkai-Zasshi, 40: 2259–2274; (Zentr. ges. Radiol., 6: 778, 1929).

——— (1928e) Die extrauterine Entwicklung und die Geschlechtsfunktion der röntgenbestrahlten Feten. Okayama-Igakkai-Zasshi, 40: 2553–2566; (author's summary, Zentr. ges. Radiol., 6: 470, 1929).

Kraemer (1930) Welche Fälle von Frucht- und Keimschädigung nach Strahlentherapie sind bis jetzt beobachtet? Inaug.-Diss. Würzburg.

Lacassagne, A., and H. Coutard (1923) De l'influence de l'irradiation des ovocytes sur les fécondations et les gestations ultérieures. Gynécologie et Obstétrique, 7: 1–25.

——— and J. Lavedan (1922) Numération des éléments du sang dans le syndrome purpurique röntgenien du lapin nouveau-né. Compt. rend. soc. biol., 86: 713–714.

———, ———, and J. de Léobardy (1922) Syndrome purpurique provoqué par les rayons X chez le lapin nouveau-né. Compt. rend. soc. biol., 86: 668–670.

Lacomme, M. (1931) Deux observations de roentgenthérapie au cours de la gestation avec accouchement à terme d'enfants bien portants. Bull. Soc. obstét. gynécol. de Paris, 20: 457–460.

Lengfellner, Karl (1906) Über Versuche von Einwirkung der Röntgenstrahlen auf Ovarien und den schwangeren Uterus von Meerschweinchen. Münch. med. Wochschr., 53: 2147–2148.

Levine, M. (1927) The influence of roentgen rays on white mice and their progeny. Am. J. Roentgenol. Radium Therapy, 17: 546–550.

Lindenfeld, B. (1913) Ein Beitrag zur Bildung rosettenartiger Figuren in der Netzhaut etc. Klin. Monatsbl. Augenheilk., 51: 440–443.

Linser, P., and E. Helber (1905) Experimentelle Untersuchungen über die Einwirkung der Röntgenstrahlen auf das Blut and Bemerkungen über die Einwirkung von Radium und ultraviolettem Lichte. Deut. Arch. klin. Med., 83: 479–498.

Mayer, M. D., W. Harris, and S. Wimpfheimer (1936) Therapeutic abortion by means of X-ray. Am. J. Obstet. Gynecol., 32: 945–957.

Miller, J. R., J. A. Corscaden, and J. A. Harrar (1936) Effects of radiation on the human offspring. Present-day views. Am. J. Obstet. Gynecol., 31: 518–522.

Mobius, W. (1951) Die Strahlenbelastung bei geburtshilflicher Röntgendiagnostik. Fortschr. Gebiete Röntgenstrahlen, 75: 734–739.

Momigliano, E. (1934) Sopra l'aborto radiologico. Annali ostet. e ginecol., 56: 1565–1622.

Murphy, D. P. (1929) Outcome of 625 pregnancies in women subjected to pelvic radium or roentgen irradiation. Am. J. Obstet. Gynecol., 18: 179–187.

——— (1947) Congenital malformations. J. B. Lippincott Company, Philadelphia, pp. 87–100.

——— and Marguerite de Renyi (1930) Post-conceptional pelvic irradiation of the albino rat (*Mus nor.*): its effect upon the offspring. Surg., Gynecol. Obstet., 50: 861–863.

———, M. E. Shirlock, and E. A. Doll (1942) Microcephaly following maternal pelvic irradiation for the interruption of pregnancy. Am. J. Roentgenol. Radium Therapy, 48: 356–359.

Nobele, de, and H. Lams (1925) Action des rayons Roentgen sur l'évolution de la grossesse et le développement du foetus. Bull. acad. roy. med. Belg., 5: 66–82.

——— and ——— (1927) Über die Wirkung der Röntgenstrahlen auf die Schwangerschaft und die Entwicklung des Fötus. Strahlentherapie, 25: 702–707.

Nürnberger, Ludwig (1920) Experimentelle Untersuchungen über die Gefahren der Bestrahlung für die Fortpflanzung. Prakt. Ergeb. Geburtshilfe u. Gynäkol., 8: 163–265.

Otis, Eileen M., and R. Brent (1952) Equivalent ages in mouse and human embryos. USAEC Report UR-194.*

Pagenstecher, H. E. (1916) Strahlenwirkung auf das fötale Auge. Experimentelle Untersuchungen über die Entstehung der Netzhautrosetten. Ber. Versamml. deut. Ophthalmol. Ges., pp. 447–456.

Parkes, A. S. (1927) On the occurrence of the oestrous cycle after X-ray sterilisation. Part II. Irradiation at or before birth. Proc. Roy. Soc. (London), B101: 71–95.

Raynaud, A., and M. Frilley (1943a) Technique d'irradiation localisée d'embryons de souris dans l'utérus au moyen des rayons X. Compt. rend., 217: 54–56.

——— and ——— (1943b) Lésions produites par irradiation avec les rayons X de différentes régions de la tête d'embryons de souris, au treizième jour de la vie intra-utérine. Compt. rend. soc. biol., 137: 419–421.

——— and ——— (1947a) Destruction, au moyen des rayons X, des ébauches de l'hypophyse de l'embryon de souris, au treizième jour de la vie intra-utérine. Compt. rend., 225: 206–207.

——— and ——— (1947b) Développement intra-utérine des embryons de souris dont les ébauches de l'hypophyse ont été détruites, au moyen des rayons X, au 13e jour de la gestation. I. Développement de l'appareil génital. Compt. rend., 225: 596–598.

——— and ——— (1947c) Destruction du cerveau des embryons de souris au treizième jour de la gestation, par irradiation au moyen des rayons X. Compt. rend. soc. biol., 141: 658–662.

——— and ——— (1949a) Structure histologique des testicules des foetus de souris dont l'hypophyse a été détruite au moyen des rayons X. Compt. rend. soc. biol., 143: 954–958.

——— and ——— (1949b) Structure histologique des ovaires des foetus de souris dont l'hypophyse a été détruite au moyen des rayons X. Compt. rend. soc. biol., 143: 959–963.

Regaud, C., T. Nogier, and H. Lacassagne (1912) Sur les effets redoutables des irradiations étendues de l'abdomen et sur les lésions du tube digestif déterminées par les rayons de röntgen. Arch. électricité méd., 343: 321–334.

Robinson, M. R. (1927) The effect of a castration dose of roentgen rays upon the rabbit ovary. An experimental study with a clinical evaluation of the problem of ovarian irradiation. Am. J. Roentgenol. Radium Therapy, 18: 1–25.

Russell, Liane Brauch (1949) X-ray induced developmental abnormalities in the mouse and their use in the analysis of embryological patterns. Thesis, University of Chicago.

——— (1950) X-ray induced developmental abnormalities in the mouse and their use in the analysis of embryological patterns. I. External and gross visceral changes. J. Exptl. Zoöl., 114: 545–602.

——— and Mary H. Major (1952) A preliminary report on radiation-induced presumed somatic mutations in the house mouse. Genetics, 36: 621.

——— and W. L. Russell (1950a) The effects of radiation on the preimplantation stages of the mouse embryo. Anat. Record, 108: 521.

——— and ——— (1950b) Changes in the relative proportions of different axial skeletal types within inbred strains of mice brought about by X-irradiation at critical stages in embryonic development. Genetics, 35: 689.

——— and ——— (1952) Radiation hazards to the embryo and fetus. Radiology, 58: 369–376.

——— and ——— (1954) An analysis of the changing radiation response of the developing mouse embryo. J. Cellular Comp. Physiol., Suppl. (In press.)

———, ———, and Mary H. Major (1951) The effect of hypoxia on the radiation induction of developmental abnormalities in the mouse. Anat. Record, 111: 455.

Russell, W. L. (1951) X-ray-induced mutations in mice. Cold Spring Harbor Symposia Quant. Biol., 16: 327–336.

Saretzky (1908) Die Röntgenisation der Eierstöcke, ihre unmittelbaren und weiterliegenden Resultate in Verbindung mit dem Einfluss auf den Verlauf der Schwangerschaft. Inaug.-Diss. St. Petersburg (Ref.: von Klot, 1911).

Schall, L. (1933) *In* Engel and Schall, Handbuch der Röntgendiagnostik und Therapie im Kindesalter. Georg Thieme, Leipzig, pp. 567–577.

Schinz, Hans R. (1923) Der Röntgenabort. Zugleich ein Beitrag zum spontanen Früchteschwund, zur Eiüberwanderung und zur Frage der innersekretorischen Gewebselemente der Keimdrüsen. Strahlentherapie, 15: 146–181.

Sébileau (1906a) Action des rayons X sur la gestation. Le Radium, 3: 287.

——— (1906b) Action des rayons X sur la gestation. Compt. rend. soc. biol., 61: 637–638.

Sonnenblick, B. P., L. J. Levinson, L. J. Furst, and J. Koch (1951) The roentgen output of fluoroscopes in routine diagnostic practice. J. Newark Beth Israel Hospital, 2: 153–163.

Toussey, S. (1905) In discussion of a paper by E. C. Titus. J. Adv. Therapy, 23: 650.

Trillmich, Fritz (1910) Experimenteller Beitrag zur Einleitung des künstlichen Abortus und zur Sterilisation durch Röntgenstrahlen. Inaug.-Diss. Freiburg, 1–63 (Zentr. Gynecol., p. 1449, 1912).

Waddington, C. H., and T. C. Carter (1952) Malformations in mouse embryos induced by trypan blue. Nature, 169: 27–28.

Warkany, J., and Elizabeth Schraffenberger (1947) Congenital malformations induced in rats by roentgen rays. Skeletal changes in the offspring following a single irradiation of the mother. Am. J. Roentgenol. Radium Therapy, 57: 455–463.

Wilson, J. G. (1949) Effects of X-irradiation on embryonic development in the rat. Anat. Record, 103: 520.

———, R. L. Brent, and H. C. Jordan (1951) Neoplasia induced in rat embryos by roentgen irradiation. Cancer Research, 12: 222–228.

——— and J. W. Karr (1950) Difference in the effects of x-irradiation in rat embryos of different ages. Anat. Record, 106: 259–260.

——— and ——— (1951) Effects of irradiation on embryonic development. I. X-rays on the 10th day of gestation in the rat. Am. J. Anat., 88: 1–33.

Manuscript received by the editor, June 3, 1952

CHAPTER 14

The Pathological Physiology of Radiation Injury in the Mammal. I. Physical and Biological Factors in Radiation Action

HARVEY M. PATT AND AUSTIN M. BRUES

Division of Biological and Medical Research, Argonne National Laboratory, Lemont, Ill.

Introduction. Nature of the biological response to radiation. Radiation quality and quantity. Biological factors in radiosensitivity: Cell and tissue sensitivity—Species sensitivity—Individual sensitivity. Induced radiosensitivity or resistence: Temperature and metabolic rate—Intermediary radiochemical events. Summary. References.

INTRODUCTION

When in 1895 Professor Röntgen reported on a "new form of radiation" to the Würzburg Physico-Medical Society, the stage was set for an energetic, though initially somewhat chaotic, development in biology. The discovery of radioactivity by Becquerel in 1896 lent further impetus to this development, although the connection between the two forms of radiation was not immediately apparent. Alopecia following X-ray photography was reported by Daniel (1896) four months after Röntgen's announcement, and the severe superficial injuries of a journeyman exhibitor of X-ray machines were eloquently described in the August 12, 1896, issue of the Electrical Review. Radiation dermatitis and epilation were observed by Leppin (1896) and Stevens (1896) at about the same time. In 1897, Freund reported the successful removal of a hairy mole with X rays, and Walsh described the unpleasant symptoms of acute radiation illness. Two years later a report on treatment of skin cancer with X rays appeared (Stenbeck, 1899), and in 1902 the earliest case of radiation-induced cancer was recorded (Frieben). Perhaps the first observation of an internal effect may be attributed to Senn, who described a decrease in size of the spleen in 1903.

As a consequence of these observations and the pressure of growing clinical usage, the biological action of ionizing radiation on animals and man was widely studied, and, although the experiments took place sporadically, with great variation in methods of exposure and dosage, many fundamental facts soon emerged. Among these were the selective action of radiation on different parts of the same cell and on different cells; the relation between differentiation, mitotic activity, and radiosensitivity; the importance of intensity-duration considerations in the radiation effect; and the latency of most biological responses.

Although many of the important effects of ionizing radiation were reported over 25 years ago, radiation dosimetry unfortunately did not keep pace with the biological approach. Advances in radiation physics and the availability of many different sources of radiation, culminating in the development of the cyclotron and other accelerators and the chain reactor, have now made possible a quantitative reinvestigation and amplification of the earlier qualitative observations and have, in addition, opened new avenues for investigation. It is our intention to present a comprehensive, though not necessarily encyclopedic, appraisal of the pathological physiology of radiation injury in the mammalian organism. The existence of several excellent reviews of the early literature has greatly simplified our task. Although we have drawn upon some early observations, our source material has largely been restricted to the more recent papers and to the Manhattan Project and Atomic Energy Commission documents. For convenience, the presentation has been divided into two parts, the first being concerned with the physical and biological factors in radiation action and the second with the specific aspects of the physiology of radiation injury.

NATURE OF THE BIOLOGICAL RESPONSE TO RADIATION

High-energy radiations dissipate their energy in tissue by ionization and excitation. The dependence of biological effectiveness upon the specific ionization or ion density of a particular radiation lends strong support to the idea that its action is related in some manner to direct local release of energy, presumably through ejection of electrons from the atoms through which it passes. While the role of excitation is not well defined, it may constitute an important secondary, if not primary, process. An interesting aspect of the energy absorption is the relatively small absolute amount that is required to produce widespread effects. One thousand roentgens, a lethal dose for most mammals, corresponds to an energy absorption of only 2×10^{-3} calorie per gram. We may examine the problem in another way by computing the fraction of molecules within a cell that is likely to be modified as a direct result of the radiation. In a cell containing about 10^{14} molecules, 1000 r would be expected to ionize only 10^{7} molecules. Although it is likely that many more molecules will be affected indirectly in consequence of the energy transformations resulting from the absorption of radiation, the total number of altered molecules is probably a small fraction of those present within a cell. It would seem, moreover, that not all the damaged molecules are of critical importance in the cell economy since most of these would be water molecules. These considerations raise the question of the localization and amplification of the early critical events. Although amplification could be accomplished by inactivation of genes or enzymes, by some disturbance in the synthesis or assembly of essential substrates, or by the formation of toxic substances, the nature of the early physicochemical events is obscure and poses the most formidable problem in radiobiology.

Two main concepts of radiation effects on living systems have been formulated. These are described most frequently as the theories of direct and indirect action and have been presented in some detail by Lea (1946) and others. Direct action postulates that ionization occurs in specific molecules that constitute a sensitive region or vital target. This idea in its classical sense is compatible with the single-hit type of effect that is characterized by its exponential relation to radiation dosage, its independence of dosage rate, and the inverse relation between its efficiency and ion density. It is perhaps best expressed in the effects on dried biological materials.

Both the direct and indirect concepts assume that chemical changes are induced by ionizing radiation, either by the alteration or inactivation of important molecular species or by the production of substances that influence cell metabolism (Zirkle, 1949). The indirect effect assumes that the initial chemical changes are due to highly reactive substances, mainly oxidants, that are formed at random in the aqueous environment and subsequently react with critical entities. Thus, localization of an effect within the living system is secondary and depends upon the nature of the acceptors as well as upon the original distribution of ions, the number of reactive substances formed, and the kinetics of their diffusion. The indirect type of action is dose rate dependent and varies, generally, directly with ion density. Organic molecules may, therefore, be modified by direct ionization and excitation or by reaction with the decomposition products of water. While it has not been possible to demonstrate these phenomena directly in irradiated biological material, there is sufficient circumstantial evidence to justify the assumption that they occur.

Perhaps the outstanding characteristic of radiobiological responses is their diversity, a not unreasonable situation when we consider that the radiant energy is absorbed at random in a heterogeneous and highly integrated system. Thus it is not surprising that many different effects are observed even on the cellular level and that not all these are in direct consequence of the radiation. It is probable that many of the seemingly discordant observations found in the literature are real and merely reflect the inherent complexity of the chain of events concerned in the radiation response and that of the responding organism.

This diversity of action increases the probability of nonspecificity, and so we observe that no single response is peculiarly specific for radiation injury, while many agents (such as urethane, nitrogen mustard, or benzol) are capable of mimicking radiation effects. Thus many of the effects of nitrogen mustard on enzymes and cells are indistinguishable from those of radiation and point to similar chemical processes (DeLong, 1950). Yet radiomimesis has its limitations in that no single agent duplicates all the radiation-induced reactions. In part at least this difference is one of spatial distribution; owing to natural barriers to the diffusion of a chemical agent from its point of entry and to conditions of its degradation, it would be almost impossible for such a radiomimetic agent to attain the uniform distribution of penetrating radiation.

Depending upon the character of the radiation and the manner of exposure, a variable period intervenes between irradiation and the various observed effects. This interval may be a matter of minutes for suppression of cell division, hours for lymphopenia, days for neutropenia and hemorrhage, weeks for anemia, or months for induction of tumors. Some of these intervals may be correlated with the life span, mitotic rate, and metabolic activity of the cells concerned with the effect. Many critical events, presumably chemical in nature, must occur during this "latent" period.

RADIATION QUALITY AND QUANTITY

As an environmental change or stimulus, radiation in general conforms to the familiar concepts of threshold, summation, intensity-duration, and adaptation. The energy required to produce different biological effects varies considerably. Retardation of growth of *Phycomyces* has been observed after only 0.001 r, while 1 r is sufficient to inhibit the activity of aged preparations of adenosinetriphosphatase (Forssberg, 1943; Barron, Dickman, *et al.*, 1949). Hematologic changes in mammals are seen with dosages of 25 to 50 r. Yet other effects such as the inhibition of contraction of striated muscle or immediate mammalian death may require many thousands of roentgens.

In general for any particular radiobiological response, there are limits within which the quantity of radiation will influence the effect in terms of latent period, severity, and recovery. In the mouse, total-body gamma-ray dosages of 140,000 r delivered in 20 min lead to immediate death (Henshaw, Snider, *et al.*, 1946). With the same dose rate, 70,000 r will kill in 1 to 5 hours, and 35,000 r in 7 to 62 hours. On the other hand, after dosages between 3500 and 14,000 r, there is no difference in survival time; all mice live 4 to 5 days. When the quantity of radiation is decreased still further to the minimum LD_{100} and below, survival time again increases, most deaths occurring at about two weeks. Similar findings have been observed with X rays and point to a distinct separation in the mode of killing which depends upon the dosage of radiation (Quastler, 1945a; Quastler *et al.*, 1951; Henshaw, 1944). Death following median lethal irradiation is the result of several factors, the most prominent of which are leucopenia, anemia, hemorrhage, bacteremia, and intestinal damage. The shocklike syndrome that appears with higher dosages and results in death within several days is initiated primarily as a consequence of intestinal injury. Finally, with still more massive dosages of radiation killing occurs within a matter of minutes or hours and is associated with disturbances of the nervous system.

A number of factors influence the threshold for different radiobiological effects. On the physical side these include the quality of the ionizing radiation, its intensity or rate of delivery, and the manner of exposure, i.e., local or total-body, external or internal, and single, continuous, or fractionated. It is generally agreed that α, β, γ, and X radiations and neutrons produce more or less similar physiological effects. However, their efficiency varies considerably since the effects of ionizing radiations depend not only upon the amount of energy absorbed per unit of volume and of time but also upon its distribution along the individual ion tracks (Zirkle, 1943; Gray, 1946). Specific ionization (ionization density) increases progressively from fast β rays to γ rays, hard X rays, soft X rays, fast neutrons, and α rays, and for most systems the biological effectiveness increases with increase in the ionization density. The time factor of irradiation and the dosage distribution among different tissues may, of course, contribute to the observed differences in efficiency and should be considered in their evaluation. The γ- to X-ray ratio of effectiveness has been found to vary from 1.3 to 2.0 for a number of biological effects (Sugiura, 1939; Lasnitzki and Lea, 1940; Mottram and Gay, 1940). When the irradiation periods are similar, the efficiency ratio for acute lethality in mice appears to be about 1.3. This is consistent with the finding that 200-kv X rays are about 1.3 times as effective as 20-Mv X rays, which have a specific ionization comparable with that of hard γ radiation (Quastler and Clark, 1945; Quastler and Lanzl, 1950). The 200-kv X rays are also about 1.4 times as efficient as Na^{24} β rays for acute killing of mice (Snyder and Kisieleski, 1950); it is worth noting, however, that the actual ratio may be somewhat lower, since the time factor of irradiation varied in these experiments. For acute effects in mammals, 1 n of fast neutrons (2.5 rep) is equivalent to 3 to 32 r, depending on the criterion (Lawrence and Lawrence, 1936; Aebersold and Lawrence, 1942; Lampe and Hodges, 1943; Mitchell, 1947; Evans, 1947; Henshaw *et al.*, 1947; Gray and Read, 1948; Dowdy, 1949). The effectiveness ratios are generally somewhat larger for periodic or protracted exposures than for acute, presumably because of a slower recovery from neutron irradiation. However, for certain effects that are related presumably to very small volumes (gene mutations or killing of small microorganisms) the efficiency varies inversely with specific ionization. It is inferred that only a few ions are required for these all-or-none effects, additional ionization being wasted.

Further evidence pointing to the similarity of the effects produced by the different radiations is given by additivity studies. Obviously, incomplete additivity of two radiations would indicate some difference in mechanism, whereas complete additivity would suggest that at least the events that are directly responsible for observed effects are identical. When the energy distribution is similar and the exposure times are relatively brief, complete additivity of the various radiations is observed (Stapleton and Zirkle, 1946; Zirkle, 1950). If the exposure time is prolonged (24 to 48 hours instead of 1 hour) additivity of γ rays and fast neutrons is incomplete (Mitchell, 1947). This may be related to differences in the recovery times, for there is reason to believe that recovery may be most rapid with β and γ rays, less with conventional X rays, and least with neutrons (Quastler and Lanzl, 1950; Lasnitzki, 1948). This point requires further amplification. Incomplete additivity is also observed after external irradiation with beta and hard gamma rays (Raper, 1947). In view of the great difference in tissue distribution of these two radiations given externally, one would hardly anticipate more than a partial additivity. It is of interest that an isotope with osseous distribution and one with reticulo-endothelial distribution are synergistic with respect to lethality (Friedell and Christie, 1951).

In the production of some biological effects (e.g., gene mutations or lethal effects in *Triton*) a given dose produces the same degree of effect regardless of the rate or time during which it is delivered (Lea, 1946; Brunst and Sheremetieva-Brunst, 1949). In a few instances, the radiation effect diminishes with very brief exposure times: the lethal effect on *Drosophila* eggs exposed to 165 r is reduced by 20 per cent when the radiation is delivered in 0.4 second instead of 1.2 seconds (Sievert and Forssberg, 1936). For most responses, especially in mammals, the effectiveness of a given dose decreases as the rate of exposure decreases. Yet the events in even this category display reciprocity over a part of the intensity spectrum, and there is little information relating to very intense instantaneous exposures, such as might be encountered in an atomic explosion. Reduction in the biological effect with protraction of the irradiation is generally explained by assuming that the recovery rate becomes appreciable during the exposure. Increasing the period of exposure 10 times reduces the lethal action in mice for a given dosage of gamma radiation to about 70 per cent (Henshaw *et al.*, 1947). The acute LD_{50} of gamma radiation for mice is 840 r when the dosage rate is 30 r per minute and 1200 r when the rate is reduced to 3 r per minute (Henshaw *et al.*, 1946). In man, the dosage required to produce an equivalent cutaneous reaction is doubled when the period of irradiation is increased about 30 times, e.g., from 435 r per minute to 15 r per minute (MacKee *et al.*, 1943).

When a particular dose is given in several fractions, it is generally less effective than when it is delivered at one time. Fractionation has been studied by exposing animals at different daily doses over a specific interval and comparing the effect produced by the same total dose given in a single exposure or by continuing the exposures until death. Such studies provide valuable information concerning lethal mechanisms and recovery constants and bear directly on the problem of radiation tolerance (MacComb and Quimby, 1936; Quimby and MacComb, 1937; Ellinger, 1943; Hagen and Simmons, 1947; Sacher *et al.*, 1949; Ellinger and Barnett, 1950; Sacher, 1950). Differences in rates of recovery may account for the lower relative efficiency of 20-Mv roentgen rays with fractionation as compared with that of 200-kv X rays (Quastler and Lanzl, 1950) or neutrons (Henshaw *et al.*, 1947; Evans, 1947). Although recovery constants can be calculated for certain radiation effects, they apparently cannot be used to predict quantitatively the recovery pattern following various modes of irradiation (Sacher, 1950).

Another aspect of the intensity-duration factor is the production of different effects with the same total dose. Acute and delayed toxic effects have been described in chick embryos, chicks, and ducklings (Karnofsky *et al.*, 1950; Jacquez and Karnofsky, 1950; Stearner, 1951). Early deaths, within 24 hours, occur with dose rates above 5 to 10 r per minute and are relatively independent of a total dose above 800 to 1000 r. There is evidence that early lethality is associated with renal failure since uricemia precedes death by several hours (Stearner *et al.*, 1950). Delayed deaths take place within one to two weeks following irradiation, and the pathological physiology parallels that seen in mammals. From dose fractionation studies it appears that the over-all time of exposure is more important than the dose rate in eliciting the early killing in chicks and ducklings (Stearner and Christian, 1951). The significance of the over-all time of exposure has been indicated in other experiments. Dose rate as such is of less importance than the dose per fraction or the intervals between fractions in determining the lethal effect of X radiation on chick fibroblasts (Paterson and Thompson, 1948).

The response to radiation depends upon the portion of the cell or organism that is irradiated. It has been shown by fractional irradiation of parts of cells that ions formed in the cell nucleus are more effective in the production of certain biological effects than those formed elsewhere (Henshaw, 1938; Zirkle, 1932). Several hundred roentgens applied locally may be relatively innocuous, whereas a similar dose administered to all or most of the body leads to widespread effects. Irradiation of the abdomen is more efficient than irradiation of the thorax, and penetrating radiations are more effective than the superficial in producing acute toxicity (Raper, 1947; Bond *et al.*, 1950). It is also apparent that different mechanisms contribute to lethality, depending upon the area that is irradiated.

The severity of cutaneous erythema is related to the size of the radiation field, and two fields a distance apart show less injury than areas that are closer together (Jolles, 1941; Jolles and Mitchell, 1947; Jolles, 1950). Partial irradiation of the frog's corneal epithelium with 3600 r results in the same over-all inhibition of mitotic division as total irradiation of the cornea with 900 r (Strelin, 1950). Thus, injury and recovery are, to some extent, dependent upon chemical interaction between the irradiated and adjacent nonirradiated areas. There is also reason to believe that injury to specific sites is more severe after a total-body exposure than after local irradiation. This may be attributed to the liberation of nonspecific toxic materials from irradiated tissue and/or to a sparing action of nonirradiated tissue. Although there is some evidence of active circulating factors following irradiation, the significance of such humoral agents is not fully appreciated (Barnes and Furth, 1943; Ahlstrom *et al.*, 1947; Van Dyke and Huff, 1949; Lawrence *et al.*, 1947; Ellinger, 1951). Parabiosis, cross-circulation, and early transfusion have been shown to diminish radiation toxicity (Barnes and Furth, 1943; Van Dyke and Huff, 1949; Salisbury *et al.*, 1951, Brecher and Cronkite, 1951, Swisher and Furth, 1951).

Shielding of relatively small volumes of tissues can decrease the severity of an otherwise total-body exposure. For example, with the spleen shielded and the remainder of the body irradiated, the 30-day LD_{50} for mice is increased from 550 to 975 r (Jacobson *et al.*, 1949). Protection of the head, the extremities, or other small areas will also diminish mortality (Abrams and Kaplan, 1951; Gershon-Cohen *et al.*, 1951; Allen, 1951). Recovery of hematopoietic tissue is also more rapid after subtotal irradiation (Boffil and Miletzky, 1946; Rekers, 1949; Jacobson *et al.*, 1951). The mechanism of these protective effects is poorly understood; Jacobson *et al.* (1950) have suggested that the mesenchymal tissues in certain shielded areas may supply a factor that facilitates regeneration of blood-forming tissue. It is of interest, in this connection, that spleen transplants or the injection of marrow suspensions or of spleen homogenates are effective in reducing radiation mortality in certain species (Jacobson *et al.*, 1951; Lorenz *et al.*, 1951; Cole *et al.*, 1952). In contrast to protection by shielding is the synergism that results when certain radioisotopes, which differ in localization, are administered in combination. When the reticulo-endothelial system of rats is irradiated with colloidal Au^{198} and the bone marrow with P^{32}, lethality is potentiated (Friedell and Christie, 1951). On the other hand, only an additive effect is obtained when two bone-seeking radioisotopes are injected simultaneously (Salerno *et al.*, 1952).

BIOLOGICAL FACTORS IN RADIOSENSITIVITY

Many of our concepts concerning the nature of radiation action are derived from studies of radiosensitivity and of the factors that influence it. The selective action of radiation on different parts of the same cell and on different cells and the relation between differentiation, mitotic activity, and radiosensitivity were described during the first decade after Röntgen's discovery of X rays. There followed numerous attempts to modify sensitivity experimentally. These included the effects of temperature, oxygen, blood flow, and hydration (Schwarz, 1909; Holthusen, 1921; Petry, 1922; Mottram, 1924; Jolly, 1924). Temperature studies were especially prominent, since temperature was a convenient tool, and it appeared that the radiation response was dependent upon metabolic activity. Unfortunately, there were few attempts to distinguish the events occurring during irradiation from those taking place after the exposure. Moreover, the early studies were restricted largely to isolated cells and tissues. These considerations, along with increasing knowledge of radiochemical reactions, have led, in recent years, to a renewed interest in the factors of radiosensitivity.

CELL AND TISSUE SENSITIVITY

The inherent difference in sensitivity of various cells and tissues attracted early attention, and in 1906 Bergonié and Tribondeau formulated the principle that actively proliferating tissues are the most sensitive to radiation and that the radiosensitivity of a tissue varies inversely with the degree of differentiation. While this view has been generally accepted, it is true only in a broad sense for there are many notable exceptions. In contrast to the large body of information pertaining to cell and tissue sensitivity is the paucity of early investigations concerned with the comparative lethal dose for animals of the same and different species and with the factors that influence the lethal dose. Our knowledge relating to this aspect of the problem is, therefore, largely a product of studies that have been conducted during the past 10 to 15 years.

Before discussing the radiosensitivities of particular cells and tissues, a discussion of what is meant by radiosensitivity is in order. If atrophy of tissues is referred to, it is obvious that this may be merely a consequence of inhibition of growth of tissues, which are continually regenerating to compensate for cells thrown off. This is particularly true of blood-forming organs. Interference with other synthetic processes (e.g., secretory activities) may be less obvious on cursory examination. In general, radiosensitivity of cells, as discussed here, will refer to destruction or degeneration of cells as living entities, and it may be well to recall that these events are prone to occur at the time of cell division.

For a given cell, the nucleus is a more sensitive indicator of damage than the cytoplasm, and the cell in mitosis is usually more susceptible to injury than the cell at rest. But even in mitosis there are differences, for cells in prophase and metaphase are the most sensitive to radiation injury (Sparrow, 1951). It is known that the absorption of radiation depends upon the atomic constitution of the absorbing medium. While nuclear sensitivity may perhaps be attributed to the differential absorption of radiation by the nucleus and cytoplasm, tissues with nearly the same cross section can vary greatly in their susceptibility. It is evident, therefore, that other intrinsic factors are involved. Although it has been demonstrated by fractional irradiation that ions produced in the cell nucleus are more effective biologically than those produced elsewhere (Zirkle, 1932; Henshaw, 1938), nuclear injury in certain cells may be a result of toxic factors originating in the cytoplasm (Duryee, 1949). A normal cell injected with cytoplasm from an irradiated cell has been shown to exhibit typical radiation effects. Thus, the special sensitivity of the nucleus to radiation may, under certain conditions, be more apparent than real, at least in terms of the initiating mechanism.

The sensitivity of the cell during division may reside in some facet of its instability, since mitosis is characterized by a number of physicochemical changes, in, for example, chromosomal mass and surface, viscosity, permeability, conductivity, and energy requirements. Polymerization and depolymerization of nucleic acids, as well as changes in the relative amounts of nuclear and cytoplasmic nucleic acids, are thought to occur during the mitotic cycle, and such changes may affect sensitivity. Recent work with pepsin-albumin films reveals that form, even on the molecular scale, can greatly influence the radiation response (Mazia and Blumenthal, 1948). The physical and chemical factors that contribute to nuclear sensitivity are numerous and only partially understood. They are discussed in some detail in the excellent review by Sparrow (1951).

Recovery phenomena have been evoked to explain the difference in response of slowly and rapidly dividing cells. It is believed that the slowly dividing cell has a greater chance to recover since the death of a cell frequently occurs at mitosis from structural alterations incurred sometime before (Lasnitzki, 1943a). However, with α and neutron irradiation, or with high dosages of X rays, degenerated cells appear in appreciable numbers before resumption of the mitotic process (Lasnitzki, 1943b; Spear and Tansley, 1944; Tansley *et al.*, 1948). Although there is ample evidence that radiation interferes with the synthesis of desoxyribonucleic acid (DNA), which could explain the postirradiation mitotic inhibition, the disturbance in rapidly growing and in adult tissues does not differ greatly (Mitchell, 1942; Hevesy, 1945, 1949; Holmes, 1949; Kelly and Jones, 1950). Unfortunately, there are few, if any, data relating the recovery of nucleic acid formation to the mitotic activity of tissues known to differ in sensitivity. It has been suggested that radiosensitivity may be related to the ratio of the nuclear and cytoplasmic nucleic acids, since the highest ratio is found in lymphoid tissue and the lowest in resistant cells (Brues and Rietz, 1951). Proliferating tissues probably show, in general, an increase in DNA per cell (Price and Laird, 1950). It is well known, however, that ribonucleic acid (RNA) also tends to be increased in proliferating cells.

That certain types of recovery may be faster in cells which are presumed to have a more rapid turnover is indicated by the finding that intestinal epithelium and lymphoid tissue exhibit less interference of mitotic activity after sublethal X irradiation than the less sensitive skin and adrenal tissue (Knowlton and Hempelmann, 1949). On the other hand, although thyroid administration increases the mitotic index of mouse epidermis, and presumably its rate of metabolism, it does not affect the response to irradiation, similar changes being observed in the epidermis of control and thyroid-fed irradiated mice (W. W. Smith, 1951).

In general, the hematopoietic and germinal tissues are the most sensitive to radiation. These are followed by the intestinal epithelium, skin, and connective tissue. Bone and glands are relatively radioresistant while muscle and nerve are the least sensitive (Warren, 1942; Henshaw and Snider, 1946; Warren and Bowers, 1950). There seems to be no relation between the susceptibility of different tissues and their basal oxygen consumption. Brain and kidney have higher rates of respiration than spleen; yet the former are relatively radioresistant, while the latter is radiosensitive. Although it has been shown that polyploidy protects certain simple organisms against radiation damage (Latarjet and Ephrussi, 1949; Clark and Kelly, 1950), there does not appear to be any reason to think that this is an important factor in radiosensitivity of the several animal tissues. Polyploid cells occur in the liver, but they are the exception rather than the rule and probably do not account for the apparent resistance of this organ to radiation.

Although radiosensitivity appears to be related to the life span, growth rate, and differentiation of tissue, this is only part of the story. For example, with the onset of mitosis germinating wheat seedlings become more resistant to the growth-retarding effect of X radiation (Henshaw and Francis, 1935), and in the eggs of *Drosophila* sensitivity does not exactly parallel the rate of division (Packard, 1930). Furthermore, radiosensitivity is not correlated with the number of premitotic or mitotic nuclei in the roots of *Vicia faba* (Mottram, 1935b). The most sensitive cells in the testis are the spermatogonia rather than the spermatocytes, which manifest greater mitotic activity (Bloom, 1947). The rapidly growing squamous cell epithelioma is fairly resistant to radiation, while the more slowly growing basal-cell tumor is sensitive (Packard, 1930). There are other exceptions; the regenerating liver does not show evidence of increased sensitivity (Brues and Rietz, 1951), and erythroblast vulnerability to radiation injury is not enhanced by an increase in mitotic activity; in fact, the hyperplastic erythroid tissue shows less injury than the normal (Jacobson *et al.*, 1948).

There are equally convincing arguments in regard to primitiveness and radiosensitivity. Susceptibility of the developing ovum of the rabbit does not depend exclusively on its differentiation (Bloom, 1947). Moreover, the primitive reticular cells are exceedingly resistant although the blast cells, which can develop from reticular cells, are quite sensitive (Bloom, 1947; Tullis, 1949). Finally, the highly differentiated nerve cell is radioresistant while the polymorphonuclear leukocyte, though well differentiated, is fairly sensitive (Warren, 1942). It would appear that many factors act to influence responsiveness of tissue under various conditions of growth and differentiation.

SPECIES SENSITIVITY

The lethal dose of ionizing radiation for the whole animal varies not only among the different species but also among animals of the same species. The dosage of total-body X radiation required to kill 50 per cent of adult warm-blooded mammals within 30 days ranges from 200 to 800 r (Dowdy, 1949). In Table 14-1 are presented the acute lethal

TABLE 14-1. COMPARISON OF THE 30-DAY LD_{50} FOR A TOTAL-BODY DOSAGE OF HARD X RAYS[a]

Animal	LD_{50}, r
Guinea pig	200–400
Swine	275
Dog	325
Goat	350
Monkey	500
Mouse	400–600
Rat	600–700
Hamster	700
Rabbit	800

[a] These dosages are approximate and may vary from time to time in the same or different laboratories (refer to text).

dosages for a number of laboratory animals. The absolute roentgen values will differ somewhat depending upon the strain, conditions of exposure, and maintenance, but the order of sensitivity remains the same. The LD_{50} for man is questionable; best estimates place it between the LD_{50} for the goat and mouse. Of interest is the radioresistance of the bat, a hibernating mammal, whose life span under laboratory conditions is shortened only after dosages of about 15,000 r (D. E. Smith *et al.*, 1951). On the other hand, the LD_{50} for the goldfish is only 850 r (Prosser *et al.*, 1947a).

Species sensitivity to penetrating radiation is not well correlated with body size or with metabolic rate, although these factors, as will be discussed later, may be important in individual animals. There is little difference in the basal heat production of the guinea pig and rat although the LD_{50} for the guinea pig is lower than that for the rat by a factor of about 2. Since a number of factors are involved in radiation death, species sensitivity may reflect, in part at least, the particular susceptibility of the different animals to the diverse mechanisms leading to morbidity, e.g., toxins, leukopenia, bacteremia, hemorrhage, impaired nutrition, and shock. There is a suggestion that species sensitivity may be related to differences in the rates of recovery from radiation injury since the mean survival time after median lethal irradiation is greater for the more sensitive species (Sacher, unpublished observation, 1951). It is of interest that a number of physiological and histological changes reflect the amount of radiation and not the lethal effect; i.e., they are more nearly independent of species (Bloom, 1947; Brues and Rietz, 1948; De Bruyn, 1948).

In contrast to the well-established differences in species sensitivity to penetrating radiations are the apparently negligible differences in the acute lethal effects of total-surface β irradiation when a correction is made for body size, i.e., for the proportion of the body mass irradiated. The median lethal dose of external β irradiation varies from 4700 rep for the mouse to 17,000 rep for the rabbit; the total integrated dose, however, is directly proportional to the body mass (Raper, 1947). That the lethal action of surface β rays is dependent upon a total mass or volume effect is assumed from the fact that all the energy is absorbed in a superficial layer of tissue whose mass is small relative to the mass of the animal. The possibility that some compensating situation, also varying with body mass, may be active is not ruled out. The lethal mechanisms are undoubtedly different for the superficial and penetrating types of radiations (Table 14-2); for example, the blood picture is unaffected by a

TABLE 14-2. DOSAGE OF EXTERNAL BETA (P^{32}) AND GAMMA (Ta^{182}) RADIATION REQUIRED TO KILL 50 PER CENT OF ANIMALS WITHIN 45 DAYS
(After Raper, 1947)

Animal	β radiation, rep	γ radiation, r
Baby rat	2,200	510
Mouse	4,700	840
Rat	7,500	1280
Guinea pig	7,750	310
Rabbit	17,000	1500

lethal dose of external β irradiation. With internally deposited β emitters, or α emitters, however, the picture more or less resembles that following penetrating external irradiation (Bloom, 1947; Prosser *et al.*, 1947b). The wider the distribution of an internal emitter, the greater is the similarity of the clinical picture to that associated with penetrating radiation.

INDIVIDUAL SENSITIVITY

Individuals in an apparently uniform population do not respond equally to radiation. Curves relating mortality to dose are of the sigmoid type and are quite steep, especially for mammals (Ellinger, 1945; Boche and Bishop, 1946). Variations in mortality of from 0 to nearly 100 per cent may occur in the LD_{50} range (Clark and Uncapher, 1949). As might be anticipated, the dose range between just lethal and completely lethal is greater in hybrid than in inbred strains, and, in addition, the LD_{50} varies under different laboratory conditions. Besides the variation in mortality, there are impressive differences in survival time during the acute period following median lethal irradiation. In the rat, deaths within 30 days are most frequent between the fourth and eighth and between the tenth and fifteenth postirradiation days (Hagen and Simmons, 1947). Mortality waves have also been observed in rabbits and chickens (Karnofsky *et al.*, 1950; Jacquez and Karnofsky, 1950; Stearner, 1951; Hagen and Sacher, 1946). In these animals the first peak of deaths occurs during the first day after irradiation, even with an LD_{50}. The existence of several processes that may lead to death in the acute period is suggested by these findings. Reference has already been made to the apparent transition from one mechanism of death to another with increasing amounts of supralethal radiation. Although there are wide variations in mortality, it is rather surprising that there are few histologic differences between animals dying after an LD_{50} of radiation and those surviving the same dose (Bloom, 1947).

Radiosensitivity of the embryo varies with its age (Karnofsky *et al.*, 1950; Wilson, 1935; Wilson and Karr, 1950). The chick embryo manifests an increasing sensitivity to early lethality (death within 24 hours) during the third to seventh day of incubation, and is most sensitive on the eighth to tenth day, after which its response is stabilized at a slightly more resistant level (Karnofsky *et al.*, 1950). Depression of growth is also related directly to the age of the chick embryo at the time of irradiation. Interestingly enough, the number of dividing cells in the non-irradiated embryo decreases markedly between the third and eighth days of incubation (O'Connor, 1950). Oxygen consumption is unchanged, but there is a threefold decrease in aerobic glycolysis during this interval.

Irradiation of the pregnant mouse before implantation of the embryo leads to a high prenatal fetal mortality with only a negligible incidence of abnormality in animals surviving to term (Russell and Russell, 1950). The earliest stages after mating are the most sensitive. When the pregnant mouse is exposed during the postimplantation stages, the relative magnitude of effects is reversed, abnormality exceeding mortality. There is a striking separation in sensitivity to lethal action. Exposure to 200 r on the ninth day of gestation is completely lethal while 400 r is required on the tenth day of gestation (Wilson and Karr, 1950). This may be related to implantation of the embryo or to beginning differentiation. Malformations of the skeleton and destruction of the developing nervous system are prominent sequelae of irradiation during the latter two-thirds of pregnancy (Russell, 1950; Hicks, 1950). In contrast, adult bone and nervous tissue are relatively radioresistant (see Chap. 13).

There is remarkably little difference in the LD_{50} for delayed deaths among the chick embryo, baby chick, and adult chicken, the embryo being, in fact, somewhat more resistant, perhaps because of the sterility of the internal environment of the egg (Karnofsky *et al.*, 1950; Jacquez and Karnofsky, 1950). This is apparently not the case in the mammal. The mammalian fetus is more susceptible than either the young or adult animal, and the former is, in general, more sensitive than the latter. There are some exceptions, however. Mice under 15 days of age are less sensitive and survive longer than 30-day-old animals, which manifest a greatly increased susceptibility (Quastler, 1945b; Abrams, 1951; Furth and Furth, 1936). Sensitivity to the lethal action of X rays decreases rapidly with increasing age beyond 30 days, and little difference is apparent between two- and three-month-old animals. The acute median lethal dose of γ rays does not differ appreciably for mice varying in age from 1.5 to 12 months (Zirkle *et al.*, 1946). The relative resistance of the newborn mouse may be related to protective influences associated with suckling (Abrams, 1951). Conversely, the sensitivity of 30-day-old mice may be a function of changes associated with puberty. It is of interest that maximal susceptibility to radiation lymphoma also occurs during the puberal period in mice (Kaplan, 1948). In contrast to these results, the amount of X radiation required for minimal depression of femoral growth following local exposure of the epiphyseal region is linear with age (Hinkel, 1942). Minimal stunting is seen with 700 r in one-month-old rats, whereas 2200 r is required at six months of age. The younger rats, however, recover more quickly than older animals.

Females may be somewhat more resistant than males, i.e., by about 50 r, but a sex difference is not apparent in all species or in different strains of the same species (Hagen and Simmons, 1947; Hagen and Sacher, 1946; Abrams, 1951; Zirkle *et al.*, 1946). The role of body weight in radiosensitivity is not well established, although it appears that heavier animals tend to be less sensitive. It is not clear, however, whether this is a reflection of weight or of age. The median lethal dose of X rays is not very dependent upon weight in rats of approximately the same age (Hagen and Simmons, 1947). However, rats of the same age, differing in weight because of dietary restrictions, vary in their sensitivity to neutron irradiation, the smaller rats being more sensitive (Ely and Ross, 1947). Rabbits of either sex weighing more than 2 kg are reported to be somewhat less sensitive than animals weighing less than 2 kg (Hagen and Sacher, 1946). The heavier rabbits survive longer in any given dose group. It has also been observed that survival time is related to body weight in mice (Quastler, 1945b). An explanation of the protective influence of weight or age is not obvious; it is probably not attributable to a simple relation between the rate of growth and sensitivity. Differences in the amount and distribution of body fat can account for small differences in sensitivity on the basis of the low effective atomic number of fat (Spiers, 1946).

A number of constitutional factors must influence the breakdown following irradiation. It is thought that preirradiation tests of functional capacity would be useful in sorting out many of these influences, thereby eliminating much of the so-called "inherent variability." Unfortunately, there is little information relating to this aspect of the problem, which is of both practical and theoretical importance.

INDUCED RADIOSENSITIVITY OR RESISTANCE

Many procedures have been employed in an attempt to modify the response to radiation. Some of these act in a general way to change the response of the organism to stress. Others are concerned more specifically with the decisive events responsible for injury to critical physiological systems or for recovery from such injury. Some of the procedures within the more specific category may be considered to act primarily upon the biological system, while others probably influence the pathways of energy dissipation within it.

Needless to say, the criterion will influence any evaluation of radiosensitivity factors. The death of an irradiated animal may be a considerable distance downstream from death of any particular cell or group of cells in the same animal. Since the death of an animal is more complex than the death of a cell, it is not surprising that more factors are found to influence sensitivity of the animal than of the cell. Likewise, it is necessary to distinguish the modification of immediate and delayed, or acute and chronic, effects. Protection against acute lethal action does not necessarily imply protection against the more chronic sequelae in so far as different mechanisms may be involved in their development.

In general, any agent that changes the body economy sufficiently modifies the lethal action of radiation. Adrenal insufficiency (Cronkite and Chapman, 1950), protein depletion (Jennings, 1949; Elson and Lamerton, 1949), vitamin deficiency (Johnson *et al.*, 1946), infection (Taliaferro and Taliaferro, 1951; Shechmeister and Bond, 1951), trauma (Brooks and

Evans, 1950), and exhaustive exercise (Stapleton and Curtis, 1946; Kimeldorf *et al.*, 1950) increase susceptibility to radiation as to most noxious stimuli. Some degree of radioresistance may be acquired as a result of previous exposures to β or X radiation (Raper, 1947; Cronkite *et al.*, 1950; Bloom, 1950), pretreatment with horse serum (Hektoen, 1918; Graham *et al.*, 1950), estrogens (Treadwell *et al.*, 1943; Patt, Straube, *et al.*, 1949), and adrenal cortical extract (Graham *et al.*, 1950), and by immunization (Kohn, 1949). There are no adequate explanations of these phenomena. In the case of the estrogens it is believed that the decreased toxicity is related to stimulation of myeloid activity following the initial estrogen-produced depression since the pretreated animals show rapid recovery from radiation granulocytopenia but not from lymphopenia (Patt, Straube, *et al.*, 1949). Along these lines, an increased resistance of erythropoietic tissues has been observed following the production of a regenerative anemia by phlebotomy, administration of phenylhydrazine (Jacobson *et al.*, 1948), or exposure to high altitude (Schack and MacDuffee, 1949).

TEMPERATURE AND METABOLIC RATE

There is general agreement that the changes incidental to irradiation are dependent upon the rate of metabolism. This is consistent with observations made in other types of injury and is not unreasonable in view of the apparent nonspecificity of radiobiological effects. An increased metabolic activity after exposure to ionizing radiation induced by thyroid extract or dinitrophenol (W. W. Smith and F. Smith, 1951; Blount and Smith, 1949), a cold environment in nonacclimatized mammals (W. W. Smith *et al.*, 1949; Hempelmann *et al.*, 1949), or exhaustive exercise (Stapleton and Curtis, 1946; Kimeldorf *et al.*, 1950) enhances lethality, while depression of metabolic rate, at least in poikilotherms and isolated tissues (Patt and Swift, 1948; Allen *et al.*, 1950; Schrek, 1946; Cook, 1939), decreases the rate of development of radiation damage. Surprisingly, administration of thiouracil and thyroidectomy appear to have little influence on lethality in adult mice and rats (W. W. Smith and F. Smith, 1951; Blount and Smith, 1949; Hempelmann *et al.*, 1949; Haley *et al.*, 1950).

Evidence that relates to the effect of temperature during exposure to radiation is equivocal, and virtually every conceivable effect has been described. Sensitivity of the eggs of *Ascaris* (Holthusen, 1921) and of *Drosophila* (Packard, 1930) is increased by elevation in temperature during irradiation. Yet temperature is without influence on *E. coli* (Lea, 1946), thymic cell suspensions (Schrek, 1946), wheat seedlings (Henshaw and Francis, 1935), or eggs of the frog and hen (Ancel and Vintemberger, 1927). Moreover, cold is reported to increase the sensitivity of the roots of *Vicia faba* and of certain tumor cells to the growth-retarding effects of irradiation and also to increase the number of dominant lethal mutations in irradiated *Drosophila* (Mottram, 1935a; Crabtree and Cramer, 1933; Baker and Sgourakis, 1950). In larger animals the results are equally confusing. Sensitivity of newborn mice and rats to irradiation of the whole body or of the skin is decreased when the ambient temperature is lowered during exposure (Lacassagne, 1942; Hempelmann *et al.*, 1949; Evans, Goodrich, and Slaughter, 1941; Evans, Robbie, *et al.*, 1941). Chilling of the adult animal does not increase the survival rate, however (Hempelmann *et al.*, 1949). Moreover, lethality and cytological damage in the frog and tadpole are not influenced by a change in body temperature during irradiation (Patt and Swift, 1948; Allen *et al.*, 1950).

Evaluation of temperature effects during irradiation is complicated since temperature may alter the quality as well as the quantity of cellular activity, which, in turn, may modify the response to irradiation. Further, reactions of injury and of recovery must rapidly follow the primary events that are associated with the absorption of energy, and it is probable that these secondary metabolic reactions appear in some degree even before the irradiation is terminated. Since the time course and temperature coefficients of the subsequent biochemical changes may vary for the different effects and systems, it is perhaps not surprising that many types of temperature responses have been described. When there is little metabolic activity initially, as in the unfertilized eggs of *Nereis*, the temperature coefficient of the events occurring during irradiation, which result ultimately in a lethal action, is found to be about 1.1 (Redfield *et al.*, 1924).

Certain temperature effects may be attributed more directly to specific changes, e.g., in blood flow or in oxygen tension. Sensitivity to radiation is dependent upon the blood flow to the exposed area, and the beneficial effects of chilling the skin can be ascribed to changes in the vascular bed (Carty, 1930). Likewise, the decreased lethality of the chilled newborn mammal may be a consequence of lowered oxygen tension resulting from the relatively greater depression of breathing than of tissue respiration in the cold. In contrast, the increase in dominant lethal mutations in *Drosophila* irradiated in oxygen at 2°C over those treated in oxygen at 27°C has been related to the higher oxygen tension within the irradiated sperm at the lower temperature (Baker and Sgourakis, 1950). Actually, these two views are not incompatible.

While it is true that fern spores and certain pollens show an enhanced radioresistance at liquid air temperatures, perhaps because of altered formation and diffusion of free radicals or of some change in the configuration of organic molecules, there is reasonable evidence that less extreme temperature changes do not directly influence the immediate radiation reactions in living systems. Temperature independence over the narrow range compatible with life is consistent with the concept of indirect as well as of direct action since the free radicals must have zero or nearly zero energies of activation. On the other hand, the events subsequent to irradiation appear to be rate-sensitive; yet, since recovery may also be influenced, the ultimate outcome is not always changed.

Consistent with these concepts are the findings that treatment of mice with desiccated thyroid both before and after irradiation gives the same enhanced effect as treatment begun after the exposure, while pretreatment alone fails to modify lethality (W. W. Smith and F. Smith, 1951). It is also noteworthy that survival is not altered by severe preirradiation exercise (Patt, Blackford, *et al.*, 1951) or by irradiating animals under Nembutal anesthesia (Hempelmann *et al.*, 1949; Patt, Blackford, *et al.*, 1951). Although lethality is diminished when mice are given a heavy dose of morphine before exposure to X rays, protection is probably a consequence of the hypoxia resulting from depression of the respiratory center (Kahn, 1951). In contrast, the lethal effect is augmented when rats are anesthetized with urethane, a radiomimetic agent, and then irradiated (Henry, 1949). This has not been observed in mice, however (Paterson and Matthews, 1951).

INTERMEDIARY RADIOCHEMICAL EVENTS

The aberrations in cell chemistry that follow irradiation are not easily resolved since the pathways of energy dissipation and the structure and properties of biologically important molecules are still obscure. From energy considerations and the widespread nature of radiation damage there is reason to believe that the primary disturbance centers around enzymes, genes, and other key molecules that are involved in the assembly and synthesis of essential substrates. Presumably, certain of these entities are inactivated or modified by direct ionization and excitation and/or by the products of irradiated water. It has been postulated by Barron (1946) and Barron and Dickman (1949) that the critically involved enzymes are those requiring sulfhydryl groups for their activity and that these are reversibly oxidized by low dosages and irreversibly denatured by higher dosages. While sulfhydryl enzymes may be inhibited by ionizing radiations under certain conditions, evidence for their selective inhibition in vivo is incomplete (Dinning *et al.*, 1950; Dubois *et al.*, 1950; LeMay, 1951). It is not known, moreover, whether changes when observed are the cause or the effect of cell injury and death.

The abundance of water in biological materials and the demonstration of activated water reactions in simple chemical systems have naturally led to much speculation concerning their implication for radiobiology. As stated by Weiss (1947), irradiated water is essentially an oxidation-reduction system that consists primarily of free hydrogen atoms and hydroxyl radicals. Although free radicals result from the ionization of water, they may also be formed in the ambient liquid when ionization occurs directly in a biological particle. Depending upon the initial spatial distribution of the ions and upon the presence and configuration of dissolved substances, recombination or further reaction of the radicals takes place. Alpha rays may produce peroxides (presumably from hydroxyl radicals) even in pure water, whereas with γ and X rays, peroxides do not appear unless dissolved oxygen is present (Bonet-Maury and Lefort, 1948; Allen, 1948). Obviously, purity conditions such as these do not obtain in biological systems, where many acceptors are available for reaction with the products of activated water. Moreover, the products of irradiated water may not be of equal consequence inside and outside of a cell. It is well to recall, in addition, that the cell represents a nonhomogeneous system with varying gradients of concentration and solubility.

The activated-water concept of radiation action has received ample confirmation in a variety of in vitro systems in which the dilution effect described by Dale (1947) (independence of ionic yield and solute concentration except at very low and high concentrations) and the protection effect (competition between solutes for the activated solvent molecules) have been demonstrated. As the solute concentration increases or with increase in radiation dosage, there is a transition from the activated-water type of reaction to the direct-hit type characteristic of nonaqueous systems. Demonstration of these phenomena in vivo is not an easy task, however. The inability to detect an immediate oxidation of sulfhydryl groups in tissues obtained from heavily irradiated animals is consistent with theoretical considerations which reveal that only an exceedingly small fraction of the available sulfhydryl reservoir could be oxidized even in the absence of the naturally occurring protective substances (Patt, Straube, *et al.*, 1950). Perhaps the most convincing evidence, admittedly indirect, in support of the theory of in vivo effects of activated water comes from studies with anaerobiosis and with protective substances. It will be remembered that direct effects of radiation on solutes also play a role, but one that cannot be well understood in the present state of knowledge regarding exact physicochemical effects and the nature of the biological targets.

Water. It was recognized long ago that desiccation of biological systems favors radioresistance. Cells exposed to ionizing radiation are frequently seen to swell and this may be a factor in, or manifestation of, cell death (Failla, 1940; Buchsbaum and Zirkle, 1949). A hypothesis has been advanced to account for this hydration phenomenon, i.e., ionization and subsequent intra- and extracellular partition of ions, followed by removal of the latter with consequent increase in cellular osmotic pressure (Failla, 1940). However, there is little evidence in support of an increase in intracellular water following lethal irradiation of the whole animal (Soberman *et al.*, 1951). While dehydration may decrease radiosensitivity by minimizing cell swelling, a more likely explanation seems to be the interference with activated-water reactions either as a result of a decrease in the available water or an increase in the concentration of protective substances. The dependence of sensitivity on the degree of hydration has been demonstrated in seeds (Petry, 1922), seedlings (Henshaw and Francis, 1935; Wertz, 1940), isolated tissues (Chambers, 1941), and tumor cells (Failla, 1940). Yet it has been difficult to determine whether this relation holds in the intact animal. Mice deprived of water for 24 to 40 hours before X irradiation tend to live somewhat longer, but the proportion surviving is not altered materially (France, 1946). Frogs kept in dry, individual containers for 3 days lose about 35 per cent of their water, yet are no more resistant to irradiation (Patt and Tyree, unpublished observations, 1949). Even though appreciable water remains, some quantitative difference at this level of dehydration should be anticipated. Perhaps the answer lies in the relative concentrations and distributions of free and bound water under these conditions of water deprivation.

Hydrogen Ion Concentration. The local changes in pH that probably occur in the neighborhood of an ion track may play a role in the development of radiation injury. The formation of hydrogen peroxide has been shown to depend upon the hydrogen ion concentration, and changes in pH have been observed in irradiated solutions (Frilley, 1947). Variation in pH during irradiation alters the radiosensitivity of germinating fern spores, *Drosophila* eggs, and paramecia, sensitivity maxima being observed at definite concentrations of acid or base (Zirkle, 1936, 1940, 1941). Zirkle has compared this behavior with the effect of irradiation on proteins in vitro, where maximal flocculation is observed at a pH near the isoelectric point. This is considered to be consistent with the hypothesis that total sensitivity is due to the added effects of several reactions having maximum yields at different acidities. There is little information in connection with pH effects in isolated mammalian tissue or in the whole mammalian organism. Change in the pH of thymic cell suspensions from 7.8 to 6.6 does not influence the action of X rays (Schrek, 1946).

Oxygen Effects. The effect of ischemia on cutaneous radiosensitivity was observed by Schwarz in 1909. The relative resistance of *Ascaris* eggs during anaerobiosis was described subsequently by Holthusen (1921), who attributed the protection to the absence of cell division. Several years later Mottram (1924) and Jolly (1924) investigated the effect of blood flow on the response of skin and lymphatic tissue to X rays, and in 1933 Crabtree and Cramer presented a detailed account of the influence of anoxia and related chemical factors on the radiosensitivity of tumor cells. The possible relation of this aspect of radiosensitivity to the reactions of activated water was suggested by Thoday and Read (1947, 1949) and Read (1950). They confirmed the observation of Mottram (1935a) that oxygen deprivation decreases the growth reduction of broad bean roots following X irradiation and observed, in addition, that oxygen lack did not afford significant protection following α irradiation. This is a biological parallel to the radiochemical reactions involving oxygen in aqueous solutions, since oxygen lack would be expected to exert a minor influence on the formation of the hydroperoxyl radical and hydrogen peroxide by α rays.

Deprivation of oxygen during exposure to γ and X radiations diminishes their action in a variety of biological systems. This is true for yeast (Anderson and Turkowitz, 1941), *E. coli* (Hollaender *et al.*, 1951), barley seeds (Hayden and Smith, 1949), *Vicia faba* (Mottram, 1935a; Thoday and Read, 1947), *Drosophila* (Baker and Sgourakis, 1950), *Tradescantia* (Giles and Riley, 1950), tumor cells (Crabtree and Cramer, 1933), and mice and rats (Lacassagne, 1942; Dowdy *et al.*, 1950). Radioresistance is said to be the same whether anaerobiosis is induced by nitrogen, helium, argon, or hydrogen. Reduced oxygen tension has been shown to decrease a number of radiation effects, including lethality (Dowdy *et al.*, 1950), growth reduction (Thoday and Read, 1947), chromosome aberrations (Giles and Riley, 1950), and sex-linked lethal mutations (Baker and Sgourakis, 1950). However, under conditions in which the radiation effect is considered to arise from the direct ionization of a biological particle, the oxygen level is without influence (Hewitt and Read, 1950).

It is well known that radiation injury to specific sites parallels the blood flow during exposure (Schwarz, 1909; Carty, 1930; Mottram, 1924; Jolly, 1924; Evans *et al.*, 1942). Thus, damage to a limb is greatly diminished when the limb circulation is blocked, and tumor sensitivity varies with its vascularity. Mechanical retardation of breathing also increases resistance to irradiation (Evans *et al.*, 1942). Since a factor common to all these examples is a reduced oxygen tension, it is assumed that anoxia accounts for the modification of sensitivity. While this seems reasonable from the preponderant evidence in support of anaerobiosis cited previously, it has not been proved.

The question naturally arises as to whether anoxia modifies radiation injury by interfering with the radiochemical reactions that involve free oxygen or by inducing a more specific biological effect, e.g., on enzymes, metabolism, or cell division. The precise mechanism must be regarded as unsettled; there is reason to think, however, that both modes of action may be involved in the oxygen effect. Although Dowdy *et al.* (1950) have shown that the 30-day LD_{50} for rats X-irradiated in 5 per cent oxygen is about twice that for rats exposed in air, it is not known whether breathing a 5 per cent oxygen mixture for several minutes before and during irradiation lowers the blood and tissue oxygen tension sufficiently to modify free radical and peroxide formation to an appreciable degree. Mice are also protected against lethal irradiation by anoxic anoxia (Dowdy *et al.*, 1950). However, the range in which protection is evident is quite narrow, protection being observed with 7 per cent but not with 10 per cent oxygen, while a 5 per cent level is lethal during the period of irradiation. As contrasted with these observations, the increase in chromosome aberration frequency in *Tradescantia* is linear between 0 and 10 per cent oxygen, after which the rise is somewhat more gradual, tending to level off above 20 per cent (Giles and Beatty, 1950).

Several chemical procedures, which bear directly on the events associated with the oxygen effect, have been employed. Histotoxic anoxia produced by cyanide apparently increases the sensitivity of tumor tissue and of *Vicia faba* to radiation (Crabtree and Cramer, 1933). On the other hand, cyanide exerts some protective action against X rays in the mouse (Bacq *et al.*, 1950; Bacq, 1951), while it is without influence in the rat and frog (Patt and Swift, 1948; Dowdy *et al.*, 1950). Iodoacetic acid and sodium fluoride which, like cyanide and oxygen deficiency, inhibit aerobic glycolysis, do not affect the sensitivity of tumor cells (Crabtree and Cramer, 1933). The failure of cyanide-induced anoxia to protect the rat and the protection afforded this animal by anoxic anoxia have been taken to indicate that radiation injury is related to the tissue oxygen tension (Dowdy *et al.*, 1950). On the other hand, it has been suggested that cyanide may protect the mouse by inhibiting the formation of peroxides by X rays and perhaps by forming a loose bond with certain enzymes (cytochrome reductase and catalase) to prevent their oxidation (Bacq *et al.*, 1950; Bacq, 1951). The important species difference between the mouse and the rat in regard to cyanide as well as its potentiation of toxicity in plant and tumor tissue cannot be taken lightly. Potentiation of tissue sensitivity by cyanide may be due to an increase in oxygen tension as a consequence of inhibition of the cytochrome system or to inactivation of catalase. Also unexplained is the finding that para-aminopropiophenone enhances the resistance of mice and rats when it is administered before X irradiation, while sodium nitrite, which produces a rather similar methemoglobinemia, gives equivocal protection (Storer and Coon, 1950; Herve *et al.*, 1950).

Chemical Protection. That oxidative reactions are important components of radiation action is also suggested from studies with protective substances. Thus, the in vitro oxidation of sulfhydryl enzymes following low doses of radiation can be prevented or reversed by glutathione (Barron *et al.*, 1949), and radiation effects in tetanus toxin (Ephrati, 1948) and bacteria (Hollaender *et al.*, 1951; Forssberg, 1950) can be diminished by a variety of reducing substances. A number of oxidizable entities also have the capacity to diminish many of the effects of X rays in mammals. Cysteine (Patt, Tyree, *et al.*, 1949; Patt, Smith, *et al.*, 1950; Smith, Patt, Tyree, and Straube, 1950; Patt, Smith, and Jackson, 1950), glutathione (Patt, Smith, Tyree, and Straube, 1950; Chapman and Cronkite, 1950; Chapman *et al.*, 1950), and BAL (Smith, Patt, and Tyree, 1950) have been shown to reduce acute toxicity in mice, rats, and dogs. Some degree of protection has been seen also with thiourea (Limperos and Mosher, 1950; Mole *et al.*, 1950), dithiophosphonate (Mole *et al.*, 1950), and massive amounts of glucose (Loiseleur and Velley, 1950a; Baclesse and Loiseleur, 1947) and ethanol (Paterson and Matthews, 1951; Patt, Mayer, and Smith, 1951a). The action of these protective substances against repeated low-dose irradiation has not, to our knowledge, been evaluated. Protection against the chronic sequelae of irradiation is also largely undetermined.

It is perhaps significant that cystine, methionine, and ascorbic acid do not modify sensitivity in the mammal (Patt, Smith, Tyree, and Straube, 1950). While all reducing agents do not appear to protect against the acute lethal action of ionizing radiations, e.g., ascorbic acid, hydrosulfite, tetraborohydride, mercaptosuccinate, and thiosulfate, this may be a consequence of their temporal and spatial distribution and biological life (Patt, Blackford, *et al.*, 1951; Patt, Mayer, and Smith, 1951a).

The time course of the protection against the acute effects of radiation may follow a somewhat different pattern in the intact animal and in certain in vitro systems. In general, however, these substances must be given before irradiation to be effective. Thus, the optimal time of cysteine administration in rats and mice is immediately before exposure, and there is no postirradiation effect (Patt, Smith, Tyree, and Straube, 1950). Although some improvement of survival has been observed in a small series of rabbits after treatment with cysteine plus ascorbic acid during the first two postexposure hours (Loiseleur and Velley, 1950b), this has not been verified in either rabbits or mice (Patt, Mayer, and Smith, 1951b). On the other hand, the survival of thymocytes irradiated in vitro is increased to the same degree whether cysteine is added one minute before or after the exposure (Patt, Blackford, and Straube, 1952). Cysteine addition 15 to 30 minutes before X irradiation is optimal, however. There is no satisfactory explanation for the apparent discrepancy other than to implicate possible differences in the kinetics of the reactions with cysteine and in the time constants for the development of irreversible injury in the thymic cell suspension and in the intact animal.

It has been suggested that glutathione protects animals by promoting regenerative mechanisms and not by preventing cellular destruction (Cronkite *et al.*, 1951). The basis for this interesting concept rests in the similarity of changes in organ weights, peripheral blood counts, and histologic appearance of certain radiosensitive tissues in treated and untreated mice during the first few days after exposure to a nearly completely lethal dose. These findings do not, however, constitute incontrovertible proof of failure to prevent injury. There is reason to believe that histologic changes, in general, reflect the amount of radiation and not the lethal effect on the animal and, moreover, that the threshold point of maximal change may be below that required for acute lethality (Bloom, 1947; De Bruyn, 1948). These considerations can also explain the failure to observe a protective effect of glutathione on organ weights (Cronkite *et al.*, 1951) and of glutathione and cysteine on the uptake of iron in the red blood cells of irradiated animals (Hennessy and Huff, 1950; Hennessy and Folsom, 1950; Hennessy, Folsom, and Glover, 1950). For example, the anticipated difference in the organ weights between 600 and 800 r, which represents the degree of protection by glutathione on the basis of survival data (Chapman, Sipe, *et al.*, 1950), is only about 5 per cent (Carter *et al.*, 1950). The failure to detect a difference in the heterophil and erythrocyte levels in the peripheral blood of glutathione-treated and untreated mice is not readily explained, however (Cronkite *et al.*, 1951).

As contrasted with the view that protection in the mammal results from some facilitation of recovery rather than prevention of injury, there is a body of evidence indicating that sulfhydryl compounds can diminish cellular destruction incident to X-ray exposure. Cysteine has been shown to decrease damage to the skin (Forssberg, 1950) and lens (von Sallmann *et al.*, 1951) after local irradiation and to increase the resistance of tumor cells (Straube *et al.*, 1950; Hall, 1951). Thymic cells have also been protected in vitro over a dosage range of 50 to 2000 r (Patt, Blackford, and Straube, 1952). Furthermore, there are indications that cysteine can modify significantly the hematologic changes in irradiated rats (Patt, Smith, and Jackson, 1950; Rosenthal *et al.*, 1950). Indeed, the changes that have been observed in rats irradiated with 800 r after cysteine treatment compare favorably with those observed after a sublethal exposure of 300 r (Patt, Smith, and Jackson, 1950). These considerations suggest that cysteine may raise the threshold for radiation effects in general, with the probable exception of those attributable to direct ionization.

The mechanism of chemical protection is poorly understood. Protective substances may increase the resistance to X rays by modifying activated water reactions, the nature of the biological targets, or the redox equilibrium of the cell. It is of interest that a given amount of cysteine accounts for a rather constant percentage of the biological effect of the radiation over a wide dose range (Patt, Blackford, and Straube, 1952; Patt, Mayer, Straube, and Jackson, in press). This has been observed in survival studies with thymic cells and with mice, but, unfortunately, can be explained equally well by postulating an interaction with either the radiation or its toxic intermediates or with the biological system.

It is not known whether reducing substances and oxygen deprivation protect in the same manner. There is, of course, no compelling reason to believe that the mode of action of either factor is identical in all living systems or indeed in a specific system under different conditions. X-ray inactivation of ribonuclease is prevented by glutathione but not by oxygen lack (Holmes, 1950). It is perhaps significant that resistance of the rat to the acute lethal action of X rays is increased to the same degree by anoxic anoxia or cysteine (Dowdy *et al.*, 1950; Smith, Patt, Tyree, and Straube, 1950) and that the effect of cysteine is enhanced in mice breathing 10 per cent oxygen during the irradiation, although the latter by itself does not offer any protection (Mayer and Patt, 1953). Certain additive effects have been observed in bacteria. The sensitivity of aerobically grown *E. coli* irradiated in phosphate buffer is reduced beyond the value obtained with anoxia alone when cysteine is present during the exposure (Hollaender *et al.*, 1952). This is not the case, however, when the organisms have been grown anaerobically. Thymic cells resemble the anaerobic bacteria in the lack of additivity (Patt, Blackford, and Straube, 1952). These considerations suggest perhaps that some of the protective substances may act by diminishing the availability of oxygen in the biological system. This does not imply, however, that oxygen deprivation per se is necessarily the decisive event in the protection afforded by such agents. Information relating to the relative effectiveness of oxygen and protective substances for the different qualities of radiation, to their additivity or lack of additivity for a specific radiation quality, and their temperature dependence should aid materially in the elucidation of the mechanism of action. A survey of some of the more important chemical and metabolic factors that have been employed in studies of animal radiosensitivity is presented in Table 14-3. Although it is not yet possible to classify these factors in terms either of their biochemical action or of radiation action, their significance is obvious since they provide a real basis for the study of the immediate chemical effects of ionization and excitation in living systems. The more recent contributions in this field have been reviewed by Patt (1953).

SUMMARY

The physical and biological factors affecting sensitivity to ionizing radiations have been discussed with emphasis directed toward the response of mammalian tissue. It has been shown that the biological effect may be influenced by the quality, quantity, manner, and completeness of irradiation. Although it is generally true that radiosensitivity is related to growth rate, it is clear that the relation is not a simple one. In view

TABLE 14-3. SURVEY OF CHEMICAL AND METABOLIC FACTORS IN RADIOSENSITIVITY

Factor	Biological object	Time relative to irradiation	Sensitivity relative to control	Possible mode of action or significance	Reference
Ischemia	Skin, lymph node, spleen, tumor	Before and during	Decreased	Decreased oxygen tension?	Carty, 1930; Schwarz, 1909; Mottram, 1924; Jolly, 1924; Evans *et al.*, 1942
Anoxia	Mouse, rat, tumor	Before and during	Decreased	Peroxides decreased, reduction of critical molecules, metabolic?	Crabtree and Cramer, 1933; Dowdy *et al.*, 1950; Lacassagne, 1942
Cyanide	Mouse, rat, frog, tumor	Before	Decreased in mouse only; increased in tumor	Mouse specificity? Tumor increase due to inactivation of catalase or to increased oxygen tension?	Patt and Swift, 1948; Crabtree and Cramer, 1933; Dowdy *et al.*, 1950; Bacq *et al.*, 1950; Bacq, 1951
Para-aminopropiophenone (PAPP)	Mouse, rat, guinea pig	Before	Decreased in intact animal	Related to oxygen effect?	Storer and Coon, 1950
Nitrite, methylene blue	Mouse, rat	Before	Unchanged?	Questionable significance of methemoglobinemia in PAPP effect	Storer and Coon, 1950; Herve *et al.*, 1950
Cysteine, glutathione, BAL	Mouse, rat, guinea pig, dog, skin, lens, thymus	Before	Decreased	Direct or indirect competition for oxidants, metabolic?	Patt, Tyree, Straube, and Smith, 1949; Patt, Smith, and Jackson, 1950; Patt, Smith, Tyree, and Straube, 1950; D. E. Smith, Patt, and Tyree, 1950; D. E. Smith, Patt, Tyree, and Straube, 1950; Chapman and Cronkite, 1950; Chapman, Sipe, *et al.*, 1950
Cystine, methionine, sulfide	Mouse, rat	Before	Unchanged	Specificity of —SH group for cysteine effect	Patt, Smith, Tyree, and Straube, 1950
Thiourea	Mouse, rat	Before	Decreased	Potential —SH groups; same as cysteine?	Limperos and Mosher, 1950; Mole *et al.*, 1950
Mercaptosuccinate	Mouse	Before	Unchanged	Difference in reactivity of —SH group or in its biological life	Patt, Mayer, and Smith, 1951
Ascorbic acid, thiosulfate, hydrosulfite, borotetrahydride	Mouse	Before	Unchanged	All reductants not effective, owing perhaps to differences in distribution and in biological life	Patt, Smith, Tyree, and Straube, 1950; Patt, Mayer, and Smith, 1951a, b
Temperature	Frog	Before	Unchanged	Rate independence of immediate events	Patt and Swift, 1948

TABLE 14-3. SURVEY OF CHEMICAL AND METABOLIC FACTORS IN RADIOSENSITIVITY.—(*Continued*)

Factor	Biological object	Time relative to irradiation	Sensitivity relative to control	Possible mode of action or significance	Reference
Temperature	Frog	After	Decreased with low temperature	Rate dependence of secondary reactions	Patt and Swift, 1948
Thyroid extract	Mouse	Before and during	Unchanged	Same as temperature	W. W. Smith, 1951
Thyroid extract	Mouse	After	Increased	Same as temperature	W. W. Smith, 1951
Thiouracil	Mouse, rat	Before and after	Unchanged	Effect of thiouracil on metabolic rate not determined in these experiments	Blount and Smith, 1949; Hempelmann *et al.*, 1949; Haley *et al.*, 1950
Exercise	Mouse	Before	Unchanged	Metabolic rate during irradiation not critical	Patt, Blackford, *et al.*, 1951
Nembutal	Rat, mouse	Before	Unchanged	Same; sedation unimportant	Hempelmann *et al.*, 1949; Patt, Blackford, 1951; Paterson and Matthews, 1951
Urethane	Rat, mouse	Before	Increased in rat only	Additivity of or sensitization to X rays	Henry, 1949; Paterson and Matthews, 1951
Glucose, ethanol, glycerol	Rat, mouse	Before	Decreased	Competition, metabolic?	Mole *et al.*, 1950; Loiseleur and Velley, 1950a; Baclesse and Loiseleur, 1947; Patt, Mayer, and Smith, 1951a; Paterson and Matthews, 1951
Iodoacetate, fluoroacetate, malonate, mercuribenzoate, fluoride, arsenoxide, Hg, Mn, Co, Cd	Mouse, rat, tumor	Before	Unchanged	Questionable role of the —SH groups and tricarboxylic acid cycle in radiosensitivity	Crabtree and Cramer, 1933; Bacq, 1951; Patt, Blackford, and Smith, 1951a

of the complexity of cell physiology and the ubiquitous nature of the energy absorption, it is not surprising that the effects of radiation are manifested in many ways and that many factors have the capacity of influencing the radiation responses.

The events that are immediately associated with the absorption of radiation are fairly independent of temperature over a wide range. However, the subsequent reactions of injury and recovery are subject to temperature influence and metabolic activity. The existence of activated-water reactions in vivo as well as in vitro is suggested by the rather parallel influence of hypoxia and protective substances on the behavior of aqueous solutions and living systems to radiation. The mode of action of these modifying factors has not been settled, however. There is reason to think that the chemical effects of ionization and excitation are responsible for the early cytological damage following moderate dosages of radiation and that this, in turn, bears a causal relation to the over-all injury in the mammalian organism.

REFERENCES

(Information regarding availability of government reports indicated by an asterisk may be obtained from the Office of Technical Services, Department of Commerce, Washington, D.C.)

Abrams, H. L. (1951) Influence of age, body weight, and sex on susceptibility of mice to the lethal effects of X radiation. Proc. Soc. Exptl. Biol. Med., 76: 729–732.

——— and H. S. Kaplan (1951) The effect of shielding on mortality following irradiation. Stanford Med. Bull., 9: 165–166.

Aebersold, P. C., and J. H. Lawrence (1942) The physiological effects of neutron rays. Ann. Rev. Physiol., 4: 25–48.

Ahlstrom, L. H., G. Hevesy, and K. Zerahn (1947) Toxische Wirkungen von Thymus-histonen Protaminen. Arkiv Kemi, Mineral. Geol., 23A: 1–10.

Allen, A. O. (1948) Radiation chemistry of aqueous solutions. J. Phys. Colloid Chem., 52: 479–490.

Allen, B. M., O. A. Schjeide, and L. B. Hochwald (1950) Relation of low temperatures to X-ray injury of hematopoietic tissue of tadpoles (preliminary account). Proc. Soc. Exptl. Biol. Med., 73: 60–62.

Allen, J. G. (1951) The beneficial effects of head shielding in 20 dogs exposed to 450 r total-body X radiation. USAEC Report ANL-4625,* p. 60.

Ancel, P., and P. Vintemberger (1927) Influence de la température sur la radiosensibilité d'oeufs d'oiseaux et de batraciens. Compt. rend. soc. biol., 97: 796–799.

Anderson, R. S., and H. Turkowitz (1941) The experimental modification of the sensitivity of yeast to roentgen rays. Am. J. Roentgenol. Radium Therapy, 46: 537–542.

Baclesse, F., and J. Loiseleur (1947) Modifications de la radiosensibilité cutanée du lapin au cours de l'hyperglycémie expérimentale. Compt. rend. soc. biol., 141: 743–745.

Bacq, Z. M. (1951) L'action indirecte du rayonnement X et ultraviolet. Experientia, 7: 11–19.

———, A. Herve, J. Lecomte, and P. Fischer (1950) Cyanide protection against X-irradiation. Science, 111: 356–357.

Baker, W. K., and E. Sgourakis (1950) The effect of oxygen concentration on the rate of X-ray-induced mutations in *Drosophila*. Proc. Natl. Acad. Sci. U.S., 36: 176–184.

Barnes, W. A., and O. B. Furth (1943) Studies on indirect effect of roentgen rays in single and parabiotic mice. Am. J. Roentgenol. Radium Therapy, 49: 662–681.

Barron, E. S. G. (1946) Effects of X rays on tissue metabolism. USAEC Report AECD-2316.*

——— and S. Dickman (1949) Studies on the mechanism of action of ionizing radiations. II. Inhibition of sulfhydryl enzymes by alpha, beta and gamma rays. J. Gen. Physiol., 32: 595–605.

———, ———, J. A. Muntz, and T. P. Singer (1949) Studies on the mechanism of action of ionizing radiations. I. Inhibition of enzymes by X rays. J. Gen. Physiol., 32: 537–552.

Bergonié, J., and L. Tribondeau (1906) Interpretation de quelques resultats de la radiothérapie et essai de fixation d'une technique rationnelle. Compt. rend., 143: 983–985.

Bloom, M. A. (1950) Acquired radioresistance of the crypt epithelium of the duodenum. Radiology, 55: 104–115.

Bloom, W. (1947) Histological changes following radiation exposures. Radiology, 49: 344–348.

Blount, H. C., Jr., and W. W. Smith (1949) Influence of thyroid and thiouracil on mice exposed to roentgen radiation. Science, 109: 83–84.

Boche, R. D., and F. W. Bishop (1946) Studies on the effects of massive doses of roentgen radiation on mortality in laboratory animals. USAEC Report MDDC-250.*

Boffil, J., and O. Miletzky (1946) Recherches expérimentales sur les perturbations produites par les rayons X au niveau de la moelle osseuse. Ann. méd., 47: 220–244.

Bond, V. P., M. N. Swift, A. C. Allen, and M. C. Fishler (1950) Sensitivity of abdomen of rat to X irradiation. Am. J. Physiol., 161: 323–330.

Bonet-Maury, P., and M. Lefort (1948) Formation of hydrogen peroxide in water irradiated with X and alpha rays. Nature, 162: 381–382.

Brecher, G., and E. P. Cronkite (1951) Postradiation parabiosis and survival in rats. Proc. Soc. Exptl. Biol. Med., 77: 292–294.

Brooks, J. W. (1951) Low temperature and radiation, *in* Symposium on burns. Natl. Acad. Sci., Natl. Research Council, Washington, D.C.

Brues, A. M., and L. Rietz (1948) Acute hematologic radiation response of the guinea pig as a function of lethality. USAEC Report ANL-4227,* p. 183.

——— and ——— (1951) Effects of external and internal radiation on cell division. Ann. N.Y. Acad. Sci., 51: 1497–1507.

Brunst, V. V., and E. A. Sheremetieva-Brunst (1949) The time factor in lethal effects of total roentgen irradiation in *Triton*. Am. J. Roentgenol. Radium Therapy, 62: 550–554.

Buchsbaum, R., and R. E. Zirkle (1949) Shrinking and swelling after alpha irradiation of various parts of large erythrocytes. Proc. Soc. Exptl. Biol. Med., 72: 27–29.

Carter, R. E., P. S. Harris, and J. T. Brennan (1950) The effect of acute doses of X-irradiation on the splenic and thymic weight of CF-1 female mice. USAEC Report LA-1075.*

Carty, J. R. (1930) The modification of the biological reaction of living tissue to X-radiation by physical and chemical agents. Radiology, 15: 353–359.

Chambers, R. J. (1941) Relative effect of X-rays on resting and actively secreting kidney tubules. J. Applied Phys., 12: 336–337.

Chapman, W. H., and E. P. Cronkite (1950) Further studies of the beneficial effect of glutathione on X-irradiated mice. Proc. Soc. Exptl. Biol. Med., 75: 318–332.

———, C. R. Sipe, D. C. Eltzholtz, E. P. Cronkite, and F. W. Chambers, Jr. (1950) Sulfhydryl-containing agents and the effects of ionizing radiations. I. Beneficial effect of glutathione injection on X-ray induced mortality rate and weight loss in mice. Radiology, 55: 865–873.

Clark, A. M., and E. M. Kelly (1950) Differential radiosensitivity of haploid and diploid prepupae and pupae of *Habrobracon*. Cancer Research, 10: 348–352.

Clark, W. G., and R. P. Uncapher (1949) Dosage-mortality in rats given total body roentgen irradiation. Proc. Soc. Exptl. Biol. Med., 71: 214–216.

Cole, L. J., M. C. Fishler, M. E. Ellis, and V. P. Bond (1952) Protection of mice against X irradiation by spleen homogenates administered after exposure. Nav. Radiol. Def. Lab. Report NRDL-339.*

Cook, E. V. (1939) Influence of low temperature on recovery from roentgen rays. Radiology, 32: 289–293.

Crabtree, H. G., and W. Cramer (1933) The action of radium on cancer cells. II. Some factors determining the susceptibility of cancer cells to radium. Proc. Roy. Soc. London, B113: 238–250.

Cronkite, E. P., G. Brecher, and W. H. Chapman (1951) Mechanism of protective action of glutathione against whole body irradiation. Proc. Soc. Exptl. Biol. Med., 76: 396–398.

——— and W. H. Chapman (1950) Effect of adrenalectomy on radiation induced mortality of the mouse. Proc. Soc. Exptl. Biol. Med., 74: 337–340.

———, C. R. Sipe, D. C. Eltzholtz, W. H. Chapman, and F. W. Chambers, Jr. (1950) Increased tolerance of mice to lethal X radiation as a result of previous sublethal exposures. Proc. Soc. Exptl. Biol. Med., 73: 184–186.

Dale, W. (1947) Action of radiation on aqueous solutions: Experimental work with enzymes in solution. Brit. J. Radiology, Suppl. 1, p. 46.

Daniel, J. (1896) The X-rays. Science, 3: 562–563.

De Bruyn, P. P. H. (1948) The effect of X-rays on the lymphatic nodule, with reference to the dose and relative sensitivities of different species. Anat. Record, 101: 373–405.

DeLong, C. W. (1950) The nitrogen mustards, a review. USAEC Report HW-18823.*

Dinning, J. S., I. Meschan, C. K. Keith, and P. L. Day (1950) Effects of X-irradiation and urethane treatment on chicken bone marrow enzymes. Proc. Soc. Exptl. Biol. Med., 74: 776–777.

Dowdy, A. H. (1949) Tabulation of available data relative to radiation biology. USAEC Report NEPA-1019-IER-17.*

———, L. R. Bennett, and S. M. Chastain (1950) Protective action of anoxic anoxia against total-body roentgen irradiation of mammals. Radiology, 55: 879.

Dubois, K., K. Cochran, and J. Doull (1950) Unpublished observations.

Duryee, W. R. (1949) The nature of radiation injury to amphibian cell nuclei. J. Natl. Cancer Inst., 10: 735.

Ellinger, F. (1943) The problem of recovery from radiation effects. Radiology, 40: 62–71.

——— (1945) Lethal dose studies with X-rays. Radiology, 44: 125.

——— (1951) Die Histaminhypothese der biologischen Strahlenwirkungen. Schweiz. med. Wochschr., No. 3, p. 61.

——— and J. C. Barnett (1950) Further studies on the influence of dose fractionation on the lethal X-ray effect produced by total-body irradiation in mice. Radiology, 54: 90–92.

Elson, L. A., and L. F. Lamerton (1949) The influence of protein content of the diet on the response of Walker rat carcinoma 256 to X radiation. Brit. J. Cancer, 3: 414–426.

Ely, J. O., and M. H. Ross (1947) Neutron effects on animals, *in* Some physiological responses of rats to neutron irradiation. The Williams & Wilkins Company, Baltimore, Chap. 17.

Ephrati, E. (1948) Mechanism of effect of X rays on bacterial toxins. Biochem. J., 42: 383–389.

Evans, T. C. (1947) Effects of small daily doses of fast neutrons on mice. USAEC Report MDDC-1450.*

———, J. P. Goodrich, and J. C. Slaughter (1941) Radiosensitivity of skin of newborn rats. III. Sensitivity at different temperatures. Proc. Soc. Exptl. Biol. Med., 47: 434–437.

———, ———, and ——— (1942) Temperature and radiosensitivity of skin of newborn rats: Effects of decreased circulation and breathing during irradiation. Radiology, 38: 201–206.

———, W. A. Robbie, J. P. Goodrich, and J. C. Slaughter (1941) Low temperature and radiosensitivity of the skin of newborn rats. II. Resistance at different dosages. Proc. Soc. Exptl. Biol. Med., 46: 662–664.

Failla, G. (1940) Some aspects of the biological action of ionizing radiations. (Janeway Lecture, 1939). Am. J. Roentgenol. Radium Therapy, 44: 649–664.

Forssberg, A. G. (1943) Studien über einige biologische Wirkungen der Röntgen- und γ-Strahlen, insbesondere am *Phycomyces blakesleeanus*. Acta Radiol., Suppl. 49, pp. 5–143.

——— (1950) On the possibility of protecting the living organism against roentgen rays by chemical means. Acta Radiol., 33: 296–304.

France, O. (1946) Changes in water content and distribution in rats and mice after chronic and acute total-body X irradiation. USAEC Report CH-3889.*

Freund, L. (1897) Cited by F. Ellinger (1941) *in* The biological fundamentals of radiation therapy. Elsevier Publishing Co., New York, p. 30.

Frieben (1902) Cited by S. Warren (1942) *in* Effects of radiation on normal tissues. Arch. Path., 34: 443–450.

Friedell, H. L., and J. H. Christie (1951) Synergistic effect of phosphorus^{32} and colloidal gold^{198} on survival in male albino rats. Proc. Soc. Exptl. Biol. Med., 76: 207–210.

Frilley, M. (1947) The radiochemistry of aqueous solutions; a survey of recent French research. Brit. J. Radiology, Suppl. 1, pp. 50–55.

Furth, J., and O. B. Furth (1936) Neoplastic diseases produced in mice by general irradiation with X-rays. I. Incidence and types of neoplasms. Am. J. Cancer, 28: 54–65.

Gershon-Cohen, J., M. B. Hermel, and J. Q. Griffith, Jr. (1951) The value of small lead shields against the injurious effect of total-body irradiation. Science, 114: 157–158.

Giles, N. H., Jr., and A. V. Beatty (1950) The effect of X irradiation in oxygen and in hydrogen at normal and positive pressures on chromosome aberration frequency in *Tradescantia* microspores. Science, 112: 643–645.

——— and H. P. Riley (1950) Studies on the mechanism of the oxygen effect on the radiosensitivity of *Tradescantia* chromosomes. Proc. Natl. Acad. Sci. U.S., 36: 337–344.

Graham, J. B., R. M. Graham, and A. J. Graffeo (1950) The influence of adrenal cortical hormones on sensitivity of mice to ionizing radiation. Endocrinology, 46: 434–440.

Gray, L. H. (1946) Comparative studies of the biological effects of X rays, neutrons and other ionizing radiations. Brit. Med. Bull., 4: 11–18.

——— and J. Read (1948) Comparison of the lethal effect of neutrons and gamma rays on mouse tumours (a) By irradiation of grafted tumours *in vivo* (b) By irradiation of tumour fragments *in vitro*. Brit. J. Radiology, 21: 5–10.

Hagen, C. W., Jr., and G. Sacher (1946) Effects of X rays on rabbits. I. Mortality after single and paired doses. USAEC Report MDDC-1252.*

——— and E. L. Simmons (1947) Effects of total body X-irradiation on rats. I. Lethal action of single, paired, and periodic doses. USAEC Report MDDC-1210.*

Haley, T. J., S. Mann, and A. H. Dowdy (1950) A comparison of the response of normal and hypothyroid mice to acute whole body roentgen radiation. Science, 112: 333–334.

Hall, B. V. (1951) Changes in the radiosensitivity of tumor fragments induced by pre-treatment *in vitro* with cysteine, methylene blue, and sodium cyanide. Cancer Research, 11: 254.

Hayden, B., and L. Smith (1949) The relation of atmosphere to biological effects of X-rays. Genetics, 34: 26–41.

Hektoen, L. (1918) Further studies on the effects of the roentgen ray on antibody-production. J. Infectious Diseases, 22: 28–33.

Hempelmann, L. H., T. T. Trujillo, and N. P. Knowlton, Jr. (1949) The effect of lethal doses of X-rays on chilled and thyroidectomized animals. USAEC Reports, Nucl. Sci. Abst., 3: 46; AECU-239.*

Hennessy, T. G., and F. B. Folsom (1950) The inability of cysteine to protect erythropoietic bone marrow against irradiation injury at a dose level of 800 r. Nav. Radiol. Def. Lab. Report AD-266(B).*

———, ———, and J. K. Glover (1950) The inability of glutathione to protect erythropoietic bone marrow against irradiation injury at a dose level of 300 r. Nav. Radiol. Def. Lab. Report AD-267(B).*

——— and R. L. Huff (1950) Depression of tracer ion uptake curve in rat erythrocytes following total body X-irradiation. Proc. Soc. Exptl. Biol. Med., 73: 436–439.

Henry, J. A. (1949) Total X-irradiation of rats under urethane anesthesia. Nature, 163: 134–135.

Henshaw, P. S. (1938) The action of X-rays on nucleated and non-nucleated egg fragments. Am. J. Cancer, 33: 258–264.

——— (1944) Experimental roentgenological injury. III. Tissue and cellular changes brought about with single massive doses of radiation. J. Natl. Cancer Inst., 4: 503–512.

——— and D. S. Francis (1935) A consideration of the biological factors influencing the radiosensitivity of cells. J. Cellular Comp. Physiol., 7: 173–195.

———, E. F. Riley, and G. E. Stapleton (1947) The biologic effects of pile radiations. Radiology, 49: 349–360.

——— and R. S. Snider (1946) Correlation of tissue responses following exposure to penetrating radiations. USAEC Report MDDC-569.*

———, ———, E. F. Riley, G. E. Stapleton, and R. E. Zirkle (1946) Comparative late effects of single doses of fission neutrons and of gamma rays. USAEC Report MDDC-1254.*

Herve, A., Z. M. Bacq, and H. Betz (1950) Chemical modification of the lethal effect of X-radiation and the mechanism of action. Sixth Intern. Congr. Radiology, London, abstracts of papers, p. 169.

Hevesy, G. (1945) Effect of roentgen rays on cellular division. Revs. Mod. Phys., 17: 102–111.

——— (1949) Effect of X-rays on the incorporation of C^{14} into desoxyribonucleic acid. Nature, 163: 869–870.

Hewitt, H. B., and J. Read (1950) Search for an effect of oxygen on the direct X-ray inactivation of bacteriophage. Brit. J. Radiology, 23: 416–423.

Hicks, S. P. (1950) Acute necrosis and malformation of developing mammalian brain caused by X-ray. Proc. Soc. Exptl. Biol. Med., 75: 485–489.

Hinkel, C. L. (1942) The effect of roentgen rays upon the growing long bones of albino rats. I. Quantitative studies of the growth limitation following irradiation. Am. J. Roentgenol. Radium Therapy, 47: 439–457.

Hollaender, A. (1952) Physical and chemical factors modifying the sensitivity of cells to high-energy and ultraviolet radiation, *in* Symposium on radiobiology (Oberlin, 1950), ed. J. J. Nickson. John Wiley & Sons, Inc., New York, pp. 285–295.

———, G. E. Stapleton, and F. L. Martin (1951) X-ray sensitivity of *E. coli* as modified by oxygen tension. Nature, 167: 103.

Holmes, B. E. (1949) The indirect effect of X-rays on the synthesis of nucleic acid in vivo. Brit. J. Radiology, 22: 487–491.

——— (1950) Inactivation of ribonuclease in dilute aqueous solutions. Nature, 165: 266–267.

Holthusen, H. (1921) Beiträge zur Biologie der Strahlenwirkung Untersuchungen an Askarideneirn. Arch. ges. Physiol. (Pflügers), 187: S1.

Jacobson, L. O., E. K. Marks, E. O. Gaston, E. L. Simmons, and M. H. Block (1948) Studies on radiosensitivity of cells. Science, 107: 248–250.

———, ———, M. J. Robson, E. O. Gaston, and R. E. Zirkle (1949) The effect of spleen protection on mortality following X-irradiation. J. Lab. Clin. Med., 34: 1538–1543.

———, E. L. Simmons, E. K. Marks, E. O. Gaston, M. J. Robson, and J. H. Eldredge (1951) Further studies on recovery from radiation injury. J. Lab. Clin. Med., 37: 683–697.

———, ———, ———, M. J. Robson, W. F. Bethard, and E. O. Gaston (1950) The role of the spleen in radiation injury and recovery. J. Lab. Clin. Med., 35: 746–770.

Jacquez, J. A., and D. A. Karnofsky (1950) The toxicity and pathological effects of roentgen rays in the chicken. Am. J. Roentgenol. Radium Therapy, 64: 289–297.

Jennings, F. L. (1949) Effect of protein depletion upon susceptibility of rats to total body irradiation. Proc. Soc. Exptl. Biol. Med., 72: 487–491.

Johnson, C. G., C. F. Vilter, and T. D. Spies (1946) Irradiation sickness in rats. Am. J. Roentgenol. Radium Therapy, 56: 631–639.

Jolles, B. (1941) X-ray skin reactions and the protective role of normal tissues. Brit. J. Radiology, 14: 110–112.

——— (1950) The reciprocal vicinity effect of irradiated tissues on a diffusible substance in irradiated tissues. Brit. J. Radiology, 23: 18–24.

——— and R. G. Mitchell (1947) Optimal skin tolerance dose levels. Brit. J. Radiology, 20: 405–409.

Jolly, J. (1924) Action des rayons X sur les cellules. Modifications de la radiosensibilité par ligature des connexions vasculaires. Compt. rend. soc. biol., 91: 351–354.

Kahn, J. B., Jr. (1951) Modification of sensitivity to X radiation by morphine sulfate. Proc. Soc. Exptl. Biol. Med., 78: 486–489.

Kaplan, H. S. (1948) Effect of age on susceptibility to development of lymphoid tumors after irradiation. J. Natl. Cancer Inst., 9: 55–56.

Karnofsky, D. A., P. A. Patterson, and L. P. Ridgway (1950) The toxicity of roentgen rays to the chick embryo. Am. J. Roentgenol. Radium Therapy, 64: 280–288.

Kelly, L. S., and H. B. Jones (1950) Effects of irradiation on nucleic acid formation. Proc. Soc. Exptl. Biol. Med., 74: 493–497.

Kimeldorf, D. J., D. C. Jones, and M. C. Fishler (1950) The effect of exercise upon the lethality of roentgen rays for rats. Science, 112: 175–176.

Knowlton, N. P., Jr., and L. H. Hempelmann (1949) The effects of X-rays on the mitotic activity of the adrenal gland, jejunum, lymph node and epidermis of the mouse. J. Cellular Comp. Physiol., 33: 73–91.

Kohn, H. I. (1949) On the modification of the toxicity of X rays by immunization. USAEC Report AECU-610.*

Lacassagne, A. (1942) Chute de la sensibilité aux rayons X chez la souris nouveau-née en état d'asphyxie. Compt. rend. acad. sci. URSS, 215: 231–232.

Lampe, J., and F. J. Hodges (1943) Differential tissue response to neutron and roentgen radiations. Radiology, 41: 344–350.

Lasnitzki, I. (1943a) The effect of X rays on cells cultivated *in vitro*. II. Recovery factor. Brit. J. Radiology, 16: 61–67.

——— (1943b) The response of cells *in vitro* to variations in X-ray dosage. Brit. J. Radiology, 16: 137–141.

——— (1948) Effect of β rays on cells cultivated *in vitro*. Brit. J. Radiology, 21: 265–269.

——— and D. E. Lea (1940) The variation with wavelength of the biological effect of radiation. Brit. J. Radiology, 13: 149–162.

Latarjet, R., and B. Ephrussi (1949) Courbes de survie de levures haploïdes et diploïdes soumises aux rayons X. Compt. rend., 229: 306–308.

Lawrence, J. H., and E. O. Lawrence (1936) The biological action of neutron rays. Proc. Natl. Acad. Sci. U.S., 22: 124–133.

Lawrence, J. S., A. H. Dowdy, and W. N. Valentine (1947) The effects of radiation on hemopoiesis. USAEC Report MDDC-853.*

Lea, D. E. (1946) Actions of radiations on living cells. Cambridge University Press, London (The Macmillan Company, New York, 1947).

LeMay, M. (1951) Effect of X radiation upon succinoxidase of rat kidney. Proc. Soc. Exptl. Biol. Med., 77: 337–339.

Leppin, O. (1896) X. Kleine Mittheilungen. Deut. med. Wochschr., 22 (28): 454.

Limperos, G., and W. A. Mosher (1950) Protection of mice against X radiation by thiourea. Science, 112: 86–87.

Loiseleur, J., and G. Velley (1950a) Immunité conférée par l'hyperglycémie, contre les rayons X administrés à dose léthale. Compt. rend., 231: 182–184.

——— and ——— (1950b) Traitement curatif des radiolesions consecutives à l'administration d'une dose léthale de rayons X. Compt. rend., 231: 529–531.

Lorenz, E., D. Uphoff, T. R. Reid, and E. Shelton (1951) Modification of irradiation injury in mice and guinea pigs by bone marrow injections. J. Natl. Cancer Inst., 12: 197–201.

MacComb, W. S., and E. H. Quimby (1936) The rate of recovery of human skin from the effects of hard or soft roentgen rays or gamma rays. Radiology, 27: 196–207.

MacKee, G. M., A. Mutscheller, and A. C. Cipollara (1943) Time factor in irradiation. Arch. Dermatol. and Syphilol., 47: 490–497.

Mayer, S. H., and H. M. Patt (1953) Potentiation of cysteine protection against X radiation by dinitrophenol or hypoxia. Federation Proc., 12: 94–95.

Mazia, D., and G. Blumenthal (1948) Inactivation of enzyme-substrate films by small doses of X rays. Proc. Natl. Acad. Sci. U.S., 34: 328–336.

Mitchell, J. S. (1942) Disturbance of nucleic acid metabolism produced by therapeutic doses of X and gamma radiations. I. Methods of investigation. Brit. J. Exptl. Path., 23: 285–295.

——— (1947) Experiments on the mechanism of the biological action of fast neutrons using the summation method for lethal effects in mice. Brit. J. Radiology, 20: 368–380.

Mole, R. H., J. St. L. Philpot, and G. R. V. Hodges (1950) Reduction in lethal effect of X-radiation by pretreatment with thiourea or sodium ethane dithiophosphonate. Nature, 166: 515.

Mottram, J. C. (1924) On the skin reactions to radium exposure and their avoidance in therapy; an experimental investigation. Brit. J. Radiology, 29: 174–180.

——— (1935a) On alteration in sensitivity of cells towards radiation produced by cold and anaerobiosis. Brit. J. Radiology, 8: 32–39.

——— (1935b) Variation in sensitivity of cells to radiation in relation to mitosis. Brit. J. Radiology, 8: 643–651.

——— and L. H. Gray (1940) The relative response of the skin of mice to X-radiation and gamma radiation. Brit. J. Radiology, 13: 31–34.

O'Connor, R. J. (1950) The metabolism of cell division. Brit. J. Exptl. Path., 31: 390–396.

Packard, C. (1930) Relation between division rate and radiosensitivity of cells. J. Cancer Res., 14: 359–369.

Paterson, E., and J. J. Matthews (1951) Protective action of ethyl alcohol on irradiated mice. Nature, 168; 1126–1127.

——— and M. V. Thompson (1948) Time-intensity factors. Brit. J. Radiology, 21: 414–419.

Patt, H. M. (1953) Protective mechanisms in ionizing radiation injury. Physiol. Rev., 33: 35–76.

———, M. E. Blackford, S. Mayer, R. L. Straube, and D. E. Smith (1951) Unpublished observations.

———, ———, and R. L. Straube (1952) Effect of X rays on thymocytes and its modification by cysteine. Proc. Soc. Exptl. Biol. Med., 80: 92–97.

———, S. Mayer, and D. E. Smith (1951a) Modification of radiation responses in mammals by chemical factors. USAEC Report ANL-4625.*

———, ———, and ——— (1951b) The failure of postirradiation cysteine and ascorbic acid to influence radiation mortality. USAEC Report ANL-4625,* p. 51.

———, ———, R. L. Straube, and E. M. Jackson (in press) Radiation dose reduction by cysteine. J. Cellular Comp. Physiol.

———, D. E. Smith, and E. Jackson (1950) The effect of cysteine on the peripheral blood of the irradiated rat. Blood, 5: 758–763.

———, ———, E. B. Tyree, and R. L. Straube (1950) Further studies on modification of sensitivity to X-rays by cysteine. Proc. Soc. Exptl. Biol. Med., 73: 18–21.

———, R. L. Straube, M. E. Blackford, and D. E. Smith (1950) Nature of cysteine induced radioresistance: sulfhydryl levels and distribution of cysteine sulfur. Am. J. Physiol., 163: 740.

———, ———, E. B. Tyree, M. N. Swift, and D. E. Smith (1949) Influence of estrogens on the acute X-irradiation syndrome. Am. J. Physiol., 159: 269–280.

——— and M. N. Swift (1948) Influence of temperature on the response of frogs to X irradiation. Am. J. Physiol., 155: 388–393.

———, E. B. Tyree, R. L. Straube, and D. E. Smith (1949) Cysteine protection against X irradiation. Science, 110: 213–214.

Petry, E. (1922) Zur Kenntnis der Bedingungen der biologischen Wirkungen der Röntgenstrahlen. Biochem. Z., 128: 326–353.

Price, J. M., and A. K. Laird (1950) A comparison of the intracellular composition of regenerating liver and induced liver tumors. Cancer Research, 10: 650.

Prosser, C. L., C. W. Hagen, Jr., and W. Grundhauser (1947) The lethal action of X radiation, stable isotopes of fission elements, Sr^{89}, and $(Ba\text{-}La)^{140}$ upon goldfish. USAEC Report ANL-4017.*

———, E. E. Painter, H. Lisco, A. M. Brues, L. O. Jacobson, and M. N. Swift (1947) The clinical sequence of physiological effects of ionizing radiation in animals. Radiology, 49: 299–313.

Quastler, H. (1945a) Studies on roentgen death in mice. I. Survival time and dosage. Am. J. Roentgenol. Radium Therapy, 54: 449–456.

——— (1945b) Studies on roentgen death in mice. II. Body weight and sensitivity. Am. J. Roentgenol. Radium Therapy, 54: 457–461.

——— and R. K. Clark (1945) Biological evaluation of 20 million volt roentgen rays. I. Acute roentgen death in mice. Am. J. Roentgenol. Radium Therapy, 54: 723–727.

——— and E. F. Lanzl (1950) Biological evaluation of 20 million volt roentgen rays. IV. Efficiency and dosage range. Am. J. Roentgenol. Radium Therapy, 63: 566–574.

———, ———, M. E. Keller, and J. W. Osborne (1951) Acute intestinal radiation death. Studies on roentgen death in mice. III. Am. J. Physiol., 164: 546–556.

Quimby, E. H., and W. S. MacComb (1937) Further studies on the rate of recovery of human skin from the effects of roentgen or gamma-ray irradiation. Radiology, 29: 305–312.

Raper, J. R. (1947) Effects of total surface beta irradiation. Radiology, 49: 314.

Read, J. (1950) The influence of oxygen tension on radiosensitivity. Sixth Intern. Congr. Radiology, London, abstracts of papers, p. 50.

Redfield, A. C., E. M. Bright, and J. Wertheimer (1924) The physiological action of ionizing radiations. IV. Comparison of beta and X rays. Am. J. Physiol., 68: 368–378.

Rekers, P. E. (1949) Transplantation of bone marrow into dogs that have received total-body single dose radiation. USAEC Report AECD-1966.*

Rosenthal, R. L., L. Goldschmidt, and B. I. Pickering (1950) Hematologic changes in rats protected by cysteine against total-body X irradiation. Nav. Radiol. Def. Lab. Report AD-215 (B).*

Russell, L. B. (1950) X-ray induced developmental abnormalities in the mouse and their uses in the analysis of embryological patterns. I. External and gross visceral changes. J. Exptl. Zool., 114: 545–601.

——— and W. L. Russell (1950) The effects of radiation on the preimplantation stages of the mouse embryo. Anat. Record, 108: 521.

Sacher, G. A. (1950) The survival of mice under duration-of-life exposure to X rays at various dose rates. USAEC Report CH-3900.*

———, J. Sackis, and A. M. Brues (1949) Analytic study of effects of various patterns of X-irradiation on survival. USAEC Report AECU-488.*

Salerno, P. R., H. L. Friedell, J. H. Christie, and M. Berg (1952) Synergistic lethal action of certain radioisotopes in rats. Radiology, 59: 564–569.

Salisbury, P. F., P. E. Rekers, J. H. Miller, and N. F. Marti (1951) Effect of early cross transfusion on X-irradiation disease. Science, 113: 6.

Schack, J. A., and R. C. MacDuffee (1949) Increased radioresistance of red bone marrow after anoxia. Science, 110: 259–260.

Schrek, R. (1946) Studies in vitro on the physiology of cells. Factors affecting the delayed cytocidal action of X-rays. J. Cellular Comp. Physiol., 28: 277–304.

Schwarz, G. (1909) Ueber Desensibilisierung gegen Röntgen und Radium-strahlen. Münch. med. Wochschr., 56: 1217–1218.

Senn, N. (1903) Case of splenomedullary leukaemia successfully treated by the use of the roentgen ray. Med. Record, 64: 281–282.

Shechmeister, I. L., and V. P. Bond (1951) Response of mice to certain avirulent bacteria after exposure to sublethal total body X-irradiation. Proc. Soc. Exptl. Biol. Med., 77: 77–80.

Sievert, R. M., and A. Forssberg (1936) The time factor in the biological action of roentgen rays. III. Investigations at very short irradiation times. Acta Radiol., 17: 290–298.

Smith, D. E., H. M. Patt, and E. B. Tyree (1950) Notes on the evaluation of materials that might be expected to alter radiosensitivity. USAEC Report ANL-4401,* p. 72.

———, ———, ———, and R. L. Straube (1950) Quantitative aspects of the protective action of cysteine against X-radiation. Proc. Soc. Exptl. Biol. Med., 73: 198–200.

———, G. Svihla, and H. M. Patt (1951) The effects of X-radiation on circulation in the wing of the bat. Physiol. Zool., 24: 249–257.

Smith, W. W. (1951) The effect of thyroid hormone and radiation on the mitotic index of mouse epidermis. J. Cellular Comp. Physiol., 38: 41–49.

———, B. J. Highman, J. R. Mitchell, and H. C. Blount, Jr. (1949) Effect of environmental temperature on the response of mice to whole-body roentgen radiation. Proc. Soc. Exptl. Biol. Med., 71: 489–501.

——— and F. Smith (1951) Effect of thyroid hormone on radiation lethality. Am. J. Physiol., 165: 639–650.

Snyder, R. H., and W. E. Kisieleski (1950) The relative biological effectiveness of beta and roentgen irradiation as shown by the radiotoxocity of Na^{24} for mice. Radiology, 54: 743–749.

Soberman, R. J., R. P. Keating, and R. D. Maxwell (1951) Effect of acute whole-body X-irradiation upon water and electrolyte balance. Am. J. Physiol., 164: 450–456.

Sparrow, A. M. (1951) Radiation sensitivity of cells during mitotic and meiotic cycles with emphasis on possible cytochemical changes. Ann. N.Y. Acad. Sci., 51: 1508–1540.

Spear, F. G., and K. Tansley (1944) The action of neutrons on developing rat retina. Brit. J. Radiology, 17: 374–379.

Spiers, F. W. (1946) Effective atomic number and energy absorption in tissues. Brit. J. Radiology, 19: 52–63.

Stapleton, G. E., and H. J. Curtis (1946) The effects of fast neutrons on the ability of mice to take forced exercise. USAEC Report MDDC-696.*

——— and R. E. Zirkle (1946) Comparative effectiveness and additivity of fission neutrons, gamma rays and beta rays on *Drosophila* eggs. USAEC Report MDDC-584.*

Stearner, S. P. (1951) The effect of variation in dosage rate of roentgen rays on survival in young birds. Am. J. Roentgenol. Radium Therapy, 65: 265–271.

——— and E. J. B. Christian (1951) The effect of over-all time of exposure upon survival of young chicks following roentgen irradiation. Am. J. Roentgenol. Radium Therapy, 65: 272–276.

———, ———, and A. M. Brues (1950) Effect of X irradiation on blood uric acid in the chick. USAEC Report ANL-4451,* p. 77.

Stenbeck, T. (1899) Cited by F. Ellinger (1941) *in* The biologic fundamentals of radiation therapy. Elsevier Publishing Co., New York, p. 113.

Stevens, L. G. (1896) Injurious effects on the skin. Brit. Med. J., 1: 998.

Storer, J. B., and J. M. Coon (1950) Protective effect of para-aminopropiophenone against lethal doses of X-radiation. Proc. Soc. Exptl. Biol. Med., 74: 202–204.

Straube, R. L., H. M. Patt, D. E. Smith, and E. B. Tyree (1950) Influence of cysteine on the radiosensitivity of Walker rat carcinoma 256. Cancer Research, 10: 243–244.

Strelin, G. S. (1950) Histological changes produced in the epithelium of the frog's cornea by total and partial irradiations with X-rays. Doklady Akad. Nauk SSSR, 73: 1283–1286; Nucl. Sci. Abst., 4: 23, 1950.

Sugiura, K. (1939) The biological measurement of gamma rays in "equivalent roentgens" with mouse sarcoma 180 as the test object. Am. J. Cancer, 37: 445–452.

Swisher, S. N., and F. W. Furth (1951) Effect of early small exchange transfusion on the X-irradiated dog. Proc. Soc. Exptl. Biol. Med., 78: 226–229.

Taliaferro, W. H., and L. G. Taliaferro (1951) Effect of X-rays on immunity: a review. J. Immunol., 66: 181–212.

Tansley, K., L. H. Gray, and F. G. Spear (1948) A preliminary note on some biological effects of alpha radiation on the frog tadpole. Brit. J. Radiology, 21: 567–570.

Thoday, J. M., and J. Read (1947) Effect of oxygen on frequency of chromosome aberrations produced by X ray. Nature, 160: 608.

——— and ——— (1949) Effect of oxygen on the frequency of chromosome aberrations produced by alpha rays. Nature, 163: 133–134.

Treadwell, A. de G., W. U. Gardner, and J. H. Lawrence (1943) Effect of combining estrogen with lethal doses of roentgen-ray in Swiss mice. Endocrinology, 32: 161–164.

Tullis, J. L. (1949) Radioresistant cells in certain radiosensitive tissues in swine exposed to atomic bomb radiation. Arch. Path., 48: 171–177.

Van Dyke, D. C., and R. L. Huff (1949) Epilation in the non-irradiated member of parabiotically united rats. Proc. Soc. Exptl. Biol. Med., 72: 266–269.

von Sallmann, L., Z. Dische, G. Ehrlich, and C. M. Munoz (1951) Study on penetration of cysteine and cystine into the aqueous humor of rabbits and its relation to early X-irradiation effects on the eye. Am. J. Ophthalmol., 34: 95–113.

Walsh, D. (1897) Deep tissue traumatism from roentgen ray exposure. Brit. Med. J., 2: 272–273.

Warren, S. (1942) Effects of radiation on normal tissues. Arch. Path., 43: 443–450.

——— and J. Z. Bowers (1950) The acute radiation syndrome in man. Ann. Internal Med., 32: 207–216.

Weiss, J. (1947) Some aspects of the action of radiations on aqueous solutions. Brit. J. Radiology, Suppl. 1, pp. 56–59.

Wertz, E. (1940) Uber die Abhängigkeit der Röntgenstrahlenwirkung vom Quellungszustand der Gewebe, nach Untersuchungen an Gerstenkörnen. Strahlentherapie, 67: 700–711.

Wilson, C. W. (1935) Some effects of γ rays of radium on the developing chick embryo. I and II. Acta Radiol., 16: 719–734.

Wilson, J. G., and J. W. Karr (1950) Difference in the effects of X-irradiation in rat embryos of different ages. Anat. Record, 106: 259–260.

Zirkle, R. E. (1932) Some effects of alpha irradiation upon plant cells. J. Cellular Comp. Physiol., 2: 251–274.

——— (1936) Modification of radiosensitivity by means of readily penetrating acids and bases. Am. J. Roentgenol. Radium Therapy, 35: 230–237.

——— (1940) The influence of intracellular acidity on the radiosensitivity of various organisms. J. Cellular Comp. Physiol., 16: 301–311.

——— (1941) Combined influence of X-ray intensity and intracellular acidity on radiosensitivity. J. Cellular Comp. Physiol., 17: 65–70.

——— (1943) Radiobiological importance of specific ionization. USAEC Report MDDC-444.*
——— (1949) Relationships between chemical and biological effects of ionizing radiations. Radiology, 52: 846–855.
——— (1950) Radiobiological additivity of various ionizing radiations. Am. J. Roentgenol. Radium Therapy, 63: 170–175.
———, E. Anderson, E. F. Riley, and H. J. Curtis (1946) The effect of age on the radiosensitivity of mice. USAEC Report MDDC-418.*

Manuscript received by the editor Apr. 17, 1952

CHAPTER 15

The Pathological Physiology of Radiation Injury in the Mammal. II. Specific Aspects of the Physiology of Radiation Injury

HARVEY M. PATT AND AUSTIN M. BRUES

Division of Biological and Medical Research, Argonne National Laboratory, Lemont, Ill.

Introduction. Blood and hematopoiesis. Abnormal bleeding. Body fluids: Blood and plasma volume—Lymph and tissue fluid—Constituents of plasma and lymph. Cardiovascular system. Gastrointestinal tract. Liver. Kidney. Endocrines: Adrenal —Thyroid—Pituitary. Nervous System. Miscellaneous tissues and organs. Metabolism and tissue breakdown. Immunity and infection. Nonspecific physiological stresses. Acute radiation syndrome. References.

INTRODUCTION

The physical and biological factors that influence the response to high energy radiation have been considered in Chap. 14. We are concerned here with the physiological aspects of irradiation of specific sites or of the whole organism. In general, the development and course of injury are similar whether ionization and excitation result from penetrating external radiations or from internally deposited radioactive materials. While biological effectiveness differs for the several radiation qualities, it is difficult to discern by physiological or histological means whether irradiation has been accomplished by slow or fast neutrons, X or γ rays when a median lethal dosage is employed. External β irradiation is distinguished by the superficial nature of the damage, and the results of poisoning with internal emitters are modified by the organ distribution and trajectory of the radiating particles.

It is clear that no single change is peculiarly specific for radiation injury. Since the ionizing energy is dissipated in a heterogeneous and highly integrated system, many different effects may ensue, and not all of these are a direct consequence of exposure. Thus, we must contend not only with the physicochemical complexities of energy absorption, but with the many ramifications of function in the organism seeking to retain physiological balance. Although the early biochemical and cytological effects probably bear a causal relation to the gross pathological physiology, the nature of this relation is poorly understood. The manifestations of the radiation syndrome and possible modes of their development will be the subject of the following discussion.

BLOOD AND HEMATOPOIESIS

The radiosensitivity of blood-forming tissues and the consequent hazard of blood damage have attracted considerable attention since the classic work of Heineke in 1903. The vast early literature on this subject has been reviewed by Dunlap (1942). Although blood and blood formation are discussed in some detail by Jacobson in Chap. 16, present concepts merit brief consideration here since the hematologic picture is an integral part of the radiation syndrome.

Peripheral blood changes depend, for the most part, upon the radiosensitivity of the parent or precursor cells, their ability to recover from injury, and the life span or rate of utilization of the mature elements in the blood. From morphological studies on acutely irradiated animals, it may be seen that changes in the peripheral blood cells reflect to a considerable extent alterations in the bone marrow, lymph nodes, and spleen (Lawrence, Dowdy, and Valentine, 1948; Lawrence, Valentine, and Dowdy, 1948; Bloom and Jacobson, 1948; Jacobson, Marks, and Lorenz, 1949; Suter, 1947; Stearner *et al.*, 1947a). This is not, however, readily apparent after chronic irradiation (Jacobson, Marks, and Lorenz, 1949). While the site of action appears to be mainly in the blood-forming organs, indirect or remote effects on hematopoietic tissue and direct effects on the morphological constituents of peripheral blood are not unknown. The alteration of lymphoid tissue in areas distant from the site of irradiation is an example of the indirect type of action (Barnes and Furth, 1943; Leblond and Segal, 1942). The utilization, destruction, and production of blood cells following irradiation of the whole animal are undoubtedly influenced indirectly by certain general derangements of body economy. Thus, infection may lead to an increased demand, damaged epithelial surfaces to an increased loss, nutritional disturbances to a decreased formation of substances necessary for normal hematopoiesis, and circulatory changes to a decreased effective blood cell mass.

Blood exposed in vitro to moderate dosages of radiation, i.e., in the lethal range for mammals, shows only slight changes. A direct cytocidal effect on lymphocytes from the thymus and spleen has been observed in the test tube with as little as 50 r and may contribute to the early decrease in circulating lymphocytes (Schrek, 1946). Mature granulocytes, on the other hand, are quite resistant and are not affected directly by radiation except in excessive dosage. Degenerate cells are not found generally in smears of mammalian blood made during the first few days after irradiation; they may be noted, however, in smears prepared from chicken blood (Murray *et al.*, 1948). Hemolysis has been seen in blood subjected to heavy X irradiation (Ting and Zirkle, 1940; Liechti and Wilbrandt, 1941; Frankenthal and Back, 1944; Halberstaedter and Leibowitz, 1947). Erythrocytes irradiated in vitro with polonium α particles first shrink and then swell before hemolysis; these changes require large dosages (5×10^5 rep) (Buchsbaum and Zirkle, 1949). Osmotic and mechanical fragility of canine erythrocytes is apparently unaltered following exposure in vivo to X rays or neutrons (Davis *et al.*, 1949; Ross and Ely, 1947), but the thermal fragility of rat erythrocytes is reported to increase during the first few hours after exposure of the whole animal to 500 to 600 r (Goldschmidt *et al.*, 1951). It is not known whether this represents a direct effect of X rays on the red cell.

That radiation anemia may be due, in part, to a hemolytic reaction is suggested by the rapid decline of red blood cells, which is in excess of that resulting solely from the absence of erythrogenesis, the active phagocytosis of erythrocytes, and the increased excretion of bile pigments (Davis *et al.*, 1949; Schwartz *et al.*, 1947; Prosser, Painter, Lisco, *et al.*, 1947). These facts do not in any sense constitute definite proof of a direct action of radiation on the mature erythrocyte. The early anemia may be partially explained by the loss of red cells from the circulation, by the increase in plasma volume, and, to some extent, by the failure of replacement. Large numbers of erythrocytes have been shown to appear in the lymph within several days after irradiation, and extensive erythrophagocytosis and hemosiderosis have been seen in the lymph sinuses of irradiated animals (Furth, Andrews, *et al.*, 1951). Destruction of erythrocytes may also be accomplished by the toxic materials that are liberated from damaged tissues or from infectious organisms. While increased excretion of bile pigments is suggestive of red cell destruction, this may also be attributed to cessation of red cell production or to some aberration in the incorporation of hemoglobin into young erythroid cells.

Although each of the ionizing radiations affects the hematopoietic organs in the same qualitative manner, their relative effectiveness varies (Lawrence and Lawrence, 1936; Jacobson and Marks, 1946). The X-ray–to–neutron ratio for the acute lymphocyte and granulocyte response in rabbits is around 6.0 (Jacobson and Marks, 1946). Only minimal blood changes are seen after external irradiation with β rays (Raper and Barnes, 1951a). This is consistent with the localization of radiation effects. Granulocytes may increase several weeks after external β-ray exposure of rabbits, but it is noteworthy that granulocytosis coincides with infection of the ulcerated skin. On the other hand, extensive damage to the hematopoietic tissues and concomitant changes in peripheral blood have been observed following poisoning with internal emitters (Bloom and Jacobson, 1948; Jacobson, Marks, and Lorenz, 1949). Differences in the hematologic effects seen after administration of various radioelements may be attributed to their anatomical distribution and the specific ionization and energy of the radiating particles.

The histological picture is characterized by disappearance of mitotic figures, cell degeneration, and death, leading, a few days later, to aplasia of the marrow and lymphoid tissue (Bloom and Jacobson, 1948). Edema and hemorrhage with subsequent fatty infiltration of the hypoplastic marrow cavity may occur several days after irradiation (Lutwak-Mann and Gunz, 1949). The early chemical changes in the blood-forming tissues are obscure. A transitory increase in oxygen consumption, carbon dioxide production, and hemin synthesis has been seen in marrow homogenates prepared from rabbits immediately after 800 r of X irradiation (Altman *et al.*, 1951). Synthesis of RNA and DNA by rabbit bone marrow is inhibited, however, while that of protein is unaffected, during the five hours following similar irradiation (Abrams, 1951). An early increase in respiration has not been observed in irradiated rat thymus (Barron, 1946). Respiration and anaerobic glycolysis of marrow and thymus decline below the preirradiation level during the first few days after exposure; recovery is apparent around the tenth day (Lutwak-Mann and Gunz, 1949; Barron, 1946). Nucleic acid phosphorus in the marrow reaches a minimum value between the second and fourth days and is still below normal at two weeks (Lutwak-Mann and Gunz, 1949). It is of interest that fatty acid synthesis is increased soon after X irradiation; this may account, in part, for the deposition of fat in the hypoplastic marrow cavity (Altman *et al.*, 1951).

Greatest sensitivity in the marrow is shown by the erythrocytic precursors (M. A. Bloom, 1948; Rosenthal, Pickering, and Goldschmidt, 1950; Denstad, 1941). Precursors of granulocytes and platelets are somewhat less sensitive, and the primitive reticular cells are quite resistant. Erythropoietic sensitivity is reflected physiologically by an early decrease in the uptake of iron by bone marrow. Twenty-four hours after exposure to 250 r, iron uptake in the rat may be decreased by a factor of 10 (Hennessy and Huff, 1950). In contrast to these findings, recovery from a standard anemia produced by phlebotomy immediately prior to irradiation with 200 r is only slightly less rapid in irradiated than in control cats (Valentine and Pearce, 1951). On the basis of functional impairment, it also appears that erythropoietic tissue is less sensitive to radiation injury than myelopoietic, but this may be a consequence of the preferential influence of phlebotomy on the relative recovery rates of the two tissues. Since cells of the reticulum appear to be the common progenitor, recovery may depend upon the factors involved in their transition to the various cell types. Formation of new cells from the reticular cells is said to be inhibited completely during the first week following median lethal irradiation (Rosenthal, Pickering, and Goldschmidt, 1950).

The blood-forming organs become actively hematopoietic within one to two weeks, but several months may elapse before regeneration is complete (Bloom and Jacobson, 1948). Overcompensation or secondary aplasia, sometimes seen during the recovery phase, can give rise to blood dyscrasias, which have been encountered especially after repeated irradiation. It is well known that a minimal exposure becomes important if repeated frequently enough to result in a significant accumulated dose. Definite hematological changes may appear in guinea pigs after exposure to as little as 1.1 r per day (Lorenz *et al.*, 1946). On the other hand, there is no evidence of any permanent functional impairment of the hematopoietic tissues when cats are subjected to a whole-body irradiation with 200 r every four months over a period of a year and a half (Valentine, Pearce, and Lawrence, 1951).

From the point of view of the time course of events in peripheral blood, the most important consideration appears to be the rate of utilization or life span of the various cellular elements. This increases progressively from the lymphocyte to the granulocyte, reticulocyte, thrombocyte, and erythrocyte, and represents the order in which changes occur in the peripheral blood after exposure to penetrating radiation in single or divided doses (Lawrence, Dowdy, and Valentine, 1948; Jacobson, Marks, and Lorenz, 1949; Suter, 1947). Significant reduction in the number of lymphocytes has been detected after a single total-body exposure to 25 r. Regeneration, however, does not follow the same pattern since recovery is ordinarily seen first in the reticulocytes, granulocytes, and thrombocytes, then in the erythrocytes and lymphocytes.

Recovery of hematopoietic tissue is more rapid after subtotal irradiation (Boffil and Miletzky, 1946; Jacobson, Simmons, Marks, Gaston, *et al.*, 1951; Rekers, 1949). The observations of Jacobson and his colleagues (Jacobson, Marks, Robson, *et al.*, 1949; Jacobson, Simmons, *et al.*, 1950; Jacobson, Simmons, Marks, Gaston, *et al.*, 1951) are of particular significance in this connection. They have shown that shielding the spleen in mice and rats or the appendix in rabbits lessens the severity of the blood changes and enhances recovery. Splenectomy performed prior to irradiation does not modify the hematologic response to X rays (Stearner *et al.*, 1947b), although it does increase the severity of the anemia that occurs after poisoning with Sr^{89} (Jacobson, Simmons, and Block, 1949). Anemia fails to develop when Sr^{89} is given to the normal mouse, apparently because of the intense ectopic erythropoiesis in the spleen. The mechanism of these protective effects is not understood; it has been suggested (Jacobson, Robson, and Marks, 1950) that mesenchymal tissues in shielded areas may supply a factor that facilitates regeneration of blood-forming tissue. It is of interest that spleen transplants (Jacobson, Simmons, Marks, and Eldredge, 1951; Jacobson, Simmons, Marks, Gaston, *et al.*, 1951) and spleen homogenates (Cole *et al.*, 1952) facilitate recovery and reduce radiation mortality in mice. Injection of lymphocytes does not protect rats against radiation damage (Campbell and Ross, 1952). Although transplants of bone marrow do not influence recovery appreciably in dogs (Rekers, 1949; Rekers *et al.*, 1950) and rats (Talbot and Pinson, 1951), intravenous or intraperitoneal administration to certain species is highly effective and, in fact, heterologous marrow (guinea pig to mouse) has considerable effectiveness (Lorenz *et al.*, 1951, 1952). The latter does not necessarily implicate a humoral substance since it has been shown that normal tissue can survive and proliferate in an X-irradiated heterologous host (Toolan, 1951).

The transient granulocytosis that occurs in the rabbit, chicken, and rat during the first hours after X irradiation has been attributed to the mobilization of granulocytes from storage depots as part of the early reaction to injury rather than to a primary stimulation of blood formation (Bloom and Jacobson, 1948). Accelerated maturation of myeloid cells has been noted, however, in the bone marrow of rats during the first hours after total-body irradiation (Rosenthal, Pickering, and Goldschmidt, 1950). The heterophils or granulocytes are the only circulating cells that are initially increased in number; monocytes and eosinophils, as well as lymphocytes, platelets, and reticulocytes, are invariably reduced. An "abortive rise" of heterophils, lymphocytes, and reticulocytes followed by a decline has been observed about one week after acute exposure to X rays or neutrons (Jacobson and Marks, 1946; Jacobson *et al.*, 1947; Jacobson, Marks, and Lorenz, 1949). There is no satisfactory explanation of this phenomenon.

Hemoglobin concentration and hematocrit, in general, parallel the changes in erythrocyte count. The anemia is, therefore, usually normocytic and normochromic (Jacobson, Marks, and Lorenz, 1949). A macrocytic anemia has been described in the rat after median lethal exposure to X radiation (Stearner *et al.*, 1947a), and similar anemias have been seen in man after poisoning with radioactive materials (Martland, 1926). While radiation-induced anemia is due primarily to the cessation of erythrocyte formation, extravasation of red cells and secondary damage are also substantial factors in its pathogenesis. The role of anemia in acute death occurring within two to three weeks after median lethal irradiation is not clear. The degree of the anemia indicates that it is at most of contributory significance during this period. Anemia may become a critical factor in the deaths seen at later periods, sometimes after a single exposure but more often after repeated irradiation.

The sedimentation rate of blood is increased after exposure to neutron or X radiation or the injection of Sr^{89} or Pu^{239} (Prosser, Painter, Lisco, *et al.*, 1947; Ross and Ely, 1947). The increase in sedimentation can be attributed only in small part to the decreased hematocrit and, therefore, is most likely related to some unknown factor in the plasma (Prosser, Painter, Lisco, *et al.*, 1947). The evidence indicates that this is probably not fibrinogen. Since the sedimentation rate in dogs may be increased by as little as 100 r to the whole animal, it is doubtful that this is a simple reflection of bacterial invasion.

In general, the sensitivity of blood and blood-forming tissues increases from rabbits to rats, mice, and chicks and then to men, goats, guinea pigs, and dogs (Jacobson, Marks and Lorenz, 1949). Since this is roughly the order of increasing sensitivity to the acute lethal action of X rays, rather comparable blood changes appear in each species after a median lethal exposure. Differences in recovery exist, however; after comparable hematologic injury recovery is more rapid in the rat than in the rabbit. There are also indications that the acute lethal dose for a species may be related to the sensitivity of its heterophils. Similar lymphopenias have been observed in the rabbit and guinea pig following irradiation with 200 r (Brues and Rietz, 1948). The heterophils, on the other hand, are decreased markedly only in the guinea pig with this dosage. Comparable heterophil depression is not observed in the rabbit until its lethal range is approached. That there may be some correlation between the heterophil response and acute lethality is also indicated by the rapid recovery of heterophils, but not of lymphocytes, in mice treated with estrogens prior to irradiation (Patt, Straube, *et al.*, 1949).

While consistent hematological differences between survivors and decedents are not always apparent, the clinical signs of acute intoxication generally parallel the hematological findings (Rekers, 1949; Ingram and Mason, 1950). It does not necessarily follow that death is due to blood damage, but the fact that morbidity and mortality can be influenced appreciably by procedures that presumably promote recovery of the blood-forming tissues suggests that such damage is a substantial factor in the radiation syndrome.

A number of agents have been employed in an attempt to modify the hematological response to radiation. Reference has already been made to the effectiveness of spleen shielding (Jacobson, Marks, Robson, *et al.*, 1949), spleen transplants and homogenates (Jacobson, Simmons, Marks, and Eldredge, 1951; Cole *et al.*, 1952), and bone marrow injections (Lorenz *et al.*, 1951, 1952). Increased resistance of erythropoietic tissues has been noted following the production of a regenerative anemia by phlebotomy, phenylhydrazine, and exposure to high altitude (Jacobson, Marks, Gaston, Simmons, and Block, 1948; Schack and MacDuffee, 1949). It is of interest that hyperplastic erythroid tissue shows less injury than normal tissue. Pretreatment with estrogens has been shown to induce a rapid recovery from radiation granulocytopenia and to minimize anemia in mice (Patt, Straube, *et al.*, 1949). The estrogen effect may be related to stimulation of activity, in this instance, of the myeloid tissues, following an initial depression. Cysteine is an effective prophylactic against the hematological changes induced in rats and mice by radiation (Patt *et al.*, 1950, 1952). Its protective action on blood is probably not specific for the hematopoietic tissues but appears rather to be related to an increase in the threshold for radiation effects generally. Enhanced recovery of blood-forming tissue is also apparent when glutathione is administered before irradiation (Cronkite *et al.*, 1951). Vitamins and other nutritional factors have been used experimentally with rather disappointing results (Simmons *et al.*, 1946; Adams and Lawrence, 1947; Stearner, 1948; Goldfeder *et al.*, 1948; Cronkite, Tullis, *et al.*, 1950; Carter, Busch, and Strang, 1950). Many of these substances are apparently useful in clinical radiation sickness (Shorvon, 1949). Post-irradiation anemia in dogs can be minimized by frequent transfusions of whole blood; granulocytopenia and thrombocytopenia are not influenced, however, nor is survival (Allen *et al.*, 1951).

ABNORMAL BLEEDING

Abnormal bleeding is usually, but not always, associated with the panhematopenia of acute irradiation. The bleeding tendency has been variously attributed to the thrombocytopenia (Shouse *et al.*, 1931; Dunlap; 1942; Holden *et al.*, 1949; Cronkite, 1950; Rosenthal and Benedek, 1950; Penick *et al.*, 1951; Dillard *et al.*, 1951), blood vessel damage (Rekers and Field, 1948; Field and Rekers, 1949a), and the presence of a circulating anticoagulant (Allen and Jacobson, 1947; Allen *et al.*, 1948). It is probable that each of these factors contributes to radiation hemorrhage, though to a different degree, depending upon species and conditions of irradiation. While hemorrhage is an almost invariable feature of the acute radiation syndrome, the extent and distribution of bleeding may vary considerably among the different species and among animals of the same species. Its severity depends, moreover, upon the completeness of irradiation and the dosage and manner of exposure.

Purpura and petechiae, though evident in the mouse, rat, and rabbit, are most severe in the dog, man, and probably the guinea pig; bleeding from the body orifices is not uncommon in these species (Allen and Jacobson, 1947; Allen *et al.*, 1948; Rekers and Field, 1948; Field and Rekers, 1949a; Kohn and Robinett, 1948; Rosenthal and Benedek, 1950; Shields Warren and Bowers, 1950). Hemorrhagic manifestations are first seen about a week after irradiation in the median lethal range and reach their peak during the second and third weeks. Extravasation of red cells results in a bloody lymph which becomes manifest several days after exposure and reaches a maximum during the period of greatest bleeding (Bigelow *et al.*, 1951). Bleeding may be widespread but is more often localized in various subcutaneous sites and in the gastrointestinal and urinary tracts, heart, and lungs. In general, the sites most subject to trauma bleed first. The distribution of hemorrhage apparently differs in animals which vary in susceptibility, being more generalized in the dog than in the rat (Allen *et al.*, 1948; Kohn and Robinett, 1948). In the dog, localized hemorrhages in the terminal state sometimes give rise to myocardial and neurological signs (Prosser, Painter, Lisco, *et al.*, 1947).

Exposure to ionizing radiation may result in a decreased coagulability of whole blood in animals and in human beings (Prosser, Painter, Lisco, *et al.*, 1947; Allen *et al.*, 1948; Field and Rekers, 1949a; Silverman, 1949). Allen and his associates (Allen and Jacobson, 1947; Allen *et al.*, 1948; Jacobson, Marks, Gaston, Allen, and Block, 1948) have observed a prolongation of clotting time in acutely irradiated dogs which is related to the appearance of a circulating heparin-like substance. The hemorrhagic diathesis in dogs is considered to be a consequence, for the most part, of the circulating heparin-like material, since various antiheparin substances, e.g., toluidine blue and protamine, can restore coagulability to normal values and prevent hemorrhage even in the presence of thrombocytopenia. The coagulation defect may occur before significant reduction of the blood platelets and in the absence of any change in prothrombin time and in blood calcium and fibrinogen. It is not altered significantly by transfusions of whole blood (Allen *et al.*, 1951) or administration of vitamins K or C. A similar clotting defect has been described in rabbits (Jacobson, Marks, Gaston, Allen, and Block, 1948) and in man (T. R. Smith *et al.*, 1948) after treatment with nitrogen mustards. The origin of the heparin-like substance is unknown; although it could arise from mast cells, the exact role of these cells after irradiation is uncertain (Kelsall and Crabb, 1952). It is of interest that chronic irradiation with low dosages, although sufficient to result in blood damage and death, does not appreciably alter blood clotting (Jacobson, Marks, and Lorenz, 1949).

While the influence of toluidine blue or protamine on the development and disappearance of radiation hemorrhage is dramatic, these agents do not alter total survival appreciably. It is noteworthy that the median lethal dosage for the rat can be reduced to that for the dog by injecting heparin after irradiation (Kohn and Robinett, 1948); yet, the distribution of hemorrhage in the heparinized irradiated rat is apparently unchanged despite the increase in bleeding. This may imply a difference between the rat and dog in the latent injuries that require "heparin-like substances" for their development; it should also be recalled that the hemorrhagic picture in traumatic shock varies greatly from species to species. As contrasted with these observations, heparinization is said to decrease the lung damage that appears in rabbits following repeated irradiation of the thorax over a two-week period (Boys and Harris, 1943). Dicumarol has also been employed to decrease pulmonary changes in man after local irradiation (Macht and Perlberg, 1950). In this case the role of vascular thrombosis in local tissue radiation damage may provide the explanation.

The existence of a circulating anticoagulant is questioned by some workers who fail to find consistent changes in the coagulability of whole blood in a number of species, although the clotting time of plasma may be increased and clot retraction diminished (Kohn and Robinett, 1948; Kohn *et al.*, 1948; Dixon, 1948; Holden *et al.*, 1949; Cronkite, 1950; Rosenthal and Benedek, 1950; Cohn, 1951). Cronkite (1950) believes that the bleeding tendency and the coagulation defect when observed can be attributed primarily to the severe thrombocytopenia and associated phenomena. Whole hemophilic blood with normal platelet levels has been found to accelerate the clotting of irradiated dog blood (Penick *et al.*, 1951). This is not the case with platelet-poor hemophilic plasma. Platelet transfusions have been shown to reverse the coagulation defect and to prevent bleeding in an irradiated dog (Dillard *et al.*, 1951). Multiple transfusions of whole blood are ineffectual, however (Allen *et al.*, 1951). We cannot account for the lack of agreement regarding the etiology of radiation hemorrhage, i.e., thrombocytopenia vs. heparin-like substances. Some of the seemingly discordant observations may be attributed to differences in experimental techniques, e.g., in the withdrawal of blood and the determination of the various components of the clotting mechanism, or in the species of animal and dosage of radiation. Recent evidence indicates that thrombocytopenia is the chief factor in the pathogenesis of abnormal bleeding.

There is some evidence that alteration in vascular fragility also plays a role in the hemorrhagic syndrome. This is largely indirect, however. Petechiae may be induced more readily in irradiated than in nonirradiated animals and bleeding is generally most severe at the points of greatest trauma (Field and Rekers, 1949a; Allen *et al.*, 1948). Bleeding cannot always be related to thrombocytopenia and the delayed clotting reaction (Field and Rekers, 1949a). Reference has already been made to the flooding of lymph by erythrocytes, indicative perhaps of capillary damage (Bigelow *et al.*, 1951). Rutin, a flavonol glucoside that is considered by some investigators to influence vascular fragility, has been shown to hasten recovery of the skin of rats after local irradiation (Griffith *et al.*, 1947) and to minimize hemorrhage and improve the survival of dogs after total-body irradiation (Rekers and Field, 1948; Field and Rekers, 1949a). To be effective, rutin must be given for a week or so before or preferably both before and after irradiation. Since reduction of hemorrhage occurs with rutin despite depression of the blood platelets and prolongation of clotting, it has been proposed (Field and Rekers, 1949a) that rutin either decreases the rate of vascular disintegration or increases its repair. It is not known whether hyaluronidase plays a role in altered capillary fragility. Hyaluronidase inhibitors have been tried in a few irradiated dogs without success (Field and Rekers, 1949b). Bleeding is said to be diminished in guinea pigs that are fed a diet supplemented with cabbage, possibly because of its high content of vitamins P and C (Lourau and

Lartigue, 1950b). On the other hand, when beets are added to the basic ration, the number of hemorrhages is increased and the LD_{50} is decreased from 350 to 150 r. This may be attributed possibly to a relative deficiency of vitamin C. Ascorbic acid does not alter the hemorrhagic state or the survival of irradiated dogs although it may act synergistically with flavonoids (Field and Rekers, 1949b). Flavonoids have been shown to improve the survival of X-rayed guinea pigs and rats, but this has not been verified by others, and the value of these substances requires further elucidation (Kohn, Robinett, and Cupp, 1948; Clark *et al.*, 1948; Sokoloff *et al.*, 1950; Cronkite *et al.*, 1949).

It is of interest that rutin does not protect the dog against dosages greater than the LD_{50} (Field and Rekers, 1949a). This suggests perhaps that the hemorrhagic tendency in the dog is a minor factor in mortality resulting from higher dosages of radiation. While hemorrhage may be extensive at the LD_{100}, its control with toluidine blue or protamine does not permit survival (Allen *et al.*, 1948). Life may, however, be prolonged for a week or two, suggesting perhaps that the control of hemorrhage in less severely irradiated animals may contribute to recovery. It is well known that many animals, including the dog, succumb with only minor evidence of hemorrhage, again emphasizing the importance of multiple factors.

BODY FLUIDS

Some disturbance in water and electrolyte metabolism may be anticipated following exposure of large areas of the body to ionizing radiation as a result of the vomiting, diarrhea, altered food and water intake, tissue breakdown, and bleeding, which are prominent features of the radiation syndrome. The degree of redistribution of body fluids will depend, in large measure, on the capacity of the homeostatic mechanisms, which may also be affected by radiation, to maintain the delicate balance of the internal environment. It is clear, therefore, that the body fluids reflect a number of influences that may vary not only with dosage and from animal to animal but also from time to time after irradiation in the same animal. While it appears that early death after massive irradiation is accompanied by hemoconcentration and dehydration, disturbances of water and electrolyte balance after median lethal dosages are, in general, comparatively mild and probably do not constitute an important cause of death.

Blood and Plasma Volume. The blood volume remains relatively constant or is only slightly diminished after irradiation of the whole body with dosages that approximate the median lethal. This obtains in the face of a greatly reduced erythrocyte volume because of the compensatory increase in the volume of plasma (Prosser, Painter, Lisco, *et. al.*, 1947; Storey *et al.*, 1950; Soberman *et al.*, 1951). The decrease in red blood cell volume has been attributed to the failure of erythropoiesis, destruction of the mature cells, and internal bleeding. Cell and plasma volumes have been determined in mice, rats, rabbits, and dogs, using P^{32} tagged erythrocytes, iodinated plasma proteins, and the conventional Evans blue technique. Following irradiation of the rabbit with 1000 r, there is a parallel decline in cell and plasma volumes that begins on the third day. By the tenth day, however, plasma volume rises, reaching a level some 10 per cent above the normal during the third week when the red cell volume is decreased by more than 40 per cent (Storey *et al.*, 1950). The blood volume is, therefore, only slightly diminished. In the irradiated dog, plasma volume may be increased by more than 50 per cent when the red cell volume and hematocrit are severely depressed (Soberman *et al.*, 1951). Rather similar findings have been observed in mice and rats (Storey *et al.*, 1950; France, 1946). Although there is some disagreement in regard to the early decline in plasma volume, this may be attributed in some instances to whether the volume is expressed as a percentage of the preirradiation body weight or of the body weight at the time of determination (Storey *et al.*, 1950; France, 1946). The rapidly falling blood pressure that is seen frequently in rabbits during the first hours after irradiation is not accompanied by significant changes in blood volume (Painter *et al.*, 1947).

When massive dosages are applied to the abdomen or whole body of the dog, death nearly always occurs during the first few days with hemoconcentration (Moon *et al.*, 1941). With less severe, but nevertheless lethal, exposure to X radiation or after injection of Sr^{89} or Pu^{239}, the usual rise in plasma volume is seen during the intermediate and acute periods as the red cell loss becomes appreciable (Prosser, Painter, Lisco, *et al.*, 1947). Thus, as contrasted with traumatic shock, hemoconcentration and appreciable diminution of blood volume are not observed in the irradiated animal unless the radiation dosage is well above the minimal LD_{100}.

There is no information concerning the blood volume after superficial irradiation, e.g., with β rays. A decrease in blood volume would perhaps be anticipated because of plasma loss in the burned areas. It is possible, however, that plasma loss might occur so slowly that compensatory mechanisms, e.g., shift in fluids from other compartments or water retention, could operate to prevent a change in blood volume. Similar information is also lacking for neutron irradiation; it is probable that the effects with neutrons would resemble those seen after X irradiation.

Lymph and Tissue Fluid. The output of lymph from the thoracic duct of cats is unchanged during the first hours after 1500 r X irradiation of the whole body (Valentine *et al.*, 1948). Lymph flow, as visualized by thorotrast, is not affected following localized X irradiation of the hind legs of rats (Hodes and Griffith, 1941). The volume of cutaneous lymph flow in man is likewise unchanged by moderate amounts of local irradiation and may actually decrease with larger dosages (Ané and Burch, 1941). However, an increased spread of intradermally injected Evans blue dye, presumably indicative of an enhanced lymph flow, has been seen in the rabbit within a few hours after irradiation (Painter *et al.*, 1947). Lymph output has not been measured in the later periods after exposure, although there is some indication of an increased flow from the thoracic duct in irradiated dogs (Bigelow *et al.*, 1951). Reference has already been made to extravasation of red cells into the lymph (Furth, Andrews, *et al.*, 1951).

Edema, especially of the face, neck, and extremities, may be observed during the acute terminal period. While edema of the viscera, particularly of the gastrointestinal tract, may also be noted in some animals, edema is more often microscopic rather than macroscopic. Consistent changes in water content have not been observed in muscle, adrenal, kidney, and gastrointestinal tract (France, 1946; Beutel and Winter, 1935; Patt *et al.*, 1947; Painter, 1948; Bowers and Scott, 1951b). In chronically irradiated rats, muscle and bone water increase slightly after the accumulation of nearly 1500 r over a period of 105 days (Brues *et al.*, 1946). Total-body water in mice is increased by about 8 per cent on the fifth day after acute X irradiation (France, 1946), but there is little change in the total water content of dogs following a nearly completely lethal dosage of X rays (Soberman *et al.*, 1951).

Extracellular fluid in rats, estimated from the thiocyanate space, has been shown to increase by about 2 cc per 100 grams of body weight during the first two weeks after whole-body X irradiation with 400 or 700 r. An increase over the range of the control animals has also been noted eight months after a single exposure to 750 r, and similar changes occur after chronic irradiation with X rays or α rays from plutonium (France, 1946). Although an early increase in the extracellular compartment has been reported in a few irradiated dogs (Prosser, Painter, Lisco, *et al.*, 1947), consistent changes are not evident from other experiments in the same dosage range (Soberman *et al.*, 1951).

Sodium retention has been described in the rat during the first few days following irradiation (Painter, 1948; Bennett *et al.*, 1949), but similar increases in sodium space do not occur in the dog after lethal irradiation (Soberman *et al.*, 1951). The lack of agreement may be related to differences in water intake between the two species, since the rat generally manifests a marked polydipsia during the first postirradiation day while water intake is reduced in the dog (Prosser, Painter, Lisco, *et al.*, 1947). On the other hand, there is reason to think that inanition, and not polydipsia, is responsible for the increased sodium space in the rat since similar changes have been seen in the gastrointestinal tracts of starved and both starved and irradiated rats (Painter, 1948). Whenever body tissue is catabolized, for example, in starvation, water is made available, and this may be a factor in the animal which is anorexic as a result of irradiation. Changes in the irradiated animal, however, are not entirely comparable to those observed in starvation; there is apparently little change in extra- and intracellular muscle water in the irradiated rat, whereas, in the starved rat, the extracellular phase is expanded and the intracellular contracted.

Water transfer is closely related to the exchange of its principal ionic solutes and both solvent and solute must be considered in any evaluation of hydration phenomena. Although there is evidence that heavy irradiation may lead to cell swelling (Buchsbaum and Zirkle, 1949; Failla, 1940), simultaneous measurements of sodium, potassium, and chloride indicate that intracellular fluid may actually be decreased at the expense of the extracellular phase in the gastrointestinal tract of rats after midlethal exposure of the whole body (Painter and Pullman, 1950). It is of interest that there is a rather parallel loss of sodium and potassium from radiosensitive tissues in the rat during the first day or two after X irradiation (Bowers and Scott, 1951a, b). This is followed by a marked increase in tissue sodium. There is also no evidence for an increase in intracellular water in irradiated dogs (Soberman *et al.*, 1951).

These considerations indicate that there is probably little serious disturbance in water balance after acute lethal irradiation. Changes appear to be more severe in rats than in dogs, which may be a result of the greater diarrhea in the former. Water intake is reduced more than water loss in most mammals. Since plasma volume may be increased in the presence of an increase in extracellular and total-body water, the extra water may be derived from metabolism or from a reduction of the respiratory loss, which may be as high as 35 per cent of the extrarenal loss under basal conditions.

Constituents of Plasma and Lymph. Plasma proteins are decreased in concentration in guinea pigs and rats, but usually not in dogs, during the first week after total-body X irradiation. The maximum decrease, amounting to about 1 gram per cent, occurs around the fifth postirradiation day in guinea pigs and rats (Kohn, 1950, 1951a; Hanschuldt and Supplee, 1949). The plasma refractive index parallels early protein change. After the initial decrease, protein concentration levels off or may return toward the normal value. In the dog, plasma protein concentration remains unchanged or may decline slightly during the first and second postexposure weeks (Prosser, Painter, Lisco, *et al.*, 1947a; Soberman *et al.*, 1951). This may be followed by a rise above the control level in nonsurvivors during the terminal period. Total protein of lymph collected from the thoracic duct fluctuates during the first two days after irradiation and then decreases slowly for several days (Brown *et al.*, 1950). Maintenance or increase of the plasma protein concentration in the presence of a rising plasma volume suggests an increased breakdown of tissue that liberates protein, a failure of mechanisms of proteolysis, or an increased synthesis of protein. Animals exposed to small daily doses of X rays do not exhibit an initial decline in plasma protein, and in the terminal period total protein may rise, fall, or remain unchanged (Prosser and Moore, 1946; Fink, 1946). Definite changes in plasma protein have not been seen in irradiated patients (Frieden and White, 1950).

The albumin-globulin ratio as determined by salt fractionation is elevated for several days after irradiation of the guinea pig or rat (Kohn, 1950, 1951a). The early increase in the A/G ratio is thought to be due to the presence in plasma of an ether-soluble factor that affects the fractionation procedure (Volkin and Kohn, 1950). There is no characteristic change in the electrophoretic pattern of plasma proteins in dogs during the first postexposure week (Muntz *et al.*, 1949). Albumin is only slightly diminished during this interval, but a marked decrease, amounting to 50 per cent, is found during the second week. Several days before death the α-globulin fraction increases sharply, especially the α_3 and α_4 fractions, and may actually be doubled. The β-globulin–fibrinogen complex is also increased but not so markedly as that of the α-globulin. Similar changes occur in dogs treated with daily doses of X rays or injected with Sr^{89} and Pu^{239} (Prosser, Painter, Lisco, *et al.*, 1947). Differences in the electrophoretic pattern have been noted in dogs and goats after X irradiation (Buchanan and Barron, 1947). In the latter, increase in the β-globulin–fibrinogen fraction predominates and little change is seen in the α-globulin.

In contrast with the results observed in X-irradiated dogs, in neutron-irradiated rabbits there is an initial decrease in the γ-globulin fraction which parallels the decline in leukocytes (Sanigar *et al.*, 1947). This, however, is followed by the increase in globulins and decrease in albumin that is seen with X rays. Direct neutron irradiation of blood plasma does not influence the electrophoretic pattern. The changes observed in irradiated animals are nonspecific and related presumably to tissue destruction, infection, and inanition. Similar patterns have been found after thermal and other injuries and after the injection of adrenal cortical hormones (Gjessing and Chanutin, 1947, 1950). It is not known whether the diminution in albumin is due to impaired synthesis or to its loss from the blood because of altered capillary permeability. Albuminuria is not evident (Muntz *et al.*, 1949).

Plasma nonprotein nitrogen rises by over 25 per cent in rats and guinea pigs during the first few days after exposure to X rays (Kohn, 1950, 1951a). On the other hand, there is little change or a gradual decline in the dog until the terminal period when a marked increase is manifest (Prosser, Painter, Lisco, *et al.*, 1947). A definite elevation of NPN and uric acid levels occurs in the lymph 4 hours after X irradiation and coincides with the period of greatest lymphocyte destruction (Brown *et al.*, 1950). Part of the late rise in plasma nonprotein nitrogen in dogs can be accounted for by the terminal anuria. Plasma urea nitrogen follows closely the change in nonprotein nitrogen. There is little alteration in nonprotein nitrogen with daily dosages of 10 to 50 r, although a sharp fall may be noted terminally with the higher dosage (Prosser and Moore, 1946). The reason for this difference in terminal behavior between dogs irradiated acutely and chronically is not clear. After neutron exposure (400 n in four divided doses) plasma NPN in the dog falls on the third day and is decreased until death (Ross and Ely, 1947).

Plasma glucose is increased in the guinea pig and rat (Kohn, 1950, 1951a; Lourau and Lartigue, 1950a). The change roughly parallels that of nonprotein nitrogen, and it has been suggested that the gluconeogenesis necessary to maintain hyperglycemia during the period of radiation anorexia is partly responsible for the rise in NPN (Kohn, 1950). Plasma glucose is also increased in the rabbit and dog after neutron or X irradiation (Ross and Ely, 1947; Prosser, Painter, Lisco, *et al.*, 1947). In the X-irradiated dog, blood sugar is increased for several days prior to the onset of fever and normal levels are found terminally. This is apparently not the case with neutron irradiation where hyperglycemia is progressive until death. Glucose concentration of lymph is unaltered during the first few days after X irradiation (Brown *et al.*, 1950).

There is a variable pattern of change in the principal electrolytes of plasma. Chloride rises in the rat and guinea pig after comparable dosage (Kohn, 1950, 1951a). The increase occurs on the third day and normal levels are evident by the second week. Blood cell chloride declines roughly in proportion to the plasma increase; thus, the total chloride is not altered appreciably. Plasma inorganic phosphorus rises slightly in the rat and parallels the hyperglycemia and elevated NPN (Kohn, 1951a). Serum sodium is also elevated in this species, while serum potassium may rise slightly or remain within normal limits (Bowers and Scott, 1951a, b; Bennett *et al.*, 1949; Kohn, 1951a). Consistent changes in the plasma levels of sodium, potassium, calcium, chloride, and phosphate have not been observed in dogs following acute or chronic exposure to X rays (Soberman *et al.*, 1951; Prosser and Moore, 1946; Fink, 1946), and only minimal effects have been seen following neutron irradiation (Ross and Ely, 1947). There are few recent data relating to acid-base balance; carbon dioxide combining power is said to be decreased in rats on the fourth day after a total-body exposure to 600 r (Kohn, 1951a).

Increased amounts of lipids have been detected in several mammalian species following total-body irradiation. Turbidity of plasma, presumably a result of the large increase in total lipid, has been observed in the rabbit and is believed to presage early death in this species (Rosenthal,

1949). Plasma turbidity is not apparent, however, in the irradiated rat, although the total lipid content of plasma is elevated (Kohn, 1951a). Plasma phospholipid may rise or remain unchanged (Kohn, 1951a; Neve and Entenman, 1951), while plasma cholesterol is reported to increase in guinea pigs, mice, rats, and dogs (Prosser, Painter, Lisco, *et al.*, 1947; Kohn, 1950, 1951a; Low-Beer, 1933). In the rat and guinea pig cholesterol rises on the second or third day after acute irradiation and returns to normal by the sixth day, the pattern resembling that of chloride. In chronically irradiated dogs (50 r per day) cholesterol is elevated only terminally. There are no significant changes in cholesterol concentration with daily dosages of 10 r or less (Fink, 1946). Alteration in the cholesterol content of serum and in the chylomicron count (mobile visible plasma lipids) has been observed in patients receiving radiation therapy. Several investigators have alluded to a relation between the direction of cholesterol change and clinical radiation sickness; the latter is not seen in patients whose serum cholesterol is elevated (Low-Beer, 1933; Hummel, 1930; Holmes, 1941). Reduction of the chylomicron count also appears to be related temporally to radiation sickness and is observed after irradiation of the abdomen or thorax but not of the extremities (Setala and Ermala, 1948).

A moderate increase in plasma alkaline phosphatase occurs in rats 24 hours after irradiation with dosages of 200 to 600 r (Ludewig and Chanutin, 1950a). Enzyme activity decreases on the second day in animals exposed to the higher dosage. Phosphatase activity in the rat is also depressed by multiple small dosages of radiation. There is little change in alkaline and acid phosphatases of plasma after chronic X irradiation of dogs (Prosser and Moore, 1946; Fink, 1946).

The sulfhydryl content of plasma is decreased in the rat about 5 days after X irradiation with 750 r (Shacter, 1951); the significance of this change is not understood. Similar effects have been observed after nitrogen mustard poisoning and surgical trauma and appear to be related chronologically to initiation of tissue regeneration. A fall in serum ascorbic acid has also been reported in animals and man (Kretzschmar and Ellis, 1947). The maximum decrease is seen about one week after exposure.

Plasma histamine is increased in the irradiated rat and rabbit (Painter *et al.*, 1947; Weber and Steggerda, 1949). In the rat given 600 r, two peaks of histamine elevation are seen, the first two hours after exposure and the second at five days (Weber and Steggerda, 1949). There is some reason to believe that histamine liberated from damaged cells and perhaps newly formed from irradiated histidine can account for certain of the radiation effects (Ellinger, 1951). Other toxic materials may be present in the plasma of irradiated animals, but these have not been identified (Venters and Painter, 1950).

Aberrations in the plasma constituents are rarely related in specific experiments to changes in water distribution, or to renal and gastrointestinal function, and this aspect of radiation injury deserves study. All the changes that have been described appear to be nonspecific reactions to the injury, and some of these are undoubtedly mediated by the pituitary-adrenal system. Yet, differences are apparent between these radiation effects and the alarm reaction (Kohn, 1950, 1951a, b). The pattern of change is said to be similar in young and adult animals and is about equal in the rat and guinea pig after comparable exposure, despite the greater sensitivity of the latter to the lethal action of radiation. The inconsistency of the plasma changes following median lethal irradiation, not only among different species but also among animals of the same species, suggests, moreover, that these effects are not critical parameters of radiation injury and probably do not constitute an important cause of death.

CARDIOVASCULAR SYSTEM

The erythematous reaction of skin is not only the most evident but perhaps also the most extensively studied circulatory response to radiation, since it plays an important role in determining the course of radiation therapy. It is well known that a smaller dosage of low-energy radiation is necessary to produce skin erythema than of high-energy radiation and that the biologic effectiveness decreases with protraction or fractionation of radiation (Shields Warren, 1943c; Schöttelndreyer, 1949; Larkin, 1941, 1942). The severity of the cutaneous erythema depends, moreover, on the size of the radiation field (Shields Warren, 1943c; Jolles, 1941, 1950; Jolles and Mitchell, 1947). Erythema has been described following exposure to the different qualities of radiation, and there is little difference in the reactions that are produced (Miescher, 1938; Shields Warren, 1943c; Larkin, 1941, 1942). The γ-to-X-ray ratio of effectiveness for cutaneous erythema is about 1.3 (Mottram and Gray, 1940).

Waves of erythema were originally defined by Miescher (1924) and may be seen in human skin during the first day, the second to third week, and at the end of the first month after irradiation. Telangiectasis may appear after heavy irradiation. Similar patterns occur in rabbit skin after local exposure to X rays. With 1000 r, erythema is seen on the first, fifth, and tenth postirradiation days (Painter *et al.*, 1947). The early cutaneous effects have been related to cell injury, the later erythema to alterations in the vascular bed (Shields Warren, 1943c). An increase in the number of patent blood vessels and dilatation of existing capillaries and lymphatics may be noted in irradiated skin (Painter *et al.*, 1947; Borak, 1942a, b, c; Pohle, 1926, 1927; Pendergrass *et al.*, 1944). The bluish cast that is sometimes observed in a hyperemic area after heavy local irradiation is thought to be due to alternate regions of constriction and dilatation in the same vessels (Borak, 1942a, b, c). Several mechanisms have been proposed to account for the vascular reactions, including a direct effect of radiation on blood vessel walls and the release of humoral agents (H substances) in the irradiated area (Ellinger, 1951; Light, 1935). Diffusible substances are postulated to account for the observation that two radiation fields a distance apart show less injury than areas that are closer together (Jolles, 1950).

Scratch tests of erythematous skin lead to a persistent vasoconstriction, and wheal formation is not induced by histamine (Larkin, 1942). Skin temperature is unchanged during the latent period between irradiation and erythema, but, with the appearance of the latter, the temperature may rise several degrees centigrade, suggestive of marked vasodilatation (Larkin, 1942). It has been pointed out that the cutaneous vessels show an increased sensitivity to dilator substances and a decreased responsiveness to constrictor stimuli during the period of skin erythema (Lazarew and Lazarewa, 1926). Blanching of the hyperemic regions can occur after injection of epinephrine, however (Larkin, 1942).

Direct in vivo observations of blood vessels in the frog's web or bat's wing reveal that radiation is a nonspecific vascular damaging agent (Painter *et al.*, 1947; Smith, Svihla, and Patt, 1951). A similar conclusion may be drawn from studies of the nail-fold area (Braasch and Nickson, 1948). Detailed studies of circulation have been made in the wing of the bat, *Myotis lucifugus*, following total-body irradiation and following local irradiation of a portion of the wing (Smith, Svihla, and Patt, 1951). Of interest is the radioresistance of the hibernating bat.[1] Circulatory changes do not occur in the wing unless the total-body dosage with 250-kv X rays exceeds 10,000 r. With dosages over the range of 10,000 to 60,000 r, adherence of leukocytes to blood vessel walls, clumping of red cells, and stagnation of blood are prominent. There are, however, no consistent changes in vessel diameter or in venomotor activity following a total-body exposure and hemorrhage is not apparent. On the other hand, there is some evidence of an increase in capillary permeability. After local irradiation of the wing, vascular reactions are confined to the irradiated area, and the threshold for circulatory disturbance is in the neighborhood of 50,000 r for 50-kv X rays. With the exception of red cell clumping, the intravascular changes noted after local exposure, e.g., leukocyte sticking and clumping, platelet thrombi, and stagnation, appear to be related to radiation dosage. Platelet thrombi and leukocyte clumps have also been observed in tissues taken from patients and from animals treated with radium and X rays, and it is presumed that these changes lead to an impairment of blood flow (Pullinger, 1932). Hepatic blood

[1] Although the bats were collected while in hibernation, observations were carried out at room temperature.

flow is decreased only by a small factor after heavy β irradiation of the mouse liver with a Y^{90} colloid (20,000 rep in 3 days) (Dobson and Jones, 1952).

The influence of radiation on vascular permeability is largely undetermined. From studies of relatively simple systems there is reason to believe that cell permeability is not affected directly unless massive dosages are employed. Although changes suggestive of altered capillary permeability have been described, it is not known whether they are a result of the action of radiation on the endothelium or of alterations in the vascular bed. Intravenously injected dyes appear sooner in patches of irradiated skin. When Evans blue dye is injected into rabbits immediately after local X irradiation, the exposed area turns blue earlier than the nonexposed (Painter *et al.*, 1947). A similar increased localization and concentration of dye has been noted with intravenous trypan blue as long as the injection is made within 1 hour of X irradiation (Rigdon and Curl, 1943). An increased spread of intradermally injected Evans blue, which is presumed to be indicative of an accelerated lymph flow, has also been seen in the irradiated skin of rabbits during the first few hours (Painter *et al.*, 1947); yet, cutaneous lymph flow in man is apparently unchanged following moderate amounts of radiation and may actually decrease with larger dosages (Ané and Burch, 1941). There is little change, moreover, in the output of lymph from the thoracic duct of the cat during the first hours after total-body irradiation (Valentine *et al.*, 1948), although an increased lymph flow has been observed in the dog several days later (Bigelow *et al.*, 1951).

Intravenous Evans blue appears in the irradiated and nonirradiated regions at the same time during the late erythematous reaction of rabbit skin, but this is not the case with fluorescein, which is seen within a few seconds in the exposed area and within several minutes in the nonexposed region (Painter *et al.*, 1947). The reason for this difference is not obvious. It has been suggested that the appearance of Evans blue may be masked by erythema of the irradiated skin. The rapid appearance of fluorescein, on the other hand, may be more a matter of hyperemia than of an increase in permeability of the vascular endothelium.

Furth and his associates (Furth, Andrews, *et al.*, 1951; Bigelow *et al.*, 1951; Wish *et al.*, 1952) have contributed several significant papers that suggest that an important part is played by endothelial damage and increased permeability after total-body irradiation. They have determined that labeled homologous and heterologous plasma, homologous and heterologous erythrocytes, Evans blue, and colloidal radiogold, in general, disappear faster from the circulation of X-rayed than of normal mice and rabbits. Maximum alteration occurs during the second postexposure week and may be correlated with the period of greatest bleeding. As contrasted with the above observations, a decreased disappearance of circulating Evans blue has been described in dogs by other investigators (Prosser, Painter, and Swift, 1947); yet plasma albumin, to which Evans blue is bound, is said to be diminished at the time of greatest reduction in dye disappearance. An increase in the rate of dye disappearance might be expected if the decline in albumin were due to its leakage through capillaries with increased permeability to colloids. The discrepancy in dye disappearance is not easily resolved; in the dog experiments determinations were made on the same animals at different postirradiation times, whereas with mice and rabbits, single determinations were made on paired control and irradiated animals.

That augmented disappearance of various tagged substances in mice and rabbits is indicative of increased permeability is perhaps strengthened by the finding that macrophage function is not altered appreciably (Wish *et al.*, 1952; Barrow *et al.*, 1949). Although colloidal gold leaves the circulation more rapidly, the absolute amount that is retained in the liver and spleen is essentially similar in both control and irradiated animals. It is conceivable that the apparent increase in permeability results, in part, from intravascular changes such as cell clumping and platelet thrombi, which lead to stagnation and decrease in the effective blood volume, although local anoxia and increased hydrostatic pressure would favor leakage under these conditions. Since capillary obstruction has been noted in in vivo preparations (Smith, Svihla, and Patt, 1951), it is difficult to guess the extent to which heightened capillary permeability is apparent or real and whether this is a direct or indirect result of the action of radiation on the vascular endothelium. It should be pointed out that there is no evidence for increased permeability of renal glomeruli and, therefore, that altered permeability following irradiation is probably not typical of capillary endothelium.

Vascular fragility is thought to be increased after irradiation since hemorrhage is not always related to the thrombocytopenia and delayed clotting, and mild trauma frequently results in showers of petechiae (Field and Rekers, 1949a). Increased fragility is suggested further by the rapid disappearance of labeled erythrocytes from the circulation and by the presence of blood in the lymph of X-rayed rats and dogs several days postexposure (Bigelow *et al.*, 1951; Wish *et al.*, 1952). Bleeding may be minimized, moreover, by certain of the flavonoids although this has not been verified universally (Rekers and Field, 1948; Field and Rekers, 1949a; Kohn, Robinett, and Cupp, 1948). Rutin is reported to antagonize hyaluronidase (Beiler and Martin, 1947), but the enzyme probably does not play a role in altered fragility. Other hyaluronidase inhibitors fail to influence radiation toxicity (Field and Rekers, 1949b), and hyaluronidase itself is inactivated by irradiation in vitro (Schoenberg *et al.*, 1950). It is, of course, possible that the relatively small dosages of radiation that are required to induce bleeding result in direct degradation of hyaluronate. While the decline in platelets and appearance of heparinoidlike substances are probably largely responsible for capillary bleeding, it is likely that other factors also play a role in its development.

The typical acute reaction to radiation injury may embarrass the circulation initially and terminally; the intermediate period, however, appears to be relatively free of any gross circulatory disturbance. This applies to penetrating radiation; unfortunately there are no data that relate to circulation after superficial irradiation other than local blood vessel effects. It is, of course, well known that these responses are separated in time by periods of relative recovery. A shocklike state has been seen in dogs following massive X irradiation of the whole body or of the abdomen (Moon *et al.*, 1940, 1941). This is characterized by progressive hemoconcentration, dehydration, and hypotension, with death occurring several days after exposure. The severity of this type of early reaction to large radiation dosages often parallels the recognizable tissue damage. Post-mortem visceral changes are described as those characteristic of circulatory failure of the shock type, and the physiological disturbances have been thought to be a consequence of acute toxicity resulting from absorption of the products of tissue necrosis, although, as in the case of irreversible shock from other causes, this has been difficult to confirm experimentally.

The shocklike syndrome is generally not observed after median lethal irradiation. Early circulatory changes may appear in some species, however. A fall in blood pressure has been detected in rats and rabbits but not in dogs during the first 24 hours after X irradiation (Prosser, Painter, Lisco, *et al.*, 1947; Painter *et al.*, 1947; Weber and Steggerda, 1949; Strauss and Rother, 1924). Hypotension is reported in the rabbit after a total-body exposure as low as 50 r (Painter *et al.*, 1947). A similar early decrease in blood pressure has been noted in patients receiving X-ray therapy (Bedürftig and Grüssner, 1949). There is reason to believe that part of the early hypotension is reflex, since vagotomy and atropinization can reduce the blood pressure response (Strauss and Rother, 1924; Painter *et al.*, 1947). That the immediate hypotension is neural in origin is suggested further by its absence in the spinal animal (Montgomery and Warren, 1951). Repeated injections of epinephrine are also effective in antagonizing initial hypotension in rabbits (Painter *et al.*, 1947). Blood pressure changes have been described after irradiation of the hind legs, but the effects are not consistent. The direction of early blood pressure change may depend upon the area that is exposed (Toyoma, 1933b). A small increase in blood pressure, which is not affected by atropine or nicotine, has been observed during irradiation of the cardiac area. A rise also occurs during exposure of midbrain; when irradiation includes the entire head of the animal, there is a decrease that can be prevented by vagotomy.

Plasma histamine rises in the rat and rabbit and this is related in time to the fall in blood pressure (Painter *et al.*, 1947; Weber and Steggerda, 1949). The presence of depressor substances receives further support from transfusion experiments (Painter *et al.*, 1947). It is of interest that vagotomy, atropine, or benadryl reduces the blood pressure response in the rabbit by about half (Painter *et al.*, 1947). It might be expected that vagotomy or atropine on the one hand and the antihistamine benadryl, on the other, would be additive in their effect on blood pressure. This is not the case, which may imply that benadryl is acting as a parasympatholytic agent or that histamine effects are decreased in the absence of parasympathetic activity. The temporal relation between histamine appearance and hypotension may, of course, be fortuitous, and other factors could be responsible for the lowering of blood pressure (Montgomery and Warren, 1951).

After the initial hypotension, arterial pressure recovers to a level somewhat below normal for a few days and then declines gradually. In the terminal period, blood pressure is frequently below 50 mm Hg (Painter *et al.*, 1947). Relatively few measurements have been made in the dog. Blood pressure is said to be constant in this species until the acute terminal period (several days before death), when it is reduced by about 25 per cent. Similar changes occur in acutely and chronically X-irradiated animals (Prosser, Painter, Lisco, *et al.*, 1947; Prosser and Moore, 1946).

Heart rate is unchanged in the dog, but it increases in the rabbit during the first few hours (Prosser, Painter, Lisco, *et al.*, 1947; Painter *et al.*, 1947). The latter probably represents a compensatory response to the initial hypotension. During the terminal period preceding death, pulse rate is increased in the dog but not always in the rabbit. Myocardial hemorrhages and abnormal electrocardiographic findings, e.g., lowered take-off level and sometimes reversal of the T wave, are described in dogs dying after acute or chronic X irradiation (Prosser, Painter, Lisco, *et al.*, 1947; Prosser and Moore, 1946). Terminal myocardial damage has also been seen in a small series of dogs following exposure to cyclotron neutrons (Ross and Ely, 1947).

While radiation may exert a direct local action on blood vessels, the myocardium appears to be quite resistant (Leach and Sugiura, 1942); changes that are observed after irradiation of the whole body are probably consequences of autonomic and humoral influences initially, and of local extravasation of blood and anoxia terminally (Prosser, Painter, Lisco, *et al.*, 1947). On the whole, the evidence for a generalized circulatory disturbance after median lethal irradiation is not impressive, although this seems to be a factor in relation to massive dosages. After smaller amounts of radiation, early severe hypotension and death are seen in some species, and failure of the circulation may develop during the last few hours or days of life. Little can be said about the efficiency of the circulation to specific sites or the capacity of the cardiovascular system to compensate for any excessive demands, such as repeated transfusions of whole blood or plasma, that may be placed upon it. These considerations deserve attention, for they pose a number of practical problems, especially in the event of combined radiation and traumatic injuries.

GASTROINTESTINAL TRACT

Many of the manifestations of irradiation of the whole body are referable to the gastrointestinal tract, which constitutes a sensitive locus for radiation action. The nausea, vomiting, and anorexia of clinical radiation sickness were first described by Walsh in 1897, and degeneration of the intestinal mucosa of irradiated animals was reported by Krause and Ziegler in 1906. Perhaps the most significant of the early observations were those by Regaud, Nogier, and Lacassagne in 1912 and by Whipple and his associates in 1919–1923. Regaud *et al.* (1912) pointed out that the small intestine of the dog is more sensitive to direct X irradiation than the stomach or colon and that the duodenum and jejunum are the most sensitive regions of it. Hall and Whipple (1919) and Stafford L. Warren and Whipple (1922a, b, c, d; 1923 a, b, c, d) described a toxic reaction following heavy irradiation of the abdomen, which was most marked at the time of greatest injury to the crypt epithelium and resembled intoxication resulting from intestinal obstruction or severe nonspecific intestinal injury. The effects of X irradiation of the abdomen were also shown to be more severe than those following exposure of other portions of the body. Similar conclusions may be drawn from more recent investigations (Moon *et al.*, 1940; Friedman, 1942; Shields Warren and Friedman, 1942; Bond *et al.*, 1950; Quastler *et al.*, 1951).

Early extensive gastrointestinal injury followed by death within several days is seen after massive dosages of radiation delivered either to the abdomen or to the whole body (Hall and Whipple, 1919; Moon *et al.*, 1941; Quastler *et al.*, 1951). Intestinal injury is generally considered to account for the toxicity resulting from such exposure. It has been found, for example, that the mean survival time in mice over the dose range of 1000 to 12,000 r is three to four days and that early killing occurs only if a large portion of the intestine is irradiated (Quastler *et al.*, 1951). Exposure of the liver, kidney, spleen, and adrenal does not lead to early death, at least in mice. This picture is probably different from that observed after lower dosages, where several competing mechanisms contribute to the lethal action. By exposing only the lower abdomen of mice, thus irradiating a considerable portion of the small intestine while sparing the liver and spleen, Chrom (1935) observed a reduction in the enterogenous infection and greatly reduced toxicity with dosages of

550 to 1100 r. Effects on radiation morbidity and mortality have also been demonstrated by Jacobson and his associates (Jacobson, Marks, Robson, *et al.*, 1949; Jacobson, Simmons, *et al.*, 1950) with spleen shielding of an otherwise totally irradiated mouse. Even in the median lethal dosage range, however, mortality has been shown to be related in time to a bacteremia of intestinal origin (Miller *et al.*, 1950b), and it is perhaps significant that maximal damage to the crypt epithelium precedes the peak mortality of chronically irradiated mice (Bloom, 1950).

Qualitatively similar effects on the gastrointestinal tract have been observed in a number of species after exposure to penetrating radiations or to internally administered radioisotopes (Friedman, 1942; Desjardins, 1931a, b, c; Lawrence and Tennant, 1937; Pierce, 1948). The most impressive changes occur in the epithelial cells, although the reactions are not confined to them. Lesions have been noted during the first hour after irradiation (Pierce, 1948; Tsuzuki, 1926; Friedman, 1945). While it is generally agreed that the crypt epithelium is the most sensitive site, destruction of the entire intestinal lining can occur with lethal dosages, leaving fragmented crypt cells, denuded villi, edema, hemorrhage, and ulcers in its wake. A marked accumulation of bacteria is often seen on the surface of the intestinal mucosa. In contrast, nuclear injury in the colon and in the surface epithelium of the stomach is usually slight, although the gastric glands are rather easily damaged. The pathological physiology does not always reflect morphological injury. The occurrence of severe diarrhea, for example, may be unrelated temporally to histological changes in the intestine (Shields Warren, MacMillan, and Dixon, 1950a, b).

As might be anticipated, intestinal damage is influenced by the rate as well as the intensity of exposure, injury of the crypt epithelium and the production of ulcers being decreased with fractionation (Stafford L. Warren and Whipple, 1923b; Engelstad, 1935, 1938). Indeed, some radioresistance of the crypt epithelium may be acquired with suitably spaced small exposures (Bloom, 1950). No doubt, much of the variance in the early investigations can be attributed to differences in the physical conditions of irradiation.

The causal relation between irradiation and morphological injury is poorly understood. Nucleic acid, protein, and ash content of the crypt epithelium is decreased soon after neutron and X irradiation (Ely and Ross, 1948a, b; Ross and Ely, 1949a). Although the rates of synthesis of DNA and RNA in rat intestine and in rabbit intestine are markedly reduced by X rays, protein synthesis is relatively unaffected (Abrams, 1951). Alkaline phosphatase activity of the crypt cells is essentially normal when assays are carried out at pH 7; phosphatase activity is increased, however, at pH 9 (Ross and Ely, 1949b). It is not known whether these chemical changes are the cause or effect of morphological injury and cell death. The same considerations may well apply to other metabolic phenomena. Respiration of all segments of the small intestine is inhibited several hours after exposure of the rat to 700 r (Barron *et al.*, 1947). Oxygen consumption is essentially normal at 24 hours, but is again depressed on the third day. Anaerobic glycolysis is apparently unaffected at all intervals.

A decrease in dry weight of the intestinal mucosa occurs during the first two days after irradiation; this is not observed in nonirradiated pair-fed controls (Ross and Ely, 1949a). In contrast, similar weight losses have been detected in the gastrointestinal tract of X-rayed and fasted rats at 4 days (Painter, 1948). Although sodium space is increased by some 50 per cent in both the irradiated and fasted animals, total water content is not changed significantly. The increase in sodium space may be related in part to an increase in extracellular fluid volume, and also to an exchange of sodium for potassium in the intestinal cells (Painter and Pullman, 1950). Radiosensitive tissues, in general, show an initial decrease in sodium and potassium followed by an increase in the former (Bowers and Scott, 1951a, b).

Anorexia and weight loss have been observed in a number of species and are reasonably good indicators of the severity of radiation injury (Prosser, Painter, Lisco, *et al.*, 1947; Ely and Ross, 1947). A transient diminution in food intake has been noted by Smith, Tyree, Patt, and Bink (1951) in the rat after only 50 r delivered to the whole body. After dosages of 250 to 10,000 r, food consumption drops to less than 10 per cent of normal on the first day. Although the initial anorexia is rather similar over a wide dosage range, recovery varies more or less directly with the magnitude of exposure, being more rapid after 250 r than after 500 r and nonexistent after 1000 r. With median lethal irradiation, food intake may return toward normal after a few days, only to decrease again several days before death. This is perhaps suggestive of some recovery in the gastrointestinal tract during the intermediate period. Anorexia apparently accounts for all or most of the weight loss that is seen after exposure to penetrating radiation (Ely and Ross, 1947; Smith, Tyree, Patt, and Bink, 1951). Observations made on a few rats after external β irradiation reveal a decreased food intake for the first week or two, followed by an increase above the normal that is maintained until death (Anderson, 1946). Body weight, however, falls progressively, perhaps as a result of extensive fluid loss.

Anorexia, vomiting, and diarrhea are generally not observed in animals after exposure of regions remote from the abdomen and are thought to be a result of direct injury of the digestive tract. Symptoms of the same general nature have been seen clinically after X irradiation of extra-abdominal areas with dosages far below those employed experimentally. The severity of the clinical reaction has been related to the size of the capillary bed in the irradiated area (Jenkinson and Brown, 1944). Since clinical irradiation is invariably confined to persons in ill health and since the immediate clinical response has a large psychosomatic component, it is not always easy to evaluate the results of such exposure. It is well known that the clinical response is influenced by the nutritional status of the person undergoing radiotherapy (Bean *et al.*, 1944). The mechanisms responsible for reactions in clinical radiation sickness and in the acute radiation syndrome may be quite different.

The initial anorexia of whole-body irradiation need not be a consequence of a direct action on the gastrointestinal tract, since exposure of only the head of the rat results in a comparable early diminution in food intake (Smith, Tyree, Patt, and Bink, 1951). This is not observed when irradiation is confined to the extremities. Weight loss during the first day or two is also rather similar in abdomen-shielded and abdomen-exposed rats (Bond *et al.*, 1950). These facts suggest that the early anorexia may be neurogenic or humoral in origin. Delayed gastric emptying (Ely and Ross, 1947; Mead *et al.*, 1950), perhaps as a result of increased tone of the pyloric sphincter, may be responsible for the anorexia. Subsequent effects on food consumption, however, are probably related more directly to injury of the intestinal mucosa. When the abdomen is shielded, late effects may possibly be attributed to damage of oral and esophageal structures.

Intestinal motility and tonus are increased by irradiation (Hall and Whipple, 1919; Martin and Rogers, 1923; Swann, 1924; Toyoma, 1933a; Conard, 1951). This has been observed in intestinal loops and in the intact animal. The increase in tonus and amplitude of contraction can be detected during irradiation. With small dosages of X rays tonus returns to normal a few minutes after the exposure is terminated. Large dosages lead to a greater and more prolonged rise in tone, and a spastic contraction, analogous to that seen after other forms of intestinal injury, may be evident. Augmented contraction and hypertonicity are largely prevented by parasympatholytic drugs and ganglionic blocking agents (Conard, 1951). Vagotomy and body shielding afford only a slight reduction of the intestinal response, which is considered to be a consequence of direct action of radiation on cholinergic elements in the intestinal tract. Increased synthesis of acetylcholine by brain (Torda and Wolff, 1950) and a reduction in blood choline esterase (Barnard, 1948) have been observed after exposure to X rays.

Irradiation of the stomach reduces gastric acidity and results in extensive atrophy of the gastric glands (Miescher, 1923; Ivy *et al.*, 1924; Ely and Ross, 1947; Simon, 1949; Hedin *et al.*, 1950; Douglas *et al.*, 1950). A transitory rise in acidity preceding the depression may occur after exposure of the whole abdomen (Ivy *et al.*, 1924). Secretory depression has been observed with X rays, β rays, and neutrons and appears to be a local rather than a systemic effect of the radiation. Peptic activity of the gastric juice is diminished but not to the same extent as the acidity (Ivy *et al.*, 1924; Ely and Ross, 1947). This is of interest, since histological observations reveal that the chief cells of the gastric mucosa are more sensitive than the parietal cells, which are more intimately concerned with acid secretion (Friedman, 1942; Hueper and de Carvajal-Forero, 1944). Radiation has been employed clinically to reduce gastric secretion in patients with ulcers; the advisability of such therapy may be questioned, however, since it may itself lead to perforation and hemorrhage (Friedman and Warren, 1942; Brick, 1947; Ricketts *et al.*, 1948).

In view of the extensive injury to the gastrointestinal tract following irradiation of the abdomen, it is reasonable to assume that absorption will be impaired. While decreased intestinal absorption has been observed by several investigators (Martin and Rogers, 1923; Buchwald, 1931; Barron *et al.*, 1947), others (Mead *et al.*, 1950) believe that there is no basic disturbance. The problem is complicated by changes in emptying time of the stomach and in intestinal motility. Inhibition of glucose absorption and diminished phosphorylation of fructose have been observed as early as 4 hours after X irradiation (Barron *et al.*, 1947). The absorption of cream is also said to be diminished (Martin and Rogers, 1923). Although an increase in fecal fat has been observed in human beings treated with X rays (Dodds and Webster, 1924), similar increases may be seen in animals on a fat-free diet (Mead *et al.*, 1950). There is little interference, moreover, with absorption of fat in irradiated mice (Mead *et al.*, 1950) and of vitamin A in irradiated rats (Bennett, Bennett, *et al.*, 1950) during the first postexposure week. There are also indications that total-body irradiation does not disturb protein absorption (Bennett *et al.*, 1951). Enteral administration of protein hydrolysates is apparently as efficacious as parenteral administration in lowering the sensitivity of irradiated protein-depleted rats (Jennings, unpublished observations, 1950). Mead and his associates (1950; Bennett *et al.*, 1951) believe that the mechanisms of absorption are not impaired by irradiation and that the changes that have been noted can be attributed in many instances to concomitant effects on motility. The available data are largely restricted to the early period after irradiation; little is known about gastrointestinal function in the intermediate and terminal periods following acute exposure. Even less can be said about the nutritional status of the irradiated organism and its potential contribution to the radiation syndrome.

LIVER

It is assumed from morphological studies that the liver is relatively resistant to radiation (Seldin, 1904; Smyth and Whipple, 1924; Pohle and

Bunting, 1932; Ely, Ross, and Gay, 1947; Rhoades, 1948a). This may be attributed, in part, to the phenomenal regenerative capacity of liver cells, and possibly to the low oxygen tension of the tissue. In an early study, Seldin (1904) compared irradiated and shielded areas of the same liver and was unable to detect any difference. The results of an extensive investigation reported by Rhoades (1948a), in which the livers of rabbits, rats, mice, and guinea pigs were examined after total-body X irradiation with dosages of 25 to 1200 r confirm the radioresistance of liver epithelium. Alterations, when observed, are considered to be secondary to the general toxicity. When irradiation is accomplished with internal emitters, histological change is also minor, with the notable exception of plutonium, in which case hepatic injury is an outstanding feature of the poisoning (Brues, 1948).

A nonspecific fatty infiltration is sometimes seen in the livers of irradiated animals. The appearance of sudanophile fat in the mouse liver has been attributed to the release of histamine-like tissue breakdown products (Ellinger, 1945). Liver cholesterol has been shown to decrease and liver glycogen to increase during the first two days after total-body irradiation (North and Nims, 1949). These changes may reflect an increased adrenal cortical activity. After local irradiation of the hepatic area of the guinea pig, glycogen disappears somewhat more slowly from the liver upon incubation (Ullmann, 1933). Inhibition of glycogen cleavage is greater with 1200 r than with 600 r but is not well correlated with the changes in total liver glycogen.

The possibility of metabolic disturbances in the liver that are not manifested by morphological alterations is indicated by the decrease in oxidative capacity of surviving liver slices obtained from animals exposed to γ and X rays or α rays from injected plutonium (Barron, 1946; DuBois, unpublished observations, 1950). It is of interest that the oxidations that are inhibited are those normally catalyzed by sulfhydryl enzymes. However, it is noteworthy that other sulfhydryl enzymes in the liver are not inhibited by large dosages of ionizing radiation. Thus there are no significant changes in succinic dehydrogenase and adenosine triphosphatase when specific assays for these enzymes are made on livers taken from mice exposed to γ rays (DuBois, Cochran, and Doull, 1951a). The activity and distribution of non-mercapto enzymes (catalase, alkaline phosphatase, esterase, arginase, and rhodanase) in liver cells and in liver connective tissue are unchanged following irradiation with 500 r (Ludewig and Chanutin, 1950b). After lethal dosages, liver catalase activity is decreased (Feinstein *et al.*, 1950), while alkaline phosphatase is increased (DuBois, unpublished observations, 1950).

Impairment of oxidative mechanisms, as well as possible changes in phosphatase activity, may account for the decrease in acid-soluble organic phosphorus, the increase in inorganic phosphorus, and the diminished turnover of phospholipid and desoxyribonucleic acid phosphorus in the livers of irradiated mice and rats (Hevesy, 1946, 1947; Kelly and Jones, 1950; Thomson, unpublished observations, 1951). A further indication of altered metabolic function as a result of irradiation is the finding that citrate accumulates in the livers of irradiated male rats after fluoroacetate treatment in contrast to the lack of effect of fluoroacetate in the nonirradiated animal (DuBois, Cochran, and Doull, 1951a). This may be attributed to an effect of radiation on the testes, since castration also leads to an increase in liver citrate that can be prevented by testosterone (DuBois, Cochran, and Zerwic, 1951b). Citrate accumulation with fluoroacetate occurs in the nonirradiated female.

Information relating to the effects of radiation on liver function is nebulous and incomplete. Alterations in serum proteins produced by radiation are not associated with significant changes in liver function as indicated by the cephalin flocculation, colloidal gold, and thymol turbidity tests (Schwartz *et al.*, 1948). Some decrease in the output of bile salts has been seen when large dosages are delivered to the liver of the dog (Smyth and Whipple, 1924). Terminal impairment of liver function may be reflected by increased urinary excretion of urobilinogen and coproporphyrin and the increased ratio of uric acid to allantoin (Schwartz *et al.*, 1948; Krizek *et al.*, 1946; Miyazaki, 1937). Abnormal function may also be indicated by the terminal rise in kynurenic acid excretion, which is perhaps suggestive of some alteration in tryptophane metabolism in the liver (Wattenberg and Schwartz, 1946a, b).

Another aspect of liver physiology is referable to its reticulo-endothelial elements. Although there is evidence of a decrease in the capacity of fixed liver phagocytes of irradiated mice to remove intravenously injected bacteria (Chrom, 1935), the uptake of a gold colloid by the reticulo-endothelial system is not impaired nor is there an appreciable difference in the fate of heterologous erythrocytes in normal and X-rayed animals (Wish *et al.*, 1952; Barrow *et al.*, 1949). There is, in fact, some evidence of an increase in phagocytic activity after irradiation. Yet, injury of liver phagocytes by radiation may be of some consequence since lethality has been shown to be potentiated when rats are injected with minimal lethal dosages of P^{32} and colloidal Au^{198} (Friedell and Christie, 1951).

KIDNEY

The kidney is another example of an organ that appears to be resistant to radiation, at least as judged by morphological studies. According to Shields Warren (1942), dosages in excess of several thousands of roentgens are required for renal changes. Kidney damage is generally not apparent in irradiated animals (Hall and Whipple, 1919; McQuarrie and Whipple, 1922; Impiombato, 1935; Ely *et al.*, 1947; W. Bloom, 1948), and the usual picture of intoxication follows heavy exposure even though the kidney is shielded (McQuarrie and Whipple, 1922). An exception to the lack of abnormalities in the kidney with moderate amounts of radiation is the acute necrosis of the developing tubules and glomeruli of baby chicks (W. Bloom, 1948; Stearner *et al.*, 1951). The severe renal damage is thought to predispose to early deaths in these animals (Stearner *et al.*, 1951).

There is some evidence of inhibition of kidney respiration and of oxidation of substrates requiring sulfhydryl enzymes (Barron, 1946); this has not been verified, however (DuBois, unpublished observations, 1950; LeMay, 1951). Although extensive studies of glomerular and tubular function have not been made, there is reason to believe that kidney function is not impaired, except possibly in the agonal period following acute irradiation of the whole body (Prosser, Painter, Lisco, *et al.*, 1947). In the dog, urinary excretion of water and nitrogen is not altered appreciably, and the specific gravity of urine remains relatively constant. Polyuria is seen in rats and rabbits during the first few postirradiation days. Excretion of sodium, potassium, and chloride is increased in the former on the first and fifth days (Edelmann, 1949). Increased urine output is not always associated with polydipsia and may be a result, at least in the rat, of an antidiuretic substance from the pituitary (Edelmann and Eversole, 1950). Several days before death, water intake is generally reduced in all species; urinary output is diminished less than water intake (Prosser, Painter, Lisco, *et al.*, 1947). Although an increased clearance of phenol red has been observed in a few dogs during the second week following median lethal dosages of X rays, a late diminished renal function is suggested by the marked terminal increase in blood nonprotein nitrogen and in urea nitrogen. This is probably not a result of direct radiation injury to the kidneys, but rather of the terminal circulatory impairment and renal hemorrhage.

ENDOCRINES

Adrenal. It is recognized universally that the adrenal glands constitute a buffer against a variety of traumatic conditions. The nonspecificity of the adrenal response to stress and its role in the general adaptation syndrome have been ably presented by Selye (1946) and elaborated upon by others (Sayers, 1950). Ionizing radiations, in common with other noxious stimuli, induce changes that are presumed to reflect an increased demand for the adrenal hormones. In the absence of these secretions susceptibility to irradiation is augmented. The functional response of the adrenals does not appear to be a direct result of their irradiation. Rather, it is mediated by the pituitary and closely resembles that seen following a host of injuries. These considerations along with the apparent lack of specificity of radiation injury raise the question of the place of the adrenal in the development of, and recovery from, the acute radiation syndrome.

The suggestion that clinical radiation sickness reflects adrenal cortical damage has been made by a number of investigators, who were either impressed with the similarity between the symptoms of radiation sickness and those of adrenal cortical insufficiency or with the efficacy of adrenal preparations in alleviating the discomfort sometimes associated with therapeutic irradiation (Narat, 1922; Hirsch, 1923; Thaddea, 1940; Weichert, 1942; Ellinger, 1948). As early as 1924, however, Martin and his associates were unable to detect functional changes in dogs from which one adrenal was removed and the other irradiated with a dosage sufficient to cause fibrotic changes. When the same dosage of X rays was applied to an isolated loop of small intestine, cachexia and death resulted. Later Fisher *et al.* (1928), employing a similar technique, observed signs of adrenal insufficiency in a dog but only after heavy irradiation and a latent period of about three months.

It appears, from morphological studies, that the adrenals are not peculiarly radiosensitive (Frey, 1928; Desjardins, 1928; Engelstad, 1936; Engelstad and Torgersen, 1937; Torgersen, 1940; Rhoades, 1948b). Although degenerative changes have been seen after heavy local irradiation (above 1500 r), dosages of 1000 r result only in minimal morphological alteration in the adrenal cortex and medulla (Engelstad, 1936; Engelstad and Torgersen, 1937). Notwithstanding the apparent resistance of the adrenals to structural change, functional responses may be elicited with relatively low dosages. Loss of adrenal cortical lipids and adrenal ascorbate occurs soon after irradiation, and urinary excretion of the 17-ketosteroids may be increased several days later (Dougherty and White, 1946; Patt *et al.*, 1947; Nizet *et al.*, 1949; North and Nims, 1949; G. H. Lawrence, 1949). Lipid depletion has also been noted in some of the victims of radiation exposure in Japan (Shields Warren, 1946). The pattern of adrenal response in X-rayed rats consists of an initial reduction in adrenal cholesterol, a normal or elevated cholesterol concentration associated with adrenal hypertrophy several days later, and a marked terminal depression (Patt *et al.*, 1947). The adrenal response does not occur in hypophysectomized animals and can be prevented, in part, by suitable administration of adrenal cortical extract (Patt *et al.*, 1948; Swift *et al.*, 1948). In contrast to the changes in adrenal lipids, oxidative capacity of adrenal slices obtained from irradiated rats is not altered appreciably (Barron, 1946).

The changes in adrenal lipids after irradiation probably reflect an increased demand for cortical secretions, which may perhaps be satisfied initially but not terminally. It is noteworthy that a single injection of adrenocorticotrophic hormone decreases adrenal cholesterol in normal animals, whereas cholesterol concentration increases after hormonal stimulation of several days duration (Sayers *et al.*, 1944). The rise in adrenal cholesterol occurring several days after median lethal irradiation may represent over-stimulation in excess of cortical hormone demand (Patt *et al.*, 1947). That the elevated cholesterol is not a result of adrenal exhaustion is suggested by its absence with higher dosages. Although adrenal lipids are usually depleted before death, it is not known whether this is a cause or an effect of the terminal events. The possibility exists that direct injury of the gland decreases its capacity to respond to the stress of irradiation, since some protection has been observed in rats when the adrenals are shielded during exposure (Craver, 1948; Edelmann, 1951a). Moderate degrees of stress (KCl and histamine) are well tolerated by the mouse after minimally lethal irradiation (W. W. Smith, 1951).

There are a few indications of altered medullary activity. However, the results are not particularly impressive. An initial discharge of epinephrine may be anticipated with irradiation of large areas of the body, but this has not been proved. Irradiation of the dog's adrenal is said to increase the pressor action of blood collected from the adrenal vein (Zunz and La Barre, 1927). On the other hand, significant changes in adrenal catechols, which include epinephrine, have not been observed after exposure of the rat adrenal to 100 or 1000 r (Raab and Soule, 1927). Therapeutic irradiation apparently prevents increased output of medullary hormone after exercise in patients with angina pectoris (Raab, 1941). Reports of a salutary effect of adrenal irradiation in hypertension are controversial (Torgersen, 1940).

The adrenals are implicated in some of the remote and indirect effects of irradiation. Generalized involution of lymphoid structures has been described following heavy local irradiation (Leblond and Segal, 1942; Halberstaedter and Ickowicz, 1947). After adrenalectomy, the changes are restricted to the irradiated area. The picture following total-body exposure is somewhat obscure, although there is general agreement that lymphoid involution after moderate dosages does not require the adrenal or pituitary for its development (Dougherty and White, 1946; Patt *et al.*, 1948). Involution of lymphoid tissues and augmentation of antibody titer subsequent to total-body exposure to 10 r have been attributed to the adrenal (Dougherty and White, 1946; Dougherty *et al.*, 1944); the indirect action of a minimal lymphopenic dose and the "anamnestic response" of antibody titer are not well substantiated, however (Craddock and Lawrence, 1948; Marder *et al.*, 1948).

The toxic reaction resulting from irradiation of large portions of the body is potentiated in the absence of the adrenals or pituitary (Leblond and Segal, 1942; Cronkite and Chapman, 1950; Edelmann, 1951b; Kaplan *et al.*, 1951; Patt *et al.*, 1948). Susceptibility of adrenalectomized mice to the lethal action of X rays is especially striking with low dosages. The degree of potentiation of radiation toxicity will, of course, depend upon the nature of replacement therapy and the time intervening between adrenalectomy and irradiation as well as the completeness of adrenal extirpation. It is significant that survival of adrenalectomized mice is similar to that of animals with intact adrenals when a constant dose of adrenal cortical extract is given daily (Straube *et al.*, 1949).

While there may be some rationale for employing adrenal corticoids to reduce radiation mortality, for the most part the results of such endeavors have been rather disappointing. Desoxycorticosterone has been shown to prevent fatty infiltration of the liver and to improve survival in mice (Ellinger, 1946, 1947). There are also some reports of its efficacy in clinical radiation sickness (Weichert, 1942; Ellinger *et al.*, 1949). These observations have not been verified by others; a number of preparations, including desoxycorticosterone, 11-dehydrocorticosterone, whole adrenal cortical extract, and cortisone have been used experimentally without success (Swift *et al.*, 1948; Straube *et al.*, 1949; Graham, Graham, and Graffeo, 1950; Graham and Graham, 1950; W. W. Smith *et al.*, 1950). This is true also of the adrenocorticotrophic hormone (W. W. Smith *et al.*, 1950). It is well to recall that negative results have been obtained with adrenal extracts in other conditions of stress. It remains to be determined whether this obtains because of the difficulty in approximating the quality and quantity of the naturally occurring internal secretions.

Thyroid. The normal thyroid is quite resistant to ionizing radiation in contrast to the relative sensitivity of the hyperplastic gland. Heavy irradiation, more than several thousand roentgens, is required to induce structural changes in the thyroids of the guinea pig, rat, rabbit, and dog (Shields Warren, 1943b; Bender, 1948). It has been found, for example, that local exposure of the thyroid area of young or mature rats to 50 or 5000 r of X rays does not alter the histological appearance of the gland, nor modify basal oxygen consumption or body weight (Bender, 1948). Uptake of radioiodine is also unaffected by local irradiation with 1000 r and is actually increased with 3000 and 6000 r (Hursh *et al.*, 1949). Increased uptake of I^{131} with the higher dosages occurs in the absence of morphological changes and is regarded as an indirect result of irradiation. The level of local X irradiation necessary to produce significant destruction of thyroid tissue in the rat is apparently greater than the highest dosage that can be administered without a fatal outcome (Bender, 1948; Hursh *et al.*, 1949). Dosages in excess of 5000 r applied to the thyroid area of the rat invariably result in death within about a week. The only grossly abnormal feature is dehydration, which has been attributed to failure to consume food and water for several days preceding death. While death may be delayed by suitable administration of fluids, the mechanism responsible for the lethal action is undetermined. It is apparently not due to damage of the thyroid, esophagus, or pituitary, nor is it related to changes in the blood. Complications have also been observed clinically after excessive irradiation of the thyroid area (Lukens, 1948).

The avidity of the thyroid for iodine and the availability of radioiodine have greatly facilitated the study of thyroid sensitivity. The results of such investigations reveal, in general, that relatively large amounts of radioiodine as equivalent roentgens are required to embarrass thyroid function (Findlay and Leblond, 1948; Feller *et al.*, 1949; Skanse, 1948; Gorbman, 1949; Goldberg, Chaikoff, *et al.*, 1950). Partial destruction of the thyroid with colloid degeneration has been seen in rats 6 days after injection of approximately 70 μc of I^{131}, at which time about 20,000 rep had been delivered to the gland (Findlay and Leblond, 1948). Thyroid function as indicated by the chemical iodine content of the gland, its retention of radioiodine, and the level of plasma iodine is not disturbed after injection of 30 μc of I^{131} in the rat (Feller *et al.*, 1949). Weight of the chick thyroid may be decreased 16 days after administration of only 10 μc, but even this tracer dose is equivalent to approximately 15,000 rep in terms of thyroid irradiation over the entire period (Skanse, 1948). In the rat, large amounts of I^{131} may result in cytological changes in the anterior pituitary that are identical with those seen after thyroid removal (Goldberg and Chaikoff, 1950).

The thyroid apparently plays a negligible role in the total-body irradiation syndrome. Radiation toxicity in the mammal is not altered appreciably by thyroidectomy or thiouracil administration (Blount and Smith, 1949; Hempelmann *et al.*, 1949; Haley *et al.*, 1950). Toxicity may be enhanced, however, when desiccated thyroid is given after irradiation (W. W. Smith and Smith, 1951a). The potentiation of injury is probably related to elevated metabolism and is not specific for radiation damage.

An increase in uptake of I^{131} by the thyroid has been noted after irradiation of the whole body or the abdomen of rats (Evans *et al.*, 1947). The thyroid response occurs in the absence of the adrenals; it is not observed in the newborn animal. While increased iodine uptake in the adult animal is suggestive of an increase in thyroid function after irradiation, the possibility exists that this may be related to anorexia and the consequent decrease in dietary iodine. The fact that a definite increase in the basal oxygen consumption of irradiated animals has not been demonstrated argues against significant alteration of thyroid activity (Kirschner *et al.*, 1949; D. E. Smith, Tyree, Patt, and Jackson, 1951; W. W. Smith and Smith, 1951b; Pratt *et al.*, 1950; Patt, Swift, and Tyree, 1949).

Pituitary. It is generally agreed that the pituitary is only slightly sensitive to X rays. The early literature has been reviewed by Shields Warren (1943b), who concludes that the normal gland is radioresistant, although he is careful to point out that the response of the diseased gland may be quite different. The relative resistance of the normal pituitary to direct irradiation is also apparent from more recent studies. Single dosages of 200 to 500 r applied to the pituitary region of adult female rats do not lead to degenerative changes in the pituitary or in the ovaries, adrenals, and thyroids (Kotz *et al.*, 1941). A transient effect of X rays on pituitary function is indicated by the reappearance of physiological signs of heat when dosages ranging from 5 to 300 r are applied to the pituitary of sexually mature female rats on the second day of their estrous cycle (Freed *et al.*, 1948). This reaction lasts for 6 to 8 hours and is accompanied by a rather definite increase in pituitary weight and a slight increase in uterine weight while ovarian weight is unchanged. Comparable irradiation of immature female rats or ground squirrels does not alter the development of their sexual systems (Freed *et al.*, 1948; Denniston, 1942). Although some increase in size and weight of the pituitaries has been described in the infantile animal 11 to 14 weeks after low-dose irradiation, there is no evidence of an increase in function (Baidens *et al.*, 1946). The early transient physiological effects of pituitary irradiation are regarded by Freed *et al.* (1948) as secondary to increased vascularity or altered permeability rather than as primary stimulation of hypophyseal activity. While injurious effects are not evident with small dosages of radiation, exposure of the pituitary region to an air dose of 1000 r or more reduces the rate of growth of young rats (Denniston, 1942). On the other hand, evidence of hypopituitarism is not apparent in man with localized dosages of 8100 to 10,000 r (Kelly *et al.*, 1951).

The functional integrity of the pituitary during the first few days after total-body irradiation is indicated by the typical pituitary–adrenal cortical response to stress (Patt *et al.*, 1947). Adrenal changes are not seen in the irradiated hypophysectomized animal and there is some evidence that pituitary ablation increases sensitivity to total-body irradiation (Patt *et al.*, 1948). It is not known whether the pituitary discharge, which apparently takes place within several hours of exposure, is a direct consequence of irradiation or of neural or humoral stimuli such as epinephrine and tissue breakdown products. Many of these considerations have already been discussed in connection with the effects of radiation on the adrenal. It is worth recalling that the adrenocorticotrophic hormone, in the one experimental study in which it was employed, did not modify X-ray toxicity (W. W. Smith *et al.*, 1950).

NERVOUS SYSTEM

The radioresistance of nervous tissue, indicated in the early experiments of Kanoky (1907), has been confirmed in numerous investigations.

Gross dysfunction of the adult nervous system is not apparent following total-body irradiation in the median lethal range (Prosser, Painter, Lisco, *et al.*, 1947), and there is no histological evidence of injury resulting from such exposures (Snider, 1948). Although it is true that cytological damage may occur following heavy irradiation, Shields Warren (1943a) has pointed out that this can be largely indirect and perhaps attributed to disturbance of the vascular system rather than to a direct effect of the radiation on the cellular components of nervous tissue. This limiting factor in the interpretation of radiation effects on the nervous system has been emphasized by others (Campbell and Novick, 1949).

Early changes consisting of chromatolysis and vacuolization of the ganglion cells have been observed following irradiation with several thousand roentgens (Campbell *et al.*, 1946; Novick, 1946). Changes in the trigeminal ganglia of rabbits after local X irradiation of the head with 3000 r can be separated temporally into three phases: an initially severe chromatolysis immediately post-exposure, a recovery phase beginning several hours later, and a second wave of chromatolysis beginning on the third day and persisting for several weeks (Novick, 1946). The clinical picture parallels the condition of the ganglion cells. Thus, dyspnea, exopthalmos, somnolence, and postural abnormalities are evident upon termination of irradiation. These signs disappear rapidly and are followed by a second phase of illness, characterized by emaciation and excessive salivation during the delayed chromatolysis of the ganglion cells. Delayed necrosis of brain cells, which appears several months after exposure, has been described in rabbits and monkeys (Davidoff *et al.*, 1938; Russell *et al.*, 1949). Localized necrosis in the central nervous system of man, notably transverse myelitis, also may follow local irradiation by 3000 r or more and may occur after months or years (Holmes and Schulz, 1950). It is thought that vascular damage may be of importance as an etiologic factor.

Local irradiation of the cerebral cortex of cats with small, high-energy radon applicators results within a few hours in a sharp gradient of tissue reactions. This technique has been used by Campbell and Novick (1949) who have found that astrocytes are the most susceptible of the various cells of the cerebral cortex; oligodendroglia and microglia are highly radioresistant. Large dosages of X rays applied to one side of the cerebrum of monkeys result in paralysis of the contralateral limbs (Davidoff *et al.*, 1938). Hemiplegia occurs rapidly with 4000 r and after several months with 2000 to 3000 r. Massive irradiation of the mid-thoracic spinal cord likewise results in a paralysis. Cerebellar lesions may appear several months after irradiation of the cerebrum.

Irradiation of the whole body of the mouse with dosages in excess of 6000 r results in a hyperacute reaction that is characterized by motor excitability (Quastler *et al.*, 1951). Motor symptoms become more conspicuous and death intervenes within a day or two after exposure to 12,000 r. These effects have been attributed to irradiation of the brain, since they do not occur when the head is shielded. The application of 50,000 r to the entire body of guinea pigs, rabbits, and mice may lead to death under the beam or within a few hours; hyperthermia, hyperesthesia, intermittent seizures, and cyanosis may be noted in these animals (Henshaw, 1944). Early death after massive irradiation occurs even though the head is shielded (Quastler *et al.*, 1951).

Peripheral nerve appears to be more resistant than brain and spinal cord. The sciatic nerve of the rat is apparently unaffected by X-ray dosages of 4000 to 10,000 r (Janzen and Warren, 1942). To accomplish complete degeneration of the nerve, approximately 75,000 r of γ radiation is required. There is some evidence that daily exposures to 80 r may interfere with regeneration of the hemisected sciatic, although there is no appreciable effect on the Schwann cells with such treatment (Gastaldi, 1949).

Synthesis of acetylcholine by brain is enhanced after sublethal X irradiation (Torda and Wolff, 1950). This may be a result, in part, of thymic involution and a consequent decrease in concentration of the choline acetylase inhibitors ordinarily present in this tissue. The capacity of peripheral nerve of hypophysectomized rats to maintain the action potential of muscle during repetitive stimulation is partially restored by low-dose irradiation (Torda and Wolff, 1950). Increased synthesis of acetylcholine may bear some relation to the parasympathomimetic effects that are evident during the initial phases of radiation sickness. It is noteworthy that atropine minimizes certain early radiation effects, including the hypotension in rabbits (Painter *et al.*, 1947) and the hypertonicity of intestinal loops (Conard, 1951); treatment with atropine has also been shown to improve slightly the survival of irradiated mice (Larkin, 1949).

The radioresistance of the adult nervous system stands in sharp contrast to the sensitivity of developing nervous tissue. The sensitivity of developing neuroblasts in mouse and rat embryos during the latter two-thirds of pregnancy has been reported by Hicks (1950). Irradiation of the pregnant animal with 150 to 200 r results in extensive destruction of the embryonic neuroblasts and severe malformations of the brain. Extraneural lesions do not appear with this dosage. Susceptibility of the embryonic nervous system to radiation injury has also been demonstrated following irradiation of selected implantation sites in pregnant rats without exposure of the mother (Wilson and Karr, 1950). The factors that act to influence responsiveness of tissue under various conditions of growth and differentiation are unknown. It is not possible at present to explain the relative sensitivities of developing and adult nerve cells other than to implicate metabolic differences that exist between the two (see also Chap. 13).

MISCELLANEOUS TISSUES AND ORGANS

The relative radiosensitivities of various tissues and detailed histologic information on radiation-induced changes within them are discussed by Bloom and Bloom in Chap. 17. In the ensuing discussion, we shall mention briefly certain physiologically important effects of ionizing radiation on some of these tissues and organs.

Skin. Radiosensitivity of the skin constitutes an important factor in radiation therapy, mainly owing to the fact that it often imposes the chief limitation on deep therapy. Since erythema is the first visible sign of radiation effects on skin and runs parallel to later and more serious effects, much attention has been given to it in clinical practice. Its vascular basis and usual course have been discussed already (p. 976). Large dosages result after a few weeks in denudation of the epithelium (moist epidermititis) (Regaud and Nogier, 1913). Treatment of the entire surface of the bodies of mice by β rays from P^{32}-containing plaques reproduces this state over large areas where the dosage is calculated as 4000 rep, beginning in four weeks and continuing for some months thereafter. New epidermis is continually formed under the sloughs throughout this period (Raper and Barnes, 1951b). These animals show a gradually increasing mortality during the years after exposure. With higher dosages, survival becomes much shorter, and above 5000 rep most of the deaths occur within three weeks.

It has been found in animals of different size (baby rats, mice, adult rats, guinea pigs, and rabbits) that the lethal dose, expressed as the 45-day LD_{50}, increases with size from 2200 rep to 17,500 rep. These dosages correspond to equivalent proportional volume dosages (gram-rep per gram) for the several species, which are fairly comparable with the respective lethal volume dosages of γ rays (Raper, Zirkle, and Barnes, 1951). The reason for this correspondence is not clear; it is obvious that external β irradiation and penetrating ionizing radiations act through different mechanisms, since they are incompletely additive (Raper and Barnes, 1951c) and since lethal external β irradiation fails to produce leukopenia (Raper and Barnes, 1951a). It seems probable that certain of the mechanisms of death are the same as those following thermal burns, although the changes in skin responsible for them are slower in developing.

Hair. Temporary epilation is produced in man by dosages of radiation of the order of 375 to 500 roentgens (Pendergrass and Mahoney, 1948). The basis for epilation is presumably inhibition of growth in the hair follicles. Permanent epilation requires a considerably higher dosage. Graying of hair is seen in mice following relatively low doses and is nearly complete in certain areas at 1000 r (Chase, 1949). Although temporary epilation is widely produced in the course of therapeutic irradiation, graying is seen rarely after regrowth takes place, and it is therefore clear that the human threshold for graying is considerably higher than that for some other species. One human case has recently been described in which the equivalent of 390 r of soft X rays resulted in temporary epilation with subsequent regrowth of normally pigmented hair (Hempelmann *et al.*, 1952). The basis of graying, which is permanent once it occurs, is probably destruction of melanoblasts; graying in mice is the characteristic effect of radiation on the inactive (nongrowing) stage, while active follicles respond by epilation. It has been suggested (Chase, 1949) that the increased melanoblast population of follicles in the active stage acts to protect these follicles against loss of potentiality to produce pigment.

Eye. Superficial effects of irradiation on the cornea and conjunctiva run parallel to effects on the skin, as regards dosage and the cyclical nature of the response. It is of interest that a sensation of pain and heat may be felt during irradiation with a few hundred roentgen equivalents (Robbins *et al.*, 1946). Many of the ocular lesions following total-body irradiation are obviously the result of the systemic changes occurring in the radiation syndrome (Wilder and Maynard, 1951).

Lenticular cataracts are among the most serious nonfatal consequences of irradiation. Although this has long been known, it received particular emphasis in 1948 when several cases were discovered in physicists who had been exposed to cyclotron neutrons (Abelson and Kruger, 1949) and when survivors of atomic bomb irradiation began to develop cataracts several years after the exposure (Cogan *et al.*, 1949). The threshold for clinically serious cataract formation by X rays in adult animals is probably close to the acute total-body LD_{50}, but is relatively much lower following exposure to neutrons, so that this effect is seen more often in survivors of total-body neutron exposure. Young animals are more susceptible than adults, and the latent period is related inversely to dose (Leinfelder and Kerr, 1936). Intermittent dosage with fast neutrons results in a particularly high ratio of effectiveness between neutrons and γ rays where cataracts are used as the criterion (Evans, 1948). The radiation cataract is seen typically in the posterior capsular area, but a cytological analysis of the course of cataract formation shows that an important component in its pathogenesis is the destruction of epithelial cells that later migrate to this area (Cogan and Donaldson, 1951).

Gonads. For a detailed account of radiation changes in the gonads the reader is referred to Chap. 17 by Bloom and Bloom. The physiologic responses resulting from irradiation of the testes and ovaries include temporary or permanent sterility, certain endocrine responses, and, in the case of the testis, evidence of impaired viability or diminished numbers of sperm.

Evidence of temporary sterility is first seen in the mouse about three weeks after a single irradiation (Glücksmann, 1947). Examination of the time course of survival of various cell types indicates that spermatogonia are most sensitive, thus accounting for the delay between irradiation and the diminution in sperm count (Eschenbrenner and Miller, 1950; Fogg and Cowing, 1951). Prior to the development of oligospermia, however, matings by the irradiated male result in a smaller than normal litter size, which may be explained by chromosome translocations in the sperm cells (Brenneke, 1937; Snell, 1935). This decrease in litter size and associated evidence of arrested segmentation of fertilized ova (Parkes, 1948) appear in the dosage range between 250 and 500 r. Local and total-body irradiation yield similar findings in the testes (Fogg and Cowing, 1951). At lower dosages, recovery is essentially complete, while no recovery occurs in mice subjected to testicular irradiation at 2000 r. After 5000 r the interstitial cells remain intact (Fogg and Cowing, 1952a). The human being may be considerably more sensitive than rodents in terms of temporary or permanent sterility (Glücksmann, 1947). Sterility induced by 2000 r in mice and 4500 r in rats does not result in feminizing changes in the submaxillary gland, which are a characteristic consequence of castration (Fogg and Cowing, 1952b). "Castration cells" do, however, appear in the pituitary after sterilizing irradiation (Liebow, Warren, and DeCoursey, 1949).

The situation regarding physiological effects of irradiating the ovaries seems to be somewhat more complicated. While temporary sterility may be produced by 170 r to the human ovaries (Glücksmann, 1947; Martin, 1950) and permanent sterility by less than twice this dose, it has nevertheless been customary to *treat* sterility with similar dosages, and pregnancies have been reported in 35 per cent of a large series of women, believed to be sterile, after X irradiation of the ovaries with about 175 r and of the pituitary with 225 r (Kaplan, 1949). The ovarian dosages required to produce permanent amenorrhea vary within wide limits (Liebow, Warren, and DeCoursey, 1949). In evaluating the effect of radiation on the human ovary, it is well to remember that amenorrhea does not necessarily imply inability to conceive. Mice show a temporary reduction in the frequency of estrus after 200 r and temporary abolition of estrus after 400 r (Bischoff *et al.*, 1944). It would appear that secondary sex characters are more sensitive to gonadal irradiation in the female than in the male (Bloom and Bloom, Chap. 17). Consideration of the circumstances involved in the production of ovarian tumors in mice after local X irradiation with 200 r suggests that this dosage, if delivered to all of the ovarian tissue, results in a gonadotrophic response by the pituitary (Lick, Kirschbaum, and Mixer, 1949).

Bone and Cartilage. Responses of these tissues have been described thoroughly by Bloom and Bloom (Chap. 17). Retardation of bone growth following moderate irradiation of the growing areas is a matter of some concern to radiotherapists treating younger individuals, since recovery is likely to be incomplete following 1000 or 2000 r or more.

Long-continued irradiation of adult bones by radium deposited in the skeleton results in the appearance of areas of rarefaction and aseptic bone necrosis, appearing late and progressing during the course of at least 20 to 25 years. Necrosis is especially likely to occur in the jaw, and the bone changes are precancerous (Martland, 1931).

Although cartilage is not remarkably radiosensitive, its recovery after irradiation to the point where necrosis occurs is very poor, perhaps owing to vascular damage (Kaplan, 1949). Consequently, therapeutic irradiation of cartilaginous areas, notably the ear and trachea, must be carried out with great caution.

METABOLISM AND TISSUE BREAKDOWN

Metabolic changes may result from the direct action of radiation on enzyme systems and other biochemical mechanisms, altered gastrointestinal, hormonal, and renal function, and the products of tissue breakdown. Certain of the metabolic consequences of exposure to X rays were described in 1907 by Edsall and Pemberton, who interpreted clinical radiation sickness as a toxic reaction to tissue breakdown. Intoxication was attributed to the inability of the organism to metabolize and excrete the products of cellular disintegration. Subsequently, Doub *et al.* (1925) observed a hyperphosphatemia that was related to radiation dosage, and noted, in addition, that irradiation of large tumor masses resulted in an early alkalosis and elevated blood levels of nonprotein nitrogen, uric acid, and guanidine. Arguments in favor of the tissue toxin hypothesis have been advanced by a number of investigators since the early work of Edsall and Pemberton (Hall and Whipple, 1919; Stafford L. Warren and Whipple, 1923d; Rolleston, 1930; Forfota and Karády, 1937; Moon *et al.*, 1941). It is quite possible that tissue breakdown products contribute to the early shock reactions with massive irradiation. Their role with smaller dosages is not well defined, although there is some evidence that circulating factors may be involved in the initial toxicity resulting from such exposures (Barnes and Furth, 1943; Painter *et al.*, 1947; Weber and Steggerda, 1949; Ellinger, 1951). Toxins may, of course, be expected in the presence of the bacteremia that occurs later.

Metabolic changes attributable to protein breakdown are also apparent from some of the more recent studies with deep roentgen therapy in man and with experimental irradiation of animals (Goldman, 1943; Robertson, 1943; Prosser *et al.*, 1947a, b). Urinary nitrogen is increased during the first hours after irradiation, and specific organ proteinases have been detected in the urine of the dog (Oster and Salter, 1938; Abderhalden, 1939). The subsequent excretion of nitrogen is usually maintained within normal limits until shortly before death. Since intake is reduced there is a negative nitrogen balance (Prosser, Painter, Lisco, *et al.*, 1947; Prosser, Painter, and Swift, 1947). These findings are suggestive of a shift in favor of catabolism.

Organ weights provide a reasonable index of tissue breakdown and repair after irradiation. The most pronounced changes are seen in the lymphoid organs and testes (Carter, Harris, and Brennan, 1950; Eschenbrenner and Miller, 1950). The weight of the gastrointestinal tract is also decreased (Painter, 1948; Ross and Ely, 1949a) as is the volume of available marrow (Brecher *et al.*, 1948). Muscle and kidney, on the other hand, undergo little change, while the adrenals are increased in size (Patt *et al.*, 1947). Changes in thymus, spleen, and testis are useful as biological dosimeters especially after low dosages; the differences in organ weights are relatively slight, however, over the narrow range from just lethal to completely lethal.

The finding that weight loss of the irradiated dog cannot be accounted for by decreased food intake (Prosser, Painter, and Swift, 1947) is suggestive of an increase in catabolism. In the rat, however, change in body weight appears to be related directly to anorexia (Ely and Ross, 1947; D. E. Smith, Tyree, Patt, and Bink, 1951). Identical weight losses have been observed, moreover, in starved and in starved-irradiated rats (D. E. Smith, Tyree, Patt, and Jackson, 1951). Since lethal irradiation does not influence the water content of muscle or the entire carcass of the starved rat, it is apparent that water retention cannot be responsible for the failure to find a greater depression of body weight in the starved-irradiated animal. Extracellular water may be increased after lethal irradiation, but the changes in total extracellular space are similar to those seen in starvation (Painter, 1948). Tissue breakdown associated with irradiation, as with starvation, does not result invariably in elevated metabolism. Although direct evidence of an increase in the metabolic rate of irradiated rats has been presented (Kirschner *et al.*, 1949), changes in oxygen consumption do not coincide with weight loss. Other investigators have been unable to verify the increase in metabolic rate in mice, rats, guinea pigs, or frogs (D. E. Smith, Tyree, Patt, and Jackson, 1951; W. W. Smith and Smith, 1951b; Pratt *et al.*, 1950; Patt, Swift, and Tyree, 1949). Measurements of oxygen consumption have not been made during the terminal febrile period in dogs.

Oxygen utilization may actually be depressed, at least in certain tissues, since the irradiated mouse is said to be more resistant to progressive asphyxia than the nonirradiated (W. W. Smith and Smith, 1951b). It is of interest that the respiratory rate of tissues obtained from irradiated animals or of tissues irradiated in vitro is either unchanged or decreased (Wels, 1924; Crabtree, 1935; Goldfeder and Fershing, 1938; Barron, 1946; Barron *et al.*, 1947; DuBois, unpublished observations, 1950). An exception to this is the brief increase in respiration that has been seen in rabbit marrow homogenates immediately after X irradiation (Altman *et al.*, 1951) and in fowl erythrocytes after massive exposure (Frankenthal and Back, 1944). While depressed tissue respiration can perhaps be attributed to specific inactivation of oxidative enzymes by the radiation, gross metabolic changes seem to be the result and not the cause of growth inhibition. In fact, effects on growth may occur at dosages considerably below those required to influence metabolism (Hubert, 1929; Fenn and Latchford, 1931–1932; Packard, 1933). The absence of profound changes in the metabolic rate of the whole animal in the presence of possible alteration in endogenous respiration of radiosensitive tissues is not unreasonable, since tissues that account for most of the oxygen consumption are notably radioresistant. Tissue breakdown products resulting from irradiation apparently do not result in an appreciable over-all increase in metabolism, perhaps because of their rapid excretion or slow release, the associated inanition, or other as yet unknown factors.

IMMUNITY AND INFECTION

It is well known that total-body irradiation decreases resistance to infection and interferes with immune reactions. The action of ionizing radiations on barriers to infection attracted early attention when it was noted that irradiation resulted in a severe depression of leukocytes (Heineke, 1903), inhibition of antibody formation (Benjamin and Sluka, 1908; Hektoen, 1915), and a terminal bacteremia of intestinal origin (Stafford L. Warren and Whipple, 1923a; Mottram and Kingsbury, 1924). The development of enterogenous infection in X-irradiated mice, including some histological evidence of local bacterial invasion of injured intestinal areas, was described subsequently by Chrom (1935), who noted also that bacteremia could be minimized by shielding the liver and spleen during irradiation. The complication of bacteremia was also observed after neutron irradiation (Lawrence and Tennant, 1937). These findings take on added significance in view of the efficacy of antibiotic therapy in certain species (Miller *et al.*, 1950b; Hammond and Miller, 1950; Howland *et al.*, 1950; Furth, Coulter, and Howland, 1951; Koletsky and Christie, 1950; Gustafson and Koletsky, 1951) and the effect of spleen shielding on hematopoietic recovery and radiation mortality (Jacobson, Marks, and Lorenz, 1949; Jacobson, Simmons, *et al.*, 1950).

The problem of radiation-induced infection has been the subject of intensive investigation in recent years, and it now seems clear that enterogenous invasion can be a substantial factor in radiation morbidity and mortality. The cause of the bacteremia still remains a moot question, however. Miller and co-workers (1950a) have observed that bacteremia in irradiated mice reaches its apogee during the period of greatest mortality. A somewhat lower incidence of positive blood cultures has been seen in the dog, but even in this species infection appears to be related to mortality in animals surviving the first two weeks of irradiation (Bennett, Rekers, and Howland, 1950). Total-body X irradiation of guinea pigs has also been shown to result in a generalized tissue invasion by cholera vibrio from the original focus of infection in the bowel (Burrows *et al.*, 1950a). The intensity of enteric infection appears to be related to a decrease in coproantibody titer. It has been suggested by Burrows and his associates (1950a) that a similar decrease in titer may account for bacteremia in irradiated animals if natural immunity to intestinal organisms is related to the coproantibody response.

Mortality of irradiated animals may be reduced with suitable antibiotic therapy. Streptomycin and terramycin afford the most effective protection to mice (Miller *et al.*, 1950b; Hammond and Miller, 1950). The incidence of diarrhea in rats is greatly diminished by terramycin or aureomycin; survival may also be prolonged (Howland *et al.*, 1950; Furth, Coulter, and Howland, 1951). Mortality from internal radiation (P^{32}) is decreased in this species when streptomycin and penicillin are given in combination (Koletsky and Christie, 1950). Definite effects on survival have not been observed in irradiated dogs with aureomycin (Furth and Coulter, 1950; Allen *et al.*, 1951). It is of interest that prophylaxis with terramycin for 2 to 3 days prior to exposure reduces radiation mortality in rats, presumably by altering the intestinal flora and consequent bacteremia (Gustafson and Koletsky, 1951). In general, antibiotic therapy leads to a reduction in the number of positive blood cultures; pancytopenia is usually not altered, however, although gastrointestinal hemorrhage and ulceration may be diminished.

Numerous reports of the effects of radiation on immunity have appeared since the detailed observations by Hektoen in 1915 of altered antibody formation following exposure to X rays. Decreased resistance of irradiated animals to infection had actually been demonstrated some years previously by Läwen (1909). Although there are some indications of a protective or beneficial action with small dosages of radiation (Glenn, 1946), the evidence, for the most part, points to an impairment of immunological responses and to an increased susceptibility to infection as a result of irradiation. X irradiation decreases the Shwartzman phenomenon of local tissue reactivity to intradermally injected bacterial endotoxins (Becker, 1948) and also diminishes the renal lesions that occur in rabbits after injection of bovine serum γ- globulin (Schwab *et al.*, 1950). These effects may be related to suppression of antibody formation. The extensive literature in this field has been the subject of recent reviews by Taliaferro and Taliaferro (1951) and Craddock and Lawrence (1948).

A marked reduction in the capacity to form antibodies has been demonstrated when irradiation is accomplished shortly before or after immunization (Hektoen, 1915; Murphy and Sturm, 1925; Craddock and Lawrence,

1948; Clemmesen and Andersen, 1948; Schwab *et al.*, 1950; Burrows *et al.*, 1950b; Kohn, 1951c). Some depression of antibody titer has been noted when immunization precedes irradiation, but a given dose of X rays becomes progressively less effective as the time of its administration is delayed after the injection of antigen (Kohn, 1951c). The excretion of fecal and urinary antibodies may be inhibited under these conditions even though a deleterious effect on the serum titer is not apparent (Burrows *et al.*, 1950b). A transitory increase in the excretion of fecal and urinary antibody has been observed in the guinea pig when immunization with cholera O vaccine is begun 1 day, but not 3 days, after irradiation (Burrows *et al.*, 1950b). The apparently contradictory findings of beneficial and detrimental effects of irradiation on infection conceivably may be explained on this basis. Sublethal irradiation does not appear to alter the rate of destruction of passively transferred homologous or heterologous antisera (Hollingsworth, 1950; Borowskaja, 1946). The capacity of the irradiated rabbit to produce antibodies to injected antigen is largely retained if the spleen or appendix is shielded during exposure (Jacobson, Robson, and Marks, 1950). It is not known whether the shielded lymphatic tissue initiates antibody formation or makes it possible for the process to be initiated elsewhere.

Augmentation of antibody titer has been observed in immunized mice after irradiation with 10 to 100 r (Dougherty *et al.*, 1944). The "anamnestic reaction" does not occur in adrenalectomized mice and is thought to be related to adrenal cortical stimulation, which results in lymphocyte dissolution and release of γ-globulin. The anamnestic response of antibody titer has not been seen in rabbits after comparable low-dose irradiation (Craddock and Lawrence, 1948). Local irradiation of the hind legs of sensitized rabbits also fails to increase the amount of circulating antibodies (Lecomte and Fischer, 1949). There are other indications that the lymphocytes do not serve as a store of antibodies, since fairly large dosages of X radiation do not result in an appreciable change in the antibody concentration of lymph, despite the widespread destruction of lymphatic tissue (Craddock *et al.*, 1949). There is no clear indication moreover of a relation between the height of antibody titer in serum and lymph. The role of the adrenal cortex in the production and release of antibody and γ-globulin has been questioned by others (Eisen *et al.*, 1947; Fischel *et al.*, 1949).

NONSPECIFIC PHYSIOLOGICAL STRESSES

In response to stress, there are evoked compensatory or buffer mechanisms whose chief function is to maintain vital processes by minimizing injury and promoting repair. The pituitary-adrenal and reticuloendothelial systems are concerned intimately with these phenomena.

Obviously, the extent to which adaptive and defensive mechanisms are successful will depend, for the most part, upon the magnitude of the stress. The nonspecific potentiation of one stress by another may be interpreted on this basis. These considerations apply to the high-energy radiations, which, because of their distribution, usually result in fairly extensive injury. It has been shown, for example, that hypophysectomy (Patt *et al.*, 1948), adrenal insufficiency (Cronkite and Chapman, 1950; Edelmann, 1951b; Kaplan *et al.*, 1951), infection (Taliaferro *et al.*, 1945; Shechmeister and Bond, 1951; Shechmeister *et al.*, 1950), trauma (Brooks, 1951), exhaustive exercise (Stapleton and Curtis, 1946; Kimeldorf *et al.*, 1950), and nutritional deficiencies (Johnson *et al.*, 1946; Jennings, 1949) enhance the susceptibility to irradiation and, conversely, that irradiation increases the toxicity resulting from many of these conditions. Moderate degrees of stress, however, may be well tolerated by minimally irradiated animals (W. W. Smith, 1951; W. W. Smith and Smith, 1951b; F. Smith and Smith, 1951). Of interest from the point of view of war disaster, is the recent finding by Brooks (1951) that 100 r total-body X irradiation, which by itself is nonlethal, increases the mortality of dogs from 14 to 75 per cent following a standardized surface burn.

ACUTE RADIATION SYNDROME

The symptom complex appearing within several weeks after irradiation of large areas of the body and the way it develops may be considered pathognomonic of radiation exposure (Shields Warren and Bowers, 1950; Howland and Warren, 1947; Jacobson *et al.*, 1949d; Painter and Brues, 1949; Hempelmann, 1950; Shields Warren and Brues, 1950; Bowers, 1951; Cronkite, 1951; Hempelmann *et al.*, 1952). The relatively mild discomfort of clinical radiation sickness, which is sometimes seen after therapeutic exposure, should be distinguished from the more serious and complex events of the acute radiation syndrome, of which it is a part. It is well to recall that chronic effects, e.g., anemia, neoplasia, lenticular opacities, and "premature aging"[2] may appear in survivors of the acute injury, or after protracted or repeated irradiation. The more chronic sequelae do not, however, constitute as discrete an entity as the acute syndrome. The pattern in man is, in general, similar to that observed experimentally. Our knowledge of acute radiation injury in man is based largely upon studies of the Japanese bomb casualties (Howland and Warren, 1947; Liebow *et al.*, 1949) and of persons injured by accidental nuclear reactions (Hempelmann *et al.*, 1952). Data relating to the Japanese victims are necessarily incomplete and complicated by the

[2] Shortening of life span is generally thought of as if it involved an acceleration of the aging process. In fact, it rests almost entirely on statistical data and so is analogous to semilethal effects in *Drosophila* (Brues and Sacher, 1952).

effects of heat and blast and the lack of precise information regarding conditions of exposure. The accident cases, on the other hand, represent uncomplicated radiation injury.

The disturbance consequent to irradiation assumes a distinctive time course, which depends not only upon the dosage, duration, and manner of irradiation but also upon the temporal relation between injury and recovery of particular cells and their rate of utilization by the organism. The initial damage leads to a complex chain of events, some of which are a direct result of the primary injury while others are secondary to it. Alteration in the cellular constituents of peripheral blood is an example of the former; in fluid balance, of the latter. All the changes are distinguished by their lack of specificity.

Supralethal irradiation is followed by a shocklike reaction and death within a few days. Severe intestinal damage and central nervous system disturbances are prominent sequelae of massive irradiation. After median lethal irradiation, there is an initially mild disturbance, a brief period of apparent respite, and a final phase of progressive injury with death or recovery. The waves of mortality that occur after moderate irradiation suggest that multiple factors may be involved. These have not been defined satisfactorily. It is apparent, however, that leukopenia, septicemia, hemorrhage, and gastrointestinal damage constitute the most important insults to the irradiated organism.

Medical management of the radiation syndrome may be resolved into three basic components: (1) correction of the panhematopenia, (2) prevention or treatment of infection, and (3) maintenance of adequate nutrition and fluid balance. Although irreversible tissue injuries occur soon after intensive irradiation, there are indications that it may be possible to prevent effectively certain of the radiation changes and to facilitate the regenerative capacity of critical tissues. It is noteworthy, for example, that morbidity and mortality are influenced by procedures that promote recovery of blood-forming tissues or prevent bacteremia, e.g., spleen and marrow transplants, and antibiotics. Data pertaining to biological protection against the acute syndrome by means of organ shielding are most impressive and should encourage further attempts to influence tissue recovery with humoral agents (cf. Chap. 16). From a practical point of view, it is imperative to establish the role of blood transfusion, hematopoietic and antihemorrhagic factors, and parenteral feeding. Early venesection and blood replacement have been shown to reduce radiation mortality in dogs; periodic blood transfusions, on the other hand, minimize anemia but apparently do not influence other radiation sequelae or mortality.

Specific chemical protection against many of the effects of ionizing radiation is of considerable theoretical importance. Elucidation of these protective mechanisms may reveal the nature of the early chemical

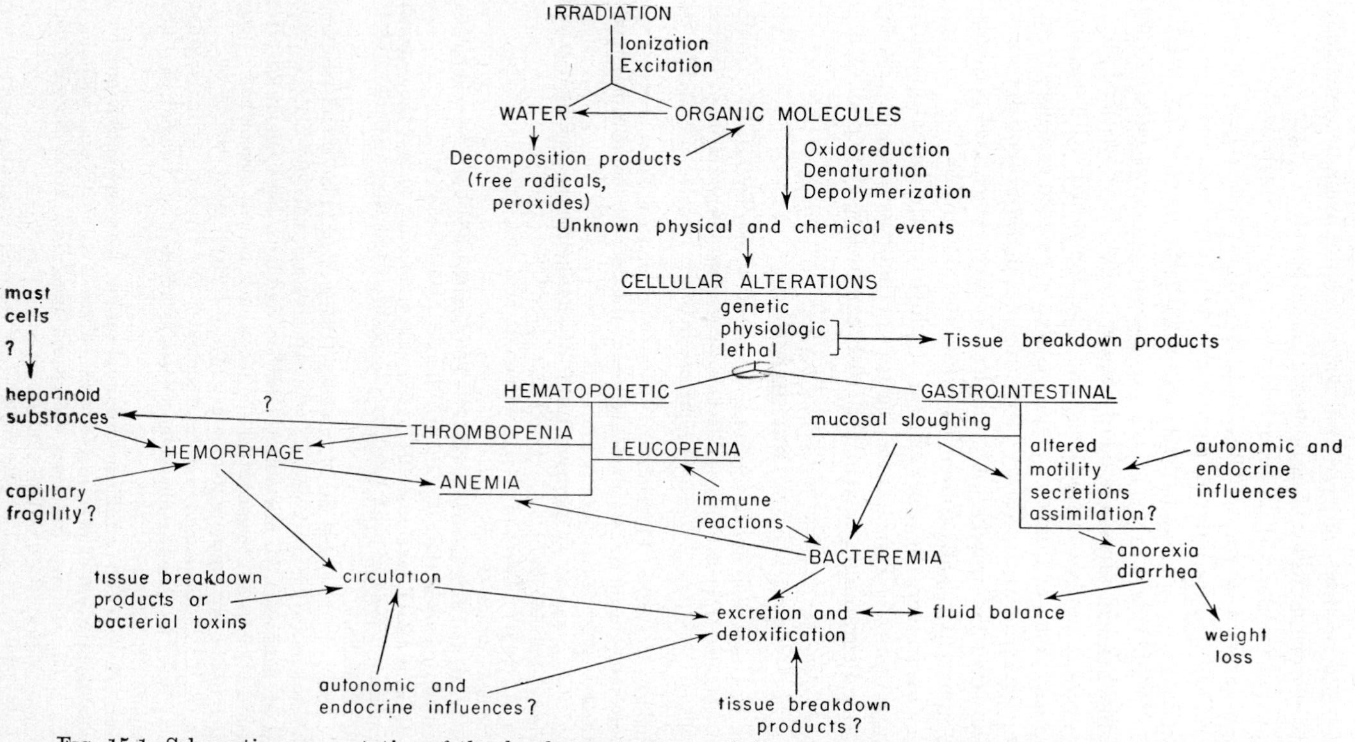

Fig. 15-1 Schematic representation of the development of acute injury following median lethal penetrating irradiation.

effects. The products of irradiated water, mainly oxidants, are probably responsible for a number of radiobiological responses; oxygen deprivation during exposure and certain reductants such as cysteine have been shown to diminish acute toxicity. Organic molecules are believed to be altered, e.g., oxidized, reduced, depolymerized, or denatured, by direct ionization and excitation as well as by interaction with the products of irradiated water. While this is in accord with effects on simple systems, the nature of the biochemical targets is poorly understood. It is assumed that the early events involve molecules that are concerned with regulatory mechanisms, e.g., enzymes or genes, as well as molecules whose integrity ensures the structural stability of the nuclear material and the ability of the cell to divide normally. Cytological damage, the earliest recognizable effect, apparently leads to deficiencies that are manifest first in areas of rapid cell turnover, the most critical of which are the hematopoietic and intestinal tissues. The essential features of the acute radiation syndrome presented diagrammatically in Fig. 15-1, can be largely explained on this basis.

REFERENCES

(Information regarding availability of government reports indicated by an asterisk may be obtained from the Office of Technical Services, Department of Commerce, Washington, D.C.)

Abderhalden, R. (1939) Further studies in the appearance of known organic specific proteinases in urine after roentgen-ray treatment. Fermentforschung, 16: 215–220.

Abelson, P. H., and P. G. Kruger (1949) Cyclotron-induced radiation cataracts. Science, 110: 655–657.

Abrams, R. (1951) Effect of X-rays on nucleic acid and protein synthesis. Arch. Biochem., 30: 90–99.

Adams, W. S., and J. S. Lawrence (1947) The negative effect of folic acid on irradiation leukopenia in the cat. USAEC Report MDDC-1538.*

Allen, J. G., and L. O. Jacobson (1947) Hyperheparinemia; cause of the hemorrhagic syndrome associated with total-body exposure to ionizing radiation. Science, 105: 388–389.

———, P. E. Moulder, and D. M. Enerson (1951) Pathogenesis and treatment of the postirradiation syndrome. J. Am. Med. Assoc., 145: 704–711.

———, M. Sanderson, M. Milham, A. Kirschon, and L. O. Jacobson (1948) Heparinemia (?) An anticoagulant in the blood of dogs with hemorrhagic tendency after total-body exposure to roentgen rays. J. Exptl. Med., 87: 71–86.

Altman, K. I., J. Richmond, and K. Saloman (1951) A note on the synthesis of fatty acids in bone marrow homogenates as affected by X-radiation. USAEC Report UR-169.*

Anderson, E. A. (1951) Influence of total-surface beta irradiation on the gross metabolic pattern of rats, *in* Biological effects of external beta radiation, R. E. Zirkle, ed. McGraw-Hill Book Company, Inc., New York, National Nuclear Energy Series, Div. IV, Vol. 22E, Chap. 8

Ané, J. N., and G. E. Burch (1941) Effects of roentgen irradiation upon linear rate of flow in cutaneous lymphatics of humans. Proc. Soc. Exptl. Biol. Med., 48: 471–473.

Baidens, A. von, L. Claesson, and A. Westman (1946) Über den Einfluss der Röntgenbestrahlung auf die gonadotrope Funktion der Hypophyse. Gynaecologia, 122: 347–362.

Barnard, R. D. (1948) A note on the depression of blood cholinesterase level following X-ray therapy and its bearing on the mechanism of radiation sickness. Medical Record, 161: 350–352.

Barnes, W. A., and O. B. Furth (1943) Studies on the indirect effect of roentgen rays in single and parabiotic mice. Am. J. Roentgenol. Radium Therapy, 49: 662–681.

Barron, E. S. G. (1946) Effects of X rays on tissue metabolism. USAEC Report AECD-2316.*

———, W. Wolkowitz, and J. A. Muntz (1947) The effect of X rays on the metabolism of the small intestine and its permeability to glucose. USAEC Report MDDC-1247.*

Barrow, J., J. L. Tullis, and F. W. Chambers (1949) The effect of total-body X-radiation, antihistine, and pyribenzamine on the phagocytic functions of the recticulo-endothelial system in rabbits injected intravenously with radioactive colloidal gold. Nav. Med. Research Inst. Report NM-007-039,* No. 24; Am. J. Physiol., 164: 822–823 (1951).

Bean, W. B., T. D. Spies, and R. W. Vilter (1944) A note on irradiation sickness. Am. J. Med. Sci., 208: 46–54.

Becker, R. M. (1948) Suppression of local tissue reactivity (Schwartzman phenomenon) by nitrogen mustard, benzol, and X-ray irradiation. Proc. Soc. Exptl. Biol. Med., 69: 247–250.

Bedürftig, G., and G. Grüssner (1949) Die indirekten Wirkungen der Roentgenstrahlen auf Herz und Kreislauf des Menschen. Strahlentherapie, 78: 445–458.

Beiler, J. M., and G. J. Martin (1947) Inhibitory action of vitamin P compounds on hyaluronidase. J. Biol. Chem., 171: 507–511.

Bender, A. E. (1948) Experimental X irradiation of the rat thyroid. Brit. J. Radiology, 21: 244–248.

Benjamin, E., and E. Sluka (1908) Antikörperbildung nach experimenteller Schädigung des hematopoetischen Systems durch Röntgenstrahlen. Wien. klin. Wochschr., 21: 311–313.

Bennett, L. R., S. M. Chastain, A. B. Decker, and J. F. Mead (1951) The effect of roentgen irradiation upon protein absorption in the mouse. USAEC Report UCLA-137;* Proc. Soc. Exptl. Biol. Med., 77: 715–718.

———, V. C. Bennett, and J. W. Howland (1949) Effect of acute X-radiation on distribution and excretion of radiosodium in the rat. Federation Proc., 8:350.

———, ———, A. Shaver, and T. Grachus (1950) Absorption and distribution of vitamin A in X-irradiated rats. Proc. Soc. Exptl. Biol. Med., 74: 439–443.

———, P. E. Rekers, and J. W. Howland (1950) The influence of infection on the hematological effects and mortality following mid-lethal X-radiation. USAEC Report UR-140;* Radiology, 57: 99–103 (1951).

Beutel, A., and K. A. Winter (1935) Das Gewebchlor bei der Ratte nach Röntgentotalbestrahlung. Strahlentherapie, 54: 89–96.

Bigelow, R. R., J. Furth, M. C. Woods, and R. H. Storey (1951) Endothelial damage by X-rays disclosed by lymph fistula studies. Proc. Soc. Exptl. Biol. Med., 76: 734–736.

Bischoff, F., H. J. Ullmann, and L. P. Ingraham (1944) The influence of irradiation of the ovaries upon estrus and neoplastic development in Marsh-Buffalo mice. Radiology, 43: 55–58.

Bloom, M. A. (1948) The bone marrow, *in* Histopathology of irradiation from external and internal sources, W. Bloom, ed. McGraw-Hill Book Company, Inc., New York, National Nuclear Energy Series, Div. IV, Vol. 22I, Chap. 5.

——— (1950) Acquired radioresistance of the crypt epithelium of the duodenum. Radiology, 55: 104–115.

Bloom, W. (1948) The kidney, *in* Histopathology of irradiation from external and internal sources, W. Bloom, ed. McGraw-Hill Book Company, Inc., New York, National Nuclear Energy Series, Div. IV, Vol. 22I, Chap. 14.

——— and L. O. Jacobson (1948) Some hematologic effects of irradiation. Blood, 3: 586–592.

Blount, H. C., Jr., and W. W. Smith (1949) Influence of thyroid and thiouracil on mice exposed to roentgen radiation. Science, 109: 83–84.

Boffil, J., and O. Miletzky (1946) Recherches expérimentales sur les perturbations produites par les rayons X au niveau de la moelle osseuse. Ann. méd., 47: 220–244.

Bond, V. P., M. N. Swift, A. C. Allen, and M. C. Fishler (1950) Sensitivity of abdomen of rat to X-irradiation. Am. J. Physiol., 161: 323–330.

Borak, J. (1942a) Radiation effects on blood vessels: erythema, edema. Radiology, 38: 481–492.

——— (1942b) Radiation effects in blood vessels: inflammation, degeneration, suppression of growth capacity, retrogression. Radiology, 38: 607–617.

——— (1942c) Radiation effects on blood vessels: telangiectasis, effects on lymph vessels. Radiology, 38: 718–727.

Borowskaja, D. (1946) Effect of roentgen irradiation on serum content of haemagglutinins in human blood. Nature, 158: 269.

Bowers, J. Z. (1951) Acute radiation syndrome. J. Am. Med. Assoc., 145: 63–65.

——— and K. G. Scott (1951a) Distribution and excretion of electrolytes after acute whole-body irradiation injury. I. Studies with radiopotassium. Proc. Soc. Exptl. Biol. Med., 78: 645–648.

——— and ——— (1951b) Distribution and excretion of electrolytes after acute whole-body irradiation injury. II. Studies with radiosodium. Proc. Soc. Exptl. Biol. Med., 78: 648–652.

Boys, F., and I. D. Harris (1943) The effect of heparinization of experimental post-irradiation tissue changes in the lung. Am. J. Roentgenol. Radium Therapy, 50: 1–8.

Braasch, N. K., and M. J. Nickson (1948) A study of the hands of radiologists. Radiology, 51: 719–727.

Brecher, G., K. M. Endicott, H. Gump, and H. P. Brawner (1948) Effects of X-ray on lymphoid and hemopoietic tissues of albino mice. Blood, 3: 1259–1274.

Brenneke, H. (1937) Strahlenschadigung von Mäuse- und Rattensperma, beobachtet an der Fruhentwicklung der Eier. Strahlentherapie, 60: 214–238.

Brick, I. V. (1947) Effect of large dosages of irradiation on gastric acidity. New Engl. J. Med., 237: 48–51.

Brooks, J. W. (1951) Low temperature and radiation, *in* Symposium on burns. Natl. Acad. Sci., Natl. Research Council, Washington, D.C.

Brown, C. S., E. Hardenbergh, and J. L. Tullis (1950) Biochemical, cellular and bacteriologic changes in thoracic-duct lymph of dogs exposed to total-body irradiation. Am. J. Physiol., 163: 668–675.

Brues, A. M. (1948) The effects of plutonium on the liver, *in* Liver injury, F. W. Hoffbauer, ed. Trans. of the 7th Conf., Jan. 15 and 16, Josiah Macy, Jr., Foundation, New York.

——— and L. Rietz (1948) Acute hematologic radiation response of the guinea pig as a function of lethality. USAEC Report ANL-4227,* pp. 183–187.

——— and G. A. Sacher (1952) Analysis of mammalian radiation injury and lethality, *in* Symposium on radiobiology (Oberlin, 1950), J. J. Nickson, ed. John Wiley & Sons, Inc., New York, pp. 441–465.

———, ———, and H. O. France (1946) Effect of total-body X ray on weights of organs in the rat. USAEC Report MDDC-1197.*

Buchanan, D. L., and E. S. G. Barron (1947) The electrophoretic patterns of the plasma of goats after X-ray irradiation. USAEC Report CH-3782,* pp. 52–63.

Buchsbaum, R., and R. E. Zirkle (1949) Shrinking and swelling after alpha irradiation of various parts of large erythrocytes. Proc. Soc. Exptl. Biol. Med., 72: 27–29.

Buchwald, K. W. (1931) The influence of X-ray lesions of the intestinal mucosa on absorption of glucose and other sugars. J. Exptl. Med., 53: 827–833.

Burrows, W., N. G. Deupree, and D. E. Moore (1950a) The effect of X irradiation on experimental enteric cholera in the guinea pig. J. Infectious Diseases, 87: 158–168.

———, ———, and ——— (1950b) The effect of X irradiation on fecal and urinary antibody response. J. Infectious Diseases, 87: 169–183.

Campbell, B., and R. Novick (1949) Effects of beta rays on central nervous tissues. Proc. Soc. Exptl. Biol. Med., 72: 34–38.

———, S. C. Peterson, and R. Novick (1946) Early changes induced in Purkinje cells of rabbit by single massive doses of roentgen rays. Proc. Soc. Exptl. Biol. Med., 61: 353–355.

Campbell, I. L., and M. H. Ross (1952) Protection experiments against radiation injury with lymphocytes. USAEC Report ORNL-1193.*

Carter, R. E., E. Busch, and V. Strang (1950) The effect of vitamin B_{12} on the leukopenia induced by radiation. Blood, 5: 753–757.

———, P. S. Harris, and J. T. Brennan (1950) The effect of acute doses of X-irradiation on the splenic and thymic weight of CF-1 female mice. USAEC Report LA-1075.*

Chase, H. B. (1949) Greying of hair. I. Effects produced by single doses of X-rays on mice. J. Morphol., 84: 57–76.

Chrom, S. A. (1935) Studies on the effect of roentgen rays upon the intestinal epithelium and upon the reticulo-endothelial cells of the liver and spleen. Acta Radiol., 16: 641–660.

Clark, W. G., R. P. Uncapher, and M. L. Jordan (1948) Effect of flavonoids (vitamin P) on mortality from total-body roentgen irradiation. Science, 108: 629–630.

Clemmesen, J., and E. K. Anderson (1948) Influence of fractioned roentgen radiation on bacterial agglutination titre. Acta Path. Microbiol. Scand., 25: 611–614.

Cogan, D. G., and D. D. Donaldson (1951) Experimental radiation cataracts. I. Cataract in the rabbit following single X-ray exposure. Arch. Ophthalmol., 45: 508–522.

———, S. F. Martin, and S. J. Kimura (1949) Atom bomb cataracts. Science, 110: 654–655.

Cohn, S. H. (1951) Effects of total-body X irradiation on blood coagulation in the rat. Nav. Radiol. Def. Lab. Report AD-298(B).*

Cole, L. J., M. C. Fishler, M. E. Ellis, and V. P. Bond (1952) Protection of mice against X irradiation by spleen homogenates administered after exposure. Nav. Radiol. Def. Lab. Report NRDL-339.*

Conard, R. A. (1951) Effect of X irradiation on intestinal motility of the rat. Am. J. Physiol. 165: 375–385.

Crabtree, H. C. (1935) The differential effect of radium radiation on the carbohydrate metabolism of normal and tumour tissues irradiated at low temperature. Biochem. J., 29: 2334–2343.

Craddock, C. G., Jr., and J. S. Lawrence (1948) The effect of roentgen irradiation on antibody formation in rabbits. J. Immunol., 60: 241–254.

———, W. N. Valentine, and J. S. Lawrence (1949) The effect of massive whole-body X ray on the antibody content of lymph, *in* The lymphocyte: studies on its relationship to immunologic processes in the cat. J. Lab. Clin. Med., 34: 166–169.

Craver, B. N. (1948) The effect of adrenal cortical injury on the toxicity of roentgen rays. Am. J. Roentgenol. Radium Therapy, 59: 404–407.

Cronkite, E. P. (1950) The hemorrhagic syndrome of acute ionizing radiation illness produced in goats and swine by exposure to the atomic bomb at Bikini, 1946. Blood, 5: 32–45.

——— (1951) The diagnosis and treatment of radiation sickness in atomic warfare. Western J. Surg. Obstet. Gynecol., 59: 55–61.

———, G. Brecher, and W. H. Chapman (1951) Mechanism of protective action of glutathione against whole-body irradiation. Proc. Soc. Exptl. Biol. Med., 76: 396–398.

——— and W. H. Chapman (1950) Effect of adrenalectomy on radiation-induced mortality of the mouse. Proc. Soc. Exptl. Biol. Med., 74: 337–340.

———, D. C. Eltzholtz, C. R. Sipe, W. H. Chapman, and F. W. Chambers, Jr. (1949) Failure of rutin to decrease the mortality of acute ionizing radiation illness in mice. Proc. Soc. Exptl. Biol. Med., 70: 125–128.

———, J. L. Tullis, C. Tessmer, and F. W. Ullrich (1950) Failure of folic acid to influence lethal radiation illness in swine. Proc. Soc. Exptl. Biol. Med., 73: 496–497.

Davidoff, L. M., C. G. Dyke, C. A. Elsberg, and I. M. Tarlov (1938) The effect of radiation applied directly to the brain and spinal cord. I. Experimental investigations on *Macacus rhesus* monkeys. Radiology, 31: 451–463.

Davis, R. W., N. Dole, M. J. Izzo, and L. E. Young (1949) "Hemolytic" effect of radiation. USAEC Report UR-99;* J. Lab. Clin. Med., 35: 528–537 (1950).

Denniston, R. H. (1942) The influence of roentgen-ray treatments of the hypophysis on reproductive systems of the ground squirrel and rat. J. Exptl. Zool., 91: 237–263.

Denstad, T. (1941) Die Strahlensensibilität des Knochenmarks. Acta Radiol., 22: 347–359.

Desjardins, A. U. (1928) The effect of irradiation on the suprarenal gland. Am. J. Roentgenol. Radium Therapy, 19: 453–461.

——— (1931a) Action of roentgen rays and radium on the gastrointestinal tract. Experimental data and clinical radiotherapy. Am. J. Roentgenol. Radium Therapy, 26: 151–190.

——— (1931b) Action of roentgen rays and radium on the gastrointestinal tract. Experimental data and clinical radiotherapy. II. Am. J. Roentgenol. Radium Therapy, 26: 337–370.

——— (1931c) Action of roentgen rays and radium on the gastrointestinal tract. Experimental data and clinical radiotherapy. III. Am. J. Roentgenol. Radium Therapy, 26: 495–510.

Dillard, G. H. L., G. Brecher, and E. P. Cronkite (1951) Separation, concentration, and transfusion of platelets. Proc. Soc. Exptl. Biol. Med., 78: 796–799.

Dixon, F. J (1948) Radiation-induced hemorrhagic disease in chickens. Proc. Soc. Exptl. Biol. Med., 68: 505–507.

Dobson, E., and H. B. Jones (1952) The behavior of intravenously injected particulate material: its rate of disappearance from the blood stream as a measure of liver blood flow. Acta Med. Scan., Suppl. 273, 144: 1–71.

Dodds, E. C., and J. H. D. Webster (1924) Metabolic changes associated with X-ray and radium treatment. Lancet, 258: 533–537.

Doub, H. P., A. Bolliger, and F. W. Hartman (1925) Immediate metabolic disturbances following deep roentgen-ray therapy. Am. J. Roentgenol. Radium Therapy, 13: 54–64.

Dougherty, T. F., and A. White (1946) Pituitary–adrenal-cortical control of lymphocyte structure and function as revealed by experimental X-radiation. Endocrinology, 39: 370–385.

———, ———, and J. H. Chase (1944) Relationship of the effect of adrenal-cortical secretion on lymphoid tissue and on antibody titer. Proc. Soc. Exptl. Biol. Med., 56: 28–29.

Douglas, D. M., W. R. Ghent, and S. Rowlands (1950) Atrophy of the gastric glands produced by beta rays; histological findings in animals. Lancet, 258: 1035–1038.

DuBois, K. P., K. W. Cochran, and J. Doull (1951) Inhibition of citric acid synthesis in vivo by X-irradiation. Proc. Soc. Exptl. Biol. Med., 76: 422–427.

———, ———, and M. M. Zerwic (1951) Influence of sex hormones on citrate synthesis in liver. Proc. Soc. Exptl. Biol. Med., 78: 452–455.

Dunlap, C. E. (1942) Effects of radiation on normal tissues. III. Effects of radiation on the blood and the hemopoietic tissues, including the spleen, the thymus, and the lymph nodes. Arch. Path., 34: 562–608.

Edelmann, A. (1949) Effects of X-radiation on water and electrolyte metabolism in the rat. Federation Proc., 8: 39.

——— (1951a) Adrenal shielding and survival of rats after X-irradiation. Am. J. Physiol., 165: 57–60.

——— (1951b) Survival of adrenalectomized rats with and without replacement therapy following X-irradiation. Am. J. Physiol., 167: 345–348.

——— and W. J. Eversole (1950) Changes in antidiuretic activity of rat serum after X-irradiation. Am. J. Physiol., 163: 709–710.

Edsall, D. L., and R. Pemberton (1907) The nature of the general toxic reaction following exposure to X-rays. Am. J. Med. Sci., 133: 426–431.

Eisen, H. N., M. M. Mayer, D. H. Moore, R. Tarr, and H. C. Stock (1947) Failure of adrenal-cortical activity to influence circulating antibodies and gamma globulin. Proc. Soc. Exptl. Biol. Med., 65: 301–306.

Ellinger, F. (1945) Response of the liver to irradiation. Radiology, 44: 241–254.

——— (1946) Protective action of desoxycorticosterone acetate against X-ray-induced liver changes. Science, 104: 502–503.

——— (1947) Some effects of desoxycorticosterone acetate on mice irradiated with X-rays. Proc. Soc. Exptl. Biol. Med., 64: 31–35.

——— (1948) The use of adrenal-cortical hormone in radiation sickness. Radiology, 51: 394–399.

——— (1951) Die Histaminhypothese der biologischen Strahlenwirkungen. Schweiz. med. Wochschr., 81(3): 61–65.

———, B. Roswit, and S. M. Glasser (1949) The treatment of radiation sickness with adrenal-cortical hormone (desoxycorticosterone acetate). A preliminary report on fifty cases. Am. J. Roentgenol. Radium Therapy, 61: 387–396.

Ely, J. O., and M. H. Ross (1947) Some physiological responses of rats to neutron irradiation, *in* Neutron effects on animals, E. MacDonald, ed. The Williams & Wilkins Company, Baltimore, Chap. 17.

——— and ——— (1948a) Nucleic acid content in intestines of rats after X-radiation. Cancer Research, 8: 285–294.

——— and ——— (1948b) Nucleic acid content in intestines of rats after neutron radiation. Cancer Research, 8: 607–612.

———, ———, and D. M. Gay (1947) Changes produced in testes, spleen, bone marrow, liver and kidneys of rats by neutron irradiation, *in* Neutron effects on animals, E. MacDonald, ed. The Williams & Wilkins Company, Baltimore, Chap. 20.

Engelstad, R. B. (1935) Ueber Magengeschwuere nach Roentgenbestrahlung. Strahlentherapie, 53: 139–170.

——— (1936) Histologische Veränderungen in den Nebennieren nach Röntgenbestrahlung. Strahlentherapie, 56: 58–68.

——— (1938) The effect of roentgen rays on the stomach in rabbits. Am. J. Roentgenol. Radium Therapy, 40: 243–263.

——— and O. Torgersen (1937) Experimental investigations on the effects of roentgen rays on the suprarenal glands in rabbits. Acta Radiol., 18: 671–687.

Eschenbrenner, A. B., and E. Miller (1950) Effect of roentgen rays on the testis: Quantitative histological analysis following whole-body exposure of mice. Arch. Path., 50: 736–749.

Evans, T. C. (1948) Effects of small daily doses of fast neutrons on mice. Radiology, 50: 811–833.

———, G. Clarke, and E. Sobel (1947) Increase in I^{131} uptake of thyroid after whole-body roentgen irradiation. Anat. Record, 99: 577.

Failla, G. (1940) Some aspects of the biological action of ionizing radiations (Janeway Lecture, 1939). Am. J. Roentgenol. Radium Therapy, 44: 649–664.

Feinstein, R. N., C. L. Butler, and D. D. Hendley (1950) Effect of whole body X-radiation and of intraperitoneal hydrogen peroxide on mouse liver catalase. Science, 111: 149–150.

Feller, D. D., I. L. Chaikoff, A. Taurog, and H. B. Jones (1949) The changes induced in iodine metabolism of the rat by internal radiation of its thyroid with I^{131}. Endocrinology, 45: 464–479.

Fenn, W. O., and W. B. Latchford (1931–1932) Increased metabolism of sartorius muscle of frog following exposure to roentgen radiation. Am. J. Physiol., 99: 454–462.

Field, J. B., and P. E. Rekers (1949a) Studies of the effects of flavonoids on roentgen irradiation disease. I. Protective influence of rutin in irradiated dogs. Am. J. Med. Sci., 218: 1–15.

——— and ——— (1949b) Studies of the effects of flavonoids on roentgen irradiation disease. II. Comparison of the protective influence of some flavonoids and vitamin C in dogs. J. Clin. Investigation, 28: 746–751.

Findlay, D., and C. P. Leblond (1948) Partial destruction of rat thyroid by large doses of radio-iodine. Am. J. Roentgenol. Radium Therapy, 59: 387–395.

Fink, K. (1946) Blood chemistry study in dogs exposed to chronic X-radiation. USAEC Report MDDC-211.*

Fischel, E. E., M. Le May, and E. A. Kabat (1949) The effect of adrenocorticotrophic hormone and X-ray on the amount of circulating antibody. J. Immunol., 61: 89–93.

Fisher, N. F., E. Larson, and A. Bachem (1928) The effect of X rays on the adrenal glands. Endocrinology, 12: 335–341.

Fogg, L. C., and R. F. Cowing (1951) The changes in cell morphology and histochemistry of the testis following irradiation and their relation to other induced testicular changes. I. Quantitative random sampling of germinal cells at intervals following direct irradiation. Cancer Research, 11: 23–28.

——— and ——— (1952a) Effect of direct X-irradiation on mammalian testicles. Exptl. Cell Research, 3: 19–32.

——— and ——— (1952b) Biologic effects of X-irradiation. Exptl. Cell Research, 3: 245–247.

Forfota, E., and S. Karády (1937) Über die biologische Allgemeinwirkung der Röntgenstrahlen vom Gesichtspunkte einer durch Histamin oder ähnlich wirkende Substanzen verursachten Schoekwirkung. Strahlentherapie, 59: 258–266.

France, O. (1946) Changes in water content and distribution in rats and mice after chronic and acute total-body X irradiation. USAEC Report CH-3889.*

Frankenthal, L., and A. Back (1944) The effect of X-rays on the respiration of fowl erythrocytes. Biochem. J., 38: 351–354.

Freed, J. H., E. J. Farris, D. P. Murphy, and E. P. Pendergrass (1948) Effect of low-dosage roentgen irradiation on the gonadotrophic function of the hypophysis of the mature and immature female albino rat. J. Clin. Endocrinol., 8: 461–481.

Frey, H. (1928) Experimentelle Untersuchungen uber die Röntgensensibilität der Nebennieren. Acta Radiol., 9: 23–53.

Friedell, H. L., and J. H. Christie (1951) Synergistic effect of phosphorus^{32} and colloidal gold^{198} on survival in male albino rats. Proc. Soc. Exptl. Biol. Med., 76: 207–210.

Frieden, J., and A. White (1950) Studies of electrophoretic serum protein patterns in subjects treated with pituitary-adrenal cortical hormones, nitrogen mustard or X-radiation. Yale J. Biol. Med., 22: 395–406.

Friedman, N. B. (1942) Effects of radiation on normal tissues. IV. Effects of radiation on the gastrointestinal tract, including the salivary glands, the liver, and the pancreas. Arch. Path., 34: 749–787.

——— (1945) Cellular dynamics in the intestinal mucosa: The effect of irradiation on epithelial maturation and migration. J. Exptl. Med., 81: 553–557.

——— and S. Warren (1942) Evolution of experimental radiation ulcers of the intestine. Arch. Path., 33: 326–333.

Furth, F. W., and M. P. Coulter (1950) The effect of aureomycin on the radiation syndrome in dogs. USAEC Report UR-146.*

———, ———, and J. W. Howland (1951) The effect of aureomycin and terramycin on the X-radiated rat. USAEC Report UR-158.*

Furth, J., G. A. Andrews, R. H. Storey, and L. Wish (1951) The effect of X-irradiation on erythrogenesis, plasma and cell volumes. South. Med. J. 44: 85–92.

Gastaldi, G. (1949) Morphological aspects of the regeneration of nerves sectioned and subjected to the action of X-rays. Riv. speriment. di freniatria, 73: 5.

Gjessing, E. C., and A. Chanutin (1947) An electrophoretic study of plasma and plasma fractions of normal and injured rats. J. Biol. Chem., 169: 657–665.

——— and ——— (1950) Studies on the proteins and lipides of plasma fractions of X-ray-irradiated rats. Arch. Biochem., 27: 191–197.

Glenn, J. C., Jr., (1946) Studies on effects of X-rays on phagocytic indices of healthy rabbits. Preliminary report. J. Immunol., 52: 65–69.

Glücksmann, A. (1947) The effects of radiation on reproductive organs. Brit. J. Radiology, Suppl. 1: pp. 101–108.

Goldberg, R. C., and I. L. Chaikoff (1950) The cytological changes that occur in the anterior pituitary glands of rats injected with various doses of I^{131} and their significance in the estimation of thyroid function. Endocrinology, 46: 91–104.

———, ———, S. Lindsay, and D. D. Feller (1950) Histopathological changes induced in the normal thyroid and other tissues of the rat by internal radiation with various doses of radioactive iodine. Endocrinology, 46: 72–90.

Goldfeder, A., L. Cohen, C. Miller, and M. Singer (1948) Agents influencing experimental radiation injury. Effects of folic acid and pyridoxine. Proc. Soc. Exptl. Biol. Med., 67: 272–278.

——— and J. L. Fershing (1938) Respiration and anaerobic glycolysis of mouse kidney in vitro following radiation. Radiology, 31: 81–88.

Goldman, D. (1943) Metabolic changes occurring as the result of deep roentgen therapy. I. The effect of 200-kv roentgen therapy. Am. J. Roentgenol. Radium Therapy, 50: 381–391.

Goldschmidt, L., R. L. Rosenthal, V. P. Bond, and M. C. Fishler (1951) Alterations in thermal fragility of rat erythrocytes following total body X-irradiation. Am. J. Physiol., 164: 202–206.

Gorbman, A. (1949) Degenerative and regenerative changes in the thyroid gland following high dosages of radioactive iodine. Trans. N. Y. Acad. Sci., 2: 201–203.

Graham, J. B., and R. M. Graham (1950) The modification of resistance to ionizing radiation by humoral agents. Cancer, 3: 709–717.

———, ———, and A. J. Graffeo (1950) The influence of adrenal-cortical hormones on sensitivity of mice to ionizing radiation. Endocrinology, 46: 434–440.

Griffith, J. Q., E. Anthony, E. P. Pendergrass, and R. Perryman (1947) Effect of rutin on recovery time from radiation injury in rats. Proc. Soc. Exptl. Biol. Med., 64: 332–333.

Gustafson, G. E., and S. Koletsky (1951) Effect of oral terramycin prior to whole body X-radiation. Proc. Soc. Exptl. Biol. Med., 78: 489–490.

Halberstaedter, L., and M. Ickowicz (1947) The effects of X-rays on the lymphatic organs of normal and adrenalectomized rats. Radiologica Clinica, 16: 240–257.

——— and J. Liebowitz (1947) Haemolysis and fixation of erythrocytes by X-rays. Biochem. J., 41: 235–239.

Haley, T. J., S. Mann, and A. H. Dowdy (1950) A comparison of the response of normal and hypothyroid mice to acute whole-body roentgen radiation. Science, 112: 333–334.

Hall, C. C., and G. H. Whipple (1919) Roentgen-ray intoxication: Disturbances in metabolism produced by deep massive doses of the hard roentgen rays. Am. J. Med. Sci., 157: 453–482.

Hammond, C. W., and C. P. Miller (1950) The effect of terramycin on postirradiation infection in mice. USAEC Report AECU-873;* Ann. N.Y. Acad. Sci., 53: 303–308.

Hanschuldt, J. D., and H. Supplee (1949) The effect of whole-body X irradiation upon the total nitrogen, total protein, and refractive index of rat plasma. Nav. Radiol. Def. Lab. Report AD-131(B).*

Hedin, R. F., W. R. Miller, and D. G. Jelatis (1950) Effect of β irradiation on gastric acidity. Arch. Surg., 61: 748–757.

Heineke, H. (1903) Uber die Einwirkung der Röentgenstrahlen auf Tiere. Münch. med. Wochschr., 50: 2090–2092.

Hektoen, L. (1915) The influence of the X ray on the production of antibodies. J. Infectious Diseases, 17: 415–422.

Hempelmann, L. H. (1950) The acute radiation syndrome. USAEC Report AECU-379.*

———, H. Lisco, and J. G. Hoffman (1952) The acute radiation syndrome: A study of nine cases and a review of the problem. Ann. Internal Med., 36: 279–510.

———, T. T. Trujillo, and N. P. Knowlton, Jr. (1949) The effect of lethal doses of X rays on chilled and thyroidectomized animals. USAEC Report AECU-239;* Nuclear Sci. Abstr., 3: 46.

Hennessy, T. G., and R. L. Huff (1950) Depression of tracer ion uptake curve in rat erythrocytes following total-body X irradiation. Proc. Soc. Exptl. Biol. Med., 73: 436–439.

Henshaw, P. S. (1944) Experimental roentgen injury. III. Tissue and cellular changes brought about with single massive doses of radiation. J. Natl. Cancer Inst., 4: 503–512.

Hevesy, G. (1946) Effect of X-rays on the rate of turnover of phosphatides. Nature, 158: 268.

——— (1947) Effect of X-rays on phosphatide turnover. Arkiv Kemi, Mineral. Geol., 24A: 26–47.

Hicks, S. P. (1950) Acute necrosis and malformation of developing mammalian brain caused by X-ray. Proc. Soc. Exptl. Biol. Med., 75: 485–489.

Hirsch, H. (1923) Zum Problem des Röntgenkaters. Strahlentherapie, 14: 679–684.

Hodes, P. J., and J. Q. Griffith (1941) Effect of roentgen irradiation upon lymphatic flow in rats. Radiology, 37: 203–204.

Holden, W. D., J. W. Cole, A. F. Portmann, and J. P. Storaasli (1949) Hypothromboplastinemia following total-body irradiation. Proc. Soc. Exptl. Biol. Med., 70: 553–556.

Hollingsworth, J. W. (1950) Effects of X-irradiation on passively transferred antibody. Proc. Soc. Exptl. Biol. Med., 75: 477–479.

Holmes, B. E. (1941) Serum cholesterol and irradiation sickness. Brit. Med. J., 1: 314.

Holmes, G. W., and M. D. Schulz (1950) Therapeutic radiology. Lea & Febiger, Philadelphia.

Howland, J. W., F. Furth, and M. Coulter (1950) Effect of aureomycin and antibiotics on whole body irradiation. Federation Proc., 9: 334.

——— and S. L. Warren (1946) The effects of irradiation from the atomic bomb on the Japanese. USAEC Report MDDC-1301.*

Hubert, R. (1929) Der Einfluss der Röntgenstrahlen auf die energieliefernden Reaktionen des wachsenden Gewebes. Arch. ges. Physiol. (Pflügers), 223: 333–350.

Hueper, W. C., and J. de Carvajal-Forero (1944) The effects of repeated irradiation of the gastric region with small doses of roentgen rays upon the stomach and blood of dogs. Am. J. Roentgenol. Radium Therapy, 52: 529–534.

Hummel, R. (1930) Über Beziehungen zwischen Cholesterinstoffwechsel und Roentgenkater. Strahlentherapie, 38: 308–314.

Hursh, J. B., J. B. Mohney, and P. A. Van Valkenburg (1949) Effect of X-irradiation on thyroid function in rats. USAEC Report AECU-615.*

Impiombato, G. (1935) La radiosensibilità del tessuto renale. Radiol. Med., 22: 487–503.

Ingram, M., and W. B. Mason (1950) The effects of acute exposure to roentgen radiation on the peripheral blood of experimental animals. USAEC Report UR-122.*

Ivy, A. C., J. E. McCarthy, and B. H. Orndoff (1924) Studies on the effect of roentgen rays on glandular activity. J. Am. Med. Assoc., 83: 1977–1984.

Jacobson, L. O., and E. K. Marks (1946) Comparative action of cyclotron fast neutrons and X rays. II. Hematological effects produced in the rabbit by fast neutrons. USAEC Report MDDC-1372.*

———, ———, E. O. Gaston, J. G. Allen, and M. H. Block (1948) The effect of nitrogen mustard and X-irradiation on blood coagulation. J. Lab. Clin. Med., 33: 1566–1578.

———, ———, ———, E. L. Simmons, and M. H. Block (1948) Studies on radiosensitivity of cells. Science, 107: 248–250.

———, ———, and E. Lorenz (1949) The hematological effects of ionizing radiations. Radiology, 52: 371–395.

———, ———, M. J. Robson, E. O. Gaston, and R. E. Zirkle (1949) The effect of spleen protection on mortality following X-irradiation. J. Lab. Clin. Med., 34: 1538–1543.

———, ———, E. L. Simmons, C. W. Hagen, and R. E. Zirkle (1947) Effects of X rays on rabbits. II. The hematological effects of total-body X irradiation in the rabbit. USAEC Report MDDC-1174.*

———, M. J. Robson, and E. K. Marks (1950) The effect of X radiation on antibody formation. Proc. Soc. Exptl. Biol. Med., 75: 145–152.

———, E. L. Simmons, and M. H. Block (1949) The effect of splenectomy on the toxicity of Sr^{89} to the hematopoietic system of mice. J. Lab. Clin. Med., 34: 1640–1655.

———, ———, E. K. Marks, and J. H. Eldredge (1951) Recovery from radiation injury. Science, 113: 510–511.

———, ———, ———, E. O. Gaston, M. J. Robson, and J. H. Eldredge (1951) Further studies on recovery from radiation injury. J. Lab. Clin. Med., 37: 683–697.

———, ———, ———, M. J. Robson, W. F. Bethard, and E. O. Gaston (1950) The role of the spleen in radiation injury and recovery. J. Lab. Clin. Med., 35: 746–770.

———, R. S. Stone, and J. G. Allen (1949) Physicians in an atomic war. J. Am. Med. Assoc., 139: 138–140.

Janzen, A., and S. Warren (1942) Effect of roentgen rays on the peripheral nerve of the rat. Radiology, 38: 333–337.

Jenkinson, E. L., and W. H. Brown (1944) Irradiation sickness: hypothesis concerning basic mechanism and study of therapeutic effect of amphetamine and dextrodesoxyephedrine. Am. J. Roentgenol. Radium Therapy, 51: 496–503.

Jennings, F. L. (1949) Effect of protein depletion upon susceptibility of rats to total-body irradiation. Proc. Soc. Exptl. Biol. Med., 72: 487–491.

Johnson, C. G., C. F. Vilter, and T. D. Spies (1946) Irradiation sickness in rats. Am. J. Roentgenol. Radium Therapy, 56: 631–639.

Jolles, B. (1941) X-ray skin reactions and the protective role of normal tissues. Brit. J. Radiology, 14: 110–112.

——— (1950) The reciprocal vicinity effect of irradiated tissues on "diffusible substance" in irradiated tissues. Brit. J. Radiology, 23: 18–23.

——— and R. G. Mitchell (1947) Optimal skin tolerance dose levels. Brit. J. Radiology, 20: 405–409.

Kanoky, J. P. (1907) Action of the roentgen ray on nerve tissue. Am. J. Dermatol. Genito-urinary Diseases, 11: 327.

Kaplan, H. S., M. B. Brown, and S. N. Marder (1951) Adrenal-cortical function and lymphoid tumor incidence in irradiated mice. Cancer Research, 11: 262–263.

Kaplan, I. I. (1949) Clinical radiation therapy, 2d ed. Paul B. Hoeber, Inc., Medical Book Department of Harper & Brothers, New York, pp. 605–606.

Kelly, K. H., E. T. Feldsted, R. F. Brown, P. Ortega, H. R. Bierman, B. V. A. Low-Beer, and M. B. Shimkin (1951) Irradiation of the normal human hypophysis in malignancy; Report of three cases receiving 8,000–10,000 r tissue dose to the pituitary gland. J. Natl. Cancer Inst., 11: 967–984.

Kelly, L. S., and H. B. Jones (1950) Effects of irradiation on nucleic acid formation. Proc. Soc. Exptl. Biol. Med., 74: 493–497.

Kelsall, M. A., and E. D. Crabb (1952) Increased mast cells in the thymus of X-irradiated hamsters. Science, 115: 123–125.

Kimeldorf, D. J., D. C. Jones, and M. C. Fishler (1950) The effect of exercise upon the lethality of roentgen rays for rats. Science, 112: 175–176.

Kirschner, L. B., C. L. Prosser, and H. Quastler (1949) Increased metabolic rate in rats after X-irradiation. Proc. Soc. Exptl. Biol. Med., 71: 463–467.

Kohn, H. I. (1950) Changes in blood plasma of guinea-pig during acute radiation syndrome. Am. J. Physiol., 162: 703–708.

——— (1951a) Changes in composition of blood plasma of the rat during acute radiation syndrome, and their partial mitigation by dibenamine and cortin. Am. J. Physiol., 165: 27–42.

——— (1951b) Effect of immaturity, hypophysectomy, and adrenalectomy upon changes in blood plasma of rat during acute radiation syndrome. Am. J. Physiol., 165: 43–56.

——— (1951c) Effect of X rays upon hemolysin production in the rat. J. Immunol., 66: 525–533.

——— and P. Robinett (1948) The effect of heparin upon the LD-50% of the X-irradiated rat. USAEC Report ORNL-116.*

———, ———, and M. N. Cupp (1948) The effects of rutin upon the response of the rat to total body X irradiation. USAEC Report AECD-2176.*

Koletsky, S., and J. H. Christie (1950) Effect of antibiotics on mortality from internal radiation. Proc. Soc. Exptl. Biol. Med., 75: 363–366.

Kotz, J., J. F. Elward, and E. Parker (1941) Non-harmful effects of irradiation of the pituitary region of rabbits. Am. J. Roentgenol. Radium Therapy, 46: 543–549.

Krause, P., and K. Ziegler (1906) Experimentelle Untersuchungen ueber die Einwirkung der Roentgenstrahlen auf tierisches Gewebe. Fortschr. Gebiete Röntgenstrahlen, 10: 126–182.

Kretzschmar, C. H., and F. Ellis (1947) The effect of X rays on ascorbic acid concentration in plasma and in tissues. Brit. J. Radiology, 20: 94–99.

Krizek, H., I. Silverbach, and S. Schwartz (1946) The effect of lethal dose of total-body X ray on uric acid and allantoin excretion in dogs. USAEC Report MDDC-1674.*

Larkin, J. C. (1941) An erythematous skin reaction produced by an alpha-particle beam. Case report. Am. J. Roentgenol. Radium Therapy, 45: 109.

——— (1942) Some physiological changes in the skin produced by neutrons. Am. J. Roentgenol. Radium Therapy, 47: 733–739.

——— (1949) Effect of atropine on acute irradiation sickness in mice. Am. J. Roentgenol. Radium Therapy, 62: 547–549.

Läwen, A. (1909) Cited by C. G. Craddock and J. S. Lawrence (1948), *in* The effect of roentgen irradiation on antibody formation in rabbits. J. Immunol., 60: 241–254.

Lawrence, G. H. (1949) The effect of total body X-radiation on 17-ketosteroid excretion in dogs. Nav. Med. Research Inst. Report NM-007-039,* No. 22; Endocrinology, 45: 383–388.

Lawrence, J. H., and E. O. Lawrence (1936) The biological action of neutron rays. Proc. Natl. Acad. Sci., 22: 124–133.

——— and R. Tennant (1937) The comparative effects of neutrons and X-rays on the whole body. J. Exptl. Med., 66: 667–688.

Lawrence, J. S., A. H. Dowdy, and W. N. Valentine (1948) Effects of radiation on hemopoiesis. Radiology, 51: 400–413.

———, W. N. Valentine, and A. H. Dowdy (1948) Effects of radiation on hemopoiesis. Is there an indirect effect? Blood, 3: 593–611.

Lazarew, N. W., and A. Lazarewa (1926) Über die funktionellen Veränderungen der Blutgefässe nach Röntgenbestrahlung. Strahlentherapie, 23: 41–78.

Leach, J. E., and K. Sugiura (1942) Late effect of high-voltage roentgen rays on the heart of adult rats. Am. J. Roentgenol. Radium Therapy, 48: 81–87.

Leblond, C. P., and G. Segal (1942) Differentiation between the direct and indirect effects of roentgen rays upon the organs of normal and adrenalectomized rats. Am. J. Roentgenol. Radium Therapy, 47: 302–306.

Lecomte, J., and P. Fischer (1949) Circulating antibodies and the alarm syndrome brought on by X-irradiation. Compt. rend. soc. biol., 143: 878–879.

Leinfelder, P. S., and H. D. Kerr (1936) Roentgen-ray cataract: An experimental, clinical, and microscopic study. Am. J. Ophthalmol., 19: 739–756.

LeMay, M. (1951) Effect of X-radiation upon succinoxidase of the rat kidney. Proc. Soc. Exptl. Biol. Med., 77: 337–339.

Lick, L., A. Kirschbaum, and H. Mixer (1949) Mechanisms of induction of ovarian tumors by X-rays. Cancer Research, 9: 532–536.

Liebow, A. A., S. Warren, and E. DeCoursey (1949) Pathology of atomic bomb casualties. Am. J. Path., 25: 853–1027.

Liechti, A., and W. Wilbrandt (1941) Radiation hemolysis. I. Hemolysis by roentgen rays. Strahlentherapie, 70: 541–567.

Light, A. E. (1935) A histologic study of the effects of X-rays on frog skin. Radiology, 25: 734–738.

Lorenz, E., C. C. Congdon, and D. Uphoff (1952) Modifications of acute radiation injury in mice and guinea pigs by bone-marrow injections. Radiology, 58: 863–877.

———, W. E. Heston, L. O. Jacobson, A. B. Eschenbrenner, M. Shimkin, M. K. Deringer, and J. Doninger (1946) Biologic effects of long-continued whole-body irradiation with gamma rays on mice, guinea pigs, and rabbits. III. Biological effect of whole body irradiation with gamma rays: effects on life span, weight, blood picture, and carcinogenesis, and the role of intensity of the radiation. USAEC Report MDDC-655.*

———, D. Uphoff, T. R. Reid, and E. Shelton (1951) Modification of irradiation injury in mice and guinea pigs by bone-marrow injections. J. Natl. Cancer Inst., 12: 197–201.

Lourau, M., and O. Lartigue (1950a) Modifications of glycemia under the influence of total X-ray radiation. Compt. rend., 230: 1426–1428.

——— and ——— (1950b) Influence du régime alimentaire sur les effets biologiques produits par une irradiation unique de tout le corps (rayons X). Experientia, 6: 25–26.

Low-Beer, A. (1933) Experimentelle Untersuchungen zur Frage der biologischen Roentgenstrahlenwirkung. Strahlentherapie, 46: 469–516.

Ludewig, S., and A. Chanutin (1950a) Effect of X-ray irradiation on alkaline phosphatase of plasma and tissues of rats. Am. J. Physiol., 163: 648–654.

——— and ——— (1950b) Distribution of enzymes in the livers of control and X-irradiated rats. Arch. Biochem., 29: 441–445.

Lukens, R. M. (1948) Complications following irradiation of the thyroid gland. Ann. Otol. Rhinol. and Laryngol., 57: 633–642.

Lutwak-Mann, C., and F. W. Gunz (1949) Effect of body exposure to X rays upon bone marrow. Biochem. J., Vol. 44, Proc. iii, No. 2.

Macht, S. H., and H. Perlberg, Jr. (1950) Use of anticoagulant (dicumarol) in preventing postirradiation tissue changes in the human lung; preliminary report. Am. J. Roentgenol. Radium Therapy, 63: 335–341.

Marder, S. N., H. S. Kaplan, and E. Lorenz (1948) Lack of effect of adrenalectomy on the lymphopenic response of C57 black mice to total-body irradiation at a low dosage level. USAEC Report ANL-4227,* pp. 21–27.

Martin, C. L. (1950) Radiation therapy in diseases of the female genital organs, *in* E. A. Pohle, Clinical radiation therapy. Lea & Febiger, Philadelphia, pp. 300–490.

——— and F. T. Rogers (1923) Intestinal reaction to erythema dose. Am. J. Roentgenol. Radium Therapy, 10: 11–19.

———, ———, and N. F. Fisher (1924) The effect of roentgen rays on the adrenal gland. Am. J. Roentgenol. Radium Therapy, 12: 466–471.

Martland, H. S. (1926) Microscopic changes of certain anemias due to radiosensitivity. Arch. Path. Lab. Med., 2: 465–472.

——— (1931) The occurrence of malignancy in radioactive persons. Am. J. Cancer, 15: 2435–2516.

McQuarrie, I., and G. H. Whipple (1922) A study of renal function in roentgen-ray intoxication. Resistance of renal epithelium to direct radiation. J. Exptl. Med., 35: 225–242.

Mead, J. F., A. B. Decker, and L. R. Bennett (1950) The effect of X-irradiation upon fat absorption in the mouse. USAEC Report UCLA-90;* J. Nutrition, 43: 485–500 (1951).

Miescher, G. (1923) Über den Einfluss der Röntgenstrahlen auf die Sekretion des Magens. Strahlentherapie, 15: 252–272.

——— (1924) Das Röntgenerythem. Strahlentherapie, 16: 333–371.

——— (1938) Vergleichende Untersuchungen zur Frage der Spezifitaet der Roentgenwirkung. Licht-, Waerm-, Roentgen-, und Thorium-X-Reaktion. Strahlentherapie, 61: 4–37.

Miller, C. P., C. W. Hammond, and M. Tompkins (1950a) The incidence of bacteremia in mice subjected to total-body X radiation. Science, 111: 540–541.

———, ———, and ——— (1950b) Reduction of mortality from X radiation by treatment with antibiotics. Science, 111: 719–720.

Miyazaki, K. (1937) Effect of X ray (50–100 r) on urinary excretion of creatine, creatinine, uric acid, and allantoin. Sei-i-Kei Med. J., 56: 2085–2104; Chem. Abstr., 32: 5011, 1938.

Montgomery, P. O., and S. Warren (1951) Mechanism of acute hypotension following total-body irradiation. Proc. Soc. Exptl. Biol. Med., 77: 803–807.

Moon, V. H., K. Kornblum, and D. R. Morgan (1940) Pathology of irradiation sickness: A new method for inducing shock. Proc. Soc. Exptl. Biol. Med., 43: 305–306.

———, ———, and ——— (1941) The nature and pathology of radiation sickness. J. Am. Med. Assoc., 116: 489–493.

Mottram, J. C., and L. H. Gray (1940) The relative response of the skin of mice to X radiation and gamma radiation. Brit. J. Radiology, 13: 31–34.

——— and A. N. Kingsbury (1924) Some researches into the action of radium and X rays correlating the production of intestinal changes, thrombopoenia, and bacterial invasion. Brit. J. Exptl. Path., 5: 220–226.

Muntz, J. A., E. S. G. Barron, and C. L. Prosser (1949) Studies on the mechanism of action of ionizing radiations. III. The plasma protein of dogs after X-ray irradiation. Arch. Biochem., 23: 434–445.

Murphy, J. B., and E. Sturm (1925) A comparison of the effects of X-ray and dry heat on antibody formation. J. Exptl. Med., 41: 245–255.

Murray, R., M. Pierce, and L. O. Jacobson (1948) The histological effects of X-rays on chickens with special reference to the peripheral blood and hemopoietic organs. USAEC Report AECD-2303.*

Narat, J. K. (1922) Treatment after irradiation with roentgen ray. J. Am. Med. Assoc., 79: 1681–1684.

Neve, R. A., and C. Entenman (1951) Changes in the plasma phospholipids in rats following whole body X-irradiation. Nav. Radiol. Def. Lab. Report AD-307(B).*

Nizet, E., C. Heusghem, and A. Herve (1949) Suprarenal cortex reactions following the administration of X-rays from a distance in the rabbit. Compt. rend. soc. biol., 143: 876–877.

North, N., and L. F. Nims (1949) Time-dose study of biochemical responses of rats to X-radiation. Federation Proc. 8: 119–120.

Novick, R. (1946) Time course of changes in sensory cells of trigeminal ganglion of the rabbit following irradiation. Proc. Soc. Exptl. Biol. Med., 61: 355–358.

Oster, R. H., and W. T. Salter (1938) Immunization against neoplasm. Its effect on the nitrogen metabolism of the host. Am. J. Cancer, 32: 422–433.

Packard, C. (1933) Biologic effects of roentgen rays and radium, *in* Science of radiology. Charles C Thomas, Publisher, Springfield, Ill., Chap. 18, pp. 319–331.

Painter, E. E. (1948) Alterations in the sodium space of the gastrointestinal tract of X-rayed and of fasted rats. USAEC Report ANL-4253,* pp. 88–95.

——— and A. M. Brues (1949) The radiation syndrome. New Engl. J. Med., 240: 871–876.

———, C. L. Prosser, and M. C. Moore (1947) Physiological observations on rabbits exposed to single doses of X rays. USAEC Report MDDC-761.*

——— and E. W. Pullman (1950) Water and electrolyte changes in rat intestine after total-body X radiation. Federation Proc., 9: 97.

Parkes, A. S. (1948) Effects on early embryonic development of irradiation of spermatozoa. Brit. J. Radiology, Suppl. 1, pp. 117–120.

Patt, H. M., S. Mayer, R. L. Straube, and E. Jackson (1952) Unpublished observations.

———, D. E. Smith, and E. Jackson (1950) The effect of cysteine on the peripheral blood of the irradiated rat. Blood, 5: 758–763.

———, R. L. Straube, E. B. Tyree, M. N. Swift, and D. E. Smith (1949) Influence of estrogens on the acute X-irradiation syndrome. Am. J. Physiol., 159: 269–280.

———, M. N. Swift, and E. B. Tyree (1949) Oxygen consumption and water balance in the X-irradiated frog. Federation Proc., 8: 124.

———, ———, ———, and E. S. John (1947) Adrenal response to total body X-radiation. Am. J. Physiol., 150: 480–487.

———, ———, ———, and R. L. Straube (1948) X irradiation of the hypophysectomized rat. Science, 108: 475–476.

Pendergrass, E. P., P. J. Hodes, and J. Q. Griffith (1944) Effect of roentgen rays on the minute vessels of the skin in man. Am. J. Roentgenol. Radium Therapy, 52: 123–127.

——— and J. F. Mahoney (1948) A consideration of the roentgen therapy in producing temporary depilation for *Tinea capitis:* a new method. Radiology, 50: 468–481.

Penick, G. D., E. P. Cronkite, I. D. Godwin, and K. M. Brinkhaus (1951) Plasma antihemophilic activity following total body irradiation. Proc. Soc. Exptl. Biol. Med., 78: 732–734.

Pierce, M. (1948) The gastrointestinal tract, *in* Histopathology of irradiation from external and internal sources, W. Bloom, ed. McGraw-Hill Book Company, Inc., New York, National Nuclear Energy Series, Div. IV, Vol. 22I, Chap. 10.

Pohle, E. A. (1926) Studies of the roentgen erythema of the human skin. I. Skin capillary changes after exposure to unfiltered radiation. Radiology, 6: 236–245.

——— (1927) Studies of the roentgen erythema of the human skin. II. Skin capillary changes after exposure to filtered roentgen rays and to ultraviolet radiation. Radiology, 8: 185–194.

——— and C. H. Bunting (1932) Studies of the effect of roentgen rays on the liver. Histological changes in liver of rats following exposure to single graded doses of filtered roentgen rays. Acta Radiol., 13: 117–124.

Pratt, A. W., B. E. Burr, M. Eden, and E. Lorenz (1950) Preliminary report: Mass spectrometer analysis of the respired air of rats. USAEC Report ANL-4531,* pp. 40–46.

Prosser, C. L., and M. C. Moore (1946) The clinical physiology of dogs exposed to daily total-body doses of X rays. USAEC Report MDDC-1271.*

———, E. E. Painter, H. Lisco, A. M. Brues, L. O. Jacobson, and M. N. Swift (1947) The clinical sequence of physiological effects of ionizing radiation in animals. Radiology, 49: 299–313.

———, ——— and M. N. Swift (1947) The clinical physiology of dogs exposed to single total-body doses of X-rays. USAEC Report MDDC-1272.*

Pullinger, B. D. (1932) Causes of cell death in irradiated human tissue. J. Path. Bact., 35: 527–540.

Quastler, H., E. F. Lanzl, M. E. Keller, and J. W. Osborne (1951) Acute intestinal radiation death. Studies on roentgen death in mice. III. Am. J. Physiol., 164: 546–556.

Raab, W. (1941) Abnormal suprarenal discharges in angina pectoris and their control by X-ray therapy. J. Clin. Endocrinol., 1: 977–982.

——— and A. B. Soule, Jr. (1927) Effect of roentgen irradiation on the hormone content and secretion of the adrenal medulla. Radiology, 41: 56–60.

Raper, J. R., and K. K. Barnes (1951a) Effects of external irradiation with beta rays on the peripheral blood of rabbits, *in* Biological effects of external beta radiation, R. E. Zirkle, ed. McGraw-Hill Book Company, Inc., New York, National Nuclear Energy Series, Div. IV, Vol. 22E, Chap. 10.

——— and ——— (1951b) Gross effects of total-surface beta irradiation, *in* Biological effects of external beta radiation, R. E. Zirkle, ed. McGraw-Hill Book Company, Inc., New York, National Nuclear Energy Series, Div. IV, Vol. 22E, Chap. 4.

——— and ——— (1951c) Additivity of lethal effects of external beta and gamma radiation, II, *in* Biological effects of external beta radiation, R. E. Zirkle, ed. McGraw-Hill Book Company, Inc., New York, National Nuclear Energy Series, Div. IV, Vol. 22E, Chap. 7.

———, R. E. Zirkle, and K. K. Barnes (1951) Comparative lethal effects of external beta irradiation, *in* Biological effects of external beta radiation, R. E. Zirkle, ed. McGraw-Hill Book Company, Inc., New York, National Nuclear Energy Series, Div. IV, Vol. 22E, Chap. 3.

Regaud, C., and T. Nogier (1913) Les éffets produits sur la peau par les hautes doses de rayons X sélectionnés par la filtration à travers 3 à 4 millimètres d'aluminium. Arch. d'électric méd., 21: 49–97.

———, ———, and A. Lacassagne (1912) Sur les effets redoutables des irradiations étendues de l'abdomen et sur les lésions du tube digestif determinées par les rayons de Roentgen. Arch. d'électric méd., 21: 321–334.

Rekers, P. E. (1949) Transplantation of bone marrow into dogs that have received total-body single dose radiation. USAEC Report AECD-1966.*

———, M. P. Coulter, and S. L. Warren (1950) Effect of transplantation of bone marrow into irradiated animals. Arch. Surg., 60: 635–667.

——— and J. B. Field (1948) Control of hemorrhagic syndrome and reduction in X-irradiation mortality with a flavanone. Science, 107: 16–17.

Rhoades, R. P. (1948a) Structures accessory to the gastrointestinal tract, *in* Histopathology of irradiation from external and internal sources, W. Bloom, ed. McGraw-Hill Book Company, Inc., New York, National Nuclear Energy Series, Div. IV, Vol. 22I, Chap. 11.

——— (1948b) The adrenal, *in* Histopathology of irradiation from external and internal sources, W. Bloom, ed. McGraw-Hill Book Company, Inc., New York, National Nuclear Energy Series, Div. IV, Vol. 22I, Chap. 17.

Ricketts, W. E., J. B. Kirsner, E. M. Humphreys, and W. L. Palmer (1948) Effect of roentgen irradiation on the gastric mucosa. Gastroenterology, 11: 818–832.

Rigdon, R. H., and H. Curl (1943) Effect of roentgen irradiation on capillary permeability and inflammation in the skin of the rabbit. Am. J. Roentgenol. Radium Therapy, 49: 250–257.

Robbins, R. L., J. C. Aub, O. Cope, D. G. Cogan, J. L. Langohr, R. W. Cloud, and O. E. Merrill (1946) Superficial "burns" of skin and eyes from scattered cathode rays. Radiology, 46: 1–23.

Robertson, J. E. (1943) Metabolic changes occurring as the result of deep roentgen therapy. Effect of 1000-kv roentgen therapy. Am. J. Roentgenol. Radium Therapy, 50: 392–399.

Rolleston, H. (1930) The harmful effects of irradiation (X-rays and radium). Quart. J. Med., 24: 101–131.

Rosenthal, R. L. (1949) Opalescence of serum after total-body X-irradiation as a prognostic sign of death. Science, 110: 43–44.

——— and A. L. Benedek (1950) Biological studies of radiation effects. Effects of total-body X-irradiation on blood coagulation in the rabbit (preliminary study). USAEC Report AECU-592;* Am. J. Physiol., 161: 505–514.

———, B. I. Pickering, and L. Goldschmidt (1950) A semiquantitative study of bone marrow in rats following total-body X-irradiation. Nav. Radiol. Def. Lab. Report AD-217(B);* Blood, 6: 600–613 (1951).

Ross, M. H., and J. O. Ely (1947) Effects of large doses of neutrons on dogs, *in* Neutron effects on animals, E. MacDonald, ed. The Williams & Wilkins Company, Baltimore, Chap. 19.

——— and ——— (1949a) Neutron and roentgen-ray effects on protein content of rat intestine. Am. J. Roentgenol. Radium Therapy, 62: 718–722.

——— and ——— (1949b) Neutron effects on alkaline phosphatase of rat intestine. Am. J. Roentgenol. Radium Therapy, 62: 723–725.

Russell, D. S., C. W. Wilson, and K. Tansley (1949) Experimental radionecrosis of the brain in rabbits. J. Neurol. Neurosurg. Psychiatr., 12: 187–195.

Sanigar, E. B., G. L. Miller, and M. N. Maddox (1947) Electrophoresis of the plasma of rabbits irradiated with neutrons, *in* Neutron effects on animals, E. MacDonald, ed. The Williams & Wilkins Company, Baltimore, Chap. 14.

Sayers, G. (1950) Adrenal cortex and homeostasis. Physiol. Rev., 30: 241–320.

———, M. N. Sayers, E. G. Fry, A. White, and C. N. H. Long (1944) The effect of the adrenotrophic hormone of the anterior pituitary on the cholesterol content of the adrenals (with a review of the literature on adrenal cholesterol). Yale J. Biol. Med., 16: 361–392.

Schack, J. A., and R. C. MacDuffee (1949) Increased radioresistance of red bone marrow after anoxia. Science, 110: 259–260.

Schoenberg, M. D., R. E. Brooks, J. J. Hall, and H. Schneiderman (1950) Effect of X irradiation on the hyaluronidase-hyaluronic acid system. USAEC Report UCLA-83;* Arch. Biochem., 30: 333–340 (1951).

Schöttelndreyer, H. (1949) Studies of the effect of the protraction of X radiation by 12 fractionations on the erythema reactions. Brit. J. Radiology, 22: 386–392.

Schrek, R. (1946) Studies in vitro on cellular physiology. The effect of X rays on the survival of cells. Radiology, 46: 395–410.

Schwab, L., F. C. Moll, T. Hall, H. Bream, M. Kirk, C. von Sandt Hawn, and C. A. Janeway (1950) Experimental hypersensitivity in the rabbit. J. Exptl. Med., 91: 505–526.

Schwartz, S., E. J. Katz, L. M. Porter, L. O. Jacobson, and C. J. Watson (1947) Studies of the hemolytic effect of radiation. USAEC Report MDDC-1342.*

———, L. Schneider, L. M. Porter, M. Tinsley, and J. Wallace (1948) Studies of liver function in experimental animals with special reference to radiation and metal exposure. USAEC Report CH-3855.*

Seldin, M. (1904) Über die Wirkung der Röntgen und Radiumstrahlen auf innere Organe und den Gesamtorganismus der Tiere. Fortschr. Gebiete Röntgenstrahlen, 7: 322–339.

Selye, H. (1946) General adaptation syndrome and diseases of adaptation. J. Clin. Endocrinol., 6: 117–230.

Setala, K., and P. Ermala (1948) On irradiation sickness. Ann. Chirurg. gynaecol. Fenniae, 37 (Suppl. 1): 1–60.

Shacter, B. (1951) Effect of X-irradiation and of radiomimetic substances on the sulfhydryl content of plasma: Relationship to adrenal activity following stress. Cancer Research, 2: 277–278.

Shechmeister, I. L., and V. P. Bond (1951) Response of mice to certain avirulent bacteria after exposure to sublethal total body X-irradiation. Proc. Soc. Exptl. Biol. Med., 77: 77–80.

———, ———, and M. N. Swift (1950) The susceptibility of irradiated mice to infection as a function of post-irradiation time. Nav. Radiol. Def. Lab. Report AD-279(B).*

Shorvon, L. M. (1949) A further survey of radiation sickness with particular reference to its treatment by pyridoxine. Brit. J. Radiology, 22: 49–55.

Shouse, S. S., S. L. Warren, and G. H. Whipple (1931) Aplasia of marrow and fatal intoxication in dogs produced by roentgen radiation of all bones. J. Exptl. Med., 53: 421–435.

Silverman, S. B. (1949) Changes in the coagulability of the blood after radiation therapy. The results of studies using the modified Waugh-Ruddick test for increased coagulability. Am. J. Roentgenol. Radium Therapy, 62: 541–546.

Simmons, E. L., L. O. Jacobson, N. Pearlman, and C. L. Prosser (1946) The effectiveness of drugs in preventing or alleviating X-ray damage. USAEC Report MDDC-1277.*

Simon, N. (1949) Suppression of gastric acidity with beta particles of P^{32}. Science, 109: 563–564.

Skanse, B. N. (1948) The biologic effect of irradiation by radioactive iodine. J. Clin. Endocrinol., 8: 707–716.

Smith, D. E., G. Svihla, and H. M. Patt (1951) The effects of X-radiation on circulation in the wing of the bat. Physiol. Zool., 24: 249–257.

———, E. B. Tyree, H. M. Patt, and N. Bink (1951) The effects of total- and partial-body irradiation upon the body weight, and intake of food and water of the rat. The effects of various feeding procedures and cysteine upon the post-irradiation changes in body weight of the rat. USAEC Report ANL-4713,* pp. 53–58.

———, ———, ———, and E. Jackson (1951) Effect of total-body X irradiation on metabolism of the rat. Proc. Soc. Exptl. Biol. Med., 78: 774–777.

Smith, F., and W. W. Smith (1951) Exercise effects on tolerance to radiation. Am. J. Physiol., 165: 662–666.

Smith, T. R., L. O. Jacobson, C. L. Spurr, J. G. Allen, and M. H. Block (1948) A coagulation defect produced by nitrogen mustard. Science, 107: 474.

Smith, W. W. (1951) Acute KCl and histamine tolerance and adrenal weight in X-irradiated mice. Am. J. Physiol., 167: 321–327.

——— and F. Smith (1951a) Effect of thyroid hormone on radiation lethality. Am. J. Physiol., 165: 639–650.

——— and ——— (1951b) Effects of thyroid and radiation on sensitivity to hypoxia, basal rate of O_2 consumption and tolerance to exercise. Am. J. Physiol., 165: 651–661.

———, ———, and E. C. Thompson (1950) Failure of cortisone or ACTH to reduce mortality in irradiated mice. Proc. Soc. Exptl. Biol. Med., 73: 529–531.

Smyth, F. S., and G. H. Whipple (1924) Bile salt metabolism. II. Proteose and X ray intoxication. J. Biol. Chem., 59: 637–646.

Snell, G. D. (1935) Induction by X-rays of hereditary changes in mice. Genetics, 20: 545–567.

Snider, R. S. (1948) The nervous system, *in* Histopathology of irradiation from external and internal sources, W. Bloom, ed. McGraw-Hill Book Company, Inc., New York, National Nuclear Energy Series, Div. IV, Vol. 22I, Chap. 18.

Soberman, R. J., R. P. Keating, and R. D. Maxwell (1951) Effect of acute whole-body X-irradiation upon water and electrolyte balance. Am. J. Physiol., 164: 450–456.

Sokoloff, B., J. B. Redd, and R. Dutcher (1950) Vitamin P protection against radiation. Science, 112: 112–113.

Stapleton, G. E., and H. J. Curtis (1946) The effects of fast neutrons on the ability of mice to take forced exercise. USAEC Report MDDC-696.*

Stearner, S. P. (1948) Effects of folic acid on the anemia induced by X irradiation. Proc. Soc. Exptl. Biol. Med., 69: 518–521.

———, E. J. B. Christian, and A. M. Brues (1951) Effects of X irradiation on renal function in newly-hatched chicks. Proc. Soc. Exptl. Biol. Med., 78: 676–679.

———, E. L. Simmons, and L. O. Jacobson (1947a) The effects of total body X-irradiation on the peripheral blood and blood-forming tissues of the rat. USAEC Report MDDC-1319;* Anat. Record, 99: 576–577.

———, ———, and ——— (1947b) The effects of X-irradiation on the peripheral blood and blood-forming tissues of splenectomized rats. USAEC Report AECD-2022.*

Storey, R. H., L. Wish, and J. Furth (1950) Changes in cell and plasma volumes produced by total body X radiation. Proc. Soc. Exptl. Biol. Med., 74: 242–244.

Straube, R. L., H. M. Patt, E. B. Tyree, and D. E. Smith (1949) Influence of level of adrenal-cortical steroids on sensitivity of mice to X irradiation. Proc. Soc. Exptl. Biol. Med., 71: 539–541.

Strauss, O., and J. Rother (1924) Strahlenwirkung auf das vegetative System. Strahlentherapie, 18: 37–63.

Suter, G. M. (1947) Response of hematopoietic system to X-rays. USAEC Report MDDC-824.*

Swann, M. B. R. (1924) A study of the immediate effects of X rays on the functions of certain tissues and organs. Brit. J. Radiology, 29: 195–220.

Swift, M. N., H. M. Patt, and E. B. Tyree (1948) The effect of adrenal cortical extract on adrenal response to total body X-irradiation. Federation Proc., 7: 121.

Talbot, J. M, and E. A. Pinson (1951) The experimental use of bone marrow in acute radiation injury. Military Surgeon, 108: 412–417.

Taliaferro, W. H., and L. G. Taliaferro (1951) Effect of X-rays on immunity: A review. J. Immunol., 66: 181–212.

———, ———, and E. L. Simmons (1945) Increased parasitemia in chicken malaria (*Plasmodium gallinaceum* and *Plasmodium lophurae*) following X-irradiation. J. Infectious Diseases, 77: 158–176.

Thaddea, S. (1940) Klinische Erscheinungsformen der Nebenniereninsuffizienz. Klin. med. Wochschr., 19: 145–151.

Ting, T. P., and R. E. Zirkle (1940) The nature and cause of the hemolysis produced by X-rays. J. Cellular Comp. Physiol., 16: 189–195.

Toolan, H. W. (1951) Proliferation and vascularization of adult human epithelium in subcutaneous tissues of X-irradiated heterologous hosts. Proc. Soc. Exptl. Biol. Med., 78: 540–543.

Torda, C., and H. G. Wolff (1950) Effect of lymphoid necrosis due to nitrogen mustard and roentgen irradiation on neuromuscular function of hypophysectomized animals. Am. J. Physiol., 163: 201–208.

Torgersen, O. (1940) Histological studies on the normal and the irradiated suprarenal gland in rabbits. Skrifter Norske Videnskaps-Akad. Oslo, I. Mat. Naturv. Klasse, No. 2.

Toyoma, T. (1933a) Über die Wirkung der Röntgenstrahlen auf die Dormbewegungen des Kaninchens. Tôhoku J. Exptl. Med., 22: 196–200.

——— (1933b) Über die Wirkung der Röntgenstrahlen auf den Blutdruk des Kaninchens. Tôhoku J. Exptl. Med., 22: 335–341.

Tsuzuki, M. (1926) Experimental studies on the biological action of hard roentgen rays. Am. J. Roentgenol. Radium Therapy, 16: 134–150.

Ullmann, T. (1933) Ueber die Einwirkung der Röntgenstrahlen auf den Kohlenhydratstoffwechsel normaler tierischer Gewebe. Strahlentherapie, 46: 705–712.

Valentine, W. N., C. G. Craddock, and J. S. Lawrence (1948) The effect of roentgen radiation on the production of thoracic duct lymphocytes. USAEC Report AECD- 2023.*

——— and M. L. Pearce (1951) Studies on the radiosensitivity of bone marrow. I. The relative sensitivity of erythroid and myeloid elements. USAEC Report UCLA-123.*

———, ———, and J. S. Lawrence (1951) Studies on the radiosensitivity of bone marrow. II. The effect of large, repeated whole-body irradiation exposure on hematopoiesis. USAEC Report UCLA-124.*

Venters, K. D., and E. E. Painter (1950) Sensitivity of X-rayed animals to infusion of histamine, adenosine and trypsin. Federation Proc., 9: 129.

Volkin, E., and H. I. Kohn (1950) A factor in the plasma of the irradiated rat which changes the A/G ratio. USAEC Report ORNL-734.*

Walsh, D. (1897) Deep tissue traumatism from Roentgen-ray exposure. Brit. Med. J., 2: 272–273.

Warren, S. (1942) Effects of radiation on normal tissues. VII. Effects of radiation on the urinary system. The kidneys and ureters. Arch. Path., 34: 1079–1084.

——— (1943a) Effects of radiation on normal tissues. IX. Effects on the nervous system. Arch. Path., 35: 127–139.

——— (1943b) Effects of radiation on normal tissues. XI. Effects on endocrine glands. Arch. Path., 35: 313–322.

——— (1943c) Effects of radiation on normal tissues. XIII. Effects on the skin. Arch. Path., 35: 340–347.

——— (1946) Pathologic effects of instantaneous dose of radiation. Cancer Research, 6: 449–453.

——— and J. Z. Bowers (1950) The acute radiation syndrome in man. Ann. Internal Med., 32: 207–216.

——— and A. M. Brues (1950) Protection against radiation hazards. Nucleonics, 7: 70–76.

——— and N. B. Friedman (1942) Pathology and pathological diagnosis of radiation lesions in the gastro-intestinal tract. Am. J. Path., 18: 499–513.

———, J. C. MacMillan, and F. J. Dixon (1950a) Effects of internal irradiation of mice with P^{32}. I. Spleen, lymph nodes, thymus, bone and bone marrow. Radiology, 55: 375–389.

———, ———, and ——— (1950b) Effects of internal irradiation of mice with P^{32}. II. Gonads, kidneys, adrenal glands, digestive tract, spinal cord, lungs, and liver. Radiology, 55: 557–570.

Warren, S. L., and G. H. Whipple (1922a) Roentgen-ray intoxication. J. Exptl. Med., 35: 187–201.

——— and ——— (1922b) Roentgen ray intoxication. II. A study of the sequence of clinical, anatomical and histological changes following a unit dose of X-rays. J. Exptl. Med., 35: 203–211.

——— and ——— (1922c) Roentgen ray intoxication. III. Speed of autolysis of various body tissues after lethal X-ray exposures. J. Exptl. Med., 35: 213–224.
——— and ——— (1923a) Roentgen ray intoxication. I. Bacterial invasion of the blood stream as influenced by X-ray destruction of the mucosal epithelium of the small intestine. J. Exptl. Med., 38: 713–723.
——— and ——— (1923b) Roentgen-ray intoxication. The cumulative effect or summation of X-ray exposures given at varying intervals. J. Exptl. Med., 38: 725–730.
——— and ——— (1923c) The path of a beam of hard rays in the living organism. J. Exptl. Med., 38: 731–739.
——— and ——— (1923d) Intestinal lesions and acute intoxication produced by radiation in a variety of animals. J. Exptl. Med., 38: 741–752.
Wattenberg, L., and S. Schwartz (1946a) Radiation-induced changes in ultraviolet absorption spectra of urine. I. General effects. USAEC Report MDDC-700.*
——— and ——— (1946b) Radiation-induced changes in ultraviolet absorption spectra of urine. II. Quantitative spectrophotometric studies. USAEC Report MDDC-701.*
Weber, R. P., and F. R. Steggerda (1949) Histamine in rat plasma: Correlation with blood pressure changes following X irradiation. Proc. Soc. Exptl. Biol. Med., 70: 261–263.
Weichert, U. (1942) Treatment of the so-called roentgen sickness with desoxycorticosterone. Strahlentherapie, 71: 127–138.
Wels, P. (1924) Zur Wirkung der Röntgenstrahlen auf die Gewebsatmung. Arch. ges. Physiol. (Pflügers), 206: 268–273.
Wilder, H. C., and R. M. Maynard (1951) Ocular changes produced by total body irradiation. Am. J. Path., 27: 1–19.
Wilson, J. G., and J. W. Karr (1950) Difference in the effects of X-irradiation in rat embryos of different ages. Anat. Record, 106: 259–260.
Wish, L., J. Furth, C. W. Sheppard, and R. H. Storey (1952) Disappearance rate of tagged substances from the circulation of roentgen irradiated animals. Am. J. Roentgenol. Radium Therapy Nuclear Med. 67: 628–640.
Zunz, E., and J. La Barre (1927) Action des rayons X sur l'adrénalinémie. Compt. rend. soc. biol., 96: 126–127.

Manuscript received by the editor June 20, 1952

CHAPTER 16

The Hematologic Effects of Ionizing Radiation

LEON O. JACOBSON

Professor of Medicine, Department of Medicine, The University of Chicago, Chicago; Scientific Director of the Argonne Cancer Research Hospital of the University of Chicago; Division of Biological and Medical Research, Argonne National Laboratory, Lemont, Illinois

Introduction. Comparative effects of ionizing radiations: Single exposures to X rays—Single exposures to fast neutrons—Comparison of effects produced by cyclotron fast neutrons and X rays—Factors concerning coagulation following single exposures. Hematologic effects of chronic total-body exposure to external radiations: Chronic exposure to X rays and fast neutrons—Chronic exposure to repeated small doses of fast neutrons—Chronic exposure to small daily doses of fast neutrons—Chronic exposure to gamma rays (radium)—Pancytopenia induced by chronic exposure to gamma radiation. Hematologic effects of exposure to externally originating radiation (radioelements): Phosphorus (P^{32})—*Sodium* (Na^{24})—*Barium-Lanthanum* ($Ba\text{-}La^{140}$)—*Yttrium* (Y^{91})—*Strontium* (Sr^{89})—*Radium—Plutonium* (Pu^{239})—*Gold* (Au^{189})—*Gallium* (Ga^{72}). *Morphologic changes in peripheral-blood cells produced by ionizing radiations: Direct vs. indirect effect of irradiation on blood formation—"Stimulation" of blood-forming tissue by radiation. Measures modifying destructive effects of irradiation or affecting recovery: Prophylactic measures—"Therapeutic" measures—Effects of combined prophylactic and therapeutic measures—Antibody-formation studies—Comment. References.*

INTRODUCTION

As a result of Heineke's (1903) pioneering research almost fifty years ago it has been recognized that the blood-forming tissues are among the most sensitive to ionizing radiations. After total-body exposure, manifestations of injury to the mammalian blood-forming tissues (such as lymphopenia) may appear in the peripheral blood even in the absence of demonstrable histopathologic change in the bone marrow or lymphatic tissues. The reviews of Warren (1943), Warren and Whipple (1922), and others (Minot and Spurling, 1924; Selling and Osgood, 1938) have covered rather adequately the significant literature up to 1942. Few observations have appeared in the past two decades that were not recorded previously in the classic descriptions of the effects of X rays on the blood and blood-forming tissues described in the earlier literature by Lacassagne and Levadan (1924), Russ *et al.* (1919), Heineke (1904),

Desjardins (1932), Aubertin and Beaujard (1905), Clarkson *et al.* (1938), Mottram and Russ (1921), Czepa (1923–1924), and Linser and Helber (1905). Because of the fact that dosage measurement was neither accurate nor accurately reproducible and because of other technical difficulties, much of the early research has been repeated in order to correlate dose with effect. In addition, new types of radiation have become available which have made comparative studies on the biological effects of various radiations desirable. This chapter is based largely on studies conducted by various investigators during the past ten years.

COMPARATIVE EFFECTS OF IONIZING RADIATIONS

In considering the irradiation of the whole body with penetrating radiations of external origin, those of significance in so far as direct effects on the blood and blood-forming tissue are concerned are X rays, γ rays, fast neutrons, and slow neutrons. The β rays and α particles that emanate from radioisotopes can, in general, be disregarded because penetration in tissue is only a few millimeters for β rays and a fraction of a millimeter for α particles. Studies on mice and rabbits by Raper and Barnes (1951), Raper, Zirkle, and Barnes (1951), Raper, Henshaw, and Snider (1951), and others have demonstrated that, although β rays may penetrate the skin, the hematologic effects, if any, are minimal and are secondary to other pathologic changes such as ulceration of the skin. No studies are yet available on the hematologic effect of exposure to β rays from a betatron source.

Studies on the effect of acute exposure of animals to a slow-neutron flux have been carried out by Zirkle (1945) and by Zirkle *et al.* (1947). This slow-neutron source was contaminated with fast neutrons, and the effect on the hematopoietic system, as reported by Raper, Henshaw, and Snider (1951), is therefore difficult to interpret. According to Zirkle (1947, 1950), however, it is not the slow neutron that produces biologic effects but rather the γ rays and fast atomic nuclei emitted upon nuclear capture of the slow neutrons. It is likely, therefore, that exposure of experimental animals to a pure slow-neutron flux would produce hematologic effects comparable to those induced by γ rays plus fast neutrons. Studies using a γ-ray source for single total-body exposures delivered in a few minutes, as reported by Henshaw *et al.* (1946) and by Henshaw, Riley, and Stapleton (1947), indicate that the effect on the blood and blood-forming tissue is qualitatively the same as that produced by X rays, and therefore no special category of discussion is devoted to this subject.

Data on single exposures of rabbits to fast neutrons in about the 30-day LD_{50} range (Jacobson and Marks, 1947) indicate that the degree of depression of the formed elements in the circulating blood and the time required for recovery are largely comparable to those observed after a

30-day LD_{50} exposure of rabbits to X rays. This information is fairly complete for dosage ranges up to the LD_{50}, but more complete data are needed for higher dosages.

Correlation between the effects of these penetrating radiations on blood-forming tissue and various hematologic constituents of the peripheral blood is generally good when the effects of dosages in the LD_{50} range for any particular species are being considered. Major deviations, however, are recognized. With doses of 100 r or less there is a lack of correlation because the changes that occur in the lymphatic tissue are difficult to quantitate histologically. The lymphocytes in the peripheral blood may be drastically reduced, although only equivocal changes are seen in the lymphatic tissues.

SINGLE EXPOSURE TO X RAYS

Studies of the effects of a single total-body exposure to X rays indicate that the rabbit (Hagen *et al.*, 1944; Jacobson *et al.*, 1947), rat (Stearner *et al.*, 1947a, b; Lawrence and Lawrence, 1936), monkey (Suter, 1947: Ingram and Mason, 1950a), mouse (Henshaw, 1943–1944a; Bloom and Bloom, 1947), chick (Murray *et al.*, 1948), goat (Swift *et al.*, 1946), pig (Cronkite *et al.*, 1949), guinea pig (Henshaw, 1943–1944b; Haley and Harris, 1949; Lorenz, 1951; Brues and Rietz, 1948), and dog (Prosser *et al.*, 1947; Allen *et al.*, 1948) show, in order, an increasing sensitivity to radiation as measured by changes in the blood and blood-forming tissues. As compared with the other species, it should be noted that the data on the hematologic effects in monkeys are conspicuously inadequate.

Effects on Leukocytes. The term "leukocyte" is applied to all the white cells in the peripheral blood. In the species discussed in this chapter the polymorphonuclear cells of the granulocyte series and the lymphocytes are the predominant forms. These constituents are discussed individually.

Aubertin and Beaujard (1908) first described the appearance of a leukocytosis prior to leukopenia after total-body X irradiation. Actually, during the first 24 hours after exposure the total leukocyte count of the peripheral blood reflects the rapidly changing status that may be described briefly as follows: With doses of 500 r an initial significant reduction occurs in the number of circulating leukocytes in the rabbit. Since the number of heterophils remains constant during this period, the reduction can be attributed to lymphocyte reduction which has been initiated and continues. On the other hand, leukocytosis is apparent at 8 hours and again at about 24 hours. This leukocytosis, which is discussed in detail later, results entirely from an increased number of heterophils.

Effects on Lymphocytes. With the possible exception of erythrocyte iron uptake, the most sensitive indicator of acute radiation effect that can be recognized by present methods in any of the various species studied is a reduction in the number of lymphocytes in the peripheral blood. In general, this effect is not significant for doses below 25 r. The pattern of acute radiation response of the rabbit lymphocyte following dosages ranging from 25–800 r is shown in Fig. 16-1. The response of the lymphocytes of the circulating blood of dogs, mice, monkeys, rats, and guinea pigs is fairly comparable to that of rabbits. According to Valentine *et al.* (1947), cats exposed to 200 r respond with a lesser lymphopenia than do the species listed. Lymphocyte values in rabbits fall below

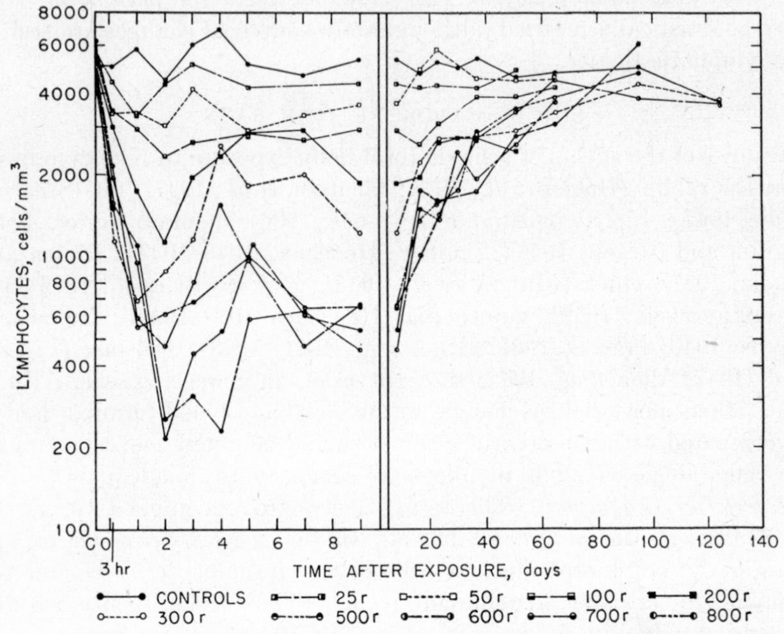

FIG. 16-1. Effect of single doses of total-body roentgen irradiation on the lymphocyte values of the peripheral blood of rabbits.

control values after 25 r and return to normal within 24–48 hours. With doses of 50 and 100 r and above, a reduction occurs within 15 minutes, and a maximum depression is reached by 24–48 hours. With dosages of 300 r and above, lymphocyte values approach the same minimum, and the time required for recovery is a function of dose. Table 16-1 gives the approximate mean time of recovery of lymphocyte values to normal limits after dosages from 25–800 r. These data are in agreement with those of Hayer (1934), Taylor *et al.* (1919), Thomas *et al.* (1919), Clarkson *et al.* (1938), Linser and Helber (1905), Siegel (1920), Russ *et al.* (1921), Russ (1921), and others.

In all species the lymphocyte values of the peripheral blood are generally the last to return to normal levels. After a dose of one-half the

LD_{50} these values may not reach the normal range for 30–90 days. According to Bloom (1947), lymphatic tissue and lymphocyte production after exposures in this range are qualitatively normal as judged by histologic methods at 20–30 days. This discrepancy between the findings in the peripheral blood and in the lymphatic tissue is understandable when it is realized that histologic findings are admittedly qualitative.

TABLE 16-1. EFFECT OF TOTAL-BODY X IRRADIATION AND EXPOSURE TO FAST NEUTRONS ON THE LEUKOCYTE VALUES OF THE PERIPHERAL BLOOD OF RABBITS

Dose	Degree of depression, per cent		Time of maximum depression, hours		Time required before normal limits attained, days	
	Lymphocytes	Heterophils	Lymphocytes	Heterophils	Lymphocytes	Heterophils
5 r	0	0				
10 r	0	0				
25 r	25	0	24	..	48 (hours)	
50 r	25	0	48	..	16	
100 r	50	..	48	..	36	
300 r	74	..	24	..	50	
500 r	90	50	48	72	50	9
600 r	90	75	48	96	50	9
700 r	90	80	48	96		
800 r	90	90	72	96	50	23
9 n	40	0	48	0	5	0
26 n	65	50	72	96	[a]	5
55 n	86	77	48	96	[a]	7
68 n	94	77	48	96	[a]	9
76 n	92	85	48	96	[a]	9
89 n	93	87	48	96	[a]	16
97 n	95	83	72	96	[a]	15
106 n	97	92	48	96	[a]	16
128 n	95	92	48	96	[a]	

[a] Recovery not complete during 37 days of observation.

Monocytes of the peripheral blood initially follow a pattern of response similar to that of the lymphocytes but characteristically return to normal values or show an absolute increase between the fourth and sixth days after exposure of the animal to 100 r or above. No change of significance has been observed in the number of plasma cells in the peripheral blood.

The polymorphonuclear leukocyte, referred to as a heterophil in the rabbit and a neutrophil in man, follows a somewhat different pattern than does the lymphocyte after total-body irradiation. The most complete data have been derived from observations on rabbits. The sensitivity of the heterophil in mice, rats, rabbits, monkeys, and swine is, in general, comparable. Although individual animals in all these species may have a reduction in the circulating heterophils after exposure to 100 r, a significant reduction in well-controlled experiments occurs only after exposure to 200 r or more. The relatively great sensitivity of the blood-forming tissue of the guinea pig, cat, and dog, however, is reflected in a significant heterophil reduction even after exposure to dosages of 200 r or less. Aubertin and Beaujard (1908) reported an initial rise in the polymorphs following exposure to dosages in the LD_{50} range, with a return to about normal in 24 hours and a maximum depression by 2–4 days. This was confirmed by Jacobson *et al.* (1947), who showed, in addition, that actually two separate elevations occur in the rabbit in the

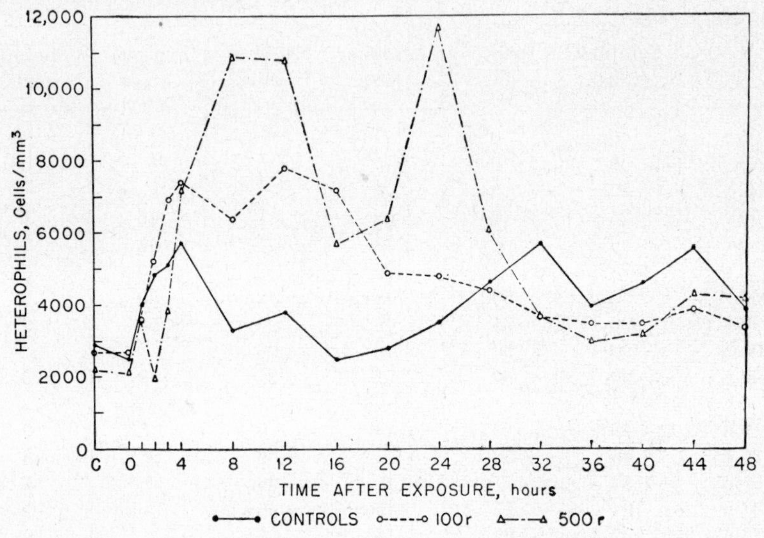

Fig. 16-2. Effect of single doses of total-body roentgen irradiation on the heterophil values of the peripheral blood of rabbits.

first 24 hours after exposure (Fig. 16-2). A heterophil rise in the first 24 hours is characteristic of all species studied, but this rise may be entirely masked in species in which lymphocytes constitute the larger percentage of the circulating leukocytes. That the initial rise in granulocytes is followed by a reduction after exposure of rabbits to dosages of 500 r or greater is shown in Fig. 16-3. Recovery is usually complete in 12–21 days even with dosages of 800 r. An "abortive rise" in the heterophil value is characteristically seen after dosages of 500–800 r. This temporary elevation appears between the fourth and eleventh day. A similar elevation is observed in lymphocyte values during the same postirradiation period (Fig. 16-1).

The mechanism of the leukocytosis within the first 24 hours after exposure is not well understood. Isaacs (1934) and Wuensche (1938) described a hastening of maturation of granulocyte precursors in the bone marrow and have suggested that the release of these cells into the circulation accounts for leukocytosis. In view of the fact that two separate peaks occur in this period, Jacobson *et al.* (1949) suggested that the first peak might be accounted for by hastening of maturation in the bone marrow and the second peak by a mobilization phenomenon in response to widespread tissue injury by irradiation. Histologic studies by Bloom (1947) have shown that the granulocyte peaks, described in the peripheral blood, are seen especially in the lymphatic tissues; an "invasion" of these tissues with granulocytes occurs concomitantly with the peaks observed in the peripheral blood.

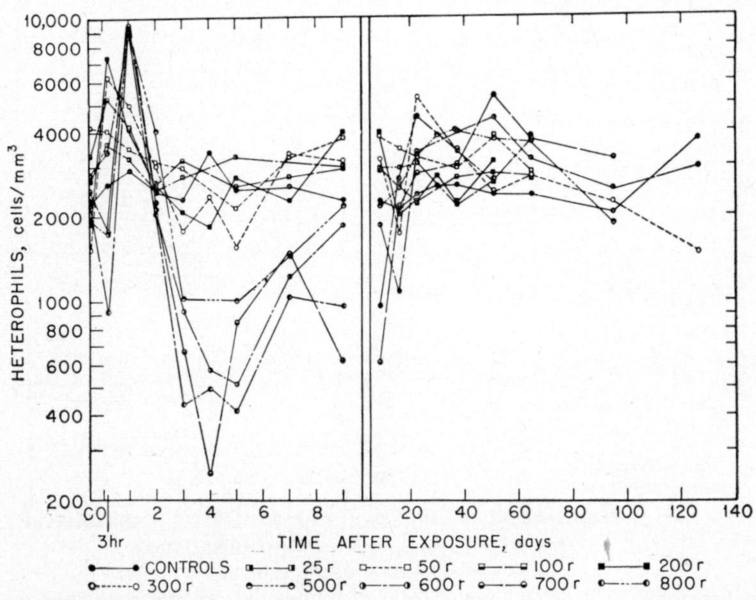

FIG. 16-3. Effect of single doses of total-body X irradiation on the heterophil values of the peripheral blood of rabbits.

Detailed studies on the effect of irradiation on the circulating eosinophils are not available. However, Aubertin and Beaujard (1908) reported an increase in animals following irradiation, and Lawrence and associates (1949) have reported an initial increase in dogs after an LD_{50} exposure.

The "Abortive Rise." An elevation in the lymphocyte, heterophil, and reticulocyte values occurs in the rabbit after exposure to dosages of 300 r and above (Figs. 16-1, 16-3). This elevation, first described by Jacobson *et al.* (1947) and Jacobson, Marks, and Lorenz (1949), has been observed by others in cats (Valentine and Pearce, 1952; Adams and Lawrence, 1947), dogs (Allen, 1947–1948), pigs (Cronkite *et al.*, 1949), rats (Cohn. 1952; Suter, 1947), and guinea pigs (Lorenz, Uphoff, and Sutton, 1949). The significance of this elevation, which appears generally between the fourth and eleventh postirradiation day, is not known. It has been suggested by Jacobson, Marks, and Lorenz (1949) that it may represent a multiplication of cells that were injured at the time of irradiation and that died after a limited number of divisions. Cells of the granulocyte series, which are grossly abnormal morphologically, are found in the peripheral blood and in the bone marrow (Bloom, 1948; Bloom and Jacobson, 1948) during this period. The temporary increase in these various cell types in the peripheral blood parallels temporary waves of

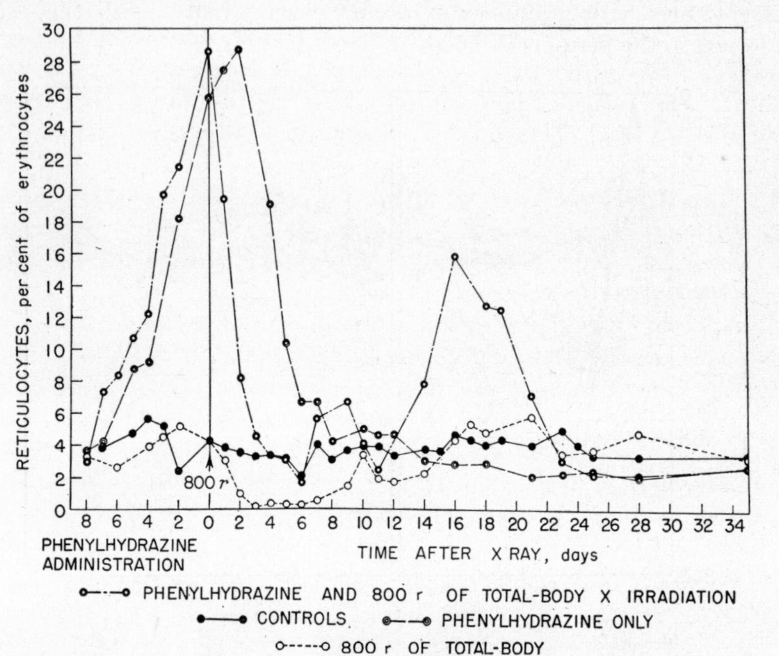

FIG. 16-4. Effect of a single dose of 800 r of total-body roentgen irradiation on the reticulocyte values in the peripheral blood of normal rabbits and rabbits with a phenylhydrazine-induced anemia. (*Originally published in Science*, 107: 249, 1948.)

regeneration observed histologically by Bloom and Bloom (1947) and Bloom (1948) in the bone marrow especially after radiation injury.

Radiation-induced Anemia. Red-cell precursors (erythroblasts) have been described by Bloom and Bloom (1947) as being the most sensitive to irradiation injury of all the cellular elements of mammalian bone marrow. This conclusion is based on histologic evidence of the degree of destruction of the erythroblasts in comparison with that of other cell types such as granulocyte precursors and megakaryocytes. These observations were made on mice, rats, chickens, and rabbits exposed to 30-day LD_{50} dosages and those well below this range. In fact it has been suggested by Bloom and Bloom (1947) that the sensitivity of erythroblasts is comparable to that of the lymphocyte. It must be pointed out, however, that Bloom compared only the immediate morphologic response of cells to irradiation. Such observations should not be construed to imply that sensitivity and rapidity of regeneration or functional reconstitution are synonymous. Rates of regeneration from an atrophic hematopoietic tissue of various cell types differ markedly.

The erythrocyte, hemoglobin, or hematocrit values of the peripheral blood do not reflect this erythroblast sensitivity in animals such as rabbits, rats, and mice unless the total-body exposure is above 300 r. On the other hand, reticulocytes, which are the immediate precursors of the erythrocytes, are significantly reduced in these species after total-body irradiation at dosages of 100 r and above. The findings of Bloom on the relative sensitivity of the erythroblast have been confirmed by Hennesey and Huff (1950). These authors studied the depression of tracer iron uptake (Fe^{59}) by rat erythrocytes following exposure to various dosages. By this method they found that a significant inhibition of erythropoiesis was apparent 24 hours after exposures as low as 5 and 25 r. On the basis of available data from peripheral-blood studies, guinea pigs have the most sensitive erythropoietic tissue of all the common laboratory animals. Lorenz (1951) has shown that a severe anemia develops in guinea pigs after exposure to 200 r, which is one-half the 30-day LD_{50} for this species. Dogs are more nearly comparable to the guinea pigs in this respect. Rabbits, which are the most resistant of the common laboratory animals to irradiation (LD_{50}, 800 r), develop a less severe anemia after an LD_{50} exposure than do dogs, cats, guinea pigs, or mice. This is apparent in material presented by Valentine and Pearce (1952) (see Table 16-2).

TABLE 16-2. EFFECT OF TOTAL-BODY X IRRADIATION ON THE ERYTHROCYTE VALUES OF THE PERIPHERAL BLOOD

Species	Dosage, r	Time of maximum reduction, days	Per cent reduction	Per cent recovery at 26 days	Reference[a]
Guinea pigs.	220	14	60	77.7	
	310	14	71.1	55.6	
	420	14	62.2	82.3	1
Rats.......	300	12	18	95	
	500	18	45	70	2
	550	250 (hours)	81.8	100 (41 days)	3
	600	14	32.2	67.7	4
	700	18	72	60.0	1
Rabbits....	500	17	19.3	85.5	5
	800	15	27.5	86.2	
Dogs.......	200	20	42.5	71.3 } 24–35 days	6
	300	23	50.0	55.6 } 24–35 days	
	350	21	32.25	79.04	7

[a] References: (1) Lorenz, 1951; (2) Suter, 1947; (3) Lawrence, Dowdy, and Valentine, 1948; (4) Bennett, Hanson, and Dowdy, 1951; (5) Jacobson *et al.*, 1947; (6) Prosser, Painter, and Swift, 1946; (7) Rekers, 1949.

Determination of the erythrocytes of the peripheral blood and their hemoglobin content by standard techniques is a rather crude means of measuring the effect of irradiation, especially during the first two weeks after exposure to X-ray dosages in the LD_{50} range or above. Even after exposure to dosages well above the lethal range it is common experience to find that no significant reduction in the erythrocyte, hemoglobin, or hematocrit values occurs prior to the sixth day. Since, after exposure to a dosage of this magnitude, destruction of the bone marrow occurs rapidly (within the first 24 hours) and thus delivery of erythrocytes ceases, a steady decline of these hematologic values would be expected to begin

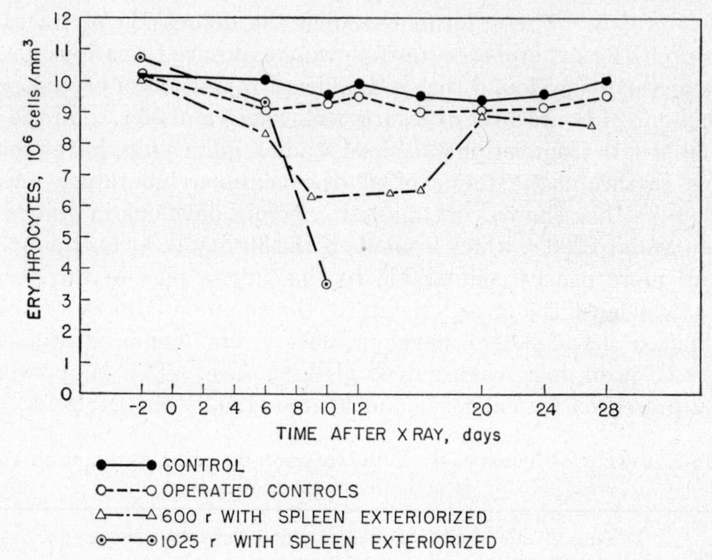

FIG. 16-5. Comparative effect of 600 and 1025 r of total-body roentgen irradiation on the erythrocyte values of CF_1 female mice.

simultaneously with exposure and continue until such time as regeneration and delivery of erythrocytes equaled or exceeded these effete cells.

As suggested by Furth *et al.* (1951) and Jacobson, Simmons, Marks, *et al.* (1950), the destruction of hematopoietic tissue and thus the cessation of erythropoiesis that occurs in dogs, rabbits, rats, pigs, guinea pigs, and mice after exposure to dosages in the LD_{50} range may be sufficient to account for the anemia observed. However, the degree and rapidity with which anemia develops above the LD_{50} range suggests that additional factors are involved. The speed and severity with which anemia appears in mice exposed to 1025 r as compared with that following 600 r exemplifies this problem (Fig. 16-5). Histopathologic investigations show that erythropoiesis ceases within 24 hours after either level of exposure. The anemia would be expected to be qualitatively the same at about 9 days if a cessation of erythropoiesis was the only aspect involved. Gross hemorrhage in mice is not a factor under these conditions. Microscopic hemorrhage and extensive erythrophagocytosis are constant histopathologic findings after exposure to 1025 r. Both processes culminate in the eventual hemolysis of the involved red cells. (As described later, gross hemorrhage may occasionally be a major factor in the production of an anemia in dogs, pigs, and guinea pigs.) Schwartz *et al.* (1947) and Lawrence, Dowdy, and Valentine (1948), and others have studied the role of red-cell hemolysis in postirradiation anemia and have found evidence of an increased excretion of the breakdown products of hemoglobin. The increased pigment excretion observed in dogs after exposure to an LD_{50} dose is not of sufficient magnitude to warrant the conclusion that increased erythrocyte hemolysis plays a role in the anemia since an indeterminate number of hemoglobin-containing erythrocyte precursors are destroyed *in situ* by irradiation. This may account for the increased pigment excretion. Davis *et al.* (1950) restudied this problem and found an increase in bile-pigment excretion in dogs exposed to 150–250 r during the first and second weeks after irradiation. No increased erythrocyte fragility (thermal or mechanical) was apparent, however, in these animals. Davis and his co-workers considered the possibility that increased pigment excretion might be based on destruction of the erythrocyte precursors. Prosser *et al.* (1947) recognized that the changes occurring in circulatory dynamics were masking actual changes in red-cell and hemoglobin levels and that the anemia that eventually developed after exposure of the dog or rabbit to LD_{50} dosages could not be accounted for by cessation of hematopoiesis or hemorrhage and postulated, as have many others (Heineke, 1905; Schwartz *et al.*, 1947; Dunlap *et al.*, 1944; Selling and Osgood, 1938), that an abnormal hemolysis of erythrocytes was probably involved.

Recently Furth and associates (Storey, Wish, and Furth, 1950; Furth *et al.*, 1951; Kahn and Furth, 1952; Ross, Furth, and Bigelow, 1952), using a number of techniques including P^{32} and Fe^{59} labeling of the red cells and I^{131} labeling of the plasma combined with regular hematologic and histopathologic investigation, have clarified many of the problems concerning postirradiation anemia. This work, based on studies of mice, rabbits, and dogs X-irradiated in the LD_{50} range and above, may be summarized as follows:

1. Erythropoiesis ceases within 24 hours after irradiation and is not resumed for 7–14 days.
2. During this same period there is a reduction in the red-cell mass as determined by isotopic studies (Fe^{59} and P^{32}), and there is a simultaneous decrease in the plasma volume. This change masks the magnitude of the drop in erythrocyte mass, especially during the first postirradiation week,

and accounts for the fact that during this period erythrocyte, hemoglobin, and hematocrit determinations are frequently within the normal range.

3. Reduction in red-cell mass results from (*a*) death of normally aging red cells and (*b*) the loss of "normal" erythrocytes from the circulation by heightened capillary permeability and thus widespread minute extravasation into lymphatic tissues and tissue spaces. Tagged red cells (Fe^{59} and P^{32}), as well as tagged plasma, were found to disappear more rapidly from the circulation of irradiated than from that of nonirradiated animals. The leakage of erythrocytes is a major factor in the production

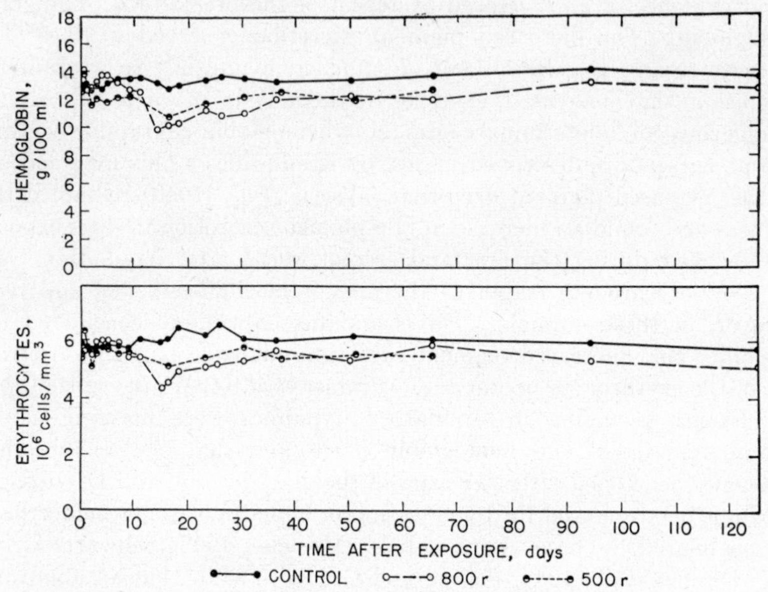

FIG. 16-6. Effect of single doses of 500 and 800 r of total-body roentgen irradiation on the hemoglobin and erythrocyte values of the peripheral blood of rabbits.

of anemia. The fate of the red cells thus extravasated as a result of primary or secondary endothelial injury is phagocytosis and eventual hemolysis.

No significant anemia, as judged by mean averages, has been observed in groups of rabbits exposed to dosages below 500 r. In individual animals, anemia may appear with exposures as low as 300 r. A progressively larger fraction develops anemia following exposure to 500 r and above (Jacobson *et al.*, 1947; Jacobson, Marks, and Lorenz, 1949). Figure 16-6 illustrates the anemia observed in rabbits after exposure to 800 r. Rats, mice, dogs, cats, swine, and guinea pigs develop anemia in response to lower doses. Figure 16-7 illustrates the anemia in guinea pigs after exposure to 220 r and above. In the absence of gross hemorrhage the anemia is normochromic and reaches a maximum at about 14 days; recovery (if the exposure was in the LD_{50} range) is usually completed in three to four weeks. With dosages above the LD_{50} the anemia develops more precipitously and is more severe, and the recovery process is delayed.

The immediate precursors of the erythrocyte are not significantly reduced in number in the peripheral blood of rabbits (Jacobson and Marks, 1947) and rats (Lawrence and Lawrence, 1936) with doses below 100 r. With doses above 100 r, reduction in reticulocytes becomes

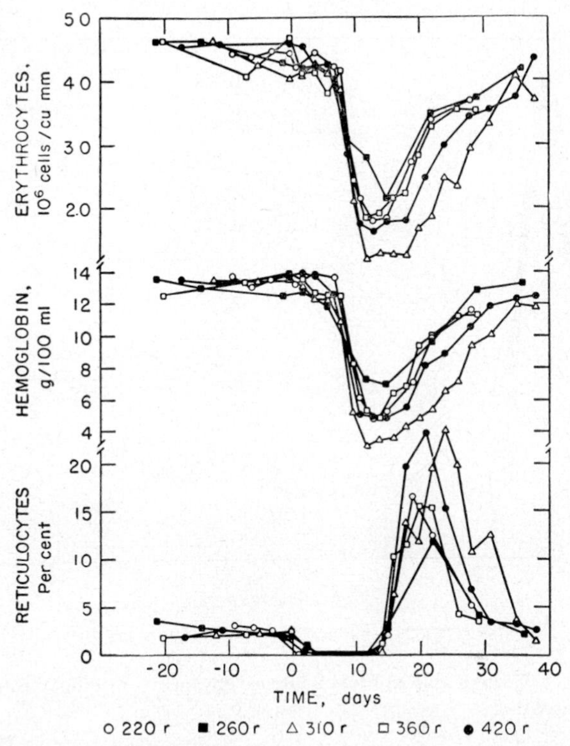

FIG. 16-7. The effect of single doses of total-body roentgen irradiation on the red-cell count, hemoglobin, and reticulocyte values of hybrid guinea pigs.

progressively more significant in all the common laboratory animals. Doses in the LD_{50} range reduce the reticulocytes from a normal of 1–4 per cent to less than 0.1 per cent. Recovery after such exposure begins at about the same time in the various species. As illustrated in Fig. 16-4, a compensatory elevation above the normal range occurs as recovery of erythropoietic tissue proceeds.

SINGLE EXPOSURE TO FAST NEUTRONS

Lawrence and Lawrence (1936) and Lawrence, Aebersold, and Lawrence (1936) reported the first study on exposure of mammals to fast neutrons.

This work, which was performed on rats, indicated that the pattern of hematologic effects was qualitatively similar to that produced by X radiation. The observations of Lawrence have been extended to other laboratory animals, including mice and rabbits (Lawrence, Aebersold, and Lawrence, 1936; Henshaw *et al.*, 1946; Jacobson and Marks, 1947). Uranium-pile fast neutrons have been explored and compared with cyclotron-produced fast neutrons (Zirkle, 1947). Henshaw exposed mice to single doses of 26, 50, 78, 90, or 105 n. These studies paralleled

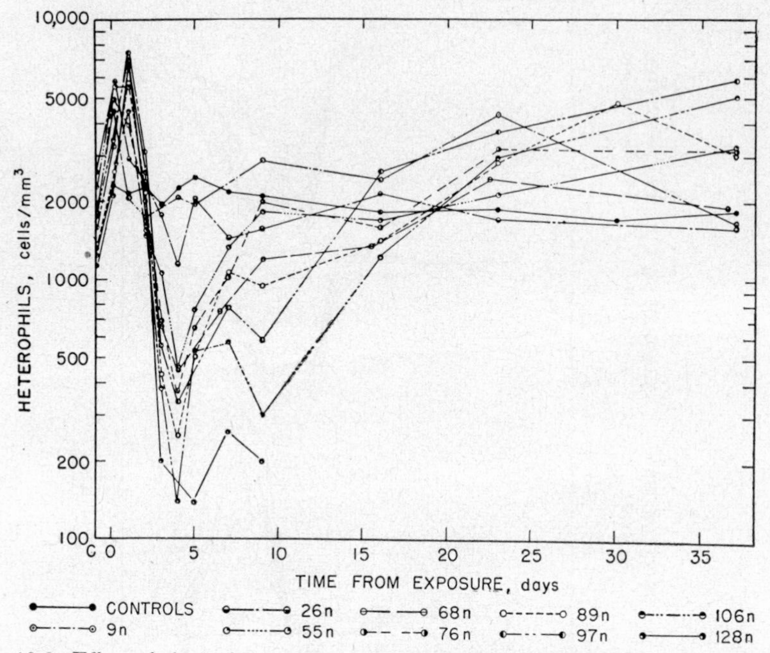

FIG. 16-8. Effect of single doses of fast neutrons on the heterophil values of the peripheral blood of rabbits.

studies on rabbits exposed to cyclotron fast neutrons, in which dosages of 9, 26, 55, 68, 76, 89, 97, 106, or 128 n were used. No difference in the hematologic effect of the LD_{50} dose of cyclotron or pile fast neutrons appears to exist.

Figures 16-8, 16-9 show the effect of cyclotron fast neutrons on the leukocyte values of rabbits, and Table 16-1 gives the comparative effect of X rays and fast neutrons on the lymphocyte response in rabbits.

An initial increase in heterophils follows exposure to fast-neutron dosages of 9–128 n, and within the first 24 hours there is also an initial rise. This is followed, after dosages ranging from 26–128 n, by a reduction, reaching a minimum in 3–5 days. No significant reduction in heterophils occurs after an exposure to 9 n. Eventual recovery to normal limits is observed in all groups exposed to total-body dosages below 128 n.

The number of lymphocytes in the peripheral blood is reduced after the administration of doses ranging from 9–128 n. This reduction is apparent as early as 3 hours after exposure, with a maximum reduction at 2–3 days. Although the lymphocyte values of animals exposed to 9 n are again within the normal control range by 5 days, the lymphocytes of those animals exposed to 26 n and above remain below control values for more than five weeks.

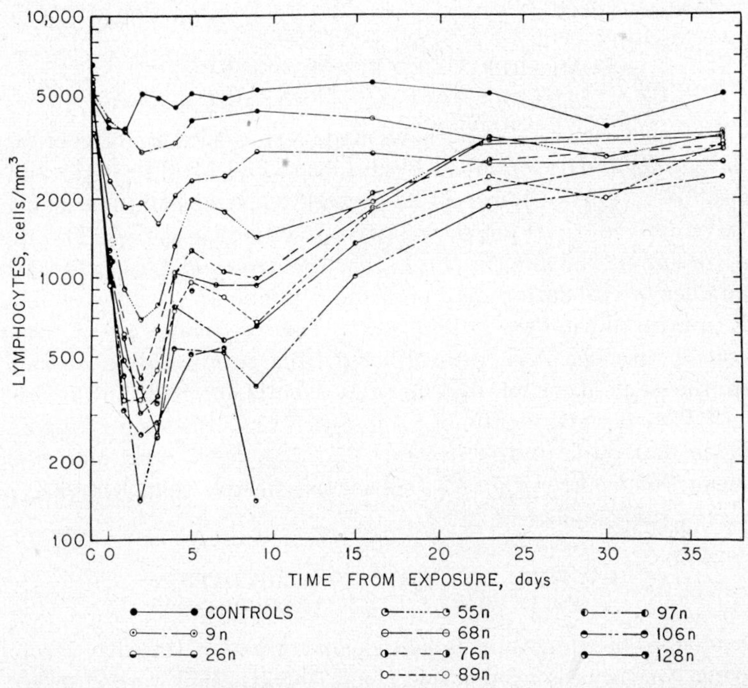

FIG. 16-9. Effect of single doses of fast neutrons on the lymphocyte values of the peripheral blood of rabbits.

A severe normochromic anemia is observed in animals exposed to a fast-neutron LD_{50}. The maximum anemia, as is also observed after exposure to a 30-day LD_{50} of X radiation, appears between the fourteenth and sixteenth days after exposure. Recovery to normal values occurs by 23 days. Reticulocytes are reduced to 0.1 per cent or less by the third day in animals exposed to doses of 128 fast-neutron units or above.

After doses of 80–89 and 100–108 n, a maximum reduction of approximately 72 per cent in the platelet values of the peripheral blood occurs between the fifth and tenth day, with return to normal values by 15 and 23 days, respectively, in the two exposure levels.

An abortive rise in heterophils and lymphocytes occurs (between the fourth and tenth day) after fast-neutron exposure and is comparable to that observed following the exposure of rabbits to X rays.

The morphologic changes in the cellular constituents of the peripheral blood after fast-neutron exposure are identical with those occurring in the peripheral blood of rabbits after "comparable" doses of X rays. These observations in rabbits are comparable with those after single exposure to X rays (Figs. 16-1, 16-3). Henshaw's observations (1946) of mice likewise are qualitatively similar to X-ray studies of these species when the differential factor of effectiveness between X rays and fast neutrons is considered.

COMPARISON OF EFFECTS PRODUCED BY CYCLOTRON FAST NEUTRONS AND X RAYS

Sacher and Pearlman (1947) have made a statistical analysis of extensive hematologic data obtained by Jacobson and Marks (1947) and by Jacobson *et al.* (1947) from rabbits exposed to X rays and fast neutrons and have derived a ratio of the relative effectiveness of these two radiations. Using the data on the effect of fast-neutron and X-ray exposure on the number of circulating heterophils and lymphocytes, they estimated the X:n ratio to be of the order of 6.3. These estimates are in essential agreement with the X:n ratio derived from survival data on rabbits (using the same type of instruments) by Hagen and Zirkle (1950). Evans (1948) derived a ratio of 8.1 in Swiss mice. It should be pointed out again that the n unit is arbitrary and that the X:n ratio given does not mean that neutrons are 6.3 times more effective than X rays in producing the same biological effect.

FACTORS CONCERNING COAGULATION FOLLOWING SINGLE EXPOSURES

A prolonged bleeding time, impaired clot retraction, fragility, thrombocytopenia, and a prolonged whole-blood clotting time were observed in laboratory animals following single exposures to dosages of penetrating radiation in the LD_{50} range and above by Shouse, Warren, and Whipple (1931), Allen and Jacobson (1947a), Allen *et al.* (1948), Cronkite (1950), Cronkite *et al.* (1949, 1950), Prosser *et al.* (1947), and others. The only cellular element in the circulating peripheral blood known to be concerned with this problem is the platelet.

Platelets are, in general, found to be reduced in the peripheral blood of all the various species of laboratory animals after exposure to dosages in the range that reduces the polymorphonuclear cells. Qualitatively, the megakaryocytes and granulocyte precursors are of approximately equal sensitivity to irradiation injury. According to Lawrence, Dowdy, and Valentine (1948) and Cohn (1952) the platelet values of the peripheral blood of the rat are significantly reduced after whole-body exposure to

300 r and above. Lorenz (1951) has demonstrated that a severe thrombocytopenia occurs in guinea pigs after exposure to 200 r. Mice, according, to Jacobson, Robson, and Marks (1950) and Jacobson, Simmons, Bethard, *et al.* (1950), are approximately equal in sensitivity in this respect to rats. With 600 r the maximum reduction occurs at about 9 days after irradiation (Fig. 16-10). Swine (Cronkite *et al.*, 1949) and dogs (Allen and Jacobson, 1947a, b; Prosser *et al.*, 1947) are roughly comparable with guinea pigs in sensitivity. In rabbits (Jacobson *et al.*, 1947; Jacobson, Marks, and Lorenz, 1949), platelets are markedly reduced after exposure to 500 or 800 r. Recovery of the platelets to normal values in all these species occurs by about the fourteenth to twenty-first day after LD_{50}

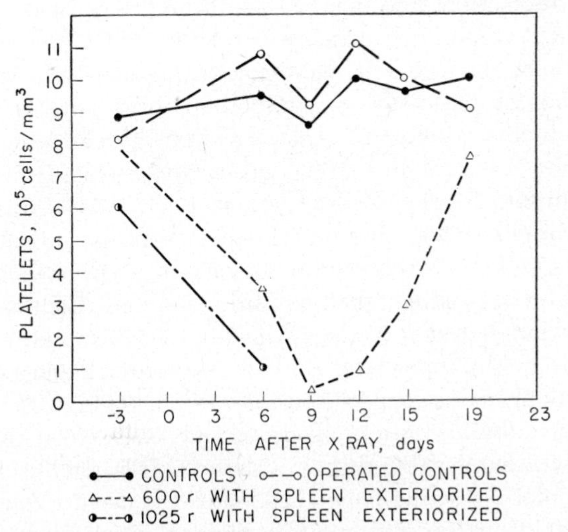

FIG. 16-10. Comparative effects of 600 and 1025 r of total-body roentgen irradiation on the platelet values of CF_1 female mice.

exposure. With doses above the LD_{50} the recovery of platelet values is, in general, a function of the dose.

The factors concerned with the hemorrhage appearing in experimental animals exposed to penetrating radiation may be multiple. With doses in the LD_{50} range or above in any of the species studied, a severe thrombocytopenia occurs, but at this time it is not known with certainty whether or not this single cellular reduction alone accounts for the widespread gross and microscopic hemorrhage which occurs in many of these species but which has been studied most extensively in the dog (Allen and Jacobson, 1947a, b; Allen, Moulder, and Enerson, 1951) and swine (Cronkite *et al.*, 1949; Cronkite, 1950). Platelets are considered to have a number of functions that are important in irradiation hemorrhage. Allen (1952) lists these functions as follows: (1) platelet agglutination and adherence to the site of vascular injury, (2) a source of thromboplastin, (3) an accelerator of prothrombin conversion, (4) an effective antiheparin, and (5) a contributor to the integrity of the capillary wall. In the absence of platelets in animals exposed to massive doses of irradiation, hemorrhage—gross or microscopic—may occur on the basis of failure of these functions. The severity of hemorrhage will vary from animal to animal, however, and local lesions such as ulcerations, abrasions, or systemic infection may also affect the severity of the hemorrhagic manifestation. In general, prothrombin studies of dogs (Allen *et al.*, 1948) and rabbits (Jacobson, Marks, Gaston, Allen, *et al.*, 1948) subjected to total-body irradiation in the LD_{50} range or above remained within normal limits except terminally. It is generally agreed that the defects of increased bleeding time, delayed clot retraction, and delayed prothrombin conversion result from the thrombocytopenia. The delay in prothrombin conversion or consumption can be corrected by addition of platelet-rich hemophilic dog plasma but not by platelet-poor hemophilic dog plasma (Cronkite *et al.*, 1950). The increased clotting time observed in dogs (Allen and Jacobson, 1947a, b; Allen *et al.*, 1948), goats and swine (Cronkite, 1950), rabbits (Jacobson, Marks, Gaston, Allen, *et al.*, 1948), and guinea pigs (Haley and Harris, 1949) may be related, in part or entirely, to platelet reduction and delayed prothrombin conversion. Other factors known to be concerned with clotting, such as fibrinogen and calcium blood levels, are normal in irradiated animals. Allen and Jacobson (1947a) and Allen *et al.* (1948) originally reported finding evidence for a heparin-like circulating anticoagulant in dogs exposed to 450 r which could usually be restored to normal by administration of protamine sulfate or toluidine blue. More recently Allen has found that, although after irradiation an increase in the whole-blood clotting time (Lee-White) is usually demonstrable in the dog, no evidence for a circulating heparin-like anticoagulant can be demonstrated unless, in addition, transfusions have been given and transfusion reactions have occurred. He has repeatedly called attention to the discrepancy that is not infrequently observed between the platelet number in the circulating blood and the whole-blood clotting time. He has reported the appearance of a prolonged whole-blood clotting time before platelets were appreciably reduced (Fig. 16-11) and a return of whole-blood clotting time to normal a week or more before evidence of platelet recovery could be detected in the peripheral blood. Although he attributes this abnormality in whole-blood clotting principally to physiologic disturbances associated with thrombocytopenia, he believes that other disturbances in the hemoplastic mechanism cannot be excluded at this time. The role of increased capillary fragility in the hemorrhagic syndrome induced by irradiation is probably of major importance. The relation of thrombocytopenia in the causation of increased capillary fragility is not understood nor has it been adequately explored. The frequent association of petechial hemorrhage with thrombocytopenic states tends to implicate the platelet in preservation of the integrity of the capillary wall. On the other hand, increased capillary fragility and petechial hemorrhage are observed in a number of toxic states, including severe systemic infection, even though platelet values of the peripheral blood are normal. The importance of the widespread microscopic hemorrhage that occurs presumably secondary to direct or indirect injury to the capillary wall has recently been emphasized by Furth *et al.* (1951). Even in the absence of gross hemorrhage a more severe anemia occurs after whole-body exposure to dosages above the LD_{50} than can be accounted for

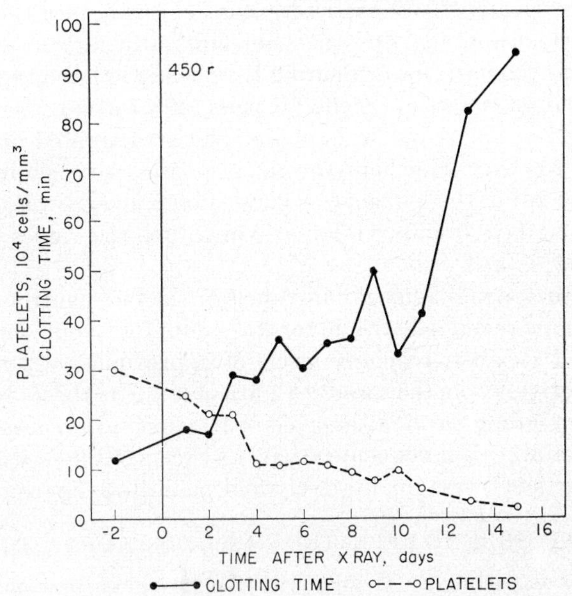

FIG. 16-11. Effect of a 450-r single dose of total-body roentgen irradiation on the platelet values and clotting time (Lee-White) of 25 dogs. (*Allen et al.*, 1948.)

by cessation of erythropoiesis alone. Furth explains this discrepancy on the basis of increased microscopic hemorrhage resulting from "leaking" through the capillary walls. No histologic abnormalities have been demonstrated that account for this loss of vascular integrity.

HEMATOLOGIC EFFECTS OF CHRONIC TOTAL-BODY EXPOSURE TO EXTERNAL RADIATIONS

The penetrating radiations to which laboratory animals have been exposed chronically (repeated or continuous exposures) include X rays, γ rays (radium and pile gammas), fast neutrons (cyclotron and pile-produced), and slow neutrons. Survival, carcinogenesis, and other biological effects have been studied in several species of mammals after exposure to these radiations. Adequate hematologic studies have been made in animals exposed chronically to γ rays, fast neutrons, and X rays. The work of Lorenz, Eschenbrenner, *et al.* (1946), Lorenz, Heston, *et al.* (1946), Lorenz, Uphoff, and Sutton (1949), and Lorenz (1951) on γ-ray exposure has been extensive and exceptionally well controlled. Evans (1948) has studied the effects of fast neutrons and, to a lesser extent, the effect of X rays on the hematopoietic system.

CHRONIC EXPOSURE TO X RAYS AND FAST NEUTRONS

For purposes of comparison of the biological effectiveness of X rays and fast neutrons, Evans (1948) exposed groups of Swiss mice to daily doses of 80 r (X rays) and 10 "N" (neutron units arbitrary). These doses were chosen as the basis for comparing the median lethal doses of the two radiations that gave a ratio (in effectiveness) of 8.1 r = 1 N. The radiations were given daily for 25 days, and the accumulated dosages were 2000 r and 250 N. The hematologic responses were similar in both groups. The fall in the leukocyte values of both groups was comparable through the 30 days of observation at which time the values were below 1000/cu mm.

The erythrocyte and hemoglobin values of the fast-neutron and X-ray exposure groups remained within control limits for about one week and thereafter fell steadily, reaching levels of approximately 2 million and 3–4 g, respectively, on the twenty-eighth day. On these findings and other data including survival and histopathologic examination of post-mortem material, Evans concluded that the effects of these two radiations at this dosage level were qualitatively and quantitatively similar.

CHRONIC EXPOSURE TO REPEATED SMALL DOSES OF FAST NEUTRONS

In another experiment, Evans (1948) exposed groups of Swiss and CF_1 male and female mice to dosages of 0.014, 0.07, 0.14, and 1.4 N/day. These dosages, according to his calculations, are equivalent biologically to a value of 1 N = 35 r. Exposure of the Swiss mice was continued for ninety weeks and of the CF_1 mice for eighty-three weeks.

Although the mean leukocyte values of all exposure groups were consistently lower than those of the control groups, only in the 1.4 N/day exposure group were significant effects observed in the peripheral blood. In this latter group, reduction in the leukocyte values was apparent within four weeks after beginning of exposure, and a reduction in the mean count of about 50 per cent was apparent at twenty-four weeks when the exposure was discontinued. This leukocyte reduction was largely due to the lymphocyte reduction; no effect on erythrocyte, hemoglobin, reticulocyte, or platelet values was noted during the period of exposure of any of the four groups.

Suter (1947) and Ingram and Mason (1950b) studied the hematologic effect of chronic X irradiation in dogs, rabbits, rats, and monkeys. With

10 r of X ray per day the erythrocyte values of the dog and rabbit were reduced by sixteen weeks, whereas it required thirty-two weeks for erythrocyte values to decrease in the rat. The same number of roentgens per day was also required to bring about a depression of the leukocyte, absolute heterophil, and platelet values in the rabbit by four, five, and twelve weeks, respectively, whereas a daily dose of only 6 r/day produced depressions of these elements in the dog by sixteen and eight weeks. The leukocyte and absolute lymphocyte values of the rat decreased in four weeks with 10 r/day, but the same elements were decreased in monkeys by one to two weeks by the same dose.

Suter (1947) also studied the effects of chronic exposure to 10.2 n/week on the peripheral blood of the dog, rabbit, and rat. A decrease in the erythrocyte values was produced by thirty-eight, thirty-two, and six weeks, respectively. The leukocytes and absolute neutrophils were reduced in the dog by 2½ weeks and the absolute lymphocytes by 4½ weeks. These same elements were decreased in the rabbit by 5, 7½, and 2½ weeks, respectively, whereas in the rat only 1½, 2½, and 1½ weeks, respectively, were required to bring about a reduction with 10.2 n/week.

CHRONIC EXPOSURE TO SMALL DAILY DOSES OF FAST NEUTRONS

Fast-neutron doses of 4.3 n/day, 6 days per week, produced a dramatic and uniform decrease in leukocyte levels in CF_1 female mice, involving both the lymphocytes and the heterophils (Henshaw, Riley, and Stapleton, 1947). Death occurred at eight to twelve weeks. In another group, daily exposures of 1.15 n were compared with 8.6 r of pile-produced γ rays (Henshaw, Riley, and Stapleton, 1947). The roentgen-to-neutron ratio of 1:7.5 for the acute killing of mice was the criterion used for selecting these dosages. Only slight hematologic changes, if any, were produced with these doses after forty to sixty weeks of exposure. Henshaw reported, however, that a daily exposure to 0.25 n of fast neutrons or to 8.6 r of pile γ rays had the same effect on survival of mice, and thus an r:n ratio of 1:35 for daily doses was calculated for these radiations. This investigator is of the opinion that threshold responses of the peripheral blood are at least ten times less sensitive than survival. Mice (C-58) treated with single weekly doses of 51.6 r (X rays) showed slightly lower leukocyte values, with a terminal drop at thirty weeks, than those exposed to the equivalent of 8.6 r of γ rays per day, 6 days per week. A significant, gradual, and progressive decline in erythrocyte values was apparent with 51.6 r/week (X rays), whereas 8.6 r/day (γ rays) produced only a slight and minimal reduction of the erythrocyte values.

CHRONIC EXPOSURE TO GAMMA RAYS (RADIUM)

The general plan of exposure employed by Lorenz, Heston, *et al.* (1946) and Lorenz, Heston, and Eschenbrenner (1947) is referred to here only to orient the reader; details may be found elsewhere. The experimental animals were placed in cages arranged about a centrally located radium source. The cages were placed at varying distances from the 2-g radium source so that given daily doses were delivered during an 8- or a 24-hour period of exposure. In Lorenz's original experiments (1946), continuous exposure (24 hours per day) was used. The data from these early experiments are available. Since more complete studies have been done using 8-hour daily exposures, only these later experiments will be considered.

Three species were studied: (1) mice, LAF_1 genetically homogeneous hybrids, strain A, C-57 black, and C_3H, (2) rabbits, crosses of Dutch and American Blue, and (3) guinea pigs, genetically heterogeneous hybrids and inbred strains.

Groups of the three species of animals were exposed to doses of 0.11, 1.1, 2.2, 4.4, or 8.8 r for 8 hours per day for periods extending in some experiments to more than three years.

Observations on Mice. Male and female LAF_1 mice received total dosages as high as 5880 r in the 8.8-r exposure group and correspondingly lower at the other exposure levels (Table 16-3).

The blood data indicate considerable radioresistance of the hematopoietic system. There was a decrease in all cellular hematologic constituents in the peripheral blood of animals exposed to 8.8 r daily. The mean reduction in erythrocyte, hemoglobin, and platelet values was relatively minimal and was not more than 30 per cent at any time. This reduction occurred slowly over a period of seventy-nine weeks. Individual animals, however, did develop severe anemia. Only a questionable reduction in the erythrocyte or hemoglobin and platelet values occurred in the groups exposed to 4.4 r. No anemia or thrombocytopenia was observed in the groups exposed to 2.2 r and below.

The mean leukocyte count was reduced in the 8.8-, 4.4-, and 2.2-r groups, but this was a reflection of the lymphocyte reduction. The heterophils remained within control limits. In general, female mice were more radiosensitive than males as far as hematologic findings were concerned.

Data available on C_3H and C_3Hb females and strain A males show that these strains are all comparable to LAF_1 in respect to their hematologic response to this chronically administered radiation.

Observations on Female Rabbits. Evidence of irradiation damage to the hematopoietic system was slight even though the highest accumulated dose was approximately 12,000 r. During the first 100 weeks of exposure the total white count of all experimental groups was lowered. The lymphocyte reduction is evident and is made more pronounced by a concomitant relative increase in heterophil values in all exposure groups except those at the 0.11-r level. As was observed in mice and guinea pigs, these changes became apparent within the first few weeks after the

Table 16-3. Effect of Daily (8 Hours) Gamma Irradiation on Hematologic Values and Survival in LAF_1 Mice[a]

Daily dose, r	Number of animals	Mean age at start, days	Mean survival time since beginning of exposure, days	Mean accumulated dose, r	Duration of experiment, days	Largest accumulated dose, r	Leukocytes		Platelets	Hemoglobin and erythrocytes	Hematologic changes
							Lymphocytes	Neutrophils			
0	59	70	703 ± 23	....	1082	....	0	0	0	0	0
0.11	45	52	761 ± 26	110	1036	164	0	0	0	0	0
1.1	48	62	684 ± 20	780	943	1040	0	0	0	0	0
2.2	47	70	630 ± 20	1400	884	2000	+	0	0	0	0
4.4	48	74	591 ± 16	2600	817	3610	+	0	+	+	+
8.8	45	85	488 ± 11	4300	667	5880	+	0	+	+	+
8.8[b]	16	78	656 ± 37	....	1025	320	−	−	−	−	−
8.8[c]	16	76	650 ± 30	....	856	680	−	−	−	−	−

[a] Acute exposure groups included.
[b] Exposed for 36 days.
[c] Exposed for 77 days.

exposure was begun and remained fairly constant at this level for the first 100 weeks. No significant effect on erythrocyte and hemoglobin values was observed in any of the exposure groups.

Observations on Guinea Pigs. As is indicated in Table 16-4, the exposure levels for this species were the same as for mice and rabbits. Within a few weeks after the beginning of exposure a decrease in the leukocyte values of the peripheral blood occurred in both males and females of the five experimental groups, and the depression persisted throughout the experiment (Fig. 16-12). The leukocyte depression was significant ($P \leqq 0.05$) even in the group exposed to 0.11 r. The degree of

TABLE 16-4. SURVIVAL OF HYBRID GUINEA PIGS EXPOSED TO GAMMA RADIATION DAILY (8 HOURS)[a]

Daily dose, r	Number of animals	Mean age at start, days	Mean survival time since beginning of exposure, days	Mean accumulated dose, r	Duration of experiment, days	Largest accumulated dose, r
0	24	151	1372 ± 95	....	2246	
0.11	17	137	1457 ± 129	180	2280	300
1.1	17	196	1224 ± 119	1380	1993	2200
2.2	18	197	978 ± 63	2170	1410	3100
4.4	18	185	653 ± 83	2900	1467	6500
8.8	18	185	187 ± 27	1670	502	4400
8.8[b]	6	199	1192 ± 142	....	1527	270
8.8[c]	6	230	968 ± 124	....	1259	540

[a] Acute exposure groups included.
[b] Exposed for 31 days.
[c] Exposed for 61 days.

leukocyte depression was correspondingly greater with the higher daily exposure.

The reduction in the leukocyte values of the various experimental groups was caused by a decrease in lymphocytes in the 0.11- and 1.1-r groups. In the 2.2-, 4.4-, and 8.8-r groups it was caused in part by a decrease in lymphocytes but was largely a result of the more significant reduction in heterophils. In fact, the characteristic terminal blood picture is one of profound neutropenia, the proportion of heterophils often being as low as 1–5 per cent. No significant alteration in the eosinophil or monocyte values was observed in these experiments. In general, there were likewise no significant morphologic changes in the leukocytes in any of these exposure groups.

No anemia of significance was produced in male or female guinea pigs exposed chronically to 0.11 and 1.1 r. The male guinea pigs exposed to

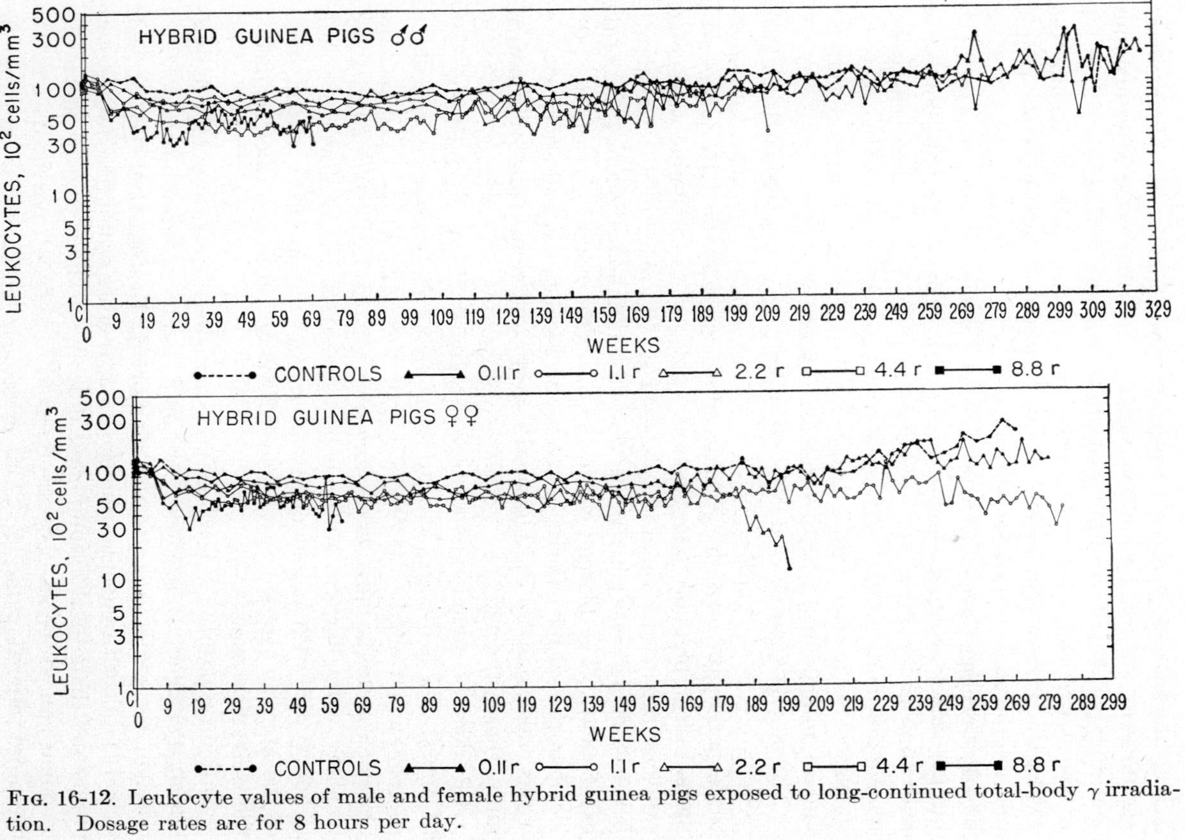

FIG. 16-12. Leukocyte values of male and female hybrid guinea pigs exposed to long-continued total-body γ irradiation. Dosage rates are for 8 hours per day.

2.2 r, however, developed a normochromic anemia of only moderate significance beginning approximately seventy-nine weeks after exposure. Within a period of forty-nine weeks both the male and female guinea pigs of the 4.4-r group developed a moderate normochromic anemia that gradually increased in severity. A reduction of about 25 per cent in hemoglobin and erythrocyte values occurred. Females exposed to 2.2 or 4.4 r developed a lesser anemia than the males at these exposure levels, but a severe terminal anemia occurred in most of the animals, both males and females, in these two exposure levels. Within nineteen weeks, female and male guinea pigs exposed to 8.8 r developed an anemia that increased in severity through sixty and sixty-nine weeks, respectively, and all animals died with a terminal anemia.

The platelets per cubic millimeter in both sexes exposed to 0.11 r daily (8 hours) remained comparable to those of the control animals throughout the experimental period. Female guinea pigs at the 1.1-r level had a normal mean platelet value when first sampled at forty-nine weeks after exposure began; the value was reduced slowly, reaching a mean slightly below control levels that was maintained throughout the remainder of the experiment. The platelet values of the male guinea pigs at this same level, however, fell slowly between the forty-ninth and seventy-ninth weeks, recovered by the hundredth week, and remained within normal limits thereafter.

In male and female guinea pigs exposed to 2.2, 4.4, and 8.8 r daily (8 hours), the reduction in platelet values was progressive, the degree of reduction roughly corresponding to the daily dose. The terminal platelet counts for individual animals were as low as 20,000/cu mm and, in many cases, lower. All animals exposed at the rate of 8.8 r daily (8 hours) died with anemia or thrombocytopenia, or both. The majority of the animals exposed to 4.4 and 2.2 r daily (8 hours) likewise died of the same disorders.

Chronic exposure to the three dose rates of 8.8, 4.4, and 2.2 r daily (8 hours) is sufficient to produce a terminal anemia or thrombocytopenia, or both, in the guinea pig. Although Lorenz, Heston, *et al.* (1946) state that it is difficult to decide from the data whether or not dose rate is more important than total accumulated dose in the induction of the severe terminal pancytopenia, they are inclined to believe that the dose rate is the more important factor. This opinion is based on the fact that no terminal anemia has been observed in the 1.1-r group even though the maximum accumulated dose was approximately 2200 r. This dose was sufficient to induce terminal anemia in the 8.8-, 4.4-, and 2.2-r groups. It seems that in the 1.1-r group the injury is compensated for by repair processes, but it is possible that in species with a similar sensitivity of the hematopoietic system, but with a considerably longer life span, injury would eventually overcome the repair process.

PANCYTOPENIA INDUCED BY CHRONIC EXPOSURE TO GAMMA RADIATION

In a series of experiments Lorenz (1951), Lorenz, Jacobson, and Sutton (1950), and Lorenz *et al.* (1950) studied the hematologic recovery pattern of guinea pigs exposed to 8.8 r (8 hours per day) until an anemia of ca. 2.8 million erythrocytes/cu mm had appeared. Leukopenia and thrombocytopenia were also invariably present when anemia reached this stage. The dose required to produce an anemia of this magnitude varied from 950–1047 r. After removal of the animals from the radiation field, three distinct hematologic recovery patterns were apparent. These three patterns will be designated as groups *a*, *b*, and *c* (Fig. 16-13).

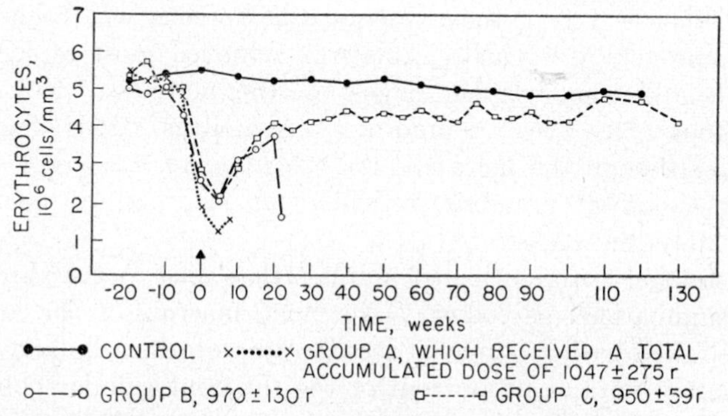

FIG. 16-13. Effect of limited chronic γ irradiation at 8.8 r daily (8 hours) on the red-cell count of inbred guinea pigs (family 2). (*Lorenz*, 1951.)

Group a. The erythrocyte, hemoglobin, and hematocrit values of the animals with recovery pattern *a* continued to decrease, and no recovery was apparent, or slight unsustained recovery was observed between six and nine weeks after the animals were removed from the exposure. The platelet values fell no lower after removal of the animals from the radiation field and, in fact, rose slowly. The leukocyte values increased rapidly after termination of the exposure. The rise in leukocytes represented a rise in both lymphocytes and heterophils. Contrary to the complete disappearance of reticulocytes following an acute X-ray exposure or a γ-ray exposure of this magnitude, no reduction of reticulocytes occurred in these three groups; in fact, a rapid increase above the control value appeared after termination of the exposure. All animals in group *a* died within approximately nine weeks after removal from the radiation field.

Group b. The hematologic findings in the animals with recovery pattern *b*, during the first nine weeks after termination of the exposure, were approximately the same as the *a* pattern. After that time the recovery processes continued for a period of several weeks. In a few animals the increase in leukocytes approached normal, but on an average it amounted to approximately one-half normal. Beginning at approximately the twelfth week and continuing to the twenty-fourth week, one animal after another developed a recurrent pancytopenia and died. There was a persistent increase in the percentage of circulating reticulocytes, and the color index also increased. Hemorrhage appeared to play no important role in the terminal picture since gross or microscopic evidence of hemorrhage was minimal or absent.

Group c. The third pattern, *c*, was one of complete recovery. The initial postirradiation hematologic findings were identical with those of the other two patterns. Recovery from the anemia began approximately six weeks after the termination of the exposure. A rapid increase of all cellular elements during the subsequent six weeks was followed by a gradual approach to normal. This was achieved most rapidly by the heterophils and was delayed longest in the platelets. However, full recovery took place over a period of many months. It is of interest to note that, although the increased red-cell diameter (macrocytosis) persisted for about sixty weeks, reticulocytes returned to normal after approximately ten weeks.

The histologic examination of animals that died in the three groups may be summarized as follows: The bone marrow of the animals of group *a* showed a slight-to-considerable decrease in cellularity with an approximately normal proportion of the different cellular components. In the animals that died in this group and in those of group *b* that died earliest, the degree of cellularity of the bone marrow was normal or nearly normal or even hyperplastic, but the proportion of the various cellular components was not normal. In the animals of group *c* the bone marrow was comparable to that of nonirradiated controls. Hemorrhage played no significant role in the development of the terminal anemia in these three groups of animals since gross or microscopic evidence of hemorrhage was minimal or absent.

HEMATOLOGIC EFFECTS OF EXPOSURE TO INTERNALLY ORIGINATING RADIATION (RADIOELEMENTS)

So far as the peripheral blood is concerned, the sensitivity and rapidity of the effect on blood-forming tissue of the radioelements and subsequent reflection in the hematologic picture depend on the dosage and the extent of localization within hematopoietic tissue. With all the radioisotopes studied by Jacobson, Marks, and Lorenz (1949), whether they localized in bone or more generally throughout the body, a reduction in the lymphocyte values of the peripheral blood was found to be the most sensitive indicator of acute or subacute effect. This was also true for radioelements such as radioiodine, which localizes promptly in the thyroid gland.

PHOSPHORUS (P^{32})

Jacobson, Skirmont, *et al.* (1948) studied the effect of a single intraperitoneal injection of 1 μc/g of body weight of P^{32} on normal and polycythemic rats. A significant depression of leukocyte values per cubic millimeter was produced in both groups. No apparent effect was produced on the hemoglobin, erythrocyte, or hematocrit values in either group. On the basis of hematologic data, no apparent difference in the sensitivity of the hematopoietic system to a single dose of P^{32} (1 μc/g) or to 300 r of total-body X irradiation was evident in rats (Fig. 16-14).

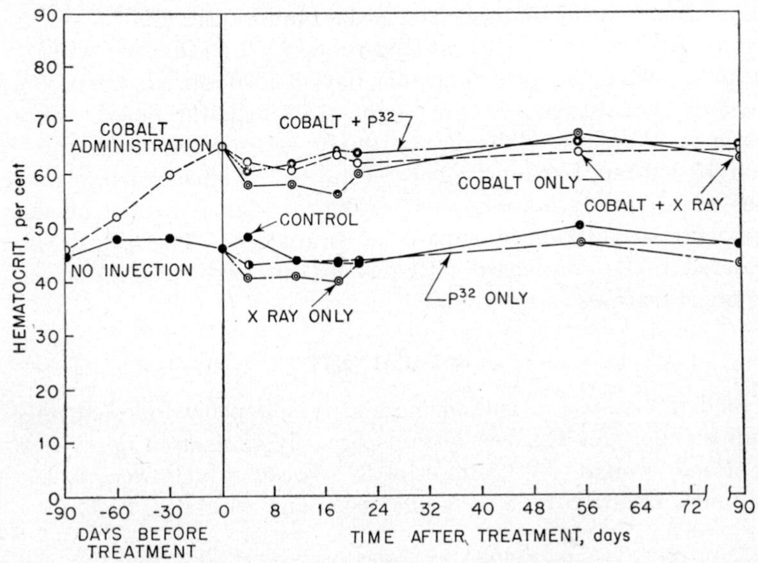

FIG. 16-14. The effect of 300 r of total-body X irradiation or a single dose of P^{32} (1 μc/g of body weight) on the hematocrit values of normal rats and those having cobalt-induced polycythemia.

However, after a total dose of 4.5 μc/g of body weight given intraperitoneally in 1.5-μc/g doses every three weeks, Bethard, Skirmont, and Jacobson (1950) reported a decrease in hematocrit and hemoglobin values by the twenty-second week, which reached a low level by twenty-eight weeks.

Warren and Dixon (1949) studied the hematologic effect of radiophosphorus on developing chicks (6–28 days). In 6-day-old chicks, given subcutaneously 235 μc of phosphorus, a rapid decrease in lymphocytes, reaching less than 1000/cu mm in 4 days, occurred followed by a gradual increase to normal values by 55 days. The erythrocytes fell gradually the first 8 days, dropped sharply to 0.63 million/cu mm by 15 days, and returned to normal value in 41 days. The leukocyte values fell rapidly during the first 4 days and then gradually disappeared completely from the blood in 15 days, recovering slowly and only approaching normal values at the end of 48 days. The same general pattern of peripheral-blood changes was found by Warren following administration of 300 μc to 19-day-old chicks and 760 μc to 28-day-old chicks. The larger doses caused a fatal anemia.

Dixon (1948) injected chickens subcutaneously with 300 or 400 μc of P^{32} every week for three weeks. A virtual agranulocytosis and thrombocytopenia developed by 7 days and remained thus during the period of observation (17 days). Erythrocyte values decreased steadily reaching 0.5 million/cu mm by 17 days.

Raper and Barnes (1951), Raper, Zirkle, and Barnes (1951), and Raper, Henshaw, and Snider (1951) studied total-surface radiation with β rays in rabbits. With doses ranging from 1500–59,000 rep, no direct effect on the cellular constituents of the peripheral blood was noted. Sporadic increase in the heterophils began three weeks after irradiation with 10,000–15,000 rep, but no evidence of individual effect on the leukocyte values was detected, nor was there evidence to substantiate the claim of lymphocyte stimulation by superficial irradiation. The lack of effect is considered to be consistent with physical properties of radiation and anatomical features of the rabbit.

SODIUM (Na^{24})

A moderate-to-severe leukopenia and lymphopenia followed injection of radiosodium (Na^{24}) given intraperitoneally to mice in doses of 23–96 $\mu c/g$ of body weight. With doses of 48–95 $\mu c/g$ of body weight, death of the animals occurred by 8 days (Jacobson and Simmons, 1946a).

BARIUM-LANTHANUM ($Ba\text{-}La^{140}$)

A dose of 1.9 $\mu c/g$ of body weight administered intraperitoneally to mice produced a significant and rapid reduction of leukocyte, lymphocyte, and heterophil values that was sustained for approximately 60 days. Rapid reduction in these values and death within 15 days followed the administration of 17 $\mu c/g$ of body weight. No significant change occurred in erythrocyte or hemoglobin values by 60 days with these doses (Jacobson, 1946). The radiation effects of these two isotopes in the mouse may be entirely due to β rays (Finkle, Snyder, and Tompkins, 1946), although both β and γ rays are emitted.

YTTRIUM (Y^{91})

Yttrium (Y^{91}) administered by gavage to rats in a single dose of 20 $\mu c/g$ of body weight produced a marked initial elevation in the erythrocyte and hemoglobin values followed by a severe anemia that reached its maximum at 20 days. A 75 per cent reduction in lymphocyte values occurred within 3 days with a return to normal values by 35 days. A dose of 10 $\mu c/g$ of body weight produced a temporary lymphopenia, whereas no hematologic effect was observed after single doses of less than 10 $\mu c/g$ of body weight. Daily ingestion of 0.3–2.0 $\mu c/g$ of body weight of yttrium produced a lymphopenia that reached a maximum at 90 days. There was prompt return to normal values upon discontinuation of the yttrium (Jacobson and Simmons, 1946b).

STRONTIUM (Sr^{89})

Hematologic studies of the peripheral blood of rabbits, rats, and mice after intraperitoneal or stomach-tube administration of strontium (Sr^{89}) as a chloride in doses from 0.015–14.5 $\mu c/g$ of body weight indicated that reduction in heterophil and lymphocyte values was about equal and that these cells were sensitive indicators of acute and subacute effects. No anemia occurred in mice following doses of 0.034 $\mu c/g$ of body weight or lower, but moderate anemia was produced with a dose of 2.0 $\mu c/g$ of body weight in this species. The minimal dose exerting a detectable reduction in heterophil values in rats and mice was 0.22 and 0.25 $\mu c/g$ of body weight. In rabbits an intraperitoneal dose of 1.0 $\mu c/g$ of body weight produced a significant reduction of heterophil values, and 3.0 $\mu c/g$ of body weight produced a significant reduction in hemoglobin and erythrocyte values (Simmons and Jacobson, 1946).

Of interest in connection with strontium (Sr^{89}) toxicity is the fact that, in mice injected with a dose of 2.0 $\mu c/g$ of body weight, only a leukopenia became apparent even though the bone marrow was markedly depleted or aplastic (Jacobson, Simmons, and Block, 1949). Concomitant with the development of aplasia in the marrow a myeloid metaplasia developed in the spleen, which was sufficient to compensate for the lack of erythrocyte production in the marrow. In splenectomized mice a severe anemia developed since compensatory blood formation in the spleen was not possible (Fig. 16-15).

RADIUM

Hematologic studies on the peripheral blood of rats, mice, and rabbits after intraperitoneal, intravenous, or intracardial injections of radium chloride indicate that a macrocytic anemia develops following parenteral administration of radium chloride in doses between 0.1 and 0.2 μg. Although doses below this range produced an anemia in rats and mice, no anemia was produced in the rabbits with this dose. A reduction in leukocyte values occurred with doses in the 0.1-μg range in the rabbit, whereas doses as high as 0.02–0.03 μg resulted in leukocyte reductions in rats and mice (Jacobson and Simmons, 1946c).

PLUTONIUM (Pu^{239})

There appeared to be no significant species difference in the sensitivity of the hematopoietic system of the mouse, rat, or rabbit to plutonium given intravenously or intramuscularly as a citrate in doses of 0.001–0.119 μc/g of body weight to rabbits and in doses of 0.003–0.125 μc/g of body weight to the rat. Doses of 0.0062 μc/g of body weight produced a moderate-to-severe and sustained leukopenia in all three species and caused an anemia in mice and rats resulting in early death in these two

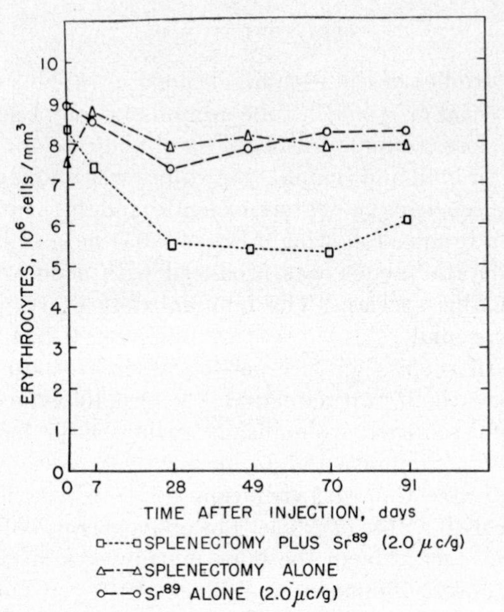

FIG. 16-15. Erythrocyte values of normal and splenectomized rats injected with a single dose of Sr^{89}, 2.0 μc/g.

species (135 days). Doses above 0.0063 μc/g of body weight produced a correspondingly more severe and sustained anemia, leukopenia, and reticulocyte and platelet reduction in mice and rats (Jacobson and Simmons, 1946c).

The fact that effects on the hematopoietic system are seen in the peripheral blood of plutonium-injected animals whereas comparable doses of injected radium produce no such changes and yet give rise to bone tumors earlier and in greater number may be related to difference in the site of deposition of the two elements.

GOLD (Au^{198})

Wheeler, Jackson, and Hahn (1951) studied the hematologic effect of radiogold in 14 dogs receiving intravenously 1 μc/kg. All dogs showed a decrease in leukocyte values, but only one had a marked leukopenia. In most dogs the sedimentation rate was increased. Liver function tests were essentially negative. The hemoglobin and hematocrit values decreased over a period of several weeks.

GALLIUM (Ga^{72})

Dudley, Louviere, and Shaw (1951) administered radiogallium as a citrate to five species of animals. The only effect of radiation observed was a reduction in total leukocytes in the mouse, rabbit, and guinea pig with dosages of 2.3–9.0 mc of Ga^{72}/kg. The degree and duration of the leukopenia vary with the dose and species. Repeated injections of Ga^{72} in dogs and rabbits indicated that this element is a cumulative poison for these species.

MORPHOLOGIC CHANGES IN PERIPHERAL-BLOOD CELLS PRODUCED BY IONIZING RADIATIONS

Morphologic changes in the various cellular constituents of the peripheral blood of animals, which are observed after exposure to penetrating radiation such as X ray, fast neutrons, and radioactive elements, have been described by a number of authors. These morphologic alterations are not specific for the various types of radiation. In fact, all the morphologic abnormalities that have thus far been described can be produced by such radiomimetic substances as the nitrogen mustards. Exposure to repeated small dosages of X rays or fast neutrons produced little or no morphologic change except macrocytosis and, occasionally, the appearance of giant platelets. Whether or not an anemia develops in mammals exposed to ionizing radiation given in repeated dosages depends on the sensitivity of the species and the size of the dose. In the event that anemia develops, then all the characteristic morphologic changes are seen in the red cells, e.g., anisocytosis, poikilocytosis, and macrocytosis. The observations of Lorenz, Heston, *et al.* (1946) on mice, guinea pigs, and rabbits exposed to dosages as high as 8.8 r/day until the accumulated dose was 5000 r or more showed surprisingly little evidence of morphologic change and form the basis for this statement.

Exposure to a single dose of externally applied radiation, such as X ray or fast neutrons, or irradiation from a single massive dose of an isotope that localizes in the blood-forming tissue produced morphologic changes that were detectable within a few hours after the exposure. These changes, which have been described by Aubertin and Beaujard (1908), Heineke (1904), Kroemeke (1926), Henshaw (1943–1944a, b), Evans (1948), Dunlap (1942), Clarkson, Mayneord, and Parson (1938), Jacobson and Marks (1947), Jacobson *et al.* (1947), and Jacobson, Marks, and Lorenz (1949), are briefly summarized.

In general, the number of morphologic abnormalities observed are directly proportionate to the radiation dosage sustained by the blood-forming tissue. There is little evidence that cells are injured in the peripheral blood (Furth *et al.*, 1951). The injury that results in the observed abnormalities in the peripheral blood is undoubtedly sustained or produced by the irradiation effects on the various maturation stages of the precursors in the blood-forming tissues. With doses in the LD_{50} range or above, an anemia was invariably produced in all the species of laboratory animals that have been investigated. In the presence of an anemia, anisocytosis, poikilocytosis, macrocytosis, microcytosis, and polychromasia were found. The degree of these red-cell abnormalities depends, in general, on the type and chronicity of the anemia.

Nucleated erythrocytes were observed soon after exposure but reached a maximum between the tenth and twenty-fifth day after irradiation. This represents the period of maximum anemia in the peripheral blood and the stage of maximum regeneration of erythropoiesis in the marrow.

Degenerative morphologic changes in the platelets were found by Jacobson, Marks, and Lorenz (1949) in the peripheral blood of animals following median lethal doses and above of roentgen radiation. Giant platelets were frequently seen concomitant with reduction in platelet values. Except for increased size and distinctive granular degeneration, no further morphologic alterations were found in the platelets of the peripheral blood. Only on rare occasions were megakaryocytes found in the peripheral blood after total-body roentgen irradiation in the LD_{50} range.

The morphologic changes in the lymphocytes of the peripheral blood increased with increasing amounts of radiation. Clumping of nuclear chromatin was seen early. Histologic studies indicate that this change, which occurred with relatively small doses ($\sim$50 r), may actually be reversible in some lymphocytes (Jacobson, Marks, and Lorenz, 1949). As it became more pronounced, pale bluish opaque areas were encountered. In addition, lymphocytes were seen with rounded chromatin masses seemingly free within the nuclear membrane. At the time of maximum lymphocyte reduction in the peripheral blood after irradiation, mononuclear cells with a somewhat basophilic cytoplasm and with nucleoli were often prominent. These latter cells are indistinguishable from "blast" forms. Occasionally mitotic blast cells appeared after semilethal or higher doses. Other lymphocytes appeared to have split nuclei and nuclei with considerable fragmentation. With the LD_{50} range of acute total-body irradiation, these destructive changes were more pronounced. Remnants of nuclear fragments, without nuclear outline and which could not be distinguished as belonging to either the myeloid or lymphoid series, appeared. Many lymphocytes were bilobed, whereas others were difficult to distinguish from monocytes. During the peak of lymphocyte destruction, phagocytic monocytes with engulfed nuclear debris were found in the peripheral-blood smears. Similar changes were described by Henshaw *et al.* (1946) in mice following large single lethal doses of γ rays.

During the phase of rapid reduction of granulocyte values in rabbits, abnormal forms of this series were seen in the peripheral blood. These cells showed nuclear deformity and disintegration to the extent that it was impossible to determine at which stage of maturity the cells were damaged (Jacobson and Marks, 1947; Jacobson *et al.*, 1947; and Jacobson, Marks, and Lorenz, 1949). The nuclear membrane was destroyed, and in most, instances, bluish nonspecific granules of uneven contour filled the entire cell, covering the nucleus and cytoplasm to such an extent that it was impossible to identify the cell other than to say it was a damaged or degenerating leukocyte. Other bizarre forms were also seen that were difficult to describe and impossible to categorize. The cytoplasm of the heterophil may undergo changes following irradiation. Occasionally it contained vacuoles and had a mottled appearance. In some instances the granules of the heterophils appeared to be damaged since cells were found in which some granules clung to the nuclear membrane while the remainder of the cytoplasm remained clear. Another type of cell seen in rabbits was one that resembled a basket cell but differed from it in having one or two distinct chromatin masses that were deep blue against a network of destroyed perichromatin and cytoplasmic disintegration.

Atypical eosinophils characterized by irregularity in the granules, both with regard to size and shape, were occasionally seen in the blood smears of dogs following LD_{50} or higher doses of total-body roentgen irradiation. Giant polymorphonuclear leukocytes were frequently seen which appeared swollen and contained multilobed nuclei spread over the cytoplasm-like globules, having an extremely fine filament branching into eight or more lobes.

DIRECT VERSUS INDIRECT EFFECT OF IRRADIATION ON BLOOD FORMATION

Lawrence, Valentine, and Dowdy (1948) reviewed the problem of indirect effects and concluded that the hematologic or histologic evidence for indirect effects of irradiation on nonirradiated blood-forming tissue was unconvincing. Jacobson *et al.* (1949, 1950) found no suppression of lymphopoiesis in the lead-shielded appendixes of rabbits given 800 r of total-body X irradiation. Exposure of rabbits to this dose with shielding of only a single Peyer's patch of the intestine did not appear to inhibit or destroy the lymphocytes in the patch (Jacobson *et al.*, 1952). It must be borne in mind that dosages above the LD_{50} may produce changes in the hematopoietic tissue of the shielded body part if the general toxicity produced by the irradiation is severe.

"STIMULATION" OF BLOOD-FORMING TISSUE BY RADIATION

The evidence that small or large doses of penetrating radiation stimulate blood formation directly is unconvincing (Bloom, 1948). On the other hand, secondary or "compensatory" increases in certain of the cellular constituents of the peripheral blood and in the blood-forming tissue have been observed repeatedly. Such compensatory "stimulation" is invariably preceded by a reduction of certain cellular constituents of the peripheral blood and destruction or inhibition of cells within the blood-forming tissue (Bloom, 1948; Jacobson, Marks, and Lorenz, 1949; Murphy, 1926). These findings are based on histologic or hematologic observations and are to be differentiated from chemical or metabolic changes within cells that may occur after irradiation and that might be labeled "stimulation." This is also true when the problem of indirect effects of irradiation is considered.

MEASURES MODIFYING DESTRUCTIVE EFFECTS OF IRRADIATION OR AFFECTING RECOVERY

Many substances that have been used to treat hematologic disorders in the human being have also been screened for their possible prophylactic or therapeutic value. Simmons *et al.* (1946) and Jacobson, Stearner, and Simmons (1947) found that, in experimental animals, substances including folic acid, liver extract, ascorbic acid, and pentnucleotide were of no demonstrable value in reducing radiation injury or in hastening recovery from this injury.

Only those prophylactic measures that have shown conclusive evidence of effect on the hematologic recovery pattern from radiation injury will be discussed in the following sections.

PROPHYLACTIC MEASURES

Induced Hyperplasia of Blood-forming Tissue. Jacobson, Marks, Gaston, Simmons, *et al.* (1948) reported that the induction of erythroblastic hyperplasia by a hemolytic agent (phenylhydrazine hydrochloride) or by repeated phlebotomy prior to irradiation prevented or reduced the atrophy of the bone marrow observed in normal adult rabbits after exposure to 800 r of total-body X irradiation. As is shown in Figs. 16-4, 16-16, and 16-17, phenylhydrazine produced an anemia, a reticulocytosis, and a hyperplastic bone marrow. Although an anemia was produced in normal rabbits which reached a maximum in 14 days, no further anemia occurred in animals with a phenylhydrazine-induced anemia at the time of irradiation, and, as can be noted by examining the reticulocyte values of histologic preparations, the production of erythrocytes was maintained within essentially normal limits. The failure of a mid-lethal dose (800 r) to produce further anemia under these conditions or to interfere materially with recovery is probably dependent on the multiplication of the surviving primitive erythroblast precursors or on the functional survival of even more primitive cells such as reticular cells. That this phenomenon was not due to a specific effect of the phenylhydrazine itself on the cells of the marrow is indicated by the fact that phlebotomy before irradiation afforded similar protection. Schack and MacDuffee (1949) have corroborated these findings using the technique of exposing mice to a

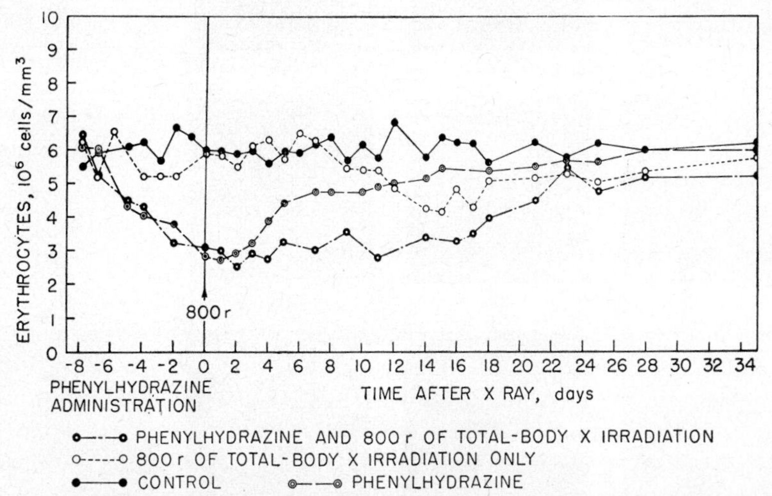

FIG. 16-16. Effect of a single dose of 800 r of total-body roentgen irradiation on the erythrocyte values in the peripheral blood of normal rabbits and rabbits with a phenylhydrazine-induced anemia. (*Originally published in Science,* 107: 249, 1948.)

low oxygen tension (simulated high altitude of 15,000 ft) and thus inducing erythroblastic hyperplasia prior to irradiation. Bethard, Skirmont, and Jacobson (1950) have demonstrated that, during the period of maximum erythroblastic hyperplasia induced by cobalt, radiophosphorus produces lesser inhibition of erythropoiesis than in normal rats (Fig. 16-18). More recently, Valentine and Pearce (1952) have compared the regenerative capacity of erythroid tissue in irradiated and nonirradiated cats. Immediately prior to irradiation (200 r, whole body) the cats were bled sufficiently to reduce the peripheral erythrocyte count by 40 per cent. It was found that recovery from the anemia induced by hemorrhage immediately prior to irradiation was only slightly less rapid than in the control nonirradiated cats. Exposure to low oxygen tension after irradiation had no effect on recovery of hematopoiesis after 400 or 500 r according to Smith, Dooley, and Thompson (1948).

The mechanism whereby phenylhydrazine-induced anemia or phlebotomy reduces the inhibition of erythropoiesis expected after a given dose of X radiation is probably unrelated to the observation of Dowdy, Bennett, and Chastain (1950) in which survival of rats exposed to lethal doses of X radiation was enhanced by reducing oxygen tension available to the animals to about 6 per cent during irradiation. This latter procedure,

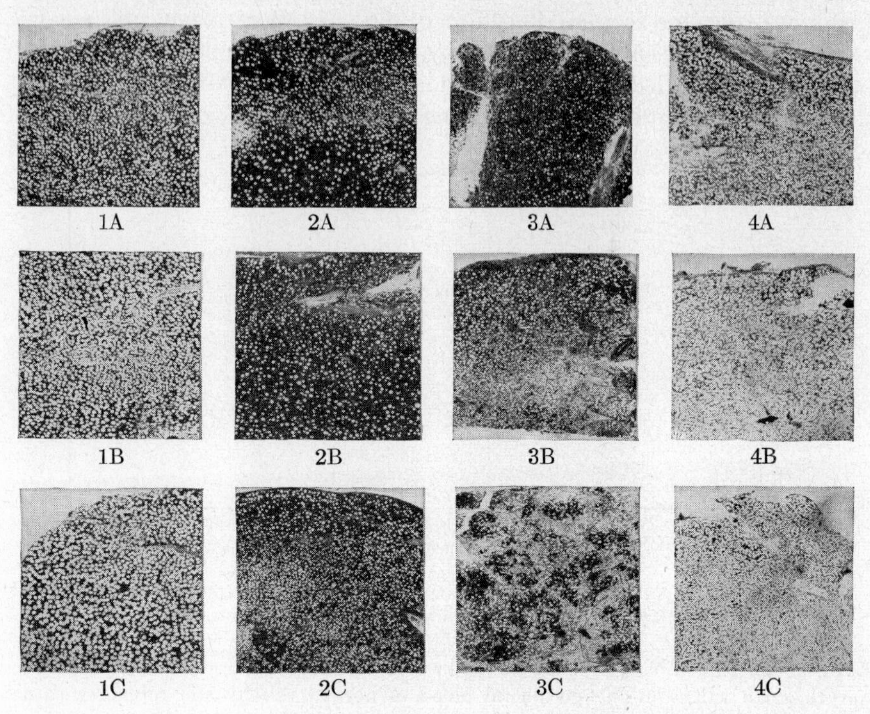

FIG. 16-17. The effect of 800 r of total-body roentgen irradiation on normal and hyperplastic bone marrow of the rabbit. (1*A*,*B*,*C*) Range of normal control marrow. (2*A*,*B*,*C*) Bone marrow after phenylhydrazine-induced hyperplasia, 3, 4, and 6 days, respectively, after phenylhydrazine withdrawal. (3*A*,*B*,*C*) Bone marrow of phenylhydrazine-induced hyperplasia at 1, 3, and 5 days, respectively, after 800 r and 3, 4, and 6 days, respectively, after phenylhydrazine withdrawal. (4*A*,*B*,*C*) Bone marrow of normal rabbits exposed to 800 r at 1, 3, and 5 days after 800 r. Magnification 16 X. (*Originally published in Science,* 107: 248, 1948.)

for all practical purposes, stops metabolic activity, whereas phenylhydrazine or phlebotomy actually enhances the metabolic activity of the cells concerned in erythropoiesis. The mechanism whereby phenylhydrazine- or phlebotomy-induced hyperplasia reduces the expected radiation effect is not known, but it must be assumed that some metabolic change within the cells renders them less susceptible to radiation.

Use of Estrogens. Treadwell, Gardner, and Lawrence (1943) demonstrated that estradiol benzoate, given 10 days prior to X radiation in the

LD_{50} range and above, significantly decreases mortality. The mechanism underlying this fact is not resolved, but studies by Patt, Straube, *et al.* (1949) have conclusively shown that the recovery of the hematopoietic tissue and subsequent return of certain constituents of the peripheral blood occurred earlier in mice given estrogens before radiation than in control irradiated nonestrogen-treated mice. The observed hematologic effect of estrogen pretreatment indicates that a greater effect is exerted on regeneration of granulocytes and erythrocytes than on lymphocytes.

Other Prophylactic Measures. Sulfhydryl enzyme systems inactivated by irradiation are reactivated in vitro by the addition of glutathione and other similar compounds (Barron *et al.*, 1949). Patt, Tyree, *et al.*

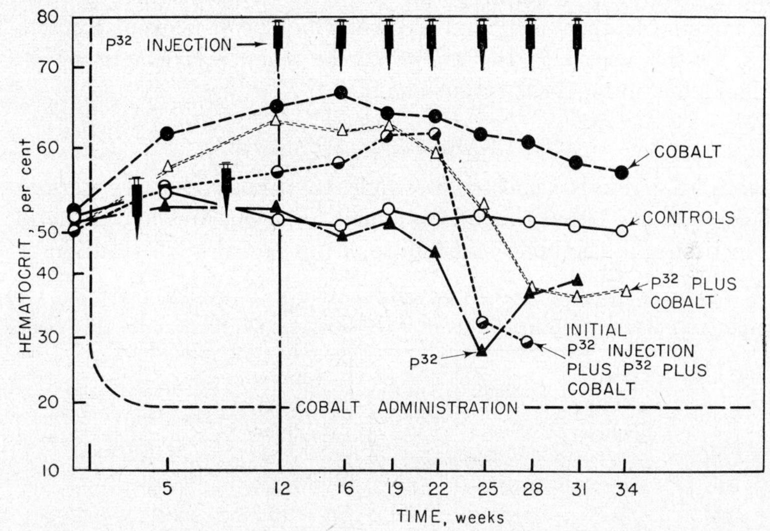

FIG. 16-18. Effect of repeated injections (1.5 $\mu c/g$) of P^{32} on the hematocrit values of the peripheral blood of rats with and without cobalt-induced polycythemia.

(1949) and Patt, Smith, and Jackson (1950) demonstrated that the administration of cysteine just prior to total-body irradiation of rats and mice increases survival of rats and, to some extent, hastens the recovery of blood-forming tissue in rats. Glutathione has since been shown by Cronkite, Brecher, and Chapman (1951) to produce an effect similar to cysteine on survival of mice and on hematopoietic recovery. Enhancement of hematopoietic recovery has been reported after severe oxygen deprivation (Bennett, Hanson, and Dowdy, 1951), but no hematologic data are available on animals subjected to cyanide intoxication during irradiation (Bacq *et al.*, 1950). The mechanism by which estrogens, cysteine, or glutathione modify the hematologic picture is not known. That the mechanism is different from the one observed after phenylhydrazine or phlebotomy is clear since the destruction of hematopoietic tissue occurs even though cysteine or estrogens have been given prophylactically. The decreased effect observed in the peripheral blood is due to a more rapid regeneration of the hematopoietic tissue from the more radioresistant precursors such as reticular cells, whereas the effect observed when phenylhydrazine is given prophylactically is that hematopoietic tissue, including reticular cells, blast forms, and perhaps even more mature forms, survives and is immediately capable of accelerated production. Regeneration of granulocytic tissue is more rapid than regeneration of lymphatic tissue when cysteine has been given prophylactically if the peripheral blood can be used as a measure of the production of granulocytes and lymphocytes. On the other hand, phenylhydrazine, although producing a panhyperplasia of the bone marrow, produces a more extreme erythroblastic hyperplasia which persists even after irradiation. Erythropoiesis is the major initial regenerative activity of the bone marrow under these conditions.

"THERAPEUTIC" MEASURES

Death of animals exposed to single total-body dosages of ionizing radiations in the lethal range is assumed to be due to the destruction of certain tissues in the body and failure of functional reconstitution of one

TABLE 16-5. SURVIVAL OF MICE EXPOSED TO VARIOUS DOSAGES OF X RADIATION WITH AND WITHOUT SHIELDING OF THE SURGICALLY EXTERIORIZED SPLEEN

Lead shielding of spleen	Dosage, r	Number of mice	Number of 28-day survivors	Survival, per cent
Yes	1025	176	134	76.0
No	1025	431	10	2.3
Yes	1100	82	30	36.5
No	1100	15	0	0.0
Yes	1200	42	23	54.7
No	1200	6	0	0.0
Yes	1300	156	5	3.2
Yes	1300[a]	48	15	31.2
No	1300	28	0	0.0
Yes	1600	46	0	0.0
No	1600			

[a] Technique differed in that the artery at the distal tip of the spleen was not severed, and thus no infarct occurred in the spleen.

or more of the tissues (e.g., the hematopoietic system) that individually or collectively are vital to the survival of the animals. Although many reasons for the importance of the blood-forming tissue to survival can be enumerated, it cannot be stated with certainty that death or survival of the irradiated animal invariably depends on the direct or indirect results of hematopoietic dysfunction. In the studies that are discussed in the following sections, a close parallelism between survival and hematopoietic regeneration is obvious, but it must be borne in mind that this correlation may be more apparent than real and that failure of tissues other than the blood-forming tissue may be critical. More precise methods of study of other organ systems and of the dependence of organ systems on one another may be necessary before the factors contributing to death or survival of irradiated animals can be clearly separated.

Lead Shielding of the Exteriorized Spleen and Other Parts of Body. Lead shielding of the surgically exteriorized spleen (average weight 0.1 g) of

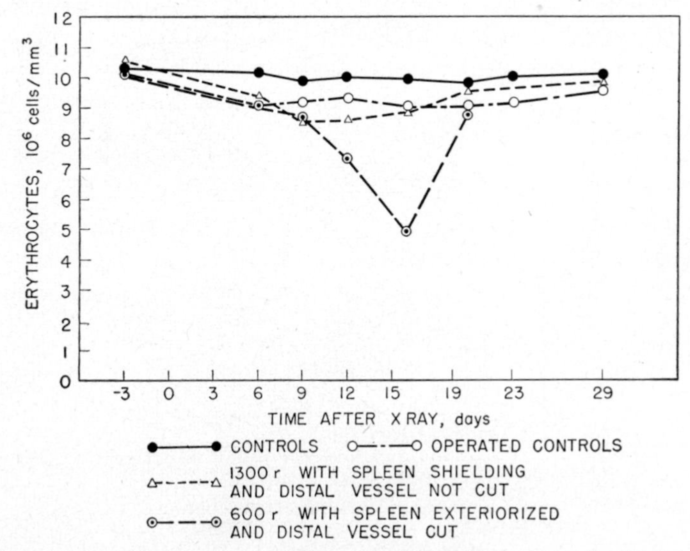

FIG. 16-19. Comparative effect of 600 r of total-body roentgen irradiation (spleen exteriorized and distal vessel cut) and of 1300 r with lead shielding of the exteriorized spleen (distal vessel not cut) on the erythrocyte values of CF_1 female mice.

adult mice during exposure to 1025 r of total-body X irradiation markedly enhances survival (Table 16-5). After exposures up to 1300 r, no anemia and only a transient leukopenia and thrombocytopenia appear in spleen-shielded mice, whereas a severe pancytopenia follows exposure to 600 r without spleen shielding (Figs. 16-19, 16-20). Recovery of hematopoietic tissue in mice exposed to 1025 r with spleen shielding occurs by 8 days, but no hematopoietic recovery is noted during this interval in unshielded mice, Fig. 16-21 (Jacobson, Simmons, Marks, *et al.*, 1950). Recovery of the lymphatic tissue in the wall of the gastrointestinal tract in spleen-shielded mice parallels recovery of the hematopoietic tissue elsewhere. These observations led to the theory that the mechanism of recovery from radiation injury under these conditions was on a humoral basis and that the factor (or factors) responsible was produced by the cells of the shielded tissue (Jacobson, Simmons, Bethard, *et al.*, 1950; Jacobson, Simmons, Marks, *et al.*, 1950).

The survival of mice exposed to 1025 r of total-body X irradiation is approximately 30 per cent if part of the exteriorized liver (0.8 g), the exteriorized intestine (2.5 g), the entire head (3.0 g), or one entire hind leg up to the thigh (1.5 g) is lead shielded during exposure. Without shielding, only 0.8 per cent survive this dose; with spleen shielding at

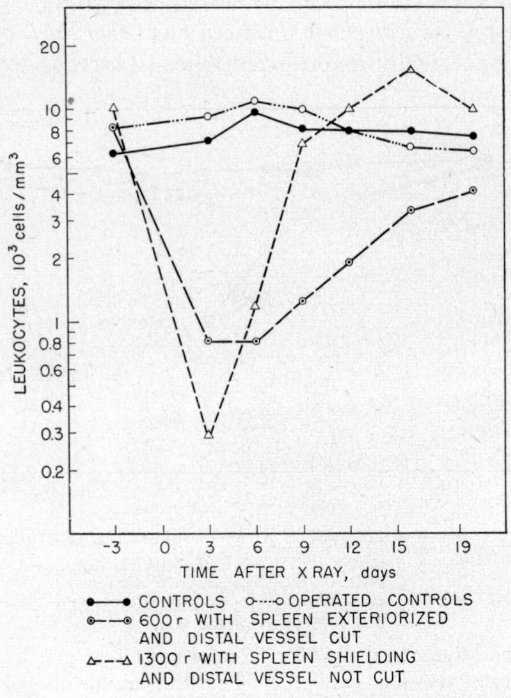

FIG. 16-20. Comparative effect of 600 r of total-body roentgen irradiation (spleen exteriorized and distal vessel cut) and of 1300 r with lead shielding of the exteriorized spleen (distal vessel not cut) on the leukocyte values of CF_1 female mice.

least 76 per cent survive. Shielding one exteriorized kidney (average weight 0.19 g) does not enhance survival. Recovery of the hematopoietic tissue, as judged by histopathologic and hematologic examination, is under way by 8 days in liver- or intestine-shielded animals, whereas after lead shielding of the head, recovery of these tissues is delayed even longer, and recovery of hematopoietic tissue is nil with kidney shielding (Jacobson, Simmons, Marks, and Eldredge, 1951; Jacobson, Simmons, Marks, Gaston, *et al.*, 1951).

The effect of spleen or appendix shielding on the survival of irradiated rabbits has not been carefully studied, but it is clear that no enhancement of survival occurs such as is observed in spleen-shielded mice or rats.

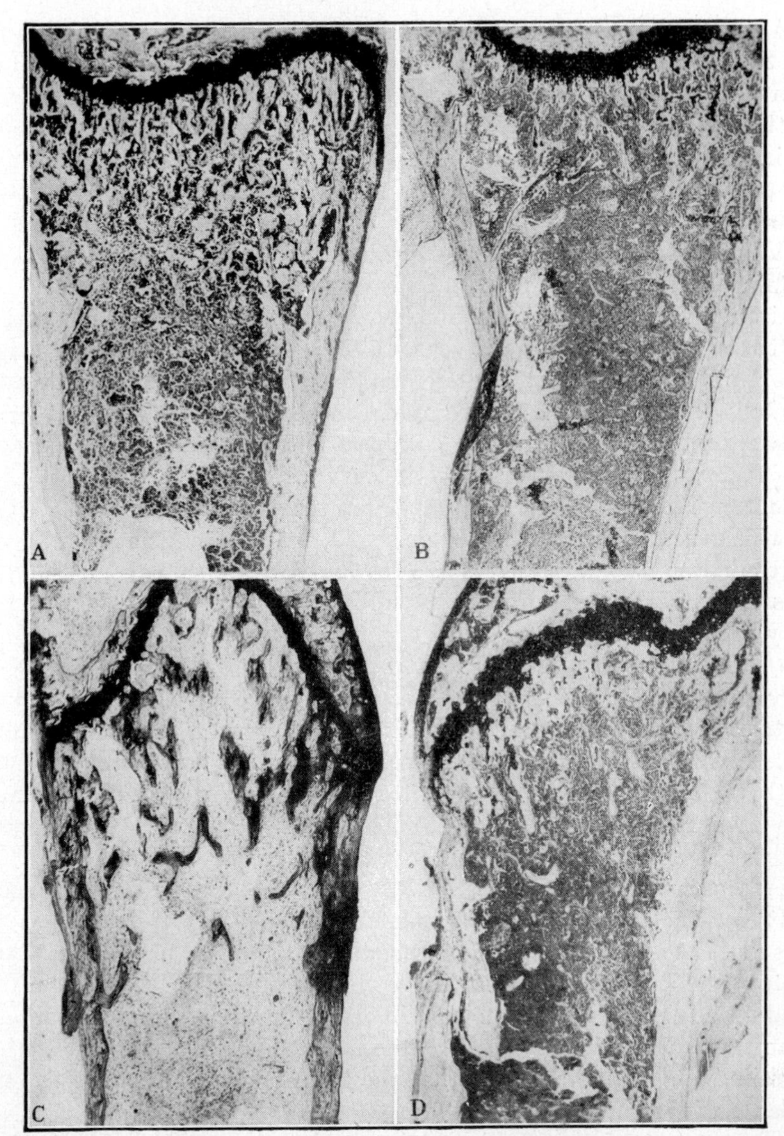

FIG. 16-21. Femoral marrow of mice 8 days after exposure to 1025 r of total-body X irradiation. (*A*) Control untreated. (*B*) Control operated only. (*C*) Total-body X irradiation without spleen protection. (*D*) Total-body X irradiation with spleen lead-shielded during irradiation.

Spleen or appendix shielding in the rabbit during exposure to 800 or 1000 r appears not to affect survival appreciably even though regeneration of blood-forming tissue precedes the recovery of this tissue in the animals without spleen or appendix shielding (Jacobson, Simmons, Marks, Gaston, *et al.*, 1951).

Allen *et al.* (1948) have reported that 450 r of total-body X irradiation is invariably lethal to dogs. With head shielding (Allen, 1951), however, mortality following this dose is reduced to 75 per cent, and other aspects of the usual postirradiation syndrome, such as hemorrhage and evidences of infection, are greatly reduced or absent. Further work on the dog comparing the relative effectiveness of shielding parts such as the head, spleen, intestine, limbs, and liver after exposure to various dosages of total-body X irradiation will be of interest if for no other reason than to obtain baselines on the potential effectiveness of these tissues for comparison with mice, rats, and rabbits and to accumulate some facts on the potential production of the factor on a tissue-weight basis, type of tissue shielded, etc. The species differences that are apparent cannot be adequately evaluated since, for example, considerable differences may exist between rabbit and mouse spleen in terms of the potential production of the factor (or factors) involved in survival or early regeneration of hematopoietic tissue. In this connection the work of Bond *et al.* (1949), in which the abdomens of rats were shielded with lead during total-body X irradiation, is of interest. The LD_{50} for these abdominal-shielded rats was 1950 r compared with ca. 700 r for nonshielded control rats. For very practical reasons it would be of interest to determine more precisely the relative importance of the various abdominal tissues in enhancing survival on a weight basis and to assess more adequately the volume-dose factor. This has been done to some extent with rats by Gershon-Cohen, Hermel, and Griffith (1951), Jacobson *et al.* (1949), Jacobson, Simmons, Bethard, *et al.* (1950), Jacobson, Simmons, Marks, *et al.* (1950), and Jacobson, Simmons, Marks, Gaston, *et al.* (1951) with mice, but further data for all species are needed. As was pointed out by Bond *et al.* (1949), the radiosensitivity of the part of the body irradiated may be more important than the gram-roentgens sustained by the balance of the body. To this must be added the fact that the actual or potential production of the factor (under consideration in this section) by the shielded or nonirradiated tissue may be more important in determining survival of the animal than the radiosensitivity of the tissue in the radiation field and, within certain limits, more important than the gram-roentgens sustained by the balance of the body.

The amount of tissue shielded in the intestine- and liver-shielding experiments in mice was greater by factors of 25 and 8, respectively, than that shielded in the mouse spleen-shielding experiments, yet survival was considerably less. These findings suggest that the potential production of a factor (or factors) by the intestine and the liver is not as great as that by splenic tissue but yet is sufficient to institute recovery early enough in a sufficient number of cells of the body to have a definite effect on survival.

It is conceivable that practically all tissues of the body are capable of producing the factor (or factors) concerned in recovery from radiation injury (Jacobson, Simmons, Marks, and Eldredge, 1951; Jacobson, Simmons, Marks, Gaston, *et al.*, 1951), but certain tissues and, in particular, the hematopoietic system have a greater potential production per unit volume.

There are several differences between head or limb shielding and spleen implantation (to be described later) and spleen shielding. According to generally accepted concepts, the reduction in volume dose when the head, limb, or intestine is shielded must be considered as playing a role in the reduction of mortality since these structures represent a fairly large proportion of the body weight (15, 7.5, and 12.5 per cent, respectively). On the other hand, the shielded spleen weighs only 0.1 g (0.005 per cent of the body weight) and spleen implants weigh 0.010 g (0.0005 per cent of the body weight) which eliminates from consideration the volume-dose factor of shielded spleen or implanted spleen. The fact that the head, hind limbs, and intestine contain reticuloendothelial tissue and other tissue of mesenchymal origin is probably more important than the volume-dose consideration.

Postirradiation Spleen Transplantation. Transplantation of spleens (total weight, 10–100 mg) from baby or adult mice into the peritoneal cavity of mice within 2 hours after exposure of the recipient adult mice to 1025 r of total-body X irradiation significantly increases the survival (ca. 50 per cent) of the irradiated mice and hastens regeneration of hematopoietic tissue (Jacobson, Simmons, Marks, and Eldredge, 1951; Jacobson, Simmons, Marks, Gaston, *et al.*, 1951). Transplantation of spleens into the peritoneal cavity of mice 1 or 2 days after exposure to 1025 r of total-body X irradiation likewise enhances survival (ca. 25 per cent) but not as effectively as earlier transplantation. Implantation of muscle into the peritoneal cavity after exposure of mice to 1025 r of total-body X irradiation has no beneficial effect on survival.

If splenectomy is performed in mice prior to irradiation, followed by implantation of fresh spleens into the peritoneal cavity after irradiation, survival is enhanced, indicating that an intact spleen is not required to make the transplant effective. Surgical removal of the transplanted spleens from the peritoneal cavity of mice 1 and 2 days after the irradiation-transplant procedure has invariably been followed by death of the animals. It is assumed that the ineffectiveness of this procedure is due to the fact that the implanted spleens are not vascularized prior to removal and are therefore incapable of elaboration and distribution of the factor. Gross and microscopic observations on mice surviving the irradiation-transplant procedure reveal that the implanted spleen or spleens have vascularized and eventually appear as normal splenic tissue. Revascularization and reconstitution of the implanted spleen are usually well under way by the sixth day after implantation. Transplantation of splenic tissue 2 days after irradiation is admittedly less effective in enhancing survival of mice exposed to 1025 r than earlier transplantation, but it has not been determined when a state of irreversibility has been reached. Actually, if establishment of a vascular supply to the transplant is essential to the manufacture and transport of the factor (or factors) in question, a conservative guess would be that supplying an optimum amount of the factor to mice as late as 6 days after exposure to 1025 r would still significantly increase the survival.

Administration of Suspension of Mashed Embryos. Intraperitoneal administration of a suspension of 12-day-old mouse embryos is effective in enhancing survival of mice exposed to 1025 r of total-body X irradiation (Jacobson, 1952; Jacobson, Marks, and Gaston, 1951). This suspension, prepared in the cold with or without the addition of normal physiological saline or buffered saline, when given intraperitoneally in a dosage of from 0.5–1.0 ml, 2–6 hours after irradiation of the recipient, results in 30 per cent survival. Suspensions of baby or adult spleens prepared and administered in a similar manner have thus far been ineffective in enhancing survival of mice exposed to 1025 r but have been effective in enhancing the survival of mice exposed to 800 r (Jacobson, 1952; Jacobson, Marks, and Gaston, 1951). Chick embryo suspensions (age of embryos, 11–14 days) prepared and administered in a similar manner to the mouse embryo suspensions have been reported by Marks (unpublished data, 1952), Stroud and Brues (unpublished data, 1952), and Jacobson (1952) to be ineffective in enhancing survival of mice exposed to X radiation in the LD_{50} range or above.

The factor (or factors) in the embryo or spleen suspensions responsible for recovery from radiation is probably the same as that responsible for the effectiveness of the spleen shielding and spleen implants. Two possible explanations for the effectiveness of cell suspensions are obvious: (1) that the cells in the suspension quickly implant and begin elaboration of the factor or factors effective in initiating tissue regeneration throughout the body or (2) that the peritoneal cavity serves as an incubator that allows the cell suspension to remain alive and to elaborate the factor responsible for increased survival and tissue regeneration in irradiated mice.

Homologous Bone-marrow Injection. Lorenz *et al.* (1951) have shown that, although 900 r is the LD_{99} for genetically homogeneous hybrid LAF_1 mice, approximately 75 per cent survive this dose if bone marrow aspirated from the long bones of normal nonirradiated mice of the same strain is injected intravenously within an hour after the exposure. If the bone marrow is administered intraperitoneally, survival is slightly less (ca. 50 per cent). The author estimates that the total weight of the injected marrow is approximately 1.5 mg. The recovery of the hematopoietic tissue of the bone-marrow–treated mice, as in the spleen-shielded, spleen-implanted, or embryo-suspension–injected mice, is hastened.

Jacobson (1952) obtained similar results in CF_1 female mice with intravenous injections of marrow from normal mice. Rekers (1948, 1950), Talbot and Pinson (1951), and Talbot and Gertsner (1951) have reported negative and equivocal beneficial effects on the radiation syndrome in dogs and rats, respectively, after bone-marrow administration.

The suspension of bone marrow that Lorenz and Jacobson injected contained mature and immature free cells such as granulocytes and megakaryocytes as well as free and fixed macrophages, reticular cells, and endothelial tissue. It seems likely that the cells injected establish as scattered foci of hematopoietic tissue and produce a factor (or factors) responsible for survival of the animal and that this factor is identical with that postulated in the spleen-shielding, spleen-implantation, and embryo-suspension experiments. Bone-marrow injection is not as effective as spleen shielding or spleen transplants in enhancing survival or hastening recovery of hematopoietic tissue in mice exposed to 1000 r or more. Since it is not known which cells in the shielded tissue or transplanted tissue (including bone marrow) are the most important in bringing about the effect, no adequate data are available to compare adequately the relative effectiveness of splenic tissue and bone marrow in enhancing survival from radiation injury.

Heterologous Transplants and Cell Suspensions. Lorenz, Congdon, and Uphoff (1952) have reported evidence of the effectiveness of heterologous tissue transplants on recovery from radiation injury. Within an hour after exposure of mice to 900 r (LD_{99}) of total-body X irradiation, approximately 25 mg of freshly aspirated guinea-pig bone marrow (in buffered saline) was injected intravenously into the irradiated mice. None of the control irradiated mice survived, but 40 per cent of the irradiated mice which received intravenous guinea-pig bone-marrow suspension survived the 28-day period of observation. As mentioned previously the survival of this strain of mice injected with homologous bone marrow (1.5 mg) after exposure to 900 r is ca. 75 per cent. The number of animals used by Lorenz, Congdon, and Uphoff (1952) in the heterologous transplant experiment is too small to warrant a positive conclusion. If further data corroborate these findings, proof that the factor (or factors) is humoral would be available.

It would not seem likely that heterologous bone-marrow injection could seed the hematopoietic tissue with cells which, by multiplication, repopulate the tissue. If heterologous tissue is effective as suggested by Lorenz, it seems more likely that this heterologous tissue lives, at least temporarily, in its new environment and produces a noncellular substance (or substances) that aids in recovery from the radiation injury.

Postirradiation Parabiosis. Barnes and Furth (1943) first demonstrated that parabiosis diminished the deleterious effects of irradiation. When one member of a parabiotic pair was irradiated, the pathological changes in the blood and blood-forming tissues of the irradiated mouse were less conspicuous than those in a single mouse similarly irradiated, while in the nonirradiated parabiont, the changes were only slight. More recently Brecher and Cronkite (1951) reported that approximately 50 per cent of rats exposed to 700 r of total-body X irradiation survive if they are joined to normal nonirradiated litter mates within a few hours after irradiation. None of the controls given the same does of irradiation survived the 28-day period of observation. Hematopoietic regeneration was more rapid in the irradiated rats with a parabion than in the irradiated controls. These findings, like those of Lorenz *et al.* (1951), corroborate Jacobson's previously reported observation that effective postirradiation "therapy" is a reality. Like the embryo-suspension experiments described, however, the experiments of Brecher do not point out the cellular source nor the identity of the effective factor (or factors) concerned.

Relation between Quantity of Shielded or Implanted Splenic Tissue and Effects on Survival. Two separate observations indicate that a definite relation exists between the quantity of implanted or shielded tissue and the effect as measured by hematopoietic regeneration or survival from irradiation (Jacobson, Simmons, Marks, Gaston, *et al.*, 1951).

1. The transplantation of two spleens (weight, ca. 5 mg) from 7- to 12-day-old baby mice into the peritoneal cavity of mice immediately after irradiation (1025 r) does not enhance survival, although the transplantation of four spleens (weight, ca. 10 mg) is effective in reversing the process in time to allow recovery of the animal (Jacobson, Simmons, Marks, Gaston, *et al.*, 1951).
2. In the regular spleen-shielding technique the main splenic pedicle is left intact, but a small blood vessel at the distal tip of the spleen is severed to facilitate exteriorization and lead shielding of the spleen. Invariably from one-fourth to one-half the spleen proximal to the severed vessel becomes infarcted and undergoes liquefaction necrosis. If this vessel is not cut and the whole spleen is shielded and remains intact, 100 per cent of the animals survive exposure to 1025 r rather than the expected 77 per cent. In fact, with a total-body exposure to 1300 r, only 3.4 per cent of the animals survive if the distal vessel of the spleen is cut during the shielding procedure, whereas 26.9 per cent survive this exposure with spleen shielding if the distal vessel is not cut (Jacobson, Simmons, Marks, Gaston, *et al.*, 1951). Hematopoietic regeneration is complete by 8 days in the animals exposed to 1300 r with spleen shielding and in which the distal vessel to the spleen is not cut. In the animals, exposed to this dose with spleen shielding but with the distal vessel cut, regeneration is not as rapid (Figs. 16-19, 16-20). This observation like observation 1 indicates that the quantity of the factor being produced is directly related

to the number of cells available in the shielded or implanted tissue and the amount of the factor available determines the survival of the animal. It would appear as though the repair process must be initiated in a minimum number of cells in the body of the irradiated animal to ensure survival of the animal exposed to dosages of 1000 r or more.

The Humoral Theory of Cell Regeneration. In mice and rabbits which had spleen shielding or spleen transplants, regeneration may occur from the scattered "free cells" in the lymphatic tissues and bone marrow that survive the radiation, but heteroplastic regeneration from reticular cells is prominent. Thus colonization from the shielded tissue and repopulation by multiplication of these colonized cells, if a factor at all, is only one aspect of the recovery process. The shielded tissue in some way restores the functional capacity of the reticular cells to repopulate the hematopoietic tissues. The shielded tissue may likewise restore the functional capacity of the residual free cells, which are not destroyed by irradiation, to multiply and thus repopulate the hematopoietic tissues. Cells coming from the shielded or implanted tissue cannot at the moment be distinguished from the residual free cells. If the cells, which do migrate out from the shielded tissue, do "lodge" in hematopoietic tissue, then it is also possible that they too contribute by division and multiplication and also by elaboration of the factor (or factors) under discussion.

Clamping Off Splenic Circulation during Irradiation-shielding Procedure. The survival of mice in which the circulation to the shielded spleen is clamped off during exposure of the animal to 1025 r and in which the clamp is released immediately after irradiation is approximately the same as survival in animals with spleen shielding but without clamping (Jacobson, Simmons, Marks, and Eldredge, 1951; Jacobson, Simmons, Marks, Gaston, *et al.*, 1951). Histologic recovery of the hematopoietic system is the same as in the spleen-shielded animals without clamping of the splenic pedicle. This observation was convincing evidence that the presence of shielded tissue in the circulation was not required during the period of irradiation in order for survival to be enhanced and hematopoietic regeneration to proceed. Reintroduction of the spleen into the circulation after irradiation could thus be considered an effective post-irradiation "therapeutic" approach to the problem.

Splenectomy after Spleen Shielding. Surgical extirpation of the initially shielded spleen at intervals after exposure of mice to 1025 r of total-body X irradiation shows that a beneficial effect (survival > 70 per cent and early regeneration of hematopoietic tissue) has already been exerted if the shielded spleen is left intact in the circulation for 1 hour (Jacobson, Simmons, Marks, Gaston, *et al.*, 1951). Leaving the spleen in the circulation for longer periods such as 6 or 24 hours or 2 or more days does not increase the percentage of animals surviving. In a previous communication (Jacobson, Simmons, Marks, and Eldredge, 1951) it was reported that, if splenectomy was performed within 10 minutes after the irradiation–spleen-shielding procedure, none survived. Further work, however, has shown that leaving the spleen in the circulation for as little as 5 minutes is sufficient to significantly increase the survival of mice exposed to 1025 r (Jacobson, Simmons, Marks, Gaston, *et al.*, 1951). Full recovery of the blood-forming tissues is delayed longer in mice splenectomized 5 minutes after irradiation than in mice splenectomized 24 hours

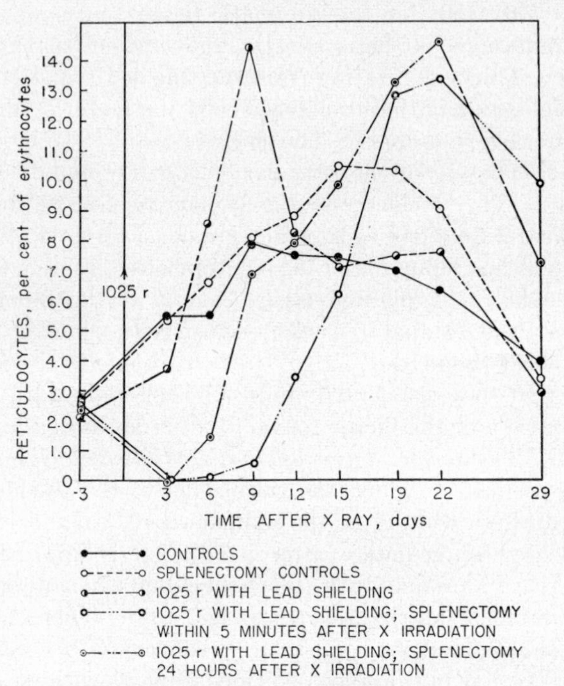

FIG. 16-22. Effect of splenectomy on the reticulocyte values of mice exposed to 1025 r of total-body roentgen irradiation with lead shielding of the exteriorized spleen.

after irradiation (Fig. 16-22). If the originally shielded spleen (whether or not the pedicle is clamped during the irradiation) is not removed, complete regeneration of hematopoietic tissue occurs earlier than in mice with splenectomy 24 hours after the shielding procedure (Jacobson, Marks, *et al.*, 1951). These facts indicate that the intact spleen may release enough of the factor in a few moments to enhance significantly the survival but that, if left in the circulation longer, an earlier and more complete regeneration of hematopoietic tissue occurs.

Total-body Exposure to 1025 *r plus* 200-*r Increments to Spleen.* Mice have been exposed to 1025 r of total-body X irradiation, and the spleen has been given various increments of the total-body dose. Doses up to and including 200 r may be given to the spleen at the same time as 1025 r of total-body exposure without reducing survival below the 75 per cent that is expected from the earlier spleen-shielding studies (Jacobson, Simmons, Marks, Gaston, *et al.*, 1951). In contrast to animals with spleen shielding and thus no irradiation of the spleen, these animals become moderately anemic and develop a severe leukopenia that persists beyond the twelfth day. Recovery of erythropoiesis as judged by the circulating reticulocytes begins by the sixth day, Fig. 16-22 (Jacobson, Marks, *et al.*, 1951). Histologic studies show that recovery of the blood-forming tissue is qualitatively complete by 10–12 days (Jacobson, Simmons, Marks, Gaston, *et al.*, 1951). Even with dosages of 400, 500, or 600 r to the spleen and 1025 r to the body, survival is significantly higher (59, 50, and 34 per cent, respectively) than in mice exposed to 1025 r without spleen shielding (1.1 per cent). Recovery of hematopoietic tissue is delayed progressively longer with increasing increments of the total-body dose delivered to the spleen. These data indicate that the capacity of the splenic tissue to elaborate the factor is still partially retained or recovery of the tissue in the spleen that produces the factor occurs early enough to enhance survival even with doses as high as 600 r to the spleen and 1025 r to the body. These observations tend to add support to the hypothesis that the factor (or factors) responsible for recovery from radiation injury under these circumstances is derived from more primitive but more radioresistant cells, such as reticular cells, rather than from the free cells of the hematopoietic system, such as lymphocytes and granulocytes. The spleen is, for all practical purposes, devoid of these free cells after a dose of 500 r, whereas the basic reticular network remains "histologically" intact. It is interesting that, following the delivery of a lethal dose to the body (1025 r) and an LD_{50} (500–600 r) to the spleen, ca. 50 per cent of the animals survive.

EFFECT OF COMBINED PROPHYLACTIC AND THERAPEUTIC MEASURES

The fact that a reduction in the mortality of animals exposed to lethal dosages of total-body X irradiation could be effected by pretreatment with estrogens (Treadwell, Gardner, and Lawrence, 1943) as well as by spleen shielding (Jacobson *et al.*, 1949) suggested to Simmons, Jacobson, and Marks (1950–1951) that these two measures might produce an additive effect on survival. Accordingly, Simmons tested this hypothesis and found that (1) mortality of mice exposed to 1025 r of total-body X irradiation was 100 per cent, (2) 61.5 per cent of the mice survived this dose if estrogens were given prior to irradiation, (3) 82.3 per cent survived if the spleen was shielded during exposure to 1025 r, and (4) 100 per cent survived 1025 r if the techniques of pretreatment with estrogens as well as spleen shielding were employed. Bethard, Skirmont, and Jacobson (1950) and Bethard and Jacobson (1951), employing the same general approach, found that cysteine and spleen shielding similarly had an additive effect on survival of mice exposed to X radiation. Furthermore, it was found that, when the techniques of pretreatment with estrogens and cysteine and spleen shielding during irradiation were all combined, an additive effect on survival was observed (Bethard, Simmons, and Jacobson, 1951). Jacobson (1952) found that pretreatment with cysteine followed by 1025 r of total-body X irradiation and postirradiation intraperitoneal transplantation of normal spleen were also additive in enhancing survival. Cysteine fails to produce any enhancing effect on survival of irradiated mice when given after 1100 r of total-body X irradiation whether or not the mice had spleen shielding during irradiation (Jacobson, 1952). These studies, although interesting, shed no light on the obvious question of whether or not the pretreatment or prophylactic techniques are related to the therapeutic techniques from the standpoint of mechanism.

ANTIBODY-FORMATION STUDIES

The fact that a single total-body exposure to X rays inhibits antibody formation is well documented (Benjamin and Sluka, 1908; Hektoen, 1918). The time of antigen injection relative to irradiation determines to a large measure the degree of inhibition (Benjamin and Sluka, 1908; Hektoen, 1918). Exposure of rabbits to dosages of total-body X irradiation ranging from 250–800 r effectively suppresses the development of appreciable antibody titer of particulate antigens administered in the 24 hours before or the 48 hours after irradiation (Benjamin and Sluka, 1908; Hektoen, 1918). It would appear from these observations that irradiation either destroys the cells concerned with antibody formation or reduces their functional capacity to react in the normal way to the injected antigen. It is not known with certainty in which cells of the body this function normally resides, but it has been postulated in a broad sense that the cells of the reticuloendothelial system are responsible. As suggested by Hektoen (1915) the degree of inhibition of antibody formation correlates well with the extent of damage to the blood-forming tissue induced by irradiation.

It has been demonstrated by Jacobson, Robson, and Marks (1950) that, if the spleen or the appendix of the rabbit is surgically exteriorized and shielded with lead during total-body exposure to 800 r, the capacity to form antibodies to a particulate antigen injected 24 hours after irradiation is retained. In another series of experiments this observation was carried a step further (Jacobson and Robson, 1952). Spleen-shielded rabbits were exposed to dosages of 800 or 500 r of total-body X irradiation. Twenty-four hours later the spleen was removed surgically. After another 24-hour period (48 hours after irradiation) a particulate antigen (sheep red cells) was given intravenously. The capacity of these animals to form antibodies (anti-sheep-cell hemolysin) was compared with various control groups given the same antigen at the same time relative to the irradiation as the experimental animals. The capacity to form antibodies to the injected antigen was retained in the rabbits, given 800 or 500 r of total-body X irradiation, which had spleen shielding during irradiation and the spleen left intact in the circulation for 24 hours and then removed surgically even though the antigen was given 24 hours after splenectomy and 48 hours after irradiation. The fact that these rabbits retained the capacity to form antibodies even though hematopoietic tissues in the body were as yet atrophic and that control rabbits exposed to the same dose did not retain this capacity is considered to be a result of the functional restoration of cells in the body (such as free and fixed macrophages and reticular cells) by a humoral (noncellular) substance entering the general circulation from the originally shielded spleen during the 24 hours prior to splenectomy.

COMMENT

It seems extremely unlikely that cell migration from the shielded or transplanted tissue and subsequent proliferation of these cells account for the reconstitution of hematopoietic tissues and increased survival of irradiated animals or that neutralization of some toxin produced by irradiation can account for these findings. Perhaps the latter possibility cannot be positively excluded on the basis of the available data. The evidence accumulated strongly suggests that the factor (or factors) responsible for recovery from radiation under these circumstances is noncellular and may be required only for the initiation of the repair process. The factor (or factors) may be quite labile or, as is more likely, may be produced in an effective quantity only by living cells. These cells may be present in shielded or implanted tissue or may migrate out and produce the factor under discussion. The factor may be a single substance such as an enzyme or coenzyme necessary for the functional reconstitution of many different cell types in the several organ systems, or several different factors may be concerned. Salisbury *et al.* (1951) found in a small number of dogs that early direct cross transfusion between irradiated (LD_{90}, X ray) and nonirradiated dogs significantly reduced mortality, reduced the severity of the expected hematopoietic depression, and reduced the severity of the usual clinical signs of irradiation sickness. Salisbury's experiments (1951) should be expanded in numbers of animals and should be more adequately controlled to make the significance of the experiment more clear cut.

The fact that 75 per cent of mice that have lead shielding of the spleen during exposure to 1025 r and then splenectomy 1 hour after the irradiation–spleen-shielding procedure survive would lead to the expectation that early administration of whole blood is effective. This seems logical since whatever the spleen accomplishes under these circumstances must be through the blood stream. That the factor (or factors) must be supplied early is also strongly supported by the fact that, in mice given a lethal dose of radiation, spleen transplants are more effective on the day of irradiation than on the second day after irradiation. In other words, supplying the factor responsible for initiating the functional repair in some unknown minimum number of cells throughout the body must be accomplished early enough to reverse the processes that ordinarily end in death of the animal. Once the factor is adequately supplied, as is clearly demonstrated by the splenectomy experiments, the process of repair is initiated; yet histologic evidence of repair or regeneration is not apparent for 4 or more days.

Indirect transfusion initiated on the fourth postirradiation day has been reported to be unsuccessful in significantly increasing survival of X-irradiated dogs (Allen *et al.*, 1952). This apparent failure of whole-blood transfusion to enhance survival and reduce morbidity effectively is understandable if it is assumed that (1) the amount of the factor (or factors) present in the blood per unit volume is small and therefore relatively large amounts of blood would be necessary to initiate effectively the recovery process or (2) the factor (or factors) was administered too late and in too small a quantity after exposure of the recipient to initiate the repair process in time and widely enough in cells of the body to have a critical effect on morbidity and survival. The preliminary experiments of Swisher and Furth (1951) indicate that the morbidity of dogs exposed to dosages of X irradiation in the mid-lethal range is reduced if as little as 250 cc of whole blood, collected in ACD solution from a compatible donor, is administered to irradiated dogs shortly after exposure. The ineffectiveness of cell-free extracts obtained from extirpated splenic tissue or embryos may only indicate that too small an amount of the factor is present or too small an amount of the factor is obtained in the extracts from these tissues by present methods. A method of preservation or concentration of the factor (or factors) or a more sensitive method of assay may be necessary before a positive result can be obtained by cell-free extracts. If the factor is present in whole blood in a concentration sufficient to alter the radiation syndrome even when given in relatively small amounts soon after irradiation of the recipient, then varying the conditions and methods of the administration of whole blood may supply important clues to the identification of the factor (or factors).

REFERENCES

(Information regarding the availability of government reports indicated by an asterisk may be obtained from the Office of Technical Services, Department of Commerce, Washington, D.C.)

Adams, W. S., and J. S. Lawrence (1947) The negative effect of folic acid on irradiation leukopenia in the cat. USAEC Report MDDC-1538.*

Allen, J. G. (1947–1948) A method for the *in vitro* titration of heparin. USAEC Report ANL-4147,* pp. 89–95.

——— (1951) The beneficial effects of head shielding in 20 dogs exposed to 450 r total-body X radiation. USAEC Report ANL-4625,* pp. 60–61.

——— (1952) Pathogenesis of irradiation hemorrhage. Conference on blood clotting and allied problems. Trans. 5th Josiah Macy Jr. Foundation, pp. 213–246.

———, C. E. Basinger, J. J. Landy, M. H. Sanderson, and D. M. Enerson (1952) Blood transfusion in irradiation hemorrhage. Science, 115: 523–526.

——— and L. O. Jacobson (1947a) Hyperheparinemia: cause of the hemorrhagic syndrome associated with total body exposure to ionizing radiation. Science, 105: 388–389.

——— and ——— (1947b) Irradiation hemorrhage. Proc. Inst. Chicago, 16: 376–377.

———, P. V. Moulder, and D. M. Enerson (1951) Pathogenesis and treatment of the postirradiation syndrome. J. Am. Med. Assoc., 145: 704–711.

———, M. Sanderson, M. Milham, A. Kirschon, and L. O. Jacobson (1948) Heparinemia (?), an anticoagulant in the blood of dogs with hemorrhagic syndrome associated with total body exposure to roentgen rays. J. Exptl. Med., 87: 71–86.

Aubertin, C., and E. Beaujard (1905) Action comparée des rayons X sur le sang dans les leucemias myelogene et lymphatique. Compt. rend. soc. biol., 58: 177.

——— and ——— (1908) Action des rayons X sur le sang et la moelle osseuse. Arch. med. exptl. anat. path., 20: 273–288.

Bacq, Z. M., A. Herve, J. Lecomte, and P. Fischer (1950) Cyanide protection against X-irradiation. Science, 111: 356–357.

Barnes, W. A., and O. B. Furth (1943) Studies on the indirect effect of roentgen rays in single and parabiotic mice. Am. J. Roentgenol. Radium Therapy, 49: 662–681.

Barron, E. S. G., S. Dickman, J. Muntz, and T. P. Singer (1949) Studies on the mechanism of action of ionizing radiations. I. Inhibition of enzymes by X-rays. J. Gen. Physiol., 32: 537–551.

Benjamin, E., and E. Sluka (1908) Antikoerperbildung nach experimenteller Schaedigung des haematopoetischen Systems durch Roentgenstrahlen. Wien. klin. Wochnschr., 21: 311–313.

Bennett, L. R., R. A. Hansen, and A. H. Dowdy (1951) The effect of anoxia on the hematological injury in rats caused by roentgen irradiation. USAEC Report UCLA-156.*

Bethard, W. F., and L. O. Jacobson (1951) Preliminary observations on the combining effect of cysteine and spleen protection on mortality of mice after exposure to X radiation. USAEC Report ANL-4571,* pp. 30–31.

———, E. L. Simmons, and L. O. Jacobson (1951) Preliminary observations on enhanced survival in X-irradiated mice following combined treatment with cysteine, estrogen and spleen protection. USAEC Report ANL-4625,* pp. 48–49.

———, E. Skirmont, and L. O. Jacobson (1950) Effect of radiophosphorus on rats with cobalt-induced polycythemia. Proc. Central Soc. Clin. Research, 23: 12.

Bloom, M. A. (1948) Bone marrow, *in* Histopathology of irradiation from external and internal sources, W. Bloom, ed. McGraw-Hill Book Company, Inc., New York, National Nuclear Energy Series, Div. IV, Vol. 22I, Chap. 6.

——— and W. Bloom (1947) The radiosensitivity of erythroblasts. J. Lab. Clin. Med., 32: 654–569.

Bloom, W. (1947) Histological changes following radiation exposure. Radiology, 49: 344–347.

——— (ed.) (1948) Histopathology of irradiation from external and internal sources. McGraw-Hill Book Company, Inc., New York, National Nuclear Energy Series, Div. IV, Vol. 22I.

——— and L. O. Jacobson (1948) Some hematological effects of irradiation. Blood, 3: 586–592.

Bond, V. P., M. N. Swift, A. C. Allen, and M. C. Fishler (1949) Sensitivity of the abdomen of the rat to X-irradiation. Nav. Radiol. Def. Lab. Report ADB-92.*

Brecher, G., and E. P. Cronkite (1951) Post-irradiation parabiosis and survival in rats. Proc. Soc. Exptl. Biol. Med., 77: 292–294.

Brues, A. M., and L. Rietz (1948) Acute hematologic radiation response of the guinea pig as a function of lethality. USAEC Report ANL-4227,* pp. 183–187.

Clarkson, J. R., W. V. Mayneord, and L. D. Parson (1938) The effect of X-irradiation on the blood and lymphoid tissue of tumor-bearing animals. J. Path. Bact., 46: 221–235.

Cohn, S. H. (1952) Effects of total body X-irradiation on blood coagulation in the rat. Blood, 7: 225–234.

Cronkite, E. P. (1950) The hemorrhagic syndrome of acute ionizing radiation illness produced in goats and swine by exposure to the atomic bomb at Bikini, 1946. Blood, 5: 32–45.

———, G. Brecher, and W. H. Chapman (1951) Mechanism of protective action of glutathione against whole body irradiation. Proc. Soc. Exptl. Biol. Med., 76: 396–398.

———, B. Halpern, D. P. Jackson, and G. V. LeRoy (1950) A study of the hemorrhagic state in dogs after a lethal dose of two million volt X-rays. J. Lab. Clin. Med., 36: 814.

———, F. W. Ullrich, D. C. Eltzholtz, C. R. Sipe, and P. K. Schork (1949) The response of the peripheral blood of swine to whole body X ray radiation in the lethal range. Nav. Med. Research Inst. Report NM 007039,* Report 21, Apr. 7.

Czepa, A. (1923–1924) Wachstumsfoerdernde und functionssteigernde Roentgen-Radium-Wirkung. Strahlentherapie, 16: 913.

Davis, R. W., N. Dole, M. J. Izzo, and L. E. Young (1950) Hemolytic effect of radiation. Observations on renal bile fistula dogs subjected to total body radiation and on human blood irradiated *in vitro*. J. Lab. Clin. Med., 35: 528–537.

Desjardins, A. U. (1932) The radiosensitiveness of cells and tissues and some medical implications. Science, 75: 569–575.

Dixon, F. J. (1948) Radiation induced hemorrhagic disease in chickens. Proc. Soc. Exptl. Biol. Med., 68: 505–507.

Dowdy, A. H., L. R. Bennett, and S. M. Chastine (1950) Study of the effect of varying oxygen tensions on the response of mammalian tissue to roentgen irradiation. USAEC Report UCLA-55.*

Dudley, H. C., L. J. Louviere, and J. C. Shaw (1951) Effects of injection of radiogallium (Ga^{72}). Nav. Med. Research Inst. Report NM 007 081.06.10,* Sept. 15.

Dunlap, C. E. (1942) Effects of radiation on the blood and the hemopoietic tissues, including the spleen, the thymus and the lymph nodes. Arch. Path., 34: 562–608.

———, J. C. Aub, R. D. Evans, and R. S. Harris (1944) Transplantable osteogenic sarcomas in rats by feeding radium. Am. J. Path., 20: 1–21.

Evans, T. C. (1948) Effects of small daily doses of fast neutrons on mice. Radiology, 50: 811–833.

Finkle, R. D., R. H. Snyder, and P. C. Tompkins (1946) Acute radiotoxicity of $(Ba\text{-}La)^{140}$ in rats and mice. Part I. Preparation and administration of the emitters. USAEC Report MDDC-1248.*

Furth, J., G. A. Andrews, R. H. Storey, and L. Wish (1951) The effect of X irradiation on erythrogenesis, plasma and cell volumes. Soc. Med. J., 44: 85–92.

Gershon-Cohen, J., M. B. Hermel, and J. Q. Griffith (1951) The value of small lead shields against the injurious effect of total-body irradiation. Science, 114: 157–158.

Hagen, C. W., L. O. Jacobson, R. Murray, and P. Lear (1944) Effects of single indirect doses of X rays on rabbits. USAEC Report MDDC-999.*

——— and R. E. Zirkle (1950) Comparative biological actions of cyclotron fast neutrons and X rays. I. Lethal action in mice and rabbits. USAEC Report CH-3903.*

Haley, T. J., and D. H. Harris (1949) The response of the guinea pig to 200 r acute body X-irradiation. USAEC Report AECU-357.*

Hayer, E. (1934) Ergebnisse von experimentellen Studien am peripheren weissen Blutbild nach Roentgenbestrahlung. Strahlentherapie, 50: 193–236.

Heineke, H. (1903) Ueber die Einwirkung der Roentgenstrahlen auf Tiere. Münch. med. Wochnschr., 50: 2090–2092.

——— (1904) Ueber die Einwirkung der Roentgenstrahlen auf innere Organe. Münch. med. Wochnschr., 51: 785.

——— (1905) Experimentelle Untersuchungen ueber die Einwirkung der Roentgenstrahlen auf innere Organe. Mitt. Grenzg. Med. Chir., 14: 21–94.

Hektoen, L. (1915) The influence of the X ray on the production of antibodies. J. Infectious Diseases, 17: 415–422.

——— (1918) Further studies on the effects of the roentgen ray antibody production. J. Infectious Diseases, 22: 28–33.

Hennesey, T. G., and R. L. Huff (1950) Depression of tracer iron uptake curve in rat erythrocytes following total body X-irradiation. Proc. Soc. Exptl. Biol. Med., 73: 436–439.

Henshaw, P. S. (1943–1944a) Experimental roentgen injury. I. Effects on the tissues and blood of C_3H mice produced with single small whole body exposures. J. Natl. Cancer Inst., 4: 477–484.

——— (1943–1944b) Experimental roentgen injury. II. Changes produced with intermediate-range doses and a comparison of the relative susceptibility of different kinds of animals. J. Natl. Cancer Inst., 4: 485–501.

———, E. F. Riley, and G. E. Stapleton (1947) The biologic effects of pile radiations. Radiology, 49: 349–360.

———, R. S. Snyder, E. F. Riley, G. E. Stapleton, and R. E. Zirkle (1946) Comparative late effects of single doses of fission neutrons and of gamma rays. USAEC Report MDDC-1254.*

Ingram, M., and W. B. Mason (1950a) The effects of acute exposure to roentgen radiation on the peripheral blood of experimental animals. USAEC Report UR-122.*

——— and ——— (1950b) The effects of chronic exposure to roentgen radiation on the peripheral blood of experimental animals. USAEC Report UR-121.*

Isaacs, R. (1934) Relation to cell types in leukemia sensitivity to radiation. Folia Haematol., 52: 414–425.

Jacobson, L. O. (1946) Acute radiotoxicity of $(Ba\text{-}La)^{140}$ in rats and mice. Part V. The effect of $(Ba\text{-}La)^{140}$ on the hematological constituents of the peripheral blood of rats and mice. USAEC Report MDDC-1261.*

Jacobson, L. O. (1952) Evidence for a humoral factor (or factors) concerned in recovery from radiation injury: a review. Cancer Research, 12: 315–325.

——— and E. K. Marks (1947) Comparative action of cyclotron fast neutrons and X rays. Part II. Hematological effects produced in the rabbit by fast neutrons. USAEC Report MDDC-1372.*

———, ———, and E. O. Gaston (1951) Effect of mouse embryo tissue on survival of irradiated mice. USAEC Report ANL-4625,* pp. 46–47.

———, ———, ———, J. G. Allen, and M. H. Block (1948) The effect of nitrogen mustard and X-irradiation on blood coagulation. J. Lab. Clin. Med., 33: 1566–1578.

———, ———, ———, and M. J. Robson (1952) Histologic studies of rabbits exposed to 800 r total body radiation with lead shielding of a single Peyer's patch. USAEC Report ANL-4794.*

———, ———, ———, ———, and R. E. Zirkle (1949) The role of the spleen in radiation injury. Proc. Soc. Exptl. Biol. Med., 70: 740–742.

———, ———, ———, E. L. Simmons, and M. H. Block (1948) Studies on radiosensitivity of cells. Science, 107: 248–250.

———, ———, and E. Lorenz (1949) The hematological effects of ionizing radiations. Radiology, 52: 371–395.

———, ———, E. L. Simmons, and E. O. Gaston (1951) Comparative hematologic studies of X-irradiated mice subjected to spleen shielding and related experimental procedures. USAEC Report ANL-4713,* pp. 23–37.

———, ———, ———, C. W. Hagen, and R. E. Zirkle (1947) Effects of X rays on rabbits. Part II. The hematological effects of total body X irradiation on the rabbit. USAEC Report MDDC-1174.*

——— and M. J. Robson (1952) Factors effecting X-ray inhibition of antibody formation. J. Lab. Clin. Med., 39: 169–175.

———, ———, and E. K. Marks (1950) The effect of X-radiation on antibody formation. Proc. Soc. Exptl. Biol. Med., 75: 145–152.

——— and E. L. Simmons (1946a) Acute radiotoxicity of injected Na^{24} for mice and rats. II. The effect of the Na^{24} on the leucocytes of the peripheral blood of mice. USAEC Report AECD-2036.*

——— and ——— (1946b) Effects of insoluble ingested Y^{91}. VIII. Hematological effects. USAEC Report AECD-2037.*

——— and ——— (1946c) Studies of the metabolism and toxic action of injected radium. Part II. The hematological effects of parenterally administered radium. A comparison of plutonium and radium effects. USAEC Report AECD-2372.*

———, ———, W. F. Bethard, E. K. Marks, and M. J. Robson (1950) The influence of the spleen on hematopoietic recovery after irradiation injury. Proc. Soc. Exptl. Biol. Med., 73: 455–459.

———, ———, and M. H. Block (1949) The effect of splenectomy on the toxicity of Sr^{89} to the hematopoietic system of mice. J. Lab. Clin. Med., 34: 1640–1655.

———, ———, E. K. Marks, and J. H. Eldredge (1951) Recovery from radiation injury. Science, 113: 510–511.

———, ———, ———, E. O. Gaston, M. J. Robson, and J. H. Eldredge (1951) Further studies on recovery from radiation injury. J. Lab. Clin. Med., 37: 683–697.

———, ———, ———, M. J. Robson, W. F. Bethard, and E. O. Gaston (1950). The role of the spleen in radiation injury and recovery. J. Lab. Clin. Med., 35: 746–770.

———, E. Skirmont, E. K. Marks, E. Gaston, and M. Block (1948) The effect of total-body X irradiation and P^{32} on the peripheral blood of normal rats and rats with cobalt-induced polycythemia. USAEC Report ANL-4147,* pp. 22–32.

———, S. P. Stearner, and E. L. Simmons (1947) The effect of folic acid on radiation induced anemia and leukopenia. J. Lab. Clin. Med., 32: 1425.

Kahn, J. B., and J. Furth (1952) The pathogenesis of postirradiation anemia. USAEC Report ORNL-1186.*

Kroemeke, F. (1926) Ueber die Einwirkung der Roentgenstrahlen auf die roten Blutkoerperchen. Strahlentherapie, 22: 608–652.

Lacassagne, A., and J. Lavedan (1924) Les modificationes histologiques due sang consecutives aux irradiationes experimentales. Paris méd., 51: 97–103.

Lawrence, J. H., P. C. Aebersold, and E. O. Lawrence (1936) Comparative effects of X rays and neutrons on normal and tumor tissue. Proc. Natl. Acad. Sci. U.S., 22: 543–557.

——— and E. O. Lawrence (1936) The biological action of neutron rays. Proc. Natl. Acad. Sci. U.S., 22: 124–133.

——— and associates (1949) Quoted in E. P. Cronkite, The hematology of ionizing radiations, *in* Atomic medicine, C. F. Behrens, 1st ed. Thomas Nelson & Sons, New York, p. 109.

———, A. H. Dowdy, and W. N. Valentine (1948) The effects of radiation on hemopoiesis. Radiology, 51: 400–413.

———, W. N. Valentine, and A. H. Dowdy (1948) The effect of radiation on hemopoiesis. Is there an indirect effect? Blood, 3: 593–611.

Linser, P., and E. Helber (1905) Experimentelle Untersuchungen ueber die Einwirkung der Roentgenstrahlen auf das Blut und Bemerkungen ueber die Einwirkung von Radium und ultraviolettem Lichte. Deut. Arch. klin. Med., 83: 479–498.

Lorenz, E. (1951) Recovery pattern of the blood picture in guinea pigs following a limited total body exposure to chronic gamma radiation. J. chim. phys., 48: 264–274.

———, C. C. Congdon, and D. Uphoff (1952) Modifications of acute irradiation injury in mice and guinea pigs by bone marrow injections. Radiology, 58: 863–877.

———, A. Eschenbrenner, M. Deringer, and W. E. Heston (1946) Biologic action of gamma and X rays. I. Exposure of mice to daily doses of gamma radiation at two rates: 5.5 r/hr and 0.11 r/8 hr. J. Natl. Cancer Inst., 6: 349–353; Cancer Research, 6: 485.

———, W. E. Heston, and A. B. Eschenbrenner (1947) Biological studies in the tolerance range. Radiology, 49: 274–285.

———, ———, L. O. Jacobson, A. B. Eschenbrenner, M. B. Shimkin, M. K. Deringer, J. Doniger, and R. Schweisthal (1946) Effects of long-continued whole body irradiation with gamma rays on mice, guinea pigs, and rabbits. Parts I–IV. USAEC Report MDDC-653,* pp. 654–656.

———, L. O. Jacobson, and H. Sutton (1950) Part I. Survival and blood picture of hybrid guinea pigs exposed to long-continued total-body gamma radiation. USAEC Report ANL-4401,* pp. 38–52.

———, ———, ———, and R. Schweisthal (1950) Part II. Recovery from anemia induced in guinea pigs by a limited exposure to chronic total-body gamma radiation. USAEC Report ANL-4401,* pp. 53–71.

———, D. Uphoff, T. R. Reid, and B. Shelton (1951) Modifications of irradiation injury in mice and guinea pigs by bone marrow injection. J. Natl. Cancer Inst., 12: 197–201.

———, ———, and H. Sutton (1949) The 30-day LD_{50} and accompanying blood picture of hybrid guinea pigs. USAEC Report ANL-4333,* pp. 57–65.
Minot, G. R., and R. Spurling (1924) Effect on blood of irradiation, especially short wave length roentgen ray therapy. Am. J. Med. Sci., 168: 215–241.
Mottram, J. C., and S. Russ (1921) Lymphopenia following exposure of rats to "soft X rays and beta rays of radium." J. Exptl. Med., 34: 271.
Murphy, J. B. (1926) The lymphocyte in resistance to tissue grafting. Monograph 21, Rockefeller Institute for Medical Research.
Murray, R., M. Pierce, and L. O. Jacobson (1948) The histological effects of X-rays on chickens with special reference to the peripheral blood and hemopoietic organs. USAEC Report AECD-2303.*
Patt, H. M., D. E. Smith, and E. Jackson (1950) The effect of cysteine on the peripheral blood of the irradiated rat. Blood, 5: 758–763.
———, R. L. Straube, E. B. Tyree, M. N. Swift, and D. E. Smith (1949) Influence of estrogens on the acute X-irradiation syndrome. Am. J. Physiol., 159: 269.
———, E. B. Tyree, R. L. Straube, and D. E. Smith (1949) Cysteine protection against X irradiation. Science, 110: 213–214.
Prosser, C. L., E. E. Painter, H. Lisco, A. M. Brues, L. O. Jacobson, and M. N. Swift (1947) The clinical sequence of physiological effects of ionizing radiation in animals. Radiology, 49: 269–365.
———, ———, and M. N. Swift (1946) Physiology of dogs exposed to single total-body doses of X rays. USAEC Report CH-3738.*
Raper, J. R., and K. K. Barnes (1951) The effects of external irradiation with beta rays on the peripheral blood of rabbits, *in* Biological effects of external beta radiation, R. E. Zirkle, ed. McGraw-Hill Book Company, Inc., New York, National Nuclear Energy Series, Div. IV, Vol. 22E, Chap. 10.
———, P. S. Henshaw, and R. S. Snider (1951) Effects of periodic total-surface beta irradiation, *in* Biological effects of external beta radiation, R. E. Zirkle, ed. McGraw-Hill Book Company, Inc., New York, National Nuclear Energy Series, Div. IV, Vol. 22E, Chap. 14.
———, R. E. Zirkle, and K. K. Barnes (1951) Comparative lethal effects of external beta irradiation, *in* Biological effects of external beta radiation, R. E. Zirkle, ed. McGraw-Hill Book Company, Inc., New York, National Nuclear Energy Series, Div. IV, Vol. 22E, Chap. 3.
Rekers, P. E. (1949) Transplantation of bone marrow into dogs that have received total body single dose radiation. USAEC Report AECD-1966.*
———, M. P. Coulter, and S. L. Warren (1950) Effect of transplantation of bone marrow into irradiated animals. Arch. Surg., 60: 635–667.
Ross, M. H., J. Furth, and R. R. Bigelow (1952) Capillary fragility caused by ionizing radiations. Changes in cellular composition of the lymph. Blood, 7: 417–428.
Russ, S. (1921) The immediate effect of X rays on the blood lymphocytes. Arch. Radiol. Electrotherapy, 26: 146.
———, H. Chambers, and G. M. Scott (1921) Further observations of the effect of X rays upon the lymphocytes. Arch. Radiol. Electrotherapy, 25: 377.
———, ———, ———, and J. C. Mottram (1919) Experimental studies with small doses of X-rays. Lancet, 196: 692.
Sacher, G. A., and N. Pearlman (1947) Comparative action of cyclotron neutrons and X-rays. Part III. Statistical analysis of blood data. USAEC Report MDDC-1387.*
Salisbury, P. E., P. E. Rekers, J. H. Miller, and N. F. Marti (1951) Effect of early cross transfusion on X-irradiated dog. Proc. Soc. Exptl. Biol. Med., 78: 226–229.

Schack, J. A., and R. C. MacDuffee (1949) Increased radioresistance of red bone marrow after anoxia. Science, 110: 259–260.

Schwartz, S. E., E. Katz, L. M. Porter, L. O. Jacobson, and C. J. Watson (1947) Studies of the hemolytic effect of radiation. USAEC Report CH-3760.*

Selling, L., and E. E. Osgood (1938) Action of benzol, roentgen rays and radioactive substances on the blood and blood-forming tissues, *in* Downey's handbook of hematology. Paul B. Hoeber, Inc., Medical Book Department of Harper & Brothers, New York, Vol. 4, pp. 2693–2801.

Shouse, S., S. L. Warren, and G. H. Whipple (1931) Aplasia of marrow and fatal intoxication in dogs produced by roentgen radiation of all bones. J. Exptl. Med., 52: 421–435.

Siegel, P. W. (1920) Die Veränderungen des Blutbildes nach gynäkologischen Röntgen-, Radium- and Mesothoriumtiefenbestrahlung und ihre klinische Bedeutung. Strahlentherapie, 11: 64–139.

Simmons, E. L., and L. O. Jacobson (1946) Radiotoxicity of injected Sr^{89} for rats, mice, and rabbits. Part IV. The hematological effects of enterally and parenterally administered Sr^{89} in mammals. USAEC Report MDDC-1387.*

———, ———, and E. K. Marks (1950–1951) Effect of pre-injection of estradiol benzoate plus spleen shielding on the survival of mice following X irradiation. USAEC Report ANL-4571.*

———, ———, N. Pearlman, and C. L. Prosser (1946) The effectiveness of drugs in preventing or alleviating X-ray damage. USAEC Report MDDC-1277.*

Smith, W. W., R. Dooley, and E. O. Thompson (1948) Simulated high altitude following whole-body radiation of mice. J. Aviation Med., 19: 227–237.

Stearner, S. P., E. L. Simmons, and L. O. Jacobson (1947a) The effects of single dose total body X irradiation on the peripheral blood of the rat. Anat. Record, 99: 576–577.

———, ———, and ——— (1947b) The effects of total body X-irradiation on the peripheral blood and blood-forming tissues of the rat. USAEC Report MDDC-1319.*

Storey, R. H., L. Wish, and J. Furth (1950) Changes in cell and plasma volumes produced by total body X irradiation. Proc. Soc. Exptl. Biol. Med., 74: 242–244.

Suter, G. M. (1947) Response of hematopoietic system to X rays. USAEC Report MDDC-824.*

Swift, M. N., C. L. Prosser, and E. S. Mika (1946) Effects of Sr^{89} and X-radiation on goats. USAEC Report AECU-108.*

Swisher, S. N., and F. W. Furth (1951) The effect of early small exchange transfusion on the X-irradiated dog. Proc. Soc. Exptl. Biol. Med., 78: 226–229.

Talbot, J. M., and H. B. Gerstner (1951) Bone marrow implants in the treatment of radiation sickness. USAF School of Aviation Med., Project 21-47-001.*

——— and E. A. Pinson (1951) The experimental use of bone marrow in acute radiation injury. Military Surgeon, 108: 412–417.

Taylor, H. D., W. D. Witherbee, and J. B. Murphy (1919) Studies on X ray effects. I. Destructive action on blood cells. J. Exptl. Med., 29: 53–73.

Thomas, M. M., W. D. Witherbee, and J. B. Murphy (1919) II. Stimulative action on the lymphocytes. J. Exptl. Med., 29: 75.

Treadwell, A., W. U. Gardner, and J. H. Lawrence (1943) Effect of combining estrogen with lethal doses of roentgen-ray in Swiss mice. Endocrinology, 32: 161–164.

Valentine, W. N., W. D. Adams, and J. S. Lawrence (1947) Blood platelets and rate of utilization in the cat. Blood, 2: 40–49.

——— and M. L. Pearce (1952) Studies on the radiosensitivity of bone marrow.

I. The relative sensitivity of erythroid and myeloid elements. Blood, 7: 1–13.

Warren, S. L., (1943) Effects of radiation on normal tissue. Arch. Path., 35: 121.

——— and D. J. Dixon (1949) Effects of continuous radiation on chick embryos and developing chicks. II. Bone marrow, lymphoid and peripheral blood. Radiology, 52: 869–882.

——— and G. H. Whipple (1922) Roentgen ray intoxication. II. A study of the sequence of clinical, anatomical, and histological changes following a unit dose of X ray. J. Exptl. Med., 35: 203–211.

Wheeler, B., M. A. Jackson, and P. Hahn (1951) Hematology of the dog following intravenous administration of radioactive colloidal gold. Am. J. Physiol., 166: 323–327.

Wuensche, H. W. (1938) Fortlaufende Untersuchungen ueber des Einflusses der Roentgenstrahlen auf das Knochenmark. Arch. Exptl. Path. Pharmakol., 189: 581.

Zirkle, R. E. (1947) Components of the acute lethal action of slow neutrons. Radiology, 49: 271–273.

——— (1950) Radiobiological additivity of various ionizing radiations. Am. J. Roentgenol. Radium Therapy, 63: 170–175.

Manuscript received by the editor Mar. 15, 1952

CHAPTER 17

Histological Changes after Irradiation

William Bloom

Department of Anatomy and Institute of Radiobiology and Biophysics, The University of Chicago

and Margaret A. Bloom

Chicago

Introduction. Visible changes in cells: Cell membrane—Organelles—Interphase nucleus—Dividing cells. Changes in tissues. Bone marrow. Lymphatic organs. Thymus. Spleen. Bone. Cartilage. Male generative system. Female generative system. Skin: Epithelium—Derma. Epidermal derivatives: Hair—Nails—Skin glands —Mammary gland. Gastrointestinal system: Mouth, nasopharynx, and esophagus—Stomach and intestines—Salivary glands —Liver—Gall bladder and biliary passages—Pancreas. Urinary system: Kidney—Urinary bladder. Respiratory system. Nervous system. Eye. Endocrine glands: Adrenal—Hypophysis—Thyroid—Parathyroid. Discussion. References.

INTRODUCTION

Within the first ten to fifteen years after their discovery, it was shown that ionizing radiations, in amounts we recognize today as under 1500 r, would produce marked degenerative changes in the skin and its appendages, parts of the gastrointestinal tract, the blood-cell-forming organs (and thus in the blood), the gonads, conjunctiva and lens, bone, and cartilage. It was also found that the skin might become ulcerated and even cancerous. Moreover, it was learned that irradiation could destroy some cancers and could produce embryological monsters. In the years which have elapsed since then much knowledge has been added, but much more is required before the *visible effects* of radiation on cells can be presented in a complete and systematic fashion.

Advances have been retarded by a number of factors. One of these is our inability to evaluate dosages in the older reports before the introduction of the roentgen. Another is the difficulty of comparing the effects on a particular organ of total-body irradiation with local irradiation of that organ, since systematic studies on this theme are lacking. Further variables which must be taken into account are the time-intensity factor for a given dosage and, closely related to this variable, whether the radiation is given at one time or in divided doses. Finally, medical interest in radiation has focused much of the investigation on the higher animal forms and on a relatively limited dose range determined by therapy in man and toxicity and survival studies in animals.

Depending in part on the amount of radiation applied and in part on the degree of susceptibility of the cells irradiated, the resulting cellular changes may be classified roughly into two groups. The first comprises subtle effects recognizable only by alterations in the actual and potential functions of the cells (including those which become manifest only in their progeny). The second group consists of more obvious changes, detectable by the optical microscope: (1) degenerative phenomena which may be reversible but which usually lead to cell death, (2) inhibition of mitosis, and (3) abnormal mitosis. Other morphological criteria must be sought especially through study of intracellular enzymes and of changes in submicroscopic structure.

Since all cells near an embedded radium needle will die if exposed long enough, there are no completely resistant cells. But with amounts of radiation which permit survival of laboratory animals for only a short time, many cells appear to be unaffected. Among the more sensitive cells, however, gradations in susceptibility are revealed.

In a number of organs the visible effect of a given dose of radiation is the death of a given type of cell, while other cell types may show no obvious damage although some of them may undergo great changes of another kind. It is thus impossible to compare their reaction to radiation using cell death as the sole criterion. For instance, spermatogonia in most mammals are destroyed by exposure to 800 r (total-body irradiation with 200-kv X rays) while spermia may show no obvious change. Yet the spermia may have been injured, although the effects will appear later only if one of them fertilizes a normal egg. For the other cells of the testis (spermatocytes, spermatids, Sertoli cells, and interstitial cells) we can find no comparison of relative radiosensitivities, as revealed by cellular degeneration, beyond the observation that they are much more resistant than the spermatogonia. Similar statements can be made about the other organs, both the sensitive and the more resistant ones. We are thus in a position to evaluate only roughly the relative radiosensitivity of a few types of cells while the other cells of the body may be grouped together as comparatively radioresistant. The data so far determined do not permit an evaluation of all cell types of the body in exact terms such as might be expressed by LD_{50} or LD_{100} values for those cells. This lack was stressed by Stafford L. Warren (Duggar, 1936, p. 475).

Although *relative radiosensitivity* is a convenient term for distinguishing varying degrees of susceptibility shown by the different parts of an organism to the same amount of radiation, it is meaningless unless the cells or tissues are being compared for the same end effect of radiation and unless the physical conditions of irradiation are the same. The idea of radiosensitivity of a given cell (or organism) must be further qualified to include consideration of its functional state at the time of irradiation and, in many cases, its present or future reproductive activity, and the species and age of the animal to which it belongs. Other terms should be used for those conditions which do not satisfy these criteria.

In contrast to a few types of injuries which cause immediate damage to cells (thermal burn, for example) the effects of irradiation, like those of many toxic agents, become apparent only after some time has elapsed. This interval may vary from a few minutes to months or years, depending mainly on the cell type, and the criterion of the injury. For instance, vast numbers of lymphocytes are destroyed in a few hours by 600 to 800 r of 200-kv X rays, while cells of the epidermis may not die for several days after three times this amount of radiation, or months or years may elapse before cataracts develop in the lens.

With the possible exception of certain effects due to specific ionization, the results of the several kinds of ionizing radiations from external sources given in equivalent amounts are identical (W. Bloom, 1948a). The same biological changes as those produced by X rays and neutrons result when the radiations are from internal sources, but these vary with the distribution of the isotope (the chemical nature of the element determining its localization, being diffuse in the case of Na^{24} or highly localized with Sr^{89}), the type of "particle" given off, and the half-life of the isotope (and its daughters). The continuous nature of internal irradiation is in contrast to that from most external sources which only exceptionally have been applied continuously.

The cold-blooded vertebrates are more resistant than the warm-blooded ones and, going down the scale of animal (and plant) complexity, the forms become increasingly resistant. Nevertheless, the kinds of cellular changes seen in vertebrate cells also occur in lower forms, although the amount of radiation necessary to elicit these changes will usually be much greater. The younger the animal the more susceptible it will be; this is also true for its cells, at least for extremes in age. It is well known that embryos are much more sensitive than postnatal animals and that resistance increases progressively with age. For instance, the nerve sheath cells in a three-week chick suffer great damage with 800 r total-body irradiation, whereas these same cells are not damaged with this dose when the animal is 11 weeks old (Snider, 1948b). Changes in temperature and metabolic rate affect the sensitivity of a particular cell strain, as shown by greater resistance at lower temperatures and when the circulation of blood is interrupted during irradiation.

It must be kept in mind that all the effects of ionizing radiations on cells, ranging from nonvisible effects on chromosomes to rapid cell death, can be brought about by certain chemical agents. This is true, for instance, for the hematopoietic organs, intestine, and testis after injection of appropriate amounts of the nitrogen or sulfur mustard gases. These and many other substances are also potent mutagenic agents. Moreover, benzol has for many years been known to deplete the blood-forming tissues in much the same fashion as X rays.

Although there is nothing known that is specific for radiation effects, it is often possible within certain dose ranges to diagnose radiation damage. Thus, "The combination of two or more of the nonspecific characteristics of radiation is strongly presumptive evidence that the injury is in fact the result of radiation. Thus the combination of giant and irregular nuclei, hyaline connective tissue, and thick-walled hyalinized blood vessels would be difficult to explain on any other basis than that of a late response to irradiation" (Shields Warren, 1944). However, the acute changes due to nitrogen mustard and irradiation are identical.

For detailed consideration of the several thousand papers dealing with changes from irradiation from external and certain internal sources, the reader is referred to a number of extensive reviews (W. Bloom, 1948a; Colwell, 1935; Desjardins, 1924, 1926, 1928, 1931; Dunlap, 1948; Ellinger, 1941; Giese, 1947; Lacassagne and Gricouroff, 1941; Packard, 1931; Regaud and Lacassagne, 1927; Shields Warren, 1942, 1943, 1944; Stafford L. Warren, 1936). Here we can only attempt to summarize the more important of these changes. Whenever possible, the data emphasized will be from experiments on laboratory animals, where control of dosage, intervals, and a large number of subjects under identical conditions is possible. In most of the organ systems the effects of moderate single doses of external irradiation will be described first, followed by the changes resulting from smaller or larger doses, then those after repeated small doses, and finally the effects of internal irradiation.

VISIBLE CHANGES IN CELLS

The first changes of irradiation are usually manifest as nuclear changes, often those involving the mitotic process. Most of the evidence since 1903 (Perthes, 1903) indicates that the nucleus is more sensitive to irradiation than the cytoplasm. This view has received direct experimental confirmation in the comparison of the effects of irradiation of cytoplasm plus nucleus with cytoplasm alone in fern spores (Zirkle, 1932). Similar conclusions were reached on *Arbacia* eggs (Henshaw, 1938). However, the opposing view that nuclear changes are secondary to changes in the cytoplasm has been strongly maintained (Duryee, 1949; see also Chap. 10 by Giles and Chap. 11 by Carlson).

Cell Membrane. There have been several reports that the cell membrane is damaged by irradiation. The most convincing instance, in the authors' opinion, is that of cells observed in tissue culture after enormous dosages of irradiation. Here it has been seen that vesicles may form at the edge of the cell and that changes in form of the membrane, as in ameboid motion, may cease. In all such cases the changes in the cell membrane have followed severe, irreversible damage to the nucleus. It has been reported that both nucleated and nonnucleated red cells swell after irradiation, and this has been interpreted as being due to injury to the cell membrane. However, the swelling may be simply a result of passage of water through the membrane because of an increased number of ions in the cell. Loss of stainability of the membrane has also been reported. The few instances in which this occurs probably are late stages after high dosage. Certainly it may be accepted that in the great mass of irradiated cells exposed to 1000 to 3000 r, the cell membrane does not lose its stainability. Early swelling of cells as a whole occurs more strikingly in some cell types than in others. It may also appear late, as in the fibroblasts of inflammatory tissue.

There is evidence in certain plants and in some cells in tissue culture of an immediate decrease in viscosity of the cytoplasm after intense irradiation. Some cells in culture have been observed to slow down, others to move faster, at least for a time. Cytoplasmic movements may proceed for many hours after the nucleus is obviously coagulated as a result of intensive irradiation.

Organelles. It has been postulated that destruction of the centrosome with its diplosome will prevent the cell from dividing. The proof for this is absent, although it is presumably correct. Ciliary motion stops after irradiation. It has been claimed that changes in the mitochondria are the first morphological evidences of radiation effects. This conclusion has been denied by others on the basis of sectioned material (W. Bloom, 1948b; Fogg and Shields Warren, 1937) and on observations of living cells irradiated in tissue culture (W. Bloom, unpublished observations). We have found no evidence that mitochondria degenerate early; on the contrary, they may persist unchanged long after the cells are obviously undergoing irreversible degenerative changes.

Minor changes in the Golgi net after irradiation of tumor cells have been described (Fogg and Shields Warren, 1937). This subject should be investigated further.

Neurofibrils and myofibrils occur in cells that are among the most radioresistant in the adult animal. We have found no reports on changes in these fibrils as a result of irradiation with therapeutic dosages or with small multiples thereof. Also, no characteristic changes have been described in cellular inclusions (fat, carbohydrates, chromophil substance, pigment granules). However, it has been noted that, in many types of cells after irradiation, there may be an increase in fat content, and there are also reports on purported changes in the glycogen in liver cells. Such changes are probably secondary to effects produced in other organs. On the other hand, iron pigment from ingested erythrocytes accumulates in macrophages in the reparative phase after irradiation, and brown pigment develops in the skin.

Interphase Nucleus. One of the first changes to be seen in sections as well as in living tissue cultures is a clumping of chromatin. This may occur in both sensitive and resistant cell strains. It is probably reversible, since it may be seen in all types of cells of the body a short time after irradiation and, depending on the dosage and the cell type, may or may not disappear after a few hours. Other changes, probably not reversible, include vacuolization of chromatin particles and nucleoli and thickening of the nuclear membrane. In the course of the next few hours such cells may show progressive pyknosis, the nuclear material condensing into one, two, or three large chromatin masses (with or without vacuoles). Sometimes the nuclei may disintegrate without passing through a pyknotic stage. There is nothing specific about these nuclear changes after irradiation, for similar effects may be produced by a variety of toxic agents.

In addition to these changes, nuclei may show marked budding in certain cell types (hepatic epithelium, megakaryocytes), particularly after long-continued action of radioactive isotopes accumulating in the organ. Multilobular nuclei may be found in myelocytes after irradiation. The swelling of nuclei is believed to be one of the most constant results of irradiation (Failla and Sugiura, 1939). It is clearly seen in the intestinal or gastric epithelium during the regenerating phase (Pierce, 1948). A pronounced swelling of the nucleus has not been a striking feature of irradiated cells in tissue culture (W. Bloom, unpublished observations).

Dividing Cells. One of the most striking nuclear effects of irradiation is the rapid cessation, after 200 to 800 r, of practically all mitosis in all the organs which normally are in a state of continuous regeneration. This interference with cellular division may be apparent about ½ to 1 hour after irradiation and may last 12 to 15 hours or much longer. The cause of this inhibition is not known. In many tissues its duration varies roughly with the dose. It is equally remarkable that "not all mitoses are inhibited, even in a heavily irradiated tissue culture" (Shields Warren, 1942, 1943). Most cells which had undergone the first morphologically evident mitotic changes seem to go through the rest of the process, although they may show lagging or otherwise damaged chromosomes. Fragmented chromosomes are thought to heal either with or without visible defects, but, in all such cases, genic material is undoubtedly lost. In total mounts of the cornea of amphibian larvae a marked clumping and eventual pyknosis of the chromatin at any stage of mitosis have been described as a primary effect of radiation (Alberti and Politzer, 1923). Some of these clumpings may be pseudo-amitotic. Then, following the period of inhibition of mitosis, the secondary effect appears, manifested by karyorrhexis in cells which were resting at the time of irradiation. In animals given a second irradiation 10 or 15 days after the first, the primary effects were complicated by secondary effects from the first irradiation.

Many of the cells which are in a resting state at the time of irradiation, as well as some that are in mitosis, may show their first evidence of damage when they divide some time later and develop visible chromosomal defects and abnormalities. A high percentage of such cells may die during this mitosis (Halberstaedter and Back, 1942; Kemp and Juul, 1930; Strangeways and Hopwood, 1926). In some instances, the chromosomes may become "sticky" and pairs of chromosomes may adhere to each other (Giese, 1947). If this occurs throughout the chromosomal content of a cell, polyploidy may result.

CHANGES IN TISSUES

Nerve and muscle, two of the four major tissues, are relatively unaffected by doses of radiation which elicit wide ranges of susceptibility in the other two primary tissues, the various connective tissues and epithelia. Some of the differences in sensitivity can be explained by the fact that, in some tissues, resting cells and cells about to divide may not show effects of damage until they divide. For example, in the epidermis there are comparatively few cells dividing at any one moment, and the full effects of irradiation do not become manifest until many of the resting cells divide. Hepatic epithelium is normally untouched by relatively large amounts of radiation. But if a large part of the liver is removed, the rest will regenerate with great numbers of mitoses and irradiation will affect the organ.

The connective tissues differ from the other tissues in two important respects: (1) the preponderance of intercellular substance, and (2) an intimate relation to the blood vascular system (although cartilage and parts of bone are exceptions). In all organs, to a greater or less extent, connective tissue separates the blood vessels from the parenchyma. Vascular connective tissue throughout the body is the tissue which reacts, by inflammation, to local injury. Much has been written about the effects of radiation on intercellular substances (see section on the derma). In the hematopoietic tissues the free cells are many times more susceptible to damage by irradiation than the cellular stroma. The adipose, pigment, tendinous, and mucous connective tissues have not been studied sufficiently for radiation effects.

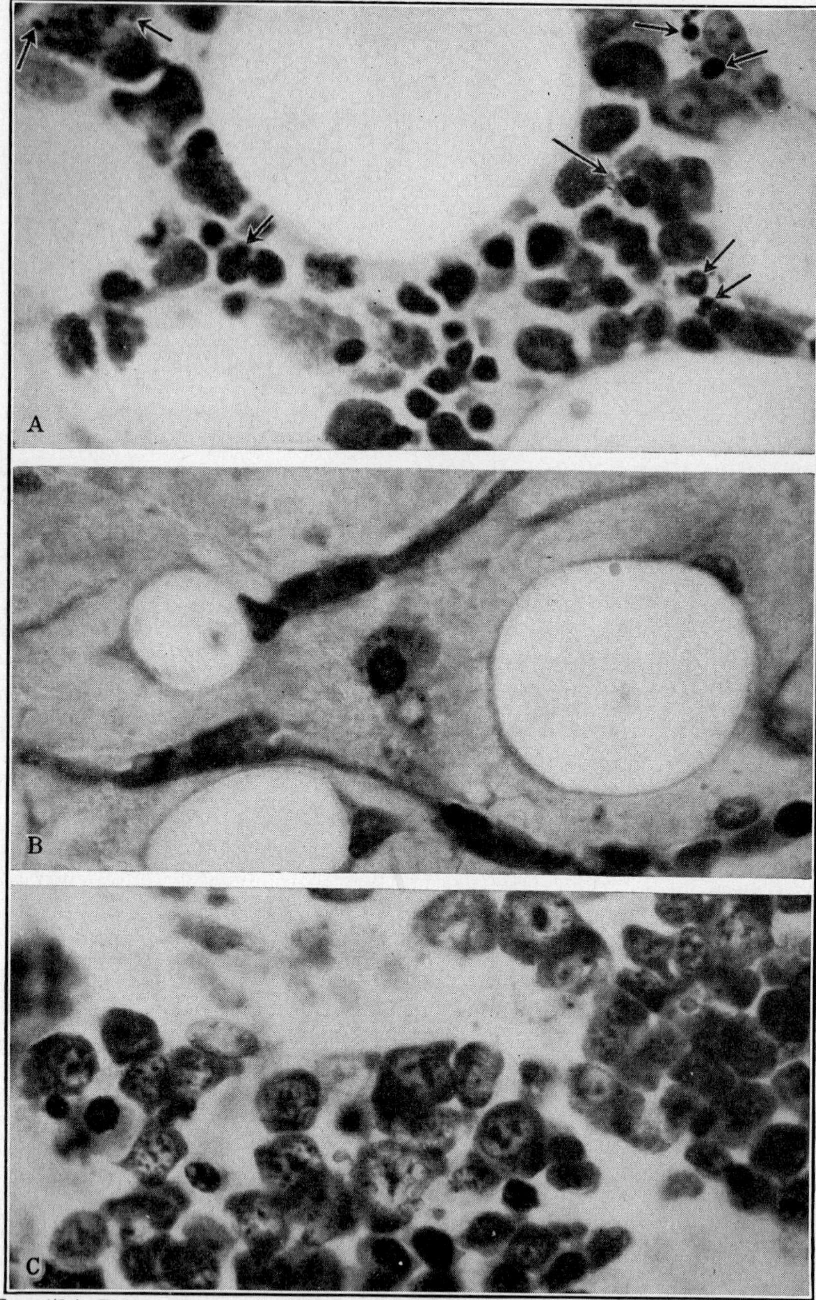

FIG. 17-1. Bone marrow of rabbit after total-body irradiation with 800 r of 200-kv X rays. The marrow at 24 hours (*A*) shows mainly various stages of granulocyte formation. The arrows point to debris, mostly of precursors of red blood cells. At 9 days (*B*) the marrow, completely depleted of hematopoietic cells, contains some fat

BONE MARROW

The framework of active mammalian marrow (myeloid tissue) consists of blood sinusoids lined with phagocytic littoral cells and a loose stroma of reticular fibers with embedded fat cells and primitive and phagocytic reticular cells. In the meshes of this framework are closely packed groups of free cells: hemocytoblasts (free stem cells), erythroblasts (precursors of red blood corpuscles), myelocytes (precursors of granular leukocytes), and megakaryocytes. In the normal adult hemocytoblasts are rare.

Ionizing radiations cause destruction of the free hematopoietic cells, and their replacement by dilated sinuses and a gelatinous or fatty type of marrow (M. A. Bloom, 1948; Dunlap, 1948; Heineke, 1903; Lacassagne and Gricouroff, 1941; Martland, 1931; Pappenheim and Plesch, 1912; Tullis, 1949). The bone marrow is much more susceptible to acute radiation damage than many of the other organs, and the changes produced are easily detectable at the LD_{50} 30-day level and, in some species, even well below this (M. A. Bloom, 1948). Thus, after 800 r total-body X irradiation in the rabbit, initial damage is revealed by a cessation of mitosis half an hour after treatment and a progressive degeneration of hematopoietic cells, already striking at 3 hours. Some cells die very soon, as evidenced by pyknosis and fragmentation of their nuclei, and are then phagocytosed by macrophages; others assume abnormal forms with swollen or distorted, often multilobed, nuclei, and, after an interval, these too may degenerate. The first of the blood-forming cells to be destroyed are the erythroblasts and hemocytoblasts, next the myelocytes, and finally the megakaryocytes. In each series the younger cells are more sensitive than the older forms of the same cell type. Thus, in the red-cell-forming series the basophil erythroblasts are more sensitive than the polychromatophil, and these in turn than the orthochromatic ones. There is also some erythrophagocytosis during this period. By 4 or 5 days the marrow is almost completely devoid of immature red and white blood corpuscles. At no stage is there any visible damage to reticular cells.

The acute destructive effects on the myelocytes are quickly reflected in the drop in granular leukocytes in the circulating blood. However, the acute destruction of erythroblasts is not reflected in a similar rapid drop in the erythrocytes of the blood, since the latter are much longer lived. The effects of irradiation on the peripheral blood cells and blood

---

cells and a gelatinous intercellular substance, in addition to an occasional macrophage (as in the center of the field) and some collapsed vessels. (*C*) After 10 days, the marrow shows a focus of regenerating hematopoiesis. Note the exceedingly large, young cells with darkly stained cytoplasm (basophilia) and the great prominence of the nucleoli. These cells are somewhat larger than the normal. 1030×.

platelets are discussed in Chap. 16 (by Jacobson). In contrast to the radiosensitivity of the free hematopoietic cells is the great resistance of macrophages, reticular cells, and fat cells, none of which show any evidence of damage even with 2000 r or more. This is important since the reticular cells are more primitive than the free stem cells and are the most important source of regenerating hematopoietic cells (W. Bloom, 1948a).

First attempts at regeneration of hematopoietic cells, sometimes during the first week after irradiation, are often abortive at the LD_{50} level of total-body X irradiation, but full recovery eventually takes place some weeks later. Regenerating erythroblasts often contain highly constricted nuclei, and regenerating myelocytes may be greatly enlarged. Regeneration follows a definite pattern: the gelatinous intercellular substance is largely replaced by fat cells and the dilated venous sinuses resume their normal size. A proliferation of stem cells—hemocytoblasts—arising from mitosis of their own cell kind or by transformation of reticular cells (homoplastic or heteroplastic origin) is followed by active erythropoiesis, later by myelocytopoiesis, and finally by the return of young megakaryocytes. After lower doses of X rays, 400 to 100 r, cellular destruction is less extensive and recovery occurs earlier. The effect of 50 r is scarcely perceptible. The morphological and temporal details of regeneration after very high doses of localized radiation have not been worked out.

X rays affect the bone marrow much less when administered at the rate of 80 r per day for several weeks than when the same quantity of radiation is given in a single dose (M. A. Bloom, 1948). Daily exposure of mice to external γ rays reveals no changes in the marrow with 1.1 r for 16 months (Eschenbrenner, 1946; Spargo *et al.*, 1951). An increased gelatinous replacement of the cellular elements of the marrow, particularly in the metaphysis, begins at four months after 8.8 r per day and at six months after 4.4 r per day. The number of immature cells of the myelocyte series (particularly hemocytoblasts) increases progressively from 8 to 16 months in the 8.8-r series. These animals also show a progressive increase in connective tissue mast cells in the marrow (Spargo *et al.*, 1951). In guinea pigs 8.8 r per day produces a low-grade anemia with a sudden terminal ending after some months (Lorenz, Heston, Jacobson, *et al.*, 1953).

A similar pattern of damage and repair results from equivalent doses of X rays, fast neutrons, and slow neutrons (M. A. Bloom, 1948; Lawrence and Tennant, 1937). With all types of radiation, damage to the bone marrow is roughly proportional to the size of the dose.

All bone-seeking isotopes tend to accumulate at the growing ends of bones and produce earlier and more severe damage in the marrow there than in the center of the shaft. A somewhat similar but less striking gradient of injury occurs with X rays and, to a less extent, with slow neutrons, but not with fast neutrons. Secondary rays, emitted by the bone spicules of the metaphysis after X irradiation and to a less extent after slow-neutron bombardment, may perhaps account for these differences.

Both depletion and regeneration take place more slowly in response to the radioactive isotopes than to any of the external ionizing radiations. Slow degeneration explains the absence of cellular debris, and delayed regeneration is undoubtedly the effect of the continued bombardment by long-lived isotopes.

In addition to the degenerative changes characteristic of bone marrow subjected to external irradiation, an atypical fibrous bone develops from spindle cells in the marrow cavity after administration of many of the radioactive isotopes. This will be described in the section on bone.

Study of aspirated vertebral marrow from atomic bomb casualties at Hiroshima disclosed the disappearance, within the first week, of myeloid tissue and the presence of atypical cells, many of them resembling plasma cells. These findings are confirmed and extended by histological sections of the long bones and sternum obtained at autopsy, in which multiplication of reticular cells is seen at 12 days (Liebow *et al.*, 1949). The failure to find in the Hiroshima material the early degeneration of erythroblasts, previously described on the basis of closely spaced specimens from laboratory animals (M. A. Bloom and W. Bloom, 1947), probably rests on the scanty material obtained during the first weeks after the explosion of the bomb. In the authors' opinion, the residual foci of erythroblasts described in the Hiroshima material may well be foci of regenerating erythroblasts.

It may not be amiss to point out here that a variety of toxins can duplicate in detail the bone marrow changes which follow irradiation.

LYMPHATIC ORGANS

Lymphatic tissue is composed of a framework of reticular cells and fibers with vast numbers of large, medium-sized, and small lymphocytes filling the meshes. The relative proportions of lymphocytes to stroma determine whether the lymphatic tissue in a given location is loose, dense, or nodular (Maximow and Bloom, 1948).

Lymph nodes and the accumulations of lymphatic tissue in other organs (tonsils, solitary nodules and Peyer's patches of the intestinal tract, and appendix) are exceedingly susceptible to ionizing radiations, and, as in the other hematopoietic organs, the degree of injury is proportional to the dose, within certain ranges. Damage is evidenced by massive destruction of lymphocytes of all sizes with consequent striking changes in the lymphatic nodules and reduction in size of the organ.

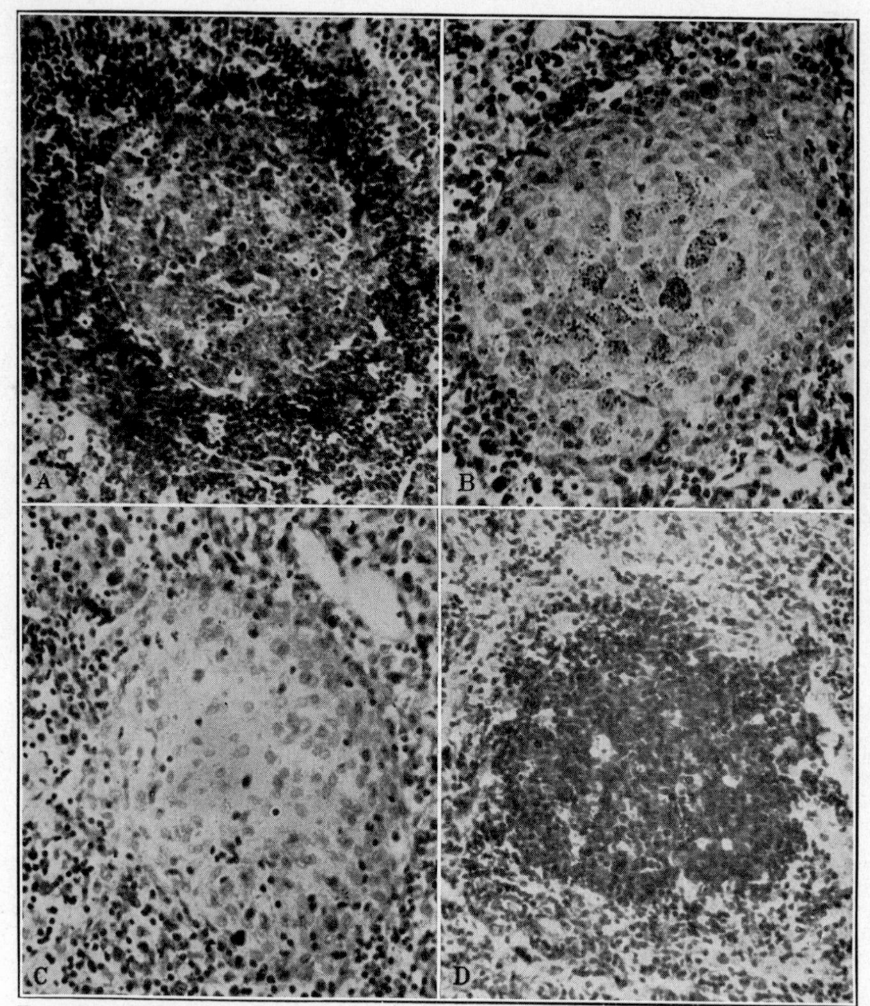

FIG. 17-2. Three stages in the degeneration and beginning regeneration of lymphatic tissue of mesenteric lymph node of rabbits after total-body irradiation with 800 r of 200-kv X rays. (*A*), untreated rabbit, shows an active germinal center with the shell of small lymphocytes extending into the dense diffuse lymphatic tissue. (*B*) 17 hours after irradiation, all the lymphocytes in the nodule have been destroyed and many of those at its periphery are also degenerating. Most of the debris is within macrophages, especially in the center of the nodule. (*C*) 24 hours after irradiation; except for a few scattered lymphocytes, the nodule consists mainly of reticular cells and a few lymphocytes, both large and small. (*D*) 31 days after irradiation; there is a focus of intense formation of lymphocytes (a new nodule) and beginning repopulation of the diffuse tissue with lymphocytes. (*After De Bruyn.*) 220×.

This destruction of lymphocytes is soon reflected in a drop in the number of lymphocytes in the peripheral blood (Chap. 16 by Jacobson).

After the administration of 800 r of total-body X radiation to rabbits, nuclear debris of lymphocytes in the lymph nodes rises from an appreciable amount at ½ hour to a maximum at 8 hours (De Bruyn, 1948). It is usually concentrated in the more active portions of the nodules rather than at their periphery. Outside the nodules it is diffusely distributed throughout cortex and medulla, sometimes with a little in the lumen of small lymphatic vessels. The reticular cells show no evidence of damage. Prompt phagocytic activity of macrophages results in almost complete disappearance of debris by 24 hours, leaving large areas of lymphocyte-poor tissue frequently characterized by dense masses of spindle-shaped reticular cells. The concentration of these cells is probably due to a collapse of the stroma rather than to a hyperplasia of the reticular cells, since none of them are in mitosis. Medium-sized and large lymphocytes frequently exhibit signs of damage, such as clumping of chromatin, lobation of nuclei, or formation of giant cells, and many, but not all of them, degenerate. As in the bone marrow, reticular cells and macrophages are not visibly affected at any stage and are the main potential source of regeneration of lymphocytes. Heterophil leukocytes appear in great numbers during the first day and persist for several days, after which they degenerate and are phagocytosed by macrophages. Edema of the connective tissue about some of the nodes is prominent as late as 10 days after irradiation. Following the disintegration and removal of the lymphocytes, most of the lymphatic nodules disappear, leaving a prominent reticular stroma for several weeks.

Early regeneration is diffuse, nodular regeneration occurring much later. Beginning at 5 days, diffuse areas of medium-sized lymphocytes, many in mitosis, appear in the cortex and to some extent in the medulla. Then, three weeks after irradiation, these cells begin to concentrate in localized areas of the cortex, forming small "bare" germinal centers, frequently associated with small areas of ectopic myelopoiesis. These bare nodules gradually grow larger, develop a shell of small lymphocytes, and by four months resume the appearance of typical nodules. Plasma cells, noted from 9 days on, especially in the medullary cords, gradually diminish after 36 days.

In the lymph node, as in the bone marrow of animals exposed to X rays (100 to 800 r), the damage is correlated with the amount of radiation. This correlation holds, not only for the quantity of cellular debris, but also for the alterations in the nodules. In contrast to complete destruction and delayed regeneration of a majority of the nodules in rabbit lymph nodes after 800 or 600 r of X rays, after 400 r there is only partial destruction and a greatly accelerated recovery, and after still lower doses the changes are correspondingly less marked. After 100 and 50 r there is a latent period of 3 hours before damage is evident. At 50 r the only injury is an increase in debris at 3 and especially at 8 hours which is not confined to the nodules. Below 50 r no damage is observed.

In different species the lymphatic tissue undergoes the same degree of damage at a particular dose level, regardless of the lethality of that dose for the species.

Equivalent doses of fast and slow neutrons and γ rays produce the same histological changes in the lymph node as do X rays.

Repeated doses of 80 r of total-body X irradiation to mice for five weeks apparently have no cumulative or sensitizing effect on the lymph node and produce no changes in the amount of lymphatic tissue or in the number and size of active nodules.

Repeated doses of external γ rays to mice, 8.8 r per day, produce changes in the lymph node only when the irradiation is continued for 10 months or more (Spargo *et al.*, 1951). Lymphocytopoietic activity decreases, the nodules becoming smaller and fewer until they disappear completely, and, concomitantly, transport of small lymphocytes through the cortical sinuses diminishes until there is none at 16 months. Lower doses, 1.1 or 4.4 r per day, even when continued for 16 months, cause no significant changes.

The changes in the lymph node after the internal administration of radioactive isotopes depend on whether the isotopes lodge in or near the organ. When present in sufficient amounts they produce the same qualitative changes as those noted after external irradiation. A quantitative comparison of effects of external and internal irradiation is more difficult, because of the uneven distribution of the isotopes in the various organs and tissues, the varying rates of excretion from the body, and the differences in their half-lives.

The intestinal lymphatic tissue undergoes the same histological alterations as the lymph node after external and internal irradiation.

THYMUS

The thymus consists of a framework of reticular cells—mainly of endodermal but also of mesenchymal origin—whose meshes are filled with dense masses of small lymphocytes in the outer (cortical) portion of the organ and with smaller numbers of small lymphocytes and a few medium-sized ones in the inner (medullary) portion of the organ. The thymus gradually "involutes" with advancing age, losing lymphocytes and some stromal cells.

Studies of the thymus after X irradiation reveal a loss in size of the organ, owing mainly to destruction of lymphocytes. In the rabbit, the effects of a single dose of 800 r total-body X ray (Murray, 1948b) include: (1) a destructive phase (1 to 8 hours), during which most of the lymphocytes die; (2) a phase of cleanup (8 hours to 2 days), when debris is removed by macrophages and possibly in part through lymphatic channels, exposing a condensed epithelial stroma and blood vessels in the cortex and leaving a few surviving lymphocytes in the medulla; (3) a phase of inactivity (2 to 9 days), during which shrinkage continues and the connective tissue becomes prominent; and (4) a phase of regeneration (10 days to four weeks), characterized by a repopulation with lymphocytes, proceeding outward from the medulla. The stromal or reticular cells are not damaged by this or even much larger amounts of irradiation. The Hassall's bodies, formed of masses of epithelial cells, are unaffected. There are suggestions of new formation of Hassall's bodies from stromal cells at 14 days.

At lower doses fewer cells die, the inactive period is shorter, and regeneration is more rapid. This sequence of changes is somewhat similar to that already described for the lymphatic tissue. As in that tissue, the reaction in different species is the same to equal single doses of X rays, irrespective of the variations in LD_{50} levels for these species.

External β rays sufficient to kill about 20 per cent of the mice (5000 rep) do not affect the thymus in these animals. Qualitatively, the reactions to fast and slow neutrons are the same as to X rays. Quantitatively, the X-ray/fast-neutron ratio has been estimated to be roughly 5 and the X-ray/slow-neutron ratio to be roughly 1 (Murray, 1948b).

Long-continued, daily low doses of total-body γ rays gradually cause depletion of lymphocytes—with 8.8 r first at 6 months and with 4.4 r at 8 months (Spargo *et al.*, 1951). With 1.1 r greater depletion than in controls is first observed at 10 months. Both in this group and in the 4.4-r group attempts at regeneration are present at 14 and 16 months. In all these animals there is a striking increase in mast cells in the depleted organs as well as in the surrounding connective tissue. Plasma cells are not prominent.

The depletion of the thymus following internal irradiation is similar to that produced by X rays, but it usually occurs more gradually and is more prolonged. Also, because of localization of the isotopes, the depletion is not always uniform. Irregular depletion results from the uneven distribution of α emitters within the thymus. For example, after administration of plutonium, areas containing the isotope, as seen in autoradiographs of adjacent sections, are depleted, whereas nearby uncontaminated areas are not. When the thymus is irradiated as a result of activity deposited elsewhere, as Sr^{89} or Y^{91} in the sternum, or Y^{91} or cerium-praseodymium (275-day) in the lung, there is a gradient of damage. The parts nearest the localized isotopes suffer the most damage, which decreases perceptibly away from the focus. However, as might be expected, the highly diffusible Na^{24} in doses of 50 to 80 $\mu c/g$ in mice (considerably above the LD_{50} 30-day level) causes a rapid, diffuse, and severe depletion of the organ in 4 days. In contrast to large single doses of external irradiation in which there is marked regeneration, there is none in those areas of the thymus in the range of long-continued bombardment from isotopes in nearby tissues.

SPLEEN

The spleen is made up of lymphatic tissue which is typical in its white pulp and atypical in its red pulp. The white pulp ensheaths the arteries; the red pulp surrounds the radicles of the veins and consists mainly of reticular cells and fibers and a few lymphocytes; it is permeated by circulating blood. Since lymphopoiesis occurs in the while pulp and, in some mammals, ectopic myelopoiesis in the red pulp, the effects of ionizing radiations on these functions may be compared here within a single organ. The white pulp, essentially dense lymphatic tissue with nodules, reacts in a fashion similar to that of lymph nodes.

After a single exposure of rabbits to 800 r of total-body X irradiation, the spleen is rapidly reduced in size during the first day, and for a week or longer it remains small and dense, with relatively small and inconspicuous areas of white pulp, lacking nodules or germinal centers (Murray, 1948a). Neither the germinal centers nor the white pulp as a whole recovers appreciably until about two weeks after treatment. Mitosis stops in a few minutes, and within the next few hours most of the lymphocytes throughout the white pulp die and the germinal centers, normally rich in medium-sized lymphocytes, are obliterated as such, leaving dense masses of reticular cells. In the red pulp, lymphocytes suffer the same change as in the white pulp, and the relatively few erythroblasts and myelocytes present show damage at early intervals and are absent at 5 and 9 days. The period from 3 to 17 hours is one of rapid phagocytosis by reticular cells of the debris from this widespread degeneration in both white and red pulp and from invading heterophil leukocytes. With the removal of the dead cells, the spleen, particularly the white pulp, shrinks, leaving the reticular cells prominent. A phase of relative inactivity ensues (1 to 9 days) with further condensation of the reticular cells, the few abortive attempts at regeneration being by transformation of reticular cells. Finally (10 days to four weeks) a phase of reconstitution takes place through mitotic activity of the lymphocytes. The regeneration of erythroblasts and myelocytes and new formation of megakaryocytes occur after the resumption of lymphopoiesis.

On the other hand, in mice and rats receiving 350 and 600 r (total-body), respectively, erythropoiesis is renewed much earlier. It expands from a few foci in the red pulp to such an extent that it sometimes encroaches upon the white pulp and apparently interferes with regeneration there. Megakaryocytes, which are numerous in the normal spleen of these animals, are greatly decreased by 3 days but begin to reappear in mice at 5 days after 350 r and in rats after three weeks following 600 r.

The sequence and type of effects are similar with lower doses, but fewer cells die, the inactive period is shorter, and regeneration is more rapid. The normal structural pattern shows little disruption below 175 r, and damage to lymphocytes is not seen below 25 r. In different species, damage to the spleen is of the same magnitude for the same size dose, irrespective of differences in the LD_{50} for these species (Murray, 1948a).

Fast and slow neutrons resemble X rays in their qualitative effects on the spleen. Equivalent fractions of the LD_{50} 30-day level produce similar effects. Estimations of their biological effectiveness on the spleen are, roughly, X/fast neutrons = 4; X/slow neutrons = 0.85.

Daily doses of 80 r of total-body X rays severely deplete the mouse spleen by 20 treatments, but erythropoiesis is definitely elevated after 24 treatments. Depletion is less than after 350 r (total-body) given in a single dose.

Seven hundred roentgens of γ rays (from an external source of radium) administered over a three-month period at the rate of 8.8 r per 8-hour day causes less damage to the spleen of guinea pigs than a single total-body dose of 175 r of X rays (Lorenz, Heston, Jacobson, *et al.*, 1953). A similar experiment with mice shows a gradual shrinkage of the organ with progressive depletion of white pulp (Spargo *et al.*, 1951). In the red pulp an increase in erythropoiesis begins at 6 months after 8.8 r per day and becomes progressively greater up to 16 months, with hemocytoblasts predominating at the latter interval. After 4.4 r per day erythropoiesis increases only at 14 and 16 months. In all these chronically irradiated mice there is a progressive increase in mast cells, reaching a maximum in the 8.8-r group of 4.5 times the number in controls.

Autoradiographs show all isotopes more concentrated in the red pulp than in the white, the deposition often being especially heavy at the transition between the two zones. With Zr^{93}-Cb^{93}, Y^{91}, and radium there is some deposition in the white pulp, mainly around the arterioles.

When radioactive isotopes lodge, even temporarily, in the spleen, the effects, with one important exception, are similar to those produced by external irradiation and consist in depletion of white pulp and shrinkage of the organ. Indeed, the changes due to administration of appropriate amounts of Na^{24} cannot be told from those due to X rays. However, the injection of bone-seeking isotopes such as Y^{91}, Sr^{89}, Ba^{140}-La^{140}, plutonium, or radium into small mammals causes an extreme depletion of hematopoietic cells in the bone marrow, and the red pulp of the spleen develops an accelerated hematopoiesis. Zr^{93}-Cb^{93}, however, in addition to producing a marked depletion of splenic white pulp, differs from the other bone-seeking β emitters in not eliciting a marked compensatory hematopoiesis in red pulp. In fact, erythrophagocytosis is striking in the red pulp after injection of this isotope. It is noteworthy that erythropoiesis does occur (except after Zr^{93}-Cb^{93}) in the red pulp, which is the site of lodgment of many isotopes. With practically all radioactive isotopes, the megakaryocytes, after a preliminary decrease, increase tremendously in number after weeks and months and often show great nuclear abnormalities (Murray, 1948a).

BONE

Bone is a specialized connective tissue consisting of bone cells (osteocytes) embedded in a matrix of collagenous fibers and amorphous cementing substance which is heavily infiltrated with small crystals of hydroxyapatite, calcium phosphate, carbonate, and small amounts of citrate. On the surface of a developing spicule of bone are cells called osteoblasts, which are believed to make the bone, and some of them become bone cells. In areas where bone is being destroyed, there are large multinucleated cells called osteoclasts. Their presumed role is the destruction of bone.

In normal animals growth of the bone in length depends on (1) continued multiplication of the cartilage cells in the epiphyseal plate and, near the bone marrow, calcification of the intercellular substance between them; and (2) continued invasion of the calcified cartilage matrix by vascular connective tissue from the bone marrow and deposition of bone in the space thus made available, often on remnants of cartilage which are not destroyed. With cessation of bone growth, multiplication of the cartilage cells and invasion by blood vessels stop, and bone is deposited on the diaphyseal side of the cartilage plate. This plate disappears in man on reaching adulthood, and continuity develops between the marrow of metaphysis and epiphysis. The epiphyseal cartilage participates in the growth of bones for a long time in rats, but in mice the period of growth lasts for only two or three months.

Bones grow in width by deposition of bone directly on the outer surface of the bony cylinder (periosteal growth). In addition, with the reconstruction of a bone which takes place as it grows, new bone may be laid down inside the bone collar (endosteal growth). This is especially true toward the growing end of a bone.

Although many believe mature bone is relatively resistant, there is little doubt that it can be severely damaged by irradiation. Thus a peculiar eburnation and devitalization of bone (Friedman, 1942) and massive necrosis after dosages which did not damage the skin (Regaud, 1922) have been described.

There is general agreement that the tissues responsible for growth of bone can be severely damaged by irradiation. Stunting of the growth of the long bones has been observed by many investigators. The rat, because of its rapid and prolonged period of growth, is a sensitive indicator of these radiation effects. After 600 r of X rays (LD_{50} 30-day

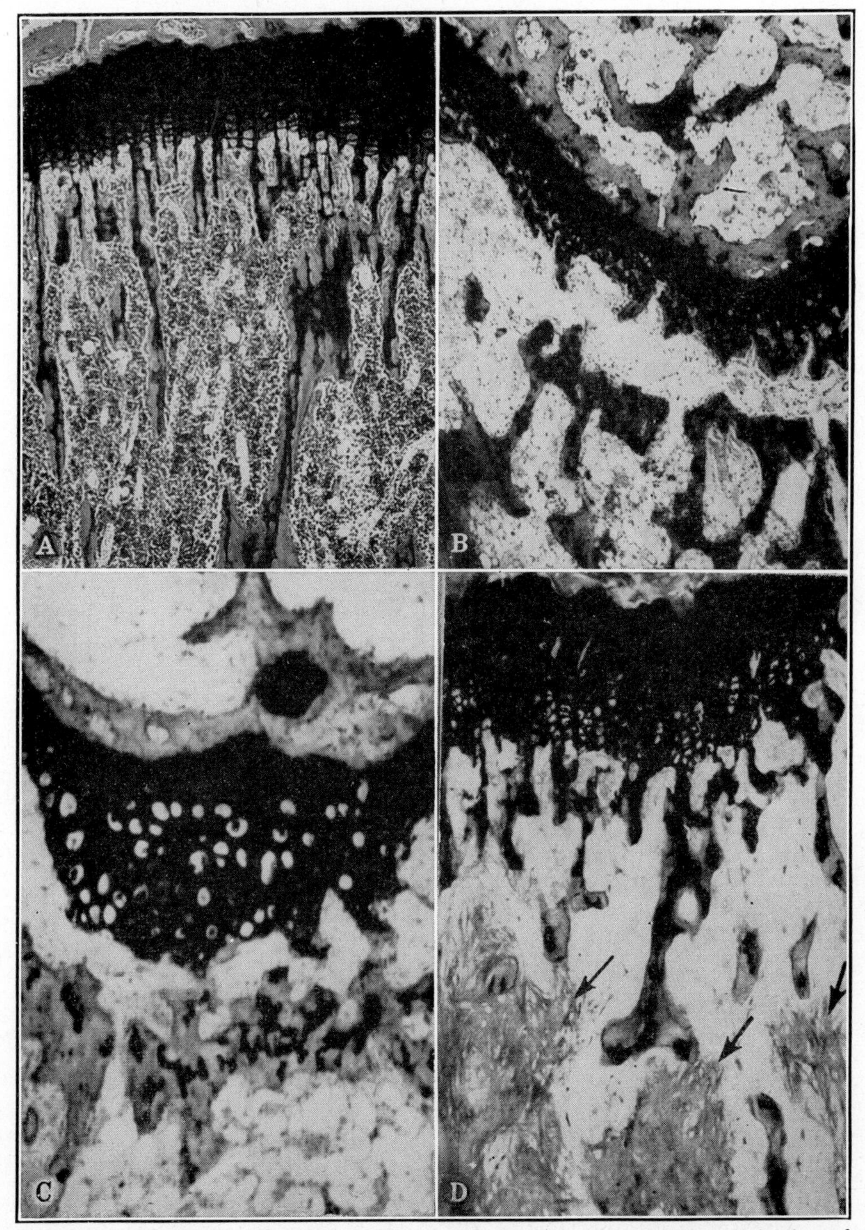

FIG. 17-3. (*A*) Metaphysis of tibia of untreated rat showing the interdigitation of primary spongiosa with cartilage; 35×. (*B*) Metaphysis of rat 9 days after 600 r total-body X rays (200 kv). Note the complete severance of the bone of the metaphysis from the cartilage; 40×. (*C*) Metaphysis of mouse femur 90 days after 3.6 μc/g of Sr^{89}. There has been severance of the spongiosa from the epiphyseal plate and the cartilage has become markedly thickened, with swelling of the cells; 50×. (*D*) Metaphysis of mouse femur 40 days after 1 μc/g of radium. Note areas of newly formed, atypical bone in the marrow; 105×. (*After Heller*, 1948.)

level), the continuity of the epiphyseal cartilage of femur and tibia with the spongiosa is frequently interrupted, resulting in a temporary cessation of bone growth in length (Heller, 1948a). Preceded by excessive hypertrophy of cartilage cells in the zone of ossification at 3 days, the normal interdigitation of cartilage and metaphyseal spongy bone is gradually lost. By 9 days the two are completely separated. In the lamellae of the spongiosa there are some dead bone cells, but none in the dense cortical bone. Osteoblasts disappear after irradiation but gradually reappear after some weeks. Only a slight increase in the number of osteoclasts accompanies the resorption of bone. In some instances this severance of cartilage and spongy bone may persist for a month, but in others a new primary spongiosa is laid down against the cartilage plate as early as 21 days or possibly sooner and growth in length is resumed. The old, disconnected spongiosa is gradually resorbed. Recovery of the growth process is complete at 70 days, although the bones are permanently somewhat stunted.

A single dose of 400 r of X rays merely reduces the number of osteoblasts at 3 and 7 days while osteoclasts are more numerous in parts of the metaphysis.

In young chicks (three weeks of age) similar changes occur. Doses of 800 or 1000 r total-body X irradiation cause severance of cartilage from spongy bone, effectively stopping growth of the bone. After 1000 r there is a steady progression of damage from 1 to 16 hours, with the disappearance of osteoblasts, increase of osteoclasts around the spongy bone, and a decrease in the erosion of cartilage. From 7 hours to 4 days occasional dead osteocytes and a number of empty lacunae are present in the spongy bone. By 4 days separation of cartilage from spongy bone is extensive, some of the latter having been resorbed, and the bone stops growing. After 800 r, the destructive process is the same as after 1000 r, only not quite so rapid. However, by 5 days severance is extensive, osteoblasts are absent, and bone growth stops. After 400 r there is a progressive reduction of osteoblasts around the metaphyseal spicules of bone from 2 to 18 hours, but at this dosage no severance or interruption of bone growth occurs. Recovery is rapid, with osteoblastic and osteoclastic activity resumed by 30 hours. No effect on chick bones is noted after 100 r.

In comparison with the effects of external irradiation on bone at LD_{50} levels, even small fractions of the LD_{50} of the bone-seeking isotopes cause disproportionately greater damage, owing to their continued activity at the points of deposition (Heller, 1948a). Among these isotopes there is a remarkable similarity of reaction, especially between radium and plutonium, and the β emitters Sr^{89} and Y^{91}. However, the weak β particles of C^{14}, which deposit heavily in bone after injection of $NaHC^{14}O_3$, do not interfere with the growth of bone, even when 2 $\mu c/g$ is injected (W. Bloom, 1949).

Autoradiographs indicate that deposition of most radioactive materials is greatest in the areas of maximum growth in length of the bones. The isotopes are also deposited along the periosteum and parts of the endosteum. Where there is intense radioactivity, osteocytes degenerate. The bone of the metaphysis is devitalized to a greater extent than that of the cortex. But in rats five and six months after radium dosage of 0.06 $\mu c/g$, even the dense cortical bone contains large numbers of lacunae devoid of their bone cells. As after X irradiation, osteoblasts disappear and interdigitation of bone and cartilage at the epiphyseal line is decreased, often leading to complete separation of epiphyseal cartilage from spongiosa and arrest of growth in length. After low doses of short-lived radioactive isotopes, as after X-ray dosage, repair occurs and growth in length is resumed. Longer-lived agents and higher doses cause an overgrowth of atypical metaphyseal bone which later becomes devitalized. This bone varies in appearance by the number of osteocytes, coarseness of connective tissue fibers, and density of the matrix; it never shows evidence of intracartilaginous ossification. It may persist in the center of the shaft months after injection of the radioactive material. The old metaphysis with its devitalized bone is very weak and fractures often occur here. This is also the site in which osteogenic sarcomas develop. Several examples of this occurred in radium dial painters (Martland, 1931). In rats receiving doses that permit survival for a long enough time, this atypical overgrowth is outstripped by the normal growth mechanism and growth in length of the bone is resumed. At still lower doses there are sometimes suggestions of partial resorption of the old spongiosa and atypical bone even with the long-lived α emitters.

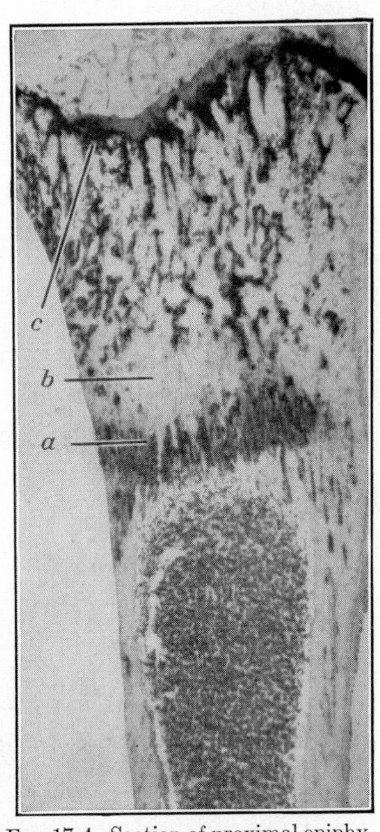

FIG. 17-4. Section of proximal epiphysis of rat tibia, five months after the injection of 0.125 $\mu c/g$ of radium showing the old metaphysis at (*a*), new bone at (*b*), and the new metaphysis at (*c*). (*After Heller*, 1948.) 9×.

However, where bone growth has ceased, as in adult mice, the picture is quite different. For example, five and seven months after the injection of plutonium or radium (0.03 $\mu c/g$), atypical bone often replaces the marrow in the metaphysis and even much of the shaft (M. A. Bloom and W. Bloom, 1949).

In a growing bone, isotope-containing bone will be in part resorbed with the remodeling and in part incorporated in new bone. The isotopes enter adult bone by incompletely understood processes of exchange with atoms in the bone-salt crystal complexes. Moreover, in the case of yttrium and plutonium, at least some of these elements become firmly adherent to the organic part of the intercellular substance of bone (Copp, Axelrod, and Hamilton, 1946; Copp, Greenberg, and Hamilton, 1946).

CARTILAGE

This tissue is distributed in the respiratory system, joints, and growing bones. In the last, a definite portion of the epiphyseal cartilage is in continuous growth, and a thin zone within it is just as continuously undergoing provisional calcification and shortly thereafter dissolution and replacement by newly formed bone. As might be expected, cartilage in these several positions and different states of activity shows great variations in susceptibility to damage by irradiation. In growing animals it is bifficult to assess accurately just how much of the change resulting from irradiation is due to failure of replacement of cartilage by ingrowth of bone. In nongrowing animals, on the other hand, it is probable that all the changes in cartilage are direct effects of irradiation. The response of cartilage may vary from rather marked resistance in adult animals to a fairly high degree of sensitivity during the period of rapid growth with resulting retardation of skeletal growth. On the basis of investigations on chicks (Perthes, 1903), on young rats (Segale, 1920), and on young rabbits (Bisgard and Hunt, 1936; Brooks and Hillstrom, 1933), it appears that localized exposure of an epiphysis of tibia or femur to 1500 r or less of X rays leads to an arrest of elongation of the bone owing to damage to the epiphyseal cartilage (Hinkel, 1942). Degenerative changes in certain cartilage cells, particularly in the zone of proliferation, occur as early as 2 days after irradiation, and at 6 days many of these cells are hypertrophic and vacuolated, with pyknotic nuclei. The columns of cells and the intercellular bridges lose their regular arrangement, the epiphysis becomes thinner, and, after two weeks, the disturbance in the growth mechanism is manifest in both cartilage and new bone of the metaphysis. By six months the epiphyseal cartilage has disappeared; this is much earlier than it disappeared on the nonirradiated side. There are indications that growing children are much more sensitive to radiation than these animals (Gates, 1943). With total-body as well as with localized irradiation, abnormally swollen cartilage cells have been noted as the first sign of degeneration in the zone of provisional calcification (Heller, 1948a). This is observed in rats 3 days after a single dose of 600 r of X rays (total-body) and is followed by partial or complete separation of epiphyseal cartilage from the primary spongiosa and eventual recovery with resumption of growth (see section on Bone).

The greater and more sustained damage to cartilage produced by certain internally administered radioactive isotopes parallels their greater injurious effects on bone, and varies with the dosage and with the age of the animal and the consequent stage of growth of its bones. Swelling and death of cells of the epiphyseal cartilage are noted early after deposition of most bone-seeking isotopes. The effects are especially severe in young rats, in which separation of the cartilage from the bone begins at 3 days and is nearly complete 7 days after a Sr^{89} dose of 2.9 $\mu c/g$ (Heller, 1948a). By 11 days the entire epiphyseal cartilage is several times the normal width and many cartilage cells are dead, especially in the zone bordering the metaphysis. The articular cartilage cells, particularly those facing the epiphyseal cavity, are either dead or greatly enlarged. In some instances the articular cartilage becomes separated into several portions by connective tissue. By three or five months (depending on the dose and the particular isotope) that portion of the cartilage not destroyed by radiation from the deposited isotope has continued its growth and moved away from the zone of damage; growth in length of the bones continues in histologically normal although slower fashion, and the animals are permanently stunted.

In rats injected with radium, 0.5 $\mu c/g$, the width of the cartilage plate, at least twice the normal at two months, increases still more at three and five months. At this last interval the cartilage has been invaded by vascular connective tissue, which extends transversely from the region of the periosteum and separates large portions of the hypertrophic cartilage, often 30 cell layers deep, from the rest.

In mice, in which growth in length of the bone ceases early, Sr^{89} also causes an abnormal hypertrophy and vacuolization of cartilage cells at most intervals, but conspicuous from 90 to 197 days after 3.6 $\mu c/g$ and as late as 70 days after 0.86 $\mu c/g$. The cartilage plate becomes thicker with marked irregularities owing to the increased number of hypertrophic cells. After higher dosages, from 5 to 15 $\mu c/g$, the same changes occur, but earlier. The effect of radium is similar but even more severe, despite its doubtful deposition in the epiphyseal cartilage at early intervals and its absence at 40 days. From 8 to 40 days after a radium dose of 1 $\mu c/g$, swollen and degenerating cartilage cells of the epiphyseal cartilage encroach even into the deeper layers of the plate. Eighty days after a dose of 0.5 $\mu c/g$, multiplication of the cartilage cells has increased the width of the plate two or three times and dead cartilage cells are numerous. The irregularity of this invasion of connective tissue results in tremendous variations in width of the epiphyseal plate and great abnormality in the appearance of the whole metaphysis.

MALE GENERATIVE SYSTEM

Total-body irradiation, whether it is carried out with single or repeated doses of X rays or γ rays or single exposure to fast neutrons, produces the same pattern of damage and repair in the testis. The degenerative changes are mainly induced through injury to the free stem cells. With all types and amounts of external and internal radiations that produce cellular depletion, the testis is reduced in size and there is a gradual cessation of spermatogenesis (Albers-Schönberg, 1903; Barratt and Arnold, 1911–1912; Bergonié and Tribondeau, 1905; Heller, 1948b; Regaud and Blanc, 1906; Schinz and Slotopolsky, 1925).

A single total-body exposure of rabbits to 800 r of X rays destroys the spermatogonia. This causes an interruption in the production of new spermatocytes and consequently of spermia several weeks later. Cell death, evidenced by dead spermatogonia (and only rarely by a dead spermatocyte) 1 day after treatment, is less obvious at 3 and 5 days (Heller, 1948b). By 9 days spermatogonia are inconspicuous in most tubules, which contain only Sertoli cells, a decreased number of spermatocytes (some damaged), spermatids and spermia, and great numbers of multinucleated and bizarre cells. Beginning regeneration (at 30 to 35 days) is indicated by the presence on the basement membrane of basophilic outstretched cells or very early spermatogonia (Heller, 1948b). Some of the tubules even contain a few spermatocytes at this time. Spermatogenesis returns to normal by four months in some specimens, while in others the tubules contain Sertoli cells alone. There is sometimes edema of the intertubular connective tissue.

After 600 r the cessation of spermatogenesis followed by regeneration is similar to that after the higher dose except that not quite so many tubules are depleted and regeneration begins earlier. Attempts at recovery are indicated at 21 days by the presence in a few tubules of spermatogonia in all stages of development, more tubules showing this appearance by 31 days and at least half the tubules showing some degree of recovery by 45 days.

In the rat the effects of 600 r of X rays on the testis are the same as in the rabbit, even in time sequence. However, in different rats 132 days after exposure, there are great differences in the degree of recovery.

The damage to the mouse testis after 350 r of X rays is much like that in the rabbit after 600 r except that regeneration begins earlier.

The cumulative effect of repeated small doses of radiation is more striking on the testis than on any other organ of the same animal, although not quite so marked as on the ovary. The testes of mice irradiated daily with 80 r of X rays show progressive damage. Twenty-four hours after

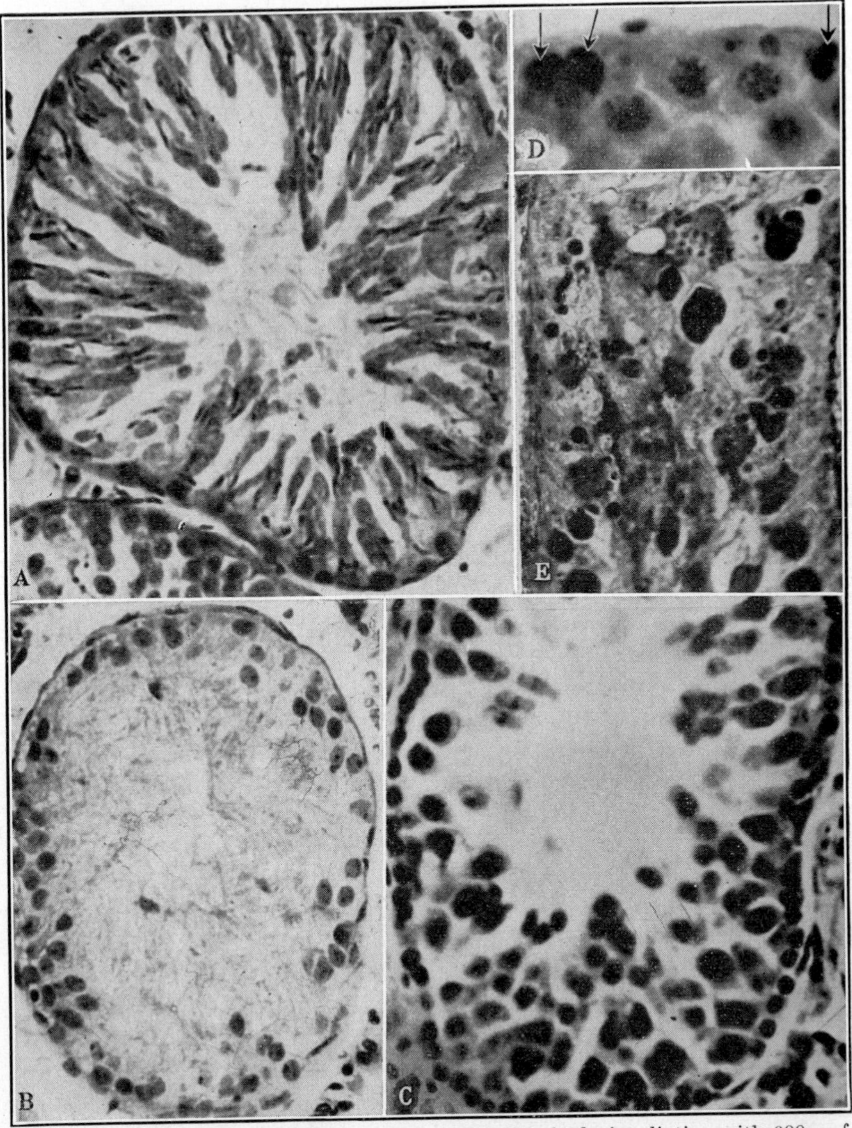

FIG. 17-5. (*A*)–(*D*) Sections of rat testes after whole-body irradiation with 600 r of 200-kv X rays. (*A*) 21 days; the tubule contains Sertoli cells and groups of spermia; all spermatogenic cells are absent; 350×. (*B*) 31 days; the tubule is further collapsed and contains only Sertoli cells; 350×. (*C*) 70 days, beginning regeneration of spermatogenesis. Note the almost continuous layer of dark-staining spermatogonia at the periphery of the tubule, the larger spermatocytes, and the clumps of smaller pale-staining spermatids; 350×. (*D*) 8 hours after irradiation; showing the intact spermatocytes and three degenerating spermatogonia indicated by the arrows; 675×. (*E*) Section of rat testis 24 days after rat was given 5μc/g of Zr^{93}-Cb^{93}. The tubule is filled with necrotic cells which stain darkly; 260×. (*After Heller*, 1948.)

four doses, dead spermatogonia are seen; 24 hours after nine doses, spermatogonia are rare and there is a marked decrease in spermatocytes; after 14, 20, 24, and 35 daily doses of 80 r, there is a gradual elimination of spermatogenesis until only the Sertoli cells remain.

In the testis of guinea pigs exposed daily to 8.8 r of γ rays from a radium source, there is early destruction of some spermatogonia while others develop into spermatocytes and eventually into spermia. With continued irradiation, no regeneration of spermatogonia occurs and the damage is progressive. After 37 daily treatments (326 r) spermatogenesis is absent (Heller, 1948b). After 46 exposures (405 r) and 81 exposures (713 r), only Sertoli cells remain and nearly all cellular debris has been removed from the lumens of the tubules. From 37 days on, large vesicular cells resembling fibroblasts are prominent around the tubules and among the interstitial cells. However, after 81 exposures the epididymis still contains spermia.

Histologically, the findings are the same in mice similarly treated, but complete cessation of spermatogenesis is less rapid. Although there is considerable generalized degeneration after two months of irradiation (8.8 r per 8-hour day), practically complete depletion of the tubules (except for Sertoli cells) is not observed until the eight-month interval (Eschenbrenner, 1946; Spargo *et al.*, 1951). In mice irradiated with 4.4 r per day, the testis shows only slight degenerative changes up to 10 months. Twelve to 16 months of treatment cause slight but progressively increasing degeneration. Irradiation at the rate of 1.1 r per day produces no visible changes in the testis up to 16 months.

Exposure of rabbits and mice to fast neutrons in comparable fractions of the LD_{50} 30-day level results in similar but even more severe damage to the testis than X irradiation (Heller, 1948b; Lawrence and Tennant, 1937). In addition to these degenerative and regenerative changes in the tubules, the interstitial connective tissue in the mouse contains focalized masses of plasma cells and some areas of hematopoiesis. There is also some inflammation in the epididymis. The testes of young rabbits show the peak of damage at 21 days, when every tubule contains a dense amorphous material and an occasional huge basophil cell. In the surrounding connective tissue there is frequently considerable extravascular and intravascular erythropoiesis.

Beta rays from an external P^{32} source produce extensive damage at the periphery of the testis near the source of the radiation. The damage decreases toward the interior of the organ. In the least damaged portions regeneration is rapid, but the outside margin is incompletely recovered 28 days after exposure to 2500 rep. Besides the dead cells in the severely injured marginal tubules, giant and bizarre cells are often prominent (Heller, 1948b).

Although the effects of internally administered radioactive isotopes are the same in kind as of the externally applied radiations, the extremes of damage are much greater at the LD_{50} 30-day level for the internally administered substances; corresponding with their localized deposition, the resulting damage tends to be localized. Radium, plutonium, and Zr^{93}-Cb^{93} appear to be more destructive to the germinal epithelium than Sr^{89}, P^{32}, Ba^{140}-La^{140}, and Y^{91}. Following very low doses, injury and repair may occur concomitantly, making it difficult or impossible to evaluate the damage.

After all types of irradiation, external and internal, the stem cells are the most sensitive and the interstitial cells are extremely radioresistant. Except in a few animals after neutron and radium treatment, the Sertoli cells show no significant changes.

There are but scanty reports on the male accessory organs and passages. They all seem to be relatively radioresistant.

FEMALE GENERATIVE SYSTEM

Irradiation of the mammalian ovary causes marked atrophy of the organ and may produce temporary or even permanent sterility if the dosage is high enough (Halberstaedter, 1905; Lacassagne, 1913; Lacassagne and Gricouroff, 1941; Shields Warren, 1942, 1943). If sterilization is not permanent, there may be a reawakening of sexual activity after the passage of months and even normal pregnancies may ensue. Dependent on and following the changes in the ovary there is atrophy of tubes, uterus, vagina, and mammary gland.

The sensitivity of the ova and of the attached follicular cells varies with their functional states at the time of irradiation (Lacassagne, 1913). There are unusually marked species differences in sensitivity. The corpora lutea and interstitial cells are relatively very radioresistant.

Irradiation of the ovaries of a rabbit with 1200 r produces dramatic effects (Lacassagne and Gricouroff, 1941). In primitive ova (surrounded by a single layer of epithelium) the signs of degeneration are pyknosis or chromatolysis and fragmentation of the cell. Debris of ovocytes is phagocytosed by the follicular cells, but these also may degenerate and the whole follicle disappear in 3 or 4 days. However, some primitive ova escape destruction and after five months or more they may begin to develop. When irradiated in the beginning growth phase, first the ovum and then follicular epithelium degenerate within 2 weeks. In irradiated large, growing follicles the first changes are seen in the follicular epithelium, but the residue of large ova may persist for months. In mature follicles the follicular epithelium disappears early after irradiation, while the ovum, with more or less visible damage, may persist for some time. There may be hemorrhages in the follicles. Apparently, definitive destruction of all ova may take place with 2000 to 2500 r.

On the other hand, interstitial gland cells show little if any effects of such an exposure, although these glands gradually decrease over some months and imperceptibly disappear, owing to failure of new cells to develop from corpora lutea. Interstitial cells give rise to cords and "glands." Some also may develop as ingrowths from surface epithelium. It should be noted that the interstitial glands, although prominent in the ovaries of rodents, are inconspicuous and may even be absent in the human ovary.

The corpora lutea are not affected by doses which destroy ova and growing follicles. Indeed, irradiation a few hours after copulation does not hinder development of corpora lutea, although such corpora lutea degenerate early. It has been reported that 500 to 1300 r administered before ovulation has no effect on development of corpora lutea, while after larger doses (1300 to 1800 r) small corpora lutea develop but their secretion does not maintain an endometrial reaction for more than 6 days (Lacassagne and Gricouroff, 1941). In any event, an amount of irradiation which destroys all developing follicles will cause failure of corpora lutea to develop.

Although 600 r produces only minimal changes in the rat, most ova are destroyed at 1600 to 1800 r, while sterilization requires 3000 r (Lacassagne and Gricouroff, 1941). However, total-body irradiation of rats with 600 r produces great degenerative changes in the ovary, there being practically no intact ova at any stage later than 2 days, although a rare corpus luteum but no ova may be found after four months (W. Bloom, 1948d). The primitive ova of the mouse are exceptionally sensitive to irradiation (Murray, 1931; Schugt, 1928). A dose of 54 r destroys many follicles, and doses of 140–150 r produce histological sterilization.

Daily irradiation with 8.8 r of γ rays per 8-hour day produces apparent sterilization of the mouse ovary at four months, with 4.4 r per day at eight months, while with 1.1 r per day there are still some growing follicles at sixteen months (Eschenbrenner, 1946; Spargo *et al.*, 1951).

The ovary is sensitive to only some of the radioactive isotopes, presumably because of the failure of many others to localize in the organ. Radium and plutonium in small doses produce marked degeneration in the ovaries of both mice and rats (W. Bloom, 1948d).

The columnar epithelium of the oviduct and uterus is much less sensitive than the stratified squamous epithelium of the vagina. In uteri of rabbits exposed to 2000 r shortly after birth, all coats of the uterus show some degeneration in a few hours and the organ atrophies (Gricouroff, 1930). But starting with the fifth day, mitoses reappear and the organ continues to grow like that of controls, although regression of the ovaries persists.

It is noteworthy that the male keeps its secondary sex characters after irradiation (Ancel and Bouin, 1907) whereas the whole female sex apparatus atrophies. This occurs in practically all mammals except the mouse—in which sterilization of all follicles in very young or adult mice does not prevent later development of estrual cycles (Parkes, 1927).

SKIN

As might be expected from the different tissues that enter its structure, the changes in the skin following irradiation vary considerably with the

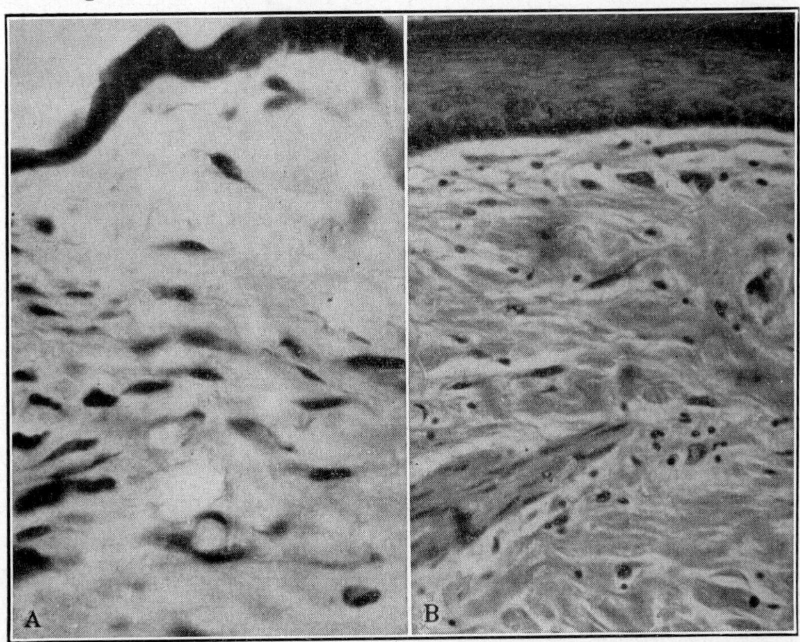

Fig. 17-6. (*A*) Section through ear of mouse 24 hours after 5000 rep of external β rays. The epidermis is of normal thickness, the derma is slightly edematous; 325×. (*B*) Lumbar skin 56 days after 12,000 rep of external β rays. The epidermis is greatly thickened and the derma still shows some infiltration with inflammatory cells. This thickening of the epithelium is typical of regeneration after severe injury to skin. Hair follicles are absent, although there is a portion of the smooth muscle of a hair in the lower left-hand part of the section; 210×. (*After Snider*, 1948.)

histological constitution of the several parts of the organ. One group of changes occurs in the epidermis with its stratified squamous epithelium and its derivatives, the hair and associated sebaceous glands, the sweat glands, and the nails. In the other category of tissues are the vascular connective tissues forming the derma and the subdermal tissues. The smooth muscles of the hair may be included with this group. The analysis of the changes in skin has been complicated by the long latent period in the epidermis and by the fact that most of the human epidermis is more sensitive and thicker than that of the laboratory mammals. This probably explains its exceptional reaction to various chemical and physical injuries; it forms blisters readily, in contrast to the skins of practically all other animals, which do not.

The gross changes in the skin extend from erythema and epilation (and, in some cases, pigmentation in human skin), which result from exposure to 500 to 800 r, to more marked changes with higher dosages, which result in thin, fragile, regenerating epidermis, sclerosis of the derma, and necrosis and ulceration. The extent of the injury to the skin varies with the amount of radiation absorbed (the effect is also greater per roentgen of soft X rays), with the animal species, with different individuals of the same species, and even with different areas on the body of the same individual. This last difference is important when using erythema as a criterion of dosage.

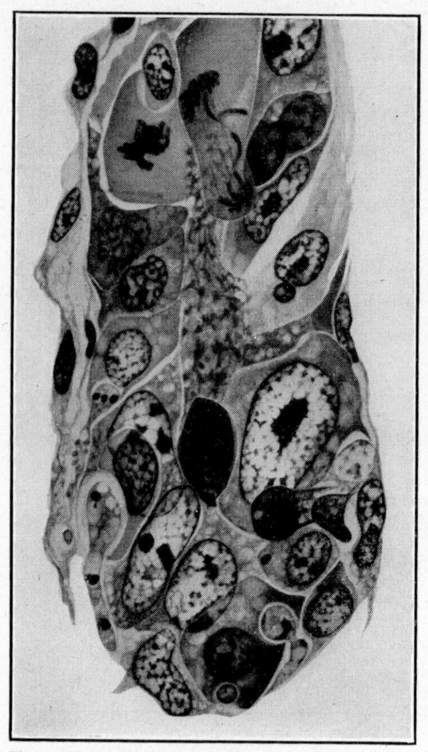

FIG. 17-7. Section of base of crypt from a duodenum of art exposed 28 hours previously to 600 r of 200-kv X rays, total-body irradiation. There is still much debris among the cells in the crypt epithelium and several mitoses indicative of beginning regeneration. There are also enormously swollen cells considerably larger than the normal cells. 1270×. (*After Pierce*, 1948.) Drawn by Esther Bohlman.

Epithelium. The first change to be seen after irradiation with doses up to several hundred roentgens is a temporary cessation of mitosis in the lower layers of the epithelium. It has even been claimed that with 35 r the mitoses in the epidermis of the mouse ear are markedly decreased (Knowlton and Hempelmann, 1949). Two to 6 or 8 days after 300 r in human skin, there are clumped chromosomes and some atypical mitoses and the debris of mitoses. No more dividing cells are found until about the twentieth day. Usually there are only a few binucleate cells. From 20 to 40 days there is a variable amount of nuclear polymorphism, with large and small cells and occasional binucleate cells (Miescher, 1938). The mitoses now are of normal appearance and the epidermis is not thickened.

Exposure of human skin to 600 to 1200 r produces some degeneration of cells of the germinative layer. With these larger doses the number of mitoses becomes very small after 5 or 6 days and many of the dividing cells are degenerate. During the second and third weeks many of the cells seem shrunken. In the succeeding weeks the polymorphism of the cells becomes greater, and many of the cells appear swollen and poorly stained. The epidermis shrinks to two or three layers of cells beneath the cornified layer. If the epidermis is not completely destroyed, a period of mitotic activity may set in (fifth to eighth week). From this time on the epidermis is composed of normal appearing cells. With still larger doses this layer degenerates, and consequently after several weeks the entire epidermis in the irradiated area has been destroyed. This epidermal degeneration has been claimed to be the result of destruction of dividing cells. More properly, it is the expression of injury to resting cells which becomes apparent only when the cells divide some time later. After complete degeneration of the epidermis, regeneration is said to occur mainly, if not exclusively, by ingrowth of epithelium from the surrounding uninjured epidermis. In laboratory animals exposed to intense or prolonged doses of external β rays, regeneration is helped also by proliferation of those hair follicles which are not destroyed by these shallow penetrating rays. The regenerating epidermis is often thin and very susceptible to mechanical and other injuries. This friable epidermis may persist for some years. After long-continued irradiation and a long latent period, it has been the source of malignant tumors, particularly following the softer X rays used so extensively in the early days of radiology.

Derma. A dose of 600 to 800 r total-body irradiation in laboratory animals calls forth an exceedingly mild inflammatory reaction characterized by slight hyperemia, a very low-grade migration of heterophil leukocytes and lymphocytes, some destruction of mast cells, and a barely perceptible edema by 24 hours (Lacassagne and Gricouroff, 1941; Schinz and Slotopolsky, 1925; Snider, 1948a).

In man an erythema due to dilatation of the blood vessels is elicited with 600 to 700 r of hard X rays over relatively small areas. The erythema appears in the first day or so, lasts for a few days, and disappears, to reappear on or about the eleventh day. This second erythema lasts three or four weeks and gradually merges into a stage of pigmentation of the skin (Ellinger, 1941).

With larger doses the inflammatory changes are more marked and persist longer. After repeated exposures, giant fibroblasts may be found many months later (Maximow, 1923). Perhaps the most important effects are on the blood vessels, which show marked arteriolar changes. It is claimed that with doses up to 1200 r the vascular changes are reversible, but that with higher doses permanent damage to endothelium and especially to the smooth muscle and elastic fibers results. The swollen or vacuolated endothelial cells may form tufts extending into the lumen.

and endothelial proliferation may be so marked as to occlude the vessels (Wolbach, 1909). Some of the small vessels may be closed by thrombi. Multinucleated endothelial cells in the derma one year after an erythema dose and arteriolar change a year and a half after the same dose in human skin have been described. Some of the dilated vessels may persist for years. An important observation is that some vessels always seem undamaged. After injection of radium, the endothelial cells may calcify and there may be calcification of the walls of small vessels (Rhoades, 1948b). Although vascular radiation lesions are well established, some believe that their importance as the cause of many of the changes observed in various irradiated organs has been exaggerated (Lacassagne and Gricouroff, 1941). These critics believe that the part played by obliterating arteritis in radionecrosis has not been proved; they hold, rather, that transformations of extracellular substances of the connective tissue and associated infection are much more important factors in the pathogenesis of this process.

Some of the changes in the derma, especially in laboratory animals, may be secondary to infections resulting from denudation of the derma with ulcer formation.

The late effect in the derma is progressive sclerosis, resulting from the inflammatory changes and characterized by hyalinization of the collagen and loss of elastic fibers. These changes, coupled with, and perhaps in part responsible for, the long-persisting, incomplete regeneration of the epidermis, leave the skin highly susceptible to further injury.

A quite different picture is called forth in the connective tissue by the local injection of those radioactive isotopes which adhere to collagen, such as plutonium and Y^{91}. In such areas the inflammatory reaction persists for weeks or months, but is atypical in that there is a continued emigration from the vessels of granular and nongranular leukocytes, which are apparently killed shortly after leaving the vessels. Consequently, there is no flooding of the field with small, medium-sized, and large inflammatory macrophages, which in ordinary inflammations develop from the nongranular leukocytes of the blood. The local macrophages (histiocytes), which are relatively few for an inflamed tissue, do not divide by mitosis but become enormously swollen and very basophilic; they do not degenerate. The local fibroblasts likewise become swollen but show no evidence of death. It is undoubtedly the continued irradiation which is responsible for the failure of a typical inflammatory reaction to develop around radium needles.

EPIDERMAL DERIVATIVES

Hair. It has been known for a long time that irradiation of the skin causes destruction of the hair follicles and falling out of the hair. In man this may be temporary, appearing in about three weeks with doses of 400 to 500 r of 200-kv X rays, but becoming permanent with 700 r or more (Shields Warren, 1942, 1943). There are marked species differences in this respect, the laboratory mammals requiring about 2000 r or more of X rays to produce permanent epilation (Ellinger, 1941).

After temporary epilation in animals the hair may grow back white in regions where previously it was pigmented (Hance and Murphy, 1926). It has also been reported that regenerating hairs in man may be darker. After a dose of radiation producing permanent epilation, the hair follicles show vacuolation, cessation of mitosis, and focal necrosis. This is sometimes associated with a slight polymorphonuclear and mononuclear infiltration, but there is generally no intense leukocytic infiltration.

During the first month the smooth muscles of the hairs increase in size with some vacuolar degeneration (Wolbach, 1909), followed by increasing atrophy, ultimately often disappearing completely.

Nails. Occasional damage to finger nails has been reported.

Skin Glands. The sebaceous glands are also highly sensitive, reduction of their secretion beginning 5 or 6 days after exposure (Ellinger, 1941). Usually one month after a dose of radiation causing permanent epilation few sebaceous glands will be visible, and those persisting frequently show some peripheral keratinization as well as accentuation of the basement membrane. It is also claimed that the sebaceous glands are destroyed in three to four weeks with a dose of 1200 r (Borak, 1936). The sebaceous glands tend to persist longer than the hair follicles but not quite so long as the sweat glands.

The sweat glands are said to be as sensitive as are the hair follicles (Flaskamp, 1930), a dose that produces temporary epilation decreasing temporarily or inhibiting completely the secretion of sweat. There are other reports which indicate that 2500 r is required to destroy these glands (Borak, 1936). In the first few days vacuolar degeneration of the epithelium is prominent, sometimes leading to great distinctness of so-called "myoepithelial cells." About a month after irradiation, the basement membrane is doubled or quadrupled in thickness, the lumens of the glands have practically disappeared, and the connective tissue adjacent to the coils is increased in amount and hyalinized. Later the sweat glands may disappear completely.

Mammary Gland. The duct system of the mammary gland, which constitutes the epithelium of the resting organ, seems to be markedly radioresistant. It has been reported that 2800 to 3600 r is necessary to prevent the development of secretory acini in the rabbit (Turner and Gomez, 1936). A dose of 720 r applied during the middle of pregnancy inhibits the subsequent ability of the epithelium to secrete milk. Lactation is completely suppressed after 2800 r, and this will persist through succeeding pregnancies.

GASTROINTESTINAL SYSTEM

There are marked variations in the radiosensitivity of the several types of epithelium lining the various segments of the digestive canal, reflecting differences in their histological constitution. The stratified squamous epithelia lining hollow viscera are about as radiosensitive as the stratified squamous epithelium of the skin (Lacassagne and Gricouroff, 1941). This is presumably due to injury of the cells in the germinative layer of the epithelium with resulting failure to produce new cells to replace those more superficial ones which will be desquamated with or without previous cornification. Those covering epithelia of the digestive system composed of columnar cells are decidedly more resistant than the stratified squamous epithelia. However, this columnar epithelium is provided with areas of less differentiated, germinative cells and these have been found to be relatively radiosensitive.

Associated with the digestive tract are the large salivary glands, the liver, and the pancreas. These show contrasts in reactivity, the liver and pancreas being very difficult to injure by radiation while the salivary glands are somewhat more sensitive.

Mouth, Nasopharynx, and Esophagus. Except in a few areas these cavities are lined with stratified squamous epithelium, and they show, after irradiation, changes similar to those shown by the epidermis. In man complete desquamation and subsequent repair in these mucous membranes occur somewhat earlier than in the skin after comparable doses of radiation, and variations in sensitivity in the mouth, tongue, inner surfaces of the cheeks, and nasopharynx have been described (Coutard, 1922). With larger doses, necrosis of the epithelia and the underlying tissues may result. As in the skin, fragility of the epithelium, marked scarring, and permanently dilated vessels persist. There seem to be no extensive studies on experimental animals.

Stomach and Intestines. Destructive changes in the gastrointestinal tract are noted as early as ½ hour after exposure to a moderately large dose (Pierce, 1948), the damage being greater in the small intestine than in the stomach or colon, greatest in the crypts, most pronounced at 8 hours, and repaired within four weeks. With smaller doses the injury is not so severe and repair is completed earlier, while with larger doses (2000 r to the abdomen of dogs), the intestine may be so greatly damaged as to lead to severe hemorrhages and ulceration with death of the animals (Regaud, Nogier, and Lacassagne, 1912; Stafford L. Warren and Whipple, 1922). There are considerable species differences and unfortunately many of the experiments are not comparable as to dosage and species.

In contrast to the paucity of reports of studies on the upper portions of the digestive tract, there is a voluminous literature on experimental and therapeutic radiation of the stomach. The changes are of two main types: (1) the functional and degenerative morphological changes and subsequent repair occurring shortly after irradiation and (2) the development of gastric ulcers some weeks later.

In rabbits, after total-body irradiation with 800 r of 200-kv X rays, some degenerate cells and absence of mitoses are seen early in the necks of the fundic glands. Mitoses reappear after 17 hours but are not normal until 5 days later. The surface epithelium and the cardiac and pyloric glands are much more resistant. In the fundic glands some of the parietal cells show wrinkling of the nuclear membrane, or pyknosis, and vacuolization of the cytoplasm from 2 hours to 5 days in some cells, but only during the first day in the majority of them. The more severely affected mucous and zymogenic cells show pyknosis for 5 days. Zymogen granules are absent from 2 hours to 5 days, and are, for the most part, irregular in size and number until 9 days (Pierce, 1948). Hemorrhages may occur, especially in the lamina propria (Engelstad, 1938).

There is agreement that irradiation causes a marked decrease in gastric secretion with a great decrease in acidity and relatively little change in pepsin content (Desjardins, 1931). It is noteworthy that in dogs the parietal cells, presumably the source of hydrochloric acid precursors, are not greatly damaged, in contrast to the destructive changes and loss of zymogen granules in the chief cells (Dawson, 1925). This decrease in production of acid after irradiation, which may last for some weeks, is the basis for the treatment of gastric ulcers by large doses of X rays (Palmer and Templeton, 1939). Many but not all authors report a decrease in secretion of gastric mucus.

The production of ulcers of the stomach by irradiation has been noted in man and animals (Delbet *et al.*, 1909; Engelstad, 1938; Ricketts *et al.*, 1949). They develop after a latent period of several weeks or more and usually occur singly along the lesser curvature. They may be shallow or may penetrate all the tunics of the organ and lead to perforation. Scarring and healing of the ulcers may occur after many months. It has been suggested that the failure to heal sooner is due to the inhibition of proliferation of connective tissue cells resulting from irradiation.

There are minor differences of opinion as to the relative sensitivity of the small intestine as compared with other tissues and organs (Friedman, 1942). Part of this absence of unanimity is due to our inability to compare dosages used in much of the experimental material before 1930, to differences in species, and to large gaps in the series of animals reported by many investigators. Nevertheless, the majority of authors agree that the small intestine is more sensitive than the stomach and that it is only slightly more resistant than lymphatic tissue.

Parts of the epithelium of the duodenum of the rabbit, more sensitive to radiation than any other part of the gastrointestinal tract, show marked degenerative changes 30 minutes after exposure to 800 r of X rays (total body) and these sometimes persist for three weeks or longer (Pierce, 1948). At 30 minutes mitosis has ceased and there are varying degrees of nuclear swelling and clumping of the chromatin in all cells of the villous, crypt, and Brunnerian epithelium. Collapsed goblet cells appear to be more numerous than normal. The most extreme damage is in the basal cells of the crypts of Lieberkühn, where nuclear fragmentation and karyolysis are present for some days. Mitotic figures reappear at 21 hours, but until 9 days degenerative changes can be detected in the epithelium. At this time regenerative changes become dominant, as evidenced by disappearance of degenerating cells, the presence of the usual number of mitotic figures, and crowding of the basal crypt cells. The Paneth cells, which have lost their normal staining properties 2 hours after irradiation, show irregular granulation until 9 days.

The epithelium of Brunner's glands, which is apparently more resistant than the villous or crypt epithelium, does not show marked degenerative changes with this dose until the 8-hour interval. However, recovery seems to be less rapid; in some animals the tubules are still distended at 21 days.

After 800 r (total-body) the destructive process in the epithelium of the ileum is less severe but is qualitatively similar to that of the duodenum and recovery is more rapid. Mitotic activity of the crypt epithelium, absent 30 minutes after exposure, is restored at 3 days. Degenerative changes are most marked in the basal crypt cells. There is only very slight nuclear damage in the epithelial cells of the colon and rectum. Increased mucus secretion, which is suggested, is difficult to evaluate because of normal variations in this function. Stafford L. Warren believes that the colon is about as sensitive as the stomach and that the more resistant rectum is about as sensitive as the mouth.

Early effects in the lamina propria are edema and absence of inflammatory cellular reaction. At 2 hours the number of small lymphocytes is reduced, and many of the lymphocytes show degenerative change. However, there is less destruction of lymphoid cells here than in the lymphatic follicles, for many appear to survive. There is a return of lymphocytes and plasma cells after 9 days. The effects on the lymphatic follicles of the ileum and appendix are much like those described in the lymphatic tissue.

After 400 r in the rabbit the damage is qualitatively similar to that produced by 800 r but quantitatively less severe, with fewer cells affected and earlier recovery. One hundred roentgens causes only a depression of mitosis and occasional dead crypt cells. Doses of 50 r or lower produce no effect.

Total-body exposure of rabbits and mice to fast neutrons and of mice to slow neutrons has the same qualitative effect on the intestinal mucosa as total-body X irradiation.

With 80 r of total-body X irradiation per day to mice there is a slight degree of acquired radioresistance so that nuclear debris in the crypts of Lieberkühn, although prominent during the first week, is rarely found from 15 to 35 days (Pierce, 1948). No changes are observed in the intestines of mice exposed daily to 8.8 r of γ rays from radium when examined at from two to sixteen months.

With larger doses (2000 to 2500 r) over the abdomen of dogs much more drastic changes are produced (Stafford L. Warren and Whipple, 1922). Within a few days the entire epithelium of crypts and villi is destroyed and sloughed off. The intestine is inflamed and hemorrhages are extensive. There is bloody diarrhea and the animals soon die. Rats and guinea pigs are slightly more sensitive than dogs, cats, or rabbits (Stafford L. Warren, 1936). It has also been found that ulceration of the small intestine may result after two or three weeks (Martin and Rogers, 1924).

Internally administered radioactive isotopes affect the gastrointestinal epithelium in the same way as do X rays, although some differences are notable (Pierce, 1948). Radium and plutonium seem to cause more nuclear swelling than the β and γ emitters. With most of the parenterally administered isotopes there is no massive destruction of the epithelium, as after a single 800-r dose of X rays. However, Zr^{93}-Cb^{93}, injected intracardially, causes marked destructive lesions throughout the small intestine, resulting in extensive areas of sloughed epithelium. Parenterally administered Na^{24} and Ba^{140}-La^{140} also cause severe damage to the gastrointestinal mucosa, notably during the first two weeks following treatment, while P^{32} (2.5 μc/g) produces moderate damage, Y^{91} (2.0 μc/g) produces less, and Sr^{89} (3.6 μc/g) still less. Changes in the gastrointestinal tract following administration of the α emitters occur at later intervals and with lower doses than with the β emitters.

The effects of Y^{91}, Sr^{89}, and fission-products mixture, administered by gavage, vary with the dose level and length of interval during which the agent may act. Large doses (23 to 33 μc/g) of fission-products mixture cause extreme necrosis of the mucosa in rats, most marked in the lower ileum and colon. Smaller single doses of fission-products mixture or of Y^{91} or daily doses of Y^{91} as high as 2 μc/g for three months cause minimal changes.

Salivary Glands. Damage to salivary glands has resulted from therapeutic irradiation of surrounding tissues. Functionally this is manifested by a marked decrease in secretion of saliva (Bergonié and Spéder, 1911; Ivy *et al.*, 1923). Histologically it has been found that the serous cells are more sensitive than the mucous (although the reverse is held by Lazarus-Barlow to be the case after exposure to radium) and both of these more sensitive than duct epithelium (Salis, 1924). After severe irradiation there is interstitial fibrosis of the organs. Desjardins, 1928, reviewing the literature, states that the salivary glands are exceptionally sensitive to irradiation. Presumably this is in comparison with other glands. Systematic studies in laboratory animals seem to be lacking.

Liver. The liver is markedly radioresistant, although there are reports of minor cytological changes. The most extensive and closely spaced work as to time intervals and dosage is by Pohle and Bunting who exposed the livers of adult rats to 600 to 2500 r at 100 and at 140 kv and studied them at daily intervals for a month. Necrosis was not seen in any liver. Minute cytoplasmic hydropic and fatty changes have been reported, including temporary atrophy of liver cells, but such changes may not have been due to irradiation. Hepatic cells may become necrotic after a dose of 1880 to 5250 r of unfiltered X rays to the exposed liver of dogs (Bollinger and Inglis, 1933) and after intravenous thorotrast, which lodges in Kupffer cells.

An unusual change results from the persistence of plutonium and yttrium in liver (Rhoades, 1948a). Enormous liver cells with budding nuclei are present after some months, and many of the dividing nuclei are clearly polyploid. Irradiation of regenerating liver in rats likewise causes marked chromosomal aberrations (Brues and Rietz, 1951).

Gall Bladder and Biliary Passages. No changes were found in the biliary epithelium after 2500 r of X rays (Pohle and Bunting, 1932). The few who have examined the gall bladder believe it is definitely more resistant than the intestine.

Pancreas. Both exocrine and endocrine portions of the pancreas are markedly radioresistant. The hypoglycemia reported after irradiation of the pancreatic region is probably not due to effects on the pancreas. The claim that irradiation of exteriorized portions of the pancreas in rabbits causes degeneration of the organ with 750 r and scarring after 1000 r (Seino, 1937) is not consonant with the other reports in the literature. In our own experience with 800 r total-body irradiation (200 kv) in rabbits and 1000 r in chickens there is no effect.

URINARY SYSTEM

Kidney. Total-body irradiation of rabbits and rats with 800 or 600 r of 200-kv X rays does not produce visible renal changes (W. Bloom, 1948c), although there are contradictory reports in the literature. On the whole, it seems that doses higher than 2000 r are necessary to produce damage to the nephron. The proximal convolution is reported to be the most sensitive portion, and with doses above 3000 r vascular damage produces secondary renal effects (Stafford L. Warren and Whipple, 1922). It is also claimed that the kidney is more sensitive than muscle (Desjardins, 1924).

Radioactive isotopes lodging in the kidney, with the possible exception of radium, have not been found to produce renal damage.

Urinary Bladder. There are but few reports on the reaction of this organ to irradiation. The epithelium is resistant, although with high doses used in man for therapy of lesions in neighboring organs, desquamation of epithelium has been observed. The most marked changes involve the connective tissue in which there is an early transient erythema and a second erythema occurring some three or four weeks later. Ulceration of the mucosa has been reported. Experimental studies are needed.

RESPIRATORY SYSTEM

The minute structure of the respiratory portion of the normal mammalian (and avian) lung is one of the unsolved problems of normal histology. The problem revolves around the delineation of the structures intervening between the vast network of blood vessels carrying blood for aeration and the air spaces. Linked with these histological uncertainties are the difficulties of analyzing mild changes resulting from any irritation and the frequent occurrence of inflammation in the lungs of laboratory animals and man. The analysis is further complicated by the relative radioresistance of the organ, it being decidedly less sensitive than any hematopoietic organ, and by the intervention of a latent period of two or three weeks. Part of the divergence of opinion in the literature has resulted from differences in the intervals between divided doses.

Just as an erythema dose delivered to the skin has a slight transient effect, so an equivalent dose delivered to the lung has a definite, though again a transient, effect. Severe damage to the lung, however, usually occurs only after the repeated doses of radiation customary for therapy, radiation pneumonitis being a frequent complication of such treatment.

In an extensive study on rabbits receiving 1500 to 9000 r Engelstad (1934) described four main stages in the pulmonary reaction:

1. An initial period with acute degenerative changes in the lymphatic tissue of the lung, increased mucus production in the conducting passages, hyperemia, and some edema with mild leukocytic infiltration in the stroma and respiratory portion. The first changes begin 2 hours after irradiation.
2. A latent period of two to three weeks.
3. Principal reaction with degenerative changes in the bronchial epithelium and acute bronchopneumonic changes about the bronchi and blood vessels. There is also a great increase in alveolar macrophages, often forming giant cells. This stage may last one to two months and gradually regresses.
4. Predominantly regenerative stage with proliferation of connective tissue, with sclerosis (at times with bone formation) and slight proliferation of bronchial epithelium.

The process may still be continuing six months after irradiation. With subepidermicidal doses the changes are mild although some fibrosis is left. Epidermicidal doses produce extensive sclerosis, often with bone formation. Such doses are often lethal. The time-intensity factor is important, since with fractionation and protracted dosing the changes are less. As the pulmonary vessels were found to react strongly to pharmacodynamic drugs in these animals, Engelstad does not believe that the primary action is on the blood vessels. Cartilage in the conducting passages is radioresistant to these doses. The bronchial epithelium shows great abnormalities, and often becomes stratified and even cornified. The pleura is resistant.

These findings have been amplified by Shields Warren and Gates (1940) in studies on a variety of species, including man. They describe the first change as swelling of cells lining the alveoli and atria. These cells may not become larger than macrophages although they may show some anaplasia, especially in man. In man, but only infrequently in animals, a hyaline membrane is prominent in influenzal and other pneumonic lesions, including irritant gas poisoning. After irradiation this membrane is usually seen close to the alveolar wall in alveoli which are distended and usually free of exudate. The membrane is not fibrin; it is probably an increased and condensed amorphous ground substance. Later, some splitting of elastic fibers occurs. Bronchial epithelium, in contrast to that of alveoli, is relatively stable. There may be some increase in mucous cells. The columnar cells become cuboidal, often with loss of cilia, but do not become stratified columnar. Bronchiolar epithelium is probably as sensitive as that of the alveolar wall. The increase in size and fusion of epithelial cells noted in animals do not occur in man. These investigators conclude: "Epithelial anaplasia, alveolar and bronchial, ruptured and reduplicated elastica, and hyaline membrane lining alveoli, combined, we have seen in no other disease process. The first two of this triad are seen in irradiated skin. The third occurs rarely in a variety of inflammatory conditions in the lung . . . " (Shields Warren and Gates, 1940).

Both post-mortem and experimental data have proved that the roentgenologic pictures and clinical symptoms usually represent transitory changes, which are generally harmless. In the late reaction, thickening of alveolar walls, patchy atelectasis, and vascular change are outstanding, but the more acute change may be present also. Fibrosis, though often present, has not been established as a radiation effect independent of intercurrent infection. There is some reason for thinking that most pleural fibrosis is a result of infection rather than injury from irradiation; the mesothelium is radioresistant. There is some clinical and experimental evidence that inflammation of the lung may render its tissues more sensitive to radiation (Shields Warren and Gates, 1940).

NERVOUS SYSTEM

The nervous tissue of adult animals seems to be very resistant to injury by irradiation (Shields Warren, 1942, 1943; Stafford L. Warren, 1936). As might be expected, the nervous system of embryos and of newborn animals does suffer severe damage, even after the period of multiplication of cells is over (Snider, 1948b). The sheath and satellite cells seem to be more sensitive than the neurons in the autonomic nervous system of young chicks.

EYE

Shortly after the discovery of X rays it was found that irradiation produces a severe inflammation of the conjunctiva, and by 1908 it was reported that cataracts very probably could be caused by irradiation (Birch-Hirschfeld, 1908). Since then many studies have been made on this subject and those before 1942 have been thoroughly reviewed (Poppe, 1942). It has been shown that 250 r produces permanent damage to this organ in the rabbit (Poppe, 1942). All authors agree on the long latent period required at approximately this dosage—as long as five to ten years in man and at least five months in rabbits. Neutrons seem to be especially effective in producing cataracts (Evans, 1947). All mice exposed to long-continued external β rays become blind owing to opacities of the eye, presumably in the lens (Zirkle, personal communication).

ENDOCRINE GLANDS

Adrenal. The adrenal glands are among the more resistant organs, and the reports of experiments involving them are unusually contradictory (Desjardins, 1928; Shields Warren, 1942, 1943). This is in part due to the extreme variations in the structure of the gland from species to species and from animal to animal, and even in the same animal in different physiological states.

In rabbits no histological changes are found after 1500 r given at one time, but degenerative changes in the cortex develop after higher doses. It has been reported (Engelstad and Torgersen, 1937) that adrenals of rabbits which received a single dose of 2200 to 2500 r of X rays locally show marked degeneration in the cortex, particularly in the zona fasciculata and the zona reticularis, but no irradiation effects in the medulla. An initial transitory hyperemia between 1 and 3 days after treatment is followed by a pronounced degeneration starting at 6 days and accompanied by hyperemia and often slight lymphocytic infiltration. The changes are greatest and most constant three months after irradiation, but are still found at six months. These authors point out a parallelism between a visible skin reaction to X irradiation and noticeable effects on the adrenal cortex. The latent period preceding degenerative changes in both may also be significant. In these experiments the glomerular zone, which is probably the main source of regeneration of the cortex, is not damaged, the changes occurring mainly in the zona fasciculata and zona reticularis. However, some investigators report no changes in the adrenals of rabbits and guinea pigs (Strauss, 1921). In general the medulla seems more resistant than the cortex.

No clear-cut changes have been observed after injection of radioactive isotopes, although some of these, such as plutonium, radium, and Zr^{93}-Cb^{93}, lodge in the organ. After insertion of radium needles, however, necrosis does occur.

Hypophysis. Most of the effects of irradiation in this organ seem to center in the anterior lobe, as degenerative changes in the other portions of the gland have been described only after very heavy irradiation. It is claimed that 3000 to 10,000 r at 180 kv produces a loss of body weight (Fehr, 1936).

The reported hypophyseal changes are very indefinite and are usually described as swelling and increase or decrease of acidophils (Fehr, 1936; Podljaschuk, 1928). Young rats exposed to 2000 to 2500 r have been said to show a reduction of 50 to 75 per cent in these cells and numerous pyknotic nuclei in the chromophils (Lawrence, Nelson, and Wilson, 1937). However, other reports hold that there are no changes in the cells of the hypophysis (Fehr, 1936; Lacassagne and Gricouroff, 1941). Irradiation of the hypophysis of young animals seems to depress the growth and development of the animals.

Larger doses administered over the whole head do not change the histological structure of the anterior hypophysis but are said to produce an increase in its content of thyrotropic and gonadotropic hormones (Grumbrecht *et al.*, 1938).

Thyroid. It is almost universally agreed that the thyroid is moderately radioresistant. Radium implants caused hemorrhage and necrosis of the thyroid (Bower and Clark, 1923). Repeated X irradiation produced no changes with doses lower than those leading to lesions of the skin (Walters, Anson, and Ivy, 1931). Some diminution of hyperplasia was noted in opossums after irradiation (Walters, Anson, and Ivy, 1932).

However, very large amounts of I^{131} are markedly effective in cancer of the thyroid and also in removing symptoms in some cases of hyperthyroidism.

Parathyroid. Little is known of the effects of radiation on the parathyroid.

DISCUSSION

It is of considerable theoretical and practical importance to evaluate the relative radiosensitivities of the different kinds of cells and organs in the body. Many such attempts have been made but all of them are deficient, owing mainly to extensive gaps in available data and to a failure to compare sensitivities for the same end effect. In Table 17-1 are listed the reactions of the cells when compared only for cell death in nearly grown rabbits exposed to 800 r of total-body 200-kv X rays. A similar table for lower doses would show many fewer dead cells. Data are not available for a complete list at double or treble this dose or for localized irradiation of each organ. Such tables do not consider many important questions, such as the time of onset and the rapidity of cell death or the rate of regeneration.

As early as 1906, Bergonié and Tribondeau felt that enough was known to enable them to make some generalizations as to the types of cells readily affected by irradiation: "The greater the reproductive activity of the cells, the longer their mitotic course ('leur devenir karyokinétique'), and the less definitively fixed their morphology and functions, the more intense is the activity of X rays on these cells." This so-called "law" obviously does not apply to the relatively great radioresistance of reticular cells which are more primitive than the free blood-cell-forming cells to which they give rise. Nor does it hold for the radioresistance of primitive ovarian follicular cells as compared with their derivatives, the growing follicular cells which are much more radiosensitive. There are numerous other instances in which this generalization does not hold. In our opinion it should be remembered only as an early attempt to focus attention on the greater susceptibility of growing organs and tissues containing dividing cells as against static ones.

Although it is true that many strains of cells which are actively in division at the time of irradiation are readily and quickly destroyed, and while it is also true that in some cell strains the destructive effects of irradiation become apparent only when the cells later undergo division, the destructive effects of ionizing radiations are not always connected with cellular reproduction. Thus, the small lymphocytes, which practically never divide, are among the most sensitive cells in the body. If those theories of hematopoiesis which hold that lymphocytes are undifferentiated cells are found to be true, then the sensitivity of these cells might be a reflection of their mitotic potential. On the other hand, plasma cells, which are recognized by all to be slightly changed lymphocytes, are exceedingly resistant. Again, spermatocytes are in continuous division (meiosis) and yet are not visibly affected by doses of radiation which will destroy all spermatogonia. It is thus clear that mitosis per se is not a prime factor determining radiosensitivity.

As is well known, small amounts of radiation may have no visible effect on the mature sex cells, and yet striking developmental changes may appear in the progeny. These effects are usually lethal mutations or malformations. Perhaps similar results may occur in somatic cells in

Table 17-1. Viability of Cells of Nearly Grown Rabbit after Total-body Irradiation with 800 r of 200-kv X Rays

All or Most Cells Die	Many or Some Cells Die	No Cells Die
Erythroblasts	Leukocytes (?)	Erythrocytes
Lymphocytes (all sizes)	Monocytes (?)	Fibroblasts
Myeloblasts (all sizes)		Reticular cells
Myelocytes		Macrophages
Thymocytes	Mast cells	Pigment cells
Megakaryocytes		Fat cells
		Plasma cells
		Endothelium
		Mesothelium
		Striated muscle
		Cardiac muscle
		Smooth muscle
		Neurons and neuroglia
Lens fibers		Retina
	Osteoblasts and osteocytes of growing bone	Osteocytes of mature bone
		Osteoclasts
	Cells of growing cartilage	Cells of resting cartilage
		Sertoli cells
Spermatogonia		Spermatocytes (?)
		Spermatids
		Spermia
Primitive ova	Mature ova	Interstitial cells of testis and ovary
Young growing ova	Growing follicular cells	Follicular epithelium of primitive ova
		Lutein cells
		Fallopian tube
		Endometrium
		Vagina
		Cornea
		Epidermis
		Hair
		Sebaceous gland
		Sudoriferous gland
		Mammary gland
		Esophagus
		Bronchial epithelium
	Cells of gastric pits	Surface epithelium of stomach
	Crypt cells of small intestine	Surface epithelium of intestine
		Hepatic and biliary epithelium
		Pancreatic cells
		Specific cells of all endocrine glands
		Kidney
		Urinary bladder

which no visible changes occur while they are in the resting state, but which do appear as abnormal, often multipolar, mitoses when the cells undergo division, frequently leading to death of the cells. Somatic lethal mutations or chromosome aberrations may perhaps explain the death of cells long after irradiation of their parent cells (Muller, 1950). This may be the explanation of the failure to persist of early regeneration of erythroblasts and myelocytes in the beginning recovery of marrow made aplastic by irradiation. In the latter case it may be that the progeny of the irradiated, but not visibly damaged, reticular cells are destined to develop somatic lethal mutations. Against this suggestion is the fact that attempts at regeneration in this tissue seem to occur in waves, whereas, on the proposed explanation, it should be a continuous process with gradual predominance of those myelopoietic cells which had not been damaged.

The normal hepatic epithelial cell undergoes mitosis only rarely. If a large part of the liver is removed, the remaining liver cells undergo such tremendous mitotic activity that in a few days a large part of the liver is regenerated—this process, as might be expected, being faster in young rats than in older ones. The liver cells normally are markedly resistant to radiation. But the rapidly dividing cells of regenerating liver are easily damaged by radiation, which calls forth great numbers of chromosome aberrations and cells with multipolar mitoses (Brues and Rietz, 1951). It is quite probable that if the liver cells were irradiated sufficiently intensely before partial hepatectomy, the irradiation damage which would become manifest in the regenerating liver would be so extensive as to interfere with or even prohibit the regenerative process.

One cannot speak of the absolute sensitivity of a particular cell type in a complex organism, for the cell in question cannot be dissociated from its environment and its functional state at a given moment. Changes in environment affect its response to irradiation just as changes in its activity also modify its reaction. Examples are seen in the greater sensitivity of lymphocytes in lymphatic nodules compared to those scattered in the lamina propria, or in bone cells of the metaphysis as opposed to the more resistant cells of compact bone. Furthermore, every cell strain becomes more radioresistant in vitro.

The radiosensitivity of an organ is not simply a reflection of the radiosensitivity of certain of its cells, for one organ may have tremendous regenerative capacities while another may not. For instance, blood cell formation may be wiped out from the bone marrow of a femur in a few days after irradiation, but this marrow can regenerate completely from its more radioresistant reticular cells. However, with the same amount of radiation, an area of skin may require weeks to manifest its complete damage and regeneration will come only from surrounding nonirradiated skin; furthermore, the friable skin may persist for years. It is difficult to decide which of these two tissues is the more radiosensitive unless it is stipulated whether one is concerned with acute or chronic injury. Another type of difference is shown after irradiation of ovary and testis. The ovary may be permanently sterilized for the production of ova and thus indirectly of ovarian hormones, while in the testis spermatogenesis can return after complete but temporary sterilization, and the production of androgen is at no time diminished. In fact, in the testis, spermatocytogenesis is relatively radiosensitive and spermiogenesis is radioresistant, but the organ as a whole is potentially radioresistant for both external and internal secretion. A third kind of reaction is that of the lens with its lack of acute damage after moderate irradiation, but which, after a long latent period, may show irreversible cataract formation from such a dose. Thus we must distinguish between acute and chronic radiation effects, and it must be determined in each case whether there is a potential for recovery or not.

In the gonads there is clear-cut evidence of the cumulative effect of repeated small doses of irradiation. A similar but less intense effect has been demonstrated in other organs, as the damage which results from localized radioactive isotopes and as the damage in spleen, thymus, and bone marrow after long-continued (eight to sixteen months) daily doses of 4.4 or 8.8 r per day. Variations on these dose-time relations, as well as the length of recovery periods between exposures, have not been thoroughly studied. In the crypt epithelium of the mouse, repeated daily exposure to 60 or 80 r per day of total-body X rays leads to a definite but small degree of acquired radioresistance (M. A. Bloom, 1950).

There is considerable evidence in favor of an indirect effect of irradiation. The symptoms of "radiation sickness" substantiate strongly the existence of such an effect. From morphological data it would seem that the best evidence rests on the following observations: (1) Radiation elicits a greater response in a particular organ when the same amount is applied to the whole body than when it is applied locally; and (2) local irradiation sometimes produces destructive changes in distant tissues. These conclusions are based on innumerable investigations carried out to study other aspects of radiation, and also on specific studies (Halberstaedter and Ickowicz, 1947; Jolles, 1950; Ssipowsky, 1934–35; Van Dyke and Huff, 1949). For example, in the thymus, pyknosis of the cells is more intense after total-body irradiation than after irradiation of either the superior or inferior part of the body (in each instance, 2000 r of X rays) (Halberstaedter and Ickowicz, 1947). Atrophy of the lead-protected thymus and spleen of rats takes place when other regions of the body are irradiated with several thousand roentgens of X rays (Leblond and Segal, 1942). However, when rats have been adrenalectomized several days before irradiation, this indirect effect on thymus and spleen does not occur. These findings have been corroborated

(Halberstaedter and Ickowicz, 1947). Adrenal hypertrophy and fatty infiltration of the liver, not reported by careful observers after direct irradiation of either the adrenals or liver, are observed as a secondary toxic effect of roentgen rays (Leblond and Segal, 1942).

The importance of the spleen (and other lymphatic organs) in radiation injury is emphasized by experiments in which the LD_{50} for mice was found to be nearly twice as great when the spleen was protected with lead during total-body irradiation as when it was not (Jacobson *et al.*, 1949). Such protection of the spleen during irradiation of the rest of the body not only lengthens the survival time of these mice, but also lessens the injury to their irradiated lymphatic tissues and bone marrow; these show greater powers of regeneration than when the whole body is irradiated (Jacobson *et al.*, 1950)—further evidence of the fact that, whereas the hematopoietic process is very radiosensitive, the hematopoietic organs are potentially radioresistant.

REFERENCES

(Information regarding availability of government reports indicated by an asterisk may be obtained from the Office of Technical Services, Department of Commerce, Washington, D.C.)

Albers-Schönberg, H. E. (1903) Ueber eine bisher unbekannte Wirkung der Röntgenstrahlen auf den Organismus der Tiere. Münch. med. Wochschr., 50: 1859–1860.

Alberti, W., and G. Politzer (1923) Ueber den Einfluss der Roentgenstrahlen auf die Zellteilung. Arch. mikroskop. Anat. Entwicklungsmech., 100: 83–109.

Ancel, P., and P. Bouin (1907) Rayons X et glandes génitales. Presse méd., 15: 228.

Barratt, J. O. W., and G. Arnold (1911–12) Cell changes in the testis due to X-rays. Arch. Zellforsch., 7: 242–276.

Bergonié, J., and E. Speder (1911) Sur quelques formes de réactions précoces après des irradiations Röntgen. Arch. d'électr. méd., 19: 241–251.

——— and L. Tribondeau (1905) Action des rayons X sur le testicule du rat blanc. Compt. rend. soc. biol., 58: 154–158, 678, 1029.

——— and ——— (1906) Interprétation de quelques résultats de la radiothérapie et essai de fixation d'une technique rationelle. Compt. rend. acad. sci., 143: 983–985.

Birch-Hirschfeld, A. (1908) Zur Wirkung der Röntgenstrahlen auf das menschliche Auge. Klin. Monatsbl. Augenheilk., 46: 129–137.

Bisgard, J. D., and H. B. Hunt (1936) Influence of roentgen rays and radium on epiphyseal growth of long bones. Radiology, 26: 56–68.

Bloom, M. A. (1948) Bone marrow, *in* Histopathology of irradiation from external and internal sources, W. Bloom, ed. McGraw-Hill Book Company, Inc., New York, National Nuclear Energy Series, Div. IV, Vol. 22I, Chap. 6.

——— (1950) Acquired radioresistance of the crypt epithelium of the duodenum. Radiology, 55: 104–115.

——— and W. Bloom (1947) Radiosensitivity of erythroblasts. J. Lab. Clin. Med., 32: 654–659.

——— and ——— (1949) Late effects of radium and plutonium on bone. Arch. Path., 47: 494–511.

Bloom, W. (ed.) (1948a) Histopathology of irradiation from external and internal sources. McGraw-Hill Book Company, Inc., New York, National Nuclear Energy Series, Div. IV, Vol. 22I.

Bloom, W. (1948b) The cell, *in* Histopathology of irradiation from external and internal sources. McGraw-Hill Book Company, Inc., New York, National Nuclear Energy Series, Div. IV, Vol. 22I, Chap. 3.

——— (1948c) The kidney, *in* Histopathology of irradiation from external and internal sources. McGraw-Hill Book Company, Inc., New York, National Nuclear Energy Series, Div. IV, Vol. 22I, Chap. 14.

——— (1948d) The ovary, *in* Histopathology of irradiation from external and internal sources. McGraw-Hill Book Company, Inc., New York, National Nuclear Energy Series, Div. IV, Vol. 22I, Chap. 13.

——— (1949) Deposition of C^{14} in the metaphysis of long bones of young rats. Anat. Record, 103: 425.

Bollinger, A., and K. Inglis (1933) Experimental liver disease produced by X-ray irradiation of the exposed organ. J. Path. Bact., 36: 19–30.

Borak, J. (1936) The radiation biology of the cutaneous glands. Radiology, 27: 651–655.

Bower, J. O., and J. H. Clark (1923) The resistance of the thyroid gland to the action of radium rays. The results of experimental implantation of radium needles in the thyroid of dogs. Am. J. Roentgenol. Radium Therapy, 10: 632–643.

Brooks, B., and H. T. Hillstrom (1933) Effect of roentgen rays on bone growth and bone regeneration. Am. J. Surg., 20: 599–614.

Brues, A. M., and L. Rietz (1951) Effect of external and internal radiation on cell division. Ann. N.Y. Acad. Sci., 51: 1497–1507.

Colwell, H A. (1935) The method of action of radium and X-rays on living tissues. Oxford University Press, London.

Copp, D. H., D. J. Axelrod, and J. Hamilton (1946) The deposition of radioactive metals in bone as a potential health hazard. USAEC Report MDDC-455.*

———, D. M. Greenberg, and J. Hamilton (1946) Deposition of plutonium and certain fission products in bone as a decontamination problem. USAEC Report AECD-2483.*

Coutard, H. (1922) Sur les delais d'apparition et d'évolution des reactions de la peau et des muqueuses de la bouche et du pharynx provoquées par les rayons X. Compt. rend. soc. biol., 86: 1140–1142.

Dawson, A. B. (1925) Histological changes in the gastric mucosa (Pavlov pouch) of the dog following irradiation. Am. J. Roentgenol., 13: 320–326.

De Bruyn, P. P. H. (1948) Lymph node and intestinal lymphatic tissue, *in* Histopathology of irradiation from external and internal sources, W. Bloom, ed. McGraw-Hill Book Company, Inc., New York, National Nuclear Energy Series, Div. IV, Vol. 22I, Chap. 8.

Delbet, P., A. Herrenschmidt, and P. Mocquot (1909) Action du radium sur l'estomac. Bull. assoc. franc. étude cancer, 2: 103–119.

Desjardins, A. U. (1924) The reaction of abdominal tumors to radiation. J. Am. Med. Assoc., 83: 109–113.

——— (1926) The reaction of the pleura and lungs to roentgen rays. Am. J. Roentgenol. Radium Therapy, 16: 444–453.

——— (1928) The effect of irradiation on the suprarenal gland. Am. J. Roentgenol. Radium Therapy, 19: 453–461.

——— (1931) Action of roentgen rays and radium on the gastrointestinal tract. Am. J. Roentgenol. Radium Therapy, 26: 145–190, 335–370, 493–510.

Duggar, B. M. (ed.) (1936) Biological effects of radiation. McGraw-Hill Book Company, Inc., New York.

Dunlap, C. E. (1942) Effects of radiation on blood and hematopoietic tissues, including the spleen, the thymus, and the lymph nodes, *in* S. Warren, Effects of radiation on normal tissues. Arch. Path., 34: 562–608.

——— (1948) Effects of radiation, *in* W. A. D. Anderson, Textbook of pathology. The C. V. Mosby Company, Medical Publishers, St. Louis.

Duryee, W. R. (1949) The nature of radiation injury to amphibian cell nuclei. J. Natl. Cancer Inst., 10: 735–796.

Ellinger, F. (1941) The biological fundamentals of radiation therapy. Elsevier Publishing Co., Inc., New York (trans. by R. Gross).

Engelstad, R. B. (1934) Ueber die Wirkung der Röntgenstrahlen auf die Lungen. Acta Radiol., Suppl. 19, pp. 1–93.

——— (1938) The effect of roentgen rays on the stomach in rabbits. Am. J. Roentgenol. Radium Therapy, 40: 243–263.

——— and O. Torgersen (1937) Experimental investigations on the effects of roentgen rays on the suprarenal glands in rabbits. Acta Radiol., 18: 671–687.

Eschenbrenner, A. B. (1946) Biological effects of long-continued whole-body γ irradiation on mice, guinea pigs, and rabbits. V. Pathological effects of γ radiation. USAEC Report CH-3644.*

Evans, T. C. (1947) Effects of small daily doses of fast neutrons on mice. USAEC Report MDDC-1450.*

Ewing, J. (1926) Radiation osteitis. Acta Radiol., 6: 399–412.

Failla, G., and K. Sugiura (1939) Experimental results supporting the "fluid flow" theory of the biological action of ionizing radiations. Science, 89: 438.

Fehr, A. (1936) Experimentelle Röntgenbestrahlung der Hypophyse bei Kaninchen. Schweiz. med. Wochschr., 17: 289–291.

Flaskamp, W. (1930) Ueber Roentgenschäden und Schäden durch radioaktive Substanzen, *in* H. Meyer, Sonderbände zur Strahlentherapie. Urban & Schwarzenberg, Berlin, Vol. 12, pp. 1–354.

Fogg, L. C., and Shields Warren (1937) A comparison of the cytoplasmic changes induced in the Walker rat carcinoma 256 by different types and dosages of radiation. I. Golgi apparatus. II. Mitochondria. Am. J. Cancer, 31: 567–577, 578–585.

Friedman, N. B. (1942) Effects of radiation on the gastrointestinal tract, including the salivary glands, the liver, and the pancreas, *in* S. Warren, Effects of radiation on normal tissues. Arch. Path., 34: 749–787.

Gates, O. (1943) Effects on bone, cartilage and teeth, *in* S. Warren, Effects of radiation on normal tissues. Arch. Path., 35: 323–340.

Giese, A. C. (1947) Radiations and cell division. Quart. Rev. Biol., 22: 253–282.

Gricouroff, G. (1930) Étude histologique de l'action des rayons X sur l'ovaire à la période d'ovogenèse. Radiophysiol. et radiothérapie, 2: 1–80.

Grumbrecht, P., F. Keller, and A. Loeser (1938) Die Wirkung von Röntgenstrahlen auf Struktur und Funktion des Hypophysenvorderlappens. Klin. Wochschr., 17: 801–805.

Halberstaedter, L. (1905) Die Einwirkung der Roentgenstrahlen auf Ovarien. Berlin. klin. Wochschr., 42: 64–66.

——— and A. Back (1942) The effect of X-rays on single colonies of *Pandorina*. Brit. J. Radiology, 15: 124–128.

——— and M. Ickowicz (1947) The effects of X-rays on the lymphatic organs of normal and adrenalectomized rats. Radiologia clinica, 16: 240–257.

Hance, R. T., and J. B. Murphy (1926) Studies on X-ray effects. XV. The prevention of pigment formation in the hair follicles of colored mice with high-voltage X-ray. J. Exptl. Med., 44: 339–342.

Heineke, H. (1903) Ueber die Einwirkung der Röntgenstrahlen auf Tiere. Münch. med. Wochschr., 50: 2090–2092.

Heller, M. (1948a) Bone, *in* Histopathology of irradiation from external and internal sources, W. Bloom, ed. McGraw-Hill Book Company, Inc., New York, National Nuclear Energy Series, Div. IV, Vol. 22I, Chap. 5.

——— (1948b) The testis, *in* Histopathology of irradiation from external and internal sources, W. Bloom, ed. McGraw-Hill Book Company, Inc., New York, National Nuclear Energy Series, Div. IV, Vol. 22I, Chap. 12.

Henshaw, P. S. (1938) The action of X-rays on nucleated and non-nucleated egg fragments. Am. J. Cancer, 33: 258–264.

Hinkel, C. L. (1942) The effect of roentgen rays upon the growing long bones of albino rats. I. Quantitative studies of the growth limitation following irradiation. Am. J. Roentgenol. Radium Therapy, 47: 439–457.

Ivy, A. C., B. H. Orndoff, A. Jacoby, and J. E. Whitlow (1923) Studies of the effect of X-rays on glandular activity. J. Radiology, 4: 189–199.

Jacobson, L. O., E. K. Marks, M. J. Robson, E. Gaston, and R. E. Zirkle (1949) The effect of spleen protection on mortality following X-irradiation. J. Lab. Clin. Med., 34: 1538–1543.

———, E. L. Simmons, W. F. Bethard, E. K. Marks, and M. J. Robson (1950) The influence of the spleen on hematopoietic recovery after irradiation injury. Proc. Soc. Exptl. Biol. Med., 73: 455–459.

Jolles, B. (1950) The reciprocal vicinity effect of irradiated tissues on a "diffusible substance" in irradiated tissues. Brit. J. Radiology, 23: 18–24.

Kemp, T., and J. Juul (1930) Influence of various agents (X-rays, radium, heat, ether) upon mitosis in tissue cultures. Acta Path. Microbiol. Scand., 7: 279–308.

Knowlton, N. P., and L. H. Hempelmann (1949) The effect of X-rays on the mitotic activity of the adrenal gland, jejunum, lymph node, and epidermis of the mouse. J. Cellular Comp. Physiol., 33: 73–91.

Lacassagne, A. (1913) Étude histologique et physiologique des effets produits sur l'ovaire par les rayons X. Thèse fac. méd. Lyon.

——— and G. Gricouroff (1941) Actions des radiations sur les tissus. Masson et Cie, Paris.

Lawrence, J. H., W. O. Nelson, and H. Wilson (1937) Roentgen irradiation of the hypophysis. Radiology, 29: 446–454.

——— and R. Tennant (1937) The comparative effects of neutrons and X-rays on the whole body. J. Exptl. Med., 66: 667–687.

Leblond, C. P., and G. Segal (1942) Differentiation between the direct and indirect effects of roentgen rays upon the organs of normal and adrenalectomized rats. Am. J. Roentgenol. Radium Therapy, 47: 302–306.

Liebow, A. A., Shields Warren, and E. DeCoursey (1949) Pathology of atomic bomb casualties. Am. J. Path., 25: 853–1027.

Lorenz, E., *et al.* (1953) Biologic effects of long-continued whole-body gamma irradiation on mice, guinea pigs, and rabbits. McGraw-Hill Book Company, Inc., New York, National Nuclear Energy Series, Div. IV, Vol. 22B.

——— and W. E. Heston (1953) Biologic effects of long-continued whole body gamma irradiation on mice, guinea pigs, and rabbits. Part I. Preliminary experiments. National Nuclear Energy Series, Div. IV, Vol. 22B.

———, ———, L. O. Jacobson, A. B. Eschenbrenner, M. Shimkin, M. Deringer, and J. Doniger (1953) Biological effects of long-continued whole body gamma irradiation on mice, guinea pigs, and rabbits. Part III. Effects on life span weight, blood picture, carcinogenesis, and the role of the intensity of radiation. National Nuclear Energy Series, Div. IV, Vol. 22B.

Martin, C. L., and F. T. Rogers (1924) Roentgen-ray cachexia. Am. J. Roentgenol. Radium Therapy, 11: 280–286.

Martland, H. S. (1931) The occurrence of malignancy in radioactive persons. Am. J. Cancer, 15: 2435–2516.

Maximow, A. (1923) Studies on the changes produced by roentgen rays in inflamed connective tissue. J. Exptl. Med., 37: 319–340.

——— and W. Bloom (1948) Textbook of histology. W. B. Saunders Company, Philadelphia.

Miescher, G. (1938) Vergleichende Untersuchungen zur Frage der Spezifität der Röntgenwirkung, Licht-, Wärme-, Röntgen-, und Thorium-X-Reaktion. Strahlentherapie, 61: 4–37.

Muller, H. J. (1950) Radiation damage to the genetic material. Part II. Effects manifested mainly in the exposed individuals. Am. Scientist, 38: 399–425.

Murray, J. M. (1931) A study of the histological structure of mouse ovaries following exposure to roentgen irradiation. Am. J. Roentgenol. Radium Therapy, 25: 1–45.

Murray, R. G. (1948a) The spleen, *in* Histopathology of irradiation from external and internal sources, W. Bloom, ed. McGraw-Hill Book Company, Inc., New York, National Nuclear Energy Series, Div. IV, Vol. 22I, Chap. 7.

——— (1948b) The thymus, *in* Histopathology of irradiation from external and internal sources, W. Bloom, ed. McGraw-Hill Book Company, Inc., New York, National Nuclear Energy Series, Div. IV, Vol. 22I, Chap. 9.

Packard, C. (1931) The biological effects of short radiation. Quart. Rev. Biol., 6: 253–280.

Palmer, W. L., and F. Templeton (1939) The effect of radiation therapy on gastric secretion. J. Am. Med. Assoc., 112: 1429–1434.

Pappenheim, A., and J. Plesch (1912) Experimentelle und histologische Untersuchungen über das Prinzip der Thorium-X-Wirkung auf die Organe im allgemeinen und den hämatopoetischen Apparat im besonderen. Folia Haematol., 14: 1–12.

Parkes, A. S. (1927) On the occurrence of the oestrous cycle after X-ray sterilization. Part III. The periodicity of oestrus after sterilization of the adult. Proc. Roy. Soc. London, B101: 421–449.

Perthes, G. (1903) Ueber den Einfluss der Roentgenstrahlen auf epitheliale Gewebe, insbesondere auf das Carcinom. Arch. klin. Chir., 71: 955–1000.

Pierce, M. (1948) The gastrointestinal tract, *in* Histopathology of irradiation from external and internal sources, W. Bloom, ed. McGraw-Hill Book Company, Inc., New York, National Nuclear Energy Series, Div. IV, Vol. 22I, Chap. 10.

Podljaschuk, L. D. (1928) Experimentelle Untersuchungen über die Beziehungen zwischen Hypophyse und anderen innersekretorischen Drüsen. II. Weitere experimentelle Beiträge zur Frage der gegenseitigen Beziehungen zwischen Hypophyse und Genitalapparat. Strahlentherapie, 30: 65–76.

Pohle, E. A., and C. H. Bunting (1932) Studies of the effect of roentgen rays on the liver. Acta Radiol., 13: 117–124.

Poppe, E. (1942) Experimental investigations of the effect of roentgen rays on the eye. Skrifter Norske Videnskaps-Akad. Oslo. I. Mat. Naturv. Klasse, No. 2.

Regaud, C. (1922) Sur la sensibilité du tissu osseux normal vis-a-vis des radiations X et sur le mécanisme de l'ostéo-radio-nécrose. Compt. rend. soc. biol., 87: 629–632.

——— and J. Blanc (1906) Actions des rayons X sur les diverses générations de la lignée spermatique; extrême sensibilité des spermatogonies à ces rayons. Compt. rend. soc. biol., 61: 163–165.

——— and A. Lacassagne (1927) Effets histophysiologiques des rayons de Roentgen et de Becquerel-Curie sur les tissus adultes normaux des animaux supérieurs. Arch. inst. radium, radiophysiol. radiothérapie, Paris, 1: 1 ff.

———, T. Nogier, and A. Lacassagne (1912) Sur les effets redoutable des irradiations étendues de l'abdomen et sur les lésions du tube digestif déterminées par les rayons de Röntgen. Arch. élect. méd., 20 (2): 321–334.

Rhoades, R. P. (1948a) Structures accessory to the gastrointestinal tract, *in* Histopathology of irradiation from external and internal sources, W. Bloom, ed. McGraw-Hill Book Company, Inc., New York, National Nuclear Energy Series, Div. IV, Vol. 22I, Chap. 11.

——— (1948b) The vascular system, *in* Histopathology of irradiation from external and internal sources, W. Bloom, ed. McGraw-Hill Book Company, Inc., New York, National Nuclear Energy Series, Div. IV, Vol. 22I, Chap. 16.

Ricketts, W. E., J. B. Kirsner, E. M. Humphreys, and W. L. Palmer (1949) Effect of roentgen irradiation on the gastric mucosa. Gastroenterology, 11: 818–832.

Salis, H. v. (1924) Zu den Röntgenveränderungen nach Bestrahlung der Gland-Submaxillaries. Strahlentherapie, 17: 395–400.

Schinz, H. R., and B. Slotopolsky (1925) Der Roentgenhoden. Ergeb. med. Strahlenforsch., 1: 443–526.

——— and ——— (1928) Strahlenbiologie der gesunden Haut. Ergeb. med. Strahlenforsch., 3: 583–641.

Schugt, P. (1928) Untersuchungen über die Wirkung abgestufter Dosen von Röntgenstrahlen verschiedener Wellenlänge auf die Struktur und Funktion der Ovarien. Strahlentherapie, 27: 603–662.

Segale, G. C. (1920) Sull' azione biologica dei raggi Röntgen e del radium sulle cartilagini epifisorie. Radiologia medica, 7: 234–246.

Seino, J. (1937) Veränderungen des Pankreas nach Röntgenbestrahlung. Strahlentherapie, 58: 449–463.

Snider, R. S. (1948a) The skin, *in* Histopathology of irradiation from external and internal sources, W. Bloom, ed. McGraw-Hill Book Company, Inc., New York, National Nuclear Energy Series, Div. IV, Vol. 22I, Chap. 4.

——— (1948b) The nervous system, *in* Histopathology of irradiation from external and internal sources. McGraw-Hill Book Company, Inc., New York, National Nuclear Energy Series, Div. IV, Vol. 22I, Chap. 18.

Spargo, B., J. R. Bloomfield, D. Glotzer, E. Gordon, and O. Nichols (1951) Histological effects of long-continued whole-body irradiation of mice. J. Natl. Cancer Inst., 12: 615–655.

Ssipowsky, P. W. (1934–35) Zur Lehre von der direkten und indirekten Wirkung der Röntgenstrahlen. Beitr. path. Anat. u. allgem. Path., 94: 1–19.

Strangeways, T. S. P., and F. L. Hopwood (1926) The effects of X rays upon mitotic cell division in tissue cultures in vitro. Proc. Roy. Soc. London, B100: 283–293.

Strauss, O. (1921) Zum Verhalten des Blutdrucks nach Röntgenbestrahlung. Fortschr. Gebiete Röntgenstrahlen, 28: 467–472.

Tullis, J. L. (1949) The response of tissue to total-body irradiation. Am. J. Path., 25: 829–851.

Turner, C. W., and E. T. Gomez (1936) The radiosensibility of the cells of the mammary gland. Am. J. Roentgenol. Radium Therapy, 36: 79–93.

Van Dyke, D. C., and R. L. Huff (1949) Epilation in nonirradiated member of parabiotically united rats. Proc. Soc. Exptl. Biol. Med., 72: 266–270.

Walters, O. M., B. J. Anson, and A. C. Ivy (1931) The effect of X rays on the thyroid and parathyroid glands. Radiology, 16: 52–58.

———, ———, and ——— (1932) The prevention of hyperplasia of the thyroid in the opossum by X rays. Radiology, 18: 583–591.

Warren, Shields (1942) Effects of radiation on normal tissues. Arch. Path., 34: 1070–1084.

——— (1943) Effects of radiation on normal tissues. Arch. Path., 35: 304–353.

——— (1944) The histopathology of radiation lesions. Physiol. Revs., 24: 225–238.

——— and O. Gates (1940) Radiation pneumonitis. Experimental and pathologic observations. Arch. Path., 30: 440–460.

Warren, Stafford L. (1936) The physiological effects of radiation upon organ and body systems, *in* Biological effects of radiation, B. M. Duggar, ed. McGraw-Hill Book Company, Inc., New York, Chap. 14.

——— and G. H. Whipple (1922) Roentgen ray intoxication. II. A study of the sequence of clinical, anatomical, and histological changes following a unit dose of X-rays. J. Exptl. Med., 35: 203–211.

Wolbach, S. B. (1909) The pathological histology of chronic X-ray dermatitis and early X-ray carcinoma. J. Med. Research, 21: 415–450.

Zirkle, R. E. (1932) Some effects of alpha radiation upon plant cells. J. Cellular Comp. Physiol., 2: 251–274.

Manuscript received by the editor Apr. 6, 1951

CHAPTER 18

Carcinogenesis by Ionizing Radiations

JACOB FURTH[1]

Biology Division, Oak Ridge National Laboratory

AND EGON LORENZ

National Cancer Institute, Bethesda, Md.

Introduction. Physical aspects of carcinogenesis by ionizing radiations. Historical. Neoplasia induced by X and gamma radiation. Neoplasia induced by radioactive substances: Artificial radioactive isotopes. Neutrons. Organ susceptibility to tumor formation. Leukemia: Leukemia among radiologists—Experimental induction of leukemia. Endocrine organs: Gonads—Pituitary tumors—Thyroid—Parathyroid. Mammary gland. Uterus. Skin. Lung: Lung tumors among miners of Schneeberg and Jáchymov—Experimental induction of lung tumors in radioactive mines—Experimental induction of lung tumors by X or gamma radiation. Bone: Bone tumors in radium dial painters—Experimental production of bone tumors. Liver. Gastrointestinal tract. Brain. General comments: Cocarcinogenesis by irradiation. Mechanism of carcinogenesis. References.

INTRODUCTION

During the past fifty years a mass of data has been accumulated on the induction of cancer in man and many species of animals by various types of ionizing radiations disclosing numerous factors. The need is felt to review these in historical perspective. Recent developments are being widely disseminated by scientists and their institutions, but little is known of past achievements in which much recent work is rooted. Excellent work by pioneers, many of whom died with cancer induced by irradiation, paved the way to safety measures enabling now the handling of large amounts of radioactive substances with perfect safety. Good monographs on the subject in French by Lacassagne (1935a, b) are available, but neither these nor the work of their author is widely known, even though the originality of his contributions is hardly matched in depth by more recent work. Among the older monographs on the subject of irradiation injuries in man and animals, those of Colwell and Russ (1924, 1934) and Colwell (1935) are outstanding. Excellent recent reviews on

[1] Work at Oak Ridge and preparation of manuscript were performed under Contract No. W-7405-eng-26 for the Atomic Energy Commission.

this subject are those of Brues (1951) and several chapters in "Medical Physics," of Glasser (1950). In locating and interpreting the enormous literature we have made much use of these publications.

The induction of neoplasia by ionizing radiations was noted accidentally soon after discovery of X radiation and radioactive substances and the clinical observations were soon verified by experimental studies in animals. Exposure to ionizing radiations arose as a new industrial and medical hazard and also as a tool of experimental carcinogenesis and cancer therapy. The artificial production of radioactive substances has increased tremendously the potentialities of application of ionizing radiations to varied fields of science and industry, but accidental or incidental exposure to large quantities of radiation has also greatly multiplied the hazards of neoplasia induction.

The use of ionizing radiations in science and industry is now in rapid ascendency; knowledge of the carcinogenic potencies of radioactive substances is still much limited. The present review aims to survey the published observations and to point to deficiencies of knowledge concerning carcinogenesis by ionizing radiations.

PHYSICAL ASPECTS OF CARCINOGENESIS BY IONIZING RADIATIONS

The interaction of ionizing radiations with biologic matter is discussed and the term of specific ionization or linear energy transfer is defined in other chapters. The specific ionization in biologic matter varies from a theoretical 6.3 ion pairs per micron (Gray, 1946) approached by the X radiation in the multimillion-volt range to several thousand for the α particles and many thousand for the heavy fission particles. This difference in specific ionization causes marked quantitative differences in the biologic effects on small biologic entities. Similar quantitative differences may not exist as concerns the acute lethal syndrome in animals. When calculated for the same absorbed energy with equal dose rates, the 30-day LD_{50} for mice is approximately the same after X irradiation as after internal α irradiation from intravenously injected radon in equilibrium with its short-lived decay products (Hollcroft and Lorenz, 1952). The slight difference observed might be explained by the nonuniformity in distribution of the α emitters. On the other hand, Zirkle (Chap. 6) has shown that cyclotron neutrons are approximately five times and X radiation 1.5 times as effective as γ radiation in killing mice (30-day LD_{50}). The application of such findings to radiation carcinogenesis is, however, merely speculative. The scant data in the literature (Henshaw *et al.*, 1947, and Upton and Furth, 1951, unpublished data) indicate no marked differences in tumor induction by neutrons as compared to X or γ radiation.

The following generalizations apply to the process of carcinogenesis: If the tumor induction is caused by a direct action of the radiation on cells and if a single ionization event can cause a carcinogenic change, the carcinogenic action should be independent of dose rate and dependent on a minimum dose, and X radiation will be more effective than α particles or neutrons. On the other hand, if several ionization events are necessary for the carcinogenic change, the action of the radiation might depend on the dose rate as concerns particles of low specific ionization (such as hard X or γ radiation), but would be independent of dose rate for heavily ionizing particles. This may apply to irradiation of small volumes of highly susceptible cells, e.g., the induction of bone tumors by localized α emitters. The situation becomes complicated, however, after whole-body irradiation when the systemic secondary reactions caused by the sum of the primary effects are dominant over the primary injury, as may be the case with induction of leukemia or ovarian tumors.

In order to arrive at a quantitative relationship, the roentgen as a dose unit is adequate for irradiation with γ or X radiation up to a few Mev, and enables a correlation of data for whole- or part-body irradiation, acute fractionated, or long-continued irradiations. When dealing with corpuscular reactions, the roentgen is of little value, especially if the radiation is localized and the particles have path lengths in tissues ranging from several μ to several mm. However, the number of particles absorbed and their average energy can be determined, and this energy can be converted to rep. The energy absorbed in 1 g of tissue by 1 r being approximately 93 ergs, the unit rep (roentgen equivalent physical) is defined as that amount of absorbed energy of corpuscular radiation that equals 93 ergs per g of tissue (Lea, 1947). Specific ionization does not enter into the determination of the tissue dose in rep. Since data on the relative efficiency of radiations of different specific ionizations on mammals are scant, but striking differences are observed on small biologic objects, the unit of rem (roentgen equivalent mammal) has been introduced. One rem equals 1 rep divided by an arbitrary factor that expresses the greater biologic effectiveness of corpuscular radiation of high ion density over X or γ radiation, e.g., as concerns fast neutrons this factor is estimated to be about 5. Hence, $1 \text{ rem} = \frac{1 \text{ rep}}{5} = 0.2 \text{ rep}$.

This brief outline of the physical aspects of ionizing radiations points to difficulties encountered in obtaining quantitative data on the carcinogenic effects. While the problem of obtaining such data for X or γ radiation is relatively simple, comparison of such data with those from radiations of different specific ionizations is exceedingly difficult, because a uniform tissue dose cannot be obtained easily by total-body irradiation with corpuscular radiation. When bone tumors are produced by X radiation, the determination of the tissue dose is simple. Bone tumors are more easily produced by β or α emitters. The amount of radioactive material deposited in the bone can be measured, but no quantitative comparison can be made with X radiation on the basis of an average computed dose, because the radioactive material is not uniformly distributed and neoplastic transformation may occur at points of greatest density of the radioactive material.

The maximum permissible amount of a radioactive element in microcuries fixed in the body of man as revised in "International Recommendations on Radiological Protection" (1951) is as follows: Ra^{226}, 0.1; Pu^{239}, 0.04; Sr^{89}, 2.0; Sr^{90} ($+Y^{90}$), 1.0; Po^{210}, 0.005; H^3, 10; C^{14} (as carbon dioxide in air), none; Na^{24}, 15; P^{32}, 10; Co^{60}, 1; I^{131}, 0.3 (0.18 in thyroid). Additional data on these elements, such as effective mean life, permissible daily deposition in body, proportion absorbed via lungs and retained in the body, proportion retained after absorption from the gut, and maximum permissible level in liquid media and in air are listed.

HISTORICAL

The first published account of the injurious effects of X irradiation, such as dermatitis and alopecia, was made in 1896 by Marcuse. Soon it became apparent that these skin lesions are excruciatingly painful, slow to heal, and likely to break down and terminate in cancer.

The dramatic sequence of events leading to carcinoma from exposure to X radiation is well recorded by Hall-Edwards in his autobiographical notes (1904, 1906) which will be read with interest and respect by those interested in the history of science.

Hall-Edwards commenced his clinical research a few weeks after publication of Roentgen's discovery. In 1896 he gave a series of demonstrations in fluoroscopy, on each occasion exposing his hands for several hours. A primitive X-ray tube in operation is shown in Fig. 18-1 and the wide-open exposure of the fluoroscopist is evident. Some two or three weeks after exposure, Hall-Edwards noticed that the skin around the roots of the nails was red and painful. Thus commenced the lesions described objectively in their full tragedy in his first communication in 1904. During the subsequent two years he did "not experience a moment's freedom from pain . . . and was rendered absolutely incapable of work, either mental or otherwise." On the back of each hand fifty to sixty warts appeared, many of them confluent. In 1908 his forearm was amputated, and he died in 1926. "As far as I know of all that early band of workers who persisted in practicing Radiography, he is the only one who escaped death from malignant disease" (Barling, 1926).

The first cancer arising in radiologists was described by Frieben (1902) and Sick (1903), who made the diagnosis, and the next by Lloyd (1903).

The first American martyr of X irradiation was Clarence Madison Dally, an assistant of Thomas A. Edison in research on the fluoroscope. Seven years after the first exposure in 1896 he developed a cancer at the site of an X-ray ulcer of the hand. This was not controlled by amputation, and he died with metastases (Brown, 1936). Elizabeth Fleischman Aschheim was one of the first, if not the first, clinical fluoroscopist. Her exposure to X radiation began in 1897, and she died in 1905 with squamous carcinoma of the fingers (Brown, 1936). Another early American martyr of irradiation was Kassabian. He wrote sixteen papers on effects of X irradiation and a textbook of roentgenology; the latter reached a second edition in the year of his death (1910).

Porter and White (1907) reviewed the first eleven verified fatal cases of X-irradiation cancers in man. The sequence of events in their first patient is characteristic. Although he stopped all X-radiation work for a

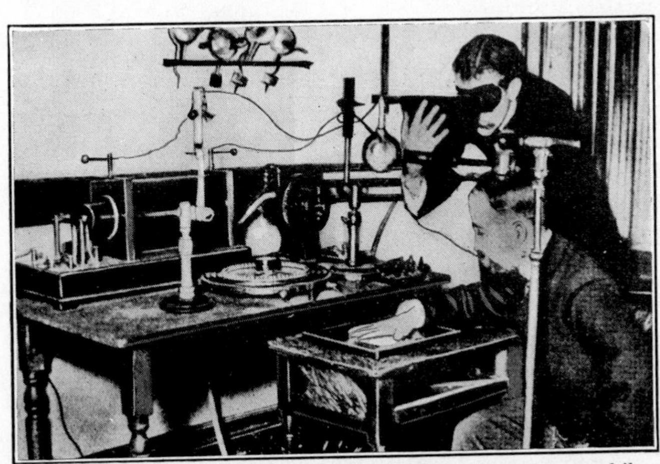

FIG. 18-1. A pioneer roentgenologist fully exposing himself to X rays while examining a patient and testing the setup by observing the opacity of bones of his hand (*after Brown*, 1936).

year, ulcers developed upon his fingers, and after the first demonstration of cancer in 1902 malignant degeneration occurred in eight different areas. Porter and White were impressed by the multiplicity of cancers produced by X irradiation.

When Rowntree (1909) gave the Hunterian lecture on cancer induction by X irradiation, it was already well established that dermatitis caused by repeated exposures to small doses of X radiation was frequently followed by the development of squamous cell carcinoma (Rowntree, 1908). X-radiation burns usually began with blistering of the skin, after which the exposure was discontinued temporarily. In the course of time warts appeared, some of which became larger and their base thickened. Some warts ulcerated and fell off, but at their base malignant cells extended into the surrounding tissue. Nearly all such cancers were multiple and occurred on both hands. Rowntree pointed out that chronic irritations can be caused by many other agents, but these are seldom complicated by cancers; malignant growths can, however, be caused also by ultraviolet radiation.

A monograph by Hesse (1911) records fifty-four cases of roentgen cancers. The pioneering spirit finds its expression in the large number of cases reported from the United States of America (26); from Germany and England each, 13 cases were recorded. Twenty-six of the fifty-four patients were physicians and twenty-four, X-ray technicians.

Feygin (1914) surveyed a number of cases of radiation-induced cancers in relation to latent periods and duration of exposure as follows:

No. of years after first irradiation......	14	13	12	11	10	9	8	7	6	5	4	3	2	1
No. of cases..........................	2	4	4	4	5	4	6	5	5	3	2			

No. of years after radiodermatitis......	11	10	9	8	7	6	5	4	3	2	1
No. of cases..........................	3	6	3	3	3	9	4	1	2	0	1

The observations in man were soon verified by experimental studies in animals by Marie *et al.* (1910, 1912) and his student, Clunet (1910), who produced sarcomas in rats by repeated administration of X radiation. Imitating the sequence of events in man, they waited until ulcers formed and healed and then administered more X radiation.

The similarity between the cutaneous changes caused by X irradiation was recognized in 1900 by Walkhoff. The first casualty (1901) from overexposure to radium radiations was Henri Becquerel himself. He carried in his vest pocket radium enclosed in a glass tube. Erythema of the skin followed by ulceration marked the site of the exposure. The ulcer healed completely a month afterward (see Colwell and Russ, 1934). It is now well established that a single local exposure is likely to cause a neoplasm only under exceptional conditions, but a single massive exposure to either X or γ radiation over the entire body may often cause cancers in some internal organs.

Wolbach (1909) and Ordway (1915), working under the Cancer Commission of Harvard University, studied in detail the injurious effects in handlers of radioactive substances. The very first changes consisted chiefly of flattening of the characteristic ridges, thickening and scaling of the superficial layers of the skin, atrophy and intractable ulcerations. These objective changes were slight compared with the subjective persisting symptoms such as paresthesia, anesthesia, tenderness, throbbing, and pain. Wolbach concluded that not a *single* trauma but *long-continued progressive* lesions of connective tissue supporting the epithelium are responsible for the acquisition of malignant properties.

The first two cases of carcinomas of the skin from exposure to radiations from radium occurred in handlers of radium tubes and applicators and were described in 1923 by MacNeal and Willis and in 1927 by Wakely. Both patients had years of repeated exposures. The lesions began with numbness in finger tips, roughness of the skin of the hand, and tingling sensation; later the nails were friable and fissured, the skin atrophic and thin but not ulcerated. Telangiectasias appeared and light brown pigmentations and hyperkeratoses; one of the last showed, on section, a squamous-cell carcinoma. These, as many other patients suffering from neoplasms induced by irradiation, were treated with radium, X radiation, and sunlight, which are carcinogenic (Colwell and Russ, 1934). This paradox is frequently discussed. Treatment with ionizing radiation causes regression of neoplasia within days or weeks but is carcinogenic only after several years and only under special circumstances.

Lazarus-Barlow (1918, 1922) was the first to induce cancer of the skin by radioactive substances. He introduced radium sulfate or silicate into the subcutaneous tissue of mice and observed the development of five malignant tumors of the skin in sixty-seven animals surviving six months. He was also believed to have induced cancer of the gallbladder by inserting radium in cholesterol stones and placing the stones in the gallbladder, but this was disputed by others. The character of an epithelial proliferation is often difficult to assess and extensive hyperplasia may mimic neoplasia, notably in the gallbladder or uterus, where, without being neoplastic, nests of epithelial cells may be established in deeper layers.

Slowly, clinical reports multiplied on induction of neoplasms in man by therapeutic irradiations. On the other hand, experimental work on this subject slackened until World War II, when developments in nuclear physics introduced the use of ionizing radiation in warfare and expanded tremendously its use in medicine and industry.

NEOPLASIA INDUCED BY X AND GAMMA RADIATION

Since 1902 when skin tumors were first observed on hands of persons who developed radiodermatitis, clinical reports appeared in steadily increasing numbers, at first on the development of cutaneous and later on internal tumors. The prophecy "La radiothérapie ne donne pas les cancers" (Belot, 1910) is now a reminder of the danger of drawing such negative conclusions. In 1911 Hesse surveyed a total of ninety-four cases, to which 126 cases were added by Krause in 1930. The clinical aspects of malignant growths induced in man are described in over thirty publications which cannot be cited here. Most of these deal with tumors of the skin and only a few with those of deep-seated organs, e.g., uterus, ovary, and larynx, and it became a matter of dispute whether

TABLE 18-1. EXPERIMENTAL INDUCTION OF NEOPLASMS BY X IRRADIATION[a]

Author	Date	X radiation		Species	Latency period, months	Type of tumor
		Total, r	Duration of administration, months			
Marie *et al.*	1910	13,200	4	Rat	13	Sarcoma, spindle-celled
	1912	6,200	12	Rat	20	
Bloch	1923	38,000	32	Rabbit	32	Carcinoma
	1924	60,000	130	Rabbit	22	
Goebel and Gérard	1925	....	5	Guinea pig	19	Sarcoma, polymorphous
Jonkhoff	1927	....	6–8	Mouse	13	Carcinoma-sarcoma
Lacassagne and Vinzent	1929	1,000	Single[b]	Rabbit	6½	Fibrosarcoma, osteosarcoma
						Rhabdomyosarcoma
Schürch	1930	30,000	15	Rabbit	24	Carcinoma
Lacassagne	1933	1,220 } 1,980 }	In 2 and 3 doses	Rabbit	33	Sarcoma, periosteal, spindle-celled
						Myxosarcoma
Sedginidse	1933	14,200	5	Mouse	6	Carcinoma, spindle-celled
Ludin	1930, 1934	8,000	6½	Rabbit	6½	Chondrosarcoma

All tumors occurred in the skin or about bones and joints.

[a] Mostly from Lacassagne (1945b).

[b] Irradiation to cause resolution of chronic bacterial abscess.

the latter were actually produced by X irradiation. No such doubt exists as concerns tumors in bones which are particularly susceptible, notably if inflamed; but even apparently normal bone, when subjected to massive irradiation, may undergo a neoplastic change (Spitz and Higinbotham, 1951).

Experimental induction of neoplasms in animals by X irradiation began eight years after the first observations in man. The procedures used imitated the conditions of exposure in man. The early literature is surveyed in Table 18-1. In his monograph, "Les Cancers Produits par les Rayonnements Électromagnétiques," Lacassagne (1945b) discusses extensively the early literature which will not be fully reviewed here.

Marie *et al.* (1910, 1912) and Clunet (1910) gave repeated doses to rats estimated by Lacassagne to be about 600 to 2000 r during four to twelve months and so induced spindle-celled sarcomas. For many years remarkably little use was made of this novel type of carcinogenesis. Bloch (1923, 1924) and Schürch (1930) induced carcinoma in the rabbit by repeated exposures to X radiation. Subsequent work on the induction of cutaneous sarcomas in guinea pigs (Goebel and Gérard, 1925), cutaneous carcinomas in mice, and bone tumors in rabbits is surveyed in Table 18-1.

The tumors of the skin were induced by relatively large doses of ionizing radiations at the sites of exposure. It is doubtful if any species would resist this type of carcinogenesis. The next important observation was that, following total-body exposures, neoplasms, leukemias, ovarian, mammary, and other tumors appeared in different organs. Mammary tumors were also induced in rats and rabbits. Subsequent research aimed to elucidate the pathogenesis and morphogenesis of the induction of internal neoplasms and to determine the relevance of observations made in one species to the animal kingdom at large. At first, single or a few large doses of X radiation were used in these studies; later, also γ radiation and chronic exposures. A large-scale chronic exposure study in mice, guinea pigs, and rabbits using γ radiation of radium was carried out by Lorenz *et al.* (1947). In mice there was a marked increase in the incidence of leukemia in the females of the groups exposed to 4.4 and 8.8 r (8 hours) daily (Fig. 18-2), an even greater increase in the incidence of ovarian tumors, and a slight increase in incidence of breast and lung tumors. In guinea pigs, there was an increase of mammary tumors, and in rabbits of uterine tumors. This and other recent work are surveyed in the sections which follow.

NEOPLASIA INDUCED BY RADIOACTIVE SUBSTANCES

While experimental induction of cancers by X irradiation followed, that by radioactive substances preceded the observations on man. Lazarus-

Barlow (1918) was the first to report on the experimental induction of carcinomas by means of radium. Although doubt was expressed as to the neoplastic nature of the epithelial proliferative changes described by him, his experimental pattern was followed by others who fully confirmed his claim. The first "radium carcinoma" was described by Wakely (1927) on the thumb of a man handling radium salts. In his first studies, Lazarus-Barlow produced carcinomas of the skin in mice and rats (1918). Later (1922) he reported on the induction of carcinoma of the gallbladder by inserting radium into gallstones and placing such stones in the gallbladder. Investigations performed during the next two decades on the

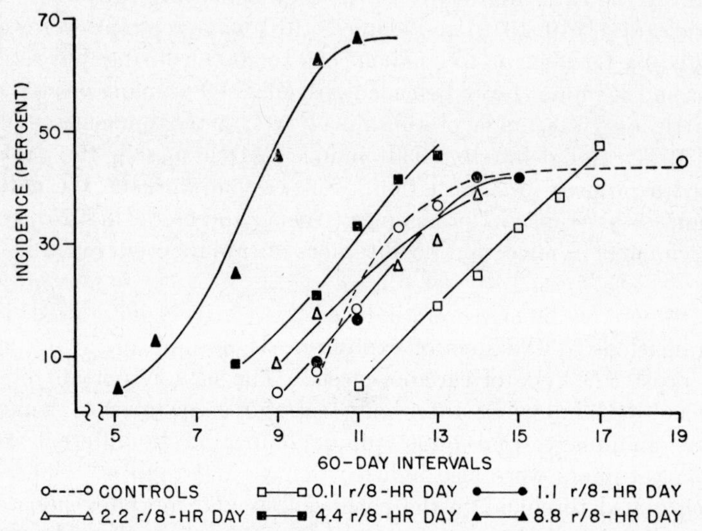

FIG. 18-2. The incidence of leukemia in female mice after chronic total-body exposure to γ rays of radium (*after Lorenz et al.*, 1947).

carcinogenic effects of radium, radon, mesothorium, and thorium are surveyed in Table 18-2.

Daels (1925) inserted radium into the subcutaneous tissue of mice and rats, inducing sarcomas after seven to twelve months. About a year later he described the induction of carcinomas by the same procedure. Daels and Biltris (1931) soaked silk strings or tissues in radium chloride solution, coated these with collodion, and inserted them in various tissues of rats and guinea pigs, inducing sarcomas of the kidney, carcinomas of the liver, and intracranial sarcomas after twelve to thirty months. The similarity of action of this carcinogen to that of chemical carcinogens such as methylcholanthrene, discovered later, is noteworthy. The type and readiness of neoplasia induction seem to depend on the tissue, species, and other factors, not on the carcinogen. When inserted in the kidney, both chemical (e.g., methylcholanthrene) and physical carcinogens induce

TABLE 18-2. EXPERIMENTAL INDUCTION OF NEOPLASMS WITH RADIOACTIVE SUBSTANCES[a]

Author	Date	Substance	Quantity, mg of Ra or mc of Rn	Duration of exposure	Species	No. of animals		Tumor induc. time, months	Type of tumor
						Used	With tumors		
Lazarus-Barlow	1918	Ra	10^{-4}–10^{-8}	Permanent	Mouse	193	5	6	Carcinoma of skin
		Ra	10^{-3}–10^{-7}	Permanent	Rat	53	?	?	
Daels and Baeten	1925–1926	Ra	10^{-6}–6×10^{-3}	Permanent	Mouse	78	3	7–12	Sarcoma, spindle-celled subcut.
					Rat	43	2		
Daels and Biltris	1931	Ra	Undeterminable	Permanent	Rat	82	4	8–22	Sarcoma of cranium, kidney, spleen
	1931–1933	Ra	....	....	Guinea pig	100	18	8–32	
	1937	Ra	....	....	Chicken	152	2	58–59	Carcinoma of biliary tract, osteosarcoma
Schürch and Uehlinger	1931	Ra	10^{-4}–5×10^{-3}	20 days	Rabbit	1	1	18	Sarcoma of bone, liver, spleen
Uehlinger and Schürch	1935–1938	Ra, Ms-Th 1	....	Permanent	Rabbit	56	18	18–50	
Sabin *et al.*	1932	Ra, Ms-Th 1	5.1 mg Ra 7.7 mg Ms-Th 1	....	Rabbit	7	2	11–19	Osteosarcoma
Petrov and Krotkina	1933	Ra	4×10^{-4}–1.8×10^{-3}	Permanent	Guinea pig	12	2	34–39	Carcinoma of biliary tract
Dobrovolskaia–Zavadskaia and Adamova	1935–1939	Rn	0.08–0.12	To exhaust. of source Rn	Mouse	262	28	7–21	Carcinoma and sarcoma of skin
Ross	1936	Ra	0.1	Permanent	Rabbit	13	6	24–32	Carcinoma of skin Fibro- and osteosarcoma
Jentzer	1937	Ra	0.5	Permanent	Rabbit	6	1	9	Osteosarcoma
Lacassagne *et al.*	1937–1942	Rn	0.65–1	To exhaust. of source Rn	Rabbit	26	8	12–39	Rhabdomyosarcoma Adenocarcinoma and sarcoma of uterus
Hellner	1938	Ra	....	....	Rabbit	...	..	24	Sarcoma, polymorphous
Selbie	1938	Thorotrast	0.2 cc	....	Mouse	...	..	17	Osteosarcoma
Dunlap *et al.*	1944	Ra	2×10^{-6}	Permanent	Rat	13	9	12	Osteosarcoma

[a] Mainly after Lacassagne (1945a).

sarcomas but do not render the renal epithelium neoplastic. The incidence of induced tumors (Daels and Biltris, 1931) was low, many animals dying too early of intercurrent disease. Biltris (1933) using the above radium-string technique, in which the carcinogenic agents were β and γ radiations, induced in guinea pigs sarcomas of the meninges, metastasizing carcinomas of the gallbladder, and malignant tumors of the spleen after a latency of eight to twenty-four months. In their last publication Daels and Biltris (1937) described the induction of osteosarcoma in two chickens by the collodion-string technique after a latency period of nearly five years.

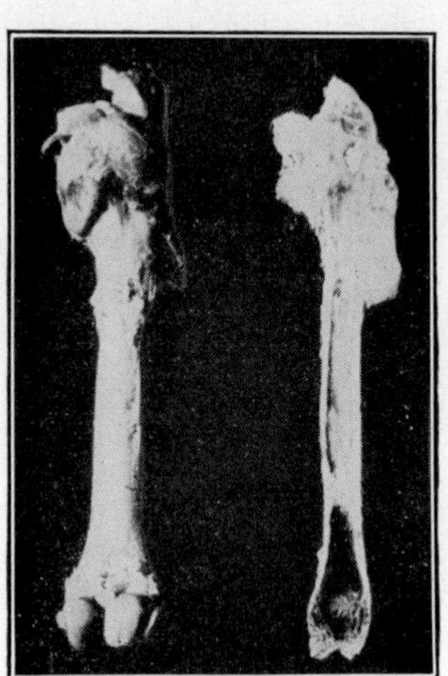

FIG. 18-3. Osteogenic sarcoma induced in a rabbit by injections of thorotrast (*after Schürch and Uehlinger*, 1935.)

Following the work of Schürch and Uehlinger (1931, 1947) (Fig. 18-3), numerous articles appeared on the induction of bone tumors in rabbits. These investigators implanted 1 mg of radium sulfate subcutaneously in the jaw of a rabbit and left it there for 20 days. The tumor appeared one and one-half years afterward. Later (1935) they placed vaseline impregnated with 2–5 mg of mesothorium in the femora of rabbits, inducing osteo- and polymorphous sarcomas. Sabin *et al.* (1932) induced bone tumors in rabbits by intravenous injection of radium chloride (approximately 5.1 mg) and mesothorium (approximately 7.7 mg) in eleven to nineteen months.

Ross (1936) implanted in the thoracic wall of rabbits 0.1 mg of radium enclosed in platinum tubes 1 cm long and with a wall thickness of 0.5 mm. Earlier, the experimental induction of neoplasms had been successful only when unscreened radioactive substance was used, with the exception of some work of Schürch and Uehlinger, and the opinion was held that α radiation was the principal carcinogenic factor. However, six of the nine experimental animals of Ross developed a tumor adjacent to the tubes; one had an osteosarcoma, the others nonosseous neoplasms, indicating that γ radiation also induced tumors. These and earlier studies are surveyed in Table 18-2.

Petrov and Krotkina (1933, 1947), repeating the disputed work of Lazarus-Barlow, implanted radium needles in the gallbladder of guinea pigs and induced carcinomas of the biliary tract. The agent causing spontaneous carcinoma of the gallbladder in man is not known; it is not likely to be a radioactive substance. Therefore, such studies do not contribute to the knowledge of spontaneous tumors or those likely to be caused in man by radioactivity, but they may disclose sensitivities to neoplastic changes.

Roussy *et al.* (1934) were first to report on the experimental induction of tumors by thorium dioxide (thorotrast) by intraperitoneal injections of this substance into rats. Subsequently, several workers induced sarcomas by subcutaneous injection of thorium dioxide in rats and mice (Roussy *et al.*, 1936; Selbie, 1936; Miyamota, 1939; Prussia, 1936; Bogliolo, 1937, 1938; and Selbie, 1938. The tumors so induced by Selbie were spindle-cell sarcomas (six), osteosarcomas (three), and one hemangioendothelioma. This recalls the extraosseous bone tumors induced in man by X irradiation and the hemangiosarcoma induced by radium. Bogliolo induced tumors in all of twenty-three rats that had been given subcutaneous injections of thorotrast. In guinea pigs Foulds (1939) induced sarcomas and a carcinoma by repeated injections of thorotrast in the nipple after a latency of three years. Andervont and Shimkin (1940) confirmed the induction of sarcoma and hemangioma in mice by subcutaneous injection of this substance and called attention to the absence of lung tumors in their mice, even though radioactive particles were demonstrated in the lungs throughout the course of the experiment and the strain of mice used was highly susceptible to lung tumors. Dunlap *et al.* (1944) fed rats each with 100 μg of radium and produced osteosarcomas in nine of thirteen animals.

The statements of Roussy and Guerin (1941), and later of Willis (1948), that tumors may appear in human beings who had been given thorotrast for diagnostic purposes, proved valid. The use of thorotrast is relatively recent and many years may elapse before tumors develop. An endothelial sarcoma developing in the liver of a seventy-year-old woman, following thorotrast injection, was described by MacMahon *et al.* (1947). Thorotrast taken up by macrophages was demonstrated microscopically in tissue sections, and this phagocytic activity was correlated with radioactivity. In spite of the wide use of thorotrast for diagnostic purposes, no other case of endothelial sarcoma of the liver was reported, even though thorotrast is retained by reticuloendothelial cells. Hence, the possibility is considered that this tumor was spontaneous. All cells of the liver are relatively resistant to induction of neoplasia. The observations of MacMahon and those made earlier by Ross suggest that endothelial cells are the most susceptible elements of this organ. Many radioactive heavy metals entering the body are retained in the liver, notably those given in suspensions or colloids. Tissue containing 1 per cent thorotrast by weight is estimated to receive approximately 3000 rep in ten years (Evans, 1950a, b).

Sarcoma of the maxilla developing nine years after intravenous injection of mesothorium was described by Gricouroff *et al.* (1943), and a solitary plasmocytoma of the humerus in a mesothorium worker by

Lumb (1950). One patient developed a carcinoma of the eyelid thirty-five years after local injection of thorium dioxide (Rudolphi, 1950).

Maisin and Dupuis (1929) induced embryomas in chickens by intravenous injection of ionium in combination with injection of embryonic extract into the pectoral muscle. Embryonic extract alone did not induce tumors. The role of the radioactivity of ionium in inducing these embryomas may be doubtful because its half life is 7.6×10^4 years. Mottram (1935) induced mesoblastic tumors in fowls by exposure to radium.

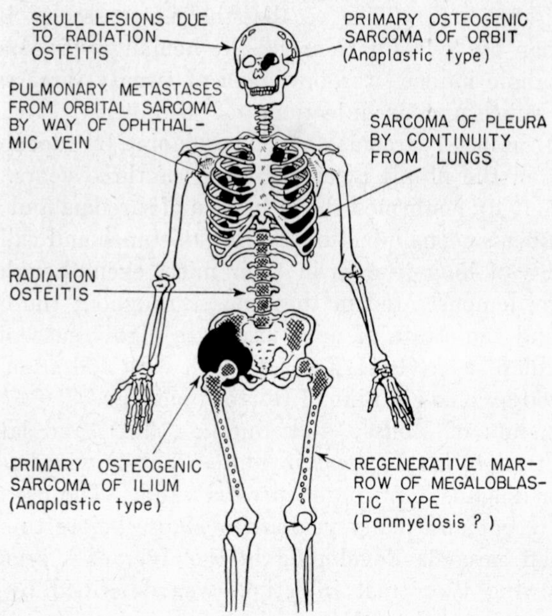

FIG. 18-4. Multicentric osteosarcoma in a dial painter with secondary tumor deposits in the lungs and foci of the precancerous radiation osteitis (*after Martland*, 1931).

The accidental induction of malignant bone tumors by radioactive substances in luminous watch dial painters (Martland and Humphries, 1929, and Martland, 1931) (Figs. 18-4 to 18-6), and skin tumors following therapeutic use of radon seeds (Evans, 1950b) will be described more fully. Nørgaard (1939) described the development of fibrosarcoma in a man following therapeutic intra-articular injection of radium chloride.

Artificial Radioactive Isotopes. Some radioactive isotopes are now standard therapeutic agents while others are being used experimentally. These include P^{32}, I^{131}, Au^{198}, Mn^{52}, Na^{24}, Ga^{67}, Sr^{89-90}, and many others (Siri, 1949). The doses employed in cancer therapy are in the carcinogenic range, but so far no patient receiving such therapy has been known to develop a neoplasm. As many as ten to thirty years may elapse before tumors appear.

Experimental studies on the carcinogenicity of radioisotopes obtained from fission products were begun by investigators of the Manhattan Project. The following observations were made by Lisco *et al.* (1947): Tumors of the colon followed ingestion of an insoluble Y^{91} compound by

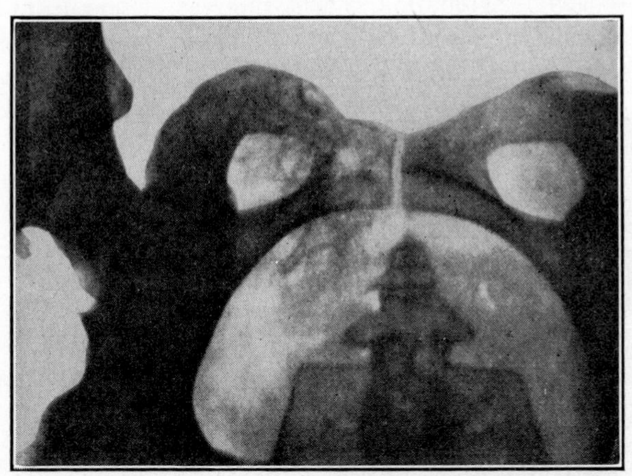

FIG. 18-5. X-ray picture of the pelvis of a dial painter with primary osteosarcoma of the pubic bone (*after Martland*, 1931).

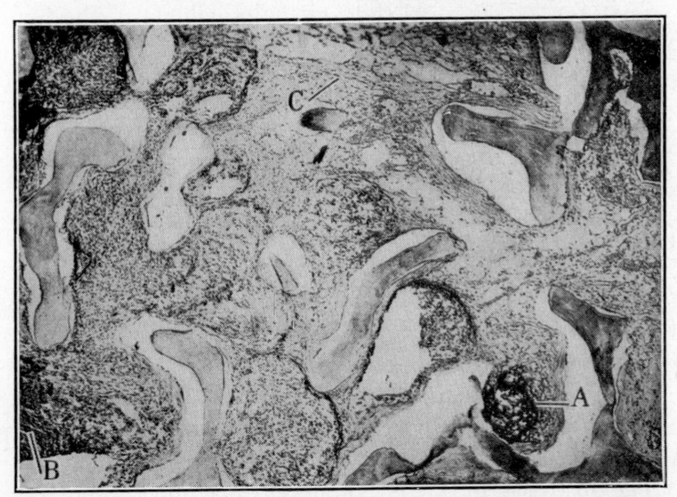

FIG. 18-6. Radiation osteitis. In the bone marrow, areas of hyperplasia alternate with areas of fibrosis. There is an increased osteoblastic activity (*after Martland* 1931).

rats. When Y^{91} was injected subcutaneously into mice as phosphate, epidermoid carcinoma and fibrosarcoma were induced. When yttrium phosphate was injected as a suspension intravenously, it induced osteogenic sarcoma in the long bones of rats. Plutonium as nitrate or citrate injected subcutaneously into mice induced fibrosarcoma at the site of injection and osteogenic tumors in distant bones. When plutonium was implanted as metal subcutaneously (Lisco and Kisieleski, 1953) the majority of the animals appeared to suffer no ill effects from the local implants or from the absorbed plutonium. When plutonium was injected as citrate or phosphate intramuscularly or intravenously into rats, it induced osteogenic sarcoma. When injected intraperitoneally into rabbits, it induced osteogenic sarcoma at distant sites. When administered intravenously, it induced, in addition to bone sarcomas, massive liver damage with secondary cirrhosis; whether this will be followed by carcinoma has not been established. Plutonium as citrate or nitrate injected intratracheally or plutonium oxide and cerium oxide produced as aerosols by burning, inhaled by rats, caused squamous and medullary carcinomas of the lung (Lisco *et al.*, 1947; Lisco and Finkel, 1949).

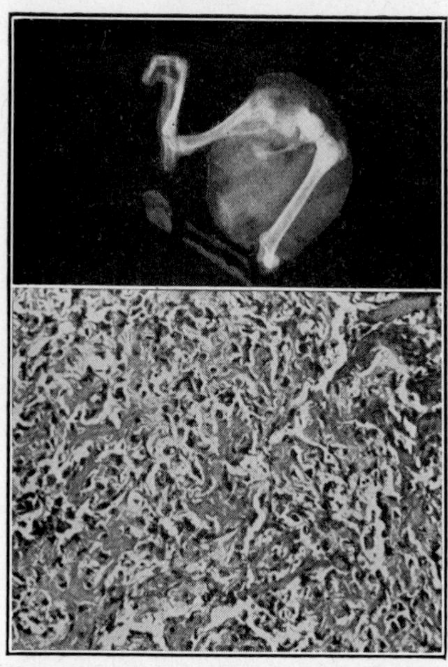

FIG. 18-7. Osteogenic sarcoma in a rat tibia produced by P^{32} (*after Koletsky et al.* 1950).

Strontium-89 given intraperitoneally induced in mice hemangioendothelioma of the femur and, more commonly, osteogenic tumors in different bones. Radium, strontium, and the rare earth and transuranic elements are all "bone seekers" which means that from the primary sites of injection they are likely to be translocated to bones.

Large doses of P^{32} (Koletsky *et al.*, 1950), injected in rats either in single or repeated doses, caused the development of osteogenic sarcomas (Fig. 18-7) in many bones and squamous cell carcinomas in about 47 per cent of the animals. Radiophosphorus, as well as many other fission products, was deposited heavily in the skeleton. The carcinomas in these rats originated in structures close to bone, as in the roof of the mouth. The dose used in rats is estimated to be about twenty times the usual therapeutic dose in man. When applied to the skin, the β radiation of P^{32} caused multicentric tumors in every rat exposed (Raper *et al.*, 1946; Raper, 1947; Henshaw *et al.*, 1947).

NEUTRONS

Henshaw *et al.* (1947) studied the effect of fast neutrons from the Oak Ridge reactor and noted a marked increase in the incidence of leukemia and ovarian neoplasms. The incidence of leukemia following a single exposure to fast neutrons was 22 to 32 per cent in groups of mice exposed to 26 and 90 N as compared to 14 per cent in controls. The variations in relation to dose seemed not significant. In parallel experiments they studied the leukemia incidence following a single dose of γ radiation and found this to be 67 per cent in mice exposed to 500 r and 64 per cent in mice exposed to 700 r.

The effects on neoplasia incidence of slow neutron exposure are being studied currently in the biological tunnel of the Oak Ridge reactor. Analyses about one year after exposure indicated a five- to tenfold increase in leukemias in the dose ranges at or moderately below the LD_{50} dose. When compared on the basis of LD_{50}, no preferential effect was noted between slow neutrons and X radiation.

The chronic effects of neutrons from cyclotrons were studied by a few investigators, but unfortunately either the animals were not observed long enough or no distinction was made between leukemias and leukemoid reactions. Leitch (1947) noted an increased incidence of mammary tumors in rats exposed to cyclotron neutrons.

In exploring the possible role of cosmic rays in carcinogenesis, Figge (1947, 1949) claimed that the potency of chemical carcinogens may be altered by slight variations in the intensity of penetrating environmental radiations. No data are available to indicate that cosmic radiation is carcinogenic. No such effect was found by Franks and Meek (1950) in a carefully controlled experiment.

ORGAN SUSCEPTIBILITY TO TUMOR FORMATION

It is probable that all cells capable of multiplication are susceptible to the induction of neoplasia by irradiation. The incidence and sites of neoplasia depend on the amount of energy absorbed by the cells, the functional state and radiosensitivity of the cells, and other factors. There are ample observations to indicate that hemopoietic cells, notably lymphocytes, are highly radiosensitive, while macrophages (histiocytes, reticuloendothelial cells) are highly resistant. Specialized cells, as osteoblasts, are highly radiosensitive; muscle, liver, and kidney cells are more resistant. The most radiosensitive organ appears to be the mouse ovary.

Studies published up to 1942 on the effects of irradiations on normal tissues have been reviewed in a series of papers by Shields Warren and associates (1942–1943) and the histological changes also by Bloom (1948). It is difficult to compare the relative sensitivity of different normal cells on the basis of total-body irradiation, since they are not in a comparable state of the reproductive cycle or under identical physiological and environmental influences. The differences in response of different types of cells and of different cells of the same type to similar ionizing radiations are truly remarkable (Lacassagne, 1936). As he phrased it:

Why does a ray passing through a certain region cause the death of one kind, e.g., the germinative cells of the gonads or certain cells of the lymphatic nodes, delayed death of certain others, e.g., those of the epidermis, simple transient alterations such as are noted in connective tissue, or no reaction at all, as in the case of nerve cells. . . . Among apparently identical cells receiving equal doses of radiation, some are killed, others show various lesions, still others are but slightly damaged and are capable of recovery. This difference in radiation effects explains the repair following irradiation, such as that of irradiated epidermis, or reversible blood changes, or the reconstitution of the germinal epithelium. It explains also the recurrences of cancer treated by irradiation. The traditional explanation of this phenomenon is biological, viz., that the cells, in their life cycle pass through stages of varying sensitivity corresponding to varying physiological conditions.

The variable radiation sensitivity of the cell can be explained, and a means of establishing this sensitivity furnished, by the discontinuous nature of radiation. The sensitivity exhibited by each cell type appears to be a function of two main factors: (1) the histological structure, which determines the size of the various zones corresponding to each lesion, and (2) the physicochemical composition, which determines the number of quanta necessary to produce ionization sufficient to cause disintegration of a sufficient number of constituent molecules of the intracellular organelle in question.

These considerations apply to the induction of neoplasms at the site of irradiation. Leblond *et al.* (1951) noted some correlation between the incidence of spontaneous neoplasms of different organs and rate of reproduction of their cells. Organs with high mitotic activity appear radiosensitive, but this is not a general rule. A different mechanism is in play when tumors arise at distant sites, as will be discussed.

LEUKEMIA

The increased incidence of leukemia among radiologists now seems to be well established, and there are numerous experimental studies elucidating the conditions of leukemia induction in mice.

Leukemia among Radiologists. As early as 1911 Jagić *et al.* described four cases of leukemia among radiologists and one in a radium worker and stated that long-continued exposure to X radiation may cause this disease. In 1912 Aubertin stated that in nineteen years he had seen five cases of leukemia among radiologists, a then relatively small fraction of physicians, and none among other physicians. In 1925 Emile-Weil and Lacassagne reported on myeloid leukemia caused by handling radioactive substances. These reports were soon amply confirmed. Henshaw and Hawkins (1944) found that during the period of 1933–1942 leukemia was 1.7 times more common among American white physicians than among the general male white population (Dublin and Spiegelman, 1947) and cited similar evidence from England and Wales. Ulrich (1946) estimated that leukemia was eight times more common among American radiologists than among other physicians; between 1935 and 1944, according to him, 3.9 per cent of 205 radiologists died of leukemia as compared to 0.44 per cent of 34,626 physicians other than radiologists. According to March (1944, 1950) the greatest excess in the mortality of physicians was found from leukemia; the death rate from this disease was 175 per cent of that for white males in the general population. The increased incidence in leukemia among physicians other than radiologists was 133 per cent of that of the general population. The incidence of leukemia in radiologists was over ten times as great when compared with other physicians, and this difference according to March was statistically significant.

Analyzing the conditions of irradiation under which leukemia developed in radiologists and was induced in mice, the following differences are noted: Chronic irradiation produces leukemia in mice only when young animals are exposed over the entire body at a dose rate far exceeding that now encountered by radiologists. Radioscopy involves exposure of only part of the body and such exposures in mice are not leukemogenic. Furthermore, radiologists are exposed to a relatively small average tissue dose. This may explain why the increase of leukemia incidence among radiologists is relatively slight.

Explosions of atomic bombs may cause leukemia predominantly by virtue of γ radiation of high energy, and the results in man (Folley *et al.*, 1952) and experimental animals (Upton *et al.*, unpublished data) are similar. In both, there is ample evidence that a massive instantaneous single exposure increases the leukemia incidence. In Hiroshima and Nagasaki the increase in incidence of leukemia during the past three years is highly significant in subjects exposed at distances less than 2000 meters and the magnitude of increase is inversely related to the distance from the hypocenter, as indicated by the following very approximate figures:

Exposure Distance from Hypocenter, m	Death Rate from Leukemia per 10^6 Living
Up to 1000	500
1000–1500	210
1500–2000	87
Over 2000	32
	Leukemia Deaths per 10^4 Total Dead
In all Japan (1943–1949)	13
United States (1940)	39

The disease occurred mostly in the early and intermediate age groups and the predominant types were acute myelocytic leukemias (Folley *et al.*, 1952).

Experimental Induction of Leukemia. Carefully controlled experimental studies with mice exposed to radiations of an atomic bomb confirm the preceding observations. Ten months after exposure over 6 per cent of a large surviving population of mice exposed to a dose above the

LD_{50} died of leukemia as compared to 0 per cent of the controls. Exposures below that dose have caused only few leukemias thus far (Upton *et al.*, unpublished data).

While depression of hemopoiesis immediately after exposure to ionizing irradiation is reversible, the liability of late changes of which leukemia is most important appears irreversible. This varies greatly with species, strains of animals, mode and dose of exposure, and is influenced by several factors. In mice the smallest dose of X radiation which depresses lymphopoiesis is about 25 r and the smallest dose which causes leukemia is somewhat below 200 r. Rats are possibly susceptible to the induction of leukemia by radiation (Metcalf and Inda, 1951); rabbits and guinea pigs, and probably also dogs, are refractory, but no large-scale studies in which animals were observed during their entire life span have been reported in species other than these.

The leukemogenic potency of X radiation was first demonstrated experimentally in mice by Krebs *et al.* (1930). Of 5500 mice exposed to sublethal doses of X radiation 3.5 per thousand developed lymphoid leukemia as compared to 0.6 per thousand of the controls. Furth and Furth (1936) exposed large numbers of mice of three unrelated strains to one or a few doses of 300–400 r of X radiation and found a sevenfold increase in lymphoid leukemia, mainly of mediastinal type, and an eightfold increase of myeloid leukemia. Subsequent work by several investigators disclosed the following: (1) Repeated, well-timed exposures are more leukemogenic than single exposures. (2) The leukemia induction rate is increased with the dose. (3) All strains of mice that were carefully tested proved susceptible although there are marked strain and sex differences in susceptibility. (4) In no species other than the mouse, and possibly the rat, has leukemia been induced experimentally, but adequate follow-up of the exposed animals has been done only in mice, rats, rabbits, and guinea pigs. (5) Gamma radiation of radium and fast and slow neutrons of the atomic reactor likewise increased the incidence of leukemia in mice. (6) Leukemia induction by radioactive substances other than P^{32} has not been reported in animals; it has been described, however, in handlers of radioactive substances.

In most strains of mice spontaneous leukemias are thymic in origin. Operative removal of this organ (Furth, 1946) or its involution brought about by cortisone (Upton and Furth, unpublished data) diminish the incidence of spontaneous leukemias or their induction by irradiation (Kaplan, 1950b; Kaplan *et al.*, 1951). Hueper (1934) exposed mice bearing spontaneous mammary tumors to repeated doses of 30–80 r of X radiation once a week over a period up to six weeks. His treatment caused extensive myeloid hyperplasia with extensive myelopoiesis of the spleen; the greatly increased incidence of leukemia in Hueper's experiments suggested that irradiation caused a leukemic transformation in these hyperplastic but nonmalignant myelopoietic and lymphopoietic tissues. Conversely, removal of the adrenals increases susceptibility to the induction of leukemia by X radiation (Kaplan *et al.*, 1951). Desoxycorticosterone is without effect. The inhibitory effect of cortisone is still manifest when its administration is deferred until six weeks after irradiation (Kaplan *et al.*, 1951).

There are few experiments bearing on the pathogenesis of leukemia induction by ionizing irradiation. Kaplan (1949) found that, in contrast to whole-body exposure, local irradiation of mice failed to increase consistently the incidence of lymphoid tumors. He concluded that the induction of these tumors is not solely the result of a direct action of radiation upon susceptible cells or their ancestors. In C57 black mice irradiation of the upper half of the body yielded leukemia in 4 per cent of the mice, lower half 2 per cent, whole body irradiation 64 per cent, when a total of ten treatments were given in twelve consecutive weeks. However, by alternating upper and lower body exposures within 24 hours many lymphoid tumors were produced (Kaplan and Brown, 1951), suggesting again that an indirect systemic mechanism is involved in leukemogenesis. Similarly, Lorenz and Eschenbrenner (unpublished data) observed the development of lymphomas in mice of strain A irradiated over the entire body with the thorax shielded, but the increase over controls was somewhat less than after total-body irradiation and exposure of the thymus alone did not increase the incidence. On the other hand, Kaplan (1949) found that shielding the thymic region of C57 black mice did not increase the incidence of leukemia and shielding the leg had a protective effect. Similarly, direct irradiation of the thymic region with the rest of the body shielded did not produce leukemias (Kaplan, 1949, 1951).

These observations led to the view that the induction of leukemia is by some indirect mechanism. Prolonged depression of hemopoietic activity may also be a factor in eliciting lymphoid tumors (Lorenz *et al.*, 1953). Kirschbaum and Mixer (1951) found that in estrogen-treated mice thymic lymphosarcoma could be induced by irradiation of the entire body except the thymus and concluded that the actual leukemogen, as Kaplan and others believe, is a humoral substance. Whether the humoral agents protecting the body from early radiation death will also lessen the likelihood of leukemia development remains to be seen.

Little attention has been given thus far to the determination of the types of experimentally induced leukemias. Some radioisotopes, as Au^{198} colloids, are selectively deposited in macrophages and the leukemogenic effect of such exposures remains to be studied. Aubertin (1931) and Emile-Weil and Lacassagne (1925) reported an increase of myeloid leukemias among radiologists but, in subsequent analyses, all types of leukemias are considered together. In mice, lymphoid tumors induced by irradiation are predominant. Furth and Furth (1936) mention also an increase of myeloid leukemias, but this lacks confirmation. The type of leukemia induced by irradiation may be influenced by the state of the hemopoietic organs at the time of irradiations. This is suggested by the observations of Hueper (1934).

The factor of age was studied by Kaplan (1948). The maximum incidence of leukemia occurred in mice of strain A when irradiated at one month (29.0 per cent), with a sharp decrease at two months (2.8 per cent) and later (at 3 months 10.9 per cent, at 4 months 6.2 per cent, at 6 months 0 per cent). In mice irradiated at two weeks of age the leukemia incidence was 14.3 per cent. The variability of values is probably due to the small number of animals used. These observations were confirmed by him with C57 black mice.

The influence of age and dose rate on leukemia induction was investigated by Brues *et al.* (1949). Throughout most of the life, the susceptibility to irradiation-induced lymphoma approximately doubled at intervals of 80 days. After 700 days of age no further increase in morbidity rate was observed. Using different patterns of X-radiation treatment, it was found that 400 r total-body X radiation is more effective if divided over a 10-day period than if given either as a single dose or divided over 40 days. Increasing doses are more effective until a saturation value is reached (Brues *et al.*, 1949). There is also evidence for a threshold dose or dose rate below which leukemia is not induced.

Lorenz *et al.* (1947), investigating the effect of chronic exposure to γ radiation of radium, induced malignant lymphomas in mice at a rate that was roughly dependent on the dose rate. The greater the dose rate, the earlier the appearance of the tumors. Their results are illustrated by Fig. 18-1. This shows that long-continued daily exposure of female LAF_1 mice to 8.8 r daily (8 hours) to the γ radiation of radium greatly increased the incidence of leukemia and hastened its onset. The total dose received by these animals over a period of twenty-three months was 5900 r. Daily exposure to 4.4 r had a similar but less marked effect, while smaller doses (2.2 r daily or less) did not increase the incidence of leukemia in comparison to untreated controls. The strain used had a very high incidence of spontaneous leukemia appearing mainly late in life.

Rats were exposed by Metcalf and Inda (1951) to doses of 0.1–10 r per day during a period of two years. Their findings suggest that leukemia may develop in this species as a result of such irradiations.

P^{32} has carcinogenic properties comparable to those of X radiation (Brues *et al.*, 1945). The rate of tumor production with both is roughly proportional to the corresponding lethal doses. P^{32} is effective whether given in a single dose or in monthly divided doses.

The carcinogenic effect of slow neutrons in the thermal column of the

Oak Ridge reactor is being studied currently. When analyzed six to sixteen months after exposure, it was found that doses of 128 r of X radiation and equivalent doses of slow neutrons increase the leukemia incidence in mice about fourfold; 512 r and an equivalent dose of slow neutrons, about sixfold. A preferential effect of neutrons as found for cataract induction was not evident for leukemia induction. This slow neutron flux has negligible quantities of fast neutrons, but it contains much γ radiation of high energy of about 5–6 r/minute (Darden *et al.*, 1951); thus an LD_{50} exposure would include exposure to 400–480 r of γ radiation and would account for about half the biological effectiveness as concerns neoplasia induction.

Earlier, Henshaw *et al.* (1947) compared the effects of fast neutrons and X radiation. The incidence of malignant lymphoma following exposure to a single dose of γ radiation was 64 and 67 per cent in groups receiving single doses of 700 and 500 r and 22–32 per cent in groups exposed to 26–90 n of fast neutrons, as compared to 14 per cent in the controls. The r-n ratio of γ radiation to fast neutrons for the different effects studied varied from 8:1 to 35:1.

The production of reticulum cell sarcoma in a rat by administration of thorotrast was described by Onufrio (1938). This tumor is not uncommon in the rat so this report is inconclusive, as are our observations on similar neoplasms in the only two mice surviving the administration of large quantities of Au^{198} colloid.

ENDOCRINE ORGANS

The induction of neoplasia in endocrine organs by ionizing radiations is of unusual interest for the following reasons: In the genesis of endocrine tumors the specific (direct) irradiation effect is minor. This carcinogenesis is reproducible in almost all mice in the two organs thus far studied extensively (ovary and pituitary). The tumor incidence is not dose-dependent in acute exposures; if a threshold dose is exceeded, almost all animals develop the neoplasm. This threshold dose may be very small, being below 32 r in the case of ovarian tumor induction by single total-body exposure (Lorenz *et al.*, 1947; Furth, 1949) or a total of 90 r by long-continued γ radiation (Lorenz *et al.*, 1947) or, in the case of pituitary tumors, many thousand rep to the thyroid (300 μc of I^{131} per mouse) (Gorbman, 1949). This dose may correspond to that required to destroy the functional capacity of this organ. The importance of hormonal imbalance in carcinogenesis has been reviewed by Gardner (1948). The ovaries are much more susceptible to irradiation than the thyroid gland. After sterilization of the mouse, subsequent irradiation does not modify the sequence of the carcinogenic process. The radiation effect can readily be counteracted or minimized by endocrine therapy;

this is proved in the case of ovarian tumors (Li and Gardner, 1949; Gardner, 1950; Kaplan, 1950a) and pituitary growths (Furth, 1951, unpublished data).

Gonads. Many studies of the early effects of radiations on the gonads have been reviewed by Warren (1942–1943). It is uncertain whether irradiation within the permissible dose would cause tumors of the testes and whether localized massive irradiation of the testis would give rise to specific tumors; on the other hand, the ovary of the mouse is highly sensitive to neoplasia induction.

In a series of excellent papers, Brambell *et al.* (1927–1929) described the changes in the ovary of the mouse for a period of approximately six months after irradiation. The possibility that the regenerative changes lead to neoplasia was then unsuspected. Irradiated mice may undergo several pregnancies, yet develop ovarian neoplasms a year and a half after irradiation (Furth, 1949; Deringer *et al.*, 1953). The induction period of the tumors is invariably long. While regenerative changes begin, depending on total dose after four to six months, tumorlike growths do not appear before about seven months; large tumors are infrequent and metastases are rare.

In the first study describing the induction of ovarian tumors by X radiation (Furth and Furth, 1936) mice of three different strains were exposed to a single dose or repeated large doses of X radiation at the age of approximately five to twelve weeks. Irradiation caused a fifteenfold increase of ovarian tumors over that of controls. Following irradiation of four- to six-weeks-old mice with single doses of 87, 175, or 350 r of X radiation (Furth and Boon, 1943), ovarian tumors began to appear when the mice were about eleven months of age. The frequency of these neoplasms increased with time and almost every mouse that lived seventeen months developed a unilateral or bilateral ovarian growth, irrespective of the dose of radiation.

The observation that total-body irradiation in female mice is frequently, if not inevitably, followed by the development of ovarian tumors has been described by numerous investigators (Bali and Furth, 1949). Lorenz *et al.* (1947) pointed out that, in mice chronically exposed to 0.1 r daily (8 hours), there is a significant increase in ovarian tumor incidence over that of controls. The maximum accumulated dose was 164 r. There is no significant decrease in mean survival time. Thus the ovarian tumor-inducing dose is cumulative and the smallest dose rate inducing ovarian tumors in mice is about 0.1 r daily, with an average total dose of 110 r.

Exposure of ovaries to X radiation causes the development of tumors (Fig. 18-8) of different types. These neoplasms are multicentric, occur frequently in both ovaries, and are of diverse histological type, each of which can be isolated as a pure line by serial transplantation. Most tumors arising in irradiated ovaries are complex (Bali and Furth, 1949). Most transplantable neoplasms are of the granulosa cell type; a small number are luteomas and tubular adenomas. All these types are frequently present in the same irradiated ovary. Less commonly encountered neoplasms were hemangiomas and endotheliomas (two of which resembled chorioepitheliomas) and sarcomas. Only two types of cells thus far transplanted were found to be associated with hormone production: granulosa cell tumors causing morphological changes indicative of the production of estrogens, and luteomas with changes indicative of progestin production. It is not known whether all small tumorlike nodules in the ovary of X-irradiated mice are autonomous growths, but

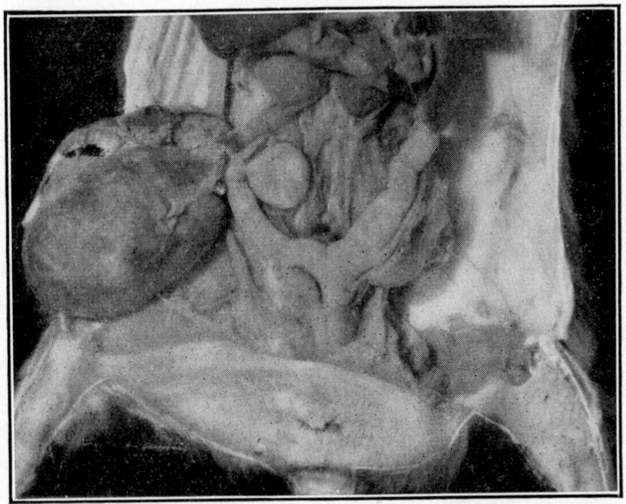

FIG. 18-8. Unilateral ovarian tumor (lacteoma) in a mouse induced by total-body exposure to X rays with hormonal hyperplasia of the uterine horns (*after Furth and Butterworth*, 1936).

five types have been grafted on normal hosts: granulosa tumors, luteomas, tubular adenomas, sarcomas, and angioendotheliomas. The granulosa tumors occur in a wide range of morphological forms similar to those seen in woman and simulate so many different types of neoplasms that their identification on a morphological basis alone is often not possible. Their common denominator is the ability to produce or initiate production of estrogens and plethorins (a hypothetical substance that raises blood volume—Sobel and Furth, 1948) although not all tumor-bearing hosts show the effects of these substances.

Investigators who have attempted to describe the morphogenesis of ovarian neoplasms have arrived at contradictory conclusions (Bali and Furth, 1949). Some trace their origin to the covering germinal epithelium, some to stromal cells (ovariocytes). The chief pacemakers of the ovarian cycle are the pituitary gland and the ova. The latter gradually die after irradiation by even small doses, and a sequence of changes ensues, leading to the development of neoplasms. Neither the morphogenesis nor the pathogenesis of this process is well understood. Some endocrine disturbance is doubtless at play, but the term "endocrine imbalance" merely covers our ignorance.

When a threshold dose is exceeded, the onset of ovarian tumors and their course follow a similar pattern; increasing the dose of radiation beyond the sterilization dose (Lorenz, 1950) does not shorten the incubation period. This is unlike the situation found with leukemia or bone tumor induction by irradiation. The induced ovarian neoplasms are always slow to grow, hardly interfere with the life span of the animals, and seldom metastasize. These findings suggest that there is some trigger mechanism causing an all-or-none response, and this is best explained on the basis of hormonal derangements initiated by the depletion of follicles of the normal ovary by irradiation (Gardner, 1950). Neither the virus nor the mutation theory can adequately explain ovarian tumorigenesis by irradiation.

Lick *et al.* (1949) have studied the pathogenesis of ovarian tumor induction. They found that X radiation did not induce tumors in an irradiated ovary if the animal's second ovary remained unirradiated and functional. Irradiation of a single ovary induced ovarian tumors only if the second ovary was extirpated. Although a second functioning ovary inhibited ovarian tumor development following unilateral contact irradiation, bilateral contact irradiation resulted in tumor development. Irradiated ovaries implanted intramuscularly into irradiated and nonirradiated groups of spayed LAF_1 hybrid mice gave rise to many granulosa-cell tumors, luteomas, and related neoplasms (Kaplan, 1950a). No such tumors occurred when irradiated ovaries were implanted into nonirradiated, nonovariectomized mice. In concluding that intact ovarian endocrine function inhibits the development of tumors in irradiated ovarian grafts, Kaplan confirmed the observations of Lick *et al.* (1949) and suggested that both a direct and an indirect mechanism may be involved in the induction of ovarian tumors by irradiation.

The induction of ovarian tumors in mice by exposure to ionizing radiations, even though it is of unusual interest, may represent a special case. Thus far (fifteen years after the original observations were made), no other species has been found to be susceptible to ovarian tumor induction by irradiation. This carcinogenesis requires no more than a single exposure, once the threshold is exceeded; it is not dose-dependent, has a long tumor-development time (approximately one year), and occurs in almost all exposed mice after about one and a half years.

Sterilization of women by X radiation was practiced some years ago. Whether X irradiation has increased the frequency of carcinoma in the reproductive organs of women has been the subject of much debate. The available information is certainly not impressive. The assumed period of latency was so short in many reported cases that many neoplasms may have been present at the time of irradiation. However, the denial of the theoretical possibility of such an event (Dehler, 1927) certainly lost its wisdom in the light of later experimental findings on the induction of neoplasms in the reproductive organs of animals. Nevertheless, the clinical observations of Depenthal (1919), Bumm (1923), Vogt (1926), and Dehler (1927) should be regarded as possibilities rather than proof of the induction of neoplasm in reproductive organs of women (uterus, ovary, vulva).

Pituitary Tumors. Large quantities of I^{131} (200–400 μc in mice) completely destroy the thyroid gland. Persistent lack of thyroid hormone causes an over-stimulation of the pituitary gland and the hyperplasia of the pituitary cells, which secrete thyrotropic hormones, gradually terminates in neoplastic growth.

The original findings of Gorbman (1949) that the destruction of the thyroid by I^{131} gives rise in mice to such growths have been fully confirmed, every mouse receiving doses of I^{131} large enough to destroy the thyroid and surviving such treatment longer than thirteen months developed pituitary tumors (Furth and Burnett, 1951). In line with this interpretation are the few observations that long-continued administration of antithyroid compounds may cause the development of similar tumors.

The pituitary growths induced by doses of I^{131} destructive to the thyroid are readily transplantable in mice, the thyroid glands of which have been similarly destroyed, but not in normal mice, with rare exceptions. Therefore, these growths are not fully autonomous but merely conditioned neoplasms even though they may metastasize. Pituitary enlargement after thyroid destruction by I^{131} can be prevented by admintration of 0.15 per cent USP desiccated thyroid in diet (thyroxine) (Goldberg and Chaikoff, 1951b); similarly, thyroid hormone restrains the growths of the grafted pituitary tumors. These tumors discharge thyrotropic and possibly gonadotropic hormones and, when grafted in young mice, cause a tremendous cystic dilatation of the extrahepatic biliary tract (Furth *et al.*, 1952). While a study of these tumors is of great interest in both endocrinology and oncology, it is not likely to become a human problem. When patients with thyroid carcinoma are given thyroid-destructive doses of I^{131}, and the symptoms of hypothyroidism become pronounced, thyroid hormone is administered, which counteracts the stimulation of the pituitary gland.

Thyroid. Administration of I^{131} localizes predominantly in the thyroid gland, and thus 300–400 μc given to mice causes complete destruction of the gland. Somewhat lower doses (200–300 μc) destroy the gland, leaving a few atypical acini which do not seem to respond to excessive amounts of thyroid-stimulating hormone circulating in the blood. Some of these thyroid remnants exhibit the morphological appearance of a precancerous lesion. Doniach (1950) administered 32 μc of I^{131} either alone or in combination with methylthiouracil to rats, and thereby increased the rate of formation of thyroid adenomas and, in one rat, a thyroid tumor was observed. Similarly, Goldberg and Chaikoff (1951a) observed multiple adenomas in two of ten rats that had been given a single injection of 400 μc of radioactive iodine.

In a later work, Goldberg and Chaikoff (1952) observed malignant thyroid tumors in seven of twenty-five rats given a single injection of 400 μc of radioactive iodine. Metastases occurred in all seven rats, the organs invaded being lung, adrenal, lymph nodes, skin, and bone.

Invasion of blood vessels, and even lung metastases, were seen by Morris and Green (1951) following long-continued administration of thiouracil to mice. Many of these tumors ultimately became autonomous in the sense that they grew in normal mice (Morris *et al.*, 1951).

The very definition of malignancy is now controversial. It is no longer possible to determine on the basis of gross or microscopic studies whether such lesions, so readily induced in different endocrine organs by irradiation, possess autonomy, or are nonneoplastic growths caused and maintained by derangement of the normal hormonal balance. Further studies on the induction of neoplasia of the thyroid gland by I^{131} alone or in combination with goitrogens are desirable. On the basis of related experience, one might expect induction of thyroid tumors in a high percentage of the experimental animals by a dose below that which completely destroys this organ. The origin of autonomy in conditioned growth has been demonstrated in several organs, including the thyroid and the pituitary (Furth *et al.*, 1952).

In man, Kindler (1943) described the development of thyroid carcinoma and that of the hypopharynx following massive prolonged irradiation of the neck. After discussing the literature, he concludes that "Überdosierung erzeugt mit Sichercheit Krebs."

Parathyroid. This appears to be resistant to radiation. No tumor has ever been described in this organ, either after total-body or local irradiation. When mice are radiothyroidectomized with I^{131}, this organ must also receive large quantities of ionizing radiations. It usually decreases in size and often little of it is found in serial sections; yet neither neoplastic nor preneoplastic changes have been noted in this organ (Furth, unpublished data).

MAMMARY GLAND

There are numerous reports on the induction of mammary tumors by ionizing irradiations in several species of animals (mice, guinea pigs, and rats). The induction of this tumor appears to take place by an indirect mechanism; in several experiments estrogens seem to be clearly implicated.

The relation of mammary tumors to irradiation has been reviewed by Lorenz *et al.* (1951). Acute massive whole-body roentgen irradiation of mice reduced the over-all incidence of these tumors in comparison with that of the controls, but the incidence of this neoplasm was high in those irradiated mice which developed granulosa-cell tumors of the ovary. These findings were attributed to the well-known decrease in estrogen production following irradiation of the ovaries and excessive estrogen production by the granulosa-cell tumors (Furth and Butterworth, 1936). Lorenz *et al.* (1951) exposed C3H mice for ten to fifteen months to doses of γ radiation of 0.044–4.4 r daily. Although the females became sterile, this type of chronic exposure had no influence upon the incidence of mammary tumors.

In another series of experiments, Lorenz *et al.* (1951) irradiated mature LAF_1 mice with doses of γ radiation ranging from 0.11 to 8.8 r daily (8 hours) during the entire life span of the animals. LAF_1 mice which do not carry the milk agent have a low spontaneous incidence of mammary tumors. All experimental groups of female mice, with the exception of that exposed to 0.11 r daily, showed an increased incidence of mammary carcinoma ranging from 4–14 per cent. Moreover, in all but the 8.8-r group irradiated during the entire life span, sarcomas of the mammary gland developed, the incidence ranging from 13–25 per cent. Most breast tumors were associated with granulosa-cell tumors of the ovary.

In their most recent paper, Lorenz *et al.* (1951) describe the effects of chronic massive γ irradiation on the mammary tumor incidence in the milk factor-free C3Hb mice. Forty-seven per cent of the females developed mammary carcinomas and sarcomas, and 88 per cent, ovarian tumors. These workers exclude the possibility that direct irradiation alone was responsible for the production of these tumors and postulate a combination of factors such as hormonal stimulation, direct effect on the mammary gland, and other unknown indirect effects of systemic origin. It is noteworthy that the mammary sarcomas like the mammary carcinomas are associated with granulosa-cell tumors. Histologic evidence of estrogen secretion is often lacking in hosts bearing primary tumors, but is invariably present in the subpassages of such tumors in young hosts. Obviously, atrophic target organs may not respond to the hormones.

It is noteworthy that estrogen induces carcinomas in mice and fibroadenomas in rats, indicating that both epithelial and connective tissue elements of the breast are under endocrine influence. This can also be demonstrated by hormonal stimulation of grafted fibroadenomas. Of twenty-eight rats living longer than 150 days after repeated doses of cyclotron neutrons, eleven had malignant tumors of which seven were mammary carcinomas (Leitch, 1947). The incidence of benign mammary tumors following X irradiation (Metcalf and Inda, 1951) was 10.8–34.6 per cent in female rats exposed to 0.1–10 r daily during a period of two years and 8.3 per cent in the controls. There was a direct relation between the daily dose of radiation and the number of benign tumors, the smallest increase occurring among rats exposed to 0.1 r and the greatest among those exposed to 10 r. Ovarian tumors were not seen in rats. It is not likely that in the same species X radiation would induce benign tumors, and neutrons, malignant tumors; the discrepancy is probably due to differences in diagnoses.

In guinea pigs of both sexes chronically exposed to 1.1 r for 8 hours daily, mammary carcinomas occurred three to five times as often as among the controls (Lorenz, 1950). These tumors were likewise not associated with ovarian neoplasms. Thus the pathogenesis of the induction of mammary tumors in rats and guinea pigs requires an explanation.

Those who practice "prophylactic" irradiation to prevent recurrence of tumors after their surgical removal may find experimental support in the work of Owen and Williams (1940), who exposed C3H mice, which have a high spontaneous incidence of breast carcinoma, to 100–400 r at approximately four months of age. They observed a decrease of cancer incidence from 65 per cent in the controls to 11–39 per cent in the irradiated mice, the decrease in cancer incidence being a function of the dose. These experiments are subject to different interpretations, and arguments can be presented in favor of both indirect (hormonal) and local mechanisms causing this change. Unfortunately, the animals were sacrificed too soon. An increase in mammary tumor incidence occurs after a longer period of time, when in the ovary the proliferation of estrogen-secreting granulosa cells supersedes the degenerative changes (Furth and Furth, 1936).

UTERUS

Chronic irradiation significantly increased the incidence of uterine carcinomas in rabbits chronically exposed to γ radiation of radium (Lorenz, 1950); the higher the dose rate, the earlier the tumor development time. The tumors did not metastasize in the controls but did so in most experimental animals, and it is possible that chronic irradiation may have enhanced the dissemination process. All but one of twelve rabbits exposed to 1.1–8.8 r daily developed a uterine carcinoma and seven of these had metastases. Two of six controls had similar tumors but none metastasized. None of three rabbits exposed to 0.11 r daily had tumors because they died early of intercurrent disease. Kaplan and Murphy (1949) described in mice a transplanted mammary tumor, which usually does not metastasize but will do so when irradiated with doses insufficient to destroy the tumor. Similarly, one of us (Furth, 1935) found that a transplantable leukemic tumor which tends to remain localized in normal hosts at the site of injection will disseminate in irradiated hosts, causing generalized leukemia.

SKIN

This organ is more resistant to induction of neoplasia by irradiation than most internal organs. Single or repeated exposures to X or γ radiation which are harmless to the skin may cause neoplasms of internal organs; leukemia in man; leukemia, ovarian, mammary, and lung tumors in mice; mammary tumors in guinea pigs; and uterine tumors in rabbits. Nevertheless cutaneous tumors were the first noted in man and reproduced in animals, mainly because of the relatively soft type of X radiation used earlier and due to lack of adequate filtration. While penetrating radiations, irrespective of type, produce internal tumors and leukemias, the carcinogenic effect of nonpenetrating radiations is limited to the skin because this is the site of greatest absorption (see also Blum, Vol. II, this series, in preparation).

During the first decades following the discovery of X radiation, radiation cancer of the skin occurred among those professionally exposed, as has been described, but in recent years therapeutic exposure has been the more common cause (Saunders and Montgomery, 1938). Self-produced radiodermatitis has not vanished, however. In one large hospital alone, 115 physicians were treated for radiodermatitis, and 39 for skin cancers. Carelessness and ignorance are the two main causes of these preventable conditions (Leddy and Rigos, 1941). Skin tumors do not develop following irradiation without an attendant reversible inflammation. Chronic radiodermatitis is encountered particularly as a result of the injudicious irradiation of various benign dermatoses. The principle that the more extensive the injury, the more likely the superimposition of cancer, is well established. Epitheliomas apparently develop with equal frequency from either keratoses or ulcerations (Saunders and Montgomery, 1938).

In man the neoplasms arising in the epidermis usually commence with a warty growth (papilloma) and terminate in squamous-cell carcinoma. Ulceration usually but not invariably precedes the development of carcinoma. Rarely, tumors (sarcomas) arise in the connective tissue. The first experimental tumors induced in rats were sarcomas, in the rabbit carcinomas, and this may be due to differences in the texture and thickness of the skin. The studies of Wolbach (1909) on the early histological changes in skin leading to carcinoma are now classical.

The earliest changes recognized by Wolbach were in the collagen. The most conspicuous and constant change in connective tissue is rarefaction immediately beneath the epidermis and a greater density in deeper layers (Saunders and Montgomery, 1938). There is homogenization of the collagen with formation of dense sclerotic areas taking on a bluish color with hematoxylin and eosin stain. Wolbach found degenerative changes in smooth muscle, obliteration of capillaries by proliferation of the endothelium, and telangiectasia of other capillaries. The obliterative changes in the veins and arteries were manifested chiefly by a great increase in the connective tissue beneath the endothelium and a marked thickening of the media. Hypertrophy of the epidermis was a constant finding. Complete absence of hair follicles and of sebaceous and coil glands was the rule in lesions of long duration. In no case was there evidence of proliferation of any of the dermal appendages. Coil glands were often found in regions in which there was a total absence of hair follicles and sebaceous glands.

Saunders and Montgomery (1938) described the characteristic histopathological picture of radiodermatitis as follows: The epidermis is hyperkeratotic and acanthotic, and usually there is an associated increase in the stratum granulosum. Necrosis and ulceration of the epidermis are frequently encountered. The formation of abscesses and spaces (*Lücken*) in the epidermis are seen infrequently. Destruction of the elastic tissues occurs in severe cases. Sometimes a few fine fibers of newly formed elastic tissue can be demonstrated. There is new formation of capillaries arising from thickened vessels in the upper cutis. The larger vessels show varying degrees of thickening of the adventitia and media and proliferation of the intima to the point of partial or complete occlusion. The infiltrate in the cutis is not consistent or characteristic, polymorphonuclear leukocytes predominating in necrotic connective tissue in areas of ulceration, and lymphocytes predominating elsewhere. The sebaceous glands are almost invariably destroyed. Next, and depending on the severity of the radiodermatitis, the hair follicles become involved and, in the case of third-degree injuries, the sweat glands are usually atrophic or completely missing. Hyperpigmentation, a feature of acute radiodermatitis, is not evident, very little melanin being demonstrable microscopically.

All epitheliomas originated in the epidermis and none in the hair follicles or sweat ducts. Most epitheliomas studied show phenomena of individual cell keratinization; many showed giant epithelial cells, representing amitotic cell division. Roentgen epitheliomas simulate and even duplicate the histologic picture of epitheliomas arising from senile and arsenic keratoses, and they tend to begin as epitheliomas *in situ*, with the various phenomena of individual cell keratinization.

Gamma radiation, from radon seeds, was widely used for the removal of hemangiomas. In a review of all the case histories of a large metropolitan tumor clinic, four cases have been found in which late radiation dermatitis or a skin carcinoma followed in thirteen to sixteen years. Two patients received much larger doses (about 110,000 r) than did the radium poisoning cases, yet the tumor development time is comparable (Evans, see Brues, 1951). The tumors so induced arise either in the epidermis or subjacent connective tissue.

The carcinogenicity of α or β emitters can be tested conveniently by direct introduction into the subcutaneous tissue. The tumors induced arise either in the epidermis or in subjacent connective tissue. Andervont and Shimkin (1940) induced subcutaneous tumors by injection of colloidal thorium dioxide and Lisco *et al.* (1947) by plutonium and colloidal yttrium phosphate. In the former experiment the effect of metallic thorium has not been excluded. Lacassagne and Rudali (1942) caused the regression of papillomas by irradiation in five rabbits, but in one rabbit a new tumor, histologically a rhabdomyosarcoma, developed at the site of the originally benign growth twenty-eight months after the irradiation. A similar sequence of events has been observed in man.

Beta radiations from P^{32} are highly carcinogenic to the skin when applied directly. The energy absorption from P^{32} is limited almost entirely to the skin (Raper *et al.*, 1946, and Raper, 1947). In experiments of Raper *et al.*, all rats receiving single doses of 4000–5000 rep developed skin tumors (see also Henshaw *et al.*, 1946, 1947) and the number of loci of tumors arising in some rabbits exceeded fifty. The lethal dose of external β radiation varied with the size of the animal, being approximately 4500 rep for mice and 7000 for rats.

LUNG

Lung Tumors among Miners of Schneeberg and Jáchymov. There is no doubt that ionizing radiations will induce lung tumors in experimental animals, but it is still controversial whether radiations emitted by radon, either inhaled as radon-contaminated air or present in the expired air from radium deposits in the body, will induce lung tumors in man. Many complicating factors make an evaluation of the problem difficult (Lorenz, 1944). With the extension of mining activity of radioactive deposits throughout the world, exposure to inhalation of radioactive dust and gases will constitute an increasing hazard, and this problem will therefore be fully reviewed.

The main information on the induction of lung tumors in man comes from the study of this disease in the miners of the uranium mines of Schneeberg and Jáchymov (Joachimsthal). The history of a strange disease called *Bergkrankheit* among the miners of Schneeberg goes back to the sixteenth century (Šikl, 1950). However, not until 1879 was it recognized (Haerting and Hesse) that this disease originated in the lungs and that about 75 per cent of all deaths of the miners was due to a neoplasm diagnosed erroneously as lymphosarcoma. These findings were confirmed by Arnstein (1913) who corrected the diagnosis to squamous-cell carcinoma and attributed 40 per cent of all deaths of miners during the period of 1875 to 1912 to this tumor. The incidence of pulmonary tumors in miners of both Schneeberg and Jáchymov was reviewed by Peller in 1939, who gave the mortality statistics contained in the accompanying tabulation. More than 87 per cent of primary tumors in these miners originated in the lung.

CANCER MORTALITY PER 1000

	Jáchymov (1929–1938)	Schneeberg		Vienna males, 15–79 years (1932–1936)
		(1895–1897)	(1895–1912)	
Lung cancer	9.8 ± 1.5	12.7 ± 1	16.5 ± 1.5	0.34
Cancer of other organs	0.7 ± 0.4	2.4 ± 0.4	2.1 ± 0.6	2.1

Early investigators attributed the high incidence of pulmonary tumors to inhalation of arsenic dust. Besides pitchblende, the mines contain silver, cobalt, arsenic, and nickel. Silicosis is as frequent as carcinoma, but no relationship could be established between the two diseases. The average time spent in mines before manifestations of carcinoma is thirteen to seventeen years. The sites in the lung, the types and the biological behavior of carcinoma are identical with those occurring in this organ throughout the world (Behounek *et al.*, 1937; Šikl, 1950).

The literature on this miner's disease is too voluminous to be fully reviewed. After the discovery of the carcinogenic properties of radioactive substances, radon was blamed for the high incidence of lung cancer. In a detailed investigation, Rajewsky *et al.* (1942) found that the radon content of air in the mines of Schneeberg and Jáchymov varied from 7×10^{-12} to 7×10^{-9} curie per liter. Measurements of the radioactive content of lungs of miners gave radium equivalent values not different from that of non-miners. Rajewsky *et al.* found an average radon content of the air of the mines to be 3×10^{-9} curie per liter and assumed a permissible dose of 1×10^{-8} to 1×10^{-9} curie per liter of air and concluded that radon is possibly one of the causes of the lung cancer of the miners.

A similar permissible dose was established by Read and Mottram (1939). Evans and Goodman (1940) arrived at a daily dose of 1×10^{-11} curie per liter as follows: 1 μg of radium stored in the body will produce 1.1×10^{-11} curie of exhaled radon per liter. Three dial painters developed carcinoma of the ethmoids and antrum (Martland, personal communication). One of these had 2 μg of stored radium in the body and exhaled 2×10^{-11} curie per liter. Typical air measurements in these mines show ten to two hundred times this value. Krebs *et al.* (1930) measured the body content of radium of eighteen persons who died with no known exposure to radium and found a range of less than 1×10^{-9} to 4×10^{-8} radium equivalent. Hursh and Gates (1950) made similar measurements and arrived at one hundred times smaller values, which are 50,000 times lower than those that were found in people with bone sarcoma induced by radium.

Assuming an average radon content of 3×10^{-9} curie per liter of mine air, Evans and Goodman (1940) estimated an hourly exposure of dry lung to be equivalent to 0.17 erg per gram, and the corresponding daily dose on the upper bronchial epithelium of the order of magnitude of 0.1 rep per day. Assuming seventeen years as an average tumor induction time, the total dose would be 600 rep (estimated to equal 3000 rem; Evans, see Brues, 1951). The dose effective in initiating the tumor would obviously be much smaller. It is not known whether α particles are more effective than X radiation for the same total dose. On the basis of blood analyses Woldrich (1931) concluded that cancer of the bronchi is caused by inhalation of radium emanation.

Induction of lung tumors in mice requires either a comparatively massive single dose or considerably higher chronic doses, as will be detailed. In comparison to the mouse, man has a low incidence of spontaneous lung tumors; most tumors in mice are benign, while most of those in man are malignant. In chronic exposures of man to radon in the Schneeberg and Jáchymov mines much smaller total doses are involved than are necessary to induce lung tumors in mice. In breathing air containing radon, the tissue dose of α radiation delivered to the epithelium is, however, greatest in the larger bronchi where the primary neoplasms are frequently located (Evans, see Brues, 1951). Radon gas which emits α radiation becomes an atom of the solid radioactive substance RaA, decays into a series of radioactive elements of varying half lives, which may adhere to the bronchial epithelium. Among other factors which may contribute to the induction of these human tumors are pneumoconiosis produced by the mine dust, and the cobalt and arsenic content of the dust. Less likely is a hereditary susceptibility due to inbreeding, mentioned by several investigators, or the carcinogenicity of nonradioactive cobalt, chromium, and arsenic (see also Schinz and Uehlinger, 1942; Hueper, personal communication).

Abrahamson *et al.* (1950) described the development of bilateral alveolar lung carcinoma in a patient who, sixteen years previously, had received an intravenous injection of 75 cc of thorotrast. The liver and spleen of the patient still contained much radioactivity at time of death. The multifocal origin of the lung tumors in this patient is cited as evidence for their induction by irradiation.

Experimental Induction of Lung Tumors in Radioactive Mines. This has been carried out either on a very small scale or without adequate controls. Dohnert (1938) exposed mice in the Schneeberg mines at places where the miners worked, but his uncontrolled experiments were inconclusive. Hereck (1939) reported on histologic changes in 110 mice similarly exposed, of which five had adenomas of the lungs. Unfortunately, no controls were observed. Lorenz (1944) injected eleven mice of a lung tumor-susceptible stock four times at weekly intervals with an aqueous radon solution totaling 1.2 mc. Some animals lived up to eight and one-half months, but no increase in lung tumor incidence was observed in the injected animals over that of controls. Rajewsky *et al.* (1943) exposed mice continuously to various doses of radon in an emanatorium. Mice exposed to 1.16×10^{-6} curie per liter lived from 161 to 453 days. Of the twelve experimental animals, ten had adenomas of the lung, one an adenocarcinoma originating from a small bronchus, while only one of the control animals had an adenoma.

Thus it is questionable whether radon can induce lung tumors in experimental animals. The work of Rajewsky *et al.* suggests this, but a problem as important as this deserves a sounder experimental foundation.

Experimental Induction of Lung Tumors by X or Gamma Radiation. This has been carried out on a much larger scale. The induction rate of lung tumors in mice by total-body irradiation is very low and the tumor development time is long.

Furth and Furth (1936) gave evidence that massive doses of X radiation given to three strains of lung tumor-susceptible mice induces lung tumors. The increase in lung tumor incidence observed in females was slight but statistically significant. Lorenz *et al.* (1946) exposed mice to chronic γ radiation giving 8.8 r daily (8 hours) and a total of approximately 2400 r over a period of ten months and found an increase in lung tumor incidence of 50 per cent over controls. In later experiments, Lorenz (unpublished data) has shown that the lung tumors are induced by a direct action of the radiation upon the lungs. The lung tumors induced in mice were alveolar in origin and benign, as were those in the controls.

Lisco and Finkel (1949) induced bronchiogenic carcinomas in rats by inhalation of an unknown quantity of radioactive cerium oxide; this compound covers the bronchi tenaciously.

Gorbman (1949) described the development of tumors of the trachea in mice that had been injected with large doses of I^{131}. This was not seen by one of us in more than thirty mice of the same strain similarly radiothyroidectomized by I^{131} and observed for over a year. The changes seen in the trachea were destructive and proliferative but not neoplastic. Cancer of the larynx was described in a woman whose thyroid received prolonged X radiation (Jacques, 1935).

BONE

The development of a malignant tumor in a normal bone or in a benign tumor that had been exposed to heavy doses of X or γ radiation was first described by Beck in 1922, and in 1945 Hatcher could collect from the literature twenty-four cases (Fig. 18-9). In all except six the irradiation was given for chronic joint infection. In three cases bone sarcoma resulted from irradiation given for the treatment of other tumors. In all but one case a large amount of radiation was administered in fractional doses over a long period. The median interval between irradiation and recognition of sarcoma was six years; the shortest interval was three years; the longest, eleven years. Chondrosarcoma occurred more frequently among irradiation-produced sarcomas than among other spontaneous bone tumors. The degree of bone formation in the tumors was variable; those in which none was found were labeled as polymorphous or spindle-celled sarcomas.

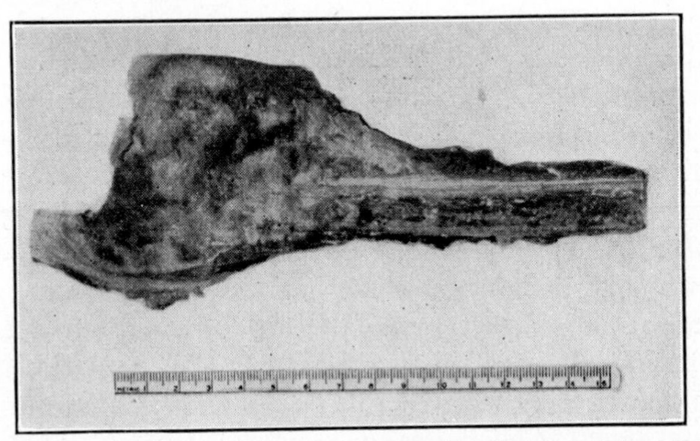

FIG. 18-9. Osteogenic sarcoma induced in man by X rays (*after Hatcher*, 1945).

Cahan *et al.* (1948) collected from the literature seventeen cases of bone sarcomas following radium or roentgen radiation therapy reported until 1948 (exclusive of Martland's cases of radium dial painters) and described eleven additional cases observed by them. The first thirteen cases noted between 1922 and 1937 occurred in patients receiving therapeutic irradiation for bone tuberculosis. The patients were eleven to forty years old at the onset of the neoplasm. Three to ten years elapsed between irradiation and the discovery of the tumor. The bone sarcomas were variously described as spindle-celled, pleomorphic, giant-celled, chondro-fibro-osteosarcoma, and osteo-chondro-myxosarcoma. The subsequent four cases described between 1939–45 occurred in patients twenty-three to fifty-six years old receiving treatment for chronic arthritis, benign giant-cell tumor, chondroblastoma, or as a "prophylactic" measure following removal of carcinoma of the breast. It was subsequently pointed out by several investigators that the irradiation of benign giant-cell tumors is hazardous, as it is likely to cause a malignant transformation of this neoplasm. Jaffe and Selin (1951) noted an apparent increase in the number of malignant metastasizing giant-cell tumors since the beginning of the era of radiation therapy of this tumor.

The eleven cases of bone tumor following X irradiation, well studied by Cahan *et al.* (1948), occurred in patients from nine to fifty-nine years of age. Some were treated for nonmalignant bone disease, such as ossifying fibroma, bone cyst, osteoid osteoma, fibrous dysplasia, and benign giant-cell tumor, or for nonosseous malignant tumor, as retinoblastoma, or for an inflammatory process, as "cloudiness" of antrum. This recalls earlier observations of bone tumor induction by X-radiation treatment given for joint tuberculosis and the experimental work of Lacassagne (1936), who induced varied neoplasms by irradiation of chronic inflammatory tissue. The estimated tumor dose in the patients of Cahan *et al.* varied between approximately 1550 to 16,000 r and the interval between the last irradiation and onset of bone tumor varied from six to twenty-two years. To one of the eleven patients, the X-radiation treatment was administered to the site of a bone fracture following radical mastectomy. It seems probable that osteoblastic activity at the time of irradiation facilitated the induction of these neoplasms; osteoblasts are highly sensitive to irradiation.

Most internal tumors in man exposed to either X radiation or radioactive substances arose in bones. Auerbach *et al.* (1951) reported an extraskeletal osteogenic sarcoma originating in soft tissues of the back. This tumor arose directly beneath the skin in an area that four years previously had received a skin dose of 4000 r of X radiation delivered in ten exposures over a period of 70 days. The rare occurrence of extraosseous bone tumors following irradiation can be explained by osteogenic metaplasia at sites of chronic inflammation.

The characteristic sequence of changes in bone following irradiation and preceding the carcinogenic transformation has been described by Ewing (1926), who named this change "radiation osteitis." This is essentially a degenerative change with necrosis and reactive atypical new bone formation and is similar following all types of irradiations. (For recent references, see Koletsky *et al.*, 1950.)

Bone Tumors in Radium Dial Painters. An industrial hazard occurring in New Jersey, well followed by Martland (1931), claimed forty-one victims during a period of some twenty years. Between 1916 and 1925 dial painters moistened, by licking, brushes which had been dipped into the luminous compound containing radium and mesothorium. This material ingested over many years lodged in the bones, causing severe anemia and bone tumors. Death occurred within four to six years after ingestion ceased. Autopsy revealed the outstanding changes were necrosis of the jaw and aplastic anemia. The bone changes first noted were those of radiation osteitis (Martland *et al.*, 1925). Later (1931), bone tumors developed in many foci, and death was caused from metastases of one of these growths. At autopsy, Martland found other primary bone tumors and transitional changes from radiation osteitis to malignant growth. Thus far (Martland, 1951, personal communication), fourteen girls had osteogenic sarcomas, all of whom died before 1930; four are still known to be alive, suffering from a crippling bone lesion, probably radiation osteitis with pathological fractures; and three died from epidermoid carcinoma that started in the mucosa of the accessory sinuses of the head. Since this type of carcinoma is rare and no other carcinoma was found in this small group, their relation to the ingested radioactive materials seems highly probable. Martland's observations gave impetus to the study of experimental induction of bone tumors, and to establish factors governing the induction of this tumor, such as the dose levels of tumor induction, permissible maximum exposure to radiation, and methods to increase the elimination of radioactive substances from the body.

In persons with chronic radium poisoning who have developed osteogenic sarcomas, the radium content varied from a few to over 20 μg. Analysis of the radium content of bone of a patient with a fibrosarcoma made after approximately fifteen years of exposure showed an average of 1.5×10^{-9} g of radium per g of dry bone, delivering approximately 1 rep per day per g of bone (Evans *et al.*, 1944; Evans, 1950a). Average dose values are of little significance unless the distribution pattern is known to be uniform. This is not the case, however, since the radium is distributed at discrete points throughout the bone.

Recent investigations of Evans (1950a) showed that persons who had received radium only and who contained from 0.3 to 22 μg of stored radium were free of bone tumors up to thirty-four years. A clinical picture similar to that of the luminous dial painters was produced in these patients by approximately five to ten times as much radioactive material. The compound ingested by the dial painters contained mesothorium, an α emitter with a half life of 6.7 years. When Martland's cases were investigated, mesothorium had already decayed many half lives and only the stored radium was determined. Mesothorium may have been involved in all cases of irradiation injury in which the stored radium was less than 5 μg. Accordingly, the maximum permissible value of 0.1 μg of radium may have a safety factor of 50. The permissible doses of the various elements given were established before these findings were known.

Experimental Production of Bone Tumors. The first bone tumors in man and experimental animals were induced inadvertently. Lacassagne and Vinzent (1929), irradiating chronic inflammatory lesions of rabbits, produced an osteosarcoma and a periosteal sarcoma. Lacassagne and Nyka (1937), attempting to induce tumors of the hypophysis with radon, caused the development of bone tumors of the sella turcica. The sequence of changes noted has been necrosis, revascularization, callus formation, and cancerization. The numerous studies made subsequently, including those with fission products, have been detailed in the section on corpuscular irradiations. It is evident from the observations described that osteoblasts are highly susceptible to neoplasia induction.

Marrow cells adjacent to radioactive bone received large doses of radiation and humans so exposed frequently developed anemia, yet only a few myeloid leukemias have been reported among them.

LIVER

Malignant liver-cell tumors resulting from exposure to ionizing radiations have not been described in man or animals, but there is some evidence that massive doses of ionizing radiations may cause endothelial sarcomas in man and benign hepatomas in mice.

Ross (1936) described an illustrative example of the consequence of prolonged exposure to γ radiation in a localized area of human liver, in which a hemangioma developed subjacent to a radium needle. Metastases were present in the lung and bone marrow. The origin of the tumor was traced to branches of the portal vein. Similarly, MacMahon *et al.* (1947) described an endothelial cell sarcoma of the liver following thorotrast injections.

Lorenz (1950, and unpublished data) noted an increased incidence of hepatomas in mice following chronic γ irradiation. The direct relation of these benign nodules to irradiation remains to be demonstrated. Au^{198} colloid had been given to man and animals, delivering to this organ many times the LD_{50} total-body dose, but thus far no local tumors have been produced. Liver damage with some cirrhosis was seen following Au^{198} therapy (Hahn *et al.*, 1951). The observations thus far are sketchy, however. It seems that, in man, the endothelial cells of the liver are susceptible to neoplasia induction by irradiation while liver cells are resistant. Chronic exposure studies with Au^{198} colloid are most desirable, since this colloid selectively localizes in the Kupffer cells, exposing the liver to thousands of rep without causing early death of the animal. The above observations suggest the possibility of neoplasia induction from its use. Radiogold colloid is currently used in the experimental therapy of human cancers. (Concerning cirrhosis in animals receiving thorium, see Hugenin *et al.*, 1931.)

Direct introduction of radium into the gallbladder will cause carcinoma of this organ (Biltris, 1933).

GASTROINTESTINAL TRACT

Lisco *et al.* (1947) produced carcinoma of the colon by feeding rats with radioactive yttrium. These tumors were associated with polypoid hyperplasia of the colon and ulcerative colitis. The pathogenesis of these tumors deserves further study, as little is known about the etiology of the common tumors of the large intestine of man, and such tumors cannot be easily induced by chemical carcinogens.

BRAIN

This organ is resistant to irradiation and thus far no human or experimental brain tumor caused by ionizing radiation is on record. Glia cells of the brain are susceptible to chemical carcinogens, and one might expect the formation of gliomas in brains exposed to large doses of ionizing radiation. Yet thus far only sarcomas of the connective tissue and bone tumors have resulted from such exposures (Jentzer, 1937; Lacassagne and Nyka, 1937).

Wilson *et al.* (1951) exposed rat embryos to X radiation on the ninth day of gestation and noted the development of discrete tumorlike growths in and around the brain and related these directly to X irradiation. They first appeared on the second day after irradiation and thereafter exhibited varying capacities for growth and differentiation. Some grew for 1 or 2 days, then disappeared as a result of dispersal of the cells; others grew rapidly until the fifth or sixth postirradiation day, then became atrophic; and still others continued to grow slowly until the seventh or eighth day, then became static or underwent atrophy and regression. It seems to us that these developmental anomalies should not be designated as neoplasms.

GENERAL COMMENTS

Ionizing radiations were the first type of carcinogens thoroughly studied and much of what has been done subsequently with chemical carcinogens is a duplication of the work with these physical carcinogens. In carcinogenic potency, ionizing radiations are second to none, as indicated by the certainty and frequency with which they induce neoplasms. In variety of neoplasms induced, precision in quantitation, and as a tool in cancer research they match any other carcinogen. Nevertheless, after the hazards of radiations were discovered and adequately controlled, research on this type of carcinogenesis waned until recent developments have made this area again a highly important field of investigation.

The dose-time relationship after administration of a single dose of a radioisotope was well worked out by Brues (1949) with the use of Sr^{89}, which causes neoplasms at the site of deposition. His findings are illustrated in Fig. 18-10. Each quantity of Sr^{89} absorbed by bone confers a given probability of bone tumor formation, the tumor development time decreasing and tumor incidence increasing with the dosage. It is not known whether a threshold dose exists for such effects, the limiting factor being the survival time. The daily tumor morbidity will constantly increase as long as further irradiation occurs.

Carcinogenesis by a bone-seeking radioisotope cannot be accurately computed on body-weight basis. The concentration in the area of susceptible cells, rate of elimination from the area, and degree or character of the specific ionization may be important. Brues (1949) found that the development period of bone tumors is comparable in mice, rats, rabbits, and dogs. His findings are illustrated in Fig. 18-1. The ordinate represents the probability that a mouse in a given dosage group will develop a tumor or possess it in a microscopic state on a given day.

Species differences doubtless exist, as illustrated by leukemia and ovarian tumor induction in mice, and difficulties of their induction in other species of animals; however, not enough work has been done in other species and the tumor development time may not have been given adequate consideration. The species differences are probably the same for all types of carcinogens, e.g., leukemias are readily induced in mice

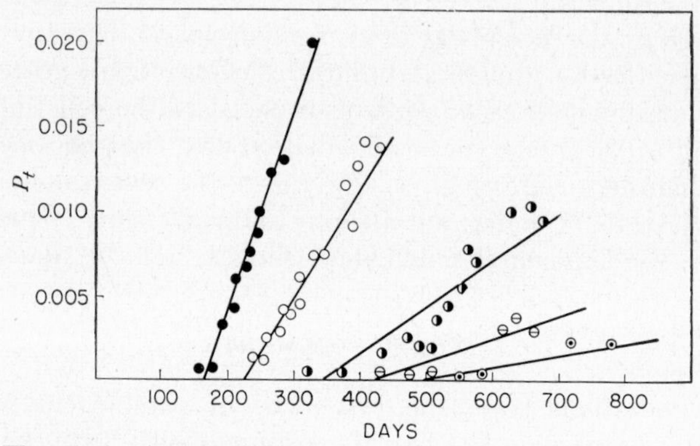

FIG. 18-10. The relation of dose of Sr^{89} to rate of induction and latency period of bone tumors (*after Brues*, 1949).

also by chemical carcinogens and hormones, but not in other species. Work in this area is, however, inadequate.

Cocarcinogenesis by Irradiation. Many observations made on the induction of neoplasms in man or animals subjected to ionizing irradiation are best explained by postulating cofactors as being operative, before, during, or after irradiation.

Observations made in the course of therapeutic use of X radiation in the control of chronic inflammatory lesions in man induced Lacassagne and Vinzent (1929) to study the promoting factor of inflammation in carcinogenesis. In a series of studies, Lacassagne *et al.* (1927–1933) have conclusively demonstrated that, in the course of inflammation, many types of cells are potentiated to the carcinogenic effects of X radiation. *Streptobacillus caviae* introduced into the thigh of the rabbit produced a suppurative inflammation which was often fatal but could be cured by X radiation. From six months to four years later infiltrative metastasizing neoplasms appeared in several rabbits so treated. Two malignant tumors (an osteoblastoma and a fibromyosarcoma) were obtained in the pectoral region of rabbits in which abscess was produced with diatomaceous earth, followed 6 days later by X irradiation. The first tumor appeared six, the second thirteen months after irradiation.

A third tumor similarly induced was atypical but also of bony origin. A fourth tumor was a periosteal sarcoma, the fifth a myxosarcoma, and the sixth an intracanalicular epithelioma. Tumors were not encountered in rabbits treated either with this bacillus or X radiation alone. The dose of X radiation was smaller than that required to produce radiodermatitis (600 r) and in three rabbits it even failed to cause epilation.

The great variety of the histological types of the tumors (osseous, periosteal, aponeurotic, loose connective tissue, muscular and ductal-epithelial) are attributed to the preparatory intervention of the inflammatory process, raising the sensitivity of different cells to X radiation.

Burrows *et al.* (1937) fully confirmed the work of Lacassagne. They produced a focus of inflammation in the groin in each of twelve rabbits by injections of kaolin and of finely powdered silica suspended in olive oil. These foci were exposed to X radiation, each receiving a single dose of 600 r. Among nine rabbits thus treated and surviving for two years or longer, tumors appeared in the irradiated tissues in six. In four of these rabbits the tumors were sarcomas that had produced metastases.

On the one hand, X radiation has been employed in the treatment of inflammation; on the other hand, there are numerous observations indicating that inflamed tissues are more readily rendered cancerous than normal tissues. Most of these observations were made in the course of therapeutic irradiation of tuberculous joints, and the bone tumors developed in the area of irradiation. The predisposing factor of inflammation frequently present in the female genital tract has been blamed for cancers in the vulva, cervix, and uterus (Bumm, 1923).

A cocarcinogenic effect of methylcholanthrene and externally applied β radiation from P^{32} was reported by Hamilton and Passonneau (1949). Each of these agents alone caused skin tumors in 13.3 per cent of the mice and, when combined in the same doses, in 53.3 per cent.

Mottram (1937) observed the cocarcinogenic effects of benzopyrene and ionizing irradiations. Painting the skin of mice twice weekly with 3,4-benzopyrene for six weeks caused some reaction of the skin but no tumors. However, with continued painting or additional application of a single dose of β or γ radiation, an appreciable number of tumors was induced. Similar results were obtained by Mayneord and Parsons (1937), who used X radiation in combination with benzopyrene or dibenzanthracene.

An enhancement of the leukemogenic action of methylcholanthrene by X irradiation was described by Furth and Boon (1943). Destruction of hemopoietic tissues by X irradiation is followed by regeneration, and during this phase mitotic figures are seen in abundance in sections of blood-forming organs. It seemed probable that, during this phase, the blood-forming organs would be particularly susceptible to leukemogenic irritants. Experiments performed to test this assumption have shown that the leukemogenic action of small doses of methylcholanthrene, which alone rarely produces leukemia, is greatly enhanced by preirradiation with doses of X radiation. It is obvious that proper timing and dosage are necessary to obtain such results. A similar coleukemogenic effect of these two agents was also noted by Mixer and Kirschbaum (1948) and a similar synergistic effect was found in inducing thymic tumors by estrogenic hormones and X irradiation (Kirschbaum *et al.*, 1949; Kirschbaum and Mixer, 1951). Agents such as cortisone, which cause involution of the thymus and depress lymphopoiesis, will probably lessen the liability of leukemia induction by X irradiation (Kaplan, 1951). Thus the reduced incidence of leukemia may be explained when pneumonia or other diseases, which cause accidental involution of the thymus, are prevalent in the animal colony.

The complexities of carcinogenesis are best illustrated by those of the mammary tumor of mice which has three major causes—genetic, hormonal, and viral; if powerful, either of the latter two may cause mammary tumors provided the genetic factor is present (Bittner, 1946–1947). Ionizing irradiation may produce mammary tumors in an agent-free strain (Lorenz *et al.*, 1951); it is not likely that this is accomplished by a direct mutagenic action on cells of the mammary gland. The genes are no doubt ever-present modifiers of all extrinsic agents but relatively little is known on genetic factors in carcinogenesis by ionizing irradiations. The uniformity of response of different strains of the same species to the same dose of ionizing radiations administered under comparable conditions is impressive. However, not enough work has been done on this subject.

Certain heavy metals not possessing radioactivity have proved to be carcinogenic under certain experimental conditions. The first experiments pointing this out were performed by Schinz and Uehlinger (1942). Hueper (personal communication) injected powdered uranium into the bone of rats, 36 per cent of which developed tumors within six months. Some of these tumors originated from the periosteum, others from adjacent muscle.

MECHANISM OF CARCINOGENESIS

Electromagnetic as well as corpuscular radiations can be considered together, since no qualitative differences have been disclosed between the two. The release of energy in cells by absorption of ionizing electromagnetic radiation is accompanied by liberation of secondary electrons which form ions along their path. These ions may be unstable, undergo chemical changes, and interact with molecules of the tissues. The greater part of the ionization will occur in the water of the tissues, resulting in the formation of OH, H, and other radicals. These radicals will interact with different cellular constituents. This fundamental ionization process is identical for all ionizing radiations whether electromagnetic or corpuscular. A biologic system can recover at least partially if sufficient time elapses between successive ionization events.

Concerning views and findings relative to the mode of action of radiations on living cells, the reader is referred to Scott (1937), Lea (1947), Tobias (1951) and Chap. 6 of this book, by Zirkle.

If a single ionization event can cause a carcinogenic change by a direct action of the radiation on the cell, the carcinogenic action will be independent of dose rate, but a minimum dose will be required to induce a macroscopic tumor during the life span of the animal. On the other hand, if several ionization events are necessary for the carcinogenic change, the action of the radiation may depend on the dose rate as is the case with particles of low specific ionization, such as penetrating X or γ rays.

A survey of the facts gathered indicates a multiplicity of mechanisms by which neoplasia is produced by ionizing radiations. Instances of both direct and indirect effects are evident, although they are not always clearly identified. The immediate cause of the neoplastic change is, however, still hidden.

In the genesis of tumors of endocrine organs, such as pituitary tumors which arise following thyroid destruction by I^{131}, radiation may do barely more than destroy the thyroid. Similarly, an endocrine "imbalance" brought about by ovarian irradiation appears to be the major if not the sole force in the genesis of ovarian tumors. It is possible that thyroid tumors arising after administration of I^{131} are caused by the combination of a local effect on the cells and excessive output of thyroid-stimulating hormones by the pituitary.

The "bone seekers" such as Sr^{89-90}, mesothorium, and radium, on the contrary, seem to exert their effect directly on osteogenic cells with which they come in contact. Injury and sustained regenerative efforts are characteristic events in the course of evolution of both bone and skin tumors.

If it is assumed that neoplasia induction requires a new type of cell with permanently altered reproduction, carcinogenesis is best looked upon either as a special type of mutation or that of abnormal differentiation (Waddington, 1947; Henshaw, 1945). Waddington relates the problem of the origin of cancer to that of cellular variations, in particular to those that are discontinuous and irreversible, but he considers carcinogenesis to be of a special type. Henshaw considers mutation a plausible explanation of neoplasia if this term is applied to irreversible changes in extrachromosomal as well as chromosomal constituents of cells. Mutation in this sense, however, does not differ from differentiation (Henshaw, 1945).

Mutagens are numerous, and ionizing radiation acting directly on a "sensitive" part of the cell is one of them. Others may be endogenous in origin.

Experiments were reported showing that cholesterol exposed to massive doses of X radiation (about 60,000 r) acquires carcinogenic power (Burrows and Mayneord, 1937), but this finding has not been confirmed. This and other ideas such as the transformation of an endogenous steroid into a carcinogenic hydrocarbon and the meaning of the presence of carcinogens in tissue extracts, are fully discussed by Lacassagne in his monograph on cancers produced by endogenous substances (1950). Concerning problems common with carcinogenesis by ultraviolet rays, see Rusch (1949) and Blum (1953).

The assumption of indirect carcinogenesis by endogenous carcinogens is also speculative, as no one has yet proved that endogenous carcinogens isolated from the body exist in that form and are not the products of the chemical techniques used for their isolation. Suggestive evidence for the mutation theory is furnished by studies on the genetic character of the neoplastic cells (Furth *et al.*, 1944), by demonstration of mutagenic power of some carcinogens (Demerec, 1948, and Latarjet *et al.*, 1949), the carcinogenic power of some mutagens (Boyland and Horning, 1949; Burdette, 1950; and Heston, 1950), and by the character of mitotic abnormalities, but direct demonstration of a chromosonal change is lacking. Mottram (1931) tested the validity of the somatic mutation hypothesis by exposing cells in vitro to high concentration of carbon dioxide and β rays which, in *Drosophila,* gives rise to derangements of chromosomes. The irradiated cells were reimplanted in the animal but only one testicular tumor was produced. Such experiments are cumbersome, yet are worth pursuing to find out whether the thesis, that mutation is proportional to the dose, applies to carcinogenesis.

That tissues which are subjected to an increased physiological or pathological regenerative process are more susceptible to neoplasia induction than normal tissues has long been demonstrated by several investigators. This may, in part, be due to the presence of an increased number of cells in a sensitive (mitotic) phase. The mere fact that ionizing radiation is one of the most powerful agents causing genetic alterations (Muller, 1938; Catcheside, 1948) lends strong support to the somatic mutation theory of cancer.

Based on studies of *Polytoma uvella*, Lacassagne (1936) postulates five types of lesions in the cell: (1) temporary suppression of growth due to absorption of energy in the cytoplasm (associated with a reparable injury to mitochondria and other cytoplasmic structures), (2) destruction of parts of chromatin resulting in abortive anomalies of division, (3) suppression of reproduction due to injury of centrosomes, (4) suppression of motility due to injury of motor centers, and (5) immediate death of cell.

The neoplastic change is explained as an anomaly of cell division. Lacassagne distinguishes between equipotential mitosis, from which arise similar daughter cells, and differentiated mitosis, which yields dissimilar daughter cells. The malignant transformation is related to alteration of the reproductive apparatus of the cells, fixing their descendants and causing preponderance of equipotential mitosis.

The tumors arising in the endocrine organs (e.g., pituitary) represent another extreme type of growth in which little if any change in character of the cell has to be postulated, since multiplication of these tumor cells, like that of their normal homologues, is caused by a sustained endocrine stimulus. Since they metastasize, they behave as malignant growths, yet they may be checked by correction of the hormonal disturbance (Furth *et al.*, unpublished data). It may be disputed that such conditioned growths could be classified as tumors. On the other hand, ignorance of the processes on which the origin and sustained growth of common neoplasms may depend is no guarantee that such processes do not exist. In any event the known dependent growths gradually or suddenly lose the dependency and sooner or later become autonomous.

The statement that irradiation may hasten the aging process and thus bring about an earlier appearance of spontaneously occurring tumors does not seem to hold for all neoplasms. Leukemia can be induced in young animals by irradiations and other carcinogens with high frequency in strains of mice in which this disease is exceedingly rare (e.g., in strain C57 black). Many neoplasms occur in young people and are of types not caused by ionizing irradiations. On the other hand, many tumors observed induced by irradiations are of the same type as found spontaneously.

The induction of neoplasms by ionizing irradiation is a fascinating chapter in the history of science. It is full of problems of increasing practical importance awaiting solution. As a tool in cancer research, it is unequaled.

REFERENCES

Most of the older literature, well reviewed in the monographs of Lacassagne (1945a, b) and Colwell and Russ (1934), is omitted for reasons of economy. Of the clinical reports, only those of historical interest and the more recent ones are listed, notably those which cite the older literature. Of the publications of authors with numerous articles, only the first, the last, and the more comprehensive ones are listed.

(Information on availability of government reports indicated by an asterisk may be obtained from the Office of Technical Services, Department of Commerce, Washington, D.C.)

Abrahamson, L., M. H. O'Connor, and M. L. Abrahamson (1950) Bilateral alveolar lung carcinoma, associated with the injection of thorotrast. Irish J. Med. Sci., 6: 229–235.

Andervont, H. B., and M. B. Shimkin (1940) Tumors in mice injected with colloidal thorium dioxide. J. Natl. Cancer Inst., 1: 349–353.

Arnstein, A. (1913) Über den sogenannten "Schneeberger Lungenkrebs." Wien. klin. Wochschr., 26: 748–752.

Aubertin, C. (1931) Leucémie myéloide chez les radiologistes. Bull. Soc. franç. électrothér. et radiol., 40: 218–226.

Auerbach, Oscar, Milton Friedman, Leo Weiss, and H. I. Amory (1951) Extraskeletal osteogenic sarcoma arising in irradiated tissue. Cancer, 4: 1095–1106.

Bali, T., and J. Furth (1949) Morphological and biological characteristics of X-ray induced transplantable ovarian tumors. Cancer Research, 9: 449–472.

Barling, G. (1926) J. F. Hall-Edwards, obit. Brit. J. Radiology (B.I.R. Sect.), 31: 455–459.

Belot, J. (1910) La radiothérapie ne donne pas les cancers. Bull. mém. soc. radiol. méd Paris, 2: 34–41.

Biltris, R. (1933) Tumeurs malignés observées chez le cobaye après introduction de sources radio-actives. Bull. Assoc. franç. étude du cancer, 22: 438–468.

Bittner, J. J. (1946–47) The causes and control of mammary cancer in mice. The Harvey Lectures, Series 42, pp. 221–246.

Bloch, B. (1923) Carcinome expérimental provoqué par les rayons X chez le lapin. Congrès Cancer Strasbourg, 2: 31.

——— (1924) Die experimentelle Erzeugung von Roentgen-Carcinomen beim Kaninchen, nebst allgemeinen Bemerkungen über die Genese der experimentellen Carcinome. Schweiz. med. Wochschr., 5: 857–865.

Bloom, William (1948) Histopathology of irradiation from external and internal sources. McGraw-Hill Book Company, Inc., New York, National Nuclear Energy Series, Div. IV, Vol. 22I.

Bogliolo, L. (1938) Sopra i blastomi sperimentali da ossido di torio. Pathologica, 30: 422–430.

Boyland, E., and E. S. Horning (1949) Induction of tumors with nitrogen mustards. Brit. J. Cancer, 3: 118–123.

Brambell, F. W. R., A. S. Parkes, and Una Fielding (1927) Changes in the ovary of the mouse following exposure to X rays. Part I. Irradiation at three weeks old. Proc. Roy. Soc. (London)., B101: 29–56.

———, Una Fielding, and A. S. Parkes (1929) Changes in the ovary of the mouse following exposure to X-rays. Part IV. The corpus luteum in the sterilized ovary and some concluding experiments. Proc. Roy. Soc. (London), B102: 385–396.

Brown, Percy (1936) American martyrs to science through the roentgen rays. Charles C Thomas, Publishers, Springfield, Ill.

Brues, A. M. (1949) Biological hazards and toxicity of radioactive isotopes. J. Clin. Invest., 28: 1286–1296.

——— (1951) Carcinogenic effects of radiation. Advances in biological and medical physics. Academic Press, Inc., New York, Vol. 2, pp. 171–191.

———, M. P. Finkel, Hermann Lisco, and G. A. Sacher (1949) Age and lymphoma incidence in CF-1 mice. Cancer Research, 9: 604.

———, G. A. Sacher, M. P. Finkel, and Hermann Lisco (1945) Comparative carcinogenic effects by X radiation and P^{32}. Cancer Research, 9: 545.

Bumm, E. (1923) Ueber Röntgenkarzinome bei der Frau. Z. Geburtsh. u. Gynäk., 86: 445–453.

Burdette, Walter J. (1950) Lethal mutation rate in *Drosophila* treated with 20-methyl-cholanthrene. Science 112: 303–306.

Burrows, H., and W. V. Mayneord (1937) A note on tumors in mice following injection of irradiated cholesterol in lard. Am. J. Cancer, 31: 484–485.

———, ———, and J. E. Roberts (1937) Neoplasia following the application of X-rays to inflammatory lesions. Proc. Roy. Soc. (London), B123: 213–217.

Cahan, W. G., H. Q. Woodard, N. L. Higinbotham, F. W. Stewart, and B. L. Coley (1948) Sarcoma arising in irradiated bone; report of 11 cases. Cancer, 1: 3–29.

Catcheside, D. G. (1948) Genetic effects of radiations. Advances in genetics. Academic Press, Inc., New York, Vol. 2, pp. 271–358.

Clunet, J. (1910) Recherches expérimentales sur les tumeurs malignes. Thèse de Paris, p. 297.

Colwell, H. A. (1935) The method of action of radium and X-rays on living tissues. Oxford University Press, London.

——— and Sidney Russ (1924) Radium, X rays and the living cell, 2d ed. George Bell & Sons, Ltd., London.

——— and ———(1934) X ray and radium injuries, prevention and treatment. Oxford University Press, London.

Daels, F. (1925) Contribution to the experimental provocation of tumours by means of radium. Brit. J. Radiology, 30: 474–476.

——— and R. Biltris (1931) Contribution à l'étude de la provocation de tumeurs malignes expérimentales au moyen de substances radioactives. Bull. Assoc. franç. étude cancer, 20: 32.

——— and ——— (1937) Essai de production de neoplasmes chez la poule par introduction de sources radioactives. Bull. Assoc. franç. étude cancer, 26: 587–601.

Darden, E. B., C. W. Sheppard, and L. C. Emerson (1951) Gamma-ray contamination in the thermal neutron exposure facility of the Oak Ridge Reactor. USAEC Report ORNL-1003.*

Dehler, H. (1927) Das gynäkologische Röntgencarcinom. Arch. Gynäkol., 130: 239–274.

Demerec, M. (1948) Mutations induced by carcinogens. Brit. J. Cancer, 2: 114–117.

Depenthal (1919) Doppelseitiges Mammakarzinom (Röntgenkarzinom). Münch. med. Wochschr., 66: 354–355.

Deringer, M., W. E. Heston, and E. Lorenz (1953) Effects of long continued total-body gamma irradiation on mice, guinea pigs, and rabbits. IV. Actions on the breeding behavior of mice, *in* Biological effects of external X and gamma irradiation, Raymond E. Zirkle, ed. McGraw-Hill Book Company, Inc., New York, National Nuclear Energy Series, Div. IV, Vol. 22B, Chap. IV.

Dobrovolskaia-Zavadskaia, N. (1935) Réaction néoplasique locale consécutive à une irradiation par le radon, chez les souris prédisposées au cancer de la mamelle. Compt. rend. soc. biol., 119: 360–363.

——— and N. Adamova (1939) Réaction à différents agents cancerigenes, de souris appartenants a la même lignée cancereuse. Bull Assoc. franç. étude cancer, 28: 76–107.

Dohnert, H. R. (1938) Experimentelle Untersuchungen zur Frage des Schneeberger Lungenkrebses. Z. Krebsforsch., 47: 209–239.

Doniach, I. (1950) The effect of radioactive iodine alone and in combination with methylthiouracil and acetylaminofluorene upon tumor production in the rat's thyroid gland. Brit. J. Cancer, 4: 223–234.

Dublin, L. I., and Mortimer Spiegelman (1947) The longevity and mortality of American physicians, 1938–1942. J. Am. Med. Assoc., 134: 1211–1215.

Dunlap, C. E., J. C. Aub, R. D. Evans, and R. S. Harris (1944) Transplantable osteogenic sarcomas in rats by feeding radium. Am. J. Pathol., 20: 1–21.

Emile-Weil, P., and A. Lacassagne (1925) Anémie pernicieuse et leucémie myéloïde mortelles provoquées par la manipulation de substances radioactives. Bull. acad. méd. (Paris), 93: 237–241.

Evans, R. D. (1950a) Quantitative aspects of chronic radium and mesothorium poisoning and their relation to the establishment of maximum permissible doses. 6th Intern. Congr. Radiology, pp. 8–9.

——— (1950b) Quantitative aspects of radiation carcinogenesis in humans. Acta Unio Intern. contra Cancrum, 6: 1229–1237.

——— and C. Goodman (1940) Determination of the thoron content of air and its bearing on lung cancer hazards in industry. J. Ind. Hyg. Toxicol., 22: 89–99.

———, R. S. Harris, and J. W. M. Bunker (1944) Radium metabolism in rats, and the production of osteogenic sarcoma by experimental radium poisoning. Am. J. Roentgenol. Radium Therapy, 52: 353–373.

Ewing, J. (1926) Radiation osteitis. Acta Radiol., 6: 399–412.

Feygin, S. (1914) Du cancer radiologique. Thèse Fac. Méd. Paris.

Figge, F. H. J. (1947) Cosmic radiation and cancer. Science, 105: 323–325.

——— (1949) Studies on the influence of penetrating radiations on carcinogenesis. Acta Unio Intern. contra Cancrum, 6: 782–784.

Folley, Jarrett H., Wayne Borges, and Takuso Yamawaki (1952) The incidence of leukemia in survivors of the atomic bomb in Hiroshima and Nagasaki. Am. J. Med., 13: 311–321.

Foulds, L. (1939) The production of transplantable carcinoma and sarcoma in guinea-pigs by injections of thorotrast. Am. J. Cancer, 35: 363–373.

Franks, W. R., and G. E. Meek (1950) Influence of background radiation on methylcholanthrene carcinogenesis in mice. Cancer Research, 10: 217.

Frieben (1902) Demonstration eines Cancroids des rechten Handrückens, das sich nach langdaurnder Einwirking von Röntgenstrahlen entwickelt hatte. Fortschr. Gebiete Röntgenstrahlen, 6: 106.

Furth, Jacob (1935) Transmission of myeloid leukemia of mice. Its relation to myeloma. J. Exptl. Med., 61: 423–445.

——— (1946) Prolongation of life with prevention of leukemia by thymectomy in mice. J. Gerontol., 1: 46–54.

——— (1949) Relation of pregnancies to induction of ovarian tumors by X rays. Proc. Soc. Exptl. Biol. Med., 71: 274–277.

——— and M. C. Boon (1943) Enhancement of leukemogenic action of methylcholanthrene by pre-irradiation with X-rays. Science, 98: 138–139.

———, ———, and N. Kaliss (1944) On the genetic character of neoplastic cells as determined in transplantation experiments. With notes on the somatic mutation theory. Cancer Research, 4: 1–10.

——— and W. T. Burnett, Jr. (1951) Hormone-secreting transplantable neoplasms of the pituitary induced by I^{131}. Proc. Soc. Exptl. Biol. Med., 78: 222–224.

——— and J. S. Butterworth (1936) Neoplastic diseases occurring among mice subjected to general irradiation with X rays. II. Ovarian tumors and associated lesions. Am. J. Cancer, 28: 66–95.

——— and O. B. Furth (1936) Neoplastic diseases produced in mice by general irradiation with X rays. I. Incidence and types of neoplasms. Am. J. Cancer, 28: 54–65.

———, E. L. Gadsden, and W. T. Burnett, Jr. (1952) Autonomous transplantable pituitary tumors arising in growths dependent on absence of the thyroid gland. Proc. Soc. Exptl. Biol. Med., 80: 4–7.

Gardner, W. U. (1948) Hormonal imbalances in tumorigenesis. Cancer Research, 8: 397–411.

——— (1950) Ovarian and lymphoid tumors in female mice subsequent to roentgenray irradiation and hormone treatment. Proc. Soc. Exptl. Biol. Med., 75: 434–436.

Glasser, Otto (1950) Medical physics. The Year Book Publishers, Chicago, Vol. 2.

Goebel, O., and P. Gérard (1925) Sarcome expérimental provoqué chez le cobaye par l'action des rayons X. Compt. rend. soc. biol., 93: 1537–1538.

Goldberg, R. C., and I. L. Chaikoff (1951a) Development of thyroid neoplasms in the rat following a single injection of radioactive iodine. Proc. Soc. Exptl. Biol. Med., 76: 563–566.

——— and ——— (1951b) On the nature of the hypertrophied pituitary gland induced in the mouse by I^{131} injections and the mechanism of its development. Endocrinology, 48: 1–5.

——— and ——— (1952) Induction of thyroid cancer in the rat by radioactive iodine. Arch. Path., 53: 22–28.

Gorbman, Aubrey (1949) Tumors of pituitary and trachea in mice after high dosages of radioactive iodine. Cancer Research, 9: 596.

Gray, L. H. (1946) Comparative studies of the biologic effects of X rays, neutrons and other ionizing radiations. Brit. Med. Bull., 4: 11–18.

Gricouroff, Georges (1943) Sarcomes consécutifs à des traitements par radiumpuncture. Mém. acad. chir., 69: 529–532.

———, Dechaume, and Baclesse (1943) Sarcome du maxillaire neuf ans après injection intraveineuse de mésothorium. Mém. acad. chir., 69: 459–463.

Haerting, F. H., and W. Hesse (1879) Der Lungenkrebs, die Bergkrankheit in den Schneeberger Gruben. Vierteljahresschr. gerichtl. Med. u. öffentl. Sanitätsw., 30: 296–309; 31: 102–129, 313–337.

Hahn, P. F., M. A. Jackson, and Horace Goldie (1951) Liver cirrhosis with ascites, induced in dogs by chronic massive hepatic irradiation with radioactive colloidal gold. Science, 114: 303–305.

Hall-Edwards, J. (1904) On chronic X-ray dermatitis. Brit. Med. J., 2: 993–996.

——— (1906) Treatment of chronic X-ray dermatitis. Brit. Med. J., 2: 826.

Hamilton, Katherine, and Janet Passonneau (1949) Cocarcinogenesis of methylcholanthrene and beta emitters. USAEC Report, ANL-4360,* pp. 56–59.

Hatcher, C. H. (1945) The development of sarcoma in bone subjected to roentgen or radium irradiation. J. Bone and Joint Surg., 27: 179–195.

Hellner, H. (1938) Experimentelle Knochensarkome und ihre Beziehungen zu allgemeinen Geschwulsproblemen. Beitr. klin. Chir. (Bruns), 168: 538–553.

Henshaw, P. S. (1945) Implications from studies with physical carcinogens. J. Natl. Cancer Inst., 5: 419–436.

——— and J. W. Hawkins (1944) Incidence of leukemia in physicians. J. Natl. Cancer Inst., 4: 339–346.

———, E. F. Riley, and G. E. Stapleton (1947) The biologic effects of pile radiations. Radiology, 49: 349–359.

——— and R. S. Snider (1946) Review of information bearing on the tumor inducing action of superficial radiations. USAEC Report MDDC-570.*

Hesse, O. (1911) Symptomatologie, Pathogenese und Therapie des Röntgenkarzinoms. J. A. Barth, Leipzig.

Heston, W. E. (1950) Carcinogenic action of the mustards. J. Natl. Cancer Inst., 11: 415–423.

Hollcroft, J., and E. Lorenz (1952) The 30-day LD_{50} of two radiations of different ion density. J. Natl. Cancer Inst., 12: 533–544.

Hueck, W. (1939) Kurzer Bericht über Ergebnisse anatomischer Untersuchungen in Schneeberg. Z. Krebsforsch., 49: 312–315.

Hueper, W. C. (1934) Leukemoid and leukemic conditions in white mice with spontaneous mammary carcinoma. Folia Haematol., 52: 167–178.

Huguenin, René, Auguste Nemours, and Guy Albot (1931) Les hépatites et les cirrhoses expérimentales au bioxyde de thorium. Compt. rend. soc. biol., 108: 879–881.

Hursh, J. B., and A. A. Gates (1950) Body radium content of individuals with no known exposure. Nucleonics, 7: 46–59.

International recommendations on radiological protection, supplement on maximum permissible amounts of radioactive isotopes. Brit. J. Radiology, 24: 50–53, 1951.

Jacques, P. (1935) Cancer du larynx chez la femme après irradiation thyroidienne prolongée. Oto-rhino-laryng. internatl., 19: 277–278.

Jaffe, H. L., and Golden Selin (1951) Tumors of bones and joints. Bull. N.Y. Acad. Med., 27: 165–174.

von Jagić, N., G. Schwarz, and Leo von Siebenrock (1911) Blutbefunde bei Röntgenologen. Berl. klin. Wochschr., 48: 1220–1222.

Jentzer, A. (1937) Sarcome ostéogénique expérimental développé à distance d'un foyer radifère. Acta Unio Intern. contra Cancrum, 2: 100–104.

Jonkhoff, A. R. (1927) Röntgencarcinom bei Mäusen. Z. Krebsforsch., 26: 32–41.

Kaplan, H. S. (1948) Influence of age on susceptibility of mice to the development of lymphoid tumors after irradiation. J. Natl. Cancer Inst., 9: 55–56.

——— (1949) Preliminary studies on the effectiveness of local irradiation in the induction of lymphoid tumors in mice. J. Natl. Cancer Inst., 10: 267–270.

——— (1950a) Influence of ovarian function on incidence of radiation induced ovarian tumors in mice. J. Natl. Cancer Inst., 11: 125–132.

——— (1950b) Influence of thymectomy, splenectomy, and gonadectomy on incidence of radiation-induced lymphoid tumors in strain C57 black mice. J. Natl. Cancer Inst., 11: 83–90.

——— (1951) Further observations on inhibition of lymphoid tumor development by shielding and partial-body irradiation of mice. Cancer Research, 11: 261.

——— and M. B. Brown (1951) Inhibition by testosterone of radiation-induced lymphoid tumor development in intact and castrate adult male mice. Cancer Research, 11: 706–708.

———, S. N. Marder, and M. B. Brown (1951) Adrenal cortical function and radiation-induced lymphoid tumors of mice. Cancer Research, 11: 629–633.

——— and E. D. Murphy (1949) The effect of local roentgen irradiation on the biological behavior of a transplantable mouse carcinoma. I. Increased frequency of pulmonary metastasis. J. Natl. Cancer Inst., 9: 407–413.

Kassabian, M. K. (1907) Cited in Hesse (1911) and Brown (1936).

——— (1910) Roentgen rays and electrotherapeutics. J. B. Lippincott Company, Philadelphia.

Kindler, K. (1943) Beitrag zur Frage der Entstehung des Röntgenkrebses in inneren Organen. Z. Krebsforsch., 54: 153–169.

Kirschbaum, A., and H. W. Mixer (1951) Rodent leukemia: recent biological studies. A review. Cancer Research, 11: 741–752.

———, J. R. Shapiro, and H. W. Mixer (1949) Synergistic action of estrogenic hormone and X rays in inducing thymic lymphosarcoma of mice. Proc. Soc. Exptl. Biol. Med., 72: 632–634.

Koletsky, Simon, Frederick J. Bonte, and Hymer L. Friedell (1950) Production of malignant tumors in rats with radioactive phosphorus. Cancer Research, 10: 129.

Krebs, Carl, Aage Wagner, and H. C. Rask-Nielsen (1930) The origin of lymphosarcomatosis and its relation to other forms of leucosis in white mice. Acta Radiol., Suppl. 10, pp. 1–53.

Lacassagne, Antoine (1933) Conditions dans lesquelles ont été obtenus, chez le lapin, des cancers par action des rayons X sur des foyers inflammatoires. Compt. rend. soc. biol., 112: 562–564.

——— (1936) Certain biological problems relating to cancer, hormones, and radiation. The International Cancer Research Foundation, Philadelphia, and the Anna Fuller Fund, New Haven.

——— (1945a) Les cancers produits par les rayonnements corpusculaires; mécanisme présumable de la cancerisation par les rayons. Actualités scientifiques et industrielles, No. 981, Hermann & Cie, Paris.

——— (1945b) Les cancers produits par les rayonnements électromagnétiques. Actualités scientifiques et industrielles, No. 975, Hermann & Cie, Paris.

——— (1950) Les cancers produit par les substance chimiques endogéne. Actualités scientifiques et industrielles, No. 1026, Hermann & Cie, Paris.

——— and W. Nyka (1937) Ostéosarcomes de la selle turcique secondaires à l'introduction d'un tube de radon dans l'hypophyse de lapins. Compt. rend. soc. biol., 124: 935–938.

——— and G. Rudali (1942) Action des radiations sur la transformation maligne du papillome infectieux du lapin. Bull. Assoc. franç. étude cancer, 30: 74–89.

——— and R. Vinzent (1929) Sarcomes provoqués chez des lapins par l'irradiation d'abcès a *Streptobacillus caviae*. Compt. rend. soc. biol., 100: 249–251.

Latarjet, R., C. Elias, and Buu-Hoi (1949) Production d'une mutation bactérienne par des cancerigenes hydrosolubles. Compt. rend soc. biol., 143: 776–778.

Lazarus-Barlow, W. S. (1918) An attempt at the experimental production of carcinoma by means of radium. Proc. Roy. Soc. Med. (Sect. Pathol.), 11: 1–17.

——— (1922) Further attempts at the experimental production of carcinoma by means of radium. Proc. Roy. Soc. Med. (Sect. Pathol.), 15: 7–12.

Lea, D. E. (1947) Actions of radiations on living cells. The Macmillan Company, New York, 181 pp. (also Cambridge University Press, Cambridge, England, 1946).

Leblond, C. P., W. F. Storey, and F. D. Bertalanffy (1951) Rate of cell renewal of organs. A comparison with cancer statistics. Acta Unio Intern. contra Cancrum, 7: 692–693.

Leddy, E. T., and F. J. Rigos (1941) Radiodermatitis among physicians. Am. J. Roentgenol. Radium Therapy, 45: 696–700.

Leitch, J. L. (1945) Relation between neutron dose and the mortality, body weight and hematology of white rats, *in* E. McDonald, Neutron effects on animals. Biochemical Research Foundation. The Williams & Wilkins Company, Baltimore.

Li, M. H., and W. U. Gardner (1949) Further studies on the pathogenesis of ovarian tumors in mice. Cancer Research, 9: 35–41.

Lick, Louis, Arthur Kirschbaum, and Harry Mixer (1949) Mechanism of induction of ovarian tumors by X-rays. Cancer Research, 9: 532–536.

Lisco, Hermann (1949) Potential hazards and pathological aspects of radioactive isotopes. Proc. 9th Intern. Congr. Ind. Med., September, 1948.

———, A. M. Brues, M. P. Finkel, and Walter Grundhauser (1947) Carcinoma of the colon in rats following the feeding of radioactive yttrium. Cancer Research, 7: 721.

——— and M. P. Finkel (1949) Observations on lung pathology following the inhalation of radioactive cerium. Federation Proc., 8: 360.

———, ———, and A. M. Brues (1947) Carcinogenic properties of radioactive fission products and of plutonium. Radiology, 49: 361–363; and demonstration at 3d Intern. Cancer Congr., St. Louis.

——— and W. E. Kisieleski (1953) The fate and pathologic effects of plutonium metal implanted into rabbits and rats. Am. J. Path., 29: 305–322.

Lloyd (1903) Epithelioma engrafted on X-ray burn. Medical Record, 63: 554.

Lorenz, Egon (1944) Radioactivity and lung cancer; a critical review of lung cancer in the miners of Schneeberg and Joachimsthal. J. Natl. Cancer Inst., 5: 1–15.

——— (1950) Some biologic effects of long continued irradiation. Am. J. Roentgenol. Radium Therapy, 63: 176–185.

———, A. B. Eschenbrenner, W. E. Heston, and D. Uphoff (1951) Mammary tumor incidence in female C3Hb mice following long continued gamma irradiation. J. Natl. Cancer Inst., 11: 947–965.

———, W. E. Heston, M. K. Deringer, and A. B. Eschenbrenner (1946) Increase in incidence of lung tumors in strain A mice following long-continued irradiation with gamma rays. J. Natl. Cancer Inst., 6: 349–353.

———, ———, A. B. Eschenbrenner, and M. K. Deringer (1947) Plutonium project; biological studies in the tolerance range. Radiology, 49: 274–285.

———, C. C. Congdon, and D. Uphoff (1953) Prevention of irradiation induced lymphoid tumors in C57 black mice by spleen protection. J. Natl. Cancer Inst., 14: 291–301.

Ludin, Max (1934) Knochesarkom nach experimenteller Röntgenbestrahlung. Acta Radiol., 15: 553–556.

Lumb, George (1950) Solitary plasmocytoma of humerus in a mesothorium worker. J. Pathol. Bacteriol., 62: 585–589.

MacMahon, H. E., A. S. Murphy, and M. I. Bates (1947) Endothelial cell sarcoma of liver following thorotrast injections. Am. J. Pathol., 23: 585–611.

MacNeal, W. J., and G. S. Willis (1923) A skin cancer following exposure to radium. J. Am. Med. Assoc., 80: 466–469.

Maisin, J., and P. DuPuis (1929) Embryomes et cancer. Rev. belge sci. méd., 1: 409–424.

March, H. C. (1944) Leukemia in radiologists. Radiology, 4: 275–278.

——— (1950) Leukemia in radiologists in a 20 year period. Am. J. Med. Sci., 220: 282–286.

Marcuse, W. (1896) Nachtrag zu dem Fall von Dermatitis und Alopecie nach Durchleuchtungsversuchen mit Rontgenstrahlen. Deut. med. Wochschr., 21: 681.

Marie, P., J. Clunet, and G. Raulot-Lapointe (1910) Contribution à l'étude du développement des tumeurs malignes sur les ulcères de roentgen. Bull. assoc. franç. étude cancer, 3: 404–426.

———, ———, and ——— (1912) Nouveau cas de tumeur maligne provoquée par une radiodermite expérimentale chez le rat blanc. Bull. assoc. franç. étude cancer, 5: 125–135.

Martland, H. S. (1931) The occurrence of malignancy in radioactive persons. A general review of data gathered in the study of the radium dial painters, with special reference to the occurrence of osteogenic sarcoma and the interrelationship of certain blood diseases. Am. J. Cancer, 15: 2435–2516.

———, Philip Conlon, and J. P. Knef (1925) Some unrecognized dangers in the use and handling of radioactive substances: with a special reference to the storage of insoluble products of radium and mesothorium in the reticulo-endothelial system. J. Am. Med. Assoc., 85: 1769–1776.

——— and R. E. Humphries (1929) Osteogenic sarcoma in dial painters using luminous paint. Arch. Pathol., 7: 406–417.

Mayneord, W. V., and L. D. Parsons (1937) The effect of X-irradiation on tumor production by a chemical compound in mice, and the associated blood changes. J. Pathol. Bacteriol., 45: 35–48.

Metcalf, R. G., and F. A. Inda (1951) Pathology in animals subjected to repeated daily exposure to roentgen rays. USAEC Report UR-88.*

Mixer, H. W., and Arthur Kirschbaum (1948) Additive effects of X rays and methycholanthrene in inducing mouse leukemia. Radiology, 50: 476–480.

Miyamoto, Sideyuki (1939) Experimentelle Sarkomerzeugung durch Thorotrast. Strahlentherapie, 64: 683–690.

Mora, J. M. (1940) Granulomatous tumor following intramammary injection of colloidal thorium dioxide. J. Am. Med. Assoc., 115: 363–364.

Morris, H. P., and C. D. Green (1951) The role of thiouracil in the induction, growth, and transplantability of mouse thyroid tumors. Science, 114: 44–46.

———, A. J. Dalton, and C. D. Green (1951) Malignant thyroid tumors occurring in the mouse after prolonged hormonal imbalance during the ingestion of thiouracil. J. Clin. Endocrinol., 11: 1281–1295.

Mottram, J. C. (1931) Experiments on the production of tumours on the somatic mutation hypothesis. Brit. J. Exptl. Pathol., 12: 378–384.

——— (1935) Mesoblastic tumours produced in fowls by exposure to radium. Proc. Roy. Soc. Med., 19: 15–18.

——— (1937) Production of epithelial tumors by irradiation of a precancerous skin lesion. Am. J. Cancer, 30: 746–748.

Muller, H. J. (1938) The biological effects of radiation with special reference to mutation. Actualités scientifiques et industrielles, No. 725.

Nørgaard, Flemming (1939) The development of fibrosarcoma as a result of the intra-articular injection of radium chloride for therapeutic purposes. Am. J. Cancer, 37: 329–342.

Onufrio, O. (1938) Su di un caso di reticulo-sarcoma sperimentale da thorotrast. Folia med. (Naples), 24: 1245–1255.

Ordway, T. (1915) Occupational injuries due to radium: personal experience, with report of cases. Trans. Assoc. Am. Physicians, 30: 657–673.

Owen, S. E., and A. E. Williams (1940) Irradiation and hereditary mammary cancer. Radiology, 34: 541–544.

Peller, S. (1939) Lung cancer among mine workers in Joachimsthal. Human Biol., 11: 130–143.

Petrov, N., and N. Krotkina (1933) Experimentelles Gallenblasen- und Leberkarzinom. Z. Krebsforsch., 38: 249–263.

——— and ——— (1947) Experimental carcinoma of gallbladder; supplementary data. Ann. Surg., 125: 241–248.

Porter, C. A., and C. J. White (1907) Multiple carcinomata following chronic X-ray dermatitis. Ann. Surg., 46: 649–671.

Prussia, G. (1936) Contributo allo studio dei tumori sperimentali di thorotrast. Lo Sperimentale, 90: 522–539.

Rajewsky, B., A. Schraub, and G. Kahlau (1943) Experimentelle Geschwulsterzeugung durch Einatmung von Radiumemanation. Naturwissenschaften, 31: 170–171.

———, ———, and E. Schraub (1942) Über die toxische Dosis bei Einatmung von Ra-Emanation. Naturwissenschaften, 30: 489–492.

Raper, J. R. (1947) Effects of total surface beta irradiation. Radiology, 49: 314–324.

———, Paul S. Henshaw, and R. S. Snider (1946) Late effects of single exposures to beta rays. USAEC Report MDDC-578.*

Read, J., and J. C. Mottram (1939) The "tolerance concentration" of radon in the atmosphere. Brit. J. Radiology, 12: 54–60.

Ross, J. M. (1932) A case illustrating the effects of prolonged action of radium. J. Pathol. Bacteriol. 35: 899–912.

——— (1936) The carcinogenic action of radium in the rabbit: The effect of prolonged irradiation with screened radium. J. Pathol. Bacteriol., 43: 267–276.

Roussy, G., and M. Guerin (1941) Le cancer expérimental provoqué par le dioxyde de thorium. Presse méd., 49: 761–763.

———, C. Oberling, and M. Guerin (1934) Action cancérigène du dioxyde de thorium chez le rat blanc. Bull. acad. méd., 112: 809–816.

———, ———, and ——— (1936) Über Sarkomerzeugung durch kolloidales Thoriumdioxyd bei der weissen Ratte. Strahlentherapie, 56: 160–167.

Rowntree, C. W. (1908) Contribution to the study of X-ray carcinoma and the conditions which precede its onset. Arch. Middlesex Hosp., 13: 182.

——— (1909) X-ray carcinoma, and an experimental inquiry into the conditions which precede its onset. Lancet, 87: 821.

Rudolphi, Hans (1950) Spätentwicklung eines Unterlidkarzinoms nach Thoriumoxydinjektion. Beitr. path. Anat. u. allgem. Pathol., 111: 158–164.

Rusch, H. P. (1949) Carcinogenesis and ultraviolet irradiation. Acta Unio Intern. contra Cancrum, 6: 844–847.

Sabin, F. R., C. A. Doan, and C. E. Forkner (1932) The production of osteogenic sarcomata and the effects on lymph nodes and bone marrow of intravenous injections of radium chloride and mesothorium in rabbits. J. Exptl. Med., 56: 267–290.

Saunders, T. S., and Hamilton Montgomery (1938) Chronic roentgen and radium dermatitis. J. Am. Med. Assoc., 110: 23–28.

Schinz, H. R., and E. Uehlinger (1942) Der Metallkrebs. Ein neues Prinzip der Krebserzeugung. Z. Krebsforsch., 52: 425–437.

Schürch, O. (1930) Studien über präcancerosen mit besonderer Berücksichtigung des experimentellen Röntgencarcinoms. Z. Krebsforsch., 32: 449–468.

——— and E. Uehlinger (1930–1931) Experimentelles Knochensarkom nach Radiumbestrahlung bei einem Kaninchen. Z. Krebsforsch., 33: 476–484.

——— and ——— (1935) Ueber experimentale Knochentumoren. Arch. f. klin. Chir., 183: 704–719.

——— and ——— (1947) Bestrahlungsversuche an experimentellen malignen Knochengeschwülsten. Schweiz. med. Wochschr., 77: 181–186.

Scott, C. M. (1937) Some quantitative aspects of the biological action of X and gamma rays. Medical Research Council Special Report Series No. 223, Her Majesty's Stationery Office, London, 99 pp.

Sedginidse, G. A. (1933) Die kombinierte Wirkung der Röntgenstrahlen und des Steinkohlenteers auf die Haut der weissen Mäuse. Z. Krebsforsch., 38: 21–34.

Selbie, F. R. (1936) Experimental production of sarcoma with thorotrast. Lancet, 231: 847–848.

——— (1938) Tumors in rats and mice following the injection of thorotrast. Brit. J. Exptl. Pathol, 29: 100–107.

Sick (1903) Ein Fall von Karzinom der Haut das auf den Boden eines Röntgenulcus entstanden ist. Munch. med. Wochschr., 50: 1445.

Šikl, H. (1950) The present status of knowledge about the Jáchymov disease (cancer of the lungs in the miners of the radium mines). Acta. Unio Intern. contra Cancrum, 6: 1366–1375.

Siri, W. E. (1949) Isotopic tracers and nuclear radiations with applications to biology and medicine. McGraw-Hill Book Company, Inc., New York.

Sobel, Harry, and Jacob Furth (1948) Hypervolemia in mice bearing granulosa cell growths. Endocrinology, 42: 436–447.

Spitz, Sophie, and N. L. Higinbotham (1951) Osteogenic sarcoma following prophylactic roentgen-ray therapy. Cancer, 4: 1107–1112.

Taylor, Grant (1951) Atomic Bomb Casualty Commission, National Research Council, unpublished data.

Teleky, L. (1938) Der benufliche Lungen Krebs. Acta Unio Intern. contra Cancrum, 3: 253–275.

Tobias, C. A. (1951) Mechanisms of biological effects of penetrating radiations. Federation Proc., 10: 595–601.

Uehlinger, E., and O. Schürch (1938) Über experimentelle Erzeugung von Sarkomen mit Radium und Mesothorium. Deut. Z. Chir., 251: 12–33.

Ulrich, H. (1946) The incidence of leukemia in radiologists. New Engl. J. Med., 234: 45–46.

Vogt, E. (1926) Weitere Beiträge zur Frage der Tumorbildung nach Röntgenkastration mit besonderer Berücksichtigung der Sarkomentwicklung im Ovarium und Uterus. Strahlentherapie, 23: 639–670.

Waddington, C. H. (1947) Organizers and genes. Cambridge University Press, Cambridge, England.

Wakely, G. P. G. (1927) Radium carcinoma of the thumb. Brit. J. Surg., 14: 677–678.

Warren, Shields (1942-1943) Effects of radiation on normal tissues. Arch. Pathol., 34: 443–450 (and C. E. Dunlap, pp. 562–608; and N. B. Friedman, pp. 749–789, 917–931, 1070–1084); 35: 121–139, 304–353.

Willis, R. A. (1948) Pathology of tumours. Butterworth & Co. (Publishers), Ltd., London.

Wilson, J. G., R. L. Brent, and H. C. Jordan (1951) Neoplasia induced in rat embryos by roentgen irradiation. USAEC Report UR-183.*

Wolbach, S. R. (1909) The pathological histology of chronic X-ray dermatitis and early X-ray carcinoma. J. Med. Research, 21: 415–449.

Woldrich, A. (1931) Radium-Vergiftungen chronische, gewerbliche in Joachimsthal. Versammlung von Vergiftungsfällen, Vogel, Berlin, 2: 79–80.

Zirkle, R. E. (1953) The radiobiological importance of linear energy transfer. Chap. 6, this volume.

Manuscript received by the editor Apr. 29, 1952

Addendum

For more recent publications see:

Furth, J., and A. C. Upton (1953) Histopathologic and carcinogenic effects of ionizing irradiation. Ann. Rev. Nuclear Sci., 3: 303–338.

——— and ——— (1954) Late effects of experimental nuclear detonation in mice. Radiology, in press.

NAME INDEX

Page numbers in **boldface** type denote bibliographical references

A

Abderhalden, R., 1000, **1008**
Abele, R. K., 160, 176, **189**
Abelson, P. H., 998, **1008**
Abrams, H. L., 926, 933, **947**
Abrams, R., 305, **308**, 962, 983, **1008**
Abrahamson, L., 1179, **1191**
Abrahamson, M. L., 1179, **1191**
Adair, R. K., 115, **141**, 161, **185**
Adamova, N., 1155, **1193**
Adams, G. D., 112, **141**
Adams, W. G., 794, 795
Adams, W. S., 966, **1008**, 1035
Aebersold, P. C., 161, **185**, 320, 330, 333, 336, 337, 339, 343*n.*, **344**, **347**, **348**, **350**, 786, **824**, 827, 830, 833, 838, **859**, 923, **947**, 1041, 1042
Ahlström, L., 276, **278**, 305, 306, **308**, 926, **947**
Ahmed, I. A. R. S., 662, 678, **704**
Albers, D., 299, **308**
Albers-Schönberg, 1114
Alberti, M., 776, 782, 799, 804, 811, 816, **817**, **822**
Alberti, W., 554, **602**, 628, 629, **696**, 1097
Albot, G., 1184, 1195
Allen, A. C., 926, **948**, 982, 985, **1010**
Allen, A. O., 328, **344**, 559, **602**, 750, 751, 753, **756**
Allen, B. M., 682, **708**, 935, 936, **947**
Allen, E., 906, **914**
Allen, J. G., 926, **947**, 966–969, 1003, 1005, **1008**, **1017**, **1018**, **1025**, 1031, 1035, 1044–1047, 1072, 1082
Allison, S. K., 68, 107, **142**
Allsopp, C. B., 272, 274, **278**, 655, **696**, 750, **756**, **757**
Almy, G. M., 112, **141**
Alper, T., 275, **278**
Altenburg, E., 362, 389, 391, 393, 395, 405, 412, 430, 446,**462**, **469**, 500, 520, 531, 534–538, 545, **602**, **618**, 629, 635, **706**
Altenburg, L. S., 534–538, 545, **602**
Altenburger, K., 131, **141**
Altman, K. I., 962, 1002, **1008**
Amato, A., 554, **602**, 627, **696**
Ames, F. B., 686, **708**, 831, 837, 841, 842, 845, 846, **859**
Amoroso, E. C., 832, 834, 835, 837, **856**
Amory, H. I., 1182, **1192**
Ancel, P., 935, **947**, 1118
Anderson, C. D., 40
Anderson, E. A., 933, **958**, 984, **1008**
Anderson, E. G., 457, **462**, 644, **696**, **697**
Anderson, E. H., 509, 561, 563, 564, 579, 580, 595, **602**, **611**, 746, **758**, 856, **858**
Anderson, E. K., 1004, **1011**
Anderson, R. S., 287, 288, **308**, 940, **947**
Andervont, H. B., 1157, 1177, **1192**
Andrews, M. B., 414, **466**
Ané, J. N., 971, 978, **1008**
Ansari, M. Y., 415, **466**
Anslow, G. A., 161, **185**
Anson, B. J., 1132
Anthony, E., 968, **1016**
Apolant, H., 553, **603**
Appleyard, R. K., 166, **185**
Araratian, A. G., 363, **467**, 480, **615**, 799, **821**
Archangelsky, B. A., 900, **914**
Ardao, M. I., 304, **309**
Arnason, T. J., 584, **603**
Arnberg, B., 509, 584, **604**
Arnold, G., 554, **603**, 1114
Arnow, L. E., **696**, **697**
Arnstein, A., 1177, **1192**
Aron, W. A., 87, **141**
Aschheim, E. F., 1149
Ashler, F. M., 692, **707**
Astaurov, B. L., 510, **603**
Aub, J. C., 998, **1024**, 1155, 1157, **1193**
Aubertin, C., 1030, 1031, 1034, 1035, 1061, 1162, 1165, **1192**
Auerbach, C., 136, **141**, 363, 415, 417, 422, 458, **463**, 507, 512, 514, 551, 577, 578, 600, **603**, 656, 657, 686, **697**, **704**, 843, **858**
Auerbach, O., 1182, **1192**
Auger, P., 34, 47
Axelrod, Dorothy, 330, 339, **344**, 1112

B

Babcock, E. B., 582, **603**
Bachem, A., 990, **1014**
Bacher, R. F., 198, **252**
Back, A., 305, **311,** 961, 1002, **1015,** 1097
Back, L., 682, **701**
Baclesse, F., 946, **947,** 1157, **1195**
Bacq, Z. M., 131, **141,** 275, **280,** 655, 656, **697,** 941, 945, 946, **947, 948, 951,** 1067
Baeten, G., 1155
Bagg, H. J., 390, **467,** 864, 865, 869, 870, 879, 893–896, 898, **914, 915**
Baidens, A. von, 994, **1009**
Baily, N., 167, 176, **186**
Baker, C. P., 5, **144**
Baker, R., 537
Baker, W. K., 509, 561, 563, 565–568, 579, 580, **603, 611,** 663, 674, 675, **697,** 746, **758,** 856, **858,** 904, 936, 940, **948**
Bakker, C. J., 66, 87, **141**
Bali, Talia, 1168, 1169, **1192**
Bancroft, F. W., 390, **467**
Bardeen, C. R., 554, **603**
Barling, G., 1148, **1192**
Barnard, R. D., 985, **1009**
Barnes, B. T., 23, **142**
Barnes, K. K., 319, 333, **348,** 1030, 1058
Barnes, W. A., 926, **948,** 960, 1000, **1009**
Barnett, J. C., 925, **949**
Barratt, J. O., 554, **603,** 1114
Barron, E. S. G., 245, 257, 262, 265, **278,** 286–289, 293, 295, 298, 299, 301–308, **310, 312, 313,** 551, 580, 599, **603,** 922, 937, 941, **948,** 962, 973, 984, 986, 987, 989, 990, 1001, **1009, 1011, 1021,** 1067
Barrow, J., 979, 988, **1009**
Bass, H., 176, **185**
Bate, R. C., 650, **703**
Bateman, A. J., 584, **603**
Bates, M. I., 1157, 1184, **1198**
Battacharya, P., 514, 515, **603**
Bauer, H., 379, 380, **463,** 481, 482, 495, **604,** 628, 630, 646, 650, 655, 662–664, 667, 670, 673, 674, 677–679, 681, 687, **697**
Baur, E., 415, **463, 511**
Baxendale, J. H., 291, **309**
Beadle, G. W., 373, 414, 461, **463, 472**
Bean, W. B., 985, **1009**
Beattie, J. W., 146, **187**
Beatty, A. V., 559, 561, 568, **609, 620,** 742–744, 746, 748, 749, 752, 753, **758, 759,** 941, **950**
Beaujard, E., 1030, 1031, 1034, 1035, 1061
Beck, 1180
Becker, R. M., 1003, **1009**
Becquerel, H., 1150
Bedichek, S., 455, **470,** 641, **707**
Bedürftig, G., 980, **1009**
Behounek, F., 1178
Beiler, J. M., 979, **1009**
Belgovsky, M. L., 363, 380, **463,** 480, 493, 553, **604**
Bell, A. L., 910, **914**
Belling, J., **368**
Belot, J., 1151, **1192**
Belser, N. O., 268, **280, 703**
Bender, A. E., 992, **1009**
Benedek, A. L., 966, 968, 974, **1024**
Benjamin, E., 1002, **1009,** 1080
Bennett, L. R., 940, 941, 944, 945, **949,** 971, 974, 985, 986, 1003, **1009, 1021,** 1037, 1066, 1067
Bennett, V. C., 971, 974, **1009**
Berg, M., 926, **955**
Berg, R. L., **480**
Bergendahl, J., 538, **602**
Bergonié, J., 553, **604,** 627, 681, **697,** 927, **948,** 1114, 1127, 1133
Berman, Z. I., 409, **463**
Bertalanffy, F. D., 1162, **1197**
Bertani, G., 417, 422, **464**
Bethard, W. F., 926, **952,** 983, 1002, **1018,** 1045, 1057, 1065, 1070, 1072, 1079, 1080
Bethe, H. A., 66, 87, 89, **141, 143,** 165, 166, **185**
Betz, H., 941, 945, **951**
Beutel, A., 971, **1009**
Bevan, E. S., 290, **310**
Bigelow, R. R., 966, 968, 971, 978, 979, **1009,** 1039
Billen, D., 580
Biltris, R., 1154–1156, 1184, **1192, 1193**
Bink, N., 984, 985, 1001, **1025**
Binks, W., 153, **187**
Birch-Hirschfeld, A., 1131
Bird, M. J., 416, 424, **463**
Birkina, B. N., 414, **463**
Bischoff, F., 999, **1009**
Bisgard, J. D., 1112
Bishop, C. J., 660, **697,** 722, 723, **757**
Bishop, D. W., 628, 665, **697**
Bishop, F. W., 932, **948**
Bishop, M., 532, 540, **606,** 677, **697**
Bittner, J. J., 1188, **1192**
Blackford, M. E., 937, 938, 942, 946, **954**
Blackwood, O., 525, 530, **604**
Blakeslee, A. F., 368, 391, **465**

Blanc, J., 1114
Blanchard, C. H., 92, **141**
Blau, M., 131, **141**
Bloch, B., 1152, 1153, **1192**
Block, M. H., 930, 935, **952,** 963, 965, 967, **1017, 1018, 1025,** 1059
Blocker, W., 97, **141**
Blomfield, G. W., 164, **185**
Bloom, M. A., 935, **948,** 962, 983, 997–999, **1009, 1010,** 1031, 1036, 1037, 1099, 1100, 1101, 1112
Bloom, W., 929–932, 943, **948,** 960–964, 988, 989, 997–999, **1010, 1022, 1023, 1026,** 1031, 1033, 1035, 1036, 1064, 1093–1096, 1100, 1101, 1110, 1112, 1118, 1128, 1161, **1192**
Blount, H. C., Jr., 935, 946, **948, 956,** 993, **1010**
Blum, H. F., 597, **604,** 811, 812, **817,** 1175, 1190
Blumel, J., 682, **697**
Blumenthal, G., 601, **616,** 928, **953**
Boche, R. D., 687, **705,** 932, **948**
Bodemann, E., 849, **859**
Boffil, J., 926, **948,** 963, **1010**
Bogliolo, L., 1157, **1192**
Bohn, G., 553, 554, **604**
Bohr, N., 51
Bollinger, A., 1000, **1013,** 1128
Bolomey, R. A., 584, **609,** 733, **758**
Bond, V. P., 926, 934, **948, 949, 956,** 961, 963, 965, 982, 985, 1005, **1010, 1011, 1016, 1025,** 1072
Bonet-Maury, P., 274, **278,** 286, **309,** 328, **344,** 567, **604,** 744, 750, 751, **757,** 938, **948**
Bonham, K., 448, **463, 465, 710**
Böni, A., 589, **609**
Bonner, D. M., 461, **462,** 593, **604**
Bonnier, G., 477, 509, 510, 513, 514, **604,** 644, **697**
Bonte, F. J., 1160, 1182, **1196**
Bonzell, V., 287, 289, **309**
Boon, M. C., 1168, 1187, 1190, **1194**
Borak, J., 976, 977, **1010,** 1123
Borchert, R., 542, **615**
Borges, W., 1163, **1194**
Borisoff, 480
Born, H. J., 574, **605**
Borowskaja, D., 1004, **1010**
Bortner, T. E., 176, **185**
Bose, I., 642, **708**
Bostian, C. H., 388, **473,** 683, 710
Bothe, W., 40, 72, 82, 83, 92, 113, **141, 142**
Bouin, P., 1118
Bouricius, J. K., 848, **856**
Boveri, T., 394, **464**
Bowen, T., 166, **185**
Bower, J. O., 1132
Bowers, J. Z., 929, **957,** 966, 1005, **1010, 1027**
Boyd, W., 589, **609**
Boyland, E., 424, **464,** 600, **605,** 1190, **1192**
Boys, F., 967, **1010**
Bozeman, M. L., 665, 679, 688–690, **697, 705**
Braasch, N. K., 977, **1010**
Bradley, Muriel, 338, **347,** 684, **705,** 798, **821**
Bragg, W. H., 87, 88, 91, 93, 157, **185**
Brambell, F. W. R., 1168, **1192**
Brandt, C. L., 304, **310**
Brandt, E. L., 424, **465**
Brar, S. S., 168–170*n.*, **185**
Braun, R., 180, **187**
Brawner, H. P., 1001, **1010**
Bream, H., 1003, 1004, **1024**
Brecher, G., 926, 942, 943, **948, 949,** 967, 1001, **1010,** 1067, 1076
Breed, H. E., 112, **141**
Brennan, J. T., 943, **948,** 1001, **1011**
Brenneke, H., 686, **697,** 826, 827, 832–835, **856, 858,** 999, **1010**
Brent, R. L., 888, **916, 918,** 1185, 1201
Bretscher, E., 139, **143,** 299, 301, **312,** 330, 331, **347**
Brewster, W., 689, **707**
Brick, I. V., 986, **1010**
Bridges, C. B., 358, 368, 393, **464,** 495, 496, **605,** 638, 643, 644, 650, 664, **698**
Bridges, P. N., 532
Bright, E. M., 936, **955**
Brinckerhoff, R. F., 167, **188**
Brinkhouse, K. M., 966, 968, **1022**
Brohult, S., 296, **313**
Bromley, D., 147, **185**
Brookhaven National Laboratory, 630, **698**
Brooks, B., 1112
Brooks, H., 116, **143**
Brooks, J. W., 934, **948,** 1005, **1010**
Brooks, R. E., 979, **1024**
Brown, C. S., 972, 974, **1010**
Brown, H. M., 555, **609**
Brown, M. B., 991, 1005, **1018,** 1164, 1165, **1196**
Brown, M. G., 303, **314**
Brown, M. S., 650, **707**
Brown, P., 1149, **1192**
Brown, R. F., 994, **1018**
Brown, W. H., 985, **1018**
Brownscombe, E. R., 328, **345**

Brues, A. M., 303, **310**, 925, 929–932, **948**, **955**, **956**, 961, 964, 965, 967, 969–975, 980, 981, 984, 987, 989, 995, 1000, 1001, 1005, **1010**, **1011**, **1022**, **1023**, **1026**, **1027**, 1031, 1074, 1128, 1135, 1146, 1159, 1166, 1176, 1177, 1179, 1184–1186, **1192**, **1197**
Brumfield, R. T., 484, 566, 578, **605**, **621**, 725, 737, **757**, **760**
Brunschwig, A., **346**
Brunst, V. V., 924, **948**
Bryson, V., 553, 592, **605**
Buchanan, D. L., 293, **310**, 973, **1011**
Buchmann, W., 414, **464**, 574, **605**
Buchsbaum, R., 938, **948**, 961, 972, **1011**
Buchwald, K. W., 986, **1011**
Buechner, W. W., 25, **141**
Bumm, E., 1171, 1187, **1192**
Bunker, J. W. M., 1183, **1194**
Bunting, C. H., 987, **1022**, 1128
Burch, G. E., 971, 978, **1008**
Burckhard, G., 865, 866, 893, 894, **914**
Burdette, W. J., 423, **464**, 650, **698**, 1190, **1192**
Burhop, E. H. S., 193, 202*n*., 205, 206, 208, 211, 236, 237, 239, 243, **253**
Burnett, W. T., Jr., 579, **605**, **611**, 1171, 1172, **1194**
Burr, B. E., 993, 1001, **1022**
Burrill, E. A., 25, **141**
Burrows, H., 1187, 1190, **1192**, **1193**
Burrows, W., 1003, 1004, **1011**
Burstone, M. S., 864, 894, 899, **914**
Burton, M., 193, **253**
Busch, E., 966, **1011**
Buschke, W., 811, 812, 816, **817**, **818**
Bush, F., 168, 169, **185**
Bushland, R. C., 441, **464**
Bushnell, R. J., 589, **625**
Bushnell, R. S., 737, **761**
Butler, C. L., 987, **1014**
Butler, E. G., 776, **817**
Butler, G. C., 289, **313**, 694, 698, 708, 754, **757**
Butler, J. A. V., 277, **278**, 290, **310**, 754, 755, **757**
Butterworth, J. S., 1169, 1173, **1194**
Buu-Hoi, 1190, **1197**
Buzzati-Traverso, A. A., 130, **141**, 437, 443, **464**, 630, **698**

C

Cade, S., 778, **817**
Cahan, W. G., 1181, 1182, **1193**
Caillot, T., 274, **280**
Caldecott, R. S., 568, 571, 572, **605**
Camerino, B., 289, **311**
Campbell, B., 995, **1011**
Campbell, I. L., 964, **1011**
Cannon, C. V., 147, 160, **185**
Canti, R. G., 773, 776, 778, 782, 788, 790, **817**
Capron, P. E., 163, **185**
Carlson, J. G., 125, **141**, 484, **605**, 628–630, 632, 643, 645, 659, 661, 666, 667, 679, 682, **698**, 748, **757**, 763, 765, 768, 769, 773–780, 782, 789, 791–794, 799–801, 804–816, **817**, **818**, 1094
Carothers, E. E., 628, **698**
Carr, J. G., 415, **463**
Carson, G., 403, 427, **472**
Carter, C. E., 300, **310**
Carter, R. E., 943, **948**, 966, **1011**
Carter, T. C., 907, **918**
Carty, J. R., 936, 940, 945, **948**
Carvajal-Forero, J. de, 986, **1017**
Caspari, E., 131, **141**, 476, **605**, 630, 656, 658, 659, 666, 701
Cassen, B., 148, **185**
Catcheside, D. G., 135, 138–140, **141**, **143**, 342, **344**, 379, 382, **464**, 480, 482, 487, 488, 490, 491, 499, 517, 521, 526–528, 530, 566, 567, **605**, **615**, 630, 632, 646, 647, 652, 653, 655, 658, 660, 663, 666, 667, 675, 678, 687, 696, **698**, **704**, 713, 714, 716, 717, 720, 721, 724, 726–729, 731, 732, 735, 741, 755, 756, **757**, **759**, 825, **856**, 1190, **1193**
Catsch, A., 481, 483, 484, 519, 535, **605**, **621**, 669–671, 684, **698**, **699**
Cattley, R., 803, **818**
Cavalli, L. L., 130, **141**, 630, **698**
Cavallo, L., 160, **189**
Chadwick, J., 42, 66, **143**
Chaikoff, I. L., 993, **1014**, **1015**, 1171, 1172, **1195**
Chambers, F. W., 264, **278**
Chambers, F. W., Jr., 308, **310**, 932, 935, 942, 943, 945, **949**, 979, 988, **1009**
Chambers, R. J., 939, **949**
Chanutin, A., 300, **312**, 973, 975, 987, **1015**, **1020**
Chapman, A. B., 848, **859**
Chapman, W. H., 264, **278**, 934, 935, 942, 943, 945, **949**, 1067
Chapman, W. J., 308, **310**
Charles, D. R., 484, **616**, 727, **759**, 844, 847, 848, 850, 851, 855, **856**
Charleton, E. E., 12, 112, **141**
Chase, H. B., 136, **142**, 997, 998, **1011**
Chase, H. Y., 811, **818**
Chase, J. H., 991, 1004, **1013**
Chastain, L. R., 1066
Chastain, S. M., 940, 941, 944, 945, **949**, 986, **1009**

Chesley, L. C., 300, **310**
Chew, G. F., 12, **142**
Christian, E. J. B., 925, **956**, 989, **1026**
Christie, J. H., 924, 926, **950**, **955**, 1002, 1003, **1019**
Chrom, S. A., 982, 988, 1002, **1011**
Cipollara, A. C., 925, **953**
Claesson, L., 994, **1009**
Clark, A. M., 388, **464**, 683, 699, 929, **949**
Clark, G. L., 287, **310**
Clark, J. B., 303, **314**, 417, **473**, 537, 544, 545, 548–552, 562, **606**, **610**, **623**, **625**, **626**, 751, **761**
Clark, J. H., 1132
Clark, R. K., 160, 167, 168, 170*n*., 176, **185**, **186**, **188**, 923, **955**
Clark, W. G., 932, **949**, 969, **1011**
Clarke, A. M., 93, **144**
Clarke, G., 993, **1014**
Clarkson, J. R., 1030, 1032, 1061
Clayton, F. E., 561, 562, 566, 567, **610**
Cleland, G. H., 417, **464**, 550, **607**, 752, **757**
Clemmesen, J., 1004, **1011**
Cloud, R. W., 93, **144**, 998, **1024**
Clunet, J., 1150, 1152, 1153, **1193**, **1198**
Cocchi, U., 685, **699**
Cochran, K., 937, **949**, 987, 988, **1013**
Cockcroft, A. L., 165, 166, **185**
Coe, W. S., 287, **310**
Cogan, D. G., 998, **1011**, **1024**
Coghill, R. D., 444, **466**, **467**, **471**, 540, **611**
Cohen, I., 769, 771, 784, 790, **820**
Cohn, M., 869, 876, 894, 900, **914**
Cohn, S. H., 968, **1011**, 1035, 1044
Cold Spring Harbor Symposia, 630, **699**
Cole, J. W., 966, 968, **1017**
Cole, L. J., 926, **949**, 963, 965, **1011**
Coley, B. L., 1181, 1182, **1193**
Collins, J. L., 582, **603**
Collinson, E., 300, **310**
Colwell, H. A., 1094, 1145, 1150, 1151, **1193**
Committee on the Standardization of X-ray Measurements, 150, **185**
Compton, A. H., 37, 38, 44, 69, 71, 102–105, 107, 137, **142**
Conard, R. A., 985, 986, **1011**
Congdon, C. C., 964, 965, **1020**, 1075, 1165, **1198**
Conger, A. D., 73, 139, **142**, 341, **345**, 386, 417, **464**, 562, 563, 573, 588, **606**, 726, 734, 737, 745, 748, **757**
Conlon, P., 1182, **1198**
Conn, E. E., 308, **310**
Conway, B. E., 755, **757**
Cook, E. V., 935, **949**
Coolidge, A. S., 216, **252**
Coon, J. M., 914, 915, **957**
Cooper, K. W., 520, **606**, 653, 654, **699**
Cope, O., 998, **1024**
Copp, D. H., 1112
Corey, R. B., 295, **313**
Corscaden, J. A., 908, **916**
Corson, D. R., 5, **144**
Cottet, P., 577, **606**
Coulson, C. A., 319, 320, **347**
Coulter, M., 1002, 1003, **1017**
Coutard, H., 893, 898, **915**, 1124
Cowing, R. F., 829, 837, **857**, 999, **1014**
Crabb, E. D., 967, **1018**
Crabtree, H. G., 275, **278**, 305, 306, **310**, 319, 339, **344**, 558, **606**, 936, 939–941, 945, 946, **949**, 1001, **1010**
Craddock, C. G., Jr., 970, 978, 991, 1003, 1004, **1012**, **1019**, **1027**
Cramer, W., 275, **278**, 558, **606**, 936, 939–941, 945, 946, **949**
Craver, B. N., 991, **1012**
Creighton, M., 628, 642, 660, **699**, 776, **818**
Crèvecoeur, E., 163, **185**
Crone, H. G., 227, **253**
Cronkite, E. P., 264, **278**, 308, **310**, 926, 934, 935, 942, 943, **948**, **949**, 966, 968, 969, 991, 1005, **1011**, **1022**, 1031, 1035, 1044–1046, 1067, 1076
Cross, C. F., 290, **310**
Crouse, H. V., 665, 679, 687, **699**
Crow, H. E., 799, **818**
Crowell, J., 811, 812, **818**
Crowther, J. A., 283, **310**, 525, **606**
Cummings, E., 584, **603**
Cupp, M. N., 968, 969, 979, **1019**
Curie, M., 134, **142**
Curl, H., 978, **1023**
Curran, S. C., 165, 166, **185**
Curtis, H. J., 933, 935, **956**, **958**, **1005**, **1026**
Curtis, L. R., 148, **185**
Czepa, A., 1030

D

Daels, F., 1154–1156, **1193**
Dainton, F. S., 236, **252**, 257, 270, **278**, **279**, 291, 300, **310**
Dakin, H. D., 297, **310**
Dalcq, A., 643, **699**
Dale, W. M., 257–263, 265, 267–269, 271, 272, 275, **279**, 293, 296, 297, 299, 300, 307, **310**, 329, **344**, 599, 656, **699**, 938, **949**
Dally, C. M., 1148
Dalton, A. J., 1172, **1199**

D'Amato, F., 275, **279**, 556, 563, 575, 576, 578, 590, **606**
Dancoff, S. M., 112, **141**
Daniel, J., 919, **949**
Daniels, D. S., 488, **614**
Darden, E. B., 1167, **1193**
Darlington, C. D., 566, 578, **606**, 660, 694, **699**, 715, 717, 721, 723, 741, 749, **757**, 784, 794, 799–801, **818**
Darwin, C., 453
Dauphin, J., 390, **464**
Davidoff, L. M., 995, **1012**
Davidson, H., 592, **605**
Davidson, N., 148, **186**
Davies, J. V., 260, 262, 263, 265, 267–269, **279**, 296, 297, **310**, 656, **699**
Davis, R. W., 961, **1012**, 1039
Dawson, A. B., 1125
Day, F. H., 107, 153, 180, **186**
Day, M. J., 147, 152, **186**, 292, **311**
Day, P. L., 937, **949**
Deal, L. J., 147, **186**
Debreuil, G., 554, **620**
DeBruyn, P. P. H., 931, 943, **949**, 1102, 1103
Dechaume, 1157, **1195**
Decker, A. B., 985, 986, **1009**, **1021**
DeCoursey, E., 999, 1005, **1020**
Dehler, H., 1171, **1193**
Delbet, P., 1125
Delbrück, M., 130, **144**, 412, 413, **464**, 476, 526, 582, 597, **606**, **624**, **625**, 630, **699**
DeLong, C. W., 922, **949**
Demerec, M., 345, 379, 380, 417, 422, **463**, **464**, 476, 478, 482, 494, 495, 505, 518, 521, 532, 533, 535, 540, 556, **604**, **606**, **608**, **611**, **620**, 630, 632, 635, 644–648, 652, 656, 658, 659, 661–663, 666–670, 673, 677, 678, 682, 683, **697**, **699-701**, **703**, 1190, 1193
Demidova, Z. A., 476, 480, **607**, **610**
Dempster, E. R., 333, 334, 339, **344**, **350**, 483, 492, 518, 521, **607**, 655, 669, 671, 683, 688, **700**, 786, **824**
Denniston, R. H., 994, **1012**
Denstad, T., 962, **1012**
Depenthal, 1171, **1193**
Deringer, M. K., 847, **856**, **858**, 963, **1020**, 1153, 1154, 1166–1168, 1180, **1193**, **1198**
Desjardins, A. U., 983, 990, **1012**, 1030, 1094, 1125, 1127, 1128, 1131
Dessauer, F., **142**, 248
Deufel, J., 774, 776, 779, 782, 799, 800, **818**
Deupree, N. G., 1003, 1004, **1011**
Devi, P., 557, **607**
DeVries, H., 353
Dickey, F. H., 417, **464**, 550, **607**, 752, **757**
Dickman, S., 551, 580, **603**, 922, 937, 941, **948**
Dickmann, S. R., 262, **278**, 298, 299, **309**
Dickson, H., 531, **607**
Di Giovanni, H., 176, **185**
Dillard, G. C. L., 966, 968, **1012**
Dinning, J. S., 937, **949**
Dirac, P. A., 40
Dische, Z., 943, **957**
Dixon, F. J., 686, **710**, 968, 983, **1012**, **1027**, 1057, 1058
Doan, C. A., 1155, 1156, **1200**
Dobrovolskaia-Zavadskaia, N., 1155, **1193**
Dobson, E. L., 978, **1012**
Dobyns, B. M., 172, **186**
Dobzhansky, T., 446, 455, **464**, **607**, 635, 640–642, 644, 648, 700
Dodds, E. C., 986, **1013**
Dognon, A., **344**, 558, **607**
Dohnert, H. R., 1179, **1193**
Dole, N., 961, **1012**
Doll, E. A., 908, **916**
Donaldson, D. D., 998, **1011**
Donaldson, L. R., 448, **465**, **710**
Donaldson, M., 788, **817**
Doniach, I., 1172, **1193**
Doniger, J., 963, **1020**
Dooley, R., 1065
Döring, H., 414, **472**, 541, 586, **607**, **623**
Dotterweich, H., 576, **607**
Doub, H. P., 1000, **1013**
Dougherty, T. F., 990, 991, 1004, **1013**
Douglas, D. M., 985, **1013**
Doull, J., 937, **949**, 987, 988, **1013**
Dowdy, A. H., 923, 930, 935, 940, 941, 944–946, **949**, **951**, 960, 963, 993, **1016**, **1019**, 1037, 1039, 1044, 1063, 1066, 1067
Downes, Helen R., **348**
Driesch, H., 353
Driessen, L. F., 865, 866, 869, 901, 908, 910, **914**
Duane, W., 286, **311**
Dubinin, N. P., 381, **465**, 480, 481, **607**, 640, **700**
Dublin, L. I., 1162, **1193**
Dubois, K. P., 937, **949**, 987–989, 1001, **1013**
Dubovsky, N. V., 410, **465**
DuBow, R., 695, **706**
Dubreuil, G., 831, **858**
Dudgeon, E., 561, 562, 566, 567, **610**
Dudley, H. C., 1061

Dudley, R. A., 172, **186**
Duggar, B. M., 630, 641, **700**, 713, **757**, 763, **818**
Dulbecco, R., 543, 544, **607**
Dunlap, C. E., 960, 966, **1013**, 1039, 1061, 1094, 1099, 1155, 1157, 1161, **1193**, **1201**
Dupuis, P., 1158, **1198**
Duryee, W. R., 628, 656, **700**, 801–804, 806, 807, **818**, 928, **949**, 1094
Dutcher, R., 969, **1026**
Dyke, C. G., 995, **1012**
Dyroff, R., 869, 894, **914**

E

Easley, M. A., 23, **142**
Eberhardt, K., 334, **344**, 480, 487, **607**, 641, **700**
Eby, F. S., 148, **187**
Eddy, C. E., 153, **186**
Edelmann, A., 989, 991, 1005, **1013**
Eden, M., 993, 1001, **1022**
Edington, C. W., 561, 563
Edison, T. A., 1148
Edmonds, H. W., 751, **760**
Edmondson, M., 546, 569, **607**
Edsall, D. L., 1000, **1013**
Efroimson, W. P., 478, 582, **607**
Ehrenberg, L., 584, **608**
Ehrlich, G., 943, **957**
Ehrlich, M., 147, **186**
Eisen, H. N., 1004, **1013**
Eldredge, J. H., 926, **952**, 963, 965, **1018**, 1070, 1073, 1077, 1078
Elias, C., 1190, **1197**
Ellinger, F., 864*n*., **914**, 925, 926, 932, **949**, **950**, **956**, 977, 987, 990, 992, 1000, **1013**, 1094, 1121, 1123
Ellis, C. D., 42, 66, **143**
Ellis, F., 788, **819**, 975, **1019**
Ellis, M. E., 926, **949**, 963, 965, **1011**
Ellis, R. H., Jr., 168, 169, 171, **188**
Elsberg, C. A., 995, **1012**
Elson, L. A., 934, **950**
Eltzholtz, D. C., 264, **278**, 308, **310**, 932, 935, 942, 943, 945, **949**
Elward, J. F., 994, **1019**
Ely, J. O., 692, 693, **700**, 934, **950**, 961, 964, 974, 981, 983–988, 1001, **1013**, **1014**, **1024**
Emerson, L. C., 1167, **1193**
Emile-Weil, P., 1162, 1165, **1193**
Emmons, C. W., 531, 535, 536, 540, 573, **608**, **611**
Endicott, K. M., 1001, **1010**
Enerson, D. M., 966–968, 1003, **1008**, 1045
Engelstad, R. B., 983, 990, **1014**, 1125, 1129–1131
Entenman, C., 975, **1021**
Enzmann, E. V., 335, **344**, 363, 386, **471**, 566, **621**, 741, **760**
Ephrati, E., 941, **950**
Ephrussi, B., 302, **312**, 461, 596, **608**, 683, **704**, 929, **953**
Erf, L. A., 339, **348**
Erickson, R., **707**
Ermala, P., 975, **1025**
Ernst, H., 553, **616**
Errera, M., 289, **311**, 696, **700**
Eschenbrenner, A. B., 829–831, 837, **857**, **858**, 963, 999, 1001, **1014**, **1020**, 1048, 1049, 1100, 1116, 1118, 1153, 1154, 1165–1168, 1173, 1180, 1188, **1198**
Euler, H. von, 276, **278**, **279**, 305, 306, **308**, 692, 696, **700**
Evans, A. T., 416, **466**
Evans, B. H., 628, 642, **699**
Evans, E. I., 935
Evans, M. G., 256, **279**, **309**
Evans, R. D., 101, **142**, 476, **608**, 1155, 1157, 1158, 1176, 1178, 1179, 1183, **1193**, **1194**
Evans, T. C., 274, **279**, 301, 303, **311**, 336, 337, **345**, 785, **818**, 923, 925, 936, 940, 945, **950**, 993, 998, **1014**, 1044, 1048, 1061, 1131
Eversole, W. J., 989, **1013**
Ewing, J., 1182, **1194**
Exner, F. M., 262, **280**, 527, **615**, 643, **708**
Eyring, H., 236, **252**

F

Fabergé, A. C., 480, 482, 488, 532, 533, 566–568, 573, **601**, **608**, 666, **700**, 727, 729, 741, 744, **757**
Fábián, G., 577, **608**
Faerber, E., 911, **914**
Faes, M., 163, **185**
Failla, G., 152–154, 157, 162, 164, 167, 176, 179, **186**, **188**, **189**, 274, **279**, 301, **311**, 319, 320*n*., 343*n*., **345**, **348**, **349**, 785, **818**, 938, 939, **950**, 972, **1014**, 1096
Fainstat, T. D., 907–908, **914**
Fairchild, G. C., 788, **819**
Fairchild, L. M., 417, **464**, 562, 563, **606**, 745, **757**
Falconer, D. S., 825, **857**
Falls, H. F., 430, **470**
Fankhauser, G., 643, **700**
Fano, L., 14, 26, 59, 116, **144**
Fano, U., 92, 109, 121, 131, 135, 139, **141**, **142**, **144**, 157, **186**, 237, **252**, 344,

Fano, U. (*cont.*), **345**, 482, 492, 494, 502, 521, **606, 608**, 630, 646, 647, 653, 656, 658, 659, 663, 666–668, 671, 672, 676, 677, 680, 682, 683, **699, 700, 701**
Farago, A., **345**
Farrant, J. L., 153, **186**
Farris, E. J., 994, **1015**
Farrow, J. G., 644, **699**
Farrow, J. H., 182, 183, **188**
Fehr, A., 1132
Feigenbaum, J., 299, **311**
Feinstein, R. M., 987, **1014**
Feldsted, E. T., 994, **1018**
Feldweg, P., 909, **914**
Fell, H. B., 805, 806, 810, **823**
Feller, D. D., 993, **1014**
Fellner, O. O., 869, 894, 900, **914**
Fenn, W. O., 1002, **1014**
Ferkel, R. L., 692, **707**
Fermi, E., 166, **186**
Fernau, A., 295, **311**
Fershing, J. L., 1001, **1015**
Feygin, S., 1150, **1194**
FIAT Review of German Science, 630, **701**
Field, J. B., 966–969, 979, **1014**
Fielding, U., 1168, **1192**
Fifth International Congress of Radiology, 151, **186**
Figge, F. H. J., 1161, **1194**
Findlay, D., 993, **1014**
Fink, K., 973–975, **1014**
Finkel, M. P., 864, 900, **914**, 1159, 1160, 1166, 1177, 1180, 1184, **1192, 1197**
Finkelstein, P., 295, **309**
Fischel, E. E., 1005, **1014**
Fischer, P., 941, 945, **948**, 1004, **1019**
Fisher, N. F., 990, **1014, 1020**
Fishler, M. C., 926, 935, **948, 949, 953**, 961, 963, 965, 982, 985, 1005, **1010, 1011, 1016, 1018**
Fitch, S. H., 147, **186**
Fitzmaurice, H. A., 879, 882, **915**
Flaskamp, W., 908, 911, **914**, 1123
Fleeman, J., 93
Fleischmann, W., 305, **312**
Flint, J., 417, **464**
Flood, V., 287, 288, 301, 303, 304, **309**, 551, 580, **603**
Focht, E. F., 86, **143**, 176, 180, 182, **188**
Fogg, L. C., 829, 837, **857**, 999, **1014**, 1095
Folley, J. H., 1163, **1194**
Folsom, F. B., 943, **951**
Ford, J. M., 538, 541, 593, **608, 615**
Forfota, E., 1000, **1015**
Forkner, C. E., 1155, 1156, **1200**
Forro, F., Jr., 139, **143**, 330, **348**
Forssberg, A. G., 262, **279**, 299, **311**, 922, 924, 941, 943, **950, 956**
Forstat, H., 165, **187**
Förster, T., 230, 233, **252**
Försterling, K., 864, **914**
Forsythe, W. E., 23, **142**
Foster, R. F., 448, **465, 710**
Foulds, L., 1157, **1194**
Fowler, W. A., 59, **143**
France, H. O., 939, **950**, 969, 971, **1011, 1015**
Francis, D. S., 274, **280**, 335, **346**, 769, 770, 784, 788–790, **820**, 929, 935, 939, **951**
Franck, J., 225, 227, 232, 233, 249, **250, 252, 253**, 270, **279**
Frankenthal, L., 305, **311**, 961, 1002, **1015**
Franks, W. R., 1161, **1194**
Frantz, F., 93
Fraser, F. C., 907, **914, 915**
Freed, J. H., 994, **1015**
Freeman, P. J., 304, **310**
Freund, L., 919, **950**
Frey, H., 990, **1015**
Fricke, H., 122, **142**, 157, **186**, 257, 258, 262, 274, **279**, 284, 287, 288, 300, 307, **311**, 328, **345**, 478, 556, 557, 599, **608**
Frieben, 919, **950**, 1148, **1194**
Friedell, H. L., 924, 926, **950, 955**, 988, **1015**, 1160, 1182, **1196**
Frieden, J., 973, **1015**
Friedenwald, J. S., 123, **142**, 811, 812, 816, **817, 818**
Friedman, M., 1182, **1192**
Friedman, N. B., 982, 983, 986, **1015, 1027**, 1108, 1125, 1161, **1201**
Friedrick, W., 153, **186**
Friesen, H., 359, 360, **465**, 582, **609**, 653, **701**
Frilley, M., 274, **278**, 299, **311**, 331, **345**, 864, 869, 876–877, 879, 888, 891, 901, **916, 917**, 939, **950**
Frings, H., 589, **609**
Fritz-Niggli, H., 589, **609**
Fry, E. G., 991, **1024**
Fry, H. J., 771, **818**
Fuerst, R., 417, **473**, 548–551, **625**, 751, **761**
Furst, L. J., 910, **918**
Furth, F. W., 926, **957**, 1002, 1003, **1015, 1017**
Furth, J., 933, **950**, 961, 966, 968–971, 978, 979, 988, **1009, 1015, 1026, 1028**, 1038, 1039, 1047, 1062, 1075, 1082, 1146, 1164, 1166–1169, 1171–1174, 1180, 1187, 1190, **1192, 1194, 1200, 1201**

Furth, O. B., 926, 933, **948, 950,** 960, **1000,** 1164, 1166, 1168, 1174, 1180, **1194**

G

Gadsden, E. L., 1171, 1172, **1194**
Gager, C. S., 390, 391, **465,** 554, **609,** 627, **701**
Gaither, N. T., 545, 564, 572, 580, **613**
Gall, E. A., **345, 347**
Gallico, E., 289, **311**
Gardner, W. U., 935, **957,** 1066, 1079, 1167, 1168, 1170, **1194, 1197**
Garrod, A., 461
Gastaldi, G., 996, **1015**
Gaston, E. O., 926, 930, 935, **952,** 963, 965, 967, 983, 1002, **1017, 1018,** 1046, 1064, 1070–1074, 1076–1079
Gasvoda, B., 293, 301–303, **309**
Gates, A. A., 1178, **1196**
Gates, O., 1112, 1130
Gaulden, M. E., 561, 569, **609,** 748, **757,** 796, 799, 808, 814, 816, **817, 818,** 904
Gauss, C. J., 908, **914**
Gavrilova, A. A., 480, **613**
Gay, D. M., 987, 988, **1014**
Gay, E. H., 520, **610**
Gay, H., 268, **280,** 503, 569, 570, **613,** 652, 657, 661, 664, 675, 676, 685, 691, 695, **696, 703,** 739, 740, **758, 759**
Geiger, H., 4
Geigy, R., 531, **609**
Gelin, O. E. V., 274, **280,** 555, **609**
Gentner, C. F., 555, **609**
Gentner, W., 5, 40, 72, 82, 83, 113, **142**
Gérard, P., 1152, 1153, **1195**
Gerritsen, A. N., 194*n.*, **252**
Gershenson, S. M., 378, 448, **469,** 664, **706**
Gershon-Cohen, J., 926, **950,** 1072
Gerstner, H. B., 1075
Gest, H., 587, **610**
Ghent, W. R., 985, **1013**
Giese, A. C., 630, **701,** 763, 811, **818, 819, 823,** 1094, 1097
Gilbert, C., 907, **914**
Gilbert, C. W., 265, 268, 271, 275, **279,** 296, 297, **310**
Gilbert, L. A., 277, **278**
Giles, N. H., Jr., 73, 139, **142,** 341, **345,** 399, **465,** 484, 517–519, 521, 558, 559, 561, 568, 584, 588, 594, 596, 597, **606, 609, 616, 620,** 656, 658, 668, **701,** 721, 723–728, 733, 734, 742–749, 751–753, **757, 758, 759,** 904, 940, 941, **950,** 1094
Gillman, J., 907, **914**
Gillman, T., 907, **914**
Gjessing, E. C., 973, **1015**
Glass, H. B., 385, **465,** 503, **609,** 679, 687, **701,** 846, **857**
Glasser, O., 23, 24, 86, 109, **142,** 157, 180, 182, **186,** 1146, **1194**
Glasser, S. M., 992, **1013**
Glenn, J. C., Jr., 1003, **1015**
Glocker, R., 331, 340, **345**
Glover, J. K., 943, **951**
Glücksmann, A., 687, **701,** 774, 776, 781, 782, 787, 797, 804–806, 810, **819, 823, 824,** 828, 831, **857,** 998, 999, **1015**
Godwin, I. D., 966, 968, **1022**
Goebel, O., 1152, 1153, **1195**
Goldberg, R. C., 993, **1015,** 1171, 1172, **1195**
Goldfeder, A., 966, 1001, **1015**
Goldhaber, G., 274, **280**
Goldie, H., 1184, **1195**
Goldman, D., 1000, **1016**
Goldschmidt, L., 943, **955,** 961, 962, 964, **1016, 1024**
Goldstein, L., 908–911, **914**
Gomez, E. T., 1123
Good, D. J., 784, **822**
Goodgal, S. H., 545–547, 579, 600, **610, 623**
Goodman, C., 1178, 1179, **1194**
Goodrich, J. P., 936, 940, 945, **950**
Goodspeed, T. H., 362, 389, **465, 610**
Gorbman, A., 993, **1016,** 1167, 1171, 1180, **1195**
Gorin, M. H., 307, **311**
Goudsmit, S., 198, **252**
Gowen, J. W., 329, **345,** 520, **610**
Gower, J. S., 827, 828, 833, 838
Grachus, T., 986, **1009**
Graffeo, A. J., 935, **950,** 992, **1016**
Graham, J. B., 935, **950,** 992, **1016**
Graham, R. M., 992, **1016**
Grasnick, W., 627, **701**
Gray, L. H., 66, 139, **142,** 154, 157, 160, 162, 165, **187,** 260, 271, 275, **279,** 296, 299, 300, 307, **310,** 317, 319, 320, 323, 328, 329, 335–337, 339, 340, **344–346, 348,** 490, 517, **614,** 628, 630, 658, **709, 710,** 725, 732, 736, 750, **758, 759,** 764, 775–777, 779, 786–788, 805, 810, **819, 823,** 923, 928, **951, 954, 957,** 976, 1002, **1021,** 1146, **1195**
Green, C. D., 1172, **1199**
Greenberg, D. M., 1112
Greenstein, J. P., 277, **281,** 289, **313,** 694, **709,** 754, **761,** 801, **823**
Greisen, K., 97, **143**
Gricouroff, G., 1094, 1099, 1117, 1118, 1121, 1122, 1124, 1132, 1157, **1195**

Griffen, A. C., 424, **465**
Griffith, H. D., 319, 333, **349**, 478, **626**
Griffith, J. Q., Jr., 926, **950**, 968, 970, 976, **1016**, **1017**, **1022**, 1072
Grimmett, L. G., 781, 790, **823**
Grobman, A., 894, 896, 898
Grodner, R., 561
Grumbrecht, P., 1132
Grundhauser, W., 930, **955**, 1159, 1160, 1177, 1184, **1197**
Grüssner, G., 980, **1009**
Gudernatsch, J. F., 864, 879, **915**
Guerin, M., 1157, **1200**
Guilleminot, M. H., 554, **610**
Gulbekian, C., 508, 516, **610**
Gump, H., 1001, **1010**
Gunz, F. W., 305, **312**, 962, **1020**
Gurney, R. W., 165, **187**
Gurtner, P., 291, **312**
Gustafson, G. E., 1002, 1003, **1016**
Gustafsson, Å., 275, **279**, 436, 442, **465**, 555, 556, 563, 575, 576, 578, 584, 590, 591, **606**, **608**, **610**, 754, **758**
Guyénot, E., 390, **465**

H

Haas, E., 249, **252**
Haas, F., 303, **313**, **314**, 417, **473**, 537, 544, 548–551, 561, 562, 566–568, **610**, **623**, **625**, 751, **761**
Haba, G. de la, 573, **615**
Haddox, C. H., 417, **473**, 548–551, **625**, 751, **761**
Haerting, F. H., 1177, **1195**
Hagen, C. W., Jr., 336, **346**, 925, 930, 932–934, **951**, **955**, 964, **1017**, 1031, 1044
Hahn, L., 696, **700**
Hahn, P. F., 1060, 1184, **1195**
Haines, R. B., 139, **143**, 299, 301, **312**, 319, 320, 330, 331, **347**
Haissinsky, M., 256, **280**
Halberstaedter, L., 274, **280**, 682, **701**, 961, 991, **1006**, 1097, 1117, 1136, 1137
Haldane, J. B. S., 411, 419, **465**, 590, 687, **701**, 854, **857**
Haley, T. J., 935, 946, **951**, 993, **1016**, 1031, 1046
Hall, B. V., 943, **951**
Hall, C. C., 982, 985, 988, 1000, **1016**
Hall, H., 166, **187**
Hall, J. J., 979, **1024**
Hall, M. E., 164, **189**
Hall, T., 1003, 1004, **1024**
Hall-Edwards, J., 1148, **1195**
Halliday, D., 6, 13, 14, **142**
Halpern, O., 166, **187**
Hamburgh, M., 907, **915**
Hamermesh, B., 117, **142**
Hamilton, J., 1112
Hamilton, K., 1187, **1195**
Hammond, C. W., 983, 1002, 1003, **1016**, **1021**
Hance, R. T., 1123
Hannah, A., 498
Hanschuldt, J. D., 972, **1016**
Hansen, R. A., 1037, 1067
Hanson, A. O., 89, 112, **141**, **142**
Hanson, F. B., **346**, 389, **465**, 478, 479, 582, **610**, 869, 876, 879, 894, 896–898, **915**
Hardenbergh, E., 972, 974, **1010**
Harrar, J. A., 908, **916**
Harrington, N. G., 779, 780, 789, 800, 801, **817**, **819**
Harris, B. B., 393, **465**
Harris, D. H., 1031, 1046
Harris, I. D., 967, **1010**
Harris, P. S., 943, **948**, 1001, **1011**
Harris, R. S., 1155, 1183, **1193**, **1194**
Harris, W., 910, **916**
Harrison, B., 287, 288, **308**
Harriss, E. B., 172, **187**
Hart, E. J., 122, **142**, 257, 262, 274, **279**, 287, 288, **311**, 556, **609**
Hartman, F. W., 1000, **1013**
Harvey, E. B., 811, **822**
Haskins, C. P., 335, **344**
Haskins, D., 907, **915**
Hatcher, C. H., 1180, 1181, **1195**
Hawkins, J. W., 1162, **1195**
Hawn, C. van Z., 1003, 1004, **1024**
Hayden, B., 559, **610**, 940, **951**
Hayer, E., 1032
Hays, F. A., 532
Hedin, R. F., 985, **1016**
Heiberg, T., 290, **310**
Heidenthal, G., 404, **472**, 667, **710**
Heilbrunn, L. V., 785, **819**
Heineke, H., 960, 1002, **1016**, 1029, 1039, 1061, 1099
Heitler, W., 98, **143**
Hektoen, L., 935, **951**, 1002, 1003, **1016**, 1080
Helber, E., 864, 900, **916**, 1030, 1032
Helfer, R. G., 662, 677, 678, **701**
Heller, M., 1109–1116
Hellner, H., 1155, **1195**
Helwig, E. R., 628, 665, **701**
Hempelmann, L. H., 776, 777, 782, 797, **820**, 929, 935–937, 946, **951**, **953**, 993, 998, 1005, **1016**, 1120
Hendley, D. D., 987, **1014**

Hennessy, T. G., 943, **951**, 962, **1016**, 1037
Henry, J. A., 937, 946, **951**
Henshaw, C. T., 788, 789, **820**
Henshaw, P. S., 274, **280**, 301, **311**, 335, 337, **346**, 647, **709**, 769–773, 784, 785, 788–790, 796, 803, **819**, **820**, 922–925, 928, 929, 935, 939, **951**, 996, **1016**, 1030, 1031, 1042, 1044, 1049, 1058, 1061, 1063, 1094, 1146, 1160, 1162, 1167, 1177, 1189, **1195**, **1199**
Henson, M., 686, **701**, 833–835, 837, **857**
Heptner, M. A., 476, **610**
Hereck, 1179
Hereford, F. L., 166, **187**
Hermel, M. B., 926, **950**, 1072
Hersh, A. H., 589, **610**
Hershey, A. D., 587, **610**
Herskowitz, I. H., 351, 416, 417, **465**, 475, 499, 506, **611**, 652, 653, **702**
Hertel, E., 811, **820**
Hertwig, G., 456, **466**, 554, **611**, 643, **702**
Hertwig, O., 554, **611**, 643, 702
Hertwig, P., 423, 456, **466**, 554, **611**, 627, 643, 686, 687, **702**, 825–830, 832–834, 836–849, 851, 852, **857**, **858**
Herve, A., 275, **280**, 941, 945, **948**, **951**, 990, **1021**
Herz, R. H., 147, **185**
Herzberg, G., 211–214, 219, **252**
Hesse, O., 1150, 1151, 1177, **1195**
Hesse, W., 1177, **1195**
Heston, W. E., 424, **466**, **856**, **858**, 963, **1020**, 1048, 1049, 1054, 1061, 1100, 1107, 1153, 1168, 1173, 1180, 1188, 1190, **1193**, **1195**, **1198**
Heusghem, C., 990, **1021**
Hevesy, G. von, 276, **278-280**, 305, 306, **308**, **311**, 692–694, **700**, **702**, 808, **820**, 926, 928, **947**, **951**, 952, 958, **1017**
Hewitt, H. B., 940, **952**
Heys, F., **346**, 479, 582, **610**
Hicks, S. P., 879, 891, 894, 896–898, 901, 904, **915**, 933, **952**, 996, **1016**
Higginbottom, C., 557, **607**
Highman, B. J., 935, **956**
Higinbotham, N. L., 1153, 1181, 1182, **1193**, **1200**
Hilcken, J. A., **345**, **347**
Hill, G. S., 794
Hill, R. F., 544, **611**
Hillstrom, H. T., 1112
Himes, M. H., 695, **702**
Hine, G. J., 167, 173, **188**
Hinkel, C. L., 933, **952**
Hinton, C. W., 653, 666, **702**
Hinton, O. T., **700**
Hinton, T., 416, **466**
Hippel, von, 869, 879, 891, 900, **915**
Hipple, J. A., 238*n*., **252**
Hirsch, H., 990, **1017**
Hirschfelder, J. O., 236, **252**
Hobbs, A. A., Jr., 909, **915**
Hoberson, J. H., 147, **186**
Hochwald, L. B., 935, 936, **947**
Hodes, P. J., 970, 976, **1017**, **1022**
Hodges, F. J., 923, **953**
Hodges, G. R. V., 264, **280**, 945, 946, **954**
Hodges, P. C., **346**
Hoecker, F. E., 172, **188**
Hoffman, B. G., 87, **141**
Hoffman, J. G., 776, 777, 782, **820**, 998, 1005, **1016**
Holden, C., **707**
Holden, W. D., 966, 968, **1017**
Hollaender, A., 127, 131, **143**, 277, **281**, 289, 301, **311**, **313**, 333, 349, 444, 466, **471**, 476, 503, 505, 506, 509, 521, 531, 532–536, 540, 543, 546, 556–558, 561, 563, 564, 569–571, 573, 578–580, 601, **605**, **606**, **608**, **611**, **613**, **620**, **622**, **623**, 675–677, 694, **703**, **709**, 738–740, 744, 754, **758**, **759**, **760**, **761**, 774–776, 779, 782, 791, 792, 794, 800, 811–815, **817**, **818**, **822**, **823**, 856, **858**, 940, 941, 944, **952**
Hollander, W., 849, **859**
Hollcroft, Joanne, 336, **346**, 1146, **1195**
Hollingsworth, J. W., 1004, **1017**
Holmes, B. E., 262, 275, 276, **280**, 300, 305, 306, 308, **310**, **312**, 692, 693, **702**, 928, 944, **952**, 975, **1017**
Holmes, G. W., 995, **1017**
Holt, M. W., 805, **823**
Holthausen, C. F., 414, **470**
Holthusen, H., 180, **187**, 554, 558, **611**, 627, **702**, 927, 935, 939, **952**
Holweck, F., 301, **312**, 330, 331, **346**, **349**
Holzknecht, G., 147, **187**
Honerjäger, R., 25, **143**
Hoover, M. E., 645, 647, 650, 683, **699**, **700**, **702**
Hopkins, D. E., 441, **464**
Hopwood, F. L., 291, **312**, 773, 776, **823**, 1097
Horlacher, W. R., 588, **611**
Horn, E. C., 335, **346**
Horning, E. S., 424, **464**, 1190, **1192**
Hornyak, W. F., 59, **143**
Horowitz, N. H., 461
Hoth, I., 574, **605**
Houlahan, M. B., 532, 540, **606**
Howard, A., 544, 546, 549, 567, **611**, 830, **858**
Howland, J. W., 971, 974, 1002, 1003, 1005, **1009**, **1017**

Hubbard, H. S., 12, **141**
Hubert, R., 1002, **1017**
Hudson, J. C., **347**
Hueck, W., **1195**
Hueper, W. C., 986, **1017**, 1164, 1166, 1179, 1188, **1195**
Huff, R. L., 926, 943, **951**, **957**, 962, **1016**, 1037, 1136
Hughes, A. F., 776, 782, 797, **824**
Hughes-Schrader, S., 646, 647, **702**
Huguenin, R., 1184, **1195**
Hummel, R., 975, **1017**
Humphreys, E. M., 986, **1023**
Humphries, R. E., 1158, **1198**
Hungate, F. P., 585, **612**
Hunt, H. B., 1112
Hursh, J. B., 992, **1017**, 1178, **1196**
Hurwitz, H., Jr., 116, **143**
Hussey, R. G., 299, **312**
Husted, L., 714, **758**
Hutchinson, W., 148, **187**
Hutner, S. H., 595, **620**

I

Ickowicz, M., 991, **1006**, 1136, 1137
Impiombato, G., 988, **1017**
Inda, F. A., 1164, 1166, 1174, **1198**
Inglis, K., 1128
Ingraham, L. P., 999, **1009**
Ingram, M., 965, **1017**, 1031, 1048
Insch, G. M., 165, 166, **185**
International Commission on Radiological Units, 150, 151, **187**
International Critical Tables, 118, **143**
International Recommendations on Radiological Protection, 1148, **1196**
Isaacs, R., 1034
Isotopes Catalogue, 14, 26, **143**
Ives, P. T., 414, 416, **466**, 588
Ivy, A. C., 985, 986, **1017**, 1127, 1132
Izzo, M. J., 961, **1012**

J

Jackson, E. M., 942, 943, 945, **954**, 966, 993, 1001, **1022**, **1025**, 1060, 1067
Jackson, M. A., 1184, **1195**
Jacobson, L. O., 337, **346**, 926, 930, 932, 935, **952**, **955**, 960–975, 980, 981, 983, 984, 989, 995, 1002, 1004, 1008, **1010**, **1017**, **1018**, **1020**, **1021**, **1022**, **1024**, **1025**, **1026**, 1029–1031, 1034–1038, 1040–1042, 1044–1046, 1055–1065, 1069–1080, 1100, 1103, 1107, 1137
Jacques, P., 1180, **1196**
Jacquez, J. A., 925, 932, 933, **952**
Jaffé, G., 194*n*.
Jaffe, H. L., 1181, **1196**
Jagić, N. von, 1162, **1196**
James, H. M., 216, **252**
Janeway, C. A., 1003, 1004, **1024**
Janossy, L., **143**
Janzen, A., 996, **1018**
Jasny, G. J., 827, 828, 838
Jelatis, D. G., 985, **1016**
Jenkinson, E. L., 985, **1018**
Jennings, F. L., 934, **952**, 986, 1005, **1018**
Jensen, K. A., 416, **466**, 547, 550, 577, **612**, 751, **758**
Jentschke, W. K., 148, **187**
Jentzer, A., 1155, 1185, **1196**
Jesse, W. P., 66, **143**, 165, **187**
Job, T. T., 864, 865, 869, 870, 873–874, 877–883, 886, 891–894, 896, 901, **915**
Joël, C. A., 686, **710**
Johannsen, W., 391, **466**
John, E. S., 971, 990, 991, 994, 1001, **1022**
Johnson, C. G., 934, **952**, 1005, **1018**
Johnson, P., 287, 288, **309**
Jolles, B., 926, **952**, 976, 977, **1018**, 1136
Jollos, V., 582, **612**
Jolly, J., 927, 939, 940, 945, **952**
Jones, D. C., 935, **953**, 1005, **1018**
Jones, H. B., 928, **953**, 978, 988, 993, **1012**, **1014**, **1018**
Jones, H. W., Jr., 908–909, **915**
Jonkhoff, A. R., 1152, **1196**
Jordan, H. C., 888, **918**, 1185, **1201**
Jordan, M. L., 969, **1011**
Jovin, J., 776, **822**
Judge, J. T., 268, **280**, **703**
Jüngling, O., 776, 777, 782, **820**
Just, E. E., 357, **466**
Juul, J., 776, 782, 799, 811, **820**, 1097

K

Kabat, E. A., 1005, **1014**
Kahlau, G., 1178, 1180, **1199**
Kahn, J. B., Jr., 937, **952**, 1039
Kaliss, N., 1190, **1194**
Kalnitsky, G., 307, **309**
Kalter, H., 907, **915**
Kamen, M. D., 587, **610**
Kanellis, A., 481, 484, 565, 576, **605**, **606**, **612**, 670, 671, 674, 698, 699, **702**
Kanoky, J. P., 994, **1018**
Kaplan, H. S., 926, 933, **947**, **952**, 991, 1005, **1018**, **1020**, 1164–1166, 1168, 1170, 1174, 1188, **1196**
Kaplan, I. I., 999, 1000, **1018**
Kaplan, R. W., 485, 537, 538, 541, 542, 555, 556, 568, 569, 575, 576, 591, **612**, **614**

Kaplan, W. D., 417, **466**
Karady, S., 1000, **1015**
Karnofsky, D. A., 925, 932, 933, **952, 953**
Karr, J. W., 864, 869, 872–873, 876, 879, 882, 887–888, 891–892, 901–904, 907, **918,** 932, 933, **957,** 996, **1028**
Karrer, E., 589, **610**
Kasha, M., 227, **252**
Kassabian, M. K., 1149, **1196**
Katz, E. J., 961, **1024**
Kaufmann, B. N., 570, **624**
Kaufmann, Berwind P., 135, **143,** 268, **280,** 378–380, 463, **466,** 483, 495, 503, 518, 521, 532–534, 569–571, 578, **604, 606, 613,** 627, 631, 632, 635, 645–648, 650–657, 659–666, 668–671, 673, 675–681, 683, 685, 695–697, **699, 700, 702, 703,** 738–740, **758, 759**
Kausche, G. A., 510, **613**
Kaven, A., 864, 869, 872, 874, 875, 879, 881–886, 890–894, 896, 898, 901–902, **915**
Kaye, G. W. C., 153, **187**
Keating, R. P., 939, **956,** 969–972, 974, **1026**
Keith, C. K., 937, **949**
Keller, M., 291, **312**
Keller, M. E., 982, 985, **1023**
Kelly, E. M., 388, **464,** 683, **699,** 838, 929, **949**
Kelly, K. H., 994, **1018**
Kelly, L. S., 928, **953,** 988, **1018**
Kelner, A., 543, 544, **613**
Kelsall, M. A., 967, **1018**
Kemp, T., 776, 782, 799, 811, **820,** 1097
Kennard, E. H., 6, 7, 11, 13, **143**
Kennedy, J. W., 587, **610**
Kennedy, R. J., 108
Kenney, R. W., 97, **141**
Kerkis, J. J., 396, 414, **466,** 508, 588, **613**
Kerr, H. D., 998, **1019**
Kerst, D. W., 112, **141**
Kersten, H. P., 299, **314**
Khvostova, V. V., 378, **471,** 480, 481, **607, 613**
Kihlman, B., 578, **613**
Kikkawa, H., 647, **703**
Kile, J. C., Jr., 561, **620,** 827, 828, **858**
Kimball, R. F., 545, 564, 572, 580, **613**
Kimeldorf, D. J., 935, **953,** 1005, **1018**
Kimura, S. J., 998, **1011**
Kindler, K., 1172, **1196**
King, E. D., 562, 565, 576, **614,** 674, **704**
King, R. C., 584, 585, **614**
Kingsbury, A. N., 1002, **1021**
Kinst, M., 403, 427, **472**
Kirby-Smith, J. S., 137, 488, **614**
Kirk, I., 416, **466,** 547, 550, 577, **612,** 751, **758**
Kirk, M., 1003, 1004, **1024**
Kirschbaum, A., 999, **1020,** 1165, 1170, 1188, **1196, 1199**
Kirschner, L. B., 993, 1001, **1018**
Kirschon, A., 966–969, **1008**
Kirsner, J. B., 986, **1023**
Kirssanow, B. A., 480, **614**
Kirwan, D. P., 538, 593, **608**
Kisieleski, W. E., 923, **956,** 1160, **1197**
Klot, B. von, 864, 898, 908, 910, **915**
Knapp, E., 476, 531, 540, 553, 555, 556, 591, **614**
Knef, J. P., 1182, **1198**
Knipling, E. F., 441
Knowlton, N. P., Jr., 681, **704,** 776, 777, 779, 780, 782, 797, **820,** 929, 935–937, 946, **951, 953,** 993, **1016,** 1120
Knuchel, H., 291, **312**
Koch, H. W., 112, **141**
Koch, J., 910, **918**
Koerner, L., 480
Koernicke, M., 554, **614,** 627, **704**
Kohn, H. I., 935, **953,** 966–969, 972–976, 979, 1004, **1018, 1019, 1027**
Koletsky, S., 1002, 1003, **1016,** 1160, 1182, **1196**
Koller, P. C., 415, **466,** 577, **614,** 629, 660, 662, 678, 681, 686, 693, **699, 704,** 722, 749, **759,** 774, 799, 804, **820,** 843, 848, **858**
Kolmark, G., 416, **466,** 547, 550, 577, **612,** 751, **758**
Komuro, H., 274, **280**
Kornblum, K., 970, 980, 982, 1000, **1021**
Kosaka, S., 864–866, 869, 872, 874, 876, 879–880, 888, 891, 893, 894, 896–898, 901, 904, **915**
Kossikov, K. V., 409, 410, **466,** 481, 522, **614**
Kostoff, D., 573, 589, **614**
Kotval, J. P., 488, 490, 517, **614,** 724, 732, 736, **759**
Kotz, J., 994, **1019**
Koza, R. W., 801, **819**
Kraemer, 908–909, **915**
Kraemer, E. A., 293, **313**
Krause, P., 554, **614,** 627, 688, 704, 982, **1019,** 1151
Krebs, C., 1164, 1178, **1196**
Krejci, L. E., 293, **313**
Krenz, F. H., 269, **280**
Kretzschmar, C. H., 975, **1019**
Krivshenko, J. D., 664, **704**
Krizek, H., 988, **1019**
Kroemeke, F., 1061
Krotkina, N., 1155, 1156, **1199**

Kruger, P. G., 148, **187**, 998, **1008**
Krumpel, O., 292, **313**
Kubowitz, F., 249, **252**
Kuck, Kathryn D., 333, **350**
Kühn, A., 461
Küntz, H., 629, **707**
Kurnick, N. B., 695, **704**
Küstner, H., 180, **187**

L

LaBarre, J., 991, **1028**
Lacassagne, A., 301, **312**, 331, **346**, 776, **822**, 869, 864, 893–895, 898, **915**, **916**, **917**, 936, 940, 945, **953**, 982, **1023**, 1029, 1094, 1099, 1117, 1118, 1121, 1122, 1124, 1132, 1145, 1152, 1153, 1155, 1161, 1162, 1165, 1177, 1182, 1183, 1185–1187, 1190, 1191, **1193**, **1196**, **1197**
Lacomme, M., 909, **916**
La Cour, L. F., 717, 721, 723, 741, 749, **757**
Laidler, K. J., 193, 205*n*., 206, 223, **252**
Laird, A. K., 929, **955**
Lamerton, L. F., 172, **187**, 934, **950**
Lampe, I., 334, 339, **350**
Lampe, J., 923, **953**
Lams, H., 865, 866, 869, 879, 893, 894, 898, **916**
Lamy, R., 388, **466**, 683, 704
Landolt-Börnstein, 229, **252**
Lane, G. R., 386, **467**, 483, 485, 486, 516, 571, 572, **615**, 727, 729, 730, **759**
Langendorff, H., 331, 332, **345**, **346**, 657, **704**, 776, 777, 782, **820**
Langendorff, M., 332, **346**
Langohr, J. L., 998, **1024**
Lanzl, E. F., 112, **141**
Lanzl, E. R., 923–925, **955**, 982, 985, **1023**
Lanzl, L. H., 89, 112, **141**, **142**
Laqueur, G., 811, 816, **822**
Larkin, J. C., 338, **349**, 976, 977, 996, **1019**
Larsh, A. E., 148, **186**
Larson, E., 990, **1014**
Lartigue, O., 969, 974, **1020**
Lasnitski, I., 319*n*., 335, **346**, 629, 682, **704**, 773, 776, 782, 787, 788, 791, 797, 804–806, 809, 810, **820**, **821**, 923, 924, 928, **953**
Laszlo, D., 305, **312**
Latarjet, A., 274, **280**, 302, **312**, 331, **345**
Latarjet, R., 549, 683, **704**, 929, **953**, 1190, **1197**
Latchford, W. B., 1002, **1014**
Laughlin, J. S., 112, **141**, 146, **187**
Laurence, G. C., 154, 155, 157, 166, 183, **187**, **188**
Lauritsen, T., 59, **143**
Lavedan, J., 630, **704**, 895, **916**, 1029
Läwen, A., 1003, **1019**
Lawrence, A. H., 1037, 1039, 1044, 1063
Lawrence, E. G., 650, **705**
Lawrence, E. O., 336, 339, **347**, 923, **953**, 961, **1019**, 1031, 1041, 1042
Lawrence, G. H., 990, **1019**
Lawrence, J. H., 320, 330, 336, 339, 343*n*., **344**, **347**, 923, 935, **947**, **957**, 961, 983, 1002, **1019**, 1031, 1035, 1041, 1042, 1066, 1079, 1100, 1132
Lawrence, J. S., 926, **953**, 960, 963, 966, 970, 978, **1008**, **1019**, **1027**, 1035
Lazarew, N. W., 977, **1019**
Lazarewa, A., 977, **1019**
Lazarus-Barlow, W. S., 1127, 1151, 1153–1156, **1197**
Lea, D. E., 81, 130, 135, 137–**141**, **143**, 180, **187**, 194, 197, **252**, 262, 263, 271, **280**, 283, 299, 301, **312**, 318–320, 323, 327, 329–331, 335, 342, 344, **346**, **347**, 479, 482, 487–491, 499, 500, 517, 521, 526–530, 542, 566, 567, **605**, **615**, 630, 632, 646, 647, 652, 653, 658, 660, 663, 666, 667, 675, 679, 685, 687, **698**, **701**, **704**, 713, 714, 716, 717, 720, 724, 726–728, 730–732, 735, 741, 750, 755, 756, **757**, **759**, 763, 770, 788, 807, **821**, 825, 835, 836, **858**, 921, 924, 935, **953**, 1147, 1189, **1197**
Leach, J. E., 981, **1019**
Le Bail, H., 256, **280**
Leblond, C. P., 960, 991, 993, **1014**, **1018**, 1136, 1137, 1162, **1197**
LeCalvez, J., 628, 646, 674, **697**
Lecomte, J., 941, 945, **948**, 1004, **1019**
Leddy, E. T., 1175, **1197**
Lederberg, E. Z., 420, 454, **467**, 584, **609**
Lederberg, J., 420, 454, **467**
Lefevre, George, Jr., 654, **704**
Lefort, M., 256, 274, **278**, **280**, 286, **309**, 328, **344**, 567, **604**, 744, 750, 751, **757**, 938, **948**
Leibold, G. J., Jr., 879, 882, **915**
Leighton, P. A., 193, **253**
Leinfelder, P. S., 998, **1019**
Leitch, J. L., 1161, 1174, **1197**
LeMay, M., 937, **953**, 989, 1005, **1014**, **1020**
Lengfellner, K., 894, **916**
Lennihan, M. R., 268, **280**, **703**
Léobardy, J. de, 895, **916**
Leppin, O., 919, **953**
Lerche, W., 667, 687, **697**
Leuchtenberger, C., 695, **707**
Levan, A., 584, **608**
LeVine, H. D., 176, **185**

Levine, M., 864, 899, **916**
Levinson, L. J., 910, **918**
Levit, S. G., 450, **467**
Levitsky, G. A., 362, 363, **467**, 480, **615**
Levy, O., 553, 554, **615**
Lewis, D., 553, 566, 568, **615**
Lewis, E. B., 650, **704**
Lewis, G. N., 581, **619**
Lewis, M., 53, 54, 56, 64, 87
Lewis, M. R., 775, **821**
Lewis, W. H., 775, **821**
Lewitsky, G. A., 799, **821**
Li, M. H., 1168, **1197**
Lick, L., 999, **1020**, 1170, **1197**
Liebmann, H., 328, **346**
Liebow, A. A., 999, 1005, **1020**, 1101
Liebowitz, J., 961, **1016**
Liechti, A., 335, **347**, 961, **1020**
Light, A. E., 977, **1020**
Limperos, G., 694, **705**, 755, **759**, 945, **953**
Lindegren, C. C., 476, 533, **615**
Lindegren, G., 476, 533, **615**
Lindenfeld, B., 908, **916**
Lingley, J. R., **345, 347**
Linser, P., 864, 900, **916**, 1030, 1032
Lisco, H., 932, **955**, 961, 964, 967, 969–975, 984, 989, 995, 998, 1000, 1001, 1005, **1016**, 1023, 1159, 1160, 1166, 1177, 1180, 1184, **1192, 1197**
Lison, L., 695, **705, 707**
Little, C. C., 355, 390, **467, 469**
Little, E. P., 274, **279**, 301, **311**, 785, **818**
Lively, E., 420, 454, **467**
Livingston, M. S., 89, **143**
Livingston, R., 227, 233, 249, **252**, 270, **279**
Lloyd, 1148, **1197**
Locher, G. L., 389, **470**, 520, **618**
Lockwood, L. B., 444, **467**
Loeb, J., 390, **467**
Loebl, H., 291, **312**
Loevinger, R., 168, 169*n*., 170, 182, **187**
Lohmann, A., 296, **313**
Loiseleur, J., 274, **280**, 289, 296, **312**, 942, 946, **947, 953**
London Conference, 630, **705**
Long, C. N. H., 991, **1024**
Loomis, A. L., 589, **610**
Loos, G. M., 811, **817**
Lorenz, E., 336, **346**, 829, 830, 847, **856-858**, 926, 953, 960, 961, 963–965, 967, 991, 993, 1001, 1002, **1017, 1020, 1022**, 1031, 1035–1037, 1040, 1045, 1048–1050, 1054–1056, 1061–1064, 1074–1076, 1146, 1153, 1154, 1165–1168, 1170, 1173, 1174, 1177, 1180, 1184, 1188, **1195, 1198**
Lotz, C., 417, **464**, 550, **607**, 752, **757**
Lourau, M., 968, 974, **1020**
Louviere, L. J., 1061
Love, W. H., 773, **821**
Low-Beer, B. V. A., 975, 994, **1018, 1020**
Ludewig, S., 300, **312**, 975, 987, **1020**
Ludin, M., 1152, **1198**
Lüers, H., 542, **615**
Luippold, H., 486, **621**, 721, 730, **760**
Lukens, R. M., 993, **1020**
Lumb, G., 1158, **1198**
Lüning, K. G., 477, 483, 504, 509, 510, 513, 514, 520, 552, 570, **604, 615**, 644, **697**
Luria, S. E., 262, **280**, 330, **349**, 527, **615**
Luther, W., 776, **821**
Lutwak-Mann, C., 305, **312**, 962, **1020**
Lyman, C. M., 305, **312**
Lyman, E. M., 89, **142**

M

McAulay, A. L., 538, 541, 593, **615**
McCarthy, J. E., 985, 986, **1017**
McClintock, B., 362, 363, 365, 366, 451, **467**, 646, 675, **705**
MacComb, W. S., 338, **347**, 925, **953, 955**
MacDonald, E., **1013, 1014, 1024**
McDonald, M. R., 268, 269, **280**, 656, 695, 696, 703
MacDowell, E. C., 906, **914**
MacDuffee, R. C., 935, **955**, 965, **1024**
MacDuffee, R. S., 1065
McElroy, W. D., 547, 573, 574, 597, **615, 624**
McGregor, J. H., 554, **616**
Macht, S. H., 967, **1020**
MacKee, G. M., 925, **953**
Mackenzie, K., 532, 540, **616, 618**
MacKey, J., 591, **610**
MacMahon, H. E., 1157, 1184, **1198**
McMaster, R., 765, 814, 816, **818**
MacMillan, J. C., 686, **710**, 983, **1027**
MacNeal, W. J., 1151, **1198**
McQuarrie, I., 988, 989, **1021**
McQuate, J. T., 532, 533, **616, 625**
Maddox, M. N., 973, **1024**
Magee, J. L., 194, **252**
Mahoney, J. F., 997, **1022**
Maier-Leibnitz, H., 5, 40, 72, 82, 83, 113, **142**
Mainx, F., 668, **705**
Maisin, J., 1158, **1198**
Major, M. H., 833, 838, 869, 877, 879, 888, 903–905, **917**
Makhijani, J. K., 480, 483, 565, **616**, 655, 671, 673, **705**
Makino, S., 642, **705**

Makki, A. I., 363, 380, **469**, 480, 481, 494, 501, **618**, 670
Maldawer, M., 555, **622**, 690, **709**, 722, **760**
Mallet, L., **347**, 782, **821**
Mann, S., 935, 946, **951**, 993, **1016**
Mannell, T., 585, **612**
Manoĭlov, S. E., 299, **312**
March, H. C., 1163, **1198**
Marchbank, Dorothy F., 333, **350**
Marcuse, W., 1148, **1198**
Marder, S. N., 991, 1005, **1018**, **1020**, 1164, 1165, **1196**
Marie, P., 1150, 1152, 1153, **1198**
Marinelli, L. D., 135, **142**, 153, 154, 157, 167–170*n*., 173, 182, 183, **185-189**, 343*n*., **349**, 484, 485, **616**, **618**, 727, **759**
Mar-Kham, R., **312**
Markham, R., 262, **280**
Marks, E. K., 337, **346**, 926, 930, 935, **952**, 960, 961, 963–965, 967, 983, 1002, 1004, **1017**, **1018**, 1030, 1035, 1036, 1038, 1040–1042, 1044–1046, 1056, 1061–1064, 1069–1074, 1076–1080
Marquardt, H., 484, 553, **616**, 776, 799, 801, 804, **821**
Marshak, A, 305, **312**, 338, 341, **347**, 575, **616**, 661, 669, 684, **705**, 775, 776, 798, 801, 811, 813, **821**
Marshak, R. E., 116, **143**
Marti, N. F., 926, **955**
Martin, C. L., 985, 986, 990, 999, **1020**, 1127
Martin, F. L., 131, **143**, 301, **311**, 333, **349**, 506, 521, 558, 579, **611**, **622**, 940, 941, 944, **952**
Martin, G. J., 979, **1009**
Martin, S. F., 998, **1011**
Martland, H. S., 964, 1000, **1020**, 1099, 1158, 1159, 1178, 1181–1183, 1198
Mason, W. B., 965, **1017**, 1031, 1048
Massey, H. S. W., 193, 202*n*., 205–207, 211, 236, 237, 239, 240, 243, **252**, **253**
Mather, K., 716, 721, **759**
Matoltsy, G., 577, **608**
Matthews, J. J., 937, 946, **954**
Mavor, J. W., 358, 359, **467**, 508, **616**, 644, **705**
Maximow, A., 1101, 1121
Maxwell, R. D., 939, **956**, 969–972, 974, **1026**
Mayer, E., 811, **821**
Mayer, M. D., 910, **916**
Mayer, M. M., 1004, **1013**
Mayer, S. H., 937, 942–946, **954**, 966, **1022**
Maynard, R. M., 998, **1028**
Mayneord, W. V., 146, 174, 185, **188**, 318, **347**, 1061, 1187, 1190, **1192**, **1193**, **1198**
Mazia, D., 601, **616**, 928, **953**
Mead, J. F., 985, 986, **1009**, **1021**
Medvedev, N. N., 565, 574, **616**
Meek, G. E., 1161, **1194**
Meredith, W. J., 259, 260, 262, 263, 271, 272, 275, **279**, 296, 299, 300, **310**, 329, **344**, 656, **699**
Merrill, O. E., 998, **1024**
Meschan, I., 937, **949**
Metcalf, R. G., 1164, 1166, 1174, **1198**
Metz, C. W., 650, 662, 665, 687–690, **705**
Meyer, H. U., 535, 536, 540, 545, 546, 569, **602**, **607**, **616**
Mickey, G. H., 565, **616**, 642, 673, 705
Miescher, G., 976, 985, **1021**, 1120
Miletzky, O., 926, **948**, 963, **1010**
Milham, W., 966–969, **1008**
Miller, B. L., 172, **188**
Miller, C. P., 983, 1002, 1003, **1016**, **1021**
Miller, E., 829, 837, 838, **857**, 999, 1001, **1014**
Miller, G. L., 973, **1024**
Miller, H., 547, 574, **624**
Miller, J. H., 926, **955**
Miller, J. R., 908, **916**
Miller, N., 270, **279**, **280**
Miller, W. R., 985, **1016**
Miller, Z. B., 307, **309**
Minder, W., 291, **312**, 335, **347**, 577, **606**
Minot, G. R., 1029
Minowitz, W., 182, **187**
Mitchell, J. R., 935, **956**
Mitchell, J. S., 163, **188**, 276, **280**, 336, 338, **347**, 692, 693, **705**, **706**, 785, 809, **821**, 924, 928, **954**
Mitchell, R. G., 976, **1018**
Miwa, M., 771, 772, 785, 787, 789, **821**, **822**, **824**
Mixer, H. W., 999, **1020**, 1165, 1170, 1188, **1196**, **1197**, **1199**
Miyamoto, S., 1157, **1199**
Miyazaki, K., 988, **1021**
Mobius, W., 910, **916**
Moelwyn-Hughes, E. A., 272, **280**
Mohler, F. L., 148, **188**
Mohler, J. D., 532, **608**
Mohney, J. B., 992, **1017**
Mohr, O. L., 358, 368, **467**, 627, 644, **706**
Mole, R. H., 264, **280**, 945, 946, **954**
Moll, F. C., 1003, 1004, **1024**
Möllendorf, W. V., 811, 816, **822**
Momigliano, E., 865, 869, 894, **916**
Montgomery, H., 1175, 1176, **1200**
Montgomery, P. O., 980, 981, **1021**

Moon, V. H., 970, 980, 982, 1000, **1021**
Moore, C. E., 198, **253**
Moore, D. E., 1003, 1004, **1011**
Moore, D. H., 1004, **1013**
Moore, M. C., 970, 971, 973–976, 978, 980, 981, 996, **1022**
Moore, W. G., 513, **616**
Mora, J. M., **1199**
Morgan, D. R., 970, 980, 982, 1000, **1021**
Morgan, L. V., 361, **467**
Morgan, T. H., 390, **467,** 638, 643, 698, 706
Mori, K., 771, 772, 785, 787, 789, **821, 822, 824**
Morris, H. P., 1172, **1199**
Morrison, P., 59, **143**
Morrow, N. M., 182, **188**
Morse, M. L., 579, **605**
Morse, S., 257, 258, **279, 345**
Moser, H., 600, **603**
Moses, J. J., 723, **760**
Moses, M. J., 695, **706**
Moses, S. G., 811, 812, 816, **817**
Mosher, W. A., 694, **705,** 755, **759,** 945, **953**
Moshman, J., 770, 796, **818**
Mott-Smith, L. M., 581, **618**
Mottram, J. C., 275, **281,** 336, 337, **345, 348,** 553, 558, **616,** 773, 776–777, 779, 782, 786, **819, 822,** 923, 927, 929, 936, 939, 940, 945, **954,** 976, **1021,** 1030, 1158, 1178, 1187, 1190, **1199**
Moulder, P. E., 966–968, 1003, **1008**
Moulder, P. V., 1045
Moyer, A. J., 444, **467**
Moyer, B. J., 12, **142**
Müller, J. H., 335, **347, 348**
Muller, H. J., 135, 136, **143,** 334, **348,** 355, 359, 362, 363, 365, 366, 377, 378, 380–382, 385, 388, 389, 391–393, 395–397, 399–401, 403, 405, 409, 411–414, 418, 419, 422, 423, 427, 430, 431, 435, 438, 446, 448, 451–453, 455, 456, 458, 460, **462, 463, 466–471,** 476, 478–484, 487, 488, 492–495, 497–503, 506, 509, 511, 513–515, 519–523, 526, 527, 529, 532, 535, 536, 538, 540, 546, 552, 563, 565, 569, 581–584, 588, 596, 598, 600, 601, **602, 604, 614, 616–618, 625,** 629, 630, 632, 635, 644, 646, 647, 650, 653, 655, 658, 661, 663, 664, 666, 668, 670, 671, 673, 676, 683, 687, **704, 706–708,** 854, **858,** 1190, **1199**
Munick, R., 168, 170*n.*, **188**
Munoz, C. M., 943, **957**
Muntz, J. A., 262, **278,** 298, 299, **309,** 551, 580, **603,** 922, 941, **948,** 973, 984, 986, 1001, **1009, 1021**
Müntzing, A., 683, **706**
Murphy, A. S., 1157, 1184, **1198**
Murphy, D. P., 864, 879, 891, 901, 908–911, **914, 916,** 994, **1015**
Murphy, E. D., 1174, **1196**
Murphy, J. B., 1003, **1021,** 1064, 1123
Murray, J. M., 687, **706**
Murray, R., 961, **1021,** 1031
Murray, R. G., 1104, 1106–1108, 1118
Mutscheller, M., 925, **953**

N

Nadson, G. A., 390, **470**
Nagai, M. A., 389, **470,** 520, **618**
Narat, J. K., 990, **1021**
National Bureau of Standards, 179, **188**
National Research Council Preliminary Report No. 8, 175*n.*, **188**
Naumenko, V. A., 417, **470**
Neary, G. J., 164, **188**
Nebel, B. R., 484, 485, **616, 618,** 727, **759,** 811, 814, **822**
Neel, J. V., 414, 430, **470**
Neill, W., Jr., 908–909, **915**
Nelms, A. T., **143**
Nelson, L., 304, **309**
Nelson, W. O., 1132
Nemours, A., 1184, **1195**
Neuberg, C., 297, **313**
Neufeld, J., 166*n.*, **188**
Neuhaus, M. E., 455, **470,** 514, **618**
Neuhaus, M. J., 654, **706**
Neumann, F., 869, 894, 900, **914**
Neve, R. A., 975, **1021**
Newcombe, H. B., 545, 572, 591, 592, 595, **618,** 724, **759**
Newcomer, E. N., 589, **625,** 737, **761**
Nichols, H. J., 182, **190**
Nickson, J. J., **952, 1011**
Nickson, M. J., 977, **1010**
Nims, L. F., 987, 990, **1021**
Nix, M., 561, **609,** 796, **818,** 904
Nizet, E., 990, **1021**
Nobele, de, 865, 866, 869, 879, 893, 894, 898, **916**
Noethling, W., 476, 531, 540, **618, 623**
Nogier, T., 863, 864, **917,** 982, **1023,** 1124
Norby, B., 558, 622
Nørgaard, F., 1158, **1199**
Norrish, R. G. W., 193*n.*, 227, **253**
North, N., 987, 990, **1021**
Northrop, J. H., 299, **313**
Novick, A., 418–420, **470,** 537, 543, 545, **619**
Novick, R., 995, **1011, 1021**
Novitski, E., 403, 427, **472,** 565, **619**
Noyes, W. A., Jr., 193, **253**

Nurnberger, C. E., 271, **281**, 296, **313**, 328, **348**
Nürnberger, L., 869, 894, 897–898, **916**
Nybom, N., 590, **610**
Nyka, W., 1155, 1183, 1185, **1197**

O

Oak Ridge Symposium, 630, **707**
Oakberg, E. F., 829*n*.
Oakley, H. E. H., 554, **623**, 776, 799, 805, **823**
Oberling, C., 1157, **1200**
O'Connor, M. H., 1179, **1191**
O'Connor, R. J., 932, **954**
Oddie, T. H., 168, 169, **188**
Oehlkers, F., 416, **470**
Offermann, C. A., 479, 497, 552, **619**, 650, **707**
Ogur, M., 695, **707**
Oldenberg, O., 220, **253**
Oliver, C. P., 476, 588, **619**, **621**, 652, **707**
Olson, A. R., 389, **465**, 581, **619**
Onufrio, O., 1167, **1199**
Oosterkamp, W. J., 180, **188**
Oppermann, K., 554, **619**
Ordway, T., 1150, **1199**
Orndoff, B. H., 985, 986, **1017**
Ortega, P., 994, **1018**
Osborne, J. W., 982, 985, **1023**
Osgood, E. E., 339, **348**, 1029, 1039
Oster, R. H., 1000, **1021**
Otis, E. M., 849, **858**, 909, **916**
Ovadia, J., 146, **187**
Owen, R., 848, **859**
Owen, S. E., 1174, **1199**

P

Packard, C., 300, **313**, **348**, 763, 784, 804, **822**, 929, 935, **954**, 1002, **1022**, 1094
Packham, Evelyn A., 339, **348**
Pagenstecher, H. E., 869, 879, 891, 898, 900, **915**, **916**
Painter, E. E., 932, **955**, 961, 964, 967, 969–981, 984, 989, 995, 996, 1000, 1001, 1005, **1022**, **1023**, **1027**, 1037
Painter, T. S., 363, 378, 446, **469**, **470**, 635, 647, **707**
Palmer, W. L., 986, **1023**, 1125
Panofsky, W. K. H., 97, **141**
Panschin, I. B., 381, **470**, 480, 493, 522, **619**, 668, **707**
Panschina, A. N., 493, **619**, 668, **707**
Papalashwili, G., 565, **619**, 673, 707
Pappenheim, A., 1099
Park, G. S., **309**
Parker, D. R., 654, **707**
Parker, E., 994, **1019**
Parkes, A. S., 832, 834, 835, 837, 839, 840, **856**, **858**, 864–866, 869, 870, 894, 896–898, **916**, 999, **1022**, 1119, 1168, **1192**
Parrish, Mary E., 331, 334, 343*n*., **348**, **350**
Parsons, L. D., 1061, 1187, **1198**
Passonneau, J., 1187, **1195**
Pasteels, J., 695, **705**, **707**
Pätau, K., 527
Paterson, E., **348**, 657, **707**, 788, 796, **819**, **822**, 925, 937, 946, **954**
Patt, H. M., 264, **281**, 308, **313**, 930, 935–939, 942–946, **953**, **954**, **956**, **957**, 965, 966, 971, 977, 979, 984, 985, 990–994, 1001, 1005, **1022**, **1025**, **1026**, 1067
Patterson, J. T., 359, 393, 399, 455, 458, **470**, 478, 514, 516, 526, **619**, 641, 644, 650, 653, 689, **707**
Patterson, P. A., 932, 933, **953**
Pauli, W., 295, **311**
Pauling, L., 32, **143**, 250, 295, **313**
Payne, F., 627, **707**
Pearce, M. L., 962, 963, **1027**, 1035, 1037, 1065
Pearlman, N., 337, **348**, 966, **1025**, 1044
Pekarek, J., 776, 782, **822**
Pelc, S. R., 172, **188**, 830, **858**
Peller, S., 1177, **1199**
Pemberton, R., 1000, **1013**
Pendergrass, E. P., 968, 976, 994, 997, **1015**, **1016**, **1022**
Penick, G. D., 966, 968, **1022**
Pennoyer, J. M., 268, **280**, **703**
Penrose, L. S., 461
Perje, A. M., 477, **604**, 644, 697
Perlberg, H., Jr., 967, **1020**
Perrot, M., 782, **821**
Perry, S. P., **346**
Perryman, R., 968, **1016**
Perthes, G., 627, **707**, 1094, 1112
Peter, O., 519, **606**, 669, 670, 698
Petersen, B. W., **345**
Peterson, S. C., 995, **1011**
Petrakis, N. L., 692, 693, **707**
Petrov, N., 1155, 1156, **1199**
Petry, E., 927, 939, **955**
Peyrou, P. P., 493, **619**, 668, 707
Pfuhl, W., 629, **707**
Philip, U., 361, **470**
Philippov, G. S., 390, **470**
Phillips, J. T., 291, **312**
Philpot, J. St. L., 264, **280**, 945, 946, **954**
Picken, D., 849, **859**
Pickering, B. I., 943, **955**, 962, 964, **1024**
Pickhan, A., 478, 572, 588, **619**
Pierce, M., 961, 983, **1021**, **1022**, 1096, 1120, 1124, 1125, 1127

Pinson, E. A., 964, **1026**, 1075
Pintner, I. J., 595, **620**
Planck, 18, 30
Platzman, R. L., 64, 88, **143**, 197, 232, 241*n*., 243, 249, 250, **253**
Plesch, J., 1099
Plomley, N. J. B., 538, 593, **615**
Plough, H. H., 414, **470**
Plunkett, C. R., 400, **471**
Podljaschuk, L. D., 1132
Pohle, E. A., 976, 986, **1020, 1022**, 1128
Poisson, S. D., 80, 133
Politzer, G., 554, **602**, 628, 629, 696, 776, 782, 799, 804, 811, 816, **817, 822**, 1097
Pollard, E. C., 139, **143**, 330, **348**
Pollister, A. W., 695, **707**
Pontecorvo, G., 365, 456, **469, 471**, 481, 482, 557, **607, 618, 619**, 646, 647, 650, 682, 685, **706–708**
Poppe, E., 1131
Porter, C. A., 1149, **1199**
Porter, G., 193*n*., **253**
Porter, L. M., 961, 988, **1024**
Portmann, A. F., 966, 968, **1017**
Portmann, U. V., 180, **186**
Powers, E. L., Jr., 586, 587, **619**
Pratt, A. W., 993, 1001, **1022**
Present, R. D., 216, **252**
Price, J. M., 929, **955**
Price, J. P., 811, 812, **817**
Pringsheim, P., 201*n*., 202*n*., 217, 230, 232, 233, **253**
Prokofyeva, A. A., 380, 448, 451, **469**, 492, 499, **618**
Prokofyeva-Belgovskaya, A. A., 377, 378, 448, **496, 471**, 493, 495, **618, 619**, 664, **706**
Promptov, A. N., 531, **620**
Prosser, C. L., 930, 932, **955**, 961, 964, 966, 967, 969–975, 979–981, 984, 989, 993, 995, 1000, 1001, **1018, 1021, 1022, 1023, 1025**, 1031, 1037, 1039, 1044, 1045
Provasoli, L., 595, **620**
Prussia, G., 1157, **1199**
Pullinger, B. D., 977, **1023**
Pullman, E. W., 972, 984, **1022**

Q

Quastler, H., 112, 136, **141, 142**, 923–925, 933, 934, **955**, 982, 993, 995, 1001, **1018, 1023**
Quimby, E. H., 86, 109, **142, 143**, 167, 173, 176, 180, 182, 183, **186, 188**, 338, **347, 348**, 925, **953, 955**

R

Raab, W., 991, **1023**
Rabinowitch, E., 230, 232, **253**
Radu, G., 48, 483, 484, **605, 606**, 670, 671, 684, **698, 699**
Raffel, D., 380, 448, **469**, 492, 493, **618**, 664, **706**
Rajewski, E. V., 294, **313**
Rajewsky, B., 1178, 1180, **1199**
Rajewsky, B. N., 567, 582, **620**, 763, **822**
Randolph, L. F., 457, **462**
Raper, J. R., 319, 333, 336, **348, 350**, 924, 926, 931, 935, **955**, 961, 997, **1023**, 1030, 1058, 1160, 1177, **1199**
Raper, K. B., 444, 466, 467, **471**, 540, **611**
Rapoport, J. A., 416, 417, **471**, 552, 557, 575, 576, **620**
Rask-Nielsen, H. C., 1164, 1178, **1196**
Raulot-Lapointe, G., 1150, 1152, 1153, **1198**
Ray-Chaudhuri, S. P., 385, **471**, 478, 480, 487, **620**, 642, 671, **708**
Raynaud, A., 864, 869, 876–877, 879, 888, 891, 901, **916, 917**
Read, J., 139, **142**, 275, **281**, 306, **314**, 320, 328, 335, 336, 339, 340, **345, 346, 348, 349**, 557, 558, 567, 599, **624**, 656, **710**, 736, 744, 751, **761**, 764, 775–777, 786, 787, **819**, 923, 940, **951, 955, 957**, 1178, **1199**
Recknagel, R. O., 796, **824**
Redd, J. B., 969, **1026**
Redfield, A. C., 936, **955**
Redfield, B., 286, **309**
Redfield, H., 654, **708**
Regaud, C., 554, **620**, 776, **822**, 831, **858**, 863, 864, **917**, 982, **1023**, 1094, 1108, 1114, 1124
Reid, T. R., 926, **953**, 964, 965, **1020**
Rekers, P. E., 926, **955**, 963–969, 979, 1003, **1009, 1014, 1023**, 1037, 1075
Remley, M. E., 148, **187**
Renyi, M. de, 864, 879, 891, 901, **916**
Reuss, A., 331, 332, 340, **345, 346**, 531, 540, **614, 620**
Reynolds, J. P., 484, **620**, 689, 690, 708
Rhoades, R. P., 987, 990, **1023**, 1122, 1128
Rice, F. O., 32, **143**
Richards, A., 783, 784, **822**
Richards, P. I., 168, **188**
Richmond, J., 962, 1002, **1008**
Richtmyer, F. K., 6, 7, 11, 13, **143**
Rick, C. M., 493, 494, 566, **620**, 668, **708**, 720, 724, 726, **759**
Ricketts, W. E., 986, **1023**, 1125
Ridgway, L. P., 932, 933, **953**

Riesen, D. E., 112, **141**
Rietz, L., 929–931, **948**, 965, **1010**, 1031, 1128, 1135
Rigdon, R. H., 978, **1023**
Rigos, F. J., 1175, **1197**
Riley, E. F., Jr., 336, 337, **346**, **350**, 922–924, 933, **951**, **958**, 1030, 1049, 1146, 1160, 1167, 1177, **1195**
Riley, H. P., 558, 559, 561, 568, 580, **609**, **620**, 656, **701**, 714, 721, 742–745, 747–749, 752, **758**, **759**, 940, **950**
Ris, H., 646, 674, **702**, **708**, 723, **759**
Risse, O., 257, **281**, 284, **313**, 328, **345**, **348**, 531, 540, **614**
Robbie, W. A., 936, **950**
Robbins, L. R., 998, **1024**
Roberts, J. E., 1187, **1193**
Robertson, J. E., 1000, **1024**
Robinett, P. W., 966–969, 979, **1019**
Robinson, C. S., 112, **141**
Robinson, J. C., 811, **817**
Robinson, J. M., 338, **349**
Robinson, M. R., 909, 910, **917**
Robinson, Robert, 461
Robson, J. M., 136, **141**, 363, 415, **463**, **466**, 551, **603**, 657, **697**
Robson, M. J., 926, **952**, 963, 965, 983, 1004, **1017**, **1018**, 1045, 1080
Rogers, F. T., 985, 986, **1020**, 1127
Rokizky, 833
Rollefson, G. K., 193, **253**
Rolleston, H., 1000, **1024**
Roman, H., 411, 454, **472**
Rosen, G. U., **707**
Rosenblum, C., 292, **313**
Rosenfeld, F. M., 277, **281**, 289, **313**, 694, **709**, 754, **760**, 801, **822**
Rosenthal, R. L., 943, **955**, 961, 962, 964, 966, 968, 974, **1016**, **1024**
Roser, F. X., 166, **185**
Ross, J. M., 1155–1157, 1184, **1199**, **1200**
Ross, M. H., 692, 693, 934, **950**, 961, 964, 974, 981, 983–988, 1001, **1011**, **1013**, **1014**, **1024**, 1039
Rossi, B., 97, **143**
Rossi, H. H., 162, 167–169, 171, 176, **186**, **188**, 320*n*., **345**, **348**, **611**, 644
Roswit, B., 992, **1013**
Rothberg, H., 570, **613**, 657, 661, 664, 676, 685, **703**
Rother, J., 980, **1026**
Rothstein, K., **348**
Roussy, G., 1157, **1200**
Rowlands, S., 985, **1013**
Rowntree, C. W., 1149, **1200**
Rubin, B. A., 168, **188**, 586, 587, **620**, **622**, 750, **760**
Rudali, G., 1155, 1177, **1197**
Rudolphi, H., 1158, **1200**
Rugh, R., 628, 643, **696**, **708**, 783, 800, 804, **822**
Rusch, H. P., 1190, **1200**
Russ, S., 773, **822**, 1029, 1030, 1032, 1145, 1150, 1151, 1191, **1193**
Russell, D. S., 995, **1024**
Russell, L. B., 561, **620**, **858**, 861, 862, 864–867, 869–871, 873–879, 882–886, 888, 891–894, 896, 898–900*n*., 901–908, 910, **917**, 932, 933, **955**
Russell, W. L., 411, 423, 429, 432, **471**, 561, 583, **620**, 825, 827, 828, 833–835, 838, 841, 845, 850–853, 855, 856, **858**, 865–867, 870, 877, 879, 900*n*., 903–906, 908, 910, **917**, 932, **955**
Rutherford, E., 41–44, 51, 66, 87, 89, **143**

S

Sabin, F. R., 1155, 1156, **1200**
Sacher, G. A., 337, **348**, 925, 931–934, **951**, **955**, 971, 1005, **1011**, 1044, 1166, **1192**
Sackis, J., 925, **955**
Sadauskis, J., 66, **143**, 165, **187**
Salaman, M. H., 329, **347**
Salerno, P. R., 926, **955**
Salis, H. von, 1127
Salisbury, P. F., 926, **955**, 1081
Sallmann, L. von, 943, **957**
Saloman, K., 962, 1002, **1008**
Salter, W. T., 1000, **1021**
Saltmarsh, O. D., 227, **253**
Sanderson, M., 966–969, **1008**
Sanigar, E. B., 293, **313**, 973, **1024**
Sansome, E. R., 476, 505, 533, 535, **611**, **620**
Saretzky, 865, 869, 893, 894, 900, **917**
Sarkar, I., 385, **471**
Sarvella, P. A., 838
Saunders, T. S., 1175, 1176, **1200**
Sax, K., 135, **144**, 362, 363, 379, 385, 386, **471**, 480, 484, 486, 487, 516, 562, 566, 571, 573, 576, **614**, **621**, 660, 666, 682, 683, **707**, **708**, 714–716, 719, 720–730, 735, 737, 740, 741, 749, **759**, **760**, 799, **822**
Sayers, G., 989, 991, **1024**
Sayers, M. N., 991, **1024**
Schack, J. A., 935, **955**, 965, **1024**, 1065
Schaefer, H., 828, 829, **858**
Schaefer, H. J., 583, 584, **621**
Schall, L., 908–911, **917**
Schechtmann, J. L., 478, **621**
Scheuer, O., 286, **311**
Schinz, H. R., 828, 837, **858**, 863, 869, 893, 894, **917**, 1114, 1121, 1179, 1188, **1200**
Schjeide, O. A., 682, **708**, 935, 936, **947**
Schmidt I. K., 479

Schmidtke, L., 576, **607**
Schmitt, O., 578, **621**
Schneider, L., 988, **1024**
Schneiderman, H., 979, **1024**
Schneiderman, H. A., 562, 576, **614**
Schoenberg, M. D., 979, **1024**
Scholes, G., 283, 290, **313**, 694, **708**, 753, 754, **760**
Scholes, M. E., 775, 779, **819**
Schön, M., 763, **822**
Schottelndreyer, H., 976, **1024**
Schraffenberger, E., 864, 869, 874, 879, 882, 891–892, 901, 907, **918**
Schraub, A., 1178, 1180, **1199**
Schreiber, H., 531, 540, **614**, 811, **821**
Schrek, R., 275, **281**, 935, 939, **955**, 960, **1024**
Schrödinger, E., 249, **253**, 597, **621**
Schugt, P., **348**, 1118
Schultz, J., 455, **465**, **621**, 652, 654, 657, 684, **708**
Schulz, M. D., 995, **1017**
Schürch, O., 1152, 1153, 1155, 1156, **1200**, **1201**
Schütze, R., 574, **621**
Schwab, L., 1003, 1004, **1024**
Schwartz, D., 560, **621**
Schwartz, S., 961, 988, **1019**, **1024**, **1028**, 1039
Schwarz, G., 927, 939, 940, 945, **956**, 1162, **1196**
Scott, C. M., **144**, 262, **281**, 297, 300, **313**, 1189, **1200**
Scott, G. M., 773, **822**
Scott, M. B., 89, **142**
Scott, M. R., 14, 26, 59, 116, **144**
Scott-Moncrieff, R., 461
Searle, A. G., 854, **858**
Sébileau, 869, 894, 898, **918**
Sedginidse, G. A., 1152, **1200**
Seemann, H. E., 180, **189**
Segal, G., 960, 991, **1019**, 1136, 1137
Segale, G. C., 1112
Segré, E., 66, 87, **141**
Seide, J., 784, 812, **822**
Seitz, F., 196, **253**
Seki, L., 303, **309**
Selbie, F. R., 1155, 1157, **1200**
Seldin, M., 986, 987, **1024**
Seliger, H. H., 92, 99, **144**, 160, **189**
Selin, G., 1181, **1196**
Sell-Beleites, I., 535, **621**
Selling, L., 1029, 1039
Selye, H., 989, **1025**
Semonov, L. F., 299, **312**
Senn, N., 919, **956**
Serebrovskaya, R. I., 409, **471**
Setala, K., 975, **1025**
Settles, F., 366, 419, **470**, 632, **706**
Seymour, A. H., 448, **465**, **710**
Sgourakis, E., 561, 563, 565–568, **603**, 655, **697**, 936, 940, **948**
Shacter, B., 975, **1025**
Shapiro, J. R., 1188, **1196**
Shapiro, N. I., 409, **471**
Shapiro, N. P., 653, 654, **708**
Shaver, A., 986, **1009**
Shaw, J. C., 1061
Shechmeister, I. L., 934, **956**, 1005, **1025**
Shefner, D., 587, **619**
Shelton, E., 926, **953**, 964, 965, **1020**
Sheppard, C. W., 160, 176, **189**, 978, 979, 988, **1028**, 1167, **1193**
Sheremetieva-Brunst, E. A., 924, **948**
Shimkin, M. B., 963, 994, **1018**, **1020**, 1157, 1177, **1192**
Shirlock, M. E., 908, **916**
Shorvon, L. M., 966, **1025**
Shouse, S. S., 966, **1025**, 1044
Shuler, K. E., 193, 205*n*., 206, 223, **252**
Sick, 1148, **1200**
Sidky, A. R., 363, 380, **469**, 480, 481, 501, 519, **618**, **621**
Sidorow, B. N., 381, **465**, 640, 700
Siebenrock, L. von, 1162, **1196**
Sieburth, L. R., 558, **622**
Siegel, P. W., 1032
Sievert, R. M., 924, **956**
Šikl, H., 1177, 1178, **1200**
Silberbach, I., 988, **1019**
Silverman, S. B., 967, **1025**
Simmons, E. L., 925, 932, 933, **951**, 960, 963–966, 1005, **1017**, **1018**, **1025**, **1026**, 1038, 1045, 1058–1060, 1064, 1069–1073, 1076–1080
Simon, N., 985, **1025**
Simon, S., 643, **699**
Simon-Reuss, J., 776, 778, 779, 782, 806, **822**
Sinclair, W. K., 584, **603**
Singer, G., 153, 179, **189**
Singer, T. P., 262, **278**, 298, 299, **309**, 551, 580, **603**, 922, 941, **948**
Singleton, W. R., 533, **621**
Sipe, C. A., 264, **278**
Sipe, C. R., 308, **310**, 934, 935, 942, 943, 945, **949**
Siri, W. E., 1158, **1200**
Skaggs, L. S., 112, 136, **141**, **142**
Skanse, B. N., 993, **1025**
Skirmont, E., 1057, 1065, 1079
Skoog, F., 276, **281**
Slack, C. M., 134, **144**
Slater, J. C., 32, **144**
Slaughter, J. C., 274, **279**, 301, **311**, 735, **818**, 936, 940, 945, **950**

Slizynska, H., 652, **708**
Slizynski, B. M., 528, 532, **622**, 645, 652, 661, 662, 668, **708**, 850, **858**
Slotopolsky, B., 828, 837, **858**, 1114, 1121
Sluka, E., 1002, **1009**, 1080
Smeltzer, J. C., 148, **189**
Smith, D. B., 289, **313**, 694, **708**
Smith, D. E., 264, **281**, 308, **313**, 930, 935, 937, 938, 942, 944–946, **954**, **956**, **957**, 965, 966, 977, 979, 984, 985, 992, 993, 1001, **1022**, **1025**, **1026**
Smith, F., 935, 937, **956**, 991–993, 1001, 1005, **1025**
Smith, H. P., 122, **142**, 257, 262, **279**, 556, **609**
Smith, K. A., 277, **278**, 290, **310**, 754, **757**
Smith, K. M., 262, **280**, **312**, 329, **347**
Smith, L., 553, 558, 559, 568, 571, 572, **605**, **610**, **622**, 940, **951**
Smith, T. R., 967, **1025**
Smith, W. W., 929, 935, 937, 946, **948**, **956**, 993, **1010**, 1065, 1067
Smyth, F. S., 986, 988, **1025**
Snell, G. D., 337, **348**, 362, 686, **708**, 825–828, 830–838, 841–850, **858**, **859**, 999, **1026**
Snider, R. S., 337, **346**, 929, **951**, 995, **1026**, 1030, 1058, 1093, 1119, 1121, 1131, 1160, 1177, **1195**, **1199**
Snyder, L. H., 355, **469**
Snyder, M. L., 776, 782, 791, 792, 794, **818**
Snyder, R. H., 923, **956**, 1058
Snyder, W. S., 163, **189**
Sobel, E., 993, **1014**
Sobel, H., 1169, **1200**
Soberman, R. J., 939, **956**, 969–972, 974, **1026**
Sokoloff, B., 969, **1026**
Sommermeyer, K., **346**, 657, **704**
Sommers, S. C., 805, **823**
Sonneborn, T. M., 424, **471**, 593, 595, **622**
Sonnenblick, B. P., 632, 647, 667, 687, 689, **709**, 910, **918**
Spargo, B., 1100, 1104, 1105, 1116, 1118
Sparrow, A. H., 277, **281**, 289, **313**, 555, **622**, 630, 688–691, 694, 695, **706**, **709**, 722, 723, 748, 750, 754, **760**, 801, 802, **822**, 928, **956**
Spear, F. G., 335, 336, 338, **345**, **348**, 628, 630, **709**, 763, 773–779, 781, 782, 786, 787, 790, 794, 797, 804–806, 809, 810, **817**, **819**, **822**, **823**, **824**, 928, **956**, **957**
Spéder, E., 1127
Spence, I., 907, **914**
Spencer, L. V., 71, 109, **144**
Spencer, W. P., 476, **622**
Sperduto, A., 25, **141**
Spiegel-Adolf, M., 292, **313**
Spiegelman, M., 1162, **1193**
Spiers, F. W., 164, **185**, **189**, 934, **956**
Spies, T. D., 934, **952**, 985, 1005, **1009**, **1018**
Spinks, J. W. T., 584, **603**
Spitz, S., 1153, **1200**
Sponer, H., 222, 225, 227, **252**, **253**
Sprague, G. F., 531, 533, 540, **622**
Spurling, R., 1029
Spurr, C. L., 967, **1025**
Ssipowsky, P. W., 1136
Stadler, L. J., 362, 363, 366, 389, 411, 454, **472**, 476, 480, 494, 531, 533, 534, 540, 552, 555, 565, 574, **622**
Stanton, Elizabeth, **346**
Stapleton, G. E., 131, **143**, 301, **311**, 333, 334, 336, 337, **346**, **349**, **350**, 506, 521, 556–558, 564, 579, 580, 605, 611, **622**, 922–924, 935, 940, 941, 944, **951**, **952**, **956**, 1005, **1026**, 1030, 1049, 1146, 1160, 1167, 1177, **1195**
Steacie, E. W. R., 193, 208, **253**
Stearner, S. P., 925, 932, **956**, 960, 963, 964, 966, 989, **1026**, 1031, 1064
Steele, R., 723, **760**
Steggerda, F. R., 975, 980, 981, 1000, **1028**
Stein, G., 147, 152, **186**, 257, 267, 268, 270, **281**, 290–292, 297, **311**–**313**, 694, **708**
Steinglass, P., 587, **620**
Stenbeck, T., 919, **956**
Stenstrom, W., 296, **313**
Stern, C., 131, **141**, 361, 368, 403, 404, 427, **472**, 476, 478, **605**, **622**, **625**, 635, 638, 653, **709**
Stevens, L. G., 919, **956**
Stewart, F. W., 1181, 1182, **1193**
Stinson, F., 71
Stock, H. C., 1004, **1013**
Stone, L. H. A., 774, **823**
Stone, R. S., 338, **349**, 1005, **1018**
Stone, W. S., 303, **313**, **314**, 417, 455, **470**, **473**, 511, 514, 537, 544, 545, 548–552, 557, 561, 562, 566, 567, 598, **606**, **610**, **619**, **623**, **625**, **626**, 641, 650, **707**, 751, **761**
Stoneburner, C. F., 153, 179, **189**
Storaasli, J. P., 966, 968, **1017**
Storer, J. B., 914, 915, **957**
Storey, R. H., 966–969, 971, 978, 979, 988, **1009**, **1026**, **1028**, 1039
Storey, W. F., 1162, **1197**
Stowell, R. E., 692, **709**
Strandskov, H. H., 826, 828, 831–833, 836–839, **859**
Strang, V., 966, **1011**
Strangeways, T. S. P., 554, **623**, 773–776, 778, 799, 805, 806, 810, **823**, 1097

Straube, R. L., 264, **281**, 308, **313**, 937, 938, 942–946, **954**, **956**, **957**, 965, 966, 990–992, 994, 1005, **1022**, **1026**, 1067
Strauss, O., 980, **1026**, 1132
Strelin, G. S., 926, **957**
Strømnaes, Øistein, 688, **709**
Stroud, A., 1074
Stubbe, H., 414, 415, **472**, 476, 478, 510, 531, 540, 541, 553, 576, 586, 589, **607**, **613**, **618**, **623**
Sturm, E., 1003, **1021**
Sturtevant, A. H., 368, 373, 382, 438, **472**, 635, 638, 643, **709**
Suche, M. L., 641, 653, **707**
Sugiura, K., 339, **349**, 923, **957**, 981, **1018**, 1096
Supplee, H., 972, **1016**
Suter, G., 960, 963, **1026**, 1031, 1035, 1037, 1048, 1049
Sutton, E., 518, 521, 538, **606**, 645, 647, 648, 661, 666, 669, **700**, **709**
Sutton, H., 1035, 1048, 1055
Svedberg, T., 296, **313**
Svenson, H. K., 359, **467**
Svihla, G., 930, **956**, 977, 979, **1025**
Swann, M. B. R., 985, **1026**
Swanson, C. P., 366, **472**, 485, 503, 504, 533, 534, 537, 546, 547, 569, 570–574, 578, 579, 597, 600, **611**, **615**, **623**, 660, 661, 682, 683, **708**, **709**, 714, 721–723, 738–741, **760**, 799, 814, **822**, **823**
Swenson, P. A., 304, **310**
Swift, H. H., 695, **709**
Swift, M. N., 926, 932, 935, 936, 940, 945, 946, **948**, **954**, **955**, 961, 964, 965, 967, 969–975, 979–982, 984, 985, 989, 993, 995, 1000, 1001, 1005, **1010**, **1022**, **1023**, **1025**, 1031, 1037
Swisher, S. N., 926, **957**, 1082
Sydow, G., 574, **605**
Szilard, B., 148, **189**
Szilard, L., 418–420, **470**, 537, 543, 545, **619**

T

Tahmisian, T., 301, **313**
Tait, J. H., 163, **189**
Takamine, N., 811, 815, **823**
Talbot, J. M., 964, **1026**, 1075
Taliaferro, L. G., 934, **957**, 1003, 1005, **1026**
Taliaferro, W. H., 934, **957**, 1003, 1005, **1026**
Tansley, K., 338, **348**, 628, **709**, 774, 776, 781, 782, 787, 805, 806, 808–810, **819**, **823**, 928, **956**, **957**, 995, **1024**
Tarlov, I. M., 995, **1012**
Tarr, R., 1004, **1013**
Tatum, E. L., 424, 461, **465**, 593, 594, 596, **624**
Taurog, A., 993, **1014**
Tavernier, G., 163, 164, **185**
Taylor, B., 277, **281**, 289, **313**, **314**, 694, **709**, 754, **761**, 801, **823**
Taylor, C. S., 148, **187**
Taylor, C. V., 303, **314**
Taylor, Grant, **1201**
Taylor, H. D., 1032
Taylor, H. S., 236, **252**
Taylor, L. S., 109, 121, **142**, 148, 152, 153, 157, 179, 182, **186**, **188**, **189**
Taylor, W. R., 632, **709**
Tazima, Y., 457
Teleky, L., **1201**
Telfer, J. D., 563
Teller, E., 32, **143**, 222, 225, 227, 252, **253**
Templeton, F., 1125
Tennant, R., 336, **347**, 983, 1002, **1019**, 1100
Tessmer, C., 966, **1012**
Thaddea, S., 990, **1026**
Thew, K., 14, 26, 59, 116, **144**
Thilo, E. R., 134, **144**
Thoday, J. M., 275, **281**, 306, **314**, 340, 341, **349**, 484, 487, 491, 517, 557, 558, 566, 567, 599, **605**, **624**, 632, 656, 660, 668, 675, **698**, **710**, 716, 717, 720, 724–728, 731, 736, 741, 744, 748, 751, 756, **761**, 940, **957**
Thomas, H., 581, **624**
Thomas, J. O., 303, **314**
Thomas, M. M., 1032
Thompson, E. C., 994, 997, **1025**
Thompson, E. O., 1065
Thompson, M. V., 657, 796, **822**, 925, 954
Thompson, W. R., 299, **312**
Thomson, J. F., 988
Thoraeus, R., 180, 182, **189**
Timoféeff-Ressovsky, N. W., 127, 130, 139, **144**, 319, 333, **349**, 394, 396, 399, 410, 412, 414, **464**, **472**, 476, 478, 479, 481, 499, 508, 509, 512–514, 516, 521, 523, 526, 565, 572, 582, 588, 597, **606**, **619**, **620**, **624–626**, 630, 658, 670, 684, **710**
Ting, T. P., 961, **1026**
Tinsley, M., 988, **1024**
Tipton, S. R., 748, **757**
Titterton, E. W., 164, **189**
Tittle, C. W., 164, **189**
Tobias, C. A., 139, 302, 316, 317, 332, 344, **349**, **350**, 1189, **1201**
Tompkins, M., 983, 1002, 1003, **1021**
Tompkins, P. C., 1058
Toolan, H. W., 964, **1026**
Torda, C., 985, 996, **1026**

Torgersen, O., 990, 991, **1014, 1027,** 1131
Toulis, W. J., 328, **349**
Toussey, S., 863, **918**
Toyoma, T., 980, 985, **1027**
Treadwell, A. de G., 935, **957,** 1066, 1079
Tribondeau, L., 553, **604,** 627, 681, **697,** 927, **948,** 1114, 1133
Trillmich, F., 865, 866, 869, 893, 894, **918**
Troland, L. T., 392, **473**
Trujillo, T. T., 935–937, 946, **951,** 993, **1016**
Trump, J. G., 93, **144**
Tsuzuki, M., 983, **1027**
Tullis, J. L., 930, **957,** 972, 974, **1010,** 1099
Turkowitz, H., 940, **947**
Turner, C. W., 1123
Tweedie, M. C. K., 259, 272, **279**
Twombley, G., 157, **186**
Tyler, W. J., 848, **859**
Tyree, E. B., 264, **281,** 308, **313,** 935, 939, 942–945, **954, 956, 957,** 965, 984, 985, 990, 992, 993, 1001, **1022, 1025, 1026,** 1067
Tytell, A. A., 299, **314**

U

Uber, F. M., 531, 534, 540, **622**
Uehlinger, E., 1155, 1156, 1179, 1188, **1200, 1201**
Uggeri, B., 685, **699**
Ullmann, H. J., 999, **1009**
Ullmann, T., 987, **1027**
Ullrich, F. W., 966, **1012**
Ulrich, H., 1162, **1201**
Uncapher, R. P., 932, **949,** 969, **1011**
U.S. Atomic Energy Commission, 442, **473**
Unterberger, F., 390, **473**
Upcott, N. B., 721, **757**
Uphoff, D., 403, 427, **472,** 476, 478, **625,** 926, **953,** 964, 965, **1020,** 1035, 1048, 1075, 1165, 1173, 1188, **1198**
Upton, A. C., 1146, 1163, 1164, **1201**
Uri, N., 256, **279**

V

Valencia, J. I., 385, 409, 411, **470,** 479, 481, 488, 493, 495, 496, 498, 500, 502, 503, 514, 519, 521–523, 533, 552, **618, 622**
Valencia, R. M., 385, 409, 411, **470,** 479, 488, 503, 514, 552, **618**
Valentine, W. N., 926, **953,** 960, 962, 963, 970, 978, 1004, **1012, 1019, 1027,** 1032, 1035, 1037, 1039, 1044, 1063, 1065
Van de Graaff, R. J., 11, 25, 93, **141, 144**
Van Dyke, D. C., 926, **957,** 1136
Van Valkenburg, P. A., 992, **1017**
Velley, G., 942, 946, **953**
Vennesland, B., 308, **310**
Venters, K. D., 975, **1027**
Villard, P., 148, **189**
Villee, C. A., 503, **625**
Vilter, C. F., 934, **952,** 1005, **1018**
Vilter, R. W., 985, **1009**
Vintemberger, P., 935, **947**
Vinzent, R., 1152, 1155, 1183, 1186, **1197**
Vogt, E., 1171, **1201**
Vogt, M., 416, **473,** 480
Volkin, E., 973, **1027**
Von Halle, E. S., 561, **603**

W

Waddington, C. H., 907, **918,** 1189, **1201**
Wagner, A., 1164, 1178, **1196**
Wagner, R. P., 417, **473,** 548, 549–551, **625,** 751, **761**
Wakely, G. P. G., 1151, 1154, **1201**
Waletzky, E., 848, **859**
Walkhoff, 1150
Wallace, B., 422, 437, **464, 473**
Wallace, J., 988, **1024**
Wallace, R. H., 589, **625,** 737, **761**
Walsh, D., 919, **957,** 982, **1027**
Walters, O. M., 1132
Warburg, O., 304, **314**
Ward, F. D., 389, **473**
Warkany, J., 864, 869, 873–874, 879, 882–886, 891–892, 901, 907, **918**
Warren, S., 686, **710,** 763, 773, 776, 805, **823,** 929, 930, **950, 957,** 966, 976, 982, 983, 988, 990–993, 996, 999, 1005, **1018, 1020, 1027,** 1094–1097, 1117, 1123, 1130, 1131, 1161, 1168, **1201**
Warren, S. L., 966, 982, 983, 1000, 1002, 1005, **1017, 1025, 1027, 1028,** 1029, 1044, 1057, 1058, 1092, 1094, 1124, 1126–1128, 1131
Washburn, M., 307, **311**
Watson, C. J., 961, **1024**
Watson, M. D., 569, 572, **625**
Wattenberg, L., 988, **1028**
Wattenwyl, H. von, 686, **710**
Way, K., 14, 26, 59, 116, **144**
Weatherwax, J. L., 109, **142,** 182, 186, **189**
Weber, R. P., 975, 980, 981, 1000, **1028**
Webster, J. H. D., 986, **1013**
Weichert, U., 990, 992, **1028**
Weinstein, A., 389, **473**
Weiss, J., 257, 267, 268, 270, **281,** 290, 291, 296, 297, **312, 313,** 694, **708,** 750, 753, 754, **761,** 937, **957**
Weiss, L., 1182, **1192**
Welander, A. D., 448, **465,** 628, 710

Wells, P. H., 811, **823**
Wels, P., 305, **314**, 1001, **1028**
Welt, P., 481, 519, **606**, 669, 670, 671, 698
Wertheimer, J., 936, **955**
Wertz, E., 555, **625**, 939, **957**
Westergaard, M., 416, **466**, 547, 550, 577, **612**, 751, **758**
Westman, A., 994, **1009**
Wettstein, W. von, 584, **608**
Wheeler, B., 1060
Whipple, G. H., 966, 982, 983, 985, 988, 989, 1000, 1002, **1016**, **1021**, **1025**, **1027**, **1028**, 1029, 1044, 1124, 1127, 1128
Whitaker, D. M., 543, **625**
White, A., 990, 991, **1013**, **1024**
White, C. J., 1149, **1199**
White, G. R., 24, 38, 40, 41, 70, 104, 105, 110, 111, **144**
White, H. E., 30, **144**
White, M. J. D., 628, 643, 646, 665, **710**, 799, **823**
White, T. N., 153, 154, **189**, 343*n*., **349**
Whiting, A. R., 384, 388, 456, **473**, 510, **625**, 643, 657, 667, 683, 688, 689, **710**, 799, 808, **823**
Whiting, P. W., 453, **473**, 668, **711**
Whittinghill, M., 653, 654, **702**, **711**
Wick, G. C., 166, **189**
Widner, W. R., 681, 779, 780, **820**
Wilbrandt, W., 961, **1020**
Wilbur, K. M., 796, **824**
Wilder, H. C., 998, **1028**
Wilhelmy, E., 478, 508, **625**
Willey, E. J. B., 193, 202*n*., 204, 205, **253**
Williams, A. E., 1174, **1199**
Williams, F. C., 87, **141**
Willis, G. S., 1151, **1198**
Willis, R. A., 1157, **1201**
Wilsey, R. B., 147, **190**
Wilson, C. T. R., **144**
Wilson, C. W., 174, **190**, 776, 782, 797, 810, **819**, **824**, 932, **957**
Wilson, G. B., 485, **618**
Wilson, H., 1132
Wilson, J. G., 864, 869, 872–874*n*., 876, 879, 882–883, 885–888, 891–892, 897, 901–904, 907, **918**, 932, 933, **957**, 996, **1028**, 1185, **1201**
Wilson, K., 675, 676, **703**, 740, **759**
Wilson, R. R., 4, 5, 81, 100, **144**
Wimpfheimer, S., 910, **916**
Winchester, A. M., 689, **707**
Winter, K. A., 971, **1009**
Wish, L., 969, 970, 978, 979, 988, **1026**, **1028**, 1039
Witkin, E. M., 125, **144**, 422, **464**, 553, **625**
Wolbach, S. B., 1122, 1123, **1143**, 1150, 1175, **1201**
Woldrich, A., 1179, **1201**
Wolf, B. S., 182, **187**
Wolff, H. G., 985, 996, **1026**
Wolfson, N. D., 769, 779
Wolkowitz, W., 984, 986, 1001, **1009**
Wollman, E., 330, **349**
Wood, F. C., **349**
Woodard, H. Q., 1181, 1182, **1193**
Woods, M. C., 966, 968, 971, 978, 979, **1009**
WPA, Federal Works Agency, 171, **190**
Wrenshall, G. A., 182, **190**
Wright, G. P., 775, **824**
Wright, K. A., 93, **144**
Wright, S., 854, **859**
Wuensche, H. W., 1034
Wyckoff, H. O., 108
Wyckoff, R. W. G., 330, **349**
Wyman, R., **703**
Wyss, O., 303, **313**, **314**, 417, **473**, 511, 537, 544, 545, 548–552, 557, 562, 598, **606**, **610**, **623**, **625**, 751, **761**

Y

Yamashita, H., 771, 772, 785, 787, 789, **821**, **822**, **824**
Yamawaki, T., 1163, **1194**
Yost, H. T., Jr., 570–572, **624**, **626**, 739, 741, **760**, **761**
Young, L. E., 961, **1012**
Young, R. A., 785, **819**

Z

Zamenhof, S., 419, 420, **473**
Zerahn, K., 306, **308**, 926, **947**
Zerwic, M. M., 988, **1013**
Ziegler, K., 554, **614**, 627, 688, 704, 982, **1019**
Zimmer, E. M., 533, 535, **611**
Zimmer, K. G., 127, 130, 139, **144**, 319, 320, 333, **349**, 478, 487, 508, 521, 523, 526, 565, 572, 574, 588, 597, **605**, **607**, **619**, **624–626**, 630, **710**
Zinder, N., 420, 454, **467**
Zirkle, R. E., 138, 139, **144**, 278, **281**, 302, 316, 319, 327, 330, 332–334, 336, 337, 343*n*., 344, **346**, **348–350**, 655, **711**, 786, 796, **824**, 921–925, 928, 933, 938, 939, **948**, **951**, **957**, **958**, 961, 963, 965, 972, 983, **1008**, **1011**, **1017**, **1026**, 1030, 1042, 1044, 1058, 1094, 1131, 1146, 1189, **1201**
Zuitin, A. I., 414, **473**
Zunz, E., 991, **1028**

SUBJECT INDEX

A

Abdomen, shielding of, 1072
Aberrations, chromatid, 715
  chromosome (*see* Chromosome aberrations)
  diagrams of types, 716, 718
  distribution in nuclei, 720
  effects of modifying factors on, 736*ff*.
  efficiencies of radiations in producing, 732
  induced by absorbed radioisotopes, 733
  induced by slow neutrons, 733
  one-hit, 723
  radiation-induced, in chromosomes of *Tradescantia*, 715–720
  relation of yield, to dose, 723
    to intensity, 727
  spontaneous vs. induced, 720
  two-hit, 723
Abnormal bleeding, 966–969
Abnormal mitosis, 628–630, 632, 646, 647, 664, 1092
Abnormalities, chromosome, induced, 627, 628
    in tumors, 338
    (*See also* Chromosome aberrations; Morphological changes following irradiation; Mutations)
  following prenatal irradiation, 879–912
    critical periods for induction of, 880–887, 891–893, 901, 902, 904, 906, 909, 912, 913
Abortion following irradiation of embryo, 866, 910–911
Absorption, of electromagnetic radiation, 17, 20, 45–48
  energy (*see* Energy absorption)
  fat, 986
  glucose, 307, 986
  from intestine, 986
  linear energy, 316
  X rays, 49
    broad-beam, 108
    narrow-beam, 107, 108
Absorption coefficient, β-ray, 102
  light, 118
  linear, 104
Absorption coefficient, mass, 104
  narrow-beam, 106
  neutrons, 114
  X rays, 103
    true (adjusted), 110
Absorption spectrum, 47
  albumin, 294
Accelerated atomic nuclei, 316–318
Accelerator, electrostatic, 11
  induction (betatron), 12
  linear, 12
Accidents, radiation, 998, 1005, 1006
Acenaphthene, 577
Acetic acid, 576
Acetylcholine synthesis by brain, 996
Acetylene polymerization, 291
Acid-base balance, 974
Acquired radioresistance, 1136
  of intestine, 1127
Acridine orange, 542
Acriflavin, 596
Activated (intermediate) complex, 220, 222, 223*n*., 224
"Activated water," 284, 937
Activation energy, 35, 60, 210, 215–216
  distribution of, 60
Activations, 60, 129
  distribution of, 135–136
  ionizing, 129
  mechanism of, 62
  and mutation, 490
  by secondary electrons, distribution of, 80
  spatial distribution of, 76
Acute radiation (*see* Radiation; X radiation)
Acute-radiation reaction, 980
Acute-radiation syndrome, 1005–1008
Adaptation syndrome, 989–990
Additivity, different radiations, 924
  radiobiological, 326
Adenosine triphosphate, 289, 987
Adenosinetriphosphatase (myosin), 298, 922
Adenylic acid, 289
Adipose tissue, 1097
Adrenal cortex, atrophy of, following prenatal irradiation, 889

Adrenal cortex, extracts of, 935, 992
  lipids of, 990
Adrenal insufficiency, 934, 992, 1005
Adrenal medulla, 991
Adrenal radiation exposure, 982
Adrenalectomy, effect on leukemogenesis, 1165
Adrenals, 306, 929, 989–992
  catechols, 991
  hyperemia, 1131
  immunity, 1004
  latent period after irradiation, 1132
  radioactive isotopes and, 1132
  radium and, 1132
  X rays and, 1131
Adrenocorticotropic hormone, 990, 992
Aerobic glycolysis, 306
Age, and radiation effects, 1093
  and radiosensitivity, 933
Alanine, 305
Albumin, 293
  absorption spectrum, 294
  egg, 293
  plasma, 295
  serum, 294–296
Albumin-globulin ratio, plasma, 973
Alcohol, 291
  ethyl, 580
Alcohol dehydrogenase, 299
Aldehydes, 417
  aliphatic, 290
Algae, 322, 445
Alkalosis, 1000
Alkaptonuria, 461
All-or-none phenomenon, 121
Allantoin, 988
Alleles, 355
  iso-, 403
  positional, 404
  pseudo-, 594
Allium, 589, 683, 737, 776, 782, 799, 801, 815
Alopecia, 919, 1148
Alpha irradiation, internal, 964, 970, 973, 1000
  oxygen effect, 940
α particles, 318, 320
  atomic weight, 7
  charge, 7
  effects of, on chromosomes, 724, 726
    as modified by oxygen, 748, 751, 752
  ejection of, 35
    spontaneous, 36
  relative efficiency in chromosome-aberration production, 732
  scattering, 42
Alpha radiation, effects of, on carboxypeptidase, 271
Alpha radiation, effects of, compared with X rays, 271
  cytosome, 785
  on glycine deamination, 271
  mechanism, 271
  mitotic, 785–787
  on tyrosine, 271
α rays, 3
  (*See also* Alpha radiation)
Altitude, 935, 965
Ambystoma, 783
Ameba, *Chaos*, 304
Amenorrhea, 999
Amino acid oxidase, X-ray effect on, 261
D-amino acid oxidase, 299
Amino acids, 307, 324, 328
  deamination, 296
  oxidation, 307
  (*See also* individual amino acids)
D-amino acids, 306
Amino groups, 292
Ammonia, 414, 575
Ammonia formation, 306, 390
Ammonium hydroxide, 575
Amorphous cementing substance and bone, 1108
Amphibia, 554, 628, 643, 656, 801, 803, 804, 806
Anaerobic glycolysis, 306
Anaerobiosis, 940–941
Anamnestic reaction, 1004
Anaphase, 628, 632, 645, 647, 661, 662, 669, 689
Androgenesis, 510
Anemia, 922, 961
  and bone marrow, 1100
  induced by acute radiation, 1036–1041, 1047, 1079
    effect on, of irradiation, 1064–1066
      mechanism of recovery from, 1038–1040
      of spleen-shielding and increments to spleen, 1079
  induced by chronic radiation, 1050–1052, 1054–1056
    by gamma rays, 1054–1056
    macrocytic, 1056
    by radioisotopes, 1058–1060
    recovery from, 1056
  induced by fast neutrons, 1043
  induced by gamma radiation (*see* Gamma radiation)
  induced by X radiation (*see* X radiation)
  pathogenesis of, 964
  phenylhydrazine-induced, and X radiation, 1064–1066
    recovery from, 1067, 1068

Anemia, radium-induced, 1059
(*See also* Cobalt-induced polycythenia; Erythrocytes)
Anesthesia, nembutal, 937, 946
Aneuploidy, 842, 849, 854
and radiation damage to embryo, 903, 913
of whole chromosomes, 358–359
Angiosperms, 554
Anlagen, optic, 458
Annihilation, 41, 69, 98
Anomalous viscosity, 289
Anorexia, 982, 984–985, 1001
neurogenic origin of, 985
Anoxia and radiosensitivity, 940, 1065–1066
Antibiotic therapy, 1002, 1003
Antibiotics, 445
Antibody formation, 1002, 1005
effect on, of appendix shielding, 1080, 1081
of spleen shielding, 1080, 1081
and splenectomy, 1080, 1081
Anticoagulants, circulating, 966
Antigens, 593, 595
Antioxidants, 308
Antirrhinum, 414, 415, 417, 476, 478, 531, 540, 541, 553, 556, 586, 589, 591
Anurans, 554
Appearance potential, 239, 240
Appendicular skeleton (limb, foot, girdle), abnormalities following prenatal irradiation, 879–882, 885, 887–888, 892, 902, 904–905, 907, 909
Appendix, 1101
effect of shielding, on antibody formation, 1080
on lymphopoiesis, 1063
on survival, 1070, 1071
Arbacia, 300, 301, 304, 766, 769, 771, 772, 784, 785, 789, 796, 803, 812, 814
Arginase, 300, 987
Argon, 559
Arsenic, 574
Arsenoxide, 946
Arteriolar change in skin, 1122
Ascaris, 554, 558, 784, 812
Ascaris eggs, 628, 674, 935
Ascomycete, 593
Ascorbic acid, 288, 942, 945, 967
of adrenals, 990
of serum, 975
Ash content of intestinal cells, 983
Aspergillus, 444, 503, 506, 521, 535, 537, 546, 547, 556, 564, 570, 578, 579
spores, 326
Asphyxia, tissue, 1001
Asters, supernumerary, X-ray-induced, 803
Astrocytes, radiosensitivity of, 995
Atmospheric oxygen, 307
Atomic-bomb effects, human, 966, 998, 999, 1005
leukemogenesis by, 1163
(*See also* Hiroshima)
Atomic nuclei, accelerated, 316–318
excitation of, 57
structure of, 27
Atomic number, 27
effective, 105*n*.
Atomic weight, 6, 27
Atoms, aggregates of, 31
excitation of, 197–208
hydrogen, 285
structure of, 27
Atrophy of tissues, causes, 927
Atropine, 980–981, 996
Atypical bone, 1101, 1111, 1112
Auger effect, 34, 47
Aureomycin, 1003
Autoradiographs of bone, 1111
Autotrophism, 462
Avian tissue, 629
Azide, 551, 562

B

Backscattering, electron, 91
neutron, 116
Bacteremia, 923, 983, 1000, 1006
Bacteria, 321, 324, 330–331, 415, 417, 444, 462, 553
endotoxins, 1003
Bacterial invasion, 965
Bacterial toxins, 1000, 1003
Bacteriophage, 543, 544, 569, 572, 587, 591, 592
Bacterium prodigiosum, 538, 541, 542
BAL, 579
protection against, 942, 945
Barium, 574
Ba^{140}-La^{140}, effect of, 1058
on intestine, 1127
on spleen, 1107
on testis, 1117
Barley, 442, 485, 552, 555, 556, 559, 565, 568, 569, 574–576, 578, 590
Barley seeds, 940
Basophilic outstretched cells in testis, 1114, 1116
Bats, radiation effect on, 930
wing circulation, 977
Beans (*see Vicia faba*)
Beets as dietary factor, 969
Bellevalia, 484, 801
Benadryl, 981

Benzene, 290, 291
  hydroxylation of, 257
  reaction with neutrons, 290
  recoil protons, 290
Benzol, 922, 1094
Benzpyrene, 577
β disintegration, 8, 35
Beta irradiation, external body, 931, 970, 984, 997
  internal, 924–926, 963–964, 970, 973, 978, 980, 993, 1003
    (*See also* specific isotopes)
β particles, negative (*see* Electrons)
  positive (*see* Positrons)
β- to X-ray ratio, 923
β rays, 3, 317, 319
  effect of, 1030, 1058, 1059
    lethal, on cells, 809
    mitotic, 771, 776, 787, 788
  emission of, 3
  energy release in tissues, 764, 785, 786
  secondary, 117
Betatron, 12, 1030
Bile pigments, excretion of, 961
Bile salts, 988
Biliary passages, 1128
Biliary tract, carcinogenesis of, 1171
Binding energy, 28, 60
Biological effectiveness, relative, 321, 322, 328–342
Biological variability, 27
Birefringency, 289
Bleeding, abnormal, 966–969
Bleeding time, effect of irradiation on, 1044–1046
Blood, dyscrasias after irradiation, 963
  electrolytes, 974
  flow of, effect on radiosensitivity, 927
    hepatic, 977–978
    and radiation injury, 940
  phosphorus content of, 1000
  platelets, 966, 978
  radiation effects, 922, 960–976, 1029–1082
    on capillary fragility, 1046
    on clot retraction, 1046
    on clotting time, 1044, 1046, 1047
  red cells (*see* Erythrocytes)
  urea of, 973, 989
  uric acid of, 925, 973, 1000
  white cells (*see* Leukocytes; Lymphocytes)
Blood calcium, 967
Blood cell mass, 960
Blood cells (*see* Erythrocytes; Leukocytes; Lymphocytes)
Blood chloride, 974
Blood clotting mechanisms, 966–968
Blood coagulation, 1044–1047
  effect on, of radiation, 1044
    of toluidine blue, 1044
Blood counts, 325, 337
  following irradiation during fetal period, 895–896
Blood-forming tissues, recovery of, 926
  regeneration of, 963–964
Blood plasma, constituents, 972–982
    globulins, 973
    histamines, 975, 980
    lipids, 974–975
    potassium, 974
    proteins, 972–973
      iodinated, 970
    sodium, 974
    sulfhydril, 969
  electrophoretic pattern, 973
  refractive index, 972
  turbidity, 974–975
  volume, 961, 969
Blood-pressure fall, 970, 980
Blood transfusions, 966, 967, 1006
  effect on irradiated dogs, 1081, 1082
Blood vessels, fragility of, 968
  obliterative changes in, 1176
Body fluids, 969–976
Body size following prenatal irradiation, 869, 876–877, 879, 896, 900, 905, 912
Body weight and radiosensitivity, 933
Bone, 1108*ff*.
  amorphous cementing substance in, 1108
  autoradiographs of, 1111
  calcium phosphate, 1108
  carbonate, 1108
  citrate, 1108
  collagenous fibers of, 1108
  cortex, 1111
  devitalized, 1111
  epiphysis, 1108
  growth, endosteal, 1108
    periosteal, 1108
    stunted, 1110
  hydroxyapatite, 1108
  metaphysis, 1108, 1109, 1111
  osteoblasts, 1108, 1110, 1111
  osteoclasts, 1108, 1110
  osteocytes, 1108
  osteogenic sarcomas and radioisotopes, 1111
  radiation effects on, 999–1000
    $carbon^{14}$, 1110
    plutonium, 1110, 1112
    radium, 1110–1112
    $strontium^{89}$, 1110
    X rays, 1110
    $yttrium^{91}$, 1110, 1112

Bone, radiosensitivity of, 929
Bone marrow, 339, 1098, 1099
  bone-seeking isotopes and, 1100
  effect of irradiation, 926, 960–965
    by fast neutrons, 1101
    gamma radiation, 1056
    nonspecificity of, 1101
    by slow neutrons, 1101
    by strontium^{89}, 1059
    by X radiation, 1066, 1099, 1101
      and phenylhydrazine-induced anemia, 1066
      and spleen shielding, 1071
  erythrocytes of, 1099
  granular leukocytes of, 1099
  Hiroshima studies of, 1101
  injections of, modification of radiation injury by, 926, 964–965, 1074, 1075
      heterologous, 964, 1075
      homologous, 1074, 1075
  macrophages, radioresistance of, 1100
  mast cells and, 1100
  megakaryocytes, 1099
  metabolism, 962
    of homogenates, 1002
  myelocytes, 964, 1099
  rabbit, glycolysis in, 305
  regeneration of, 1101
  uptake of iron by, 962
Bone-marrow changes and toxins, 1101
Bone matrix, 1108
Bone repair, 1111
Bone-seeking isotopes and bone marrow, 1100
Bone tumors, 1147, 1152, 1155, 1157, 1160, 1170, 1180–1184
  induced by plutonium^{239}, 1060
Bragg curve, 87
Brain carcinogenesis, 1185
"Breakage-first" theory, 480
Breathing retardation, 940
Bremsstrahlung, 23, 69
Broad bean (*see Vicia faba*)
Bromus, 798
Bronchial epithelium of lung, 1130
Bronchogenic carcinoma, 1153, 1157, 1160, 1177–1180
Brownian movement, 383
Brunner's glands, 1126
Budding of nuclei, 1096
Build-up, neutrons, 116
  X rays, 108
Build-up factor, 108, 116
    calculations, 109
Butterflies, 390

C

Cabbage as dietary factor, 968
Cadmium, 946
Caffeine, 576
Cage effect, 231, 246
Calcium, 295
  in blood, 967, 974
Calcium phosphate, 1108
Callitroga americana, 441
Cancer (*see* Carcinogenesis; Carcinogenic agents; Leukemia; Leukemogenesis; Radiation; Radioactive elements; Tumors; specific animals and sites)
Cancer Commission of Harvard University, 1150
Cancer theory, mutation, 1170, 1189
  virus, 1170
Cancerogenic agent (*see* Carcinogenic agents)
Cancerolytic agent, 283
Capillaries, dilatation of, 976
Capillary fragility, effect of irradiation on, 1044
Carbamates, 417
Carbohydrates, 298
  in cells, 1095
Carbon^{14}, 305
  and bone, 1110
Carbon dioxide, 575
  combining power of, 974
  production of, 962
Carbon monoxide, 562
Carbon tetrachloride, 291
Carbonate and bone, 1108
Carboxylic acids, salts of, 580
Carboxypeptidase, 297, 299, 307
  radiation effect on, 258, 271
    alpha-, 271
Carcinogenesis, endocrine imbalance and, 1167, 1170
  ionizing radiation compared with other carcinogens, 1185–1188
  mechanism of, 1188–1191
  physical aspects of, 1146–1148
  radiation-induced, and treatment, 919
  by radioactive elements (*see* Radioactive elements)
  relative effectiveness of different radiations, 1146, 1147
  threshold dose in, 1167
  (*See also* specific animals and organs)
Carcinogenic agents, 283
  aging, 1191
  bone seekers (*see* Radioactive elements)
  cosmic rays, 1161
  endogenous, 1190
    by radioactive substances, 1153–1160

Carcinogenic agents, estrogen, 1173
  fission products, 1159
  ionizing radiations, 1145–1201
  neutrons, 1160, 1161, 1166, 1167
    cataract, 1167
  ultraviolet radiation, 1150, 1190
  (*See also* Radioactive elements)
Carcinogenicity and mutagenicity, 421–424
Carcinoma in rats, 684
Cardiovascular system, 976–982
Cartilage, degenerative changes of, 1112
  ear, 1000
  hypertrophic, 1112, 1113
  provisional calcification, 1112
  radiation effects, 999–1000
    radioactive isotopes, 1113
    radium, 1113
    strontium^{89}, 1113
    X rays, 1113
  trachea, 1000
Cascade showers, 63, 70, 95, 111
Castration cells, 999
Cat, 863
Catalase, 286, 288, 299, 300, 303, 544, 549, 551, 562, 581, 941, 987
Cataracts, 325, 337, 1131
  following prenatal irradiation, 879, 896, 909, 912
  radiation, 943, 998
    induced by neutrons, 1167
Catechols of adrenal, 991
Cathepsin II, 300
Cathode rays, 3
Cell damage and radiation effects on embryos, 903–904, 906, 913
Cell death, 1092, 1133
  X rays, 1134
Cell division, 289, 682
  interference with, 357–359
Cell membrane, 1094, 1095
Cell physiology, 462
Cell viability (*see* Viability effects, cell)
Cells, metabolism of, 922
  swelling of, 938, 972
  turnover of, in radiosensitivity, 929
Cellular functions, effects on actual and potential, 1092
Cellular inclusions, 1095
Central nervous system (brain, spinal cord), damage following prenatal irradiation, 880, 881, 883, 888–891, 896–898, 902, 909, 912
Centrifugation, effect on radiation-induced chromosome aberrations, 737
  and mutation, 573, 589
Centriole, 525
Centromere, 354, 850
Centrosome, 1095
Cerebellum lesions, 995
Cerium-praseodymium and thymus, 1105
Cessation, of mitosis, 1096
  of spermatogenesis, 1116
Chaetomium, 531, 538, 541, 593, 595
Chaetopterus, 804
Chain reaction, 264, 270
Characters, 395
Charge exchange, 237–238, 245
  (*See also* Electron-transfer processes)
Charged particles, acceleration of, 11
  collision of, 41
    elastic, 42
  heavy (positive ions), 7
  sources of, 10
    nuclear, 13
Cheese, 445
Chemical bond, 31
  energy of, 28, 31, 60
Chemical changes, 60
Chemical forces, 34, 60
Chemiluminescence, 201
Chemostat, 418, 419
Chiasma, 357
Chick embryo, 335
Chickens, 774, 776–778, 781, 782, 787, 788, 790, 794, 796, 797, 805, 806, 809–811
  carcinogenesis in, 1155, 1158
  eggs, 935
  radiation effects, 925
  time of death, 932
Chloride, excretion of, 989
  of plasma and blood cells, 974
  in tissue, 972
Chlorine, 552
Chloropicrin, 551
Chloroplastids, 595
Cholera vibrio, 1003
Cholesterol, 291
  of adrenals, 990
  of liver, 987
  of plasma, 975
Cholic acid, 291
  acetylation, 291
Choline acetylase inhibitors, 996
Chortophaga (*see* Grasshopper)
Chromatid breaks, 717
  relation of, to radiation dose, 724
    to radiation intensity, 727
Chromatid exchanges, 717
  relation of, to fast-neutron dose, 726
    to radiation intensity, 727
    to X-ray dose, 725
  symmetrical and asymmetrical, 720
Chromatids, in chromosomes, 628, 632, 642, 647–650, 659–661, 664, 675
  sister, 354

Chromatin, 1096
Chromatolysis of ganglian cells, 995
Chromonema effects, 801, 802, 814
Chromophil substance, 1095
Chromophoric groups, 74, 84, 289
Chromosome aberrations, 289, 324–326, 334, 338, 341–342, 627, 628, 717, 798, 825, 1135
  in animal cells, induced, 627, 629, 630, 632–635, 642, 645, 648, 650, 652, 653, 655, 656, 659, 666, 669, 671, 673, 674, 676, 682–690
  in mammals, 826, 831, 832, 835–837, 839, 842, 843, 854, 855
    and radiation damage to embryo, 902–904, 913
  in microspores, 715
  oxygen tension, 940
  radiation-induced, effect on, of centrifugation, 737
    of colchicine, 737
    of sonic vibration, 737
    in *Tradescantia*, 713–761
  regenerating liver, 1128
  tumors, 338
  Vicia faba, 306
Chromosome breaks, 124, 132, 135, 136, 138, 140, 272, 364, 446, 598, 717, 801, 802, 836, 839, 846, 847
  in animal cells, induced, 628–630, 632–635, 637, 641, 642, 647, 649–671, 673–682, 687, 688, 690
  distribution in chromosomes, 720
  and dosage, 482, 724
  frequency per cell, 125
  healing of, 366, 491
  and infrared, 571
  intragenic, 497
  and ionization, 480–492
  isochromatid, 490
  multiple, 366–377
  point mutation, 496–507
  restitution of, 363, 483, 499, 500, 722
  reunion of, 722, 730, 749
  single, 362–366
Chromosome changes, in form, 801, 814
  nonrandom incidence of, 377–380
  and ultraviolet radiation, 531–535
Chromosome exchanges, 717
  relation of, to fast-neutron dose, 726
    to radiation intensity, 727
    to X-ray dose, 725
Chromosome matrix, 555
Chromosome matrix effects, 814
Chromosome number, in *Drosophila melanogaster*, 631, 642
  in *Tradescantia*, 631
Chromosome rearrangements, 132
  in animal cells (*see* Chromosomes)
  gross, and ionization, 380, 480–488
  minute, 380
Chromosome ring, 372, 497, 498, 500, 514
Chromosome stickiness, 777, 779, 798–801, 814, 1097
  dose and, 800
  thymonucleic acid depolymerization and, 800, 801
  time after treatment and, 798–800
Chromosomes, 352, 355, 1096
  acentric, 363, 364
  adhesive ends, 446
  aneuploidy of whole, 358–359
  in animal cells, adhesion, induced, 694, 695
    chromatids, 628, 632, 642, 647–650, 659–661, 664, 675
    deficiencies, 640–642, 645–650, 661–663, 667–670
    division, 628, 677–680
    duplications, 636, 637, 640–642, 645, 648–650, 660, 662, 689
    fragmentation, induced, 628, 629, 631, 632, 659, 665, 668
    inversions, 635–638, 647, 650, 651, 654, 661–663, 670, 677–680, 685, 687, 689
    isochromatid breaks, 632, 660
    neuroblast, 635, 638, 648, 651, 659, 660, 666, 667, 679
    rearrangement, 627, 629, 630, 632, 635–637, 641, 642, 649–657, 660, 661, 663–666, 668–681, 684, 685, 688, 689
    recombination, 630, 642, 649, 652–655, 660, 661, 663, 665, 670, 671, 674–680, 682, 687, 690
    reconstitution, induced, 628, 629
    salivary-gland, 447, 494–496, 507, 635–637, 646, 648–652, 660, 661, 663–665, 668–670, 673, 677–679, 689
    translocation, induced, 635, 637–642, 651, 652, 659, 661–663, 669–671, 673, 674, 679, 680, 685, 687, 689
    transpositions, 650, 651, 689
  arrangement in sperm, 520
  balancing, 457
  breakage-fusion-bridge cycle, 365, 451, 456, 515, 560
  bridge formation, 482
  centric, 363, 364
  and deficiency, 449
  deletion in, 371, 372
  dicentric, 364
  distribution, 630

Chromosomes, euchromatic region in, 645, 663, 664, 677, 678, 681
extended, 447
fragmented, 1096
heterochromatic regions in, 635, 636, 645, 651, 652, 663–665, 677–681
homologous, 370
indirect radiation effects, 753, 754, 756
intranuclear disorientation, X-ray-induced, 804
inversion in, 374
iso-, 363
metastable, 571
minute structural changes in, by ionizing radiation, 492–496
monocentric, 370
radiation effects in *Tradescantia*, 713–761
"shift" rearrangement in, 376
sticky (*see* Chromosome stickiness)
structural changes, 362
telomeres, 366, 446
terminal deficiency, 366
time of division, 721
translocation, 999
union of fragments, 446
variations in radiosensitivity, 721
X, 377, 378, 396, 407, 497, 498, 500, 514, 641, 644–648, 650, 654, 661, 663–668, 677, 678, 680, 682, 839, 842
Y, 455, 514, 641, 644, 645, 649, 651, 654, 663, 668, 674, 842
(*See also* Chromosome aberrations; Chromosome breaks)
Chronic-radiation effects (*see* Anemia; Erythrocytes)
Chylomicron count, 975
Ciliary motion, 1095
Circulation, radiation effects, 960, 976–982
and radiosensitivity, 940
Citrate, and bone, 1108
in liver, 988
Cleavage, irradiation during, 868
multipolar, X-ray induced, 803
retarded, following irradiation of early mouse embryo, 866
Cleavage furrow, ultraviolet-induced change in position, 815, 816
Cleavage time, 304
Clinical literature on prenatal irradiation, 908–911, 913
Clot retraction, effect of irradiation on, 1044
Clotting time, effect of irradiation on, 1047
Cloud chamber, 4
Cluster, 80
Coat color, mammalian, 461
Cobalt, 946
Cobalt-induced polycythemia, effect on, of phosphorus[32], 1065
and X radiation, 1067
of X radiation, 1067
erythropoiesis in, 1065
Cocarcinonogenesis factors, 1186–1188
Cohesive forces, 31
Colchicine, 577, 578
effect on radiation-induced chromosome aberrations, 737
Cold environment, 935
Collagen changes, 1175
Collisions, average energy dissipated, 55
cooperative action, 138
distance, 77
law of probability, 79–80
elastic, 42, 45, 49, 50
charged particles, 42
energy dissipation by, 67
neutrons, 74
fast, 50
of first kind, 200
glancing, 51, 56, 62
characteristics of, 63
inelastic, 49, 62
energy dissipation by, 51
mechanism of, 50
probability of, 55
interval, 136
knock-on, 51, 56, 63
neutralizing one another, 140
radiative, 42, 49, 50, 63, 95
relative frequency, 55–56
resonance rule in, 205, 207, 208, 220, 235, 237–238
of second kind, 200, 202–208, 219–220, 228–229, 237–238
slow, 50
spin-conservation in, 205, 208, 220
Colloid retention, 978
Coloboma following prenatal irradiation, 879, 883, 887, 902, 909
Colon, 982, 1124
carcinoma induced by Y^{91} in, 1159
Colony formation, inhibition of, 330–331, 333
Columnar epithelium of digestive system, 1124
Compound (heterozygote), 404
Compound nucleus, 58
Compton effect, 38, 69
Compton scattering (*see* Scattering)
Conjunctiva, 1131
radiation effects, 998
Convariant reproduction, 352

Conversion, internal, 34
Copper sulfate, 414
Coproantibodies, response, 1003
Coproporphyrin, 988
Cornea, epithelium, 926
  radiation effects, 998
Corpora lutea, 1117, 1118
Corpuscular radiation (*see* Radiation)
Cortisone, effect of, on leukemogenesis, 1164, 1188
    on mouse embryo, 907
Corynebacterium creatinovorans, 301
Cosmic rays, 3
Crepis, 363, 589
Critical periods for induction of abnormalities by prenatal irradiation, 880–887, 891–893, 901, 902, 904, 906, 909, 912, 913
Crocus, 774
Crop plants, 442
Cross circulation, 926
Cross section, definition of, 37*n*.
Crossing over, 356, 359–362, 508
  in *Drosophila*, 635, 638, 642, 653, 654, 668
  somatic, 458
Crypt epithelium of intestine, 982
Crystal diffraction, neutrons, 115
  X rays, 105
Cumingia, 784
Cumulative dose, 766, 770
Cumulative effect, 1136
Curie (unit), 13
Current, oscillating, 20, 30, 33
    frequency of, 30
  resonating, 17, 20
Cyanide, 551, 562, 577, 580
  of potassium, 576
  and radiosensitivity, 941, 945
Cyclotron, 12
Cysteine, 295, 304, 551, 579, 586
  liberation of H_2S from, 267–268
  modification of radiation injury by, 1067, 1068
    and estradiol, 1068
    and estrogens plus spleen shielding, 1079, 1080
    and/or spleen shielding, 1080
  protection by, 942–945, 965
    mechanism of protective effect, 1067, 1068
Cytochemical techniques and analysis in radiobiology, 692, 693, 695
Cytochrome *c*, 287
Cytochrome oxidase, 544, 550, 551, 562, 576
Cytochrome reductase, 941
Cytological techniques and analysis in radiobiology, 632, 635, 638, 648, 673, 696
Cytoplasm, decrease in viscosity of, 1095
  injections of, 928
  and nucleus, 928–929
    relative radiosensitivity of, 1094
Cytoplasmic inheritance, 595, 596
Cytoplasmic movements, 1095

D

Daily irradiation of ovary, 1118
Datura, 391
Deamination, of amino acids, 296
  glycine, effect of alpha radiation on, 271
  by X rays, 265–266
    effect of solute concentration, 268–270
    pH dependence, 266–267
Death, genetic, 426, 430
  (*See also* Mortality)
Decrease in viscosity of cytoplasm, 1095
Decticus, 358
Deficiency, 449, 854, 855
Degenerative phenomena, 1092
  cartilage cells, 1112, 1113
  epidermis, 1121
Dehydration, 969
11-Dehydrocorticosterone, 992
Delayed effects, 1097
Deletions, 480, 498, 842
δ rays, 81, 271
Dermatitis, radiation, 919, 1148
Desoxycorticosterone, 992
Desoxyribonucleic acid (DNA), 305
  chromosome breakage, 723
  radiation effects on, 276, 277, 753–755
    depolymerization, 277
    inhibition of formation, 276
  oxygen and radiosensitivity of, 755
  synthesis, 929, 962
Desoxyribonucleic acid depolymerase, 299
Desquamation, 338
Deuterons, 3
  atomic weight, 7
  charge, 7
Development, 458–462
  mammalian prenatal, broad divisions of, with respect to radiation response, 862–863, 886, 911
    radiation effects on, 861–918
Developmental anomalies, 861–918, 1185
Devitalized bone, 1111
Diagnostic irradiation and hazards to embryo, 910, 913

Diarrhea, 969, 984, 1127
Diazomethane, 547
Dicumarol, 967
Diet and radiosensitivity, 933
Differentiation, 459
  as related to radiosensitivity, 927
  and type of radiation damage to embryo, 902–903
Digestive system, columnar epithelium of, 1124
Dilution effect, 259, 274
Dinitrophenol, 551, 935
Diphenyl, 290
Diphosphopyridine nucleotide, 288, 289
Diploid, 354
Diploid cells, 642–644, 647, 683
Direct action theory of radiation (*see* Target theory)
Direct effects of radiation (biological), 245–252
  on chromosomes, 735, 753
Disability, average, 432
Disintegration, 32, 35
  different modes of, 35
Disordering of solids, 196
Dissipation of energy (*see* Energy dissipation)
Dissociation, 33, 213–219, 224–225, 238–239, 246, 248
  following ionization, 225, 235, 238–239
Dithiophosphonate, 942
Divided doses, 1092
Dog, 863
  LD_{50} for, 930
Dominance, 402–405
  effective, 427
Dosage compensation, 401, 449
Dosage rate, effects of, 924
    on chromosome aberrations, 727
    lethal, on cells, 810
    mitotic, 788–793, 813
Dose, 120
  cumulative, 766, 770
  divided, 1092
  effect of varying, in prenatal irradiation, 882–887, 904–907, 913
  and mitotic effects of ionizing radiation, 769, 772, 782, 783
  permissible average or total, 433, 434
Dose action (*see* Dose effect)
Dose effect, exponential curves, 123–125, 130, 131, 135, 136
    range of validity, 125–127
    shape of, 326
    theoretical significance, 126
  sigmoid curves, 132, 135
Dose-effect relations, 123
Dosimetry, 145
  comparison of units, 149, 150
  of internal emitters, 166–174
  of ionizing particles, 164–165
  by means of ionization in gases, 148–150
  of neutrons, 161–164
  of photons, 151–154, 177
  practical aspects of, 174–185
    ionizing particle, 174–177
    photons, 181–183
  survey of dosimetric methods, 146–148
  of very-low-energy X ray, 179–180
  (*See also* Dosage rate; Dose; Radiation)
Drosophila, 324, 325, 333–335, 358–363, 373, 375, 377, 378, 380–383, 387, 389, 390, 392, 394–396, 399, 403, 405–412, 414, 416–423, 427, 437, 438, 443, 447–450, 452–455, 457, 458, 460, 476–479, 481–486, 492–494, 497, 502–507, 509, 512, 513, 516, 518, 519, 521, 524–526, 529, 531, 532, 534, 535, 539, 542, 545–547, 551, 557, 561, 565–572, 575–578, 581–584, 589, 595, 600, 738–740, 746, 807, 924, 935, 936, 939, 1005
  carcinogenesis in, 1190
  crossing over, 635, 638, 642, 653, 654, 668
  eggs, 682, 687, 689
  embryos, 683
  funebris, 410
  genetic effects in, compared with mammals, 825, 835, 836, 842, 844, 846, 847, 849, 854–856
  melanogaster, 410, 456, 553
    chromosome number in, 631, 642
  simulans, 410, 456, 553
  spermatogonia, 685, 686
  spermatozoa, 631, 632, 635, 644, 669, 670, 673–676, 682, 686
  stocks, 457
  testes, 685, 686
Drugs, parasympatholytic, 985
Ducklings, radiation effects, 925
Duodenum, 982
Duplication, 353
Dye, 289, 292, 295
Dyspnea, 995

E

Ear cartilage, 1000
Echinoderms, 357, 811
Ectopic erythropoiesis, 963
Ectopic myelopoiesis, 1103, 1106
Edema, 971
  intestinal, 983
  lymphatic organs, 1103

Effective areas, 128
Effective volume, 128, 130, 137
Electric relaxation, 69
Electrocardiograph, 981
Electrolytes, metabolism, 969
Electromagnetic radiation (*see* Radiation)
Electron attachment to neutral molecules, 240–241
Electron tracks, 90
Electron-transfer processes, 232, 237, 242–243
Electron volt, 8
Electronic equilibrium (X rays), 111
Electrons, atomic weight, 6
  average deflection, 92
  backscattering, 91
  capture, 69
  charge of, 6
  energy dissipation at various depths, 93
  energy distribution, 90
  excitation of atomic, 30
  negative, 6
  penetration, 90, 99
  penetration data, 100
  positive (*see* Positrons)
  primary, 57
  recoil, 38
  secondary, 21, 57, 69, 138
    energy dissipation by, 68
  sources of, 10
Electrophoretic mobility, change in, 328
Electrophoretic pattern of plasma, 973
Electrostatic accelerator, 11
Elementary processes, 26, 45
  chains of, 62
  free atomic particles, 44
  in mercury vapor, 199, 200, 202, 206–208, 215
Embryo, human, effects of radiation on, 908–911, 913
  mammalian, 861
    irradiated during period of major organogenesis, 862, 868–893, 909–910, 912
    irradiated in preimplantation stages, 862, 864–868, 911–912
    irradiation, of individual, 864, 901
      of selected parts of, 864, 877, 889–890, 911
    mechanism of radiation effect on, 900–908, 913
      role of maternal body in, 861, 900–901, 911, 912
  radiation effects, 925
  radiosensitivity, 932
    hypoxia and, 904–906, 913
Embryo mash, effect on radiation injury, 1074
Embryology, mammalian experimental, radiation effects and, 861–862, 911
Embryonic precursor, radiation effect on, 902–904, 906, 908, 913
Emitters, internal (*see* specific elements)
Endocrine imbalance and carcinogenesis, 1167, 1170
Endocrine organs, carcinogenesis in, 1167–1172
  radiation effects, 989–994
Endosteal growth and bone, 1108
Endothelium, damage to, 978
Endotoxins, bacterial, 1003
Energy, activation, 210, 215–216
  average, per ion pair, 65, 66, 158, 165, 166, 237, 241, 251
  binding, 28, 60
  of chemical bond, 28, 31, 60
  migration of, 202, 233–234, 246*n.*, 248*n.*, 249
Energy absorption, linear, 316
  and neutron flux, 163
  per roentgen, 150
  in tissues, ultraviolet radiations, 764
Energy dissipation, average, in collisions, 55
  by elastic collisions, 67
  by electrons at various depths, 93
  by inelastic collisions, 51
  rate of, 87
  by secondary electrons, 68
Energy distribution, electrons, 90
Energy flux per roentgen, 159
Energy loss, rate of, 316
Energy scales, 9
Energy transfer, linear, 316
Enterase, 987
Enterogenous infection, 982–983, 1002
Entropy, 291
Environment of cells and radiosensitivity, 1135
Enzyme systems, 297
Enzymes, 937, 941
  amino groups, 297
  double bonds, 297
  flavone, 562
  and genes, 354, 462
  hydroxyl groups, 297
  inactivation of, 324, 329
  prosthetic group, 297
  sulfhydryl, 937
  sulfhydryl groups, 297
Eosin, 541
Eosinophils, effect of irradiation on, 1063
Epidermis, 1097, 1119
  cellular polymorphism, 1121

Epidermis, degeneration of, 1121
 friable, 1121
 latent period in, 1119
 loss of elastic fibers in, 1122
 regeneration of, 1121
Epidermititis, moist, 997
Epididymis, 1116
Epilation, 337, 919, 997, 1120, 1123
Epilobium, 553
Epinephrine, 977, 980, 991
Epiphysis of bone, 1108
Epithelioma radiosensitivity, 929
Epithelium, intestinal, 982, 983
 radiation damage, 960
 stratified squamous, 1124
Epoxides, 417
Erythema, 338, 1120, 1121, 1150
 of skin, 926, 976–997
Erythroblasts, 1009
 sensitivity to radiation, 930, 1036–1037
Erythrocytes, 960–961, 970, 974, 979, 1002
 and bone marrow, 1099
 chloride, 974
 chronic-radiation effects, 1048, 1049, 1136
  and cutting of distal vessel of spleen, 1069
  on fragility, 961, 1039
   of red-cell mass, 1039, 1040
    and hemolysis, 1039
  of gamma radiation, 1050–1052, 1054–1056
  of radioisotopes, 1056, 1061
   strontium[89] and splenectomy, 1060
  and spleen shielding, 1038
  of X radiation, 1037–1041, 1067
   in phenylhydrazine-induced anemia, 1065
 disappearance of, 979
 fowl, metabolism, 1002
 iron[59] uptake in, 1037
 mass, 960
 morphological changes in, 1061–1062
 nucleated, 305
 tagged, 970
Erythropoiesis, ectopic, 963
 induced by phenylhydrazine and/or bleeding, 1064–1066
  inhibition of, 1037–1039, 1047, 1065–1066
 and spleen, 1107, 1108
Erythrosine, 542
Escherichia coli, 417, 418, 420, 454, 537, 542–546, 549, 564, 572, 579, 587, 591, 592, 935, 940, 944
Esophagus, 1124
Ester linkages, 290
Esterase, 300
Estradiol, effect of, on peripheral blood, 1067
 and modification of radiation injury, 1066–1067, 1077–1080
  by cysteine, 1080
   and/or spleen shielding, 1079, 1080
Estrogens, treatment with, 935, 965
 (*See also* Estradiol)
Estrus suppression, 337
Ethanol, 942, 946
Ethyl alcohol, 580
Euchromatic region in chromosome, 645, 663, 664, 677, 678, 681
Euchromatin, 361, 450
Evans blue, 971, 978
Evaporation, 36
Exchange reactions, 205–206, 220
Excitation, 60, 193–194, 197–234, 920
 of atoms, 30, 197–208
 in condensed systems, 229–234
 of diatomic molecules, 209–220
 effects of, 32
 energy sharing, 32
 interatomic motion, 32
 of polyatomic molecules, 220–229
Exercise, 934, 937, 946, 1005
External beta rays and thymus, 1105
Extracts, cell-free, effect of, 1082
Extremities, protection of, 926
Eye, latent period, 1131
  in lens, 1136
 radiation effects, 943, 998
  damage following prenatal irradiation, 879–881, 883, 887–889, 891–892, 896–898, 909, 912
   (*See also* specific abnormalities)
  gamma rays, 1131
  neutrons, 1131
  X rays, 1131
Eye pigments, insect, 461
Eyelid carcinoma caused by ThO_2, 1158

F

Fallopian tubes, 1117
Fast neutrons, 1033, 1042–1044, 1048
 anemia induced by, 1043
 biological effectiveness of, and X rays, 1048
 comparative effect of, and X rays, 1044
 effect of intensity, 723*ff*.
 effects of, on abortive rise, 1043–1044
  on chromosomes, 723*ff*.
  modified by oxygen, 747, 752
  on morphological cell changes, 1044
  on peripheral blood, 1033, 1042, 1043

Fast neutrons, relation of aberration yield to dose, 726
relative efficiency in chromosome-aberration production, 732
toxicity of, 923, 961, 998
Fat, absorption of, 986
in cells, 1095
Fat cells, bone marrow, 1100
Fat infiltration of liver, 987
Fatty acids, 298
Fenton reagent, 290
Fern, 576, 786, 796
Fern spores, 322, 324, 333, 936, 939
Ferric sulfate, 575
Ferricytochrome *c*, 289
Ferrocytochrome, 287
Ferrocytochrome *c*, 307
Fertility, effects of radiation, in mammals, 826–831
effects of prenatal irradiation on, 889–890, 896–898, 909, 912
(*See also* Mutations, partial sterility, sterility; Sterility)
Fetal period, irradiation during, 862, 863, 893–900, 912
and time of parturition, 898–899
Fetus, human, effects of radiation on, 908–911
mechanism of radiation effect on, 900–908
(*See also* Fetal period)
Fibrinogen, 965, 967, 973
Fibroblasts, 321, 335–336
Fish, LD_{50} for, 930
Fission, 14, 36
Fission products and intestine, 1127
Flavone enzymes, 562
Flavonoids, 968–969, 979
Flavoproteins, 551
Flower pigments, 461
Fluids, body, 969–976
extracellular, of intestine, 984
Fluorescein, 978
Fluorescence and phosphorescence, 22, 46, 201–202, 216–217, 224, 227, 230, 231, 233, 246
quenching of, 202, 203, 206, 207, 231
sensitized, 203, 207, 228, 237*n.*, 248*n.*
X-ray, 47, 69
yield, 107
Fluoride, 941, 946
Fluoroacetate, 946, 988
Fodder, 445
Follicular epithelium of ovary, 1117
Food consumption, 984
Food production, 445
Formaldehyde, 417, 422, 547
Formate, 581
Formic acid, 288
Fractionated doses, 925
effects on chromosome-aberration yield, 729
Fragility, capillary, 1044
vascular, 979
Franck-Condon principle, 204–206, 208, 214–218, 220, 223–224, 227, 235, 238
Frog eggs, 935
Frog radiosensitivity, 936
Fructose phosphorylation, 986
Fucus, 543
Fungi, 324, 333, 415, 444, 462, 505, 531, 535, 543, 557

G

Galactose, 304
Galactozymase, 304
Gall bladder, 1128
carcinogenesis in, 1154, 1156, 1184
Gallium[72], effect on peripheral blood, 1061
Galls, 444
Gamma radiation, 408, 518, 521–523
anemia induced by, 1050–1052, 1054–1056
effect of, on bone marrow, 1056
on peripheral blood, 1049–1056
on survival, 1052
and eye, 1131
genetic effects of, in mammals, 825, 830, 847
genetic hazards of, 854–856
and lymph nodes, 1104
and mutation, 479, 487
pancytopenia induced by, 1055, 1056
and spleen, 1107
and testis, 1114, 1116
γ rays, 3
anemia induced by (*see* Gamma radiation)
definition of, 20*n.*, 21
energy release in tissues, 764, 785, 786
lethal effect on cells, 805, 808–810
measurement of, 318–319
mitotic effects, 771, 776–779, 782, 784, 786, 787, 789–794, 797
and mutations, 479, 487
ratio to X rays, 923, 976
secondary, 117
sources of, 26
(*See also* Gamma radiation; X rays)
Ganglion cells, 995
Gastric acidity, 985–986
Gastric atrophy, 985–986
Gastric secretion, 1125

Gastrointestinal tract, 982–986
  carcinogenesis in, 1184
  fluid content, 972
Geiger counters, 4, 204
Gelatin, viscosity of solutions, 295
Gels, 292
Genes, 352
  accessory, 402
  as catalyst, 353
  conjugator, 447
  dosage, effects of changing, 396–402
  and enzymes, 354, 462
  equilibrium frequency of, 430
  linkage of, 638, 642
  marker, 406
  modifying, 401
  mutations (*see* Mutations)
  mutator, 414, 496
  noncompoundness of, 601
  and nucleic acid, 353
  number of, estimates, 407
  primary, 402
  sensitive volume of, 526, 527, 529
  shape of, 527
  size of, 527, 528
Genetic death, 426
  overlapping in, 430
Genetic effects, 135, 136
  of radiation, in mammals, 825–859
    proportionality to dose, 126
Genetic hazards of radiation, 854–856
  (*See also* Radiation)
Genetic "load" or disability, 427
Genetic material, fundamental properties of, 352–354
  transmission of, 354–357
Genetic-strain differences in response to prenatal irradiation, 872, 906–907, 913
Genetic technique and analysis in radiobiology, 632, 635, 638, 639, 641, 668, 670, 673, 677
Genetics, developmental, 459
Genomeres, 452
Germ-cell age and mutation, 504, 552
Germinal centers, 1103, 1106
Germinal selection, 408, 502, 685, 687, 689, 837–839, 846
Germinal tissues, radiosensitivity of, 929
Germination inhibition, 331, 333
Gesonia, 385
Gestation period, length of, and prenatal irradiation, 898–899, 912
  survey of radiation effects on entire, 862, 880
Globulins of plasma, 973
Gluconeogenesis, 974
Glucose, 303, 942, 946
  absorption of, 307, 986
  of plasma and lymph, 974
Glucosides, flavonol, 968–969
L-Glutamate, 306
Glutathione, 287, 298, 299, 304, 308
  liberation of H_2S from, 267
  modification of radiation injury by, 941–945, 1067
Glutathione reductase, 308
Glycerine, 580
Glycerol, 946
Glycine, 296, 297
Glycogen, 1095
  metabolism, 987
Glycols, 580
Glycolysis, 305
  aerobic, 306, 941
  anaerobic, 306
  bone-marrow, 305
  inhibition of, 339
Glycosidic linkages, 290
Goat, LD_{50} for, 930
Gold, colloidal, 979, 988
$Gold^{198}$ irradiation, 926
  effect of, on peripheral blood, 1060, 1061
    on sedimentation rate, 1061
  toxicity of, 988
Goldfish, LD_{50} for, 930
Golgi net, 1095
Gonadotrophic response, 999
Gonads, 325
  carcinogenesis in, 1168–1171
  radiation effects, 998–999
Gradient of injury, bone marrow, 1101
Granular leukocytes and bone marrow, 1099
Granulocytes (heterophils), 965
Granulocytopenia, 935
Granulocytosis, 960, 964
Graphite hydrosol, 324, 328
Grasshopper (*Chortophaga*), 484, 486, 569, 628, 629, 632, 659, 660, 666, 667, 682, 685, 766, 768, 772, 774, 776, 777, 779–781, 783, 791–796, 801, 803, 806, 808, 811–815
Grasshopper eggs, 301
Graying of hair, 997–998
Growing follicles of ovary, 1117, 1118
Growth, 459
  and oxygen tension, 940
  retardation of, 339, 340, 869, 876–877, 879, 896, 900, 905, 912, 922
Guanidine of blood, 1000
Guinea pigs, 825, 826, 828, 831, 833, 836, 838, 839, 863

Guinea pigs, anemia induced by gamma radiation in, 1052, 1054–1056
survival of, 1052
broad developmental divisions of, 863
carcinogenesis in, 1152, 1153, 1155, 1164, 1174
effect of bone-marrow injections from, on irradiated mice, 1075
irradiation of, during fetal period, 894, 897–898
during period of major organogenesis, 869, 874, 879, 880
during preimplantation period, 864–866
LD_{50} for, 930–931, 969
Gynandromorph, 359, 514, 515

H

Habrobracon, 384, 388, 453, 454, 510, 643, 657, 667, 683, 688, 689, 799, 808
Hair, 1119, 1122
epilation, 1123
permanent, 1123
temporary, 1123
graying of, 998
radiation effects, 997
X rays, 1123
Hair follicles, carcinogenesis in, 1176
destruction of, 1122
Half deaths, 426
Half-value layer, 104
Hamster, LD_{50} for, 930
Haploid cells, 335, 642–644, 668, 683
Hassall's bodies of thymus, 1105
Hatching, inhibition of, 325, 334–335
Hazards of radiation, human, 854–856, 910, 913
(*See also* Radiation illness; Radiation injury)
Head protection, 926
by shielding, 1070, 1072, 1073
Heart-muscle damage, 981
Heart rate, 981
Heavy particles, deflection of, 89
penetration of, 87
Helianthus, 589
Helium, 559
Hematocrit, 964
effect of radiation on, 1037, 1038, 1055
and phosphorus[32], 1057
in cobalt-induced polycythemia, 1067
Hematologic effects of ionizing radiations, 1029–1090
Hematopoiesis, radiation effects, 960–969
in testis, 1116
Hematopoietic cells, regeneration of, 1100
Hematopoietic tissues, radiosensitivity of, 929
Hemin synthesis, 962
Hemoconcentration, 969–970
Hemocyanin, 295
Hemocytoblasts, 1099, 1107
Hemoglobin, 295
effect of radiation on, 1037–1041
(*See also* Erythrocytes)
Hemoglobin concentration, 964
Hemolysis, 961
Hemophilia, 460
Hemorrhage, 922, 923
induced by radiation, 1039–1040, 1045–1047, 1056, 1072
intestinal, 983
Heparin injections, 967
Heparin-like material, circulating, 967
Hepatic blood flow, 977–978
Hertzian waves (radio waves), 3, 14, 20
Heterochromatic regions in chromosomes, 635, 636, 645, 651, 652, 663–665, 677–681
Heterochromatin, 361, 448, 450, 493
Heterochromatin blocks, 378, 447
Heterophil leukocytes, 1103, 1106
abortive rise in, 1034–1036
effect on, of fast neutrons, 1042–1044
of gamma radiation, 1050–1052, 1055, 1056
Heterosis, 429
Heterozygote, 402
Hibernation, 930
radioresistance during, 977
Hiroshima, bone-marrow studies, 1101
leukemia incidence, 1163
Histamine of plasma, 975, 980
Histidine, 292
Histology of damage following prenatal irradiation, 880, 897, 904, 912
Hit theory (*see* Target theory)
Homozygote, 402
Hormone imbalance, 1167, 1170
Horse serum, 935
Human cells, 629
Human fetus (*see* Fetus)
Human radiation effects (*see* Man)
Human subjects, 338, 339
(*See also* Man)
Humoral theory of regeneration, 1077–1081
Hyaline membrane in lung, 1130
Hyalinization of collagen in skin, 1122
Hyaluronidase, 968, 979
Hybrids, introgressive, 456
species, 553
Hydration of ions, 232, 242–243, 247, 250–251

Hydrocarbons, carcinogenic, 422
Hydrocephalus following prenatal irradiation, 879–881, 883, 909
Hydrogen atoms, 285
Hydrogen bonding in protein, breaking of, by radiation, 250–252
Hydrogen chloride, 291
Hydrogen effect on radiation-induced chromosome aberrations, 746, 753
Hydrogen ion concentration and radiosensitivity, 939
Hydrogen peroxide, 256, 271, 274, 275–277, 303, 306, 939
  formation of, 285, 286, 328
  and mutation, 547–552, 581
  origin in irradiated water, 750
  in relation to radiation-induced chromosome aberrations, 751
Hydroperoxyl radicals, 294
  origin in irradiated water, 751
  in relation to radiation-induced chromosome aberrations, 752
Hydrosulfite, 942, 945
Hydroxyapatite and bone, 1108
β-Hydroxyglutamic acid, 292
Hydroxyl groups, 292
Hydroxyl radicals, 285
  origin in irradiated water, 750
  in relation to radiation-induced chromosome aberrations, 752*ff*.
Hydroxylation of benzene, 257
Hydroxyproline, 292
Hymenoptera, 454
Hyperesthesia, 996
Hypertension and adrenal irradiation, 991
Hyperthermia, 996
Hypopharynx, carcinogenesis in, 1172
Hypophysectomy, 1005
Hypophysis, 1132
  anterior lobe, 1132
  growth, 1132
Hypotension, 980
Hypoxia, effect on radiation-induced genetic damage, 856
  and radiation sensitivity of embryos, 904–906, 913

I

Immunity to radiation effects, 1002–1004
Immunization, 935
Implantation process, radiation effect on, 868
Inactivation of viruses, 324, 329–330
Indirect action of radiations, 960
Indirect action theory of radiation, 257–260, 272
Indirect effects of radiation, biological, 244–245, 1136
  on chromosomes, 753, 754, 756
  as related to radiodecomposition of water, 750
Individual radiosensitivity, 932
Infections, 934, 960, 1002
  enterogenous, 982–983, 1002
Inflammation facilitating carcinogenesis, 1186–1187
Inflammatory reaction in skin, 1121, 1122
Infrared effects in combination with X rays, 739
Inheritance, cytoplasmic, 595, 596
Intensity, duration factor, 925
  (*See also* Dosage rate)
Interference, 356
Internal conversion, 34, 225, 226–228, 246–249
Interphase, 628, 682, 684
Interphase nucleus, 1096
Interstitial cells, 1116–1118
  of ovary, 1117, 1118
  of testis, 999, 1116, 1117
Interstitial deletions, 717
  in relation to X-ray dose, 726
Intestinal absorption, 986
Intestinal edema, 983
Intestines, 929, 982–983, 1006, 1124
  acquired radioresistance of, 1127
  duodenum, 1125
  effect on, of, Ba^{140}-La^{140}, 1127
    of fast neutrons, 1126
    of fission products, 1127
    of $phosphorus^{32}$, 1127
    of plutonium, 1127
    of radium, 1127
    of shielding, 1070, 1072, 1073
    of slow neutrons, 1126
    of $sodium^{24}$, 1127
    of $strontium^{89}$, 1127
    of $yttrium^{91}$, 1127
    of Zr^{93}-Cb^{93}, (Zr^{95}-Nb^{95}), 1127
  epithelium of, 929
  hemorrhages, 1124
  motility of, 985
  small, 306, 307, 1124
  ulceration, 1124
Inversion, paracentric and pericentric, 374
Iodine, 414, 552
$Iodine^{131}$, effect of, on lymphopoiesis, 1057
  on thyroid, 1132
  toxicity of, 993
  uptake, 992–993
Iodoacetate, 941, 946
Ion beams, 3

Ion density, 315, 920, 923
Ion pairs, definition of, 5
per cluster, 81
Ionic yield, 259*n.*
of dry substances, 272
of small and macromolecules, 272
and solute concentration, 268
Ionization, 32, 234–244
biological effect, 920
and chromosome breakage, 480–488
number required, 488–492
in condensed systems, 241–243
definition of, 5
density of, 197, 243–244, 248
dissociation following, 225, 235, 238–239
and gross chromosomal rearrangements, 480–488
mean energy per ion pair, 65, 66, 158, 165, 166, 237, 241, 251
measurement of, 5
multiple, 196, 243
and point mutation, 475–479
recombination of, 194*n.*, 239–240
spatial distribution of, 194, 197
specific (*see* Specific ionization)
by X-ray beam, 113
yield, 65
Ionization chambers, 6
air wall or thimble, 154, 157–161
calibration in roentgens, 177–179
correction factors, 155, 156
extrapolation, 176, 182
standard air, 151–154, 179
Ionization potential, 28, 29
Ionizing radiations (*see* Radiation)
Ions, charge of, 67–68
columnar distribution of, 83
hydration of, 232, 242–243, 247, 250–251
negative, 80
formation of, 69
positive, 7
sources of, 10
recombination, 68
spatial distribution of, 194, 197
Iron, 574
uptake by bone marrow, 962
Iron[59] uptake by rat erythrocytes, 1037
Iron pigment, 1096
Iron porphyrin, 287
Irradiation (*see* Alpha irradiation; Beta irradiation; Gamma radiation; Radition; X radiation)
Ischemia, 939, 945
Isochromatid breaks, 632, 660, 717
relation of, to radiation dose, 724
to radiation intensity, 727
Isotopes, 27
radioactive (*see* Radioactive isotopes)

J

Japanese bomb casualties, 996, 998, 999, 1005
(*See also* Hiroshima)
Jaw abnormalities following prenatal irradiation, 880–881, 892

K

Karyorrhexis, 1097
Ketones, 417
17-Ketosteroids, excretion, 990
Kidney, 306, 1128
carcinogenesis in, 1154, 1155, 1161
chick, damage to, 989
failure of, 925
radiation effects, 982, 988–989
and shielding, 1070, 1072, 1073
Knock-on collisions, 51, 56, 63
Kynurenic acid excretion, 988

L

Lactate, 305
Lactation suppression in mammary gland, 1123
Lactic acid formation, 305
Larynx, carcinogenesis in, 1151, 1180
Latent period, 922, 1136
in adrenal, 1132
in epidermis, 1119
in eye, 1131
lens, 1136
in lung, 1129
in lymphatic tissue, 1104
of protein denaturation, 294
in skin, 1121
Lead, 574
Lens, cysteine protection, 943
Lethal action, acute, 336
Lethal dose (LD_{50}), at birth, following prenatal irradiation, 875, 912
for mammals, 930
(*See also* specific animals)
Lethal effects, cell (*see* Viability effects, cell)
Lethal mutations (*see* Mutations)
Leukemia, 1153, 1154, 1162–1167, 1170, 1191
induction of (*see* Leukemogenesis)
lymphoid, 1164, 1165
myeloid, 1162, 1163, 1165, 1166, 1184
among physicians, 1162, 1163, 1165
in radium workers, 1162

Leukemia, in relation to myeloid hyperplasia, 1164
reticulum cell, 1167
thymic, 1164
Leukemogenesis, by atomic bomb, 1163
effect on, of adrenalectomy, 1165
of cortisone, 1188
in dogs, 1164
dose rate, 1166
factors of, 1165
indirect mechanism, 1165
Leukocytes, 922–923, 930, 935, 960, 964–965, 977
abortive rise in, 1035, 1036, 1043, 1044
after exposure to fast neutrons, 1043, 1044
acute-radiation effects, 1031–1036
and cutting of distal vessel of spleen, 1070
of fast neutrons, 1033, 1042–1044
of gamma radiation, 1049–1053, 1055–1056
of radioisotopes, 1056–1061
of X radiation and fast neutrons, 1033
adherence to blood vessels, 977
morphological changes in, 1062, 1063
polymorphonuclear, 930
Leukocytosis, 964
Leukopenia, 922, 923
Lewisite, 551
(*See also* Mustard gas)
Liberation of H_2S, from cysteine, 267–268
pH dependence of, 267
from glutathione, 267
Life span, decrease in, 337
of mammals, 922
shortening of, 1005*n*.
Light, 3, 14
absorption coefficient of, 118
infrared, definition of, 20
penetration of, 118
primary action of, 74
production of, 21
ultraviolet, definition of, 20
visible, definition of, 20
Light effects, characteristics of, 84
Linear accelerator, 12
Linear energy absorption, 316
Linear energy transfer, definition, 316
Linkages, 356
ester, 290
gene, 638, 642
glycosidic, 290
Lipids, of adrenal cortex, 990
of plasma, 974–975
Liquid solutions, 229–233
Litter size, 826, 830–840, 843, 848, 849, 855
from females irradiated during pregnancy, 866, 870–874, 890–891
Liver, 306, 1128
blood flow, 977–978
carcinogenesis in, 1157, 1160, 1184
irradiation of, 978, 982, 986–988
effects of shielding, 1070, 1072, 1073
plutonium and, 1128
regeneration of, 1128, 1135
and radiosensitivity, 929
retention of colloids, 979, 988
sensitivity of, to prenatal irradiation, 880, 886–889, 896–898, 902, 904
thorotrast, 1128
uric acid of, 988
yttrium and, 1128
Liverwort, 531
Local irradiation, 1136
vs. total-body irradiation, 1091
Loci, 356
duplicate, 455
groups of, 454
Locust, 358, 385
Loss of elastic fibers in skin, 1122
Lotus, 583
Luminescence (*see* Fluorescence and phosphorescence)
Lung, 1129
bronchial epithelium, 1130
carcinogenesis in, 1153, 1157, 1160, 1177–1180
latent period in, 1129
relative radioresistance of, 1129
Lupin, 567
Lycopersicum, 776
Lymph, constituents of, 972–976
extravasation of red cells, 966, 968, 971, 979
flow of, 970
Lymph nodes, 960–966, 1101, 1103, 1104
effect on, of fast neutrons, 1104
of repeated X irradiation, 1104
of slow neutrons, 1104
Lymphatic organs, 1101
edema of, 1103
involution, 991
latent period, 1104
Peyer's patches, 1101
radioactive isotopes and, 1104
regeneration of, 1103
solitary lymphatic nodules, 1101
spleen (*see* Spleen)
tissue, 1101
tonsils, 1101
Lymphatic vessels, dilatation of, 976

Lymphocytes, 1101, 1103, 1104, 1133
effect on, of acute radiation, 1031–1036
fast neutrons, 1042, 1043
gamma radiation, 1049–1052, 1055
morphological changes, 1062, 1063
radioisotopes, 1056–1060
Lymphoid tissue, indirect action, 960
nucleic acids, 929
Lymphoma after irradiation, 933
Lymphopenia, 922, 935
Lymphopoiesis, effect on, of appendix shielding, 1063
of spleen shielding, 1063
and spleen, 1106

M

Macrophages, 1100, 1103
Maize, 363, 410, 450, 454, 457, 531, 533–536, 540, 560
Malformations (*see* Morphological changes following irradiation)
Malonate, 946
Mammalian coat color, 461
Mammals, 415
radiation effects, on embryo, 861–918
genetic, 825–859
on reproduction, 826–831
(*See also* Radiation)
Mammary gland, 1117, 1123
during pregnancy, 1123
suppression of lactation, 1123
Man, 410
LD_{50} for, 930
mutations in, 419, 583, 854–856
radiation effects, 338, 339, 919, 966, 998, 999, 1005
on development, 862, 908–911
radiation hazards, 854–856, 910, 913
Manganese, 946
Maps, linkage, 356
Mass number, 27
Mast cells, 1100, 1105, 1107
Maternal body, role of, in radiation effect on mammalian embryo, 861, 900–901, 911, 912
Mature follicles of ovary, 1117
Mature sex cells, 1133
Mean square deviation, 80
Mechanism, of radiation effect on embryo and fetus, 900–908, 913
of radiobiological action, 327–328
Megakaryocytes, 1099, 1106, 1108
Meiosis, 354
Meiosis-meiotic cycle, 640, 642–644, 653, 654, 689, 690
Melanoblasts, 998
Menadione, 551, 552
Meninges, carcinogenesis in, 1156
Mercaptocarboxylic acids, 479
Mercaptosuccinate, 942, 945
Mercuribenzoate, 946
Mercury, 946
Mercury vapor, elementary processes in, 199, 200, 202, 206–208, 215
Mesons, 3, 59
Mesothelium, 1130
Metabolic activity, 922
Metabolic processes and gene mutation, 418–421
Metabolic rate and radiosensitivity, 931, 935–937
Metabolism, radiation effects on, 1000–1002
Metals, heavy, and mutation, 574
Metaphase, 628, 632, 638, 643, 659, 662, 689, 690, 928
Metaphysis of bone, 1108, 1109, 1111
Metastasis facilitated by irradiation, 1174–1175
Methemoglobinemia, 941
Methionine, 942, 945
Methyl-3: 12-diacetoxy-7-keto cholanate, 291
Methylacrylate, 291
Methylcholanthrene, 422
Methylene blue, 289, 945
Methylmethacrylate, 291
Microcephaly following prenatal irradiation, 880, 889, 909
Micrococcus (*Staphylococcus*) *aureus*, 537, 545, 548–552, 562
Microglia radioresistance, 995
Microphthalmia following prenatal irradiation, 879, 883, 887, 888, 902, 907, 909
Microspores, 341
chromosome aberrations in, 715
Microwaves, 3, 20
Midbrain radiation exposure, 980
Migration of energy, 202, 233–234, 246*n*., 248*n*., 249
Milk agent in mammary tumor induction, 1173
Miners, carcinogenesis in, 1177–1179
Mitochondria, 1095
Mitosis, 289, 354, 1096, 1133, 1135
abnormal, 628–630, 632, 646, 647, 664, 1092
cessation of, 1096
inhibition of, 322, 325, 331–333, 335–336, 340, 561, 1092
multipolar, 1135
potential, 1133

Mitosis, rate (frequency) of, 922
correlated with type of radiation damage to embryo, 902, 906, 908, 913
sensitivity of cell, 928
Mitosis-mitotic cycle, 627, 628, 642, 644, 655, 659, 677, 681, 682, 684, 685, 688, 691, 695, 696
Mitotic activity and radiosensitivity, 1162
Mitotic effects, 766–798, 811–814
of alpha radiation, 785–787
of ionizing radiations, 766–798
acceleration of, 783, 784
calcium and, 796
cell structures involved, 784, 785
chromosome number and, 798
critical period, 768, 769
dosage rate and, 788–793
dose and, 769, 772, 782, 783
for different species, 781, 782
duration of mitotic decrease and, 775–777
on egg, 769
fractionated treatment and, 793, 794
kind of radiation and, 785–788
α rays, 786, 787
β rays, 785, 787, 788
γ rays, 785–787
neutrons, fast, 786, 787
X rays, 786–788
kind of tissue and, 797, 798
length of mitotic cycle and, 775
mechanism of action, 785
normal mitotic rate and, 778–781
oxygen concentration and, 796
pH and, 796
recovery from, 770, 782
in relation to dose, 782
retardation of, 768, 769, 771, 772, 782, 783
reversion of, 768
sensitivity of different stages, 768, 769, 771–774
on sperm, 769
temperature and, 794–796
during treatment, 794
following treatment, 794–796
type of preparation and, 797
urethane and, 796
methods of study of, 766–768
counting of mitotic stages, 767, 768
timing of cells, 766, 767
of ultraviolet radiations, 811–814
acceleration of, 811, 812
chemical treatment and, 813, 814
intensity and, 813
regression of, 813
retardation of, 811
sensitivity of different stages, 812, 813
Mitotic effects, of ultraviolet radiations, wave length and, 811, 812
Mitotic mechanism, injury of, and radiation damage to embryo, 902–904
Mitotic spindle (*see* Spindle)
Modification of radiation effects (*see* Radiation injury)
Modifying factors, effects of, on radiation-induced chromosome aberrations, 736*ff*.
Molds, 391, 399, 417, 444, 461
Molecular chaos, 392
Molecular rays, 3
Mongolism following prenatal irradiation, 909
Monkey, LD_{50} for, 930
Monochromatic radiation, 16
Monocytes, effect of radiation on, 1033
morphological changes in, 1063
Monosomics, 644
Monsters (*see* Morphological changes following irradiation)
Morphine, 937
Morphological changes following irradiation, compared with effects of other agents applied to embryos, 907–908, 913
during fetal period, 863, 895–898
of human embryos, 908–911, 913
intermediate effects of maternal body on, 901, 911, 912
nature of primary damage leading to, 902–904, 906, 913
during period of major organogenesis, 862, 868–869, 878–893, 909–910, 912–913
during preimplantation period, 862, 864, 866–867, 886
(*See also* names of specific abnormalities)
Mortality, dose curves, 932
neonatal, and irradiation, during fetal period, 893–894
during period of major organogenesis, 869, 874–875, 890, 904–905, 912
during preimplantation period, 875
postnatal, and irradiation, during fetal period, 893–895
of human embryo or fetus, 911
during period of major organogenesis, 869, 904
prenatal, influence of radiation effects on mother, 900–901
and irradiation, during fetal period, 862, 893–894

Mortality, prenatal, and irradiation, during period of major organogenesis, 862, 868–874, 888, 890, 904, 912
during preimplantation period, 862, 864–868, 872, 911–912
Mosaics, 481, 507, 513, 514, 560
in *Drosophila*, 648, 649, 653, 661
tobacco, 510
Motility of intestine, 985
Motor excitability, 995
Mouse, 336, 337, 390, 432, 459, 561, 583, 776, 777, 797, 806, 809
broad developmental divisions of, 863, 909
carcinogenesis in (*see* specific site)
effects of radiation, during fetal period of, 871, 894, 896–899
genetic, 825–859
during period of major organogenesis of, 869–892, 905–908
during preimplantation period of, 864–868, 871
on reproduction, 826–831
LD_{50} for, 924, 930–931
mutation rate in, 850–856
Mouth, 1124
Mucous tissue, 1097
Multilobular nuclei, 1096
Multiple-hit, 133
determination of number of hits, 134
Muscle, 1097
carcinogenesis in, 1177
effect of implants of, on radiation injury, 1073
radiosensitivity of, 929
striated, contraction of, 922
Muscle cell, radiosensitivity of, 1161
Mushrooms, 442
Mustard, nitrogen (*see* Nitrogen mustards)
Mustard gas, 415, 512, 514, 547, 548, 551, 579, 594, 600, 1094
derivatives, 424
Mutagenesis, and biological conditions, 552–555
and chemicals, 574–581
and infrared, 565–574
and physical factors, 565–574
selective, and radiations, 590–597
and temperature, 565–574
and ultraviolet radiation (*see* Ultraviolet radiation)
and water and oxygen, 555–564
Mutants, achaete, 507
albino, 590, 591
alboviridis, 590
alboxantha, 590
Bar M2, 493
Mutants, Beaded wings, 390
cubitus interruptus, 481, 487
bithorax, 454
dumpy, 454
histidineless, 537, 542
inositol, 594
kappa, 595
lozenge, 454, 507
Minute bristles, 449
mottled eye, 595
Notch, 494, 495
phage, 595
purine, 564
R and Q type, 556, 591
scute, 452, 493, 507
streptomycin, 564, 587, 591, 592, 595
Stubble, 454
tigrina, 590
Truncate wings, 390
tryptophane, 592
viridis, 590, 591
white, 454, 504, 507, 515, 516, 526
yellow, 504, 507
xantha, 590
Mutational spectrum, 590, 594, 596
Mutations, 121, 138, 249, 289, 303, 324, 333, 334, 352
accumulation of, 424–432, 855, 856
and activations, 490
and active radicals, 551
amorphic, 398, 597
antimorphic, 398
biochemical, 462
and carcinogens, 421–424
and centrifuging, 573
clustered, 523, 853
and cosmic radiation, 581–584
cryptic, 404
deficiency, 449, 854, 855
delayed, 512, 514, 600
detrimental class of, 395
in different species, 410–412, 835, 836, 844, 854–856
direct or abnormad, 398
dominant, 381, 402
elimination of, 424–432, 837, 839, 842, 843, 846, 855, 856
and energy levels, 597
expression of, 424–432
and fluorescent substances, 541
fractional, 512
and gamma rays, 479, 487
(*See also* Gamma radiation)
gene, 389, 394, 598, 630, 638, 675, 825, 843, 854
and abnormalities from irradiation of embryos, 903, 908, 913
and metabolic processes, 418–421

Mutations, gene, radiation-induced, 405–409
in mammals, 825–859
spontaneous, 405–409
and germ-cell age, 504, 552
and heavy metals, 574
and hydrogen peroxide, 547–552
hypermorphic, 398, 597
hypomorphic, 397, 449, 597
lethal, 394, 652, 653, 666, 1133
cell, 838
dominant, 359, 504, 632, 644, 646, 655, 657, 663, 666–668, 670, 675, 676, 682–685, 687–689, 825, 831–840, 844, 847, 854, 856
and abnormalities from irradiation of embryos, 903, 913
recessive, 851–855
sex-linked, 140, 405, 476, 851
somatic, 1135
in mammals, 825–859
in man, 419, 583, 854–856
and natural radiation, 581–584
neomorphic, 381, 399, 597
not radiation-induced, 412–418
and nuclear transmutation, 584–590
and nucleic acid, 540
and oxygen, 561, 856
and ozone, 557, 563
partial sterility, 825, 840, 842–850, 854
point, 389, 394, 411, 825, 826, 836, 837, 839, 855
and ionization, 475–479
relation to chromosomal breakage, 496–507
and temperature, 565
and ultraviolet radiation, 531–542
pre-, 511
and pressure, 573
proportionality of, to dose, 477
radiation, 389–396
spacially limited, 507–511, 517–525
time-limited, 511–517
and radiation duration and intensity, 478
and radioactive phosphorus, 585, 587
and radioactive sulfur, 585
rate of, critical, 433
of immature female germ cells, 552
of individual genes, 407, 853
mammalian, 903
in man, 583, 854–856
and meiotic stage, 566
in mouse, 850–856
of spermatogonia, 552, 850–853, 855, 856
of spermatozoa, 552, 850, 851, 855
recessive, 381, 402, 450
Mutations, reverse or normad, 398, 596, 597
semilethal, dominant, 831–840
recessive, 851–855
semisterility, 825, 840, 842–850, 854
sex-linked, 140, 405, 476, 851
somatic, in mouse, 903
and sonic vibrations, 572
specific loci, 850–856
spontaneous, 389–396
in statosphere, 582
sterility, 840–843, 854, 855
sublethal class of, 395
subvital, 831–840, 851, 852, 855
and supersonics, 589
"suppressor," 399, 441
and target hypothesis, 525–531
and temperature, 412
and thermal neutrons, 588
translocations, 842–844, 846–850, 854
transverse induction of, 509
and undernourishment, 576
"unit loads" of, 434
and viability, 395, 853–856
viable, recessive, 851–854
visible, 395, 477, 502, 506
dominant, 850–851, 855
recessive, 851, 852
and X-ray wave length, 478
Myaesthenia gravis, 460
Myelocytes, 1099, 1106
Myeloid cells, maturation of, 964
Myocardial damage, 967, 981
Myofibrils, 1095
Myosin (adenosinetriphosphatase), 298
Myotis lucifugus, 977

N

Nails, 1119
Narcissus, 489
Nasopharynx, 1124
Nausea, 982
(*See also* Radiation illness)
Necrosis following prenatal irradiation, 897
Nembutal anesthesia, 937, 946
Nephritis, 305
Nerve cells, radiosensitivity of, 929, 930
Nerves, 1097, 1131
peripheral, 996
Nervous system, radiation effects, 994–996, 1006
Nervous tissue, developing, 996
of embryos, 1131
of newborn, 1131
Neuroblasts, radiosensitivity of, 996
Neurofibrils, 1095
Neurogenic origin of anorexia, 985

Neurological damage, 967
Neurospora, 382, 399, 454, 461, 476, 505, 533, 535, 541, 545–550, 562, 576, 585, 586, 594, 596, 751
Neutrino, 3
Neutrons, 3, 27, 318, 320, 479, 492, 517–524, 526, 528, 588
atomic weight, 7
backscattering, 116
capture, 58, 114, 116
collisions, 113
crystal diffraction, 115
dosimetry of, 161–164
ejection of, 36
elastic collisions, 74
energy distribution in space, 116
energy release in tissues, 786
and eye, 1131
fast (*see* Fast neutrons)
genetic effects of, in mammals, 825, 827, 830, 833, 838, 841, 845, 846
in n units, 320
no electric charge, 7
penetration of, 113, 114
scattered, 116
secondary, 116
slow, chromosome-aberration production by, 733
effect of, on blood-forming tissue, 1030
on bone marrow, 1101
on intestinal mucosa, 1126
on lymph nodes, 1104
on spleen, 1107
on thymus, 1105
relation of, to biological efficiency, 734
sources of, 14
and testis, 1114, 1116, 1117
Neutropenia, 922
Neutrophils (*see* Heterophils)
Nicotine, 980
Nicotiana, 589
Nitrite, 941, 945
Nitrobenzene, 291
Nitrogen, 559–561, 576
excretion by urine, 1000
nonprotein of blood, 973, 989, 1000
Nitrogen mustards, 285, 424, 507, 577, 922, 967
effect of, on morphological changes in peripheral blood, 1061
on rat embryo, 907
Nitrophenols, 291
Nondisjunction, 358, 508
Nonspecificity of radiation effects, 1093
on bone marrow, 1101
Nor-di-guairetic acid, 550
Nuclear changes, 60
production of, 62
Nuclear forces, 27
effect of, 44
Nuclear reactions, injuries, 1005
Nuclear reactor, 14
Nuclear resonance effect, 58
Nuclear transformations, types of, 59
Nuclear transmutation and mutation, 584–590
Nucleated red cells, 305
Nucleic acids, 290, 303, 527, 540, 550, 587, 692, 696, 929
intestinal, 983
of liver, 988
synthesis of, 305, 962
Nucleolus, 1096
ultraviolet-radiation effects, 816
X-ray effects, 803
Nucleoproteins, 290, 580
Nucleotides, 498
Nucleus, 1094
budding, 1096
compound, 58
and cytoplasm, 928–929
relative radiosensitivity of, 1094
membrane, 1096
structure of, 27
swelling of, 1127
Nutrition, disturbances of, and blood effects, 960, 965
and radiosensitivity, 985
Nutritional deficiency, 1005

O

Oenothera, 382, 390, 553, 566
Oligodendroglia, radioresistance, 995
One-hit aberrations, 723
$1/r^2$ law, 85
Onion, 578, 580
Oöcytes, 387, 837, 844, 847
Oötid, 374
Optic anlagen, 458
Organic chemistry, 462
Organic matrix of bone, 1112
Organogenesis, irradiation during period of major, 862, 868–893, 905, 909–910, 912
Organs, reduplication of, 325, 335
susceptibility of, to tumor induction, 1161–1162
weights of, 1001
Oscillating current, 20, 30, 33
Osmotic pressure, cellular, 938
Osteoblasts and bone, 1108, 1110, 1111
Osteoclasts and bone, 1108, 1110
Osteocytes, bone, 1108, 1110, 1111

Ova, 1117, 1118
  developing, 930
  primitive, 1117
Ovarian tumors, 999, 1151, 1153, 1168–1171
Ovaries, 1117, 1136
  daily irradiation of, 1118
  follicular cells of, 1117
  interstitial cells of, 1117, 1118
  plutonium and, 1118
  radiation effects, 994, 998–999
  radium and, 1118
  sterility, 1117
"Overlapping" in genetic death, 430
Oviduct, 1118
Ovocytes, 1117
Ovulation, 1118
Oxidants in physiological effects of radiation, 921
Oxidation and mutations, 417
Oxidation-reduction, 256
Oxidation-reduction potentials, 307
Oxidation-reduction systems, 286, 289
Oxygen, 417
  atmospheric, 307
  dissolved, 284, 286
  effect of, on blood-forming tissue, 1065, 1067
    on radiation-induced chromosome aberrations, 736, 744*ff*.
    on radiosensitivity, 927, 939–941
  influence of, on high-energy mutagensis, 552, 555–564, 577
    (*See also* Hypoxia)
  as related, to radiation intensity, 749
    to temperature effects, 742
  tissue utilization of, 1001
Oxygen concentration, influence on radiation action, 131
Oxygen consumption, 962
Oxygen tension in mammals, 936
Ozone and mutation, 557, 563

P

Pair production, 39, 44, 69
  cross section, 40
Palate, cleft, following injections of cortisone, 907
    following prenatal irradiation, 883, 892, 907, 909
Pancreas, 1128
Pancreatic fibrosis, 460
Pancytopenia, effect of spleen shielding on, 1069
  induced by gamma radiation, 1055–1056
Papain, 299
Para-aminopropiophenone, 941, 945
Parabiosis, 926
Paramecium, 424, 545, 564, 572, 580, 581, 586, 587, 593, 595, 939
Parasites, insect, 444
Parasympatholytic drugs, 985
Parathyroid, carcinogenesis in, 1172
Partial body irradiation, 925
Pathology, 458–462
Penetration, 84–119
  β rays in thick foils, 100
  electrons, 90
    data on, 100
    thick foils, 99
    thin foils, 99
  exponential law, 103–104
  heavy charged particles, 87
  light, 118
  neutrons, 113, 114
    narrow-beam, 114
  X rays, 102
    broad-beam, 108
    narrow-beam, 103
Penicillin, 1003
Penicillin resistance, 303
Penicillium, 444, 535, 594
Pentaploid cells, 643
Pentaploidy, 357
Pepsin, 299
Periosteal growth and bone, 1108
Permeability, vascular, 978–979
Peroxides, 417, 937, 939, 941
  organic, and mutation, 303, 550, 752
  (*See also* Hydrogen peroxide)
Persistence, 426
Petechiae, 966
Peyer's patch, effect of shielding, on lymphocytes, 1063
pH, 575
Phenol, 290
Phenotype, 396
  and gene dosage, 401
Phenylhydrazine, 935, 965
  stimulation of erythropoiesis by, 1064–1066
Phenylhydrazine-induced anemia, effect of X radiation on, 1064–1066
  mechanism of recovery from, 1067, 1068
Phenylpyruvic amentia, 461
Phlebotomy-induced anemia (*see* Phenylhydrazine-induced anemia)
Phosphate, inorganic, 290
Phosphatase, alkaline, 987
  of intestine, 983
  of plasma, 975
Phosphoglyceraldehyde dehydrogenase, 298, 299

Phospholipids, liver turnover, 988
of plasma, 975
Phosphorus (P^{32}), 305, 476
effect of, 1057, 1058
on bone marrow, 926
on erythropoiesis, 1065
external irradiation by, 997
on intestine, 1127
on polycythemic rats, 1057
on testis, 1116, 1117
inorganic, of plasma, 974
radioactive, and mutation, 585, 587
toxicity of, 988, 1003
Phosphorus content, of blood, 1000
of liver, 987
Phosphorus^{32}-tagged erythrocytes, 970
Phosphorylation of fructose, 986
Photochemical reactions, 46, 193, 194
primary processes in, 195–196
sensitized, 195, 208
Photoelectric effect, 18, 20, 46, 69
Photoelectric threshold, 18
Photoelectrons, 20
Photon-electron equilibrium, 150, 183–185
Photon flux per roentgen, 159
Photons, definition of, 19
dosimetry of, 151–154, 177
Photoreactivation, 543, 569
Phycomyces, 922
Pigment, loss of, 997–998
Pigment granules, 1095
Pigment tissue, 1097
Pigmentation in skin, 1120, 1121
Pile, 14
Pilocarpin, 576
Pisum, 776
Pituitary-adrenal system, 1004–1005
Pituitary damage following prenatal irradiation, 877, 889
Pituitary gland, 991–994
Pituitary tumor, 1167–1169, 1171
(*See also* Radioactive elements)
Placenta, degenerative changes in, following irradiation, 901
Planck constant, 18, 30
Plankton, 445
Planorbis, 783
Plasma (*see* Blood plasma)
Plasma cells, 1103, 1116, 1133
effect of radiation on, 1033
Plasma proteins, iodinated, 970
Plasma volume, 961, 969
Platelet transfusion, 968
Platelets, effect on, of fast neutrons, 1043, 1048
of gamma radiation, 1050, 1051, 1054–1056
of radioisotopes, 1056–1061
Platelets, morphological changes in, 1062
thrombi, 977
Pleura, 1130
Ploidy, 683
Plutonium^{239}, effect of, on bone, 1110, 1112
on intestine, 1127
on liver, 987, 1128
on ovary, 1118
on peripheral blood, 1060
on skin, 1122
on spleen, 1107
on testis, 1117
on thymus, 1105
toxicity of, 964, 970, 973
Pneumococci, 353
Point heat, 62
"Point sensible," 283, 284
"Poison" produced by radiation (*see* Toxins)
Poisons, effects of, on embryonic development, 862, 907–908, 913
Poisson distribution law, 80, 133
Polar cap, 531
Polar force, 31
Polarization effects, 75
Pole cells, 534, 536, 538, 539, 545, 546
Pollen, 341–342, 936
Polonium sources, 320
Polycythemia, cobalt-induced, effect of phosphorus^{32} on, 1065
Polydipsia, 971
Polymerization, 290, 291, 292
acetylene, 291
acrylonitrile, 257
Polymorphonuclear neutrophils (*see* Heterophils)
Polyphenol, 290
Polyploidy, 357–358, 1097
and radiosensitivity, 929
Polysomics, 644
Position effects, 376, 380–383, 450, 487, 502, 503, 505, 507, 516, 849
Positrons, 7
atomic weight, 6
charge of, 6
penetration of, 98
sources of, 10
Posture abnormalities, 995
Potassium, 581
cyanide of, 576
excretion of, 989
of intestine, 984
permanganate of, 417, 552
of plasma, 974
in tissue, 972
Potency, 8, 61, 135–136
corpuscular radiations, 8
electromagnetic radiation, 18

Potential, appearance, 239, 240
Potential barrier, 35
Potential curves, 211–215, 226–227
Potential surfaces, 220–226
Poultry, 459
(*See also* Chickens)
Precursor, embryonic, radiation effect on, 902–904, 906, 908, 913
Predissociation, 218–219, 224–225, 227, 246
Pregnancy, irradiation during, 932
and mammary gland, 1123
termination of, following irradiation, 867, 870, 910, 912
unsuspected, and radiation-induced abnormalities, 910, 913
(*See also* Abnormalities; Embryo; Fetus)
Preimplantation period (of embryo), irradiation during, 862, 864–868, 875, 886, 911–912
Pressure and mutation, 573
Primitive ova, 1117
Primitiveness and radiosensitivity, 930
Primordium damage as result of prenatal irradiation, 887*n.*, 902–904, 913
Progynon, 576
Propane-1,3-dithiol, 287
Prophase, 628, 635, 638, 643, 648, 653, 660, 664, 682, 688–690, 696, 928
Propylene glycol, 305
Protamine, 967–968
Protecting agent, 307
Protection, by hypoxia against radiation damage to embryo, 904–905, 913
from radiation effects, 245, 934, 1006
ionizing radiations, 656
Protection effect, 260–262, 274
and reactivity of solutes, 262–264
Protein depletion, 934
Protein molecule, 292
Proteins, 692, 695, 696
breakdown of, 306
concentration of, 293
degrees of reactivity, 292
denaturation of, 292, 293, 294, 308
latent period of, 294
by radiation, 250–252
hydrogen bond rupture, 292
of intestinal cells, 983
of lymph, 972–973
molecular weight, 292
of plasma, 972–973
prevention of enzyme inhibition, 307
shape, 292
side groups, 292, 295
solutions, 292, 294, 295
spiral structure, 295
subunits, 195
Proteins, synthesis of, 305
Prothrombin-concentration studies, 1046
Prothrombin time, 967
Protons, 3, 27
atomic weight, 7
charges of, 7
ejection of, 36
energy release in tissues, 764, 786
range of, 87
sources of, 10
Protozoa, 303, 444
Prunus, 553
Pseudocentrotus, 771, 772, 785, 787
Pulse rate, 981
Purine, 290
Purine bases, 290
Purine derivatives, 578
Purine ring, 290
Purpura, 966
Pyknosis, 1096
Pyrimidine ring, 290
Pyruvate, 305, 306

Q

Quality of radiation in physiological effects, 922
Quantity of radiation in physiological effects, 922

R

Rabbit, 336, 554, 629, 825, 831, 833–835, 837, 863, 900–901
bone-marrow glycolysis, 305
broad developmental divisions of, 863
carcinogenesis in, 1152, 1153, 1155, 1164, 1174, 1183
irradiation of, during fetal period, 893–896, 898
during period of major organogenesis, 868–869, 876, 879, 880, 891
during preimplantation period, 865–866
LD_{50} for, 930–931
time of death, 932
Radiation, action of, 85
influence of oxygen concentration on, 131
working models, 119, 130
acute, effects of, 1136
on peripheral blood, 1031–1041
by fast neutrons, 1041–1044
by X radiation, 1031–1041
(*See also* Anemia)
and age, 1093
alpha, 526, 540, 964, 970, 973, 1000
effects of, 271, 940
breaking of hydrogen bonding in protein by, 250–252

Radiation, classification of, 2
  comparative effectiveness of, 135–136
  corpuscular, analysis of, 4
    classification of, 2
    definition of, 2
    electric charges, 6
    energy transport by, 4
    masses, 6
    methods of detection, 4
    potency of, 8
    secondary, 21, 57
    types of, 6
  cosmic, and mutation, 412, 581–584
  damage by (*see* Radiation injury)
  definition of, 2
  delta-ray, and mutation, 479
  denaturation of protein by, 250–252
  direct action theory of, 258, 272
  dose (*see* Dosage rate; Dose; Dose effect; Dosimetry)
  earth, 412
  and effect of cell stage on chromosomal breakage, 383–389
  effects of, biological, direct, 245–252
      indirect, 244–245
        on chromosomes, 753, 754, 756
      protection from, 245, 656, 934, 1006
    on fertility in mammals, 826–831
      (*See also* Mutations, partial sterility, sterility)
    immunity to, 1002–1004
    modification of (*see* Radiation injury)
    and temperature, 1093
    in water, 244*n.*, 273, 274
  electromagnetic, 2
    absorption of, 17, 20, 45–48
    action of, 16
    classification of, 2, 20
    detection of, 21
    mechanism of, 15
    potency of, 18
    scattering of, 37, 45–48
  gamma (*see* Gamma radiation)
  grenz-rays, 478
  hemorrhage induced by, 1039–1040, 1045–1047, 1056, 1072
  indirect action theory of, 257–260, 272
  infrared, 503
    and chromosome breakage, 571
    influencing high-energy mutagenesis, 565–574
  ionizing, 61, 1029–1082
    comparative effectiveness of, 139
    degradation of, 61
    differences in cell sensitivity to, 681–691

Radiation, ionizing, effects of, on blood coagulation, 1044–1047
      on blood-forming tissue, 1063, 1064
        comparative, 1030–1031
      direct vs. indirect, 1030
    and minute structural chromosome changes, 492–496
    mitotic effects (*see* Mitotic effects)
    and mutations, limited by space, 507–511, 517–525
      limited in time, 511–517
    protection from, 656
    secondary, 63
    similar effects, 84
  massive doses, 922, 923, 995, 996
  and metastasis, 1174–1175
  monochromatic, 16
  mutation and fractionated doses, 485
  natural, and mutation, 581–584
  nuclear particle, effect on atomic nuclei, 58
  poison produced by, 245
  practical genetic applications of, 440–445
  quality and quantity of, in physiological effects, 922
  resonance, 199, 202, 206, 216
  secondary, 72
  and selective mutagenesis, 490–497
  and speed of evolution, 435–440
  stimulation of blood-forming tissue by, 1064
  as tool for study, of biochemistry, 458–462
    of chromosome behavior, 445–448
    of chromosome properties, 445–448
    of development, 458–462
    of gene evolution, 448–458
    of gene properties, 448–458
    of pathology, 458–462
    of physiology, 458–462
  ultraviolet (*see* Ultraviolet radiation)
  visible, and mutation, 588
  X (*see* X radiation)
Radiation accidents, 998, 1005, 1006
Radiation action (*see* Radiation, action of)
Radiation chemistry, 194
  primary processes in, 196–197
Radiation illness, acute, 919
  clinical, 966
  following irradiation during fetal period, 893
  of mother and effect on embryo, 190
  nausea, 982

Radiation injury, 553, 934, 1005
  mechanism of recovery from, 1069, 1074–1075, 1079–1082
  modification of, 274–276, 1064–1077, 1079, 1080
    by absence or presence of oxygen, 275
    by combined prophylactic and therapeutic measures, 1079, 1080
    by prophylactic measures, 579, 1064–1068
      cysteine, 1067
      estradiol, 1066, 1067
      glutathione, 1067
      HO_2, 274, 275
      H_2O_2, 274, 275
      H_2S and ammonia, 276
      induced hyperplasia, 1064–1066
      oxygen deprivation, 275, 1067
      sulfhydral compounds, 1067
    by therapeutic measures, 1068–1077
      blood transfusions, 1081, 1082
      embryo mash, 1074
      heterologous bone-marrow injections, 1075
      heterologous transplants, 1075
      homologous bone-marrow injections, 1074, 1075
      parabiosis, 1075, 1076
      spleen implants, 1073–1076
      spleen shielding, 1068–1073
      splenectomy, and spleen implants, 1073, 1074
        and spleen shielding, 1077–1081
      tissue shielding, 1069–1073
  neurological, 967
  in subsequent generations, 432–435
  (*See also* Chromosome aberrations; Morphological changes following irradiation; Mutations)
Radiation length, 96
Radiation quantum (photon), 19
Radiation syndrome, acute, 960, 1005–1008
  treatment, 1006
Radiationless transition, 34–35
Radiative collisions, 42, 49, 50, 63, 95
Radicals from water, by irradiation, 256–257, 262, 270, 750
  number of, 270
  specificity of reaction of, 265–268
Radio waves, 3, 14, 20
  and mutation, 588
Radioactive elements, 13
  artificial isotopes (P^{32}, I^{131}, Au^{198}, Mn^{52}, Ga^{67}, Sr^{89-90}), 1158
  bone seekers, rare earth, 1160
    transuranic elements, 1160
Radioactive elements, carcinogenesis by, Au^{198}, 1158, 1165, 1167, 1184
    I^{131}, 1167, 1171
    ionium, 1158
    mesothorium, 1156, 1157
    P^{32}, 1148, 1158, 1160, 1166, 1177
    Po^{210}, 1148
    Pu^{239}, 1148, 1159, 1160, 1177
    Ra^{226}, 1147–1148, 1151, 1153–1158, 1160, 1177
    radon, 1155, 1158, 1176–1177, 1178, 1180, 1183
    Sr^{89-90}, 1160, 1185
    thorium dioxide (thorotrast), 1155, 1157, 1158, 1167, 1177, 1179, 1184
    uranium, 1177
    Y^{91}, 1159, 1177, 1184
  maximum permissible amount of [Ra^{226}, Pu^{239}, Sr^{89-90} ($+Y^{90}$), Po^{210}, H^3, C^{14}, Na^{24}, P^{32}, Co^{60}, I^{131}], 1148
  strontium, 586
  sulfur, 585
  (*See also* Radioactive isotopes)
Radioactive istopes, 1093
  artificial (*see* Radioactive elements)
  chromosome aberrations produced by, 733
  effect of, on adrenal gland, 1132
    on bone, 1110
    on bone marrow, 1100
    on cartilage, 1113
    on gastrointestinal epithelium, 1127
    injected into pregnant females, 864, 899–900
    on kidney, 1128
    on lymphatic tissue, 1104
    on osteogenic sarcomas, 1111
    on ovary, 1118
    on skin, 1122
    on spleen, 1107
    on testis, 1116
    on thymus, 1105
    on thyroid, 1132
  (*See also* specific elements)
Radioactive transformations, 13
Radiobiological action, mechanism of, 327–328
Radiobiological additivity, 326
Radiobiology, primary processes in, 194–195, 197
Radiochemical events in biological systems, 937
Radiodermatitis, 1151, 1175–1176
Radiomimetic agents, 285, 922, 937
Radioresistance, 1092, 1133, 1135
  acquired, 1127, 1136
  induced, 934–944
  of lung, 1129

Radioresistance, of macrophages in bone marrow, 1100
of reticular cells, 1133, 1135
Radiosensitivity, 1133
alteration of, by combined measures, 1079, 1080
by prophylactic measures, 1064–1068
by therapeutic measures, 1068–1077
by tissue shielding, 1068–1073
biological factors, 927–934
and cellular environment, 1135
of chromosomes, 721, 741, 748
of cold-blooded vs. warm-blooded vertebrates, 1093
dependent on developmental stage, 861–862, 867–868, 874–877, 879–882, 906–907, 909, 911
differential, of parts of embryo, 862, 889, 892, 899–900
(*See also* Critical periods for induction of abnormalities by prenatal irradiation)
effect of induced hyperplasia on, 1064–1066
experimental modification of, 927–934
induced, 934–944
of organs, 1135
physical factors, 927–934
recovery in, 928
in relation to water, 754
relative, 1092, 1094, 1132
Radiothyroidectomy by I^{131}, 1171–1172
Radium, 390, 391
anemia induced by, 1059
calcification of vessels by, 1122
effect of, on adrenal gland, 1132
on bone, 1110–1112
on cartilage, 1113
on intestine, 1127
on peripheral blood, 1059
on ovary, 1118
on skin, 1122
on spleen, 1107
on testis, 1117
and mutations, 478, 581
toxicity of, 1000
Radium workers, leukemia among, 1162
tumor incidence in, 1158, 1182–1183
Radon sources, 321
Raman effect, 46
Rana, 802
Rana spermatozoa, 643
Randomness of atomic events, 26
Range, 87
extrapolated, 100
maximum, 100, 102
relative, of electrons and photons, 111
true, 92, 100
Rate of energy loss, 316
Rats, 774, 776, 781, 805, 806, 808, 809, 811, 812, 816, 825, 827, 831–835, 837, 848, 863, 907
baby, LD^{50} for, 931
broad developmental divisions of, 863
carcinogenesis in, 1152, 1157, 1159, 1164, 1172, 1174, 1180, 1184
carcinoma in, 684
irradiation of, during fetal period, 893–894, 896–898
during period of major organogenesis, 869, 872–874, 876–888, 891–892, 901
during preimplantation period, 864–866
LD_{50} for, 930–931
sarcoma in, 693
Reactor, nuclear, 14
Reciprocity, 924
Recombination, 355
of ions, 194*n*., 239–240
Recovery in radiosensitivity, 928
Red cells, 960–961, 970, 974, 979, 1002
nucleated, 305
(*See also* Erythrocytes)
Red pulp of spleen, 1106, 1108
Reduplication of organs, 325, 335
Refractive index of plasma, 972
Regeneration, 459, 1135
of blood-forming tissues, 963–964
of bone marrow, 1101
hematopoietic cells, 1100
capacity for, and type of radiation damage to embryo, 902
of epidermis, 1121
following injury from prenatal irradiation, 880, 888
inhibition of, 335
of liver, 1128, 1135
of lymphatic tissue, 1103
of spleen, 1106
Regression of tumors, 325, 339
Regulatory powers of mammalian blastomeres, 868, 904
Relative biological effectiveness, 321, 322, 328–342
Relative radiosensitivity, 1092, 1132
nucleus and cytoplasm, 1094
Relaxation, electric, 69
Relaxation length, 104
Relaxation time, 76
Rem (roentgen equivalent mammal), 1147
Remodeling of bone, 1112
Renal failure, 925
Rep (roentgen equivalent physical), 1147
Repair of bone, 1111

Repeated X irradiation of lymph nodes, 1104
Reproduction, convariant, 352
in mammals, effect of radiation on, 826–831
Reproductive system, effects of prenatal irradiation on, 889–890, 896–898, 909, 912
Resonance, 16, 46
Resonance effect, neutron collisions, 114
nuclear, 58
Resonance radiation, 199, 202, 206, 216
Resonance rule in collisions, 205, 207, 208, 220, 235, 237–238
Resonating current, 17, 20
Resorption, of bone, 1110
of embryos after irradiation, 864, 866, 873
(*See also* Mortality, prenatal)
Respiration, endogenous, 302
of intestinal tissue, 984
single cells, 300
Restitution, average time for, 728
of chromosome breaks, 363, 483, 499, 500, 722
oxygen effect on, 749
proportion of breaks undergoing, 731
space factor in, 730
Retardation, of breathing, 940
of growth, 339, 340, 869, 876–877, 879, 896, 900, 905, 912, 922
Reticular cells, 930, 1135
bone marrow, 1099
lymphatic organs, 1101, 1103
radioresistance of, 1133, 1135
bone marrow, 1100
spleen, 1106
thymus, 1104
Reticulo-endothelial system, 926, 1004–1005
Reticulocytes, effect on, of fast neutrons, 1043, 1048
of gamma radiation, 1055
of spleen shielding, 1078
and splenectomy, 1078
of X radiation in phenylhydrazine-induced anemia, 1036
Retina, 306, 339
damage to, following prenatal irradiation, 880, 889, 891, 897–898, 909, 912
degeneration in, 338
Reunion of chromosome breaks, 722
oxygen effect on, 749
space factor in, 730
Reversible degenerative phenomena, 1092
Rhodanase, 987
Rib abnormalities following prenatal irradiation, 882, 884, 887, 892, 904
Ribonuclease, 299
inactivation of, 944
Ribonucleic acids, 289, 305, 929
synthesis of, 962
Rodents, 686, 687
Roentgen rays, 3
Roentgen units, 120, 319
definition of, 149
Root-mean-square deviation, 80
Roots, pea, 341
sunflower, 340
tomato, 341
Vicia faba, 322, 325, 340, 341
wheat, 339
Rotifers, 583
Ruminants, 444
Rutherford scattering, 41, 43, 44, 51
Rutin, 968, 969, 979

S

Salamander, 335, 554, 776, 811, 816
Salivary-gland chromosomes in animal cells, 635–637, 646, 648–652, 660, 661, 663–665, 668–670, 673, 677–679, 689
Salivary-gland secretion, 1127
Salivation, excessive, 995
Salmon, 448, 628, 629
Saltants, 593
Sarcoma, Jensen, 305
rat, 693
Saturation effect, 140
Scatterer recoil, 43
Scattering, α-particle, 42
coherent, 104
Compton, 37, 38, 44
angular distribution of, 39
distribution of energy, 38
of electromagnetic radiation, 37, 45–48
probability of, 39
Rutherford, 41, 43, 44, 51
Schwann cells, 996
Sciara, 484, 689, 690
Scilla, 776, 799, 804
Scintillation counters, 233
Scintillations, 4
Sclerosis in skin, 1122
Sea urchins (*Arbacia*), 554, 766, 769, 771, 772, 784, 785, 789, 796, 803, 812, 814
sperm, 300, 301, 304
Sea water, 576
Sebaceous glands, 1119, 1123
carcinogenesis in, 1176
Secale, 363
Secondary radiation, 72

Secondary sex characters, 1118
Sedimentation rate of blood, 964
  effect of radiogold on, 1061
Sedimentation velocity, 295
Seedlings, pea, 341
  sunflower, 340
  Vicia, 340, 341
  wheat, 339, 935
Seeds, 939
Segmental interchange, 367, 368, 847
Segregation, Mendel's law of, 355
Semilethal effects, 1005
Semipermeable membrane, 301
Semisterility, 825, 840, 842–850, 854
Sensitive area, 140, 283, 284
Sensitive volume, 130, 140
Sensitivity of cells, differences in, to ionizing radiations, 681–691
Separation of cartilage from bone, 1113
Sequoias, 583
Sertoli cells, 828, 831, 1114, 1116, 1117
Serum, horse, 935
Serum phosphatase, 299
Sex and radiosensitivity, 933
Sex determination, 455
Sex ratio, 839, 840
  following prenatal irradiation, 877–878, 912
Shielding, 926
  of parts of pregnant females during irradiation, 864, 901, 911
  spleen (*see* Spleen shielding)
Showers, cascade, 63, 70, 95, 111
Shwartzman phenomenon, 1003
Silkworm, 457, 510
Single-hit, 132
Single-hit curves (*see* Dose effect, exponential curves)
Situs inversus following prenatal irradiation, 886, 888, 892
Skeleton, skeletal abnormalities, effects of prenatal irradiation on, 882–887, 909
  (*See also* specific abnormalities)
Skin, 325, 337–338, 1119
  cysteine protection, 943
  damage following prenatal irradiation, 881, 886, 896–898, 912
  derma, 1119, 1120
  epidermis, cellular polymorphism, 1121
    degeneration of, 1121
  epilation of, 1120
  epithelium, 1120
    atypical, 1120
    cessation of mitosis, 1120
  erythema of, 926, 976–977, 1120
  inflammatory reaction, 1121, 1122
  latent period in, 1121
Skin, loss of elastic fibers in, 1122
  mammary gland, 1123
  necrosis, 1120
  nuclear polymorphism of, 1120
  papilloma, 1175
  pigmentation of, 1120
  radiation effects, 997
    plutonium, 1122
    radium, 1122
    $yttrium^{91}$, 1122
  radiosensitivity of, 929
  sclerosis of, 1120
  sebaceous glands, 1123
  sweat glands, 1123
  temperature of, 977
  tumors, 1151, 1153, 1155, 1159, 1175–1177
  ulceration, 1120, 1149
Skin glands and X rays, 1123
Skull abnormalities following prenatal irradiation, 879, 881, 883, 887, 889, 909
Slow neutrons (*see* Neutrons)
Small intestines, 306, 307, 1124
Smear techniques in radiobiology, 632, 635
Sodium, excretion of, 989
  of plasma, 974
  retention of, 971
  of tissue, 972
Sodium fluoride, 941
Sodium hydrosulfite, 580
Sodium nitrite, 941, 945
Sodium space of intestine, 989
$Sodium^{24}$, 1093
  effect of, 1058
    on intestine, 1127
    on spleen, 1107
    on thymus, 1105
  toxicity of, 923
Somnolence, 995
Sonic vibration, effect on radiation-induced chromosome aberrations, 737
  and mutation, 572
Soret band, 287
Spatial distribution of ions, 194, 197
Species, radiosensitivity of, 930–934
Species heterozygotes, 456
Specific ionization, 87, 315, 920, 923, 1093
  and carcinogenesis, 1146, 1147
  as related, to oxygen effect on chromosome-aberration production, 752
    to radiation efficiency in chromosome-aberration production, 732
Spectral analysis, 18

Spectrum, 18
absorption, 47
albumin, 294
bands, 47
continuous, 47
line, 47
mutational, 590, 594, 596
nuclei, 49
optical, 20
Sperm, fertilization power of, 301
formation of, 998–999
motility of, 455
restitution of breaks, 483
Spermatids, 828–831, 842, 1114
Spermatocytes, 828–830, 842, 844, 1114, 1116, 1133
radiosensitivity of, 929
Spermatogenesis, 829, 830, 842, 843, 854, 1114, 1116, 1136
cessation of, 1116
Spermatogonia, 829, 830, 837–839, 842, 843, 846, 847, 852, 855, 1114, 1116, 1133
radiosensitivity of, 929, 999
Spermatozoa, 826, 828, 830–832, 834, 835, 837, 839, 842–844, 846–848, 855, 856
Spermia, 1114
Sphaerocarpus, 476, 531, 540, 553
Spiderwort, 484
Spin-conservation rule in collisions, 205, 208, 220
Spindle, mitotic, destruction of, ultraviolet-induced, 814, 815
suppression of, X-ray-induced, 804
Spleen, 306, 919, 926, 960–966, 979, 982, 1106
ectopic erythropoiesis, 963
ectopic myelopoiesis, 1106
effect on, of clamping off circulation in shielding-irradiation procedure, 1077, 1078
of cutting distal vessel in shielding-irradiation procedure, 1069, 1070, 1076
of transplants, 963, 965
effect of increments to, on survival, 1078, 1079
erythropoiesis, 1107, 1108
germinal centers, 1106
hemocytoblasts, 1107
heterophil leukocytes, 1106
homogenates, 926, 963, 965
lymphatic tissue, 1106
lymphocytes, 1106
lymphopoiesis, 1106
mast cells in, 1107
megakaryocytes, 1106, 1108
Spleen, myelocytes, 1106
radiation effect on, 919
Ba^{140}-La^{140}, 1107
fast neutrons, 1107
gamma rays, 1107
plutonium, 1107
radioactive isotopes, 1107
radium, 1107
slow neutrons, 1107
$sodium^{24}$, 1107
$strontium^{89}$, 1107
$yttrium^{91}$, 1107
Zr^{93}-Cb^{93} (Zr^{95}-Nb^{95}), 1107
radiation exposure, 982
prenatal, sensitivity to, 880, 897–898
red pulp, 1106, 1108
regeneration of, 1106
retention of colloids, 979
reticular cells, 1106
sarcoma of, 1155, 1156
white pulp, 1106
(*See also* Spleen shielding; Spleen transplants)
Spleen shielding, 926, 963, 965, 1068–1073
comparison of, with head shielding, 1073
with intestine shielding, 1072
with limb shielding, 1073
with liver shielding, 1072
effect of, on peripheral blood, 1069–1070
on survival of mice, 1068
and cysteine, 1079
plus estrogen, 1079, 1080
and estrogen, 1079
hematopoietic recovery, 1069–1076
splenectomy effects after, 1077–1081
on antibody formation, 1080, 1081
before radiation and with spleen transplants, 1073–1074
on survival of mice, 1073, 1074, 1077, 1081
Spleen transplants, 926
modification of radiation injury by, 1074–1075
quantity of transplanted tissue on survival, 1076
Splenic suspensions, 1074
Staphylococcus (*Micrococcus aureus*), 537, 545, 548–552, 562
Stationary states, 29–30
within a molecule or crystal, 32
oscillatory or rotary, 32
Stem cells in testis, 1117
Sterility, 826–831, 840–843, 854, 855
following prenatal irradiation, 897–898
(*See also* Reproductive system, effects of prenatal irradiation on)

Sterility, and ovary, 1117
partial, 825, 840, 842–850, 854
production of, 999
treatment of, 999
Sterilization, 337
Stichococcus, 322
Sticky chromosomes (*see* Chromosome stickiness)
Stillbirths, 835, 836, 839
following prenatal irradiation, 874, 898, 900, 911
(*See also* Mortality, neonatal)
Stimulation of blood-forming tissue by radiation, 1064
Stock, "sifter," 458
Stomach, 1124
radiation effects, 985–986
ulcers, 1125
Stopping number, 52, 53
Stopping power, 52, 87, 158, 165, 166
of different materials, 88
of water, electron, 54
proton, 54
Straggling, 88
Stratified squamous epithelium, 1124
Streptomyces, 543, 544
Streptomycin, 585, 1003
Stresses, nonspecific, 1004
Stromal cells of thymus, 1104
Strontium, radioactive, 586
$Strontium^{89}$, 1093
effect of, on bone, 1110
on bone marrow, 1059
on cartilage, 1113
on intestine, 1127
on peripheral blood, 1059, 1060
on spleen, 1107
on testis, 1117
on thymus, 1105
and splenectomy, effect on erythrocytes, 1059, 1060
toxicity of, 963, 970, 973
Styrene, 291
Submaxillary glands, 306
feminizing changes, 999
Succinate, 306
Succinic dehydrogenase, 987
Succinoxidase, 298
Sugars, 307
(*See also* individual sugars)
Sulfhydryl compounds, 551, 579
effect on radiation injury, 1067
Sulfhydryl content of plasma, 975
Sulfhydryl groups, 937–938, 941
oxidation, 287, 290, 292
Sulfhydryl enzymes, 937, 941, 987
Sulfide, 945
Sulfur, 285, 576, 586
radioactive, and mutation, 585
Supersonics and mutation, 589
Supralethal irradiation, 1006
Survival, mean time of, 931, 932
Sweat glands, 1119, 1123
Swelling, of cells, 1095
of nuclei, 1096, 1127
Swine, LD_{50} for, 930
Symbiosis, 444
Synapsis, 355
Synchrotron, 12

T

Tadpole, 776, 786, 804–806, 810
Tail abnormalities following prenatal irradiation, 881, 884, 892, 902, 905, 907
Target theory (hit theory, *Treffertheorie*), 129, 130, 132, 140, 245, 248, 252, 258, 272, 283, 284, 301, 921
and mutation, 525–531, 552
Telangiectasias, 1151
Telomeres, 366, 446
Temperature, effect of, on chromosome aberrations in absence of oxygen, 743
on radiation-induced chromosome aberrations, 741
and mutation, 412, 565
and oxygen effect, 742
and radiation effects, 1093
and radiosensitivity, 927, 935–937, 945–946
Temperature changes in skin, 977
Tendon, 1097
Termites, 444
Terphenyl, 290
Terramycin, 1003
Testes, 306, 828, 829, 831, 842, 843, 1114
basophilic outstretched cells in, 1114, 1116
carcinogenesis in, 1168–1171, 1190
interstitial cells of, 1116, 1117
radiation effects, 998–999
Ba^{140}-La^{140}, 1117
fast neutrons, 1114, 1116, 1117
gamma rays, 1114, 1116
$phosphorus^{32}$, 1116, 1117
plutonium, 1117
radium, 1117
repeated irradiation, 1114
$strontium^{89}$, 1117
$yttrium^{91}$, 1117
Zr^{93}-Cb^{93} (Zr^{95}-Nb^{95}), 1117
spermatogenesis, 1136
Tetanus toxin, 941

Tetraborohydride, 942, 945
Tetrads, 355
Tetraploid cells, 642, 643, 683
Thiocyanate space, 971
Thiol compounds, 307
Thiol groups, 298, 304
Thiols, 286–289, 303, 308
Thiosulfate, 942, 945
Thiouracil, 935, 946, 993
Thiourea as protection, 942, 945
Thorax abnormalities following prenatal irradiation, 884, 906
Thorotrast, 970
Threshold dose in carcinogenesis, 1167
Thrombi, platelet, 977
Thrombocytes (*see* Platelets)
Thrombocytopenia, 966
Thrombosis, vascular, 967
Thymic cell suspensions, 935, 939, 942, 960
Thymonucleic acid, 289
Thymus, 306, 1104
  effect on, of cerium-praseodymium, 1105
    of external beta rays, 1105
    of fast neutrons, 1105
    of plutonium, 1105
    of radioactive isotopes, 1105
    of slow neutrons, 1105
    of sodium^{24}, 1105
    of strontium^{89}, 1105
    of yttrium^{91}, 1105
  Hassall's bodies, 1105
  lymphocytes, 1104
  mast cells in, 1105
  sensitivity of, to prenatal irradiation, 880, 897–898, 912
  stromal cells, 1104
Thyroid, 1132
  administration of, 929, 935, 937, 946
  carcinogenesis in, 1167, 1171–1172
  iodine^{131} and, 1132
  radiation effects, 942
Thyroidectomy, 935, 993
Time-intensity factor, 134, 1091, 1130
Tissue breakdown, 1000–1002
Tobacco mosaic virus, 510
Toluidine blue, 967–968
  effect on radiation-induced hemorrhage, 1046
Tonus of intestine, 985
Tooth primordia, effect of P^{32} on, 899–900
Total-body vs. local irradiation, 1091
Totipotency, 868, 904
Toxins, bacterial, 1000, 1003
  produced by radiation, 245, 877, 890, 900
Trachea, carcinogenesis in, 1180
  cartilage, 1000
Tracks of high-energy particles, 77, 82, 83, 315
Tradescantia, 363, 385, 386, 484–488, 490, 491, 493, 516–518, 522, 524, 525, 533, 534, 559, 561, 562, 566–568, 570–573, 578, 584, 774, 799, 804, 807, 814, 940, 941
  chromosome number in, 631
  microspores and chromosomes, 631, 632, 659, 668, 669, 675, 679
    diploid, 683
      haploid, 683
  radiation-induced aberrations in chromosomes of, 713–761
Transfusions, blood, 966, 967, 1006, 1081, 1082
Transition effect (X rays), 111
Translocations, aneucentric, 367, 386
  chromosome, 999
    in animal cells (*see* Chromosomes)
  deletion-insertion type, 376
  eucentric, 367, 369, 386
  in mammals, 842–844, 846–850, 854
  mutual or reciprocal, 367, 368
  rate with dose, 480
  and temperature, 565
  whole-arm, 369
  X-ray induced, 484, 487
Transport of small lymphocytes, 1104
Trauma (*see* Radiation injury)
Treatment of radiation syndrome, 1006
Treffertheorie (*see* Target theory)
Tricarboxylic acid cycle, 946
Trichophyton, 531, 535, 540, 570
Trigeminal ganglia, 995
Trillium, 689, 691, 695, 722, 799, 802
Triols, 291
Triploids, 456, 643, 683
Triticum, 589, 798
Tritium, 587
Triton, lethal effects, 924
Triturus, 807
Trypan blue, effects of, on mammalian embryo, 907
Trypsin, 299
Tryptophane metabolism, 988
Tumor cells, 935, 939–940
Tumor induction (tumorigenesis), 922
  latency of, 1150, 1158, 1171, 1178, 1181
  pathogenesis of, 1174
  by radioscopy, 1148, 1163
  (*See also* Carcinogenesis; Carcinogenic agents)
Tumors, 305
  carcinoma (*see* specific animals and sites)
  chondrosarcoma (*see* Bone)

Tumors, chorioepithelioma induced by X rays, 1169
- chromosome abnormalities in, 338
- embryoma, 1158
- endothelioma, 1157, 1169, 1184
- hemangioendothelioma, 1157, 1160, 1169, 1176, 1184
- incidence of, in painters of radioactive watch dials, 1158, 1182–1183
- inhibition of "takes," 339
- lymphoma (*see* Leukemia)
- mammary, 1153, 1161, 1164, 1172–1174, 1188
  - milk agent, 1173
- neoplasms (*see* Carcinogenesis; Carcinogenic agents; specific sites)
- osteosarcoma, 1111
- papilloma, 1175
- plasmocytoma, induction by mesothorium, 1157
- radiosensitivity of, 929
- regression of, 325, 339
- sarcoma (*see* specific animals and sites)

Turbidity of plasma, 974–975
Two-hit aberrations, 723
Tyndall effect, 119
Tyrosine, 292, 293, 296
- dissociation of hydroxyl group, 293
- effect of alpha radiation on, 271

U

Ulcers, intestinal, 983
Ultraviolet radiation, 362, 390, 399
- action spectrum for mutation, 540, 541, 545
- and chromosome changes, 531–535, 738
- chromosome effects, 738, 814
- cleavage furrow, change in position, 815, 816
- in combination with X rays, 738
- and deletions, 532, 533
- and dominant lethal mutations, 532
- energy absorption in tissues, 764
- excitations, 539
- and inversions, 533
- lethal effect on cells, 816, 817
- mitotic effects (*see* Mitotic effects)
- mutagenesis, by irradiation of medium, 548–552
  - repair and enhancement in, 542–548
- and mutation, 504, 592–595
  - intensity, 538
- nucleolar spheration, 816
- and point mutations, 531–542
- spindle effects, 814
- and terminal deletions, 532
- and translocations, 532, 533
- (*See also* Light)

Uranium, 295, 574
Uranyl nitrate, 575
Urea of blood, 973, 989
Urease, 299
Urethane, 922, 937, 946
- ethyl, 416, 424

Uric acid, of blood, 925, 973, 1000
- of liver, 988

Uricemia, 925
Urinary bladder, 1129
Urine composition, 989
Urobilinogen, 988
Urogenital-system abnormalities following prenatal irradiation, 886–888, 892, 896–897, 907, 909
Uterus, 1117, 1118
- carcinogenesis in, 1151, 1153, 1174–1175

V

Vacuolization of cartilage cells, 1113
Vagina, 1117, 1118
Vagotomy, 980–981, 985
van der Waals force, 32
Variability, biological, 27
Variance, 80
Vascular calcification and radium, 1122
Vascular changes in skin, 1121
Vascular damage, 966
Vascular fragility, 968, 979
Vascular permeability, 978–979
Vascular thrombosis, 967
Vascularity and radiosensitivity, 940
Velocity, sedimentation, 295
Velocity gradient, 289
Vertebral-column abnormalities following prenatal irradiation, 884, 887, 902, 906–907, 909
Viability and mutations, 395, 853–856
Viability effects, cell, 804–810, 816–817
- chromosome losses and, 807, 808
- degenerative changes described, 804–807
- DNA formation and, 808
- dosage rate and, 810
- kind of radiation and, 809, 810, 816, 817
  - α rays, 810
  - β rays, 809
  - γ rays, 809, 810
  - neutrons, 809
  - ultraviolet radiation, 816
  - X rays, 809
- mitotic stage and, 805, 806
- radiosensitivities of different kinds of cells, 808
- temperature and, 810, 816
- in vivo and in vitro, 806

Vicia faba, 363, 391, 558, 577, 589, 736, 744, 748, 755, 774, 776–778, 782, 784, 786, 799, 801, 811, 929, 935, 940, 941
  chromosome aberrations, 306
Vinyl acetate, 291
Virus, 527
  inactivation of, 324, 329–330
Visceral abnormalities and retarded development following prenatal irradiation, 886, 888, 896–898
Viscosity, 289
  anomalous, 289
  of cytoplasm, 1095
  of gelatin solutions, 295
Vitamin-A absorption, 986
Vitamin C, 942, 945, 967, 975, 990
Vitamin deficiency, 934
Vitamin K, 967
Vitamin P, 968
Vitamins, 934, 965, 967–968, 986
Vomiting, 969, 982, 984

W

Water, 256, 273
  "activated," 284, 937
  and cell organization, 273
  effects on, 324, 328
  extracellular, 1001
  influence on high-energy mutagenesis, 555–564
  metabolism, 969
  "pure," 285
  radicals from (*see* Radicals from water)
  radiodecomposition of, 750
  role of, in radiation effects, 244*n*., 273, 274
    on chromosomes, 751*ff*.
    and radiosensitivity, 754
Water content, effect on radiosensitivity, 927
  of organs, 1001
  of tissues, 971
Wave length, 16
Wave length effect, 137
Weeds, noxious, 444
Weight, at birth (*see* Body size)
  loss of, 984
  of organs, 1001
Wheat seedlings, 935
Whole-body irradiation, 1136
  of pregnant females, 864, 901
  (*See also* Embryo; Fetus)
Wines, 445

X

X radiation, anemia induced by, biological effectiveness of fast neutrons and, 1048
  comparative effect of fast neutrons and, 1044
  effect of, on adrenal glands, 1131
    in mammalian prenatal development, 861–918
  effect on peripheral blood, of acute exposure, 1031–1041
    of chronic exposure, 1047–1049
    (*See also* Bone marrow)
  effect of tissue shielding on injury induced by acute exposure, 1068–1073
  genetic effects, 629
    in mammals, 825–859
  mitotic inactivity, 628
  primary effect, 628, 694
  secondary effects, 628, 629
X-ray fluorescence, 47, 69, 107
X rays, 3, 14
  absorption of, 49, 107, 108
  absorption coefficient, 103, 110
  asters, induced supernumerary, 803
  build-up, 108
  chromonema effects, 801, 802
  chromosome breakage, 801
  chromosome change in form, 801
  chromosome stickiness (*see* Chromosome stickiness)
  crystal diffraction, 105
  cytosome effect, 803
  deamination by, 265–270
  definition of, 20
  distribution of, 86
  effect of intensity of, 727
  effects of, on chromosomes, 723*ff*.
  effects on, of modifying factors, 736*ff*.
  electronic equilibrium of, 111
  emission, 44
  energy distribution, 109
  energy release in tissues, 764, 786
  lethal effect on cells, 805–810
  measurement of, 318–319
  mitotic effects, 768–791, 794–798
    (*See also* Mitosis; Mitotic effects)
  penetration of (*see* Penetration)
  probability of different effects, 70
  production of, 23
  relation of aberration yield to dose, 723
  relative efficiency, 732
  scattered, 107
  secondary, 106
  spindle suppression, 804
  thymonucleic acid depolymerization, 800, 801

X rays, transition effect, 111
translocations induced by, 484, 487
(*See also* Chromosome aberrations; Mutations; Radiation; X radiation)

Y

Yeasts, 321, 324, 325, 331–332, 445, 595, 940
diploid, 303, 321, 324
haploid, 302, 303, 321, 324
hexokinase, 298
Saccharomyces cerevisiae, 304, 325
Yttrium, radioactive, 586
$Yttrium^{90}$ colloid, 978
$Yttrium^{91}$, effect of, on bone, 1110, 1112
on intestine, 1127
on liver, 1128
on peripheral blood, 1058, 1059
on skin, 1122
on spleen, 1107
on testis, 1117
on thymus, 1105

Z

Zr^{93}-Cb^{93} (Zr^{95}-Nb^{95}), effect of, on intestine, 1127
on spleen, 1107
on testis, 1117
"Zone sensible," 301